CONTEMPORARY MEDICAL PHYSIOLOGY

Robert L. Vick, Ph.D.

Professor of Physiology
Baylor College of Medicine

Addison-Wesley Publishing Company
Medical Division • Menlo Park, California
Reading, Massachusetts • London • Amsterdam
Don Mills, Ontario • Sydney

To Rose and Suzanne

Sponsoring Editors: *Richard W. Mixter, Katherine Pitcoff*
Production Coordinators: *Charles Hibbard, Fannie Toldi*
Cover Designer: *Michael A. Rogondino*
Book Designer: *John Edeen*
Art Coordinator: *Julie Kranhold*
Cover Photo: *From* Tissues and Organs: A Text-Atlas of Scanning
Electron Microscopy *by Richard G. Kessel and Randy H. Kardon. W.H.*
Freeman and Company. Copyright © 1979.

Library of Congress Cataloging in Publication Data
Vick, Robert L., 1929–
   Contemporary medical physiology.

   Includes bibliographies and index.
   1. Human physiology. I. Title. [DNLM: 1. Physiology.
QT 104 V636c]
QP34.5.V53 1984   612   83–21423
ISBN 0–201–08095–8

BCDEFGHIJ–MA–8987654

The authors and publishers have exerted every effort to ensure that drug selection, dosage, and composition of formulas set forth in this text are in accord with current formulations, recommendations, and practice at the time of publication. However, in view of ongoing research, changes in government regulations, the reformulation of nutritional products, and the constant flow of information relating to drug therapy and drug reactions, the reader is urged to check product information on composition or the package insert for each drug for any change in indications of dosage and for added warnings and precautions. This is particularly important where the recommended agent is a new and/or infrequently employed drug.

Addison-Wesley Publishing Company
Medical Division
2725 Sand Hill Road
Menlo Park, California 94025

CONTRIBUTING AUTHORS

Robert P. Borda, Ph.D.
Assistant Professor of Neurology
Baylor College of Medicine

Stephanie I. Deavers, Ph.D.
Assistant Professor of Physiology
Baylor College of Medicine

Cutberto Garza, M.D., Ph.D.
Assistant Professor of Physiology
   and Pediatrics
Baylor College of Medicine

G. Harley Hartung, Ph.D.
Assistant Professor of Physical Medicine
Baylor College of Medicine

Carlton F. Hazlewood, Ph.D.
Professor of Physiology
Baylor College of Medicine

Jack N. Hunt, M.D., Ph.D.
Professor of Physiology
Baylor College of Medicine

George W. Pettit, M.D., Ph.D.
Visiting Assistant Professor of Physiology
Baylor College of Medicine

William J. Schindler, M.D., Ph.D.
Associate Professor of Physiology
Baylor College of Medicine

Charles L. Seidel, Ph.D.
Assistant Professor of Physiology and
   Medicine
Baylor College of Medicine

Hwai-Ping Sheng, Ph.D.
Assistant Professor of Physiology
Baylor College of Medicine

Lois A. Sutton, Ph.D.
Assistant Professor of Otorhinolaryngology
   and Communicative Sciences
Baylor College of Medicine

Robert L. Vick, Ph.D.
Professor of Physiology
Baylor College of Medicine

PREFACE

PURPOSE AND GOALS OF THE BOOK

Contemporary Medical Physiology was conceived and written to provide health science students with an introduction to physiology that is thorough, understandable, and current. These are challenging and important goals for any textbook, reflecting the needs of today's students, who must repeatedly draw upon their understanding of physiological concepts and information in order to keep up with rapid advances in the health sciences and clinical practice. This book is written primarily for use by students in medical schools and upper division college courses.

The principal author and contributing authors of this textbook all are active teachers of physiology. In determining what material to include and how to present it, the contributors and I have drawn on our own extensive experience and our understanding of the needs of students. The contributing authors have not worked in isolation. As principal author and editor, I have worked closely with each of the contributors, virtually as a co-author on every chapter, to attempt to attain *the accuracy and depth of understanding of a multiauthored text* without sacrificing *the uniformity of style and presentation of a single-authored text.*

Throughout the text we have placed *emphasis on understanding the principles and concepts of physiology.* The student is encouraged to learn by using fundamental concepts to understand how systems work, and to use logic, internal consistency, and integration of ideas without depending on rote memorization. By placing special emphasis on building under-standing from fundamentals, the book gives the student a foundation on which to learn. By presenting the fundamental, natural bases of physiological phenomena, we encourage the student by example to learn to solve problems rationally. Thus, we hope to prepare the student for a lifetime of learning. I do not contend that all learning of "facts" can be avoided, for these are part of learning physiology. However, whenever possible, the fundamental physical, chemical, and mathematical bases for why systems act as they do are pointed out, and the student is encouraged to use them.

Much of the study of physiology is the study of *control systems,* and much of disease is related to control systems gone awry. Thus, the control systems that operate in every organ and across organ systems are given early and thorough attention.

Although physiological concepts rely on research using both humans and animals, we emphasize interpretation of the experimental data and theories that arise from them in terms of *human* physiology. Generally, the student is not left to choose among conflicting theories; we have presented what we believe are the best explanations for how things work, but there is no pretense that all problems have been solved. Where knowledge is incomplete or the answers simply are not known, it is so stated.

SPECIAL FEATURES

A special feature of the book is a *study outline* at the end of each chapter. This is intended to help students summarize their knowledge or refresh their understanding quickly and easily.

The *clinical correlations* are another special feature of this book which I expect will serve several purposes. They are intended to increase the student's appreciation of basic physiology by showing its application in practical situations and to introduce more of the pathophysiology associated with each organ system. A disease cannot alter the function of one organ system without affecting others; the clinical correlations are therefore designed to integrate the material of the various sections. They also are intended to introduce the student to methods of clinical evaluation and the use of clinical data. When clinical laboratory data or findings from physical examination are given, the ranges of normal values also are given, to help the student put the data into perspective. The clinical correlations are intended not to teach clinical medicine, but to give the student a glimpse of physiology in action. Although presented in a case format, the clinical correlations do not represent real cases. Rather, they are hypothetical and composite cases based on real clinical records. Each case has been checked for accuracy and appropriateness by practicing clinicians.

Several criteria have been used in choosing the *bibliography*. Some of the references were chosen because they are classics, documenting fundamental ideas that have not changed. Others were selected because they represent current thinking in areas where ideas are changing. Some give broad coverage of a subject, or place an idea in perspective, and others are intended to illustrate clinical relevance. Each reference has been perused for the quality of its own bibliography, which provides entree into the related literature.

ACKNOWLEDGMENTS

The author wishes to express his appreciation to all of the contributors for their courtesy and cooperation, and to Mr. Richard W. Mixter, Medical Editor, Addison-Wesley Publishing Company, for his encouragement and support. The writing of this textbook has been a challenging, rewarding, and humbling experience. The book is dedicated to all teachers and students of physiology.

Robert L. Vick

BRIEF
CONTENTS

ix

DETAILED
CONTENTS

PART III

MUSCLE   159

PART IV

CARDIOVASCULAR PHYSIOLOGY 193

PART V

BLOOD AND IMMUNITY   357

PART VI

RESPIRATORY PHYSIOLOGY   403

PART VII
RENAL PHYSIOLOGY AND BODY FLUIDS   537

PART VIII

GASTROINTESTINAL PHYSIOLOGY   657

PART IX
ENDOCRINOLOGY AND REPRODUCTION   747

PART X
METABOLISM AND NUTRITION 885

PART
I

INTRODUCTION TO
PHYSIOLOGY

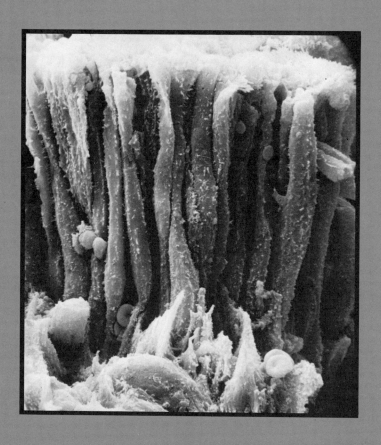

1

Physiological Principles

CHAPTER CONTENTS

GENERAL BACKGROUND

Physiology is the study of the functions of the organs and systems of the body. Simply to know *what* an organ or system does, however, is not enough—physiologists want to know *how* it functions. Physiologists also try to understand function at the cellular and subcellular levels. This should be thought of not as an attempt to neglect knowledge at the organ or tissue level, but to expand the range of understanding to include both the tissue and the cellular levels.

How an organ is controlled is just as important as how it functions. Because the individual tissue, organ, or system is a member of the physiological community that comprises the body, it is important to understand how all of the organs and systems work together: how they influence, complement, and regulate one another and how they may assist, compete, or cooperate when resources are limited. Although it is necessary to organize the study of the body by systems and to analyze the systems separately, one should bear in mind that the systems of the body do not function separately.

Physiological actions are described in physical, chemical, and mathematical terms as much as possible. Thus, the expression "physiological principles" applied to the material in this chapter may seem too inclusive. Many principles are indeed physical, chemical, and mathematical, but physiology is not a primary (or fundamental) science; therefore, physiology must use the principles of the more basic sciences. Thus, this chapter discusses principles that are applied to physiology, although they did not originate in physiology. These principles are given in general terms here and developed more specifically in subsequent chapters.

THE INTERNAL ENVIRONMENT: HOMEOSTASIS

Although the atmosphere of the earth may be thought of as the environment of the human body, only the surface cells of the body and the linings of the oral cavity and the respiratory tract come into direct contact with the atmosphere. The vast majority of the cells of the body are surrounded by neighboring cells and the extracellular fluid that bathes them. Thus, the body actually lives within itself, in an internal environment that is regulated and protected from the wider range of conditions that exist in the external environment.

The cells of the body take oxygen, energy, and chemical substrates from their environment and excrete wastes and by-products into their environment. Because the cells are arranged compactly and the volume of the internal environment is small, the amounts of energy and chemical substrates immediately available to the cells are small and the capacity of the immediate environment to absorb by-products and wastes is limited. To maintain the proper environment for the cells, the body must bring in energy and materials from internal stores or the external environment and take wastes out. Thus, the body must have a system for monitoring and adjusting the composition of its internal environment. Much of the study of physiology is concerned with the maintenance of the constancy of the internal environment (*homeostasis*).

The internal environment is renewed by exchange with the larger, external environment. The interstitial fluid that bathes the cells exchanges with the blood through the capillaries. The blood, pumped by the heart, circulates between the cells and the lungs, with which it exchanges gases, and through the gastrointes-

tinal tract, from which it obtains water, nutrients, and substrates. It flows through the kidneys, which filter it, adjust its composition, and return to the external environment water, solutes that are not needed, and the waste products of the cells. In addition, it flows to the surface of the body, where it dissipates excess heat.

Oxygen is added to the blood in the lungs and given up in the tissues; carbon dioxide is added to the blood in the tissues and given up in the lungs. The respiratory system brings the external environment (air) into contact with the blood in the capillaries of the lungs (*inspiration*) and releases the excess carbon dioxide into the external environment (*expiration*). Water vapor also is lost from the body through the respiratory tract.

The gastrointestinal, or alimentary, tract is a specialized tube that extends through the core of the body, from the mouth to the anus. The lumen of the tube is outside the internal environment of the body. Food, water, and, sometimes, other materials are placed in the alimentary tract (swallowed) and made available to the body. Fluids and enzymes are secreted from the body into the alimentary tract to aid in the breakdown and absorption of materials. Fat, carbohydrate, protein, salts, and water come into contact with special absorptive surfaces in the small intestine and, ultimately, are absorbed into the capillaries of the intestinal villi. The composition of the internal environment is protected by the liver, through which all of the blood that comes through the gastrointestinal tract must pass before reentering the general circulation. The liver removes materials from the blood, adds other materials to the blood, and stores, synthesizes, modifies, and detoxifies materials. The substrates for energy, structure, and specialized compounds are obtained through the gastrointestinal tract; substances that cannot be excreted by the kidneys (because they are not soluble in water) are excreted into the gastrointestinal tract for subsequent elimination. The mass of material that remains in the alimentary tract after foodstuffs, water, and salts have been absorbed and waste materials have been excreted is returned to the external environment as feces.

Important exchange between the internal and external environment occurs at the surface of the body. Water is lost by evaporation from the skin, and water and salts are lost through the perspiration. Heat is lost from the skin by radiation, conduction, and evaporation of water from the perspiration.

The temperature of the internal environment is maintained rigorously in the core of the body, which contains the vital organs (brain, heart, lungs, liver, and kidneys), but the external surface (mostly skin) and the appendages are permitted to be cooler than the core. Excess heat is produced, and its rate of dissipation is controlled. Heat is carried by the blood from the core to the surface, where it is lost to the external environment. When the external environment becomes colder and heat must be conserved, blood flow to the skin is decreased, the skin becomes cooler, and less heat is lost.

To maintain its integrity, the internal environment must be isolated from the external environment, except through the routes of controlled exchange, and precautions must be taken to avoid extremes of the external environment that might exceed the capacity of the body to compensate for them. Humans have learned to supplement the control systems that act to keep the internal environment constant. They have learned to control their immediate external environment by wearing clothing, building shelter, and using fuel for heating and cooling.

CONTROL SYSTEMS

Feedback

The elements of a formal control system are (1) a *sensor*, which monitors the rate of output of a system or the level of a product, (2) an *integrator*, which receives information from the sensor, compares the rate of output or the level of the product with a set point and directs any adjustments to be made, and (3) an *effector,* which makes the necessary adjustments (Figure 1-1A). In this kind of control system the information about the output or level is called *feedback*—in a sense, a sample of the output or level is "fed back" to keep the integrator informed about the working of the system.

The example used traditionally to illustrate a control system is the automatic heating system of a house. A thermometer senses the temperature of the air, and the furnace provides the heat. When the temperature of the air decreases more than the permissible amount from the set point, the thermostat, which is the integrator, turns on the furnace and turns it off again when the temperature has increased sufficiently.

Thus, the temperature of the air in the house is controlled around a set point.

NEGATIVE FEEDBACK

In physiological functions, most control is exerted through *negative feedback*. In a negative-feedback system, deviation of the output or level from the set point initiates adjustment to increase or decrease the output or level until it matches the set point, just as the thermometer-thermostat-furnace example does. The system is called a negative-feedback system because a deviation of the output from the set point elicits a response that negates the deviation. Thus, systems controlled by negative feedback tend to operate at a constant level or to adjust frequently to maintain constancy (Figure 1-1B). It is easy to see how a negative-feedback control is the kind of control that is needed to maintain homeostasis.

An example of a physiological function that is controlled by negative feedback is the systemic arterial pressure (see Chapter 15). The arterial pressure is sensed by the baroreceptors in the carotid sinuses and the aortic arch, which stretch as pressure increases. If the arterial pressure tends to decrease in the resting subject, the baroreceptors are stretched less, and information about the magnitude and direction of the change is coded through cranial nerves IX and X to the cardiovascular control center in the medulla (brain stem). The control center, through the autonomic nervous system, increases the heart rate, the contractility of the heart, the systemic venous tone, and the peripheral (arteriolar) resistance enough to return the arterial pressure to the set level. If the arterial pressure increases, the baroreceptor detects more stretch, different information is encoded, and the heart rate, cardiac contractility, venous tone, and peripheral resistance decrease enough to lower the pressure to normal again.

The concentration of glucose in the blood is another example of a physiological value that is controlled by negative feedback. The level of glucose is sensed in the blood as it perfuses the pancreas and is corrected by the secretion of insulin or glucagon. If the blood glucose increases, as it does after food is eaten, insulin is released. Insulin stimulates the transport of glucose into the cells, where the glucose may be stored in the form of glycogen or used in the synthesis of fat. An increase of the glucose level also decreases the secretion of glucagon, which has effects on blood sugar opposite to those of glucose. If the blood glucose decreases, as it does during fasting, glucagon is released. Glucagon increases the blood glucose by breaking down glycogen in the liver, promoting the synthesis of glucose from amino acids, and opposing the synthesis of fat from glucose. This two-effector arrangement gives the system more effective control on either side of normal.

These two systems have been described in oversimplified fashion to illustrate a fundamental principle. Although the systems are more complex in action, and although they interact with, and are influenced by, other systems, the principle still holds. The body contains many negative-feedback control systems that will be characterized in subsequent chapters.

POSITIVE FEEDBACK

Positive-feedback control acts oppositely to negative feedback. Rather than producing constancy, positive feedback accelerates change; rather than stability, positive feedback promotes instability. The positive-feedback system could be likened to a chain reaction or a vicious circle. In the positive-feedback system, deviation from the beginning value generates further deviation, in explosive fashion (Figure 1-1C). Positive-feedback systems are rare in physiology; however, two examples can be given: (1) the action potential of excitable tissues, and (2) ovulation in the female.

The rising phase of the action potential develops through positive feedback (see Chapter 2). When the cellular potential is more negative than a certain critical value, the permeability of the membrane to sodium ions (Na^+) is very low. When the cell is depolarized—by propagated activity, pacemaker activity, or a generator potential—the permeability of the membrane to Na^+ increases, because it is determined by the cellular potential. Because the concentration of Na^+ outside the cell is greater than the concentration of Na^+ inside the cell, and because the inside of the cell is negatively charged, whereas Na^+ is positively charged, Na^+ flows into the cell down an electrochemical gradient. As Na^+ flows into the cell, the cellular potential decreases, the permeability to Na^+ increases further, Na^+ flows in at a greater rate, the cellular potential decreases more, and the permeability to Na^+ increases more. In true positive-feedback fashion, the action potential is formed in regenerative, explosive, and irreversible fashion. The rise of the action potential is limited by the electrochemical gradient that drives Na^+ into the cell and by the action of

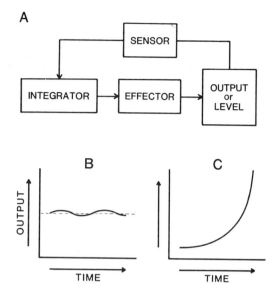

Figure 1-1. A. Feedback control. The signal from the sensor to the integrator may be either negative or positive, but in physiological systems, it most often is negative. **B.** Type of control exerted by negative feedback. The oscillation has been exaggerated for purposes of illustration; however, negative feedback systems can oscillate, depending on the fineness of control. **C.** Type of control exerted by positive feedback.

another, more slowly developing, positive feedback that decreases Na^+ permeability as the cell is depolarized.

Positive feedback in another system is illustrated by the action of estrogen on the cyclic center of the hypothalamus in the female. Estrogen formed by the ovaries causes the release of luteinizing hormone-releasing hormone (LRH) from the hypothalamus, which, in turn, causes the release of luteinizing hormone (LH) from the anterior pituitary gland (see Chapter 63). During the proliferative phase of the menstrual cycle, the plasma level of estrogen increases; this increase stimulates the release of LRH, which, in turn, stimulates the production of LH, and causes further secretion of estrogen by the ovaries. The cycle continues until the burst of estrogen causes ovulation (release of an egg from one of the ovaries).

RATE

The concept of *rate* is important in physiology. Rate indicates a quantitative relationship between two entities by relating change in one to a unit change of the other. The most important base for rate is *time*. For example, heart rate (beats per minute), velocity (centimeters per second), bulk flow (milliliters per second), and so on. Other bases also are used. For example, pressure (force per unit area), tension (force per unit length), distensibility (volume per unit force), electrical capacity (charge per unit potential), or surface area of a body (area per unit mass). *Concentration* (e.g., moles per unit weight, moles per unit volume, or mass per unit volume) is a very important rate relationship that expresses the amount of an ionic species, an energy supply, a hormone, oxygen, or other material that is contained in a volume of solution (e.g., plasma or interstitial fluid). In a rate relationship, one entity may vary with another directly, inversely, or exponentially, within physiological limits (Figure 1-2).

GRADIENT

The concept of the *gradient* is very important in physiology. Gradient is used most frequently to refer to an uneven distribution of mass or energy (e.g., a gradient of pressure, chemical activity, temperature, or electrical potential). Blood flows, ions diffuse, and heat is transferred down gradients. Movement down a gradient dissipates energy and increases *entropy* (the system becomes less organized and more random). When gradients disappear, the system is in *equilibrium*. Thus, the gradient represents the driving force for passive transfer, or the force against which active transfer must proceed. A gradient may involve only one compartment or two or more; it may be shallow or steep (Figure 1-3). Much of the work of the body goes toward the development and maintenance of gradients.

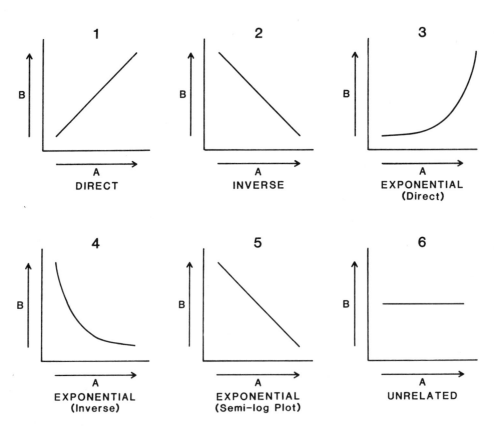

Figure 1-2. Different relationships between related entities *A* and *B* within the limited range that the relationship holds. *A* is varied systematically and *B* follows. Thus, *A* is the independent variable, and *B* is the dependent variable.

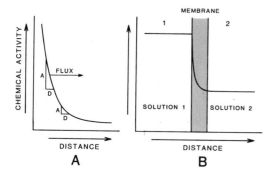

Figure 1-3.   Chemical activity gradients shown in two dimensions. **A.** One compartment. The chemical activity decreases exponentially away from the source, and the net flux proceeds passively down the gradient. **B.** Two compartments separated by a membrane. A steep gradient is maintained in the membrane, which is much less permeable than the solutions in the compartments. The solute diffuses rapidly to the membrane in compartment 1 and rapidly away from it in compartment 2, so that no discernible gradient develops in either compartment.

PRESSURE

Pressure is defined as force per unit area. Pressure is a very important principle in the cardiovascular system, in which it is the force that causes blood to flow; in the respiratory system, in which it causes air to flow; in the renal system, in which it causes glomerular filtration; and in the gastrointestinal system, in which it moves the contents of the esophagus, stomach, and intestines. Pressure in a fluid is exerted uniformly in all directions, against all enclosing surfaces. The fluid is displaced (propelled) if a gradient, or difference, of pressure exists in the system.

Measurement of Pressure

PRIMARY UNIT

In the laboratory and the clinic, pressure is measured in millimeters of mercury (mm Hg), which is a unit of length, not force. However, the height of the column of mercury reflects the force that is required to lift the column of mercury against the force of gravity. Pressure could be measured in this way using any liquid; mercury is used because it is very dense (13.6 g/cm^3, at 15 C). Thus, a column of mercury 10 cm high exerts the same force as a column of water 136

cm high. When high pressures are measured, the use of mercury is convenient because it does not require such a tall column. For example, arterial pressure in an animal (a horse) was first measured by permitting blood to flow upward in a tube (Stephen Hales, 1733). The pressure that was measured was 8 ft 3 in of blood, which is equivalent to only 185 mm, or 7.3 in, of mercury. An even more convenient arrangement is mercury in a U-tube (Figure 1-4). The pressure to be measured is directed against the mercury on one side, which pushes that side down and raises the other. The force that is exerted is equal to the difference between the heights of the two columns.

STANDARD UNIT

The force that is exerted by the column of mercury is the force of gravity acting on the mass of the mercury. Thus, the pressure in a system is measured indirectly as the equivalent of a known force exerted by gravity. Mass is simply the amount of matter; mass is the same everywhere, but the gravitational force that is exerted on a mass can vary. For example, a given mass

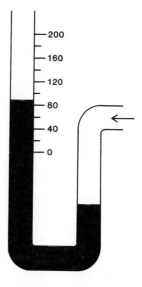

Figure 1-4.   The U-tube mercury manometer. Pressure at the side tube (*arrow*) forces the mercury down in one side and up in the other. 0 is the point at which both sides are equal, and the numbers are half-scale because the mercury moves both ways. To provide an accurate reading in this way, the tube must be of uniform bore throughout. The force that is measured is the accelerating effect of gravity on the mass of the mercury, which is equal to the pressure of interest.

weighs less on the moon than it does on earth because the force of gravity is less on the moon.

A force is measured by its action on a mass during a unit of time. Because a force acting on a mass displaces that mass, continued application of the force continues to displace the mass. Thus, a force *accelerates* a mass; and so force, *F*, is measured as the product of mass, *m*, × acceleration, *a*. The unit of mass in the cgs (centimeter-gram-second) system is the gram (g), and the unit of acceleration is (cm/sec)/sec, or cm × sec^{-2}. The unit of force is the *dyne*, which is the force that is required to impart a velocity of 1 cm/sec to a mass of 1 g in 1 second. Thus,

$$F = m \times a = g \times cm \times sec^{-2}$$
$$= g\ cm\ sec^{-2} = dyne$$

Since pressure expressed as the height of a column of mercury is a measure of the force of gravity on the mass of the mercury, pressure is the weight of the column of mercury. The size of the column does not matter—since the weight varies directly with the cross-sectional area, that factor is included automatically. However, if the pressure is expressed in standard dimensions of force per unit area (e.g., dynes per square centimeter), the mass of mercury per unit of cross-sectional area of the tube must be considered. The unit of area in the cgs system is cm^2. To convert mm Hg to $dyne/cm^2$, one can begin with a column of mercury 1 mm (or 0.1 cm) high that covers an area of $1\ cm^2$.

The *volume* of the column is

$$1\ cm^2 \times 0.1\ cm = 0.1\ cm^3$$

The *mass, m,* is given by the product of volume and density:

$$m = 0.1\ cm^3 \times 13.6\ g\ cm^{-3} = 1.36\ g$$

The force of gravity acting on the mass, that is, the weight of the column, is obtained from the relationship

Force = Mass × acceleration ($F = m \times a$)

The acceleration caused by gravity is not the same at all points on the earth. The factor that is used in the United States is obtained at the Smithsonian Institution, in Washington, D. C. ($980\ cm\ sec^{-2}$). Thus, the force per unit area of 1 mm Hg is the weight of mercury per unit area:

$$
\begin{aligned}
F\ cm^{-2} &= (m \times a)\ cm^{-2} \\
&= 1.36\ g \times 980\ cm\ sec^{-2} \times cm^{-2} \\
&= 1333\ g\ cm\ sec^{-2}\ cm^{-2} \\
&= 1333\ dyne\ cm^{-2}
\end{aligned}
$$

By substituting in the equation above, one finds that 1 mm Hg = 1333 $dyne/cm^2$. This expresses pressure in a standard system of units, so that it can be used in other calculations. However, the primary unit, mm Hg, has the advantage that it can be measured directly. In recent years, the eponym *torr* has been applied to the primary unit, mm Hg.

RELATIONSHIP TO ATMOSPHERIC PRESSURE

The pressure of the atmosphere is applied uniformly to all bodies that are contained in the atmosphere. It is the weight of the air in an imaginary column above each unit of area of the earth's surface. At sea level, atmospheric pressure is 760 mm Hg; at higher elevations, it is less. When the pressure in a system (e.g., arterial pressure) is measured with a mercury manometer at sea level, the atmospheric pressure that is applied to both the blood and the mercury is 760 mm Hg. If an arterial pressure of 100 mm Hg is measured, the pressure on the blood in the artery is 760 + 100 = 860 mm Hg, and the pressure on the mercury that is open to the atmosphere is 760 mm Hg + 0 = 760 mm Hg. Thus, all pressures, except in special circumstances, are measured in reference to atmospheric pressure (i.e., as the difference from atmospheric pressure), which is taken as 0. Some pressures, such as intrapleural pressure, which is measured in the respiratory system, are lower than atmospheric pressure. This occurs because certain spaces, or potential spaces, are enclosed in such a way that a small "vacuum" is generated (see Chapter 28). Pressures in these areas may be called subatmospheric, or they may be given negative values (e.g., −5 mm Hg). One should always remember, however, that the values are only relative, and truly negative pressure does not exist. Under some conditions, an investigator might wish to refer the pressure in one area directly to the pressure in another area, rather than to atmospheric pressure. For example, one side of the manometer might be connected to a pulmonary artery and the other side to the interpleural "space." This would permit the investigator to measure directly the pressure across the wall of the pulmonary artery, which is contained in the intrapleural space. These special conditions of measurement must be indicated, however, because pressure is assumed to be measured relative to atmospheric pressure unless otherwise specified.

FLOW

Rate of Flow

Fluids *flow* in all of the systems that generate pressure, if the pressure is not the same in all parts of the system. When force is applied to a fluid by the contraction of cardiac muscle or by contraction of the smooth muscle in the wall of the intestine, for example, a gradient of pressure develops, and fluid is displaced down the gradient (i.e., it flows). Thus, the flow of fluid is caused by differences of pressure ($P_1 - P_2$, or ΔP), regardless of the absolute pressures involved.

The *rate of flow* of fluid is measured as the volume of fluid displaced per unit of time. Blood flow may be measured as milliliters per second or liters per minute, and air flow in the lungs (air is a fluid) usually is measured as liters per minute.

Velocity of Flow

When a fluid flows, it attains a velocity. *Velocity* is speed, or distance of displacement in a unit of time. In physiological systems, it usually is measured in centimeters per second. Velocity is not related directly to volume of flow because the same volume may flow (e.g., cm³/sec) at widely different velocities, depending on the size (cross-sectional area) of the conduit. Suppose, for example, water flows at a rate of 100 cm³/sec in a pipe that has a uniform inside diameter of 2 cm (Figure 1-5A). Since a column of water 2 cm in diameter and 100 cm³ in volume is displaced completely in 1 second, one can calculate the velocity of displacement (flow) by finding the length of the column. This can be done by using the formula for the volume of a cylinder

$$V = \pi r^2 h$$

where V is volume, r is the radius, and h is the height, or length, of the cylinder. Rearranging to solve for h,

$$h = \frac{V}{\pi r^2} = \frac{100 \text{ cm}^3}{\pi (1 \text{ cm})^2} = 31.8 \text{ cm}$$

Thus, the column of water moved 31.8 cm in 1 second; hence, the velocity of flow was 31.8 cm/sec.

The difference between rate of flow and velocity is illustrated dramatically when the diameter of the tube decreases to 1 cm (Figure 1-5B). The volume of the column that is dis-

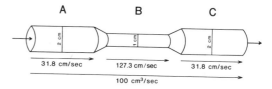

Figure 1-5.   Change of velocity with constant rate of flow through tubes of different size. Flow proceeds from left to right at the rate of 100 cm³/sec. Calculations are shown in text.

placed remains the same, but the column is narrower; hence, it must be longer. One can solve for the length of the column again, using the new dimension for radius

$$h = \frac{V}{\pi r^2} = \frac{100 \text{ cm}^3}{\pi (0.5 \text{ cm})^2} = 127.3 \text{ cm}$$

Thus, the velocity of flow in the narrow part of the tube is 127.3 cm/sec. When the fluid reaches the wide part again, the velocity decreases to 31.8 cm/sec again (Figure 1-5C).

Viscosity and Resistance to Flow

Fluids have *viscosity*, or what seems intuitively to be resistance to displacement. A homogeneous fluid that wets the walls of a tube through which it flows is considered to flow in monomolecular *laminae*, or layers (Figure 1-6). The layer of fluid in contact with the wall adheres to the wall and does not move at all. A second layer of fluid slides over the first (adhering) layer because the layers are sheared apart by the force (difference of pressure) that causes the movement. A third layer slides over the second layer, and the velocity of the third layer is greater than that of the second layer because the

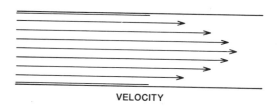

VELOCITY

Figure 1-6.   Laminar flow. As flow accelerates down a gradient of pressure, the lamina in contact with the wall does not move, but each successive lamina toward the center moves faster than the one outside it, until the maximum velocity is reached at the center. The resistance to flow arises from the friction between successive laminae.

third layer moves with the second layer, and then, because of the propulsive force, moves ahead of it, undergoing additional shear. Thus, each successive layer moves faster than the layer outside it, and the effect is one of concentric tubes moving along a gradient of force, with a gradient of velocity that goes from zero at the wall to a maximum at the center. The internal fluid friction of the laminae sliding over one another is the source of the resistance of fluids to flow.

A certain amount of resistance must be overcome to make any fluid flow through a tube. In practical terms, this *resistance* can be defined as the gradient of pressure that is required to move a unit of volume past a point of reference in a unit of time. Thus, the resistance is not expressed as a primary unit but as a ratio of the force that is imposed and the flow that results

$$R \simeq \frac{P_1 - P_2}{\dot{Q}} = \frac{\Delta P}{\dot{Q}}$$

where R is resistance, ΔP is the difference of pressure between points 1 and 2, and $\dot{Q}$ is the rate of flow. The variables that contribute to resistance can be identified and measured, under limited conditions. The variables that increase resistance are the viscosity (η) of the fluid and the length (l) of the tube between the sites at which P_1 and P_2 were measured. Thus,

$$R \simeq \eta l$$

where the unit of η is the *poise*, 1 dyne sec cm^{-2}.

Viscosity is an expression of the interaction between successive laminae as one layer slides over another: cohesive forces, which produce a "drag" or "shear," must be overcome. Viscosity is proportional to the shear force between layers, in dyne cm^{-2} of layer surface, and inversely proportional to the gradient of velocity between layers (Figure 1-6), in cm sec^{-1} cm^{-1}, from the wall to the center. Thus,

$$\eta \simeq \frac{\text{dyne cm}^{-2}}{\text{cm sec}^{-1} \text{cm}^{-1}} = \text{dyne sec cm}^{-2}$$

The resistance varies inversely with the radius of the tube because the force that is required to produce flow decreases as the distance from the lamina that adheres to the wall increases. The relationship is

$$R \simeq \frac{1}{\pi r^4}$$

where r is the radius of the tube. Combining both sets of variables gives

$$R \simeq \frac{\eta l}{1} \times \frac{1}{\pi r^4} = \frac{\eta l}{\pi r^4}$$

These relationships are expressed as *Poiseuille's equation*, which usually is given the form that corresponds to $\dot{Q} = \Delta P \times 1/R$

$$\dot{Q} = \frac{\Delta P \pi r^4}{8 \eta l}$$

The numerical constant 8 arose from the integration used to find the velocity gradient (0 at the wall of the tube to maximum at the center).

One can use cgs units to show that Poiseuille's equation does indeed describe flow $\dot{Q}$ in milliliters (cm^3) per second

$$\dot{Q} = \frac{\text{dyne cm}^{-2} \times \text{cm}^4}{\text{dyne sec cm}^{-2} \times \text{cm}} = \frac{\text{cm}^3}{\text{sec}}$$

Turbulent Flow

Fluid flows through tubes in discrete laminae only up to certain velocities. At a critical velocity, the laminae begin to break up, and some flow occurs at right angles to the mainstream, tending to form eddies and vortices. Although the resistance to flow at lower velocities occurs between the laminae, when the laminae break up, the resistance becomes even greater. Turbulent flow occurs in both the cardiovascular system (blood) and the respiratory system (air).

The critical velocity (V_c) for turbulent flow varies directly with the viscosity of the fluid; thus

$$V_c \simeq \eta$$

and inversely with the density (ρ) of the fluid and the radius (r) of the tube; thus

$$V_c \simeq \frac{1}{\rho r}$$

Combining both sets of variables gives

$$V_c \simeq \frac{\eta}{1} \times \frac{1}{\rho r} = \frac{\eta}{\rho r}$$

In cgs units this is

$$V_c \simeq \frac{\text{dyne sec cm}^{-2}}{\text{g cm}^{-3} \times \text{cm}} = \text{cm sec}^{-1}$$

If a constant is added, the proportionality becomes mathematically precise

$$V_c = \mathrm{Re}\,\frac{\eta}{\rho r}$$

where Re is *Reynold's number*. For blood flowing in straight tubes, Reynold's number is about 1000.

Turbulent flow produces vibration that may be perceived as sound. This vibration occurs when the velocity of blood flow exceeds the critical velocity because of constricted or occluded vessels (*bruits*) or damaged cardiac valves (*murmurs*). It also occurs normally at the peak of ventricular ejection (*innocent murmur*), particularly when the cardiac output is increased.

KINETIC ENERGY AND INERTIA

Pressure represents force applied against a surface; hence, pressure represents potential energy. If pressure is applied to a fluid that is not completely enclosed, the fluid is *displaced*, or put into motion. When a mass is put into motion, energy is put into it. If the body in motion is arrested, energy must be taken from it. Thus, a body remains motionless until energy is put into it, or it continues in motion until energy is taken out of it. The property of a body to resist being put into motion or to resist being stopped after it is in motion is called *inertia*. An example of energy being put into a mass is a pitcher throwing a baseball; an example of energy being taken from a mass is the impact of the ball on the catcher's mitt. The energy put into a body to displace it, or taken out to bring it to rest, is called *kinetic energy*, or the energy of motion. Kinetic energy is related to the mass of the body and its velocity.

Since a force acting on the mass of a body displaces the body, a force acting continuously produces *acceleration*, and, after the body has moved through a unit of distance, *velocity*. Thus

$$a \times D \simeq v$$

where a is acceleration, D is distance, and v is velocity. The cgs units of $a \times D$ are cm sec^{-2} × cm = cm^2/sec^{-2}, which are the units of velocity squared (cm sec^{-1})^2

$$a \times D \simeq v^2$$

Since the rate of acceleration is constant, the mean velocity at which the body moves through the unit of distance is the average of v_1, the initial velocity, and v_2, the velocity when the distance has been traversed: $(v_1 + v_2)/2$. Since $v_1 = 0$, the mean velocity is ½ the velocity attained at the end of the unit of distance. Therefore,

$$a \times D = \tfrac{1}{2}v^2$$

Since the force applied, F, is the product of m, the mass displaced, and a, the acceleration produced

$$F = m \times a$$

and, rearranging

$$a = F/m$$

Substituting F/m for a in the expression developed above

$$F/m \times D = \tfrac{1}{2}v^2$$

and rearranging, we have

$$F \times D = \tfrac{1}{2}mv^2$$

Since $F \times D$ (force × distance) = work, or energy

$$E_k = \tfrac{1}{2}mv^2$$

Thus, the kinetic energy, E_k, = ½ the product of the mass and the square of the velocity.

The concepts of potential energy, kinetic energy, and inertia are applied in the cardiovascular system. The energy that accelerates blood and moves it through the systemic circulation is provided by the contraction of the left ventricle. The heart is an intermittent pump, but blood flows continuously. The heart transmits energy to the blood in the forms of pressure (potential energy) and flow (kinetic energy). Some of the kinetic energy is transformed to potential energy and stored in the tension of the elastic arteries to be given back again to help keep arterial blood flowing after the heart has finished emptying and has relaxed to fill again. By the time the blood returns to the heart, all of the energy that was imparted to it by the ventricle has been dissipated as heat or transformed to potential energy (electrical and chemical).

SOLUTIONS

True, or Molecular, Solutions

A *solution* is a homogeneous molecular mixture of two or more substances. In biological systems, water is the solvent; solids, liquids, and gases are the solutes. Because water is a polar, or charged, compound, substances that dissolve in water to any significant extent also must have some degree of *polarity*, or charge. Small inorganic compounds that ionize dissolve easily in water (e.g., Na^+Cl^-). Inorganic compounds that ionize only slightly do not dissolve well in water (e.g., AgCl). Small organic compounds that contain a hydroxyl group (alcoholic), which interacts with water (e.g., methanol and ethanol), and larger organic compounds that have several hydroxyl groups dissolve easily (e.g., glucose and sucrose). Small organic acids and bases (e.g., acetic acid and ethylamine), which dissociate to some extent, are water-soluble. Larger organic acids and bases are less soluble but can be made more soluble by the formation of salts (e.g., with Na^+, K^+, or Cl^-). The water solubility of large organic compounds that contain alcoholic hydroxyl groups is related to the number of hydroxyl groups. For example, the drug digitoxin (a cardiac glycoside), a steroid compound that has a sugar moiety and only one hydroxyl group, is soluble at the rate of less than 1 g/10,000 ml of water. By contrast, ouabain, a closely related compound, has 5 hydroxyl groups and is soluble at the rate of 1 g/75 ml of water.

Large organic molecules that have both water-soluble and lipid-soluble portions can serve as an interface between water and water-insoluble organic compounds. Indeed, this is the basis of detergent action. In biological systems, water-solubility is advantageous because all of the body fluids are aqueous. However, substances that are not lipid-soluble must have special carriers or be able to enter via special pores to get through the lipid membrane into the cell. In the gastrointestinal tract, the bile salts, which are steroid molecules that contain both hydroxyl (alcohol) and carboxyl (acid) groups, are essential in the digestion of fats. The bile salts make the fats soluble in water and help to transport fats through the lumen of the intestine to the enterocytes (absorbing cells). In the bloodstream, fats are transported by other compounds (lipoproteins) that have both water-soluble and lipid-soluble moieties.

Colloidal Solutions

Particles that are larger than about 1 nm in diameter usually do not form homogeneous, or true, solutions but are considered to exist in two distinct *phases*, in *colloidal* solution. The particles form the *dispersed phase*, and the medium, usually a liquid, is the *dispersion medium*. Particles smaller than about 1 nm form homogeneous solutions, and particles larger than about 1–5 μm settle out. Colloidal particles are kept in solution by intimate association with the dispersion medium, by molecular motion, and by mutual repulsion through the electrical charges they bear.

Because of the sizes of the molecules, most soluble proteins in the body function in colloidal solution, and soluble proteins are the most important colloidal solutions in the body. Most of the plasma proteins are about 8 nm or more in diameter and remain in the plasma because they are too large to pass through the capillary pores. Thus, they are separated by ultrafiltration when isotonic solution is forced through the walls of the regular capillaries and glomerular capillaries of the kidneys. Because they do not pass readily through the capillary walls, the plasma proteins generate an osmotic force (*osmotic pressure*) of about 25 mm Hg, which opposes the tendency of the capillary hydrostatic pressure to cause ultrafiltration (see "Osmosis").

Colloids that dissolve in water are called lyophilic (signifying "water-loving"). Each particle has a layer of water adsorbed around it. Proteins have many charged sites, formed by carboxyl and amino groups that are not involved in the peptide linkages, which can adsorb water. The carboxyl and amino groups on a protein molecule react with one another to a certain extent, which decreases their interaction with water. When unequal numbers of oppositely charged sites exist on the surface of the protein, more sites are available to associate with water. The concentration of hydrogen ion, $[H^+]$, of the solution strongly influences the balance of the charged sites. In mild alkaline solution, for example, because of the decreased $[H^+]$, dissociation of the carboxyl group is increased:

$$R\text{-COOH} \rightleftarrows R\text{-COO}^- H^+$$

while the dissociation of the amino group is suppressed. On the other hand, in mild acid solution the dissociation of the carboxyl is suppressed but the amino group is charged:

$$R\text{-C-NH}_2 \rightleftarrows R\text{-C-NH}_3^+$$

If both groups are equally ionized, the charges

balance one another, the least water is adsorbed, and the protein is least soluble (more easily precipitated from solution). The [H⁺] at which this occurs is called the *isoelectric point* (IEP). As one might expect, the IEPs of the body proteins are not near the [H⁺] at which the proteins usually function. For example, the IEP of serum albumin is about pH 5, which is far from the normal plasma pH of 7.4. The electrical charges on proteins also cause the proteins to migrate in an electrical field; this property is used in electrophoresis.

Emulsions

Emulsions are dispersions of water in oil or oil in water. Emulsions in biological systems are the latter, because water is the solvent and dispersing medium in the body. Emulsions are similar to colloidal solutions, except that in emulsions the dispersed particles are larger and a stabilizing substance that associates partly with water surrounds the oil particles and keeps them dispersed. Proteins probably act as emulsifying agents in the cytoplasm, in which colloidal solutions and emulsions intermingle. Bile salts act as emulsifying agents for fats in the intestinal lumen, where they facilitate digestion and transport (see previous section, "Colloidal Solutions").

Dilution Principle

The dilution principle is widely applied in physiology. It is used to measure various body fluids, such as the extracellular fluid, the blood, and the intracellular volume. A variant of the basic principle, called the *Fick principle*, in which time is included, is used to measure the cardiac output and the clearance of substances from the plasma by the kidney.

In applying the dilution principle, a known amount of a solute, A, is added to an unknown volume of solvent, V, and mixed to produce a uniform solution. A sample is taken, and the concentration, C, of the solute in the solvent is determined. Since the concentration is the amount dissolved in the volume, we have

$$C = A/V$$

and, rearranging to solve for V,

$$V = \frac{A}{C}$$

The applications of this principle are given in the sections on cardiovascular physiology (Chapters 12–23), respiratory physiology (Chapters 27–35), and renal physiology (Chapters 36–45).

Diffusion

Substances in solution tend to be distributed evenly because of the random movement of their molecules. If, for example, a crystal of copper sulfate ($CuSO_4$) is placed in a small beaker, and the beaker is filled with water, the $CuSO_4$ begins to dissolve. The solution can be seen because of its blue color. At the top of the beaker is colorless water. The chemical activity of $CuSO_4$ is highest in the water immediately around and above the crystal, and the color is deep blue. Away from the crystal, the color is light blue and eventually disappears. If the beaker is covered and not disturbed, the solution spreads, although slowly. The solution spreads because of the random movement of the copper and sulfate ions. Net movement like this, from an area of a given chemical activity to an area of lower chemical activity is called *diffusion*. The decreasing chemical activity of $CuSO_4$ farther away from the crystal constitutes a *gradient* of chemical activity (see the section entitled "Gradient" earlier in this chapter). Diffusion proceeds down gradients. The water molecules also diffuse down gradients. The chemical activity of the water that forms the solution of $CuSO_4$ is less than the chemical activity of the pure water farther away. Hence, the water diffusing toward the $CuSO_4$ helps to equalize the solution. Eventually, by diffusion alone, the $CuSO_4$ will be in uniform solution throughout the beaker.

Osmosis

Suppose the beaker that is used to prepare the solution of $CuSO_4$ that was discussed in the preceding section were divided in half by a special membrane that stretched from side to side and top to bottom and was sealed against the glass at the sides and the bottom. The crystal of $CuSO_4$ is placed on one side and dissolved in water by stirring. Pure water is placed on the other side of the membrane. The beaker is only half filled on each side. Suppose, also, that water can pass easily through pores in the membrane, but Cu^{++} and $SO_4^=$ cannot. Because the chemical activity of the water is decreased by the $CuSO_4$, the rate of movement (*flux*) of water out of the solution, through the membrane, into the pure water, will be slower than the flux from the pure water into the solution. Thus, there will be a net flux of water into the $CuSO_4$ solution. The diffusion of water through a semipermeable membrane from an area of higher chemical activity to an area of lower chemical activity is called *osmosis*. The force of osmosis is measured by the hydrostatic pressure that is required to stop it; thus, the force of osmosis is called *osmotic pressure*. In the body, water moves freely through most cell membranes, whereas the movement of most solutes is somewhat restricted. Thus, body solutions, for the most part, have equal osmotic activity, and the maintenance of the homeostasis of the internal environment requires osmotic equality.

TENSION

Wall Tension: The Law of Laplace

In a sphere formed by a membrane (e.g., a soap bubble) the tension T in the wall increases with the volume V, and, since the system is elastic, the pressure P increases with the volume; hence, $T \simeq V$, $P \simeq V$, and $P \simeq T$. At any given constant size of bubble, the forces that tend to expand the system and those that tend to contract the system must be at equilibrium, as expressed by the pressure in the system, the tension at a given point, and the curvature of the wall at that point. The curvature is expressed by the radii of intersecting circles that share a common center (Figure 1-7A): the greater the radius, the greater the tension. Thus, the pressure required to maintain the distention is directly proportional to the tension produced and inversely proportional to the radii of curvature

$$P = T \left[\frac{1}{r_1} + \frac{1}{r_2} \right]$$

where r_1 and r_2 are the radii of the intersecting circles. Since $r_1 = r_2$ in a sphere,

$$P = T \times 2 \left[\frac{1}{r_1} \right] = \frac{2T}{r}$$

This is the law of Laplace. Although it is strictly correct only for very thin membranes, such as soap bubbles, it is used in principle to describe the relationship between volume and wall ten-

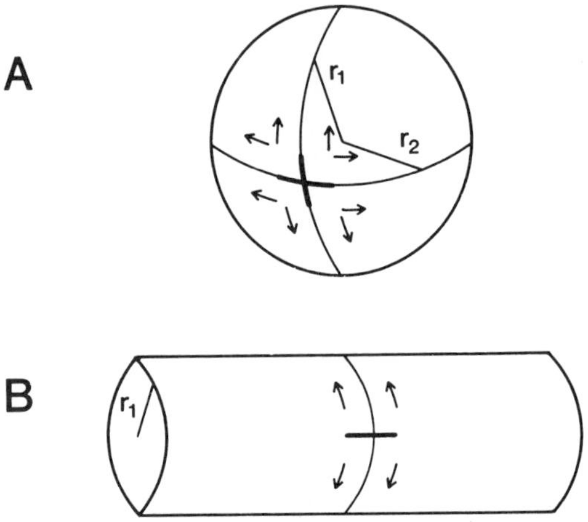

Figure 1-7. Concept of wall tension. **A.** In a sphere. The tension may be thought of as the force that is required to hold together the edges of a cut along each of two intersecting radii, r_1 and r_2. Because the tension is shared along two cuts, each cut must oppose only half of the tension. Hence, $T = \frac{1}{2} Pr$. **B.** In a cylinder. The tension is applied to only one radius; hence, $T = Pr$.

sion in the heart, and the relationship between adjoining alveoli in the lungs.

The principle of the law of Laplace also is applied to cylinders, such as blood vessels and intestines. A cylinder has only one radius of curvature (r_1); the surface is straight in the other dimension (Figure 1-7B). Since the radius of curvature of a straight line is infinite, $1/r_2 = 0$. Thus, for a cylinder,

$$P = T \times \frac{1}{r_1} + 0 = \frac{T}{r}$$

Rearranging, we can calculate wall tension by

$$T = Pr$$

In the cgs system,

$$T = Pr = \text{dyne cm}^{-2} \times \text{cm} = \text{dyne cm}^{-1}$$

The tension is directed along the surface of the sphere or the cylinder. It may be thought of as the force required to hold together the edges of a cut in the surface. Thus, a tension of 1 dyne cm^{-1} means that a force of 1 dyne would be required to hold together the edges of a cut 1 cm long.

Surface Tension

Molecules of a given chemical element or compound are attracted to one another. Thus, a large group of molecules in a liquid that have freedom of movement will arrange themselves in such a way as to obtain the closest association possible. A free-falling drop takes the form of a sphere because that shape puts the mass into the smallest possible space; hence, on the average, all of the molecules are as close together as they can be. When it is on a surface or in a container, however, a liquid spreads out because of the effect of gravity and its own fluidity.

A container of a liquid acts as if its surface layer forms a stretched membrane. Thus, a probe that is not wet by the liquid (i.e., to which the liquid does not adhere) depresses the surface when placed carefully in contact with the liquid. This phenomenon can be explained by the attraction of the molecules of the liquid for one another. Well beneath the surface of the liquid, a given molecule is surrounded on all sides by other molecules that mutually attract one another. The molecules on the surface, however, can share attraction only with other molecules below them or to their sides. Because there are no molecules above the surface, the attractive forces acting on the surface molecules are unbalanced. The surface molecules are attracted strongly toward the body of the liquid and to each side; the downward and sideways pull produces the effect of a stretched membrane. The tension in the "membrane" can be measured in dyne cm^{-1}, just as wall tension is. This phenomenon is called *surface tension*. A number of other phenomena that really are caused by the cohesive qualities of liquids, of which surface tension is one manifestation, are attributed directly to surface tension.

The surface tension of water is unusually high for such a small compound because of the polar nature of the water molecule. The surface tension (coherence) of water is decreased by heating, which increases the motion of the molecules, and by the use of materials called detergents, or surface-active agents. The consequences of the surface tension of water are particularly important in the respiratory system, where it can affect seriously the expansion of the lungs (see Chapter 28).

COMPLIANCE AND ELASTICITY

Compliance is the tendency of a material to be extended, or stretched, by a force. Compliance is the reciprocal of *elasticity*, which is the tendency of a material to return to its unstretched

length. Thus, it is impossible to consider compliance and elasticity separately. When applied to simple elongation and recoil, compliance and elasticity are expressed in the units of *length* and *tension*.

In structures such as the heart, the blood vessels, and the lungs, compliance and elasticity are expressed in units of pressure and volume. In this context, compliance sometimes is called *distensibility*. Compliance in these organs and tissues is expressed as change of volume with change of pressure (dV/dP, ml/mm Hg, or cm^3/dyne cm^{-2}). The compliance of the cardiac ventricles is very important to the filling of the heart and, hence, the maintenance of a normal stroke volume. The enlarged stroke volume of the athlete's heart is caused by increased cardiac compliance that was developed by training (see Chapter 73). The compliance of the large arteries is an important factor in making the flow of blood continuous despite the intermittent flow from the heart. Elasticity, measured as dP/dV in mm Hg/ml, or dyne cm^{-2}/cm^3, also is important in the arteries. In hardening of the arteries (*arteriosclerosis*), both compliance and elasticity are lost, and the arteries become somewhat dilated, rigid tubes. Consequently, arterial pressure is abnormally high during systole and abnormally low during diastole, and pulsatile flow is exaggerated (see Chapter 21).

Compliance also is important in the lungs, because it is a significant factor in determining the work of breathing. For example, compliance is decreased in respiratory distress syndrome (see Chapter 28). The elasticity of the lungs is important in the recoil, or emptying, of the lungs. In emphysema, for example, the lungs have lost much of their elasticity, which makes expiration difficult (see Chapter 35).

BIOELECTRICAL PARAMETERS

Currents

In biological systems, electrical current is carried by ions, such as Na$^+$, K$^+$, Cl$^-$, and so on. Cations, such as Na$^+$, and K$^+$, flow toward areas of negative ($-$) potential, and anions, such as Cl$^-$ and HCO$_3^-$, flow toward areas of positive ($+$) potential. Experimentally, sites of potential difference are formed by placing electrodes on the surface of tissues and connecting them to sources of electrical potential (stimulating electrodes). If the potential difference is great enough and the resistance between the electrodes is not too great, current flows in the tissue between the electrodes. The anions flow to the positive electrode (anode), and the cations flow to the negative electrode (cathode). Since the currents are equivalent, either of them could be used as a reference. By convention, nonspecific currents are expressed in terms of the flow of positive charges, regardless of whether they actually are carried by anions flowing toward an anode or by cations flowing toward a cathode.

Resistance and Potential

According to Ohm's law of electricity, the current I (in amperes) that flows in a conductor is directly proportional to the electrical potential difference E (in volts) across the circuit and inversely proportional to the resistance R (in ohms). Thus,

$$I = \frac{E}{R}$$

During the propagation of excitation, when currents flow outside excitable cells (nerve and muscle), differences of electrical potential develop along the lines of current flow because of the small but finite resistance of the extracellular fluids. These gradients of potential, described by a rearrangement of Ohm's law

$$E = IR$$

are reflected in the electrocardiogram and in action potentials of nerve and muscle that are recorded externally.

Capacitance

When resistance is high, as it is across the resting cell membrane, the current is very small. Since the interior of the cell is negative, the outside of the cell is positive, and the membrane is thin (e.g., 7–8 nm), negative charges on the inside and positive charges on the outside line up close to one another on opposite sides of the membrane (Figure 1-8A). This arrangement is like that of an electrical condenser, in which the membrane is the dielectric and the charges that attract one another across the membrane constitute the electrical capacity. If a pair of stimulating electrodes, insulated except at the tips, is placed on the membrane and connected to a source of electrical potential, positive charges at the outer surface of the membrane flow into the cathode, and negative charges at the outer sur-

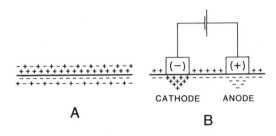

Figure 1-8. The membrane as a charged condenser. **A.** In the resting cell, negative charges line the inside of the membrane, and positive charges line the outside of the membrane. **B.** When a pair of stimulating electrodes is placed in contact with the tissue, positive charges outside the cell flow into the cathode and positive charges inside the cell flow to the membrane under the cathode. Corresponding movements of negative charges occur at the anode. Current flows into and out of the capacity of the membrane when the potential changes, as if the current had flowed through the membrane. When the capacity of the membrane is charged, however, no more current flows until the potential changes again.

face flow into the anode. The negativity of the cathode also attracts positive charges to the inner surface of the membrane (Figure 1-8B), decreasing the cellular potential under the cathode (*depolarization*). The opposite effect occurs under the anode, where the increased density of negative charges at the inner surface of the membrane increases the cellular potential (*hyperpolarization*). Effects like those under the cathode precede the formation of the action potential during the propagation of excitation (see Chapter 2).

Because current flows toward the membrane on one side and away from it on the other, the effect is as if the same amount of current had flowed *through* the membrane. However, the magnitude of the current that flows is limited by the size of charge the membrane can hold, that is, its capacity. The rate of charging or discharging is maximal initially and decreases exponentially as the capacity is filled or emptied. Once the capacity has been charged in accordance with the electrical potential difference across the membrane (*dielectric*), no more current flows. Thus, direct current (D.C.), generated by a constant potential, is blocked by a condenser; however, alternating current (A.C.), generated by a continually reversing, or alternating, potential (e.g., 60 Hz electricity in a power line), is not impeded.

STUDY OUTLINE

GENERAL BACKGROUND Physiology is the study of the function of organs and systems.

Important to know *how* organs and systems work, at both tissue and cellular levels.

Physiology is described in physical, chemical, and mathematical terms.

THE INTERNAL ENVIRONMENT: HOMEOSTASIS Body lives within itself in protected and regulated internal environment.

Internal environment exchanges with larger external environment through lungs, gastrointestinal tract, kidneys, and skin.

Circulatory system communicates between cells and routes of exchange.

Much of the study of physiology is concerned with maintaining constancy of internal environment (homeostasis).

CONTROL SYSTEMS

FEEDBACK Sample of output or level of product fed back to guide adjustment of rate of output.

NEGATIVE FEEDBACK Deviation of output or level of product from set point initiates adjustment to correct deviation.

Tends to maintain constancy—ideal for homeostasis.

Examples are control of arterial pressure and blood glucose level.

POSITIVE FEEDBACK Causes accelerating change and instability; much less application than with negative feedback.

Examples are action potential of excitable tissues and burst of estrogen that causes ovulation.

RATE Expresses relationship between two entities by stating one in terms of units of the other.

Most important rate base is time, but others also are used.

GRADIENT Uneven distribution of mass or energy.

Passive processes driven by movement down gradients; equilibrium-seeking.

Active processes proceed up gradients; much of work of body is to develop and maintain gradients.

PRESSURE Force per unit area.

Pressure gradients propel fluids and semi-solids.

MEASUREMENT OF PRESSURE

PRIMARY UNIT Pressure expressed as mm Hg.

Force required to raise column of mercury against force of gravity.

Mercury is convenient because of its high density.

STANDARD UNIT Standard unit of pressure is dyne/cm^2.

Pressure is measured indirectly as equivalent of known force exerted by gravity.

Mass is same everywhere; weight varies with effect of gravity on mass.

Force accelerates mass; unit is dyne—g cm/sec/sec.

One mm Hg = 1333 dyne/cm^2.

RELATIONSHIP TO ATMOSPHERIC PRESSURE Weight of atmosphere is on everything; all pressures are related to atmospheric pressure as 0, except in special circumstances.

FLOW

RATE OF FLOW Fluids flow down gradients of pressure.

Measured as volume displaced/unit of time (e.g., cm^3/sec).

VELOCITY OF FLOW Depends on rate of flow and size of conduit.

Measured as distance displaced/unit of time (e.g., cm/sec).

VISCOSITY AND RESISTANCE TO FLOW Fluid flows in laminae that slide apart under pressure gradient; faster in center of tube to stationary at wall.

Resistance is directly proportional to viscosity (friction between adjacent laminae) and length of tube; inversely proportional to radius of tube.

Measured practically as ratio of gradient of pressure required to cause unit of flow.

TURBULENT FLOW At critical velocity, laminar flow breaks up, producing turbulence.

Occurs in constricted vessels and damaged cardiac valves and, normally, at peak of ventricular ejection.

KINETIC ENERGY AND INERTIA Kinetic energy is put into a body to move it and taken out to stop it.

Related to mass of body and velocity.

Resistance to being moved or stopped—inertia.

Together with elastic arteries helps to convert intermittent output of heart into continuous flow.

SOLUTIONS

TRUE, OR MOLECULAR, SOLUTIONS Homogeneous mixture of two or more substances.

Water is the solvent in biological solutions.

Solutes in water must interact with water through polarity, or charge.

Soluble inorganic components are ionized.

Organic compounds are made soluble by ionization, salt formation, or alcoholic hydroxyls.

Large organic molecules that have both water-soluble and lipid-soluble portions serve as interface between water and water-insoluble organic compounds; form special carriers for fats in gastrointestinal tract and plasma.

COLLOIDAL SOLUTIONS   Particles larger than about 1 nm in diameter; uniformly mixed, but exist in distinct phases.

Kept in solution by interaction with dispersion medium (water in biological systems), molecular motion, and mutual repulsion caused by electrical charges.

Proteins form colloidal solutions—interact with water through carboxyl and amino groups.

Proteins are least soluble at isoelectric point (pH at which carboxyl groups and amino groups interact most with each other and least with water).

Plasma proteins are too large to pass through capillary walls; generate osmotic force that helps to keep fluid in capillaries.

EMULSIONS   In biological solutions, dispersions of oil in water; particles larger than in colloidal solutions.

Substances that associate partly with oil, partly with water (emulsifying agents) keep particles dispersed.

Bile salts emulsify fats in lumen of gastrointestinal tract; aid digestion and transport.

DILUTION PRINCIPLE   Solute dissolved in unknown volume of solvent; concentration of sample is used to solve for volume.

Variant that includes time—Fick principle—is used to measure cardiac output and renal clearance of substances from plasma.

DIFFUSION   Substances in solution tend to distribute uniformly because of diffusion down gradients of chemical activity.

OSMOSIS   Diffusion of water from one compartment to another of lower chemical activity through membrane not permeable to solutes.

Osmotic pressure—hydrostatic pressure required to stop osmosis.

Solutes decrease chemical activity of water.

TENSION

WALL TENSION—THE LAW OF LAPLACE In a soap bubble, wall tension equals ½ product of internal pressure and radius ($T = Pr/2$).

Principle is applied to elastic spheres and cylinders.

In cylinders $T = Pr$.

Important in cardiovascular, respiratory, and gastrointestinal sytems.

SURFACE TENSION   Unbalanced attraction of molecules at surface of liquid to those in body of solutions produces effect like stretched surface membrane.

Affects wetting properties of water.

Cohesive force among water molecules is an important factor in work required to expand lungs.

COMPLIANCE AND ELASTICITY   Reciprocals.

Compliance is tendency of material to be stretched or distended; measured as dV/dP.

Elasticity is tendency of stretched material to return to unstretched length; measured as dP/dV.

Important properties of cardiovascular and respiratory systems.

BIOELECTRICAL PARAMETERS

CURRENTS   In biological systems, carried by ions down gradients of electrical potential.

Expressed as flow of positive charges (cations).

RESISTANCE AND POTENTIAL   Potential difference develops as current flows through resistance—can be measured as external action potentials of nerve and muscle.

CAPACITANCE   Charges line up across cell membrane—negative inside, positive outside—similar to electrical condenser.

Amount of charge held is capacity of membrane.

Small currents flow into capacity on one side and out on other—as if flowing through membrane, up to limit of capacity.

Capacitative currents flow during excitation, before and after action potential.

BIBLIOGRAPHY

Adolph, E.F. 1982. Physiological integrations in action. *The Physiologist* 25: (Suppl.).

Aird, E.G.A. 1975. *An Introduction to Medical Physics.* London: William Heinemann Medical Books.

Albergoni, V. 1974. *Biological Systems: An Engineering Approach to Physiology.* Bologna: Pitagura.

Astin, A.V. 1968. Standards of measurement. *Sci. Am.* 218:50.

Aukland, K., and Nicolaysen, G. 1981. Interstitial fluid volume: Local regulatory mechanisms. *Physiol. Rev.* 61:556.

Basar, E. 1976. *Biophysical and Physiological Systems Analysis: Based on Lectures to Graduate Students.* Reading, Massachusetts: Addison-Wesley Publishing Co.

Bayliss, L.E. 1959. *Principles of General Physiology.* London: Longman.

Brown, B.H. 1981. *Medical Physics and Physiological Measurement.* Oxford: Blackwell Scientific.

Burton, A.C. 1972. *Physiology and Biophysics of the Circulation.* Chicago: Yearbook Medical Publishers, Inc.

Cannon, W.B. 1939. *The Wisdom of the Body* (2nd ed.). New York: W.W. Norton and Co.

Frisancho, A.R. 1979. *Human Adaptation.* St. Louis: C.V. Mosby Co.

Giese, A.C. 1979. *Cell Physiology* (5th ed.). Philadelphia: W.B. Saunders Co.

Hedeskov, C.J. 1980. Mechanisms of glucose-induced insulin secretion. *Physiol. Rev.* 60:442.

Hobbie, R.K. 1978. *Intermediate Physics for Medicine and Biology.* New York: John Wiley and Sons.

Jensen, J.T. 1982. *Physics for the Health Professions.* New York: John Wiley and Sons.

Kalmus, H. (ed.). 1966. *Regulation and Control in Living Systems.* New York: John Wiley and Sons.

Manning, J.W. (chairman). 1980. Central integration of cardiovascular control. (Symposium) *Fed. Proc.* 39:2485.

Marshall, A.G. 1978. *Biophysical Chemistry: Principles, Techniques, and Applications.* New York: John Wiley and Sons.

Milhorn, H.T. 1966. *The Application of Control Theory to Physiological Systems.* Philadelphia: W.B. Saunders Co.

Mitchell, J.H. (chairman). 1980. Regulation in physiological systems during exercise. (Symposium) *Fed. Proc.* 39:1479.

Moncrief, J.W., and Jones, W.H. 1977. *Elements of Physical Chemistry.* Reading, Massachusetts: Addison-Wesley Publishing Co.

Riggs, D.S. 1970. *Control Theory and Physiological Feedback Mechanisms.* Huntington, New York: Krieger.

Schmidt-Nielsen, K. 1981. Countercurrent systems in animals. *Sci. Am.* 244:(5)118.

Sears, F.W., Zemansky, M.W., and Young, H.D. 1982. *University Physics* (6th ed.). Reading, Massachusetts: Addison-Wesley Publishing Co.

Zierler, K. (chairman). 1981. Roles of electrical potentials across membranes in functions of living systems (Symposium) *Fed. Proc.* 40:119.

2

Cell Physiology

CHAPTER CONTENTS

STRUCTURE AND CONTENTS OF THE CELL

The generalized cell (Figure 2-1) is bounded by a plasma membrane and filled with cytoplasm that contains two types of structures: (1) organelles, which have definite functions and are essential to the life of the cell, and (2) inclusions, which may perform functions but without which the cell can survive. Examples of inclusions are secretory granules, pigments, and stored nutrients, such as fat or glycogen granules.

Organelles

NUCLEUS

In tissue preparations stained for light microscopy, the most prominent organelle is the *nucleus,* which is filled with a dark-staining substance called *chromatin.* Modern techniques by which nuclei can be removed from the cell and purified have revealed that chromatin is a complex of *deoxyribonucleic acid* (DNA), *ribonucleic acid* (RNA), and specific proteins. DNA has been identified as the genetic material of the body. During cell division, the chromatin is condensed into *chromosomes,* each of which is composed of a series of DNA molecules bound to the protein histone. A *gene* is a portion of a DNA molecule that carries the genetic information needed to construct an enzyme, which, by its role in a metabolic chain, helps to determine the structure or function of the body. The amount of DNA in the nucleus is constant in all of the tissues of a particular species. This is consistent with the function of DNA as the genetic material. The nucleus contains a smaller amount of RNA, most of which is in the nucleolus. The amount of RNA in the nucleus varies with the metabolic state of the cell.

The nucleus is surrounded by a double membrane system, the *nuclear envelope.* Openings called *nuclear pores* extend through the membrane and align with channels of nucleoplasm. The membranes join to form the edges of the pores, and the chromatin attaches to the inner membrane.

Most of the activities of the cell are initiated and regulated by the nucleus. The nucleus contains enzymes that are necessary for the synthesis of DNA, RNA, coenzymes, and high-energy phosphate bonds. Although most of the RNA of the cell is in the cytoplasm, RNA is synthesized in the nucleus and passes through the nuclear pores. RNA directs the synthesis of protein on the ribosomes of the endoplasmic reticulum. Messenger RNA (mRNA) is formed by the DNA of the nucleus and carries the genetic message to the sites of protein synthesis.

ENDOPLASMIC RETICULUM

The endoplasmic reticulum (ER) first was observed as a lacy structure within the cytoplasm. Subsequently, ER was discovered to be a series of tubules and flattened sacs, called *cisternae,* that extend from the surface of the cell into the cytoplasm. This system may serve to communicate and transport substances between the exterior and the interior of the cell. In muscle, in which it is called the *sarcoplasmic reticulum* (SR), it conducts the electrical potential that excites myofibrils deep within the cell (see Chapter 9). The SR also takes part in excitation-contraction coupling, through the release and uptake of Ca^{++}.

The endoplasmic reticulum consists, in different cells, of rough ER and smooth ER. Rough ER derives its name from its appearance, which is caused by the occurrence of ribosomes on the cytoplasmic surface. Rough ER is prominent in cells that produce and secrete enzymes or other proteins; thus, the *ribosomes*

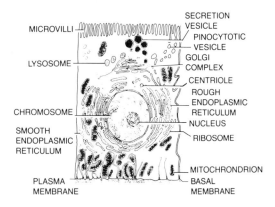

Figure 2-1.   Structure of the generalized cell.

are associated with the synthesis of protein. About 65% of the ribosome is ribosomal RNA (rRNA), and structural protein forms the remaining 35%. The synthesis of protein in the ribosome is directed by DNA, which carries the genetic code, through the synthesis of mRNA and transfer RNA (tRNA). mRNA is synthesized in the nucleus and transported through the nuclear pores into the cytoplasm, where it combines with and activates ribosomes on the ER. mRNA carries the genetic template that is obtained from DNA. The synthesis of protein begins with the activation of an amino acid by reaction with adenosine triphosphate (ATP) in the presence of a specific activating enzyme. tRNA carries activated amino acids to the mRNA on the ribosome, where they are added to the growing peptide, and the tRNA is released. Groups of ribosomes acting together are called *polysomes.*

The smooth ER is involved in the synthesis of carbohydrates and lipids and in detoxifying chemicals. Enzymes that synthesize glycogen, triglycerides, steroids, phosphatides, and other lipids have been identified. The ER of liver cells contains enzymes that conjugate, hydroxylate, deaminate, decarboxylate, and carry out other reactions that make some compounds available for synthesis (see Chapter 51) and make other compounds water-soluble, so that they can be excreted.

Through differential centrifugation, biochemists have isolated a fraction that consists of fragments of the cell membrane and various parts of the ER, the vacuolar system, and the Golgi complex. This fraction, called the *microsomal system* because of the small size of the particles in it, contains a number of enzymes. However, this microsomal system is produced in the laboratory and is not a discrete component of the intact cell.

GOLGI COMPLEX

The Golgi complex was discovered by its staining characteristics long before its function was known. Thought to be an extension of the ER, the Golgi complex is most prominent in neurons and secretory cells. It consists of secretory vesicles and a series of cisternae that appear to be stacked. In cells that have a definite secretory surface, such as the acinar cells of the pancreas (see Figure 50-3), the Golgi complex is located between the nucleus and the secretory membrane. In liver and nerve cells, the cisternae are not so localized. The Golgi complex forms secretions of mucus and mucopolysaccharides (e.g., in the endothelium of the alimentary tract) and participates in secretion in some tissues (e.g., the endocrine pancreas) by providing a phospholipid coating for packets of enzymes. These packets merge with the cell membrane when the secretory contents are delivered outside the cell.

MITOCHONDRIA

The mitochondria are the sites of oxygen use in the cell. The mitochondria contain the enzymes that extract energy from substrates and store it in the phosphate bonds of adenosine triphosphate (ATP). ATP diffuses to areas of the cell where the energy is used to do work. Oxygen accepts hydrogen to form water and combines with carbon to form carbon dioxide (CO_2). Water and CO_2 contain no biologically available energy and are easily eliminated when they are in excess.

Mitochondria are distributed in the cytoplasm, and in many cells they are free to move about. Usually, the mitochondria are concentrated in the cell near areas of activity, such as the regions where contraction (muscular), absorption, secretion, and synthesis occur. The numbers vary depending on the level of cellular activity. A normal liver cell, for example, may contain between 1000 and 2000 mitochondria, which comprise 30%–35% of the protein in the cell. Mitochondria take the form of short rods with rounded ends, about 0.5 μm in diameter and up to 7 μm long.

The detailed structure of the mitochondrion was not known until electron microscopy was

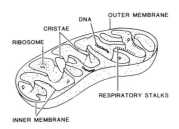

Figure 2-2.   Mitochondrion.

developed (Figure 2-2). The mitochondrion is surrounded by two membranes about 7 nm apart. The outer membrane is permeable to ions, water, and other molecules up to a molecular weight of about 10,000 daltons. The inner membrane forms folds, or crests, that extend much of the way across the interior of the structure. The inner membrane is selectively permeable and contains proteins that serve as carriers for specific substances. Through the use of energy (i.e., active transport), the mitochondrion accumulates K^+, Ca^{++}, Mg^{++}, and phosphate against electrochemical gradients. Because of its selective permeability and accumulation of certain ions, the mitochondrion, like the cell, is sensitive to the osmolarity of its surroundings. The infoldings of the inner membrane to form the crests greatly increase the inner surface of the mitochondrion. Many of the enzymes appear to be fixed to the surface in a three-dimensional matrix that groups related enzymes and facilitates sequential reactions. The interior of the mitochondrion is filled with a proteinaceous material, which is called the *mitochondrial matrix*. The matrix contains a small amount of DNA and a few ribosomes, and may contain filaments and granules. A few of the mitochondrial enzymes and a small amount of the proteinase are coded by mitochondrial DNA, but most of the enzymes are coded by nuclear DNA, formed in the ribosomes of the cytoplasm, and incorporated into the mitochondria.

LYSOSOMES

Lysosomes are small cytoplasmic particles, 0.2–0.8 μm in diameter, which are filled with hydrolytic enzymes and surrounded by a single membrane. Lysosomes contain enzymes that hydrolyze protein, carbohydrate, lipid, nucleic acids, and organic phosphate, although a given lysosome need not contain all of these enzymes. The membrane protects the cell from *autolysis* (digesting itself). Lysosomes appear to have been derived from either the ER or the Golgi complex; possibly, lysosomes come from both cellular components. Lysosomes rupture spontaneously in injured or dying cells, thus serving to remove noncontributing units. In circulatory shock, lysosomes released from damaged cells contribute to the progression of the condition (see Chapter 23). Lysosomes contribute to the growth and remodeling of cells by removing obsolete or outgrown structures.

PEROXISOMES

Peroxisomes, also called *microbodies,* resemble lysosomes but differ in that they contain oxidative enzymes that produce hydrogen peroxide (H_2O_2) and contain catalase, which decomposes the H_2O_2 to water and oxygen. The peroxisomes isolate the reactions that produce peroxide and destroy this toxic substance as it is produced. Peroxisomes are formed from the ER.

MICROTUBULES AND MICROFILAMENTS

Before the development of the electron microscope, cytoplasm was thought to be amorphous. Although there were some suggestions of structural material in the cell, this material could not consistently be distinguished from artifacts. Electron microscopy has revealed a three-dimensional matrix of microtubules and microfilaments among the organelles. Cytosol fills the spaces of the cells and forms the internal environment of the cell.

The microtubules are straight pipes that are about 25 nm in outside diameter and several μm long. Microtubules appear to be important in maintaining processes and extensions, as well as the physical shape of the cell in general. They function to shape the cell during differentiation and are involved in the distribution of organelles, the transport of macromolecules within the cell, and the transduction of energy in sensory processes. The microtubules are composed of the protein *tubulin.*

Microfilaments, which are 6–10 nm thick, form a lattice that extends throughout the cell from the plasma membrane to the nucleus. This lattice appears to support or contain vesicles of the ER, microtubules, and polysomes. It consists mostly of actin, but also contains myosin, tropomyosin, troponin-C, and α-actinin. The presence of the contractile proteins suggests that this microfilament lattice plays a role in contraction or movement.

Structure of the Cell Membrane

DANIELLI–DAVSON MODEL

The plasma membrane was not seen until after electron microscopy was developed. On the basis of studies of permeability, Overton, in 1902, proposed that the cell membrane consisted of a thin layer of lipid. Subsequently, it was found that the membrane of the red blood cell, the cell that has been studied the most, contained enough lipid for two thin layers. However, the surface tension at the interface of the cell and the surrounding water is too low to support the hypothesis of a simple lipid sheet. Therefore, Danielli and Davson, in 1935, proposed that the cell membrane is a lipid bilayer covered, at least to some extent, by globular protein. Danielli and Davson thought that the lipid consisted of a nonpolar hydrocarbon and another group, such as phosphate, that could take on an electrical charge. The nonpolar hydrocarbon tails were thought to face toward the interior of the membrane, and the charged heads were believed to face toward the intracellular and extracellular fluids (Figure 2-3A and B). The globular protein also was viewed as having hydrophobic and hydrophilic surfaces, so lipid and protein formed a loose polar bond.

The model soon was modified, because research had shown that the protein-lipid bond was much tighter than had been thought initially. The second model added an "unrolled" layer of protein that had a hydrophobic layer bound to the lipid heads and a hydrophilic surface dotted with globules of protein (Figure 2-3C). The description of the cell membrane in this model was consistent with the movement of most molecules that are found in the intracellular and extracellular fluids; however, Danielli found that some substances traversed the membrane more quickly than simple diffusion through the membrane would allow. He felt that channels or pores must exist, through which these molecules could travel and bypass the lipid barrier; further, Danielli believed that these active regions might be filled with some form of enzyme (which consists of protein).

The final model of Danielli and Davson (in 1955) described the lipid bilayer as being surrounded by two layers of bound protein that were interwoven to some degree, and active patches, or channels, of absorbed, unrolled protein (Figure 2-3D). Since then, this model has been found to be too inflexible to describe the dynamics of the cell membrane.

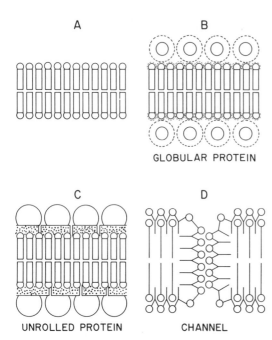

GLOBULAR PROTEIN

UNROLLED PROTEIN   CHANNEL

Figure 2-3. Models of the membrane proposed by Danielli and Davson. **A.** The bilayer of polar lipid in water has hydrophilic "heads" in contact with the water, and hydrophobic "tails" that face one another. **B.** The original membrane model of bilipid layer contained by protein globules (1934). **C.** A revision of the model (1937) that incorporated a layer of unrolled protein. **D.** The final unit-membrane model that has protein channels available for communication between the extracellular and intracellular fluids. (**A** and **C:** Redrawn, with permission, from Danielli, J.F., and Davson, H. 1970. *The Permeability of Natural Membranes.* New York: Cambridge University Press. **B:** Redrawn, with permission, from Danielli, J.F. and Davson, H. 1936. *J. Cell. Comp. Physiol.* 5:498. **D:** Redrawn, with permission, from Stein, W.D. and Danielli, J.F. 1956. Structure and function in red cell permeability. *Disc. Faraday Soc.* 21:249.)

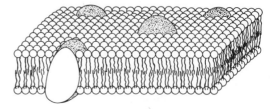

Figure 2-4. Singer-Nicolson membrane model. The functional protein communicates with both extracellular and intracellular fluid, presumably to participate in ionic transport at the active sites of the cell membrane.

MODEL OF SINGER AND NICOLSON

Singer and Nicolson's model describes the cell membrane as being like "icebergs" of protein embedded in a "sea" of lipid. The base is a lipid bilayer that contains two layers of proteins: structural and functional. The proteins and the lipids both are believed to have hydrophobic and hydrophilic areas (Figure 2-4). The functional proteins traverse the entire lipid bilayer and project into the intracellular and extracellular fluids. Structural proteins embedded in the lipid bilayers are free to move laterally through the membrane, whereas the func-

tional proteins define the active areas of the membrane.

The process of freeze-etching has allowed investigators to split the cell membrane between the lipid bilayers. The Singer-Nicolson model predicts that protein bumps will be evident on a rather smooth background. Electron micrographs show a roughened surface, that is, protuberant particles above the split in the lipid bilayer. All of the types of membranes that have been examined demonstrate this rough surface.

Recent experimental evidence shows that abundant internal extensions of molecular structures are attached to the plasma membranes (see the earlier section entitled "Microtubules and Microfilaments") of most cells, and, therefore, in the view of some physiologists, it is difficult to know where the internal surface of the membrane ends and the aqueous cytoplasmic phase begins. Thus, anatomically, the membrane may not be a single sheet that separates two solutions; physiologically, however, the cell appears to function as it would if it possessed a well-defined, semipermeable outer membrane.

SURFACE RECEPTORS

Many of the effects of intercellular communication are mediated through specialized areas of the cell membrane. Since early in the twentieth century, physiologists have thought that neurotransmitters react with specific sites on the surface. Pharmacologists also thought along this line, because many drugs are active in such low concentrations that they could not possibly form even a monomolecular layer on the surface of all of the cells they affect. Thus, pharmacologists proposed that the molecules of drugs must interact with "receptive patches" on the surface of the cells. Ultimately, the notion of *receptors* was developed, and this concept has been very useful in explaining the actions of drugs, hormones, transmitters, peptides, antigens, and bacterial toxins.

Many receptors in cell membranes are coupled to enzymes, such as adenylate cyclase and guanylate cyclase, which are located at the inner surface of the membrane. The circulating chemical binds to a specific receptor protein that interacts with the enzyme, most often adenylate cyclase, and exerts its characteristic effect on the cell by altering the activity of the enzyme. Adenylate cyclase acts on adenosine triphosphate (ATP) to produce 3', 5'-cyclic adenosine monophosphate (cyclic AMP), which is released into the cytoplasm. The effect of cyclic AMP in the cell depends on the organ or system that is involved. Cyclic AMP is known to mediate the actions of norepinephrine, acetylcholine, epinephrine, growth hormone, antidiuretic hormone (ADH), thyroid hormone, parathyroid hormone, adrenocorticotrophic hormone (ACTH), glucagon, and luteinizing hormone. The effects of cyclic AMP may include activation of additional enzymes, changes of cellular permeability, synthesis of protein, synthesis of steroid compounds, and other physiological actions. The cell regulates the actions of cyclic AMP through the enzyme phosphodiesterase, which changes cyclic AMP to AMP.

Cyclic AMP usually acts on additional intermediaries. In the action of epinephrine to break down glycogen in the liver cell, for example, cyclic AMP activates protein kinase, which, in turn, activates phosphorylase kinase, which activates glycogen phosphorylase, which degrades glycogen to glucose. Through these *cascades* of enzymes, the original signal is amplified in the cell.

Although each hormone, transmitter, or other activator reacts with a specific receptor protein in a given cell, several kinds of receptors can couple to adenylate cyclase. Adenylate cyclase can interact with two or more different receptors in the same cell (e.g., epinephrine and glucagon in the liver cell) or with a variety of different receptors in the cells of different organs. The mobility of the membrane proteins permits adenylate cyclase to have this wide range of associations.

PHYSIOLOGY OF
THE CELL MEMBRANE

Much of our knowledge of the cell membrane has been derived from studies of the red blood cell, or erythrocyte, and the properties of membranes in general are assumed to be similar, if not identical to the membrane of the red blood cell. The concentrations of substances inside the cell are quite different from the concentration of substances outside the cell, and the differences are believed to be related to the selective permeability of the cell membrane and the transport of certain specific substances across the cell membrane.

Passive Transport

Generally, lipid-soluble substances that dissolve in the membrane pass through it by simple, nonionic *diffusion*. (Diffusion is the random movement of particles in solution from one area to another area of lower chemical activity.) Some substances that dissolve in the membrane also are water-soluble (e.g., ethanol). Other substances, such as fatty acids and triglycerides, are not water-soluble and must be transported to the membrane by special water-soluble carriers (see Chapter 53).

Inorganic ions, such as K^+, Cl^-, and Na^+, and other polar, water-soluble compounds generally do not move through the lipid of the membrane very easily and may not move through it at all, in fact. These solutes are believed to diffuse through pores in the membrane or to be transported by special proteins in the membrane.

DIFFUSION

Nonionized substances move down their chemical gradients; ions move down chemical gradients, electrical gradients, or both (electrochemical gradients). The net rate of diffusion, or *flux,* for any given species of particle is proportional to (a) the gradient of chemical activity (the difference between the chemical activity of the species inside the cell and outside the cell), (b) the electrical potential difference between the inside of the cell and the outside, (c) the cross-sectional area of the pores through which the particles pass, and (d) the temperature of the system. The rate of diffusion is *inversely* proportional to (a) the molecular weight of the particle and (b) the thickness of the membrane.

FACILITATED DIFFUSION

Some substances combine with specific proteins in the membrane, called *permeases,* which aid the movement of these substances across the membrane. If the substance that is transported moves through the membrane faster than it could move alone, but cannot move against a chemical or electrical gradient, the process is called *facilitated diffusion*. Permeases are available only for certain substances; hence, they show specificity. Since only a certain number of carrier molecules can cross the membrane in a unit of time, the system can be saturated. When saturation occurs, increasing the concentration of the substance does not increase the rate of transport of the substance. Sometimes, closely related members of a class of chemical compounds can be transported by the same permease system. Molecules of each member of the class combine with the carrier in proportion to their chemical activities and affinities. Hence, the compounds compete for the carrier, and none of them is transported at the rate it would be if the others were not present.

Active Transport

Transport of a substance across the membrane from one area to another area of higher chemical activity or against an electrical potential gradient is called *active transport* (see the section on active transport of K^+ and Na^+ in this chapter and Chapter 40). Active transport requires the use of energy, which is supplied by cellular metabolism. Active transport is identified closely with the action of specific enzymes (e.g., Na^+, K^+-activated ATPase), and the occurrence of these enzymes in a tissue often is taken as evidence of active transport. Systems of active transport depend on special transport proteins, which are located in the membrane and have specific binding affinities. Hence, these special transport proteins are specific, can be saturated, and may be competed for by chemically related substances.

Water

In addition to ions and molecules of solute, water also passes through the cell membrane. If the membrane were relatively *impermeable* to particles, but water could diffuse through it, water would flow through the membrane from any region where its activity is higher to any other region where its activity is lower. This process of net diffusion of water caused by differences of the chemical activity on each side of the cell membrane is called *osmosis*. The chemical activity of the water is determined by the number of particles that are dissolved in the water. It is higher in a dilute solution of particles than it is in a concentrated solution. The effect of particles in solution on the chemical activity

of water is recognized in the term *osmolality*. The net flow of water can be demonstrated by placing erythrocytes in a solution of NaCl. If the osmolality of the NaCl solution is equal to the osmolality of the intracellular fluid (i.e., the solutions are *isosmotic*), and the volume of the cell does not change, the solution is said to be *isotonic*. However, if the NaCl solution is *hypertonic* (of higher osmolality than the intracellular fluid), water diffuses out of the cell and the erythrocytes shrink. On the other hand, if the saline solution is *hypotonic* (of lower osmolality than the intracellular fluid), water diffuses into the cells and the erythrocytes swell. If the swelling is great enough, the plasma membrane eventually ruptures, or *hemolyzes,* and hemoglobin leaves the cell.

The terms *isosmotic* and *isotonic* are not synonymous. Isosmotic means that a solution has the same osmotic activity as plasma. Isotonic means that the volume of the cell does not change. Suppose red blood cells were placed in an isosmotic solution of a solute to which they are permeable (e.g., 0.3 osmolal urea). If urea did not penetrate the cells, the activity of the water inside the cell would be the same as the activity of water outside the cell, and the volume of the cell would not change. Because urea enters the cell, however, it decreases the activity of the water inside the cell, water enters down its activity gradient, and the cell swells. Thus, an isosmotic solution may or may not be isotonic, depending on the properties of the membrane in question.

The force of osmosis can be demonstrated by placing a membrane that is permeable to water but not to NaCl between the two halves of an apparatus that forms a U-tube (Figure 2-5). A solution of NaCl in water is placed in side 1, and an equal volume of water is placed in side 2. Two fluxes of water develop—from side 1 to side 2, and from side 2 to side 1 (Figure 2-5A). The fluxes are carried by two forces: (1) osmosis, the movement of water down its chemical activity gradient, and (2) filtration, the movement of water down its hydrostatic pressure gradient. Because the height of the two columns is the same, the fluxes caused by filtration will be the same, and no net filtration flux occurs.* How-

---

*This is not strictly true, because the *specific gravity* (weight of a unit volume) of the NaCl solution is slightly greater than the specific gravity of the pure water; hence, the flux caused by filtration from side 1 to side 2 exceeds the flux from side 2 to side 1. However, the difference of the flux caused by filtration is very small relative to the flux caused by osmosis and can safely be ignored.

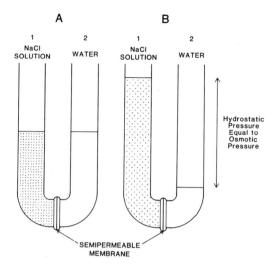

Figure 2-5. The force of osmosis (osmotic pressure). The membrane is permeable to water but not to NaCl. **A.** A solution of NaCl in water is placed in side *1* and pure water is placed in side *2*. **B.** At equilibrium. The net movement of water into side *1* has increased the hydrostatic pressure in side *1* and decreased the hydrostatic pressure in side *2*. The difference of hydrostatic pressure has stopped osmosis.

---

ever, the fluxes caused by osmosis are not equal—the flux from side 2 to side 1 exceeds that from side 1 to side 2 because the chemical activity of the pure water in side 2 exceeds that in the solution of NaCl in side 1. Thus, a net osmotic flux between the two sides is established. Because of the net movement of water from side 2 to side 1, the level of solution in side 1 rises, and the level of water in side 2 falls. Because the height of the two columns differs, the hydrostatic pressure of each differs. The greater pressure (force per unit area) on side 1 increases the filtration flux from side 1 to side 2, while the filtration flux from side 2 to side 1 decreases as the pressure on side 1 decreases. Thus, the rate of transfer of water from side 2 to side 1 decreases, and, eventually, no more water is transferred (Figure 2-5B). The difference of hydrostatic pressure caused by the difference of height of the two columns has generated a filtration flux equal to the osmotic flux. Thus, it has stopped osmosis. The force that stops osmosis is called the osmotic pressure of the solution. Osmotic pressure, as such, does not exist in biological systems, but it does represent the force that causes osmosis.

The osmotic pressure π of a solution can be calculated by the expression

$$\pi = RT[S_a]$$

where R is the universal gas constant, T is the temperature in degrees Kelvin (K), and $[S_a]$ is the sum of the chemical activities of each substance in solution. By these means, the osmotic pressure can be calculated as 19.3 mm Hg per milliosmole. Thus, the osmotic pressure of isotonic NaCl solution (0.9%) is 5500 mm Hg (285 mOsm $\times$ 19.3 mm Hg/mOsm). This is a considerable force (remember that the mean arterial blood pressure in humans is about 90 mm Hg).

The *osmolality* of a solution, or the amount by which the chemical activity of the water has been decreased, can be determined by the method of freezing-point depression. When its chemical activity is decreased, the tendency of water to form the crystalline structure that is characteristic of ice is decreased, and the water must be colder to freeze. One mole of an ideal solute depresses the freezing point of 1 kg of water by 1.86 C. This is a 1 osmolal solution. (An ideal solute has a chemical activity coefficient of 1.0, which means that its own molecules do not restrict the freedom of movement of each other.) Human blood plasma decreases the freezing point of water by 0.536 C; thus, plasma is a 0.536/1.86 = 0.288 osmolal solution, or 288 milliosmolal (mOsm). Isotonic NaCl solution (9 g/liter) contains 308 mEq/liter of NaCl. Isotonic NaCl depresses the freezing point of water by 0.53 C; thus, it is 0.53/1.86 = 285 mOsm. Its activity coefficient is (285/308 =) 0.925.

The osmotic pressure that is generated by the plasma proteins (also called *plasma oncotic pressure* or *colloidal osmotic pressure*) is a special case of osmosis. Here, the capillary wall forms the semipermeable membrane (see Chapter 12). The total chemical activity of the plasma proteins, mostly albumin but also consisting of globulin and fibrinogen, is 1.3 mOsm. Thus,

$$\pi = 19.3 \text{ mm Hg/mOsm} \times 1.3 \text{ mOsm}$$
$$= 25.1 \text{ mm Hg}$$

This force opposes the capillary blood pressure, which tends to filter plasma water and small solutes (Na^+, Cl^-, K^+, etc.) into the interstitium (see Chapter 12).

Electrical Gradients

Because many of the particles in the fluid inside and outside the cell have an electrical charge, the movements of these particles involve electrical as well as chemical forces. A salt of a strong acid and a strong base, for example, ionizes into cations and anions, which are charged oppositely.

Each ion is attracted by any other ion of opposite charge and is repelled by any other ion that has the same charge. If the cation, for example, diffuses more rapidly or is transported actively through a membrane and its associated anion lags behind, an electrical gradient develops across the membrane. The potential difference accelerates the movement of the anion, so that the distance between the cation and the anion and the magnitude of the potential difference become constant. This potential, called a *diffusion potential,* develops at any permeability barrier that the cation and the anion do not penetrate at the same rate, or, if the motilities of the cation and the anion are different, a diffusion potential develops at any junction of the solution with another solution of different composition or concentration. The two sides of the membrane are like the poles of a battery—an electrical potential difference exists between them, and an electrical current flows between them when they are connected by a conductor.

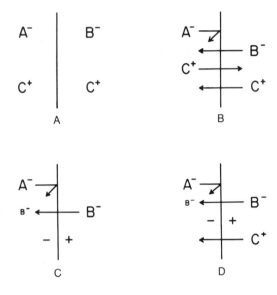

Figure 2-6.   Donnan equilibrium. **A.** A semipermeable membrane separates dilute solutions of two salts, C^+A^- and C^+B^-. **B.** The membrane is permeable to B^- and C^+ but not to A^-. **C.** B^- crosses the membrane down its gradient of chemical activity; the accumulation of anions creates a negative potential difference. **D.** The cation enters the cell down the electrical gradient.

DONNAN EQUILIBRIUM

The model system developed by Donnan describes the relationship between chemical species and electrical potentials. Although it is a far simpler system than the system to which the cellular potential is related, it is useful in illustrating the potential developed by passive diffusion.

Suppose that a membrane separates two aqueous solutions of ionized salts (Figure 2-6A). The cation (C^+) is the same in each solution and is small enough to cross the membrane easily. The anion on one side (B^-) is small and can cross the membrane easily, but the anion (A^-) on the other side is large and cannot cross the membrane (Figure 2-6B).

The occurrence of a particular species of anion on one side of the membrane but not on the other constitutes a gradient of chemical activity. The anion that can permeate the membrane does so, as a consequence of its chemical gradient. As the permeating anion moves down its chemical gradient, an electrical gradient develops—negative on the side to which the anion is diffusing (Figure 2-6C). As a consequence of the electrical gradient, the cation follows the permeating anion (Figure 2-6D). Three gradients that affect the flux of ions can be identified: (1) the chemical gradient of the per-

meating anion, which has existed from the beginning, (2) an electrical potential gradient, which develops as the permeating anion moves down its chemical gradient, and (3) a chemical gradient of the cation, which develops as the cation moves down the electrical gradient (Figure 2-7). The chemical gradient of the nonpermeating anion is not recognizable directly as a force; however, all of the effective gradients are related to it, and, if it disappeared, all of the other gradients would disappear (Figure 2-8).

Each of the gradients is an *energy* gradient, regardless of its source, and the energy is exchangeable. Random molecular motion causes net movement of each species of ion down the appropriate gradient, which tends to dissipate the gradient. However, as reduction of any one gradient increases another (e.g., movement of an ionic species down an electrical gradient decreases the electrical gradient but increases the chemical gradient), none of these gradients can be neutralized, and a steady state is reached, in which the *sum* of all of the gradients is zero, and there is no free energy. The system is in *equilibrium*, yet all three forces remain; ions move down each of the gradients, forming electrical currents. Since the oppositely directed currents

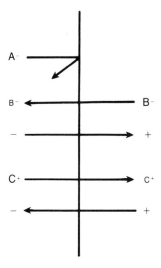

Figure 2-7. Three gradients exist at electrochemical equilibrium in the presence of a nonpermeating anion: (1) the chemical activity gradient of the permeating anion, (2) the chemical activity gradient of the permeating cation, (3) the gradient of electrical potential.

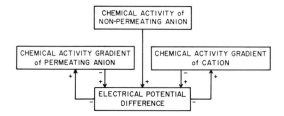

Figure 2-8. The forces involved in the Donnan equilibrium. The nonpermeating anion maintains a constant electrical potential difference (negative). Because the nonpermeating anion cannot be distributed at equilibrium, neither can the permeating ions. The electrical and chemical gradients that result are interlocked; dissipation of one gradient builds up another gradient, which restores the first gradient, and so on. For example, when the permeating anion crosses the membrane, down its gradient of chemical activity, the gradient of chemical activity decreases (–); however, the movement of the anion increases (+) the electrical potential difference, which increases the flux of the permeating anion in the opposite direction, thereby decreasing (–) the electrical potential again and restoring (+) the chemical activity gradient. A corresponding circle of events can be developed for the cation. Since the electrical potential affects both chemical gradients, neither species of permeating ion can move without affecting the other.

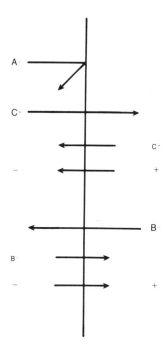

Figure 2-9. The ionic fluxes at electrochemical equilibrium. The chemical activity of the cation on the left supports a flux from left to right, and the chemical activity of the cation on the right supports a flux from right to left. The difference between these unidirectional fluxes is the net flux caused by chemical activity, from left to right. It is equal to the flux of C^+ from right to left down the electrical gradient. The corresponding fluxes of the anion are opposite to the fluxes of the cation.

are equal, they represent no net movement (Figure 2-8).

At equilibrium, one could measure (1) an electrical potential difference, negative on the side of the nonpermeating anion, (2) a chemical gradient of the permeating anion that is opposed by the negative potential, and (3) a chemical gradient of the cation that is opposed by the positive potential (Figure 2-9).

NERNST EQUATION

Because all of the forces interrelate, the magnitude of the potential and the magnitudes of the chemical gradients of each of the permeating ions are related quantitatively *at equilibrium*. This relationship can be expressed for each species of ion by the Nernst equation

$$E_s = \frac{RT}{FZ} \log_n \frac{[S_a]_1}{[S_a]_2}$$

Where S is a permeating ion in a system that includes a selectively permeable membrane and a nonpermeating ion; R, the universal gas constant, describes the random movements of the ions; T, the absolute temperature, affects the random movements of the ions; F, Faraday's number, gives the amount of electrical charge in a mole of univalent ions (i.e., 96,500 coulomb); Z is the valence of the ion S; $\log_n$ is the natural (i.e., napierian, or base e) logarithm; 1 and 2 are the two sides of the membrane; and $[S_\alpha]$ is the chemical activity (in osmoles) of the ion S.

E_s is the *electrochemical equilibrium potential*, which exactly balances the effect of the chemical gradient to move ions across the membrane. Thus, it is the electrical equivalent of the chemical gradient. If $\log_n$ is converted to $\log_{10}$ and the temperature is 37 C, $RT/FZ = 61.5$ mv for a monovalent ion or 30.75 mv for a divalent ion.

The Nernst equation can be used in biological systems to determine whether a given species of ion is distributed at equilibrium. The chemical activity of the ion on each side of the membrane is measured, and the electrochemical equilibrium potential is calculated. The cellular potential is measured, and if the two potentials are equal, the ion is distributed at equilibrium. If the potentials are not equal, the ion is not at equilibrium. If the system is in *steady state* but the ion is not at equilibrium, the chemical gradient is being maintained against an electrical gradient, which suggests active transport (Figure 2-10).

Electrochemical Equilibrium Potentials

For the sake of convenience, chemical *concentration*, rather than chemical activity (which reflects the extent of molecular motion), often is used to calculate the equilibrium potential. This introduces error since chemical activity always is less than chemical concentration because of various factors that restrict molecular motion. However, according to conventional theory, the differences are not great enough to be significant, and the activity coefficient of each of the major ions often is assumed to be 1.0.

POTASSIUM

A typical chemical activity of extracellular potassium, $[K_\alpha^+]_o$, is 4 mOsm, and a typical chemical activity of intracellular potassium, $[K_\alpha^+]_i$, is 120 mOsm. Substituting in the Nernst equation

$$E_K = 61.5\,\text{mv}\ \log_{10}\frac{4}{120} = -91^*\,\text{mv}$$

Thus, a cellular potential of 91 mv, negative inside, is required to produce an influx of K^+ equal to the efflux of K^+ produced by the chemical activity gradient of 120 mOsm intracellular to 4 mOsm extracellular. If the measured cellular potential were -91 mv, K^+ would be distributed at equilibrium. In this example, the measured cellular potential is -82 mv; therefore, K^+ is not distributed at equilibrium.

SODIUM

Typical chemical activities of sodium are $[Na_\alpha^+]_o = 148$ mOsm and $[Na_\alpha^+]_i = 16$ mOsm. Therefore,

$$E_{Na} = 61.5\ \text{mv}\ \log_{10}\frac{148}{16} = +59\,\text{mv}$$

Thus, Na^+ is far from equilibrium, because the cellular potential would have to be 59 mv, *positive* inside, to produce an efflux of Na^+ equal to the influx of Na^+ produced by the chemical activity gradient of 148 mOsm outside to 16 mOsm inside.

CALCIUM

Typical chemical activities of calcium are $[Ca_\alpha^{++}]_o = 2.7$ mOsm and $[Ca_\alpha^{++}]_i = 0.000035$ mOsm (estimation). Therefore,

$$E_{Ca} = 30.75\ \text{mv}\ \log_{10}\frac{2.7}{0.000035} = +150\,\text{mv}$$

Thus, Ca^{++} also is far from equilibrium.

CHLORIDE

Typical chemical activities of chloride are $[Cl_\alpha^-]_o = 130$ mOsm and $[Cl_\alpha^-]_i = 6$ mOsm. Therefore,

$$E_{Cl} = 61.5\ \text{mv}\ \log_{10}\frac{6}{130} = -82\,\text{mv}$$

Because the measured cellular potential is -82 mv, Cl^- is distributed at equilibrium.

According to the calculations above, K^+, Na^+, and Ca^{++} are not at equilibrium. Therefore, these ions are kept at steady state by some other means, presumably by the input of energy, that is, by active transport (Figure 2-10).

---

*The convention is to write a *negative* number, but the number is positive, and the *electricity* is negative.

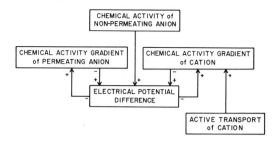

Figure 2-10. Imposition of active transport of the cation on the Donnan equilibrium. The chemical activity gradient of the cation is increased and maintained in excess of the equilibrium value. Therefore, the electrochemical equilibrium potential of the cation is increased, and the influence of the chemical gradient of the cation on the electrical potential is increased. The meanings of (+) and (–) are the same as in Figure 2-8.

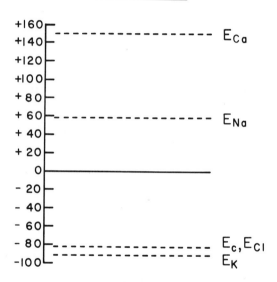

Figure 2-11. Electrochemical equilibrium potentials of potassium (E_K), chloride (E_{Cl}), sodium (E_{Na}), and calcium (E_{Ca}); and the cellular potential (E_c). The scale is in millivolts, negative inside.

Relationships Between Cellular Potential and Equilibrium Potentials

When the equilibrium potential of a given species of ion differs from the cellular potential (Figure 2-11), an ionic current, proportional to the difference of potential and the permeability of the membrane to the ion, flows down the electrochemical gradient. This current tends either to change the cellular potential toward the equilibrium potential of the species or to alter the distribution of the species in such a

way as to bring its equilibrium potential toward the cellular potential. The net influence of a particular species of ion on the cellular potential depends on the magnitude of the current the ion carries relative to the magnitude of the current carried by each of the other species of ion.

POTASSIUM

The Nernst equation expresses the chemical gradient in terms of an equivalent electrical gradient. Thus, the chemical gradient of K^+ (120 mOsm inside the cell to 4 mOsm outside) is equivalent to an electrical gradient of −91 mv. Since the cellular potential is −82 mv, the difference of 9 mv is a net force that causes an efflux of K^+ from the cell (Figure 2-12), and the maintenance of intracellular K^+ at 120 mOsm requires an additional influx, which is supplied by active transport (Figure 2-13).

As long as $[K_\alpha^+]_i$ is maintained at 120 mOsm and $[K_\alpha^+]_o$ is kept at 4 mOsm, the passive efflux of K^+ (K^+ current) is sufficient to increase the cellular potential to −91 mv. The persistence of E_c at only −82 mv reflects primarily the influx of Na^+ along its electrochemical gradient (Na^+ current), which continues as long as E_c is negative to E_{Na}. The maintenance of E_c closer to E_K than to E_{Na} reflects the greater permeability of the membrane to K^+. Thus, under equal driving forces, K^+ leaves the cell more rapidly than Na^+ enters the cell (K^+ current > Na^+ current), and E_c moves toward E_K. As E_c moves farther from E_{Na} and closer to E_K, the net driving force on Na^+ increases, the net driving force on K^+ decreases, and the fluxes, or currents, become about equal.

SODIUM

All of the net passive forces that act on Na^+ are directed inward. The electrical gradient, which is the cellular potential, is −82 mv, and the chemical gradient is equivalent to +59 mv; thus, the *electrochemical gradient* that tends to move Na^+ into the cell and to decrease E_c is the equivalent of 141 mv (Figure 2-12). The net efflux of Na^+ is caused by active transport, and at steady state, the active efflux of Na^+ equals the passive influx of Na^+ (Figure 2-14).

CALCIUM

All of the net forces that act on Ca^{++} are directed inward. The electrical gradient is −82 mv, and the chemical gradient is +150 mv; thus, the

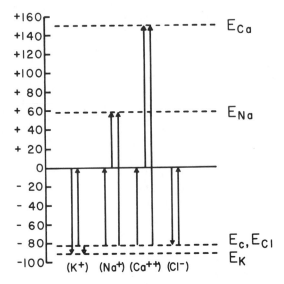

Figure 2-12. The passive forces that influence the cellular potential. The chemical gradient of K^+ acts to move K^+ out of the cell, hence to make the interior of the cell negative. The chemical gradient of K^+ would disappear at -91 mv (E_K) (indicated by arrow from 0 to -91 mv). The electrical gradient (the cellular potential, E_c), which acts to move K^+ to the cell, would disappear at 0 mv (indicated by arrow from -82 to 0 mv). Thus, the electrochemical gradient of K^+, -9 mv (indicated by arrow from -82 to -91 mv), acts to move K^+ out of the cell, thereby increasing E_c. Both the electrical gradient E_c and the chemical activity gradient, represented by E_{Na}, act to move Na^+ into the cell. The electrical gradient would disappear at 0 mv (indicated by arrow from -82 to 0 mv). The chemical activity gradient, which tends to make the interior positive, would disappear at $+59$ mv (E_{Na}) (indicated by arrow from 0 to $+59$ mv). Thus, the electrochemical gradient of Na^+ is $+141$ mv (indicated by arrow from -82 to $+59$ mv). Both the electrical gradient E_c and the chemical activity gradient, represented by E_{Ca}, act to move Ca^{++} into the cell. Thus, the electrochemical gradient of Ca^{++} is $+232$ mv (indicated by arrow from -82 to $+150$ mv). The chemical activity gradient of Cl^-, which acts to move Cl^- into the cell, would disappear at -82 mv (E_{Cl}) (indicated by arrow from 0 to -82 mv), and the electrical gradient E_c, which acts to move Cl^- out of the cell, would disappear at 0 mv (indicated by arrow from -82 to 0 mv). Thus, the electrochemical gradient of Cl^- is 0, and Cl^- is distributed at equilibrium.

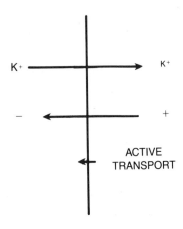

Figure 2-13. Flux of K^+ across the membrane. At steady state, the net influx and the net efflux are equal. All of the efflux of K^+, from left to right in the diagram, is passive and moves down the chemical gradient. The electrical equivalent of the chemical gradient E_K is -91 mv in this example. The influx is largely passive and moves down the electrical gradient, which is the cellular potential of -82 mv. Thus, a net passive (electrochemical) force of 9 mv (91 mv – 82 mv) acts to move K^+ out of the cell. The remaining influx of K^+, which is equal to the difference between the passive efflux and the passive influx, is attributed to active transport.

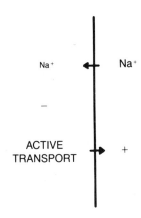

Figure 2-14. Flux of Na^+ across the membrane. Both of the passive forces that act on Na^+, the chemical gradient and the electrical gradient, tend to move Na^+ into the cell. Thus, the outward flux of Na^+, which equals the inward flux in the steady state, is caused by active transport.

electrochemical gradient, which tends to move Ca^{++} into the cell and to make E_c positive, is the equivalent of 232 mv (Figure 2-12). The net efflux of Ca^{++} is caused by active transport, and at steady state, the active efflux of Ca^{++} equals the passive influx of Ca^{++}. In nerve and skeletal muscle, the movement of Ca^{++} through the membrane is negligible relative to the movement of K^+, Na^+, and Cl, but the Ca^{++} current is important in cardiac muscle and smooth muscle.

CHLORIDE

The electrochemical gradient of Cl^- in the resting cell at steady state is zero. The electrical gradient of -82 mv opposes the entry of Cl^-, and the chemical gradient, which favors the entry of Cl^-, also is equivalent to 82 mv (Figure 2-12). Cl^-, appears not to be transported actively; therefore, it is directed solely by passive forces (Figure 2-15). Net movement of Cl^- occurs when the cellular potential changes; thus, Cl^- differs from K^+, Na^+, and Ca^{++}, all of which are transported actively, maintain electrochemical gradients, and tend to influence the cellular potential.

GOLDMAN-HODGKIN-KATZ EQUATION

The algebraic sum of all of the electrochemical gradients in the resting cell, weighted by their relative permeabilities P, is given by the Goldman-Hodgkin-Katz equation

$$E_c = \frac{RT}{FZ} l_n \frac{P_K [K_\alpha^+]_o + P_{Na} [Na_\alpha^+]_o + P_{Cl} [Cl_\alpha^-]_i}{P_K [K_\alpha^+]_i + P_{Na} [Na_\alpha^+]_i + P_{Cl} [Cl_\alpha^-]_o}$$

This equation is useful, conceptually, to identify the limits of the forces that contribute to the cellular potential; however, it is difficult to apply to an active tissue, in which permeabilities and electrochemical gradients are changing.

Conductance

The influence of the electrochemical gradient of a particular ionic species on the cellular potential is mediated through the permeability of the cellular membrane to that ion. Because an ion is a charged particle, its permeability can be measured as a conductance, which is reflected by the magnitude of the current that flows under the influence of a given potential difference (Ohm's law)

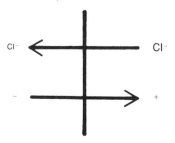

Figure 2-15. The flux of Cl^- across the membrane. Only passive forces act on Cl^-. In the steady state, the flux inward, along the chemical gradient, is equal to the flux outward, along the electrical gradient.

$$Current = \frac{Potential\ difference}{Resistance}\ or\ I = \frac{\Delta E}{R},$$

which can be written as

$$I = \frac{\Delta E}{1} \times \frac{1}{R}$$

and

$$\frac{1}{R} = conductance\ g;$$

therefore,

$$I = \Delta E g$$

In the examples given earlier, ΔE is the electrochemical gradient, which is the difference between the equilibrium potential and the cellular potential. Thus,

$$\Delta E = E_s - E_c$$

For potassium,

$$\Delta E = E_K - E_c$$
$$= -91\ mv - (-82\ mv)$$
$$= -9\ mv\ (see\ Figure\ 2\text{-}12)$$

In this context, a negative value for ΔE means that the equilibrium potential of that ion exceeds (is more negative than), and therefore helps to establish and maintain, the cellular resting potential.

For sodium,

$$\Delta E = E_{Na} - E_c$$
$$= +59\ mv - (-82\ mv)$$
$$= +141\ mv\ (see\ Figure\ 2\text{-}12)$$

A positive value for ΔE means that the equilibrium potential of that ion is less negative than (or is positive to), and therefore opposes, the cellular resting potential. Because the net current carried by K^+ in the resting cell at steady state (see Figure 2-13) approximately equals the net current carried by Na^+ ($I_K = I_{Na}$) (Figure 2-14), and the electrochemical gradient that causes I_K (9 mv) is much smaller than the electrochemical gradient that causes I_{Na} (141 mv), it follows that $g_K > g_{Na}$.

Active Transport of Sodium and Potassium

Although both Na^+ and K^+ pass through the cell membrane, neither ion is distributed at electrochemical equilibrium. Therefore, the concentrations of these ions on either side of the membrane must depend in part on some mechanism that requires the use of energy. Most physiologists believe that an ionic "pump" within the membrane actively transports Na^+ out of the cell and transports K^+ into the cell. In the erythrocyte, in which most of the studies on the active transport of ions have been conducted, the transport of Na^+ and the transport of K^+ appear to be linked in a ratio of three Na^+ transferred for every two K^+ transferred. Neither ion can be transported independent of the other. The energy source for this Na^+-K^+ "pump" is the same as that for other cellular functions (i.e., ATP). It has been determined that for the pump to work, ATP must be present *inside* the cell and that the conversion of one molecule of ATP to adenosine diphosphate (ADP) provides the energy to transport the three Na^+ and two K^+. The function of this transport system depends on the presence of Mg^{++} within the cell because Mg^{++} is necessary for the hydrolysis of ATP to ADP and inorganic phosphate. Because of the importance of the ATP energy source, active transport is related strongly to the presence of ion-specific ATPases.

The actual mechanism by which Na^+ and K^+ are transported across the membrane is not known. In one model that has been proposed, the essential element is a protein molecule in the cell membrane that possesses receptor sites specific for the binding of K^+ and Na^+. Once the ions are bound, phosphorylation of the protein by ATP causes a conformational change that reverses the Na^+ and K^+ binding sites, so that the Na^+ bound to the protein on the interior of the cell is displaced to an extracellular location, while the K^+ bound to the protein on the exterior of the cell is displaced to an intracellular location. Once transported in this manner, both ions are released and the process is repeated. A slightly different model postulates only a single type of binding site. In this model, Na^+ is bound within the cell, transported across the membrane, and released; K^+ then binds to that same site and is transported into the cell as the protein returns to its original conformation. Neither model explains why the transfer of Na^+ and K^+ is linked in a 3 : 2 ratio.

ELECTROGENIC PUMP

It follows logically that continuous transfer at the rate of three Na^+ out of the cell for each two K^+ into the cell would generate an electrical potential difference, making the inside of the cell more negative. Early work with the giant axon of the squid seemed to indicate that the entire cellular potential could be accounted for by the equilibrium potentials of K^+ and Na^+; therefore, the transport process was thought to be neutral. In some conditions, however, investigators have found data that can be explained most readily by postulating an "electrogenic" pump, which pumps some cations (Na^+) out of the cell faster than it pumps other cations (K^+) into the cell. If the pump contributes to the cellular potential, the potential should decrease when the pump is inhibited. Compounds of the digitalis family and similar compounds from other plant and animal sources inhibit the transport of Na^+ and K^+ in the red blood cell. Chemically, these compounds are glycosides, and they have marked effects on the rhythm and contractility of the heart. Hence, they are called *cardiac glycosides*. One such glycoside, ouabain, is widely used as a test of active transport because it is very active and dissolves readily in water. Thus, the decrease of the cellular resting potential or prevention of an increase of potential by including ouabain in the physiological solution that bathes the tissue is taken as evidence of an electrogenic pump. In general, a cellular resting potential greater than the equilibrium potential of K (i.e., $E_c > E_K$), which can be obtained under certain experimental conditions, is explained by the action of an electrogenic pump, particularly if the potential is decreased by ouabain. It seems to be generally accepted now that electrogenic pumping may occur in certain tissues under certain circumstances; however, there seems to be no need to invoke that source of potential for most normal physiological activity.

EXCITABILITY

Concept

Virtually all cells of the body carry an electrical potential that is related to the nonuniform distribution of ions. Nerve and muscle cells have, in addition, a property such that altering the cellular potential initiates a series of events that is reflected not only within that cell but in adjacent cells. This property is referred to as *excitability*.

Action Potential

In the giant axon of the squid, in which the membrane theory of excitation was developed, decrease of the resting potential to a critical (or threshold) value evokes a rapid, regenerative, temporary increase of g_{Na} followed by a delayed increase of g_K. The resulting currents, which flow down the electrochemical gradients represented by the differences between the cellular potential (E_c) and E_{Na} and E_K, respectively, change E_c to produce the characteristic pattern of the action potential (Figure 2-16). In nerve and skeletal muscle, the entire event lasts for only about 2 milliseconds. In cardiac muscle and smooth muscle, the event may last for several hundred milliseconds, and significant currents are carried by Ca^{++} during the action potential. In the resting cardiac cell (diastole) $g_K > g_{Na}$, and $g_K \gg g_{Ca}$.

Decrease of E_c to the critical level—which is accomplished by generator potentials of receptors, by pacemaker potentials, or by propagated excitation—changes the characteristics of the membrane so that g_{Na} increases rapidly. The electrochemical gradient of Na^+ is tapped, and the cellular potential moves rapidly toward E_{Na}, producing the rising phase of the action potential. The increase of g_{Na} is self-limiting. According to the original formulation of Hodgkin and Huxley, g_{Na} is determined by two factors, both of which are controlled by the cellular potential. When the cell is depolarized, one factor (m) activates g_{Na} rapidly, and the other factor (h) inactivates g_{Na} slowly (Figure 2-17). Thus, g_{Na} is increased and decreased sequentially by the depolarization of the cell; when the

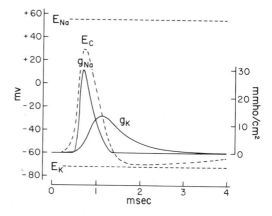

Figure 2-16. Calculated changes of specific conductance during and after an action potential in the giant axon of the squid. The initial depolarization is caused by currents that flow ahead of a propagated action potential; the sodium conductance g_{Na} is increased as the cell depolarizes. Thereafter, g_{Na} is increased progressively by the depolarization that forms the remainder of the rising phase of the action potential. Thus, increasing g_{Na} and increasing depolarization are interrelated. The current that causes the action potential is carried by Na^+ flowing down its electrochemical gradient; the limit is given by E_{Na}. As E_c approaches E_{Na}, the gradient is dissipated; in addition, g_{Na} decreases and g_K increases. The increased efflux of K^+, combined with the decreased influx of Na^+, repolarizes the cell. (Redrawn, with permission, from Hodgkin, A.L., and Huxley, A.F. 1952. A quantitative description of membrane current and its application to conduction in nerve. *J. Physiol.* (London) 117:500.)

threshold potential is reached, I_{Na} contributes regeneratively to the depolarization (Figure 2-18). In cardiac cells, g_{Ca} increases during the plateau of the action potential, tapping the electrochemical gradient of Ca^{++}, which produces an influx of Ca^{++} that contributes to the formation of the plateau and causes contraction.

Active transport maintains steady state by removing from the resting cell the Na^+ (and Ca^{++}) that entered during depolarization and by returning to the cell the K^+ that left during repolarization. In cardiac cells, g_K decreases when the cell is depolarized. Since the force that keeps K^+ inside the cell, the negative resting potential, disappears during the action potential, K^+ would leave the cell rapidly if its conductance did not decrease, and the duration of the action potential would be decreased. The

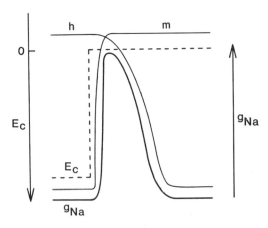

Figure 2-17. The control of sodium conductance (g_{Na}) by the cellular potential. According to theory, g_{Na} is controlled by two hypothetical variables, h and m, which are determined by the cellular potential E_c. Both h and m must be in a favorable position (represented by the top of the figure) for g_{Na} to increase. In the fully polarized, resting cell, h is in the favorable position but m is not. When the cell is depolarized, m moves rapidly into the favorable position, and g_{Na} increases rapidly; however, h moves slowly out of the favorable position, and g_{Na} decreases again. In the diagram, E_c is held in two states: at the resting level and at 0 mv. Depolarization initially increases g_{Na} and then decreases it; thus, the action potential is self-limiting.

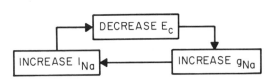

Figure 2-18. Interaction of the cellular potential (E_c), sodium conductance (g_{Na}), and sodium current (I_{Na}). This is an example of positive feedback in a physiological process (see Chapter 1).

action potential is terminated by the decreasing influx of Na^+ and Ca^{++}, as g_{Na} and g_{Ca} decrease, and by the efflux of K^+, as g_K increases again (Figure 2-19).

Propagation of Excitation

The excitable cell is polarized, inside to outside, like an electrical capacitor because the surface membrane has a high resistance and charges are separated across it (Figure 2-20). If electrodes, insulated except at the tip, are placed on a nerve and connected to a battery, current flows into

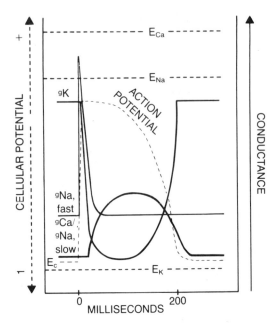

Figure 2-19. The probable changes of specific conductances during the propagation of an action potential in cardiac muscle. The initial depolarization is caused by currents that flow ahead of the propagated action potential; the fast sodium conductance, fast g_{Na}, is increased as the cell depolarizes. Thereafter, fast g_{Na} is increased progressively by the depolarization that forms the remainder of the rising phase of the action potential; subsequently, fast g_{Na} reaches a peak and falls rapidly to its resting value. The potassium conductance, g_K, decreases as the action potential develops, and remains low during the plateau phase. The calcium conductance, g_{Ca}, and the slow sodium conductance, slow g_{Na}, increase during the plateau. Repolarization is accomplished mainly by the restoration of g_K to its high resting value, aided by the return of g_{Ca} and slow g_{Na} to their low resting values.

the capacity of the membrane and along the inner core of the nerve (Figure 2-21). Outside the cell, current flows from the capacity of the membrane into the electrodes, completing the circuit. Because the resistance of the membrane is high, very little current flows through it. If the cellular potential is recorded in the area of each electrode, it is found to increase at the anode (the electrode connected to the positive terminal of the battery) and to decrease at the cathode (the electrode connected to the negative terminal). These changes reflect the polarities of the charges that accumulate under each electrode. The charge at the anode is the same as the charge of the cell and adds to it; the charge at the cathode is opposite to the charge of the cell and subtracts from it.

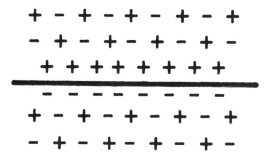

Figure 2-20. Distribution of charges inside and outside the excitable cell. The line represents the cell membrane; above the line is outside the cell, and below the line is inside the cell. Negative charges line up along the inside of the membrane, and positive charges line up along the outside. Away from the membrane, the distribution of charges is even; therefore, the membrane is charged like an electrical condenser.

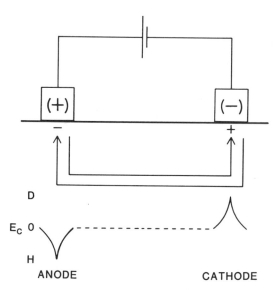

Figure 2-21. The electrical currents and the local changes of the cellular potential under each of a pair of stimulating electrodes. The heavy line represents the membrane of a nerve axon, and the arrows indicate electrical currents. The electrodes are insulated, except for the surface in contact with the membrane. E_c is the cellular potential; 0 is the resting level, D denotes depolarization, and *H* denotes hyperpolarization. Positive ions flow from beneath the anode (+) and collect under the cathode (–); negative ions flow from beneath the cathode and collect under the anode. The result of each current is the same—more negative (and less positive) under the anode, and more positive (and less negative) under the cathode. The same effect can be expressed by referring to only one of the currents. By convention, the flow of positive ions is followed.

If the current at the cathode (Figure 2-22A) is large enough and reaches its maximum value quickly (*square wave*), E_c decreases to threshold, Na^+ channels open (which greatly decreases the resistance of the membrane), and Na^+ flows into the cell at that site. A circuit is formed, as current flows down the core of the nerve, into the capacity of the membrane on the inside, out of the capacity of the membrane on the outside, and along the outside of the nerve into the area of low resistance (Figure 2-22B). The cellular potential in the area around the site of excitation decreases, as it would under a cathode (Figure 2-22C). Reduction of the potential to the critical value (*threshold*) causes Na^+ channels to open, and current flows in at the new site. Therefore, eddy currents are formed as new areas are depolarized, and activity is *propagated* away from the original site (Figure 2-22D). This is propagation, rather than conduction, because the action potential is regenerated from each area of the cell membrane engaged. The action potential produced is both the sign of activity and the stimulus for continued propagation of activity.

After a brief period, g_{Na} (or g_{Ca}, or both) inactivates, g_K activates, the potential is restored, and the cell becomes "excitable" again. During the time that the properties of the

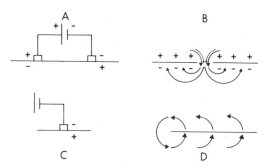

Figure 2-22. Changes of potential and electrical currents during excitation and propagation. **A.** The cellular potential is decreased under the cathode (negative pole), as positive charges accumulate and neutralize the negative charges that already were there. **B.** When the cellular potential is decreased to less than the threshold value, specific channels open in the membrane, and current, carried by Na^+, enters the cell. The positive ions flow into the capacity of the adjacent areas of membrane and decrease the potential. **C.** The effect here is similar to the effect that occurs at the cathode. **D.** The action potential is propagated by circuits that develop sequentially in adjacent areas.

membrane were changed, the cell was "refractory" to excitation; hence, that period is called the *refractory period.*

Recording

BIPHASIC POTENTIAL

If appropriate electrodes are placed on a nerve and connected to a recording device, and the nerve is excited at a distant point, propagated activity can be recorded (Figure 2-23). No potential difference is recorded initially from the surface of the resting nerve (Figure 2-23A). Activity that is propagated toward and eventually past the first electrode causes current to flow in the fluid outside the nerve. Although the resistance in the external fluid is low, it is finite, and a potential difference develops along the line of flow. The first electrode becomes negative relative to the second electrode (Figure 2-23B). If the electrodes have been placed far enough apart, they become isopotential again as excitation is propagated between them (Figure 2-23C). The second electrode becomes negative when the activity reaches it; however, the first electrode, which is used as the recording electrode, becomes positive (Figure 2-23D). After activity has passed both electrodes and the extracellular currents have ceased, a biphasic action potential has been recorded (Figure 2-23E).

MONOPHASIC POTENTIAL (INJURY POTENTIAL)

Historically, the first evidence of the cellular resting potential was the recording of the injury potential. If one area of nerve is crushed, the resistance of the cell membrane decreases in the area of injury, current flows, and a potential difference can be recorded between the inside and the outside of the cell. When the nerve is at rest, a steady potential is recorded; the electrode on the injured area is negative to the other one, which is called the recording electrode (Figure 2-24A). The injury potential is smaller than the true resting potential because of the leakage of current through the site of injury. When activity propagates under the recording electrode, the potential difference is cancelled (Figure 2-24B). After the activity has passed the recording electrode, the baseline (injury potential) is restored (Figure 2-24C), and a monophasic action potential has been recorded (Figure 2-24D).

INTRACELLULAR RECORDING

The cellular potential can be recorded most accurately by inserting a microelectrode (a glass micropipette filled with an electrically conductive fluid) into the cell. The tip of the electrode is less than 1 μm in diameter, and the cell is not injured significantly; the high resistance of the membrane persists, and no current of injury flows. The sequence of excitation and recovery as recorded by this technique are shown diagrammatically in Figure 2-25.

Because of intracellular recording, the conventional representation of the action potential has been altered. The external electrode is used as the reference, and the intracellular electrode is the recording electrode. When both electrodes are outside the cell, no action potential is recorded (Figure 2-25A), but when the microelectrode is inserted, it records the negativity of the cell, and the baseline shifts to a negative value (Figure 2-25B). When excitation is propagated past the internal electrode, the region temporarily becomes positive relative to the exterior and then returns to its resting value (Figures 2-25C and 2-25D). When the microelectrode is withdrawn from the cell, the isopotential line is recorded again (Figure 2-25E).

In the early theories of excitation, the action potential was thought to reflect the temporary disappearance of the cellular potential; hence, the cell was said to be "depolarized." In most cells, however, the potential does not disappear; rather, the cell temporarily is polarized in the opposite direction. Therefore, the action potential is larger than the resting potential. The "reversal" of the action potential is related to the influx of Na^+ down the electrochemical gradient represented by E_{Na}. The phases of the action potential are illustrated in Figure 2-25.

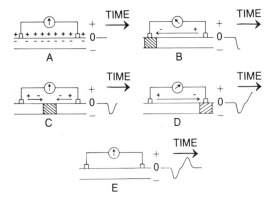

Figure 2-23. Recording of the biphasic action potential. See the text for a description of the events.

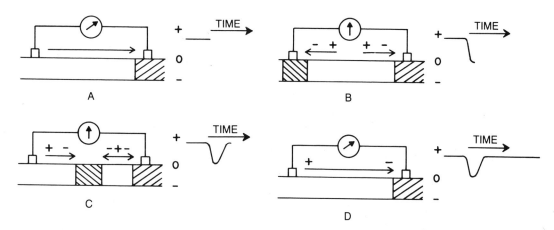

Figure 2-24.   Recording of the injury potential and the monophasic action potential. See the text for a description of the events.

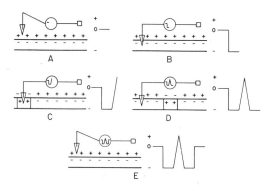

Figure 2-25.   Recording of the cellular potential and the monophasic action potential. See the text for a description of the events.

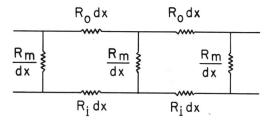

Figure 2-26.   Equivalent circuit of the resistances of the membrane, the internal fluid medium, and the external fluid medium. dx is an infinitesimal unit of length, R_o is the longitudinal resistance of the external medium, and R_i is the longitudinal resistance of the internal medium. Each variable increases with length (ohms per centimeter). R_m is the transverse resistance of the membrane; R_m decreases with length, that is, with increasing area (ohm centimeters). R_m is much greater than either R_o or R_i.

Electrotonic Conduction

Although the action potential is not "conducted" as an insulated wire conducts current (by the flow of electrons) or even as a salt solution conducts current (by the flow of ions), the local circuits that initiate propagation are conducted.

CABLE THEORY

The model for classical electrophysiology is the "cable theory," in which the cell is considered to be an insulated core conductor. The insulation appears not to be very effective, and a potential difference applied between the inside of a nerve and the outside of the nerve diminishes along the length of the cell, apparently short-circuited through the leaky insulation (i.e., the membrane). Hence, the cell is made analogous to a "leaky cable."

Although the membrane is not considered to be a good insulator, its resistance is much greater than the resistance of the extracellular fluid or the interior of the cell. The pathways of resistance (or conductance) are illustrated in Figure 2-26 by means of an equivalent circuit.

The cable properties of the nerve are illustrated in Figure 2-27. A brief anodal potential (depolarizing) is applied between an intracellular electrode and an electrode in the medium that bathes the nerve (Figure 2-27A). If the insulation of the cell were perfect, the same potential difference would be recorded at any point between the inside and the outside of

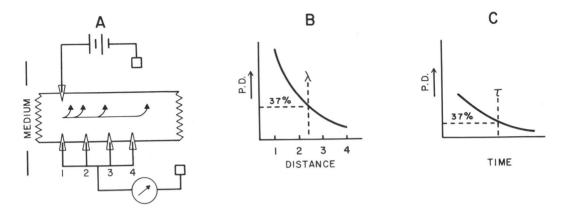

Figure 2-27. The cable properties of the nerve. **A.** A diagrammatic illustration of an axon contained in a physiological medium. A subthreshold potential difference of brief duration is applied between the interior of the nerve and the external medium. The lines and arrows indicate pathways of electrical current. The potential difference between the interior of the axon and the external medium is measured by electrodes 1-4. A switching device permits successive, independent measurements by each electrode. **B.** The maximum potential difference measured at each electrode and plotted as a continuous curve. Because the curve is an exponential, the length constant, λ, can be derived. **C.** The maximum potential difference measured at electrode *2*, and its rate of decline after the source of the current is disconnected. Because the curve is an exponential, the time constant, τ, can be derived. The measurements indicate that the membrane is leaky and that it has capacity.

the cell. However, the potential recorded at electrodes 1 through 4 diminishes as the distance from the point of application of the potential to the point of recording increases (Figure 2-27B), which seems to indicate that current leaks across the membrane, as shown by the arrows. Because the potential declines exponentially, the insulating characteristics of the cell can be expressed as a *length constant,* which is the distance from the source at which the potential has declined to $1/e$* (about 37%) of the beginning value. The lower the resistance, the more rapid the decline of potential with distance; hence, the shorter the length constant. The higher the resistance, the farther the potential spreads electrotonically from the source, and the longer the length constant.

The rate of decrease of potential at any of the recording electrodes when the stimulus is discontinued indicates that the membrane also has *capacity* (see Chapter 1). The potential declines exponentially with time (Figure 2-27C); if the membrane were purely resistive, the potential would disappear immediately when the stimulus was discontinued. The more complete equiv-

*The base of natural (or Napierian) logarithms, equal to 2.7182818. This value often is used to compare exponential curves.

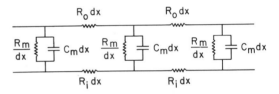

Figure 2-28. Equivalent circuit of the membrane expanded to include electrical capacity. C_m is the capacity of the membrane; C_m increases with length, hence, with increasing area (farad per centimeter). The other symbols were identified in Figure 2-26.

alent circuit of the membrane is shown in Figure 2-28.

The effect of electrical capacity is seen only with change of potential, which occurs at the onset and the termination of the flow of current. For example, an applied square-wave stimulus changes the cellular potential exponentially (Figure 2-29). This effect, which is related to electrotonic *conduction,* also precedes propagation. The extrinsic current that flows from the source of excitation into the capacity of the cell on the inside, and out of the capacity of the cell on the outside, decreases the cellular potential to threshold, initiating and maintaining

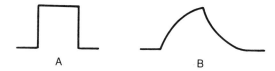

Figure 2-29. Effect of the capacity of the membrane on the response to a subthreshold stimulus. **A.** Diagrammatic representation of a square-wave stimulus (current begins abruptly, is sustained briefly, stops abruptly). **B.** The change of cellular potential that is produced.

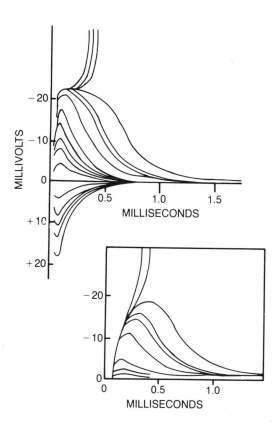

Figure 2-30. The effects at the cathode (depolarization, upward) and the anode (hyperpolarization, downward) of successive stimuli of increasing intensity. The last three stimuli produced action potentials (*off scale*) at the cathode. The inset shows the active response at the cathode, which was obtained by subtracting the hyperpolarization at the anode from the depolarization at the cathode. (Redrawn, with permission, from Hodgkin, A.L., 1938. The subthreshold potentials in a crustacean nerve fibre. *Proc. Roy. Soc. Lond.* (Series B) 126:87.)

propagated excitation. Thus, during propagation, excitation spreads electrotonically.

SUBTHRESHOLD DEPOLARIZATION

Application of an electrical stimulus depolarizes the cell at the cathode and hyperpolarizes the cell at the anode (see Figure 2-21). When the stimulus is very small, the effects are opposite and about equal. The flow of current is capacitative; the charges do not actually pass through the membrane, but rather flow into and out of the capacity of the membrane (see Figure 2-31A). As the magnitude of the stimulus increases, the change of potential at the cathode is greater and lasts longer than the change of potential at the anode (Figure 2-30). The change of potential at the anode remains purely passive, like the change of potential that occurs in an instrumental resistor-capacitor element. The response at the cathode is active; it is explained by activation of g_{Na} through the m factor (see "Propagation of Excitation" in this chapter) un-

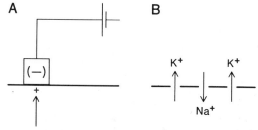

Figure 2-31. Currents and ionic fluxes involved in the local response. **A.** The flow of current (*arrow*) into the capacity under the cathode (–) partially depolarizes the membrane, and, if it is large enough, produces an active response that increases the magnitude and duration of the depolarization (see Figure 2-30). If the local depolarization reaches threshold, an action potential is initiated. **B.** The active response at the cathode is caused by the influx of Na^+ through channels that open when the cell is depolarized (increase of g_{Na}). The active response is opposed by efflux of K^+ through channels that already are open ($g_K \gg g_{Na}$ in the resting cell) and through additional channels that open after the cell is depolarized, although slower than the Na^+ channels open. Depolarization decreases the force that holds K^+ inside the cell, and the resulting efflux of K^+ tends to stabilize the cellular potential. If the influx of Na^+ exceeds the efflux of K^+, depolarization becomes regenerative, and an action potential is produced.

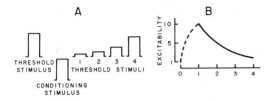

Figure 2-32. Increase of excitability caused by a brief, subthreshold, cathodal stimulus. **A.** The symbols represent square-wave stimuli; the current begins abruptly, is sustained briefly, and stops abruptly. The magnitude of the threshold stimulus is determined; a subthreshold conditioning stimulus then is applied, and the threshold stimulus is determined again. Immediately after the conditioning stimulus, the threshold stimulus is decreased greatly. The threshold stimuli depicted at 1-4 show how the magnitude of the threshold stimulus increases as it is determined at successively longer intervals after the conditioning stimulus. **B.** The change of threshold stimulus in A expressed as change of excitability (the reciprocal of the threshold stimulus).

der the influence of decreased cellular potential. The response at the cathode reflects the opening of Na^+ "channels" and the flow of Na^+ inward along pathways of low resistance (Figure 2-31B). Hence, the change of potential is caused by the selective movement of positive ions into the cell, which charges the inner surface of the membrane. At rest, the cell is kept polarized by the efflux of K^+, and the inward Na^+ current must exceed the outward K^+ current before the action potential can be formed. The potential at which the increase of the inward Na^+ current becomes regenerative and irreversible is called the *critical,* or *threshold,* potential.

SUMMATION OF LOCAL RESPONSES

The action potential is an *all-or-nothing response;* that is, it is triggered at a threshold, and beyond the threshold, is independent of the magnitude of the stimulus. The local response is not an all-or-nothing phenomenon, because it varies with the magnitude of the stimulus (see Figure 2-30). A brief, depolarizing current pulse applied to an excitable cell decreases the potential in the region where it is applied. If this depolarization reaches or exceeds the threshold level for that cell, an action potential is generated, and the stimulus is said to have been *threshold* or *suprathreshold.* A weaker pulse may not cause an action potential and is said to have

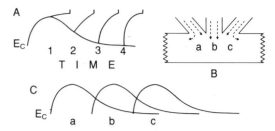

Figure 2-33. **A.** Temporal summation. The local depolarization that follows a subthreshold, cathodal, conditioning stimulus temporarily decreases the amount of depolarization needed to produce an action potential. The effects of the conditioning stimulus and the test stimulus summate to reach threshold. **B.** and **C.** Spatial summation. **B.** The current that flows during the propagation of excitation in a small fiber may be inadequate to excite a large fiber that the small fiber joins. The current is diluted into the greater capacity of the larger fiber and may produce only a subthreshold depolarization. However, if several such fibers join a larger one close together, the local effects may summate. **C.** The local depolarization produced by the converging fibers illustrated in B. If two or more of these responses occur simultaneously, their summation could produce an action potential.

been *subthreshold.* Subthreshold depolarization increases excitability temporarily (Figure 2-32), and hyperpolarization decreases excitability. Local responses can summate and alter excitability if the interval between them is brief enough (Figure 2-33A). This is summation in time, or *temporal summation.* Thus, a single local response can facilitate the excitation of a nerve, or a series of subthreshold stimuli can cause excitation. A series of local responses produced simultaneously through anatomically converging pathways also alters excitability or produces excitation (Figures 2-33B and C). This is summation in space, or *spatial summation.*

INHIBITION BY LOCAL RESPONSE

A subthreshold, depolarizing stimulus initially increases excitability (Figure 2-32); the effect is temporary, however, and if the stimulus persists, excitability decreases (Figure 2-34). The initial active response and increase of excitability depends on the increase of g_{Na} and the influx of Na^+ that is caused by depolarization (effect of m factor). However, persistent depolarization eventually inactivates, or decreases, g_{Na} and the influx of Na^+ (effect of h factor). In addition,

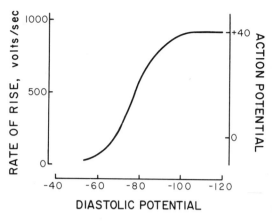

Figure 2-34. The initial increase and subsequent decrease of excitability caused by a prolonged, subthreshold, cathodal stimulus (accommodation). The symbols represent square-wave stimuli (see Figure 2-32). The magnitude of the threshold stimulus is determined; the prolonged subthreshold stimulus then is applied, and the threshold stimulus is determined at successively longer intervals during the conditioning stimulus. Immediately after the conditioning stimulus is begun, the threshold stimulus is decreased; however, as the conditioning stimulus persists, the threshold stimulus increases to greater than the initial value.

Figure 2-35. Relationship between the resting potential and the rate of rise of the action potential. The amount of "overshoot" of the action potential is plotted. According to theory, a variable, h, which helps to determine g_{Na}, is activated more fully at greater resting potentials (see also Figure 2-17).

prolonged depolarization activates g_K, and the efflux of K^+ that follows opposes further depolarization. This phenomenon is termed *accommodation,* or *depolarization block;* because it occurs at the cathode, it also may be called *cathodal block.* Hyperpolarization inhibits the cell by moving the membrane potential farther from the threshold level, and this, because it occurs at the anode, is called *anodal block.*

Just as a prolonged, subthreshold depolarizing stimulus causes inhibition, a depolarizing stimulus that is applied slowly (i.e., has a long rise time) may be ineffective because of the inactivation of g_{Na} and the activation of g_K before the threshold level is reached. When stimuli that are effective as square waves are applied slowly and the nerve is not excited, the nerve is said to have "accommodated" to the stimulus; therefore, this is another form of accommodation block.

Factors that Affect the Velocity of Propagation

Because electrotonic, subthreshold events precede the action potential in each segment of tissue that is invaded by the process of excitation, the resistive and capacitive properties of the cell (impedance) affect the velocity of propagation. Furthermore, the larger the potential difference, the more rapidly the capacity is charged; therefore, the magnitude of the cellular resting potential is an important determinant of the magnitude and rate of rise of the

action potential (Figure 2-35). Factors that decrease the resting potential slow the velocity of propagation. These factors may include intrinsically low resting potentials, delayed repolarization, effects of certain drugs, and, in the heart, latent pacemaker activity (see Chapter 18). In pathological conditions such as hypoxia, increase of extracellular $[K^+]$, or injury to the cell membrane, the magnitude of the action potential may be decreased by the inability of the tissue to maintain ionic gradients or selective permeabilities. Since the current that flows into the cell and produces the action potential flows out again and sustains propagation, small or slowly rising action potentials may prove to be inadequate stimuli, and propagation may decrement and fail, producing only a local response beyond the block.

The propagation of the action potential also is affected by the diameter of the fiber and, in a nerve, the presence of a myelin sheath (see Chapter 3). The propagation velocity of unmyelinated fibers is proportional to the square root of the diameter of the fiber ($V \simeq \sqrt{D}$). This property reflects the influence of the cross-sectional area of the core on the longitudinal resistance (see Figure 2-27).

SALTATORY PROPAGATION

A myelinated nerve propagates more rapidly than would be expected from its size alone, and the velocity is proportional to the diameter of

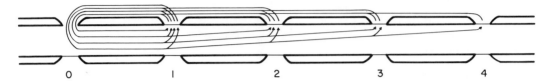

Figure 2-36. Saltatory propagation. The figure represents a myelinated axon; the numbered spaces are nodes of Ranvier. The internodal distance, relative to the diameter of the axon, actually is much greater than the distance shown here; the proportions are altered to permit the effects at several nodes to be illustrated. The lines and arrows represent electrical currents; current flows all around the axon, but for the sake of clarity, it is shown in only one place. An action potential is being produced at node 0; g_{Na} is high, and current is flowing into the capacity of the nodes; the circuit is completed externally. The cellular potential is decreased to threshold at nodes *1* and *2*, and to subthreshold levels at nodes *3* and *4*. The velocity of propagation is increased because (1) the length constant is increased, as current is forced to flow farther down the core, and (2) excitability is increased at adjacent nodes by subthreshold depolarization.

the fiber. Myelin insulates the nerves except at the *nodes of Ranvier,* where the myelin is thin or discontinuous. The resistance of the membrane is very high in the myelinated areas, and the local circuits flowing along the core discharge the capacity only at the spaces; the membrane in between is not excited (Figure 2-36). In effect, the length constant (see "Cable Theory" in this chapter) is increased enormously by the insulated internodal areas. Propagation is speeded greatly because the internodal distance is traversed electrotonically (conduction of electrical current) rather than by the initiation and propagation of excitation. The electrotonic spread includes several nodes; the closer nodes are excited, and excitation is increased by subthreshold depolarization in several more distal nodes.

STUDY OUTLINE

STRUCTURE AND CONTENTS OF THE CELL   Cell is bounded by plasma membrane and is filled by cytoplasm that contains:

Organelles, which have definite functions and are essential for life, and

Inclusions, which may have functions but are not necessary for life (e.g., fat, glycogen, and pigments).

ORGANELLES

NUCLEUS   Most prominent inclusion; filled with dark-staining material called chromatin; initiates and regulates activities of cell.

Chromatin, genetic material of body, is complex of deoxyribonucleic acid (DNA), ribonucleic acid (RNA), and proteins.

During cell division, chromatin condenses into chromosomes, which contain genes.

Gene—portion of DNA molecule—carries genetic information for synthesis of specific peptide.

Amount of DNA in nucleus is constant; RNA varies with metabolic state of cell.

Nucleus is surrounded by double membrane system that has openings called nuclear pores.

RNA is synthesized in nucleus, passes through pores into cytoplasm; messenger RNA carries genetic message to sites of protein synthesis.

ENDOPLASMIC RETICULUM (ER)   Series of tubules and cisternae that provide communication and transportation between cell surface and cytoplasm.

Rough ER contains ribosomes—associated with synthesis of protein.

Smooth ER is involved with synthesis of carbohydrates and lipids and with detoxifying chemicals.

GOLGI COMPLEX   Secretory vesicles and cisternae associated with secretion.

MITOCHONDRIA   Sites of oxygen usage in cells.

Contain spatially oriented series of enzymes that extract and store energy in bonds of phosphate compounds (ATP).

Number of mitochondria varies with metabolic activity of cell.

LYSOSOMES   Small particles that contain hydrolytic enzymes; destroy injured cells, aid in growth and remodeling.

PEROXISOMES Contain enzymes that produce and destroy hydrogen peroxide (H_2O_2).

MICROTUBULES AND MICROFILAMENTS Form three-dimensional matrix among organelles.

Microtubules help to maintain shape of cell, are involved in transport of macromolecules.

Microfilaments form lattice throughout cell—consist mostly of actin.

STRUCTURE OF THE CELL MEMBRANE

DANIELLI-DAVSON MODEL Lipid bilayer with globules of protein scattered throughout; proteins form channels through which ions are transported.

MODEL OF SINGER AND NICOLSON Functional proteins traverse lipid bilayer, project into intracellular and extracellular fluids.

SURFACE RECEPTORS Active sites that interact with hormones, transmitters, peptides, antigens, and bacterial toxins.

Receptor proteins in membranes of many cells are coupled to adenylate cyclase.

Stimulation of adenylate cyclase increases 3'-5'-cyclic AMP (cyclic AMP) in cell, produces effects that depend on organ or tissue involved.

Cyclic AMP mediates actions of transmitters, many hormones; cyclic AMP is inactivated by phosphodiesterase.

Effects include changes of cellular permeability, synthesis of protein, synthesis of steroid and other compounds.

More than one type of receptor protein can interact with adenylate cyclase, in same cell or in cells of different organs.

PHYSIOLOGY OF THE CELL MEMBRANE Concentrations of substances in cell different from concentrations of substances outside because of selective permeability of membrane and specific transport processes.

PASSIVE TRANSPORT Lipid-soluble substances diffuse through membrane.

Ions and other polar, water-soluble compounds diffuse through pores in membrane or are transported by special proteins in membrane.

DIFFUSION Nonionized substances move down chemical gradients.

Ions move down chemical and/or electrical gradients (electrochemical gradients).

Flux is proportional to electrochemical gradient, pore size, and temperature; inversely proportional to particle size and membrane thickness.

FACILITATED DIFFUSION Substance combines with specific protein in membrane, moves faster than it could by simple diffusion.

Not transported against electrochemical gradient.

System is specific for certain chemical classes, but competition can occur; system can be saturated.

ACTIVE TRANSPORT Substance is transported against electrochemical gradient.

Process requires energy; associated with specific enzymes (ATPases).

System is specific; competition can occur; system can be saturated.

WATER Passes through membrane by osmosis—movement of water down chemical activity gradient.

Osmolarity—measure of chemical activity of solute by effect on chemical activity of water.

Isotonic solution—erythrocytes neither swell nor shrink; chemical activity of water in solution is same as chemical activity of water in cell.

Hypertonic solution—chemical activity of water in solution is less than chemical activity of water in erythrocyte; erythrocyte shrinks.

Hypotonic solution—chemical activity of water in solution is greater than chemical activity of water in erythrocyte; erythrocyte swells.

Osmotic pressure—force required to stop osmosis.

ELECTRICAL GRADIENTS Ions are separated by cell membrane.

Diffusion potential—separation of ions when one of pair moves faster than other; develops at permeability barriers or at junctions with solutions of different composition or concentration.

DONNAN EQUILIBRIUM Describes relationship between chemical and electrical gradients at equilibrium in system that contains nonpermeating ion.

NERNST EQUATION Used to calculate electrical potential for any given ion in system at equilibrium; expresses electrical equivalent of chemical gradient.

ELECTROCHEMICAL EQUILIBRIUM POTENTIALS Electrical gradient required to balance chemical activity gradient.

Chemical activity should be used, but concentration often is used for convenience.

POTASSIUM Inside of cell must be negative to balance chemical activity gradient of cation inside to outside.

Because $E_K > E_c$, K^+ is not distributed at equilibrium.

SODIUM Inside of cell must be positive to balance chemical activity gradient of cation outside to inside.

Far from equilibrium.

CALCIUM   Positive inside; far from equilibrium.

CHLORIDE   Identical to E_c in resting cell; distributed at equilibrium.

RELATIONSHIPS BETWEEN CELLULAR POTENTIAL AND EQUILIBRIUM POTENTIALS
If equilibrium potential of ion is different from cellular potential (E_c), electrochemical gradient is equal to difference.

Current flows; proportional to electrochemical gradient and permeability of cell to ion.

Ionic current either changes cellular potential or redistributes ion.

Influence of particular ionic species depends on permeability and electrochemical gradient.

POTASSIUM   Cell membrane is most permeable to K^+, resting E_c is close to E_K; difference is due mostly to Na^+.

Because of greater permeability of K^+, small electrochemical gradient makes K^+ current equal to Na^+ current.

SODIUM   Net passive forces tend to drive Na^+ into cell; Na^+ is extruded by active transport.

Because of low permeability, large electrochemical gradient produces Na^+ current equal to K^+ current.

CALCIUM   Net passive forces act to move Ca^{++} into cell; Ca^{++} is removed by active transport.

Low permeability in resting cell.

CHLORIDE   Not transported actively; net movement of Cl^- when E_c changes.

GOLDMAN-HODGKIN-KATZ EQUATION
Summation of all electrochemical gradients in cell at rest; weighted by relative permeabilities of each ion species.

CONDUCTANCE
Permeability of ion expressed in terms of current flow and driving force (Ohm's law).

ACTIVE TRANSPORT OF SODIUM AND POTASSIUM
Mechanism is not known; three Na^+ are transferred for two K^+.

Energy for "pump" is provided by conversion of ATP to ADP.

Presence of ion-specific ATPases is important to concept.

ELECTROGENIC PUMP   If more Na^+ is pumped out than K^+ is pumped in, electrical potential difference is developed by pump.

Inhibition of cellular potential by cardiac glycosides often is taken as evidence of electrogenic pump.

May occur in certain circumstances, but probably is not involved in most physiological activity.

EXCITABILITY

CONCEPT   Change of cellular potential initiates further changes of potential in cell and adjacent cells.

ACTION POTENTIAL   Rapid regenerative changes of cellular potential when cell is depolarized to critical (threshold) value.

Rapid, temporary increase of g_{Na} and/or g_{Ca}; followed by rapid decrease of g_{Na} and/or g_{Ca} and increase of g_K.

Na^+ and Ca^{++} are removed and K^+ is returned by active transport after event.

PROPAGATION OF EXCITATION   Current flow during action potential depolarizes adjacent areas of cell—when threshold is reached, also generates action potential.

RECORDING
BIPHASIC POTENTIAL   Depolarization first at one electrode and then at the other.

MONOPHASIC POTENTIAL   One electrode on intact nerve surface, other on injured area; monophasic potential is recorded as action potential passes beneath electrode on intact cell.

INTRACELLULAR RECORDING   With microelectrodes—reflects cellular potential more accurately.

ELECTROTONIC CONDUCTION   Nonpropagated spread of current by flow of ions.

CABLE THEORY   Electrotonic conduction is subject to resistance and capacitance, like insulated cable.

Brief subthreshold stimulus causes subthreshold depolarization by flow of current into capacity of membrane.

Effect declines exponentially—distance is expressed by length constant; duration is expressed by time constant.

Action potential is preceded by electrotonic depolarization to threshold.

SUBTHRESHOLD DEPOLARIZATION
Electrical stimulus depolarizes cell at cathode, hyperpolarizes cell at anode.

With very small stimulus, effects are equal; as stimulus increases, effect at cathode becomes larger, lasts longer than effect at anode.

At cathode, Na^+ conductance increases, Na^+ flows into cell, decreasing cellular potential.

When Na^+ influx exceeds K^+ efflux (critical potential, or threshold), depolarization becomes regenerative (i.e., action potential is formed).

SUMMATION OF LOCAL RESPONSES
Subthreshold local responses may summate if repeated (temporal summation) or occurring in converging pathways (spatial summation).

INHIBITION BY LOCAL RESPONSE
Subthreshold cathodal stimulus initially increases excitability (g_{Na} increased through m factor); inhibitory if prolonged (g_{Na} decreased through h factor and g_K increased)—*accommodation, depolarization block, cathodal block.*

Block may occur at anode because of hyperpolarization and stabilization of membrane—*anodal block.*

Slowly increasing stimulus also causes inactivation of g_{Na}, activation of g_K—another form of accommodation.

FACTORS THAT AFFECT THE VELOCITY OF PROPAGATION Subthreshold depolarization that precedes excitation involves resistive-capacitative properties of cell; affects velocity of propagation.

Large current flow associated with large action potential charges capacity rapidly; speeds propagation.

Hypoxia, high extracellular [K^+], certain drugs, or partial depolarization cause small action potentials that propagate slowly, may die out (decremental propagation).

Velocity of propagation increases with size of nerve fiber.

SALTATORY PROPAGATION In myelinated nerve, action potentials generated only at nodes of Ranvier; excitation skips from node to node, proceeds faster than in unmyelinated fiber.

BIBLIOGRAPHY

Cheung, W.Y. 1982. Calmodulin. *Sci. Am.* 246:(6)62.

Coraboeuf, E. 1978. Ionic basis of electrical activity in cardiac tissues. *Am. J. Physiol.* 234:H101.

Danielli, J.F., and Davson, H. 1935. A contribution to the theory of permeability of thin films. *J. Cell. Comp. Physiol.* 5:193.

Davson, H., and Danielli, J.F. 1952. *The Permeability of Natural Membranes.* Darien, Connecticut: Hafner Publishing Co.

de Duve, C. 1983. Microbodies in the living cell. *Sci. Am.* 248(5):74.

DeRobertis, E.D.P., and DeRobertis, E.M.F., Jr. 1980. *Cell and Molecular Biology.* Philadelphia: W.B. Saunders Co.

Dustin, P. 1980. Microtubules. *Sci. Am.* 243:(2)66.

Garrahan, P.J., and Glynn, I.M. 1967. The stoichiometry of the sodium pump. *J. Physiol.* (London) 192:217.

Giese, A.C. 1979. *Cell Physiology.* Philadelphia: W.B. Saunders Co.

Hodgkin, A.L. 1938. The subthreshold potentials in a crustacean nerve fibre. *Proc. Roy. Soc. Lond.* (Series B) 126:87.

Hodgkin, A.L. 1958. Ionic movements and electrical activity in giant nerve fibres. *Proc. Roy. Soc. Lond.* (Series B) 148:1.

Hodgkin, A.L. 1964. The ionic basis of nervous conduction. *Science* 145:1148.

Hodgkin, A.L., and Huxley, A.F. 1952a. Currents carried by sodium and potassium ions through the membrane of the giant axon of *Loligo. J. Physiol.* (London) 116:449.

Hodgkin, A.L., and Huxley, A.F. 1952b. The components of membrane conductance in the giant axon of *Loligo. J. Physiol.* (London) 116:473.

Hodgkin, A.L., and Huxley, A.F. 1952c. The dual effect of membrane potential on sodium conductance in the giant axon of *Loligo. J. Physiol.* (London) 116:497.

Hodgkin, A.L., and Huxley, A.F. 1952d. A quantitative description of membrane current and its application to conduction in nerve. *J. Physiol.* (London) 117:500.

Hodgkin, A.L., Huxley, A.F., and Katz, B. 1952. Measurements of current-voltage relations in the membrane of the giant axon of *Loligo. J. Physiol.* (London) 116:424.

Hodgkin, A.L., and Katz, B. 1949. The effect of sodium ions on the electrical activity of the giant axon of the squid. *J. Physiol.* (London) 108:37.

Huxley, A.F. 1964. Excitation and conduction in nerve: Quantitative analysis. *Science* 145:1154.

Huxley, A.F., and Stampfli, R. 1949. Evidence for saltatory conduction in peripheral myelinated nerve fibers. *J. Physiol.* (London) 108:315.

Keynes, R.D. 1979. Ion channels in the nerve-cell membrane. *Sci. Am.* 240:126.

Keynes, R.D., and Aidley, D.J. 1981. *Nerve and Muscle.* New York: Cambridge University Press.

Morell, P., and Norton, W.T. 1980. Myelin. *Sci. Am.* 242:(5)88.

Robertson, J.D. 1966. Granulofibrillar and globular substructure in unit membranes. *Ann. N.Y. Acad. Sci.* 137:421.

Rogart, R. 1981. Sodium channels in nerve and muscle membrane. *Annu. Rev. Physiol.* 43:711.

Singer, S.J. 1975. Architecture and topography of biologic membranes. In *Cell Membranes: Biochemistry, Cell Biology, and Pathology.* Edited by G. Weissman and R. Claiborne. New York: HP Publishing Co. p. 35.

Singer, S.J., and Nicolson, G.L. 1972. The fluid mosaic model of the structure of cell membranes. *Science* 175:720.

Stein, W.D., and Danielli, J.F. 1956. Structure and function in red cell permeability. *Disc. Faraday Soc.* 21:238.

Thomas, R.C. 1972. Electrogenic sodium pump in nerve and muscle cells. *Physiol. Rev.* 52:563.

Tsein, R.W. 1983. Calcium channels in excitable cell membranes. *Annu. Rev. Physiol.* 45:341.

PART
II

NEUROPHYSIOLOGY

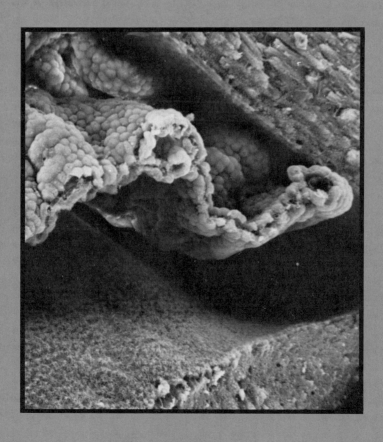

Photomicrograph from *Tissues and Organs: A Text-Atlas of Scanning Electron Microscopy* by
Richard G. Kessel and Randy H. Kardon. W.H. Freeman and Company. © 1979.

3

The Neuron

CHAPTER CONTENTS

MORPHOLOGY OF NERVE CELLS

The basic unit of the nervous system is the *neuron;* it is the cell that receives, transfers, and processes information. Neurons vary in size and shape, depending on their specific functions and locations. The classification of neurons is based on the number of processes (*neurites*) and their extent and form of branching. *Unipolar* neurons have only one process extending from the cell body, whereas *bipolar* neurons have two processes. Cells that have more than two processes are *multipolar*. Regardless of these variations in shape, certain aspects are shared by all neurons: each neuron has (1) a receptive portion, called the *dendrite,* (2) an organizational area, called the *soma* or cell body, and (3) a transmitting portion, called the *axon* (Figure 3-1).

Soma

Typically, the soma lies centrally, between the dendrite and the axon. The soma contains the nucleus and such cytoplasmic ultrastructures as

mitochondria, the Golgi apparatus, and the Nissl substance. The *Nissl substance* appears to consist of areas of endoplasmic reticulum that are associated with numerous ribosomes and, thus, are involved in protein synthesis. Nissl substance is found only in the soma and basal

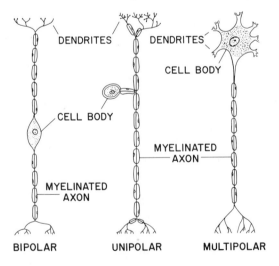

Figure 3-1. Types of neurons.

areas of the dendrites. The Nissl method of staining (using basic aniline dyes) often is used to examine the cytoarchitecture of various cell groups. Neurons may be identified and classified on the basis of the shape and size of the cell body, the position of the nucleus within the soma, and the appearance of the Nissl substance (Figure 3-2).

Axon

The axon originates in the *axon hillock,* which is a thickening on one side of the soma. The axon hillock and the axoplasm contain no Nissl

bodies or ribosomes. The hillock contains bundles of neurotubules, which pass into the axon; silver stains are used to impregnate the neurotubules and the slender neurofibrils. These stains color the entire extent of the neuron and its ramifications, but they mask the inner structures of the neuron. Stains specific for the myelin sheath that covers some axons may be used to trace the course and terminations of the nerve fibers.

Dendrites

Although most neurons have axons, not all neurons have dendrites as such. When they are present, dendrites tend to be short and to branch considerably. The cytoplasm of dendrites essentially is the same as the cytoplasm of the soma.

Synapses

GENERAL PROPERTIES

The specialized junctions between nerve cells or between nerve cells and muscle cells are known as *synapses*. The dendritic area of a neuron, for example, is the site of many synapses (Figure 3-3). Substances called *neurotransmitters,* which either depolarize or hyperpolarize the postsynaptic cell, are released at most synapses. Trans-

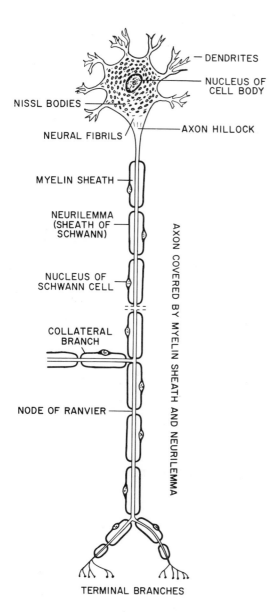

Figure 3-2.   Structure of a typical neuron.

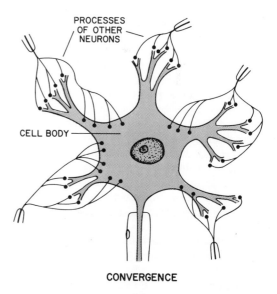

CONVERGENCE

Figure 3-3.   Synapses to soma and dendrites as several neurons converge on one neuron. This multiplicity of connections provides the basis for the integration of information in the nervous system.

mitters depolarize the cell by increasing g_{Na} or g_{Ca}, or by decreasing g_K. Because the resting potential of a nerve usually is less than E_K (the equilibrium potential of K^+) (see Chapter 2), a transmitter that increases g_K hyperpolarizes the cell and produces a local inhibitory effect. The summation of local effects at the synapse is an important mechanism in the integration of sensory information because the interaction of excitatory and inhibitory stimuli causes graded changes of the cellular potential, which determine whether the cell will produce an action potential. Synapses serve to organize tissue functionally, that is, to build pathways by which information may be transferred.

GRADED POTENTIALS

The nomenclature of graded potentials depends on the type of cell involved. At neural junctions, graded potentials are called *excitatory postsynaptic potentials* (EPSP), or *inhibitory postsynaptic potentials* (IPSP), depending on their effects. At the neuromuscular junction of the skeletal muscles, graded potentials are called *end-plate potentials* (EPP). Sensory receptors produce *generator,* or *receptor, potentials.*

TYPES OF SYNAPSES

Anatomically, there are three types of synapses (Figure 3-4). At a *tight junction,* the outermost lipid layers of the cells actually fuse, whereas at a *gap junction,* a definite intercellular space exists. Tight junctions impose a sharp physical separation between two areas. The endothelial lining of the cerebral blood vessels consists of cells that are joined by tight junctions, forming the blood-brain barrier (see Chapter 16). Electron microscopy of gap junctions has shown channels that cross the intercellular cleft and pass through the presynaptic and postsynaptic membranes, thus serving to join the cytoplasm of the two cells. In the third form of synapse, there is an intercellular cleft between the cells, and there are no membrane or cytoplasmic connections; this will be referred to as an *open,* or *free, cleft.*

Information is transferred at gap junctions by electrotonic conduction; the currents associated with the propagation of action potentials flow into each succeeding cell as if the entire pathway were simply a single cell. Ionic currents do not cross the open cleft. In this type of synapse, the presynaptic cell releases a chemical (neurotransmitter) that diffuses across the

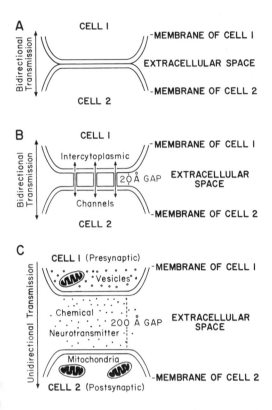

Figure 3-4. Three types of synapses. **A.** Tight junction. The outer surfaces of each cell membrane actually fuse, and there is no discernible intercellular space. **B.** Gap junction. A small but distinct intercellular space is present but is bridged by "tubes" of protein that permit certain molecules to move from the cytoplasm of one cell to the cytoplasm of the other. **C.** Open-cleft junction. Information is transferred in one direction only, because this type of synapse involves the release of a chemical neurotransmitter from the presynaptic cell membrane into the relatively wide cleft that separates the two cells. Specialized receptor sites on the membrane of the postsynaptic cell bind the neurotransmitter; this changes the conductance, and hence the potential, of the postsynaptic cell.

synapse, reacts at specific sites on the postsynaptic cell, and produces a local response. Mammalian synapses are predominantly, but not entirely, chemical. The neuromuscular junction is a well-known chemical synapse, and electrotonic junctions occur in the retina, cerebellum, and vestibular nuclei.

Chemical and electrotonic synapses differ both functionally and anatomically. An action potential is propagated much more quickly across an electrical synapse than across a chemical synapse, simply because of the time that is required for the release, diffusion, and reaction of the transmitter at the postsynaptic element. Chemical synapses are more susceptible to drug and metabolic interferences than electrical synapses are. For example, a drug may block the release of the transmitter or inactivate the postsynaptic membrane but not alter the current-conducting characteristics of the cell. A chemical synapse passes information in one direction only—from the presynaptic membrane to the postsynaptic membrane. The traditional concept states that current may travel bidirectionally at electrotonic synapses; this is generally true at tight junctions. However, current also may flow in only one direction at some gap junctions (e.g., at the abdominal nerve cord of the crayfish).

At one time, physiologists thought that integration of information, based on local responses and summation, could not occur at electrical synapses; however, it appears now that it can. Although there is a high probability that the presynaptic activity will give rise to a postsynaptic potential in an electrical synapse, the degree of coupling between the cells determines the amount of current that flows between the cells. It is possible for the current from one synapse to be insufficient to generate an action potential; however, convergence of several electrical synapses on a single neuron allows the summation of local responses at the postsynaptic membrane and the possibility that an action potential may be generated (see "Spatial Summation," Chapter 2).

CHEMICAL SYNAPSE

As early as the nineteenth century, some physiologists proposed neural and neuromuscular transmission by the flow of current and by the secretion of an excitatory substance. Most early investigators supported the concept of the electrical synapse, because they thought that excitation was transferred across the synapse too quickly to be mediated by chemical action. Research on the concept of excitatory substances did not begin until the first two decades of the twentieth century.

CHEMICAL TRANSMITTERS

Evidence that supported the notion of chemical transmitters came from studies of the autonomic nervous system and the actions of certain plant alkaloids (nicotine and muscarine)

on involuntary muscle and gland cells (see Chapter 7). Investigators concluded that sympathetic nerves release epinephrine and that parasympathetic nerves secrete a chemical similar to muscarine. Initially, choline was found to produce effects like those of the parasympathetic nerves; subsequently, acetylcholine (ACh) was shown to produce the same effects in much smaller concentration. ACh injected into the bloodstream of an animal produced rapid and intense but brief action, and investigators proposed that an enzyme in the blood hydrolyzed the ACh.

The existence of a chemical transmitter was demonstrated by Loewi in 1921. Loewi perfused a frog heart, stimulated the vagus nerve, and observed the expected slowing of the heart rate. Perfusion of a second heart with the fluid from the first heart also inhibited the second heart. The chemical that was isolated from the fluid, and which apparently was responsible for the inhibitory response, was identical to ACh. A repetition of the study in which the sympathetic fibers to the heart were stimulated showed that excitatory elements also could be transferred in the perfusion fluids. The excitatory substance was believed to be adrenaline (epinephrine), which supported the earlier conclusions.

The criteria for classifying a chemical as a neurotransmitter are complex. The chemical must be synthesized within the cell and released from the nerve ending when the nerve is stimulated. When the chemical is administered exogenously, as ACh was, the action must mimic the normal presynaptic-postsynaptic chain of events. Finally, drugs that affect synaptic transmission in the normal system must have the same effects on the postsynaptic response caused by the administered substance. Substances that have been accepted as neurotransmitters include ACh, norepinephrine, dopamine, serotonin (5-hydroxytryptamine, or 5-HT), and GABA (γ-aminobutyric acid).

SYNTHESIS, STORAGE, AND RELEASE OF TRANSMITTERS

Examination of the presynaptic cholinergic nerve ending shows many granular vesicles that contain ACh. These vesicles are not merely chemical granules, but rather are units bounded by a membrane; this explains why they are pharmacologically inactive when isolated and injected into a neural preparation. The vesicles keep the transmitters isolated during periods of inactivity.

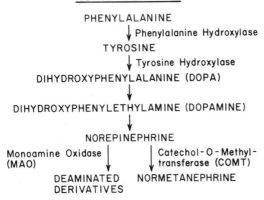

ACETYLCHOLINE

ACETYLCOENZYME A
↓
ACETATE
↓
ACETATE + CHOLINE
↓ Choline Acetyltransferase
ACETYLCHOLINE
↓ Acetylcholinesterase
ACETATE + CHOLINE

NOREPINEPHRINE

PHENYLALANINE
↓ Phenylalanine Hydroxylase
TYROSINE
↓ Tyrosine Hydroxylase
DIHYDROXYPHENYLALANINE (DOPA)
↓
DIHYDROXYPHENYLETHYLAMINE (DOPAMINE)
↓
NOREPINEPHRINE
Monoamine Oxidase ↓   ↓ Catechol - O - Methyl-
(MAO)   transferase (COMT)
DEAMINATED   NORMETANEPHRINE
DERIVATIVES

Figure 3-5. Summary of the steps in the synthesis and breakdown of the neurotransmitters acetylcholine and norepinephrine. The enzymes involved in some of the steps are shown in parentheses.

The enzymes and molecules that produce the transmitters are known (Figure 3-5), but the exact site of formation is not known. For example, ACh is produced when an acetyl group from acetylcoenzyme A combines with choline; the reaction is catalyzed by choline acetyltransferase. Coenzyme A is not found within the vesicles, however, so ACh must be formed outside the vesicles. The formation of ACh may begin in the soma, in which ribosomes and the required protein are abundant. The transmitter then would be carried to the tip of the axon by axoplasmic flow.

QUANTAL RELEASE OF TRANSMITTERS

Discrete miniature potentials can be measured in the postsynaptic cell even while the presynaptic cell is at rest. It is assumed that each of these potentials is caused by a packet, or quantum, of transmitter (i.e., a synchronous

discharge of many transmitter molecules) into the synaptic cleft. The simple leakage of a few transmitter molecules does not produce the postsynaptic potentials that are observed. The terms *quantum,* or *packet,* refer to the smallest effective unit of transmitter molecules. At the neuromuscular junction, the small amount of depolarization of the postsynaptic membrane caused by the spontaneous release of the transmitter contained in a single packet is called a *miniature end-plate potential* (MEPP).

EFFECT OF $[Ca^{++}]$

At the neuromuscular junction, ACh is released only if the surrounding fluid contains sufficient Ca^{++}. Depletion of Ca^{++} prevents release of the transmitter but does not alter the excitability of the presynaptic neuron. When Ca^{++} is removed from the extracellular fluid, the postsynaptic potentials (MEPP) decrease in unit steps; this effect provides further support for the notion of the quantal release of neurotransmitter.

ROLE OF VESICLES

It is generally accepted that a single vesicle contains a quantum of neurotransmitter; for ACh, this is less than 10,000 molecules. Correlation of the size of a quantum with the storage of ACh within vesicles is complicated by the occurrence of free pools of newly synthesized ACh and by the lack of understanding of how ACh is released from the vesicles.

The newly synthesized ACh is released in preference to the ACh that is stored. However, electron microscopic investigations have shown that the number of vesicles decreases after stimulation, which indicates an active role for the vesicles. When the release of transmitter is inhibited by the depletion of Ca^{++}, the number of vesicles does not diminish.

The sequence of events that lead to the discharge of neurotransmitter may be summarized as follows: stimulation, influx of Ca^{++}, lineup of vesicles, and release of neurotransmitter. The vesicles may either form a tunnel, such that several vesicles discharge into the same channel, or they may line a troughlike area of the presynaptic membrane. The orientation of the vesicles is not as important as their synchronous discharge.

The fate of the vesicles after the release of the transmitter also is not known. If they are extruded, the vesicles either may be destroyed in the synaptic cleft or resorbed to be refilled with neurotransmitter. The overall number of vesicles remains relatively constant. If the vesicles are destroyed or damaged, they are replaced.

After release, the neurotransmitter diffuses across the open cleft to bind at receptor sites on the postsynaptic membrane. The effect of the neurotransmitter is to open ionic channels in the postsynaptic membrane. These channels permit the localized or graded changes of potential that were described in Chapter 2.

SYNTHESIS AND RELEASE OF NOREPINEPHRINE

The steps that are involved in the synthesis of norepinephrine (NE) include the hydroxylation of the amino acid phenylalanine to p-tyrosine and subsequently to dihydroxyphenylalanine (dopa), and the decarboxylation of dopa to dihydroxphenylethylamine (dopamine). A final hydroxylation of dopamine produces NE (Figure 3-5).

Although the synthesis of NE (see Figure 3-5) is more complex than the synthesis of ACh, it also is achieved within the postsynaptic neuron (sympathetic nerves of the autonomic nervous system). NE also is stored in vesicles within the neuron and released in quantum fashion into the synaptic cleft.

OTHER TRANSMITTERS

Several amino acids that are found in neurons of the central nervous system alter excitability of central neurons and are assumed to function as transmitters. The best known of these amino acids is γ-aminobutyric acid (GABA), which is inhibitory. GABA increases the membrane conductance of K^+ (g_K), which either hyperpolarizes the membrane or stabilizes it. If the cellular potential (E_c) is less than the equilibrium potential of K^+ (E_K) (see Chapter 2), GABA increases the cellular potential. If E_c is near or equal to g_K, GABA stabilizes the membrane, making it more resistant to depolarization. Other inhibitory amino acids are glycine and taurine. In contrast, glutamate and aspartate excite central neurons by causing depolarization. This effect is caused by a nonspecific increase of membrane permeability similar to the increase of membrane permeability that occurs at the neuromuscular junction (see Chapter 10). The cellular potential moves toward an equilibrium value near zero.

INACTIVATION OF TRANSMITTERS

Neurotransmitters act for only a short time and then are degraded enzymatically or taken up again by the presynaptic cell. For example, acetylcholinesterase hydrolyzes ACh quickly into choline and acetate. At least half of the choline that is produced is taken up by the cell to form new ACh. The acetate also eventually reenters the cell to be recycled. Although norepinephrine and dopamine may be degraded within the neuron by monoamine oxidase (MAO) or in the synaptic cleft by catechol-O-methyltransferase (COMT), those enzymes act slowly. The primary process that ends the synaptic action of these transmitters is uptake of the intact molecule by the presynaptic neuron. The centrally active amino acid transmitters also are inactivated by a combination of reuptake and enzymatic degradation.

The chain of events that is involved in synaptic transmission is long and may be interrupted at several points. Drugs may block the formation of the transmitter, prevent its uptake into the vesicles, block transmitter release, inhibit transmitter destruction, compete for postsynaptic binding sites, interfere with the uptake of the transmitter, or block changes in the postsynaptic membrane. Other substances may cause an increase in transmitter release or increase the effect of the transmitter at the postsynaptic site and block transmission by these mechanisms. Table 3-1 lists several drugs that act on the neuromuscular junction and demonstrate the blocking characteristics listed above. Other compounds, such as local anesthetics, block neural transmission by acting specifically on the cell membrane to prevent the propagation of an action potential. Table 3-2 lists several compounds that can affect synaptic transmission at different sites.

Myasthenia Gravis

Myasthenia gravis (MG) is one of the more intriguing neuromuscular disorders. MG is characterized by muscle fatigue, which increases with exercise and improves with rest. Research has demonstrated neither decreased numbers of synaptic vesicles nor decreased content of ACh in MG. Changes in the morphology of the postsynaptic membrane and in the distance between the presynaptic membrane and the postsynaptic terminal have been

TABLE 3-1

Drugs that can interfere with transmission at
the neuromuscular junction

Drug	Effect
Atropine	Competes with ACh at muscarinic receptor sites
Black widow spider toxin	Increases release of ACh, causes depolarization block
Botulinus toxin	Prevents release of ACh
Curare	Competes with ACh for skeletal muscle receptor sites
Hemicholinium-3	Blocks synthesis of ACh by binding with acetylcoenzyme A
Neostigmine	Cholinesterase inhibitor—prevents breakdown of ACh, produces depolarization block
Succinylcholine	Competes with ACh at skeletal muscle receptor sites; broken down by cholinesterase

demonstrated, however, and secondary folding of the postsynaptic ending is lost. Certain toxins that bind to the ACh receptor are less effective on postsynaptic terminals of the patient who has MG than on normal postsynaptic terminals. Sensitivity of the synapse to iontophoretically applied ACh also is decreased.

The evidence suggests that MG has an autoimmune component. Antibodies to the ACh receptor have been found in the sera of approximately 85% of MG patients, and immune complexes have been found at the end-plate. The exact pathogenesis of MG is not known, however. Immunologic induction of the alterations in the postsynaptic terminal has not been accepted, and it is possible that MG represents more than one disease process. Regardless of the pathogenesis, the postsynaptic terminal of the neuromuscular junction is the site of dysfunction.

Coding of Information in the Nervous System

The *action potential* (AP) is the only signal by which the activity of a cell can be conveyed to distant portions of the nervous system. In the most simple case, a cell can be thought of as being either at rest or engaged in producing an AP. In this case, the coding would be based on which cells are firing at any given moment and how frequently they are firing. Much of the coding in the central nervous system occurs in this manner; for example, the chain of cells that

originates in the retina of the eye is segregated anatomically from the chain of cells that originates in the cochlea of the ear. Stimulation of one of the cellular networks that originate in the eye will cause only a sensation of vision, regardless of the mode of stimulation (electrical, mechanical, or chemical); this is the essence of Müller's *doctrine of specific nerve energies*.

In a simple system, the resting state of a neuron may be characterized by the absence of action potentials. However, neurons in the central nervous system produce action potentials spontaneously, even in their "resting state." This arrangement increases greatly the amount of information that the cell can convey. In the simple illustration of an action potential or no action potential, a cell could convey only the information that net excitatory influences exceeded net inhibitory influences. In a cell that is reexcited continuously, however, the condition in which net inhibitory influences exceed excitatory ones can be signalled by a *decrease* in the frequency of excitation; thus, the range of information conveyed by the cell is extended.

The rate of formation of APs usually varies with the magnitude of the input, because high amplitude (i.e., summated) EPSPs cause APs to occur more frequently. These relatively simple encoding mechanisms provide the basis for fairly complex neural processing. First, information is derived from a determination of *which* fibers are firing. Second, information is derived from the *rate* at which the fibers are firing and whether that rate is higher or lower

TABLE 3-2
Effects of various drugs at the neural synapse

Block transmitter formation	Increase transmitter release	Bind at receptor sites
Hemicholinium-3	α-Bungarotoxin	Curare
Tyrosine hydroxylase blockers	Tyramine, ephedrine	α-Bungarotoxin
	Amphetamine	Chlorpromazine
	Reserpine	

Block transmitter release	Block transmitter breakdown	Prevent changes in cellular permeability
Botulinus toxin	Cholinergic	Local anesthetics
Bretylium	Reversible	(e.g., lidocaine, procaine,
	Neostigmine	cocaine)
	Physostigmine	Tetrodotoxin (TTX)
	Edrophonium	
	Irreversible	Tetraethylammonium
	Organophosphates	(TEA)
	(insecticides)	
	Adrenergic	
	MAO and COMT inhibitors	

Block transmitter uptake
Reserpine

than the resting rate. Third, the total *number* of cells that are excited by a stimulus increases with the magnitude of the stimulus (*recruitment*), and additional information is conveyed in this manner. Fourth, some nerve cells do not simply increase or decrease their rates of firing, but fire in complex *patterns*. Specific examples of different types of coding will be given in Chapter 5, which deals with the special sensory systems.

STUDY OUTLINE

MORPHOLOGY OF NERVE CELLS   Unipolar, bipolar, and multipolar.

SOMA   Cell body—organizational portion of cell; contains nucleus, mitochondria, Golgi apparatus, and Nissl substance.

AXON   Originates in axon hillock; transmission portion of cell.

DENDRITES   Receptive portion of cell; short, branching fibers extending from soma.

SYNAPSES   Junctions between nerve cells or between nerve and muscle cells.

  GENERAL PROPERTIES   Neurotransmitters released at most synapses; either excite or inhibit postsynaptic cell.
  Local effects summate—important mechanism for integration of sensory information.
  GRADED POTENTIALS   Nonpropagated—EPSP, IPSP, EPP, and receptor potentials.

TYPES OF SYNAPSES   Gap junctions conduct electrotonically; open clefts transmit chemically.

CHEMICAL SYNAPSE Neurotransmitter released by presynaptic cell alters cellular potential in postsynaptic cell.

CHEMICAL TRANSMITTERS   Include ACh, dopamine, norepinephrine, serotinin, and GABA.

SYNTHESIS, STORAGE, AND RELEASE OF TRANSMITTERS   ACh is synthesized in cholinergic nerves; stored in vesicles near presynaptic membrane; released into synaptic cleft by action potential.

QUANTAL RELEASE OF TRANSMITTERS   Discharge of vesicles, each containing fixed amount of ACh.

EFFECT OF $[Ca^{++}]$ Required for release of ACh.

ROLE OF VESICLES   Store and transport ACh to presynaptic membrane; discharge ACh into cleft.

SYNTHESIS AND RELEASE OF NOREPINEPHRINE   Derived from phenylalanine via *p*-tyrosine, dopa, and dopamine.

Stored in vesicles and released in quantum fashion.

OTHER TRANSMITTERS   GABA, glycine, and taurine are inhibitory in central nervous system; glutamate and aspartate are excitatory.

INACTIVATION OF TRANSMITTERS Degradation (ACh) or combination of degradation and uptake (others).

MYASTHENIA GRAVIS   Muscle fatigue; disorder of neuromuscular junction.

CODING OF INFORMATION IN NERVOUS SYSTEM   Which fibers are active.
Frequency of activity.
Number of cells active.
Pattern of activity.

BIBLIOGRAPHY

Axelrod, J. 1959. The metabolism of catecholamines in vivo and in vitro. *Pharmacol. Rev.* 11:402.

Bloom, F.E. 1981. Neuropeptides. *Sci. Am.* 245:(4)148.

Ceccarelli, B., and Hurlbut, W.P. 1980. Vesicle hypothesis of the release of quanta of acetylcholine. *Physiol. Rev.* 60:396.

Eccles, J.C. 1964. *The Physiology of Synapses.* New York: Springer-Verlag.

Farner, D.S., and Lederis, K. (eds.). 1981. *Neurosecretion: Molecular, Cells, Systemic.* New York: Plenum Press.

Giaume, C., and Korn, H. 1983. Bidirectional transmission at the rectifying synapse: A voltage-dependent process. *Science* 220:84.

Hertzberg, E.L., Lawrence, T.S., and Gilula, N.B. 1981. Gap junctional communication. *Annu. Rev. Physiol.* 43:479.

Kandel, E.R. (ed.). 1977. In *Handbook of Physiology.* Section 1. The nervous system. Volume 1. Cell biology of neurons, Part 1. Washington, D.C.: American Physiological Society.

Kandel, E.R., and Schwartz, E.R. (eds.). 1981. *Principles of Neural Science.* New York: Elsevier North-Holland.

Keynes, R.D., and Aidley, D.J. 1981. *Nerve and Muscle.* New York: Cambridge University Press.

Lee, C.-M., Javitch, M.A., and Snyder, S.H. 1983. Recognition sites for non-epinephrine uptake: Regulation by neurotransmitter. *Science* 220:626.

Lester, H.A. 1977. The response to acetylcholine. *Sci. Am.* 236:121.

Llinás, R.R. 1982. Calcium in synaptic transmission. *Sci. Am.* 247(4):56.

Millar, R.P. (ed.). 1981. *Neuropeptides: Biochemical and Physiological Studies.* Edinburgh: Churchill Livingstone.

Morell, P., and Norton, W.T. 1980. Myelin. *Sci. Am.* 242:(5)88.

Schwartz, J.H. 1980. The transport of substances in nerve cells. *Sci. Am.* 242:(4)152.

Seeman, P. 1980. Brain dopamine receptors. *Pharmacol. Rev.* 32:229.

Snyder, S.H. 1980. Brain peptides or neurotransmitters. *Science* 209:976.

Stevens, C.G. 1979. The neuron. *Sci. Am.* 241:(3)54.

Tauc, L. 1982. Nonvesicular release of neurotransmitter. *Physiol. Rev.* 62:857.

Waxman, S.G. 1982. Membrane, myelin, and the pathophysiology of multiple sclerosis. *N. Engl. J. Med.* 306:1529.

Whittaker, V.P. 1975. Membranes in synaptic function. In *Cell Membranes: Biochemistry, Cell Biology and Pathology.* Edited by G. Weissman and R. Claiborne. New York: HP Publishing Co. p. 167.

4

Organization of
the Nervous System

CHAPTER CONTENTS

MAJOR DIVISIONS

The human nervous system is composed of three sections: the *central nervous system* (CNS), the *peripheral nervous system* (PNS), and the *autonomic nervous system* (ANS). The PNS transmits information to and from the CNS. The CNS sorts and processes incoming sensory information and controls body reactions, from simple spinal reflexes to complex, coordinated motor responses. The ANS regulates the general vegetative functions of the body, such as heart rate, digestive functions, blood pressure, and blood flow.

NEURAL AND
SUPPORTIVE CELLS

The *neuron* is the basic unit of the nervous system. The neuron does not exist alone, but rather is surrounded by supportive cells, or *neuroglia*, of ectodermal origin. In addition to functioning as connective tissue, glial cells participate in metabolic functions, phagocytosis, and excita-

tion. Neuroglia include ependymal cells, astrocytes, and oligodendroglia in the CNS, and satellite and Schwann cells in the PNS. *Ependymal cells* line the ventricular system and the central canal of the spinal cord, *astrocytes* occur between neurons and blood vessels at nonsynaptic areas of the neuron, and *oligodendroglial cells* form the myelin sheaths of axons within the CNS.

The counterpart of oligodendroglia in the PNS is the *Schwann cell*, which surrounds all axons. In some cases, an axon may run through a Schwann cell without being myelinated (Figure 4-1). In other cases, a coil of Schwann cell membrane wraps around the axon and forms a layered sheath of protein and lipid (*the myelin sheath*) (Figure 4-2). The myelin is interrupted periodically in such a way that the axonal membrane is exposed. These bared portions are known as the *nodes of Ranvier* (see Chapter 2); each node is the gap between one Schwann cell and the next. The distance between nodes is inversely proportional to the thickness of the myelin sheath but generally is approximately 1 mm.

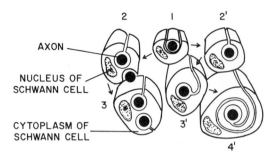

Figure 4-1. Stages in the development of axonal sheaths. The axon becomes partially embedded in a supporting cell, such as a Schwann cell, as indicated in *1*. If the axon is destined to remain unmyelinated, it and other axons may become more or less embedded in the same Schwann cell, as in *2* and *3*. If the axon ultimately will become myelinated, the same initial events occur (*2'*), but only a single axon is myelinated by a given Schwann cell. (In the central nervous system, an oligodendrocyte may myelinate a large number of axons.) The line of fusion of the Schwann cell processes that envelop the axon is the mesaxon. With further development, the mesaxon elongates as the Schwann cell processes grow in a spiral about the axon, as in *3'* and *4'*. Eventually, the cytoplasm between adjacent layers of mesaxon is extruded, and the membranes fuse.

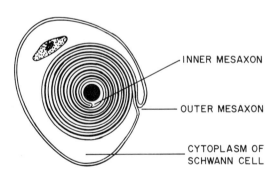

Figure 4-2. Structure of myelin.

Nerve Bundles

Collections of peripheral neurons that course together form nerves, or nerve bundles. When several neural cell bodies occur at the same place, the collection is termed a *ganglion* in the PNS and a *nucleus* in the CNS. An axon may travel a long distance before synapsing with another neuron. Groups of axons that course together in the CNS are termed *fiber tracts*.

The simplest way to classify nerve fibers and nerve bundles is to label them as afferent nerves or efferent nerves. *Afferent nerves* carry impulses from sensory receptors to the CNS, and *efferent nerves* carry impulses from the CNS and the ANS to muscles and glands.

PERIPHERAL NERVOUS SYSTEM

The spinal and cranial nerves and their associated ganglia make up the PNS. In general, peripheral nerves are mixed nerves that contain both afferent axons and efferent axons. The axons, or nerve fibers, in a peripheral nerve vary in diameter and may or may not be covered by a myelin sheath (Table 4-1). As is summarized in Table 4-2, the susceptibility of individual nerve fibers to anesthetics, ischemia, and electrical stimulation is related to the diameter of the fiber and the characteristics of the lipid sheath.

Compound Action Potential

After a nerve has been stimulated, "compound" action potentials may be recorded by electrodes placed close to the nerve bundle. The compound action potential differs from a single-unit action potential in two ways. First, the size of the compound action potential increases, within limits, as the strength of the stimulus increases. Second, when the compound action potential is recorded at a site distant from the point of stimulation, the waveform contains several peaks. Thus, in contrast to the single-unit action potential, the compound action potential is not an all-or-nothing phenomenon.

The largest fibers have the lowest threshold for excitation. As the strength of the stimulus increases, the thresholds of the smaller fibers are reached. The compound action potential represents the sum of the activity of all of these fibers. Although the compound action potential is not a linear summation of the action potentials of the single units, its size is proportional to the number of neurons excited.

The shape of the compound action potential depends on the distance between the site of stimulation and the recording electrode. The speed at which the action potential moves along a neuron (i.e., the velocity of propagation) varies among different types of fibers. When the

TABLE 4-1
Classification schemes for peripheral axons

Myelination	Electrophysiological group	Subserves	Fiber type
Myelinated (1–21 μm diameter)	A–α (9–21 μm diameter)	Muscle spindles, (primary) motor neurons	I
	A–β (5–12 μm diameter)	Joint position receptors, large cutaneous neuron receptors	II
	A–Δ (1–6 μm diameter)	Crude touch, temperature, nociceptors, fusimotor	III
Unmyelinated (0.1–0.8 μm diameter)		Crude touch, temperature, nociceptors	IV

TABLE 4-2
General properties of peripheral axons

Effects of ischemia	Effects of local anesthetic	Threshold for electrical stimulation	Velocity of propagation
Myelinated most sensitive	Myelinated least sensitive	Largest have lowest threshold	Largest are fastest
Unmyelinated least sensitive	Unmyelinated most sensitive	Smallest have highest threshold	Smallest are slowest

recording electrode is far enough away from the stimulating electrode, the propagated action potentials of the various types of fibers arrive at the recording electrode at slightly different times. Hence, the waveform of the compound action potential has several peaks.

Spinal Nerves

The spinal nerves form a subset of the PNS. A total of 31 pairs of spinal nerves (8 cervical, 12 thoracic, 5 lumbar, 5 sacral, and 1 coccygeal) attach to each side of the spinal cord, each by a ventral root and a dorsal root. The dorsal root carries sensory information, mainly from the periphery but also from the interior, whereas the ventral root carries primarily motor impulses to the periphery. The spinal nerves emerge between vertebral sections. The verte-bral column lengthens as it matures, so that the spinal cord is shorter than the vertebral column; hence, in the adult the segments of the spinal cord are not aligned with the corresponding vertebral segments, and some of the spinal nerve roots must descend along the cord before exiting from the vertebral column (Figure 4-3).

Cranial Nerves

The cranial nerves form another subset of the PNS. The 12 pairs of cranial nerves enter and leave the brain from the medulla upward. They provide not only the general sensory and motor functions for the head and neck, but also subserve the special senses of vision, hearing, taste, and smell. Table 4-3 outlines the cranial nerves.

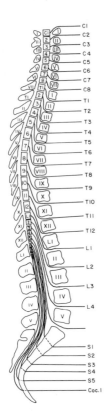

Figure 4-3. Diagram of the position of the spinal cord segments and existing spinal nerves, with reference to the bodies of the vertebrae.

CENTRAL NERVOUS SYSTEM

The CNS is composed of the brain and spinal cord. Both are encased by bone and float in the cerebrospinal fluid (CSF) (Chapter 16), and both are wrapped in the *meninges*, which are composed of three anatomically distinct membranes. The innermost layer is the *pia mater*, a thin membrane that adheres directly to the neural tissue. The next layer is the *arachnoid membrane*. The *subarachnoid space,* between the pia and arachnoid, is filled with CSF, and several cranial arteries course through the space. The *dura mater*, the outermost covering, is a thick, tough, two-layered membrane. The outer layer of the dura is similar to *periosteum* and attaches to the inner surface of the cranium at multiple points. The inner layer covers and protects the brain. At several points, this layer of dura folds inward to form membranes that separate the two cerebral hemispheres (the falx cerebri), the two hemispheres of the *cerebellum* (the falx cerebelli), and the cerebellum from the

occipital lobes of the cerebrum (tentorium cerebelli). Fingerlike extensions of the arachnoid, the *arachnoid villi*, pierce the dura mater and carry CSF to the *venous sinuses*, which lie between the inner and outer layers of dura.

Brain

The major divisions of the brain are the *cerebral hemispheres,* the *brain stem*, and the *cerebellum.* The cerebral hemispheres appear to mushroom out above the brain stem and turn downward in such a way that the upper brain stem, which consists of the *diencephalon* and the *midbrain*, lies between the temporal lobes of the hemispheres. The lower brain stem consists of the *medulla* and the *pons*. The surface of the cerebral hemispheres is convoluted, with ridges, or *gyri,* and dips, or *sulci.* The gray matter, which consists of the cell bodies of neurons, is exterior to the white matter, which consists of tracts of axons. The convolutions of the brain greatly increase the surface area and, therefore, the amount of gray matter (Figure 4-4).

The hemispheres are partially separated by the *medial longitudinal fissure,* which extends inward to the *corpus callosum,* the largest commissure between the hemispheres. Each hemisphere is divided into four lobes. The *frontal lobe* mediates the motor activity of the contralateral side of the body and many social behaviors, such as ambition and anxiety. The *parietal lobe* is separated from the frontal lobe by the *central sulcus.* The *precentral gyrus* is called the *motor cortex,* and the *postcentral gyrus* is the *somatosensory cortex.* The two often are grouped together as the *sensorimotor* cortex. Sensations such as pain, temperature, touch, and pressure

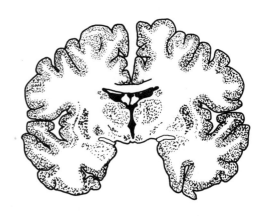

Figure 4-4. Frontal section of the cerebral cortex demonstrating the increased surface area of gray matter that is produced by the convolutions.

TABLE 4-3

The cranial nerves

Cranial nerve	Function and/or structures supplied
I (Olfactory)	Smell
II (Optic)	Vision
III (Oculomotor)	Superior, medial, inferior rectus muscles Inferior oblique muscle Levator palpebrae superioris Sphincter muscle iris Ciliary muscle
IV (Troclear)	Superior oblique muscle
V (Trigeminal)	Muscles of mastication Tensor tympani muscle Sensation, anterior two-thirds of head (general, pain, and temperature)
VI (Abducens)	Lateral rectus muscle
VII (Facial)	Muscles of facial expression Stapedius muscle Acoustic reflex Taste, anterior two-thirds of tongue Major glands of head, except parotid
VIII (Auditory)	Hearing Postural equilibrium
IX (Glossopharyngeal)	Pharyngeal muscles Parotid gland Taste, posterior one-third of tongue
X (Vagus)	Muscles of palate Somatic muscles of esophagus Pharynx Larynx Thorax, upper abdomen
XI (Spinal accessory)	Muscles of neck and shoulder
XII (Hypoglossal)	Muscles of tongue

are processed in the postcentral gyrus, although primary sensations actually may be processed subcortically. The *occipital lobe,* the primary visual cortex, is separated from the parietal lobes by the *parietooccipital fissure.* The *temporal lobe* is separated from the frontal lobe by the *lateral sulcus,* or Sylvian fissure, but is continuous with the parietal and occipital lobes. The temporal cortex contains the primary auditory cortex, the visual pathways, and portions of the limbic system (Figures 4-5 and 4-6).

The rostral area of the brain stem is the *diencephalon,* which consists of the thalamus and hypothalamus. The *thalamus* is a major relay station or processing center between lower centers and the cortex. The *hypothalamus,* which is the region just below the thalamus, regulates body temperature (see Chapter 66),

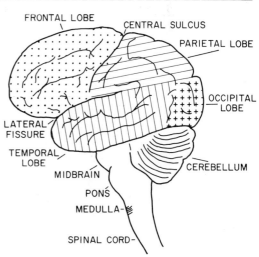

Figure 4-5. Major divisions of the central nervous system.

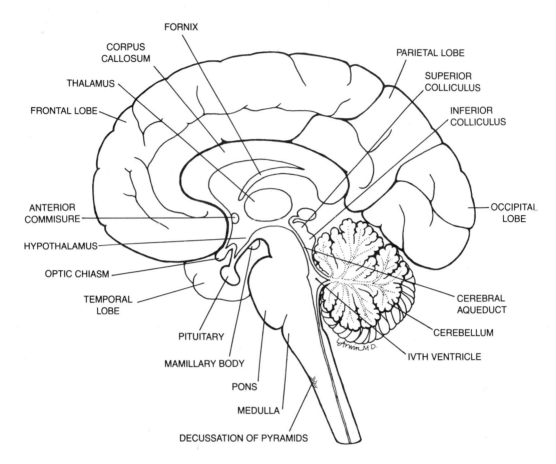

Figure 4-6.   Sagittal section of the brain and brain-stem showing major internal structures.

sleep, appetite (see Chapter 67), and some emotions (such as pleasure and fear). The hypothalamus also controls the ANS (see Chapter 8) and is the site of interaction between the nervous system and the endocrine system (see Chapter 57). The *midbrain* lies between the diencephalon and the *pons*. The pons consists of fibers that connect the midbrain, the *medulla oblongata*, and the cerebellum.

The *cerebellum*, which lies within the posterior fossa of the cranium against the dorsal surface of the brain stem, helps to coordinate voluntary motor activity and to maintain muscle tone. The cerebellum is divided into three portions: the anterior lobe, the posterior lobe, and the flocculonodular lobe. The connections of the cerebellar-vestibular system lie within the flocculonodular lobe. The cerebellum is separated from the occipital lobes by a flat sheet of dura, the *tentorium*.

The *medulla oblongata* occupies the area between the pons and the spinal cord. The motor tracts that descend from the cortex cross at the level of the medulla. The transition from medulla to spinal cord occurs at the *foramen magnum* of the skull.

Spinal Cord

The segments of the spinal cord are labelled to correspond with the vertebral segments in the infant. The spinal cord grows less in length than the vertebral column does, however, and a given segment of the spinal cord actually lies above, or rostral to, the corresponding vertebral segment in an adult; for example, spinal cord segment C8 lies at vertebral column C6, and the sacral cord extends from vertebra T12 to L1. The space below the tip of the spinal cord is filled by nerve roots that angle downward to exit at the appropriate vertebral level. This collection of nerves is called the *cauda equina;* spinal taps are performed at this level. The needle that is inserted merely pushes the nerve roots aside without penetrating them, and the cerebrospinal fluid can be withdrawn easily (Figure 4-7).

The spinal cord is roundish in shape and varies in diameter with the size of the afferent and efferent tracts at any particular level. The white axonal tracts surround the butterfly-shaped gray area. The central canal is near the middle of the cord in the gray matter.

At the lower levels, the spinal cord is small and contains about equal amounts of gray matter and white matter. The amount of gray matter increases in the lumbar and cervical spine because of the number of neurons that are necessary to control the arms and legs. The amount of white matter is greater nearer to the brainstem simply because of the larger number of axons within the ascending pathways at successively higher levels. Cross-sections of the spinal cord may be seen in Figure 4-8.

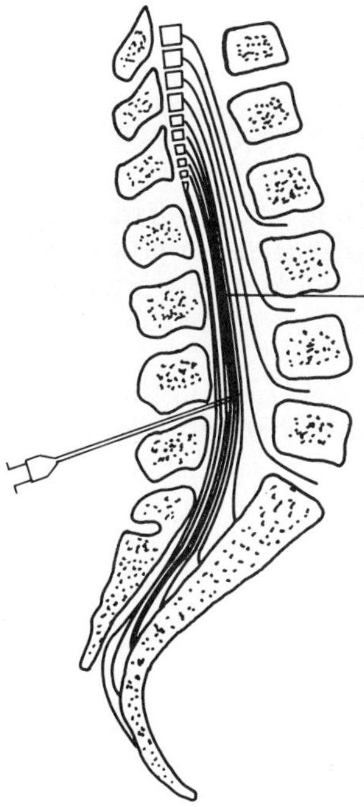

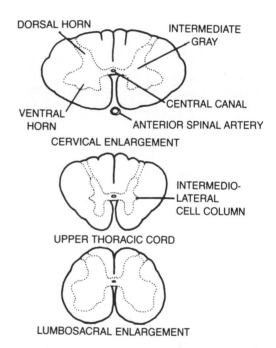

CAUDA EQUINA

Figure 4-7. Position and angle of needle for lumbar puncture in the fourth lumbar interspace below the level of the spinal cord. The cauda equina is pushed aside without being punctured.

Figure 4-8. Cross-sections of the spinal cord showing cord size and relation of white matter (tracts) and gray matter (cell bodies) at successive levels.

STUDY OUTLINE

MAJOR DIVISIONS Central nervous system (CNS), peripheral nervous system (PNS), and autonomic nervous systems (ANS).

NEURAL AND SUPPORTIVE CELLS Neuron is basic unit of nervous system.

Neuroglia serve as connective tissue; participate in metabolism, phagocytosis, excitation.

Oligodendron forms myelin sheath (layered sheath of protein and lipid around many axons) in CNS; Schwann cell forms myelin sheath in PNS.

In myelinated axons, gaps between Schwann cells form nodes of Ranvier.

NERVE BUNDLES Collections of nerve fibers (axons) that course together; also termed simply *nerves*.

Afferent—propagate impulses toward CNS.

Efferent—propagate impulses away from CNS.

PERIPHERAL NERVOUS SYSTEM Spinal and cranial nerves and associated ganglia; generally mixed (afferent fibers and efferent fibers).

COMPOUND ACTION POTENTIAL Nerves contain fibers of different sizes—myelinated and unmyelinated; action potentials propagated at different velocities.

Electrode located at distance from stimulation site records polyphasic, or compound, action potential.

SPINAL NERVES Eight cervical, 12 thoracic, 5 lumbar, 5 sacral, and 1 coccygeal; attached to spinal cord by dorsal (primarily afferent) root and ventral (primarily motor) roots.

CRANIAL NERVES Leave CNS from medulla and more rostral structures.

12 pairs—sensory and motor for head and neck; special senses of vision, audition, taste, and smell.

CENTRAL NERVOUS SYSTEM Brain and spinal cord.

Both are encased in bone, float in CSF; both covered by meninges (pia mater, arachnoid, dura mater).

BRAIN Cerebral hemispheres—each is subdivided into frontal, temporal, parietal, and occipital lobes.

Brain stem—medulla, pons, midbrain, and diencephalon.

Cerebellum—anterior, posterior, and flocculonodular lobes.

SPINAL CORD Segments are named according to associated vertebral segments in infant; relationship does not hold in adults.

Cord is roundish in shape, contains both gray matter and white matter; extends caudally to L1 in adult.

Diameter of cord varies with size of tracts and number of cell bodies at any level; gray matter (cell bodies) increases in lumbar and cervical areas because of neurons needed to control arms and legs.

Spinal column below L1 contains spinal nerves (cauda equina) that serve lower extremities.

BIBLIOGRAPHY

Carpenter, M.B. 1978. *Core Text of Neuroanatomy.* Baltimore: Williams and Wilkins Co.

Clark, R.G. 1979. *Essentials of Clinical Neuroanatomy and Neurophysiology.* Philadelphia: F.A. Davis.

Cowan, W.M. 1979. The development of the brain. *Sci. Am.* 241:(3)112.

Hubel, D.H. 1979. The brain. *Sci. Am.* 241:(3)44.

Kandel, E.R., and Schwartz, J.H. 1981. *Principles of Neural Science.* New York: Elsevier North-Holland.

Kuffler, S.W., and Nicholls, J.G. 1966. The physiology of neuroglial cells. *Ergeb. Physiol.* 57:1.

Nauta, W.J.H., and Feirtag, M. 1979. The organization of the brain. *Sci. Am.* 241:(3)88.

5

Sensory Systems

CHAPTER CONTENTS

CLASSIFICATION OF RECEPTOR CELLS

Functional

The sensory receptor cells of the body may be classified in several different ways. Consistent with the classification of Sherrington, receptors are grouped according to the function they serve, as follows:

1. *Proprioceptors*—located in muscles and joints; proprioceptors provide information about movement and body position.

2. *Exteroceptors*—located in the skin; exteroceptors provide information about the adjacent external environment.

3. *Interoceptors*—located in the viscera; interoceptors provide information about the internal evironment.

4. *Teleceptors*—located in the eyes, ears, and nose; teleceptors provide information about the distant environment.

5. *Nociceptors*—located throughout the body; nociceptors respond to extremes of mechanical force, temperature, and other potentially destructive stimuli.

Physiological

In the contemporary context, receptors more commonly are grouped physiologically. According to this type of classification, receptors are grouped as follows:

1. *Mechanoreceptors*, which respond to physical deformation of the receptor-cell membrane, occur in the somatosensory, auditory, vestibular, circulatory, renal, and respiratory systems.

2. *Chemoreceptors*, which respond to specific chemicals in solution, are found in the olfactory and gustatory systems and in the systems that regulate osmolarity, blood pressure, respiration, and the secretion of hormones.

3. *Photoreceptors,* which respond to light through a chemical reaction and are responsible for vision.

4. *Thermoreceptors*, which respond to increases or decreases of temperature but otherwise are not well understood.

5. *Nociceptors*, which respond (as in the previous classification) to extremes of stimulation, possibly through the release of chemicals.

RECEPTOR MECHANISMS

Transducer Function

SPECIFICITY

Receptors function as transducers, which convert one form of energy into another. Proprioceptors, for example, convert mechanical energy into electrical energy, by which the nervous system functions. In addition, a given receptor is most sensitive to one particular form of energy. An example of this specificity is provided by the retinal photoreceptors, which can respond to mechanical stimulation (as demonstrated by exerting gentle pressure on the eye and noting the accompanying visual sensation), but are most sensitive to light. A stimulus of the appropriate modality and of threshold intensity for a given receptor is said to be an adequate stimulus for that receptor.

The example given above, in which pressure on the eye can cause visual sensation, also is an example of *Müller's doctrine of specific nerve energies.* This doctrine holds that, regardless of the form of energy used to stimulate a particular sense organ, the sensation will be the same as the sensation that is elicited by any other adequate stimulus.

GENERATOR POTENTIALS

An appropriate stimulus applied to a receptor alters the cellular potential, usually by decreasing it. This effect is graded and nonpropagated (see Chapter 2). In general, the initial phase of the receptor potential represents a nonselective increase in ionic permeability. Receptor potentials may be generated within a separate cell and transmitted to a nerve fiber, as in the cochlea and retina, or they may be generated within a specialized ending of an afferent nerve fiber, as in the pacinian corpuscle. These potentials, which are like subthreshold potentials in an excitable cell, summate spatially and temporally to initiate an action potential in the afferent nerve. Within physiological limits, the frequency of excitation of the nerve fibers varies with the magnitude of the receptor potential (see Figure 5-1).

Adaptation

The rate of firing of a nerve fiber in response to a sustained stimulus generally is highest when the stimulus is first applied; the rate of firing

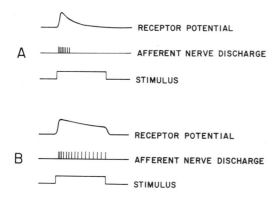

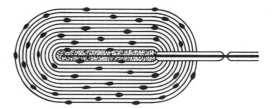

Figure 5-2.   Longitudinal section through a pacinian corpuscle showing the concentric lamellae and associated myelinated nerve fiber with an unmyelinated portion inside the corpuscle.

Figure 5-1.   Receptor potentials and associated afferent nerve responses in **A** rapidly adapting and **B** slowly adapting receptors.

decreases with time. This is described as *adaptation* of the receptor. If the firing ceases soon after the stimulus is applied, the receptor is said to be *rapidly adapting;* if firing continues throughout the duration of the stimulus, the receptor is said to be *slowly adapting* (Figure 5-1).

Cutaneous Receptors

The sensations of pressure (deep touch), discriminative (light) touch, pain, and temperature are served by various anatomically distinct receptors in the skin. These receptors include nerve fibers of small diameter, either myelinated (such as hair follicle receptors and Ruffini endings) or unmyelinated (such as free nerve endings), and encapsulated receptor organs, such as pacinian corpuscles, Meissner's corpuscles, and Krause's end bulbs. In humans and several other mammals, the skin contains special receptor complexes, called *touch corpuscles*, which are identifiable as small but distinct mounds in the epidermis. These mounds, which have a rich vasculature and therefore are slightly redder than the surrounding skin surface, contain numerous receptors, called *Merkel disks,* which are associated with the endings of unmyelinated nerve fibers. In general, distortion of these receptors causes an alteration, usually an increase, of ionic permeability.

PACINIAN CORPUSCLE
One of the most widely studied cutaneous receptors is the *pacinian corpuscle* (Figure 5-2), an encapsulated receptor organ found in the tissue

around joints and tendons, in subcutaneous tissue, and in the mesentery. The pacinian corpuscle consists of multiple concentric layers, or *lamellae*, that surround a single nerve fiber. The nerve fibers associated with pacinian corpuscles generally are myelinated, but the myelin sheath terminates in the outer lamellae of the corpuscle. Pacinian corpuscles are extremely sensitive, rapidly adapting mechanoreceptors that respond to deformation, possibly as small as 0.5 μm. Their rapid adaptation allows them to respond to trains of high-frequency stimuli; vibration, such as that provided by a tuning fork, is an effective stimulus for these receptors. The lamellae are free to slide over one another slightly, and this property may account for some of the adaptation that is evident in the potentials recorded from pacinian corpuscles. Even if the outermost layers remain displaced, the innermost layers can return toward their resting positions; the net result is decreased deformation of the unmyelinated fiber and a decrease of the associated receptor potential.

Muscle Receptors

Numerous receptor cells, including muscle spindles, Golgi tendon organs, pressure-pain endings, and pacinian corpuscles, are located in muscles and tendons. Most of these receptors do not cause conscious sensations but are involved in the coordination of movement and the regulation of muscle tone. These processes are considered in detail in Chapter 6.

PRESSURE-PAIN ENDINGS
The pressure-pain endings, which are located in fascia, are bare nerve endings—the terminations of small-diameter myelinated axons. These receptors respond to both pressure and noxious

stimuli and can produce conscious sensations. The fascia also contain pacinian corpuscles that function in a manner similar to the pacinian corpuscles that are located in the skin. These receptors, which respond to pressure and vibration, also give rise to perceptible sensations.

TENDON ORGANS

Large myelinated nerve fibers (Group Ib afferents) innervate tendons of skeletal muscles and terminate in numerous small-diameter, unmyelinated branches near bundles of collagen fibers. This complex of fine, branching fibers, which is called a *Golgi tendon organ*, encodes the tension that is generated in the tendon, primarily by contraction of the muscle, but also by passive stretch. These receptors adapt slowly but continue to respond as long as the tendon is stretched. The information they provide is used only at the subconscious level.

MUSCLE SPINDLES

The muscle spindle is a complex receptor organ that has been investigated extensively. It contains specialized contractile fibers in the muscle, called *intrafusal fibers* (the common contractile fibers of skeletal muscle are termed *extrafusal*), and motor and sensory nerves that innervate the specialized fibers. The motor innervation is provided by the γ-efferent fibers, which are activated independently of the motoneurons that serve the extrafusal fibers. The sensory fibers belong to both group IA, the largest of the myelinated fibers in the peripheral nervous system, and group II, which are medium-sized, myelinated axons. These two types of afferent nerve fibers end in bare axons that wrap around the intrafusal fibers and are encapsulated (Figure 5-3). The encapsulated portion of the intrafusal fiber does not contract, but the portions on either side of it do, in response to input from the γ-efferents. Thus, the afferent endings act as stretch receptors for the central portion of the intrafusal fibers that respond to both passive stretch of the whole muscle, which stretches both intrafusal and extrafusal fibers, and γ-activation of the contractile portions of the intrafusal fibers, which stretches the encapsulated central portion. Muscle spindles provide information about the length of the muscle and the rate of change of length (i.e., velocity of contraction). Afferent fibers from the spindles end directly on and excite primary motoneurons in

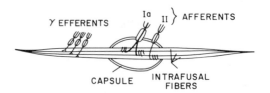

Figure 5-3. The units that comprise the muscle spindle, including the modified fibers of skeletal muscle (intrafusal fibers); the motor fibers that innervate these muscle fibers (γ-efferents); the large myelinated (group Ia) afferents; the smaller (group II) afferents, the bare fiber endings of which wrap around the intrafusals; and the capsule that surrounds the afferent endings.

the spinal cord. Passive stretch activates the spindles, which cause the α-motoneurons to fire and the extrafusal fibers to contract. This counteracts the stretch. This response probably is the major component of the *tendon-jerk* (or stretch) reflex.

Physiologically, the muscle spindles and γ-efferent fibers comprise a feedback system that regulates the activity of the skeletal muscles. A slight increase in γ-activity produces tension in the intrafusal fibers and brings the spindles closer to the threshold for excitation, making them more sensitive to stretch of the muscles. This function is considered in more detail in Chapter 6.

Joint Receptors

Various receptors are located within the joints. Some of these receptors adapt slowly, and others adapt rapidly; however, all of them convey information about position and movement of the joints. The receptors are innervated by both myelinated and unmyelinated fibers. The myelinated fibers end primarily in the spraylike *Ruffini endings* and the *paciniform corpuscles* (encapsulated structures that resemble miniature pacinian corpuscles). The unmyelinated nerves terminate primarily in a network of small fibers, some of which end within the connective tissue that surrounds the joint and, presumably, mediate pain. The other receptors are involved in the conscious perception of joint position and motion and the unconscious processing of information about joint position and motion.

SOMATOSENSORY SYSTEM

Traditionally, the somatosensory system consists of an exteroceptive division, which provides information from the external environment, an interoceptive division, which supplies information from the internal environment, and a proprioceptive division, which gives information about the orientation of the body in space. Many subdivisions of these major categories will be considered in sections on the special senses (auditory, visual, vestibular, olfactory, and gustatory) that follow in this chapter; therefore, the discussion here will cover only the sensations of touch, joint position, vibration, pain, and temperature.

Touch

LIGHT TOUCH
The sensation of touch is subdivided into two clinically and subjectively distinct categories. The first category, termed *discriminative*, or *light, touch*, is the sense that permits one to determine the surface characteristics of an object. For example, discriminative touch permits one to distinguish the coarseness of sandpaper by touch alone or to identify an object that is placed in the hand but not seen. This sense can be tested clinically by placing the points of a caliper on the skin of a patient and determining how far apart they must be for the patient to perceive them separately. The ability to recognize objects by touch alone, which is called *stereognosis*, is tested routinely in a neurological examination. Although this ability also depends on the integrity of muscle activity in the hand, its sensory component is discriminative touch.

DEEP TOUCH
If a person lacked the capability of light touch, the sensation that remained would be that of pressure or deep touch. With only this component of touch intact, one could determine that something was being pressed against the skin but would be unable to tell whether it was sharp or dull or whether more than one site was being touched simultaneously.

Pain and Temperature

Pain and temperature usually are discussed together because they share some common properties. Pain and temperature are the least understood of the somatic sensations, and information in both modalities may ascend the spinal cord in the same fiber tracts (the lateral spinothalamic tracts). Certain specific receptors for pain (*nociceptors*) in the body may be stimulated either directly by damage to the receptor cell or secondarily by the release of chemicals from damaged tissue in the region of the receptors. Free nerve endings usually are thought to provide these functions. However, much of the sensation of pain must arise from the central integration of input from widely varied types of receptors received through a diffuse network of ascending pathways. Attempts to relieve intractable pain by sectioning dorsal roots associated with discrete tracts in the spinal cord generally have been ineffective, presumably because of the multiplicity of pathways involved. Moreover, cognitive and emotional factors strongly affect the perception of pain. The discovery of peptides in the central nervous system (CNS) that have the qualities of opiates and receptors that are specific for these peptides and for opiate compounds also suggests the existence of a central network that is concerned with pain.

GATE-CONTROL THEORY
This theory proposes a physiological basis for the reduction of perceived pain by gentle tactile stimulation over the affected area (e.g., abdominal pain is subjectively reduced by lightly stroking the skin over the abdomen). A network of "t-cells" (cells that transmit painful stimuli from slowly propagating fibers) and interneurons that can inhibit the t-cells is postulated to form a "gate" within the spinal cord. The interneurons are activated by the faster propagating fibers that carry information about light touch. According to the theory, tactile stimulation activates the interneurons, which inhibit the t-cells and decrease the transmission of pain impulses. Although the exact locus of the gate network is unknown, the principles of the theory generally have been accepted and applied clinically. Tactile stimulation that is used to "close the gate" can be replaced by electrical stimulation of the pathways for light touch through electrodes placed on the skin (transcutaneous electrical nerve stimulation, or TENS).

REFERRED PAIN

Pain associated with visceral disorders usually is perceived to be qualitatively different from the pain that originates at cutaneous receptors: it is intense, diffuse, persistent, and poorly localized. However, such disorders may be associated with hypersensitivity and pain in specific areas of the skin, which can help to identify the sources. Although the physiological mechanisms that underlie this association are poorly understood, some mechanisms have been proposed. Neural activity that originates from affected internal organs may lower the threshold for transmission (t) cells within the cord, so that impulses from the skin carried in peripheral nerves that enter the cord at the same level produce painful sensations. The pain seems to originate in the area of the skin served by the peripheral fibers, and the pain of the visceral disorder is "referred" to the skin. In a sense, this proposed mechanism of referred pain can be thought of as "opening the gate" for painful sensations from the skin. Consistent with the theory, local anesthetic drugs injected into the hypersensitive area of skin block the referred pain, although intense pain can overcome the block.

Some examples of referred pain seen clinically are pain in the left shoulder and arm associated with ischemia of the heart, the pain of appendicitis felt just below the sternum, and pain in the skin of the lower back and groin associated with kidney stones or infections of the kidneys. In each instance, the nerves that supply the painful region of skin and the fibers that subserve the affected internal organ enter the same segment of the spinal cord.

PROJECTED PAIN

The *doctrine of specific nerve energies*, stated by Johannes Müller in the nineteenth century, emphasizes that each kind of sensory receptor and its associated pathways are dedicated to a particular type of sensation. Stimulation of the visual system, for example, whether by the action of light on the photoreceptors of the eye or electrical stimulation of the optic nerve, produces visual sensations. Regardless of where the system is stimulated, the sensation is perceived to have arisen in the receptors, or is "projected" to the periphery. In this manner, sensations of pain initiated by irritation of the sensory pathways (caused by inflammation, trauma, tumor, or pressure) are perceived to come from the region served by the receptors associated with

those pathways. Inflammation of a dorsal root, for example, is associated with pain projected to the dermatome (area of skin) supplied by nerves that enter the cord through that root. Knowledge of this fact helps the neurologist to identify the site of the lesion.

TEMPERATURE

The mechanisms that underlie sensations of temperature are understood even less well than the mechanisms that underlie pain. Although specific "thermoreceptors" in the skin are supposed to exist, they have not been identified. Two different populations of receptors appear to function—one more sensitive to cold, which responds to temperatures in the range of 10–35 C, and another more responsive to heat, which responds to temperatures in the range of 25–45 C. Both types of receptors respond to temperatures in the "comfort zone" between 25 and 35 C. Temperatures higher than about 45 C elicit the sensation of pain. Both types of receptors adapt (i.e., are more sensitive to change of temperature), but some response continues even in the absence of change. To illustrate the adaptation, if one finger is placed in cold water and another finger is placed in hot water, each sensation initially is perceived sharply, after which the sensation wanes. If both fingers then are placed in the same container of warm water, the cold-adapted finger feels "hot" water and the hot-adapted finger feels "cold" water. In each case, the sensory input is unbalanced by the adaptation of one type of receptor, which allows the other (unadapted) receptor to give the dominant signal of hot or cold. Receptors for cold are more numerous than receptors for heat, although each type of receptor tends to be located in discrete spots in the skin, rather than distributed evenly.

Information about temperature is carried in specific tracts in the spinal cord and brainstem (lateral spinothalamic tracts; see Figure 5-7). Temperature sensitivity is assessed in the neurological examination by touching the skin with metal tubes that contain warm or cool water. False sensations of temperature change may accompany lesions of the somatosensory pathway.

Vibration and Joint Position

The sensation of vibration is evaluated by applying a tuning fork (vibrating in the range of 150–200 Hz) to various bony prominences and

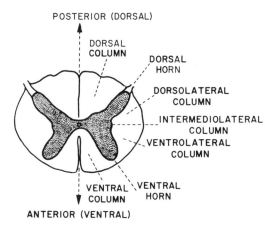

POSTERIOR (DORSAL)

DORSAL COLUMN

DORSAL HORN

DORSOLATERAL COLUMN

INTERMEDIOLATERAL COLUMN

VENTROLATERAL COLUMN

VENTRAL COLUMN   VENTRAL HORN

ANTERIOR (VENTRAL)

Figure 5-4. Cross-section of spinal cord showing major divisions. Shaded area represents gray matter, which contains cell bodies and unmyelinated fibers. Unshaded portions represent white matter, which consists of ascending and descending myelinated fibers.

---

determining whether the subject can perceive the vibration. The sense of joint position is tested by moving the subject's fingers, toes, or limbs and requiring him to report, without looking, in which direction the appendages were moved. The sense of joint position also is involved, at an unconscious level, in the coordination of movements.

Spinal Pathways

Discriminative touch and deep touch are considered separately because the nerve fibers that carry information about these two senses are routed through different neural pathways, or tracts, within the spinal cord. Thus, these two senses may be involved in different disease processes. The major divisions of spinal cord tracts are shown diagrammatically in Figure 5-4.

Since much of the information carried in the various somatosensory pathways is involved in the unconscious coordination of motor activities, many of these fibers also connect with structures in the CNS that are responsible for motor control. These systems are discussed in Chapter 6.

LIGHT TOUCH, JOINT POSITION, AND VIBRATION

The peripheral nerve trunks that carry light touch, joint position, and vibration consist of neurons that have cell bodies in the dorsal root ganglia adjacent to the spinal cord. The central

extensions of these neurons enter the cord, and most ascend toward the brain in the dorsal column on the same side of the body as the peripheral nerve and dorsal root ganglion (Figure 5-5). Thus, at the spinal level, this pathway is mostly uncrossed. In the nucleus gracilis or nucleus cuneatus of the medulla, the axons synapse with cell bodies that send fibers across to the opposite side. These fibers ascend and connect with nuclei in the upper thalamus, and the system terminates eventually in the somesthetic receiving area of the cortex (Figure 5-6), still on the side opposite to the original sensory receptors. This pathway illustrates one of the general, but not inviolate, principles of the major sensory and motor pathways: a particular portion of the body is served by cortical regions that lie on the opposite side of the midline.

PAIN AND TEMPERATURE
Information from the body about pain and temperature is carried in a pathway that is located in the ventrolateral columns of the spinal cord (Figure 5-7). Unlike the pathways for light touch, the fibers that carry information about pain and temperature usually synapse just after entering the cord. The next axons in the series cross the midline and ascend in the lateral portions of the cord; thus, the pathway primarily is crossed, that is, it carries information from the opposite side of the body. A relatively small lesion that involved only one side of the spinal cord could affect the sensation of pain and temperature from the side of the body opposite (contralateral to) the lesion, but it would affect light touch from the same side as (ipsilateral to) the lesion. At the cerebral level, however, both senses are represented on the opposite side.

DEEP TOUCH
The sense of deep touch is carried by fibers in two different portions of the lateral columns of the spinal cord, one of which is crossed and one of which is uncrossed. As in the other two pathways, however, all of the representation in the cerebrum essentially is contralateral to the receptors that are stimulated.

Disorders of the Somatosensory System

Through either irritation or destruction of fibers, lesions of somatosensory pathways can produce *paresthesias* (spontaneous needlelike

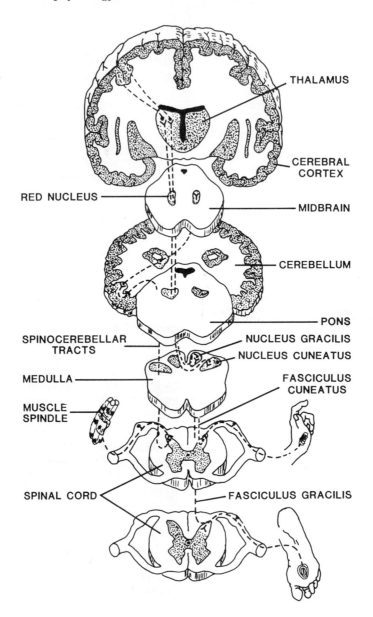

Figure 5-5. Sensory pathways for touch, pressure, and proprioception within the fasciculus gracilis and fasciculus cuneatus, and for proprioception within the spinocerebellar tracts.

sensations, burning, tingling, numbness, or sensations of warmth or cold), *hyperesthesias* (enhanced sensitivity to tactile stimuli), or *hypesthesias* (diminished sensitivity to tactile stimuli). Complete loss of sensitivity, even if confined to a specific region, is termed *anesthesia.*

BROWN–SÉQUARD SYNDROME

Although the somatosensory system is made complex by segregation of the various types of somatic sensation in well-defined, independent pathways, the specialization of its component tracts helps the clinician to localize pathology. The symptoms caused by hemisection of the spinal cord (Brown–Séquard syndrome), which may be caused by trauma or neoplasm, illustrate how a lesion can be localized through neuroanatomical considerations alone. Because the pathways that carry the sensations of pain and temperature mostly are crossed in the spinal cord, these sensations, after hemisection, are lost on the side of the body that is opposite to the lesion, beginning slightly below the level of the lesion. The pathways that carry vibration,

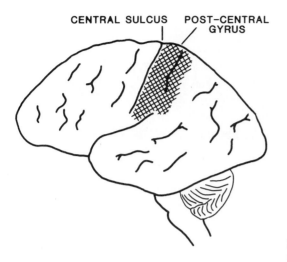

CENTRAL SULCUS POST–CENTRAL GYRUS

Figure 5-6. Lateral view of the brain showing the primary cortical receiving area for somatosensory information.

Figure 5-7. Sensory pathways for pain and temperature within the lateral spinothalamic tracts.

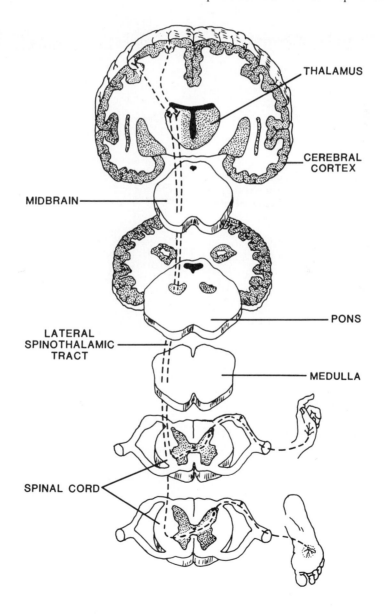

CLINICAL CORRELATION

5.1   Tumor of the Spinal Cord

CASE REPORT

The Patient: A 27-year-old man.

Principal Complaints: Weakness of the left leg and difficulty walking.

History: Approximately two months before the current admission, the patient noted pain in the left hip and over the dorsal surface of the left thigh. The painful sensations gradually resolved, and the affected regions became somewhat numb. He noted progressive difficulty walking during the next month, and often tripped over objects with the left leg. He stated that his leg always felt "asleep."

Clinical Examination: Physical examination revealed slightly reduced muscle mass (wasting) in the left leg. Deep tendon reflexes (Ch. 6, "Clinical Applications of Spinal Reflexes") were normal in the upper extremities and the right leg, but were hyperreactive in the left leg. Abdominal reflexes were intact bilaterally; the cremasteric reflex (retraction of the testis on the same side) was not elicited by stimulating the medial aspect of the left thigh, but could be elicited on the right side. Testing with a sharp pin revealed markedly diminished pain sensation in the right leg, although this sense was preserved in the left leg. Vibration sense and sense of joint position were diminished in the left leg; both of these senses were normal in the right leg and in the upper extremities. Strength was normal in the upper extremities and right leg but was markedly reduced in the left leg. No other muscle weakness or wasting was found, and cranial nerve function was intact. No abnormalities of cerebellar function were evident.

A myelogram was obtained by introducing a radio-opaque dye through a needle inserted into the subarachnoid space below the termination of the spinal cord (e.g., between the 3rd and 4th lumbar vertebrae). Sequential x-ray pictures of the spinal column showed the dye progressing through the column, outlining the cord. Myelography revealed displacement of the cord and the dura to the right, with narrowing of the subarachnoid space at the level of L1–L2. The outline of the nerve root could not be identified at that level on the left side. Analysis of spinal fluid withdrawn at the time of the lumbar puncture showed a slight increase in the concentration of protein, but the concentration of glucose was normal.

Comment: The patient's symptoms and the findings of the neurological examination indicated a small lesion in the spinal cord (Brown-Séquard syndrome), at the level of L1–L2. The early symptoms of pain implicated the second lumbar nerve root on the left side, whereas the other neurological findings were associated with ascending and descending spinal pathways. The weakness, muscle wasting, and hyperactive tendon reflexes in the left leg indicated involvement of the ventral cord (descending corticospinal and vestibulospinal pathways) on the left side, whereas the diminished senses of vibration and joint position were related to the dorsal columns. Because the lateral spinothalamic pathways are crossed, involvement of these fibers on the left side of the cord accounts for the diminished perception of pain in the right leg.

Outcome: All of the clinical findings indicated an extradural mass at L1–L2 on the left side, probably a tumor. The patient was referred to the neurosurgical service for further diagnosis.

sense of position, and touch mostly are un-crossed in the spinal cord; therefore, these elements are lost on the same side of the body as the lesion. Destruction or irritation of dorsal roots at the site of the lesion can produce a band of anesthesia in the appropriate area of innervation on the same side as the lesion. The descending motor pathways also are interrupted, which causes partial paralysis.

VISUAL SYSTEM

Structure and Function

The importance of the visual system is indicated by the large part of the CNS that is engaged in visual function. Four of the twelve cranial nerves are devoted exclusively to efferent fibers and afferent fibers that are related to the eyes. Each of the optic nerves has approximately 1 million fibers, and the number of cortical cells involved in the processing of visual input is so great that all of the occipital lobe and part of the parietal lobe are used almost exclusively for this sensory function.

The sensation of vision is elicited by a narrow band of the electromagnetic spectrum, in the range of about 400–700 nm. This portion of the electromagnetic energy band is called the visible spectrum because the visual system is sensitive to it. The term *light* also includes the wavelengths that are a little longer (infrared) or shorter (ultraviolet) than the wavelengths that usually are considered to be visible. The visual systems of animals other than humans may respond to slightly different portions of the electromagnetic spectrum.

The eye is roughly analogous to a fluid-filled hollow sphere. The tough, white outer covering is called the *sclera* (Figure 5-8). In all but the more anterior portions of the globe, a highly vascular layer, called the *choroid,* lies inside the sclera, and a third layer, the *retina*, is within the choroid. The photoreceptors, which are sensitive to light, are located within the retina. In vertebrates, the retina is inverted; that is, the light-sensitive tips of the photoreceptors point away from the light. Although this arrangement has the disadvantage of scattering light somewhat because the light must pass first through the layers of other neural elements in the retina before it strikes the photoreceptors, it has the advantage of permitting the layer of receptor cells to be imbedded in the light-absorbent

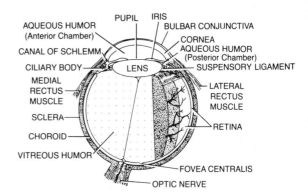

Figure 5-8. The structures of the eye.

pigment epithelium (see Figure 5-13). The retinal pigment epithelium (RPE) not only provides a nonreflective surface that reduces the scatter of light within the eye, but it also is important in the metabolism of the receptor cells. Mammals that lack the light-absorbing RPE have instead a *tapetum lucidum,* an epithelial lining of the choroid that increases the reflection of light. Although the increased reflectance decreases the sharpness of the perceived image, it increases the sensitivity of the eye in dim light, and, therefore, is advantageous to animals that are at least partially nocturnal. The tapetum also causes the eyes of some animals to reflect headlights or flashlight beams.

The eye often is compared to a camera, with the retina analogous to the photographic film. Actually, the function of the eye resembles more closely that of a TV camera, because elaborate self-adjusting circuits focus the image and compensate for a wide range of ambient light conditions. The eye contains image-sharpening and contrast-enhancing circuits and color-coding mechanisms; instead of discrete pictures, the eye continuously transmits encoded images. The basic physiological mechanisms that underlie the various "circuits" of this elaborate and fascinating system will be discussed in the section that follows.

Image Focusing

CORNEA

The anterior portion of the eye is specialized to regulate the amount of light that enters the eye and to focus the image on the retina. A slight bulge on the anterior aspect causes the globe to deviate from its otherwise nearly spherical shape; this bulge is called the *cornea*, a clear, avascular sheet of tissue that forms a convex lens. Like all convex lenses, this optical surface causes the incoming light rays to converge. The cornea provides most of the focusing that is necessary to form a sharp image on the surface of the retina. The remainder of the focusing comes from the crystalline lens, a biconvex lens of variable focal length.

CRYSTALLINE LENS

The crystalline lens is held in place in the center of the optical axis, an imaginary line that goes through the globe from the center of the cornea to the posterior pole, by the suspensory ligaments and the ciliary muscle. In a young person the lens is an elastic, nearly spherical capsule filled with viscous material. When the lens is under no tension, its anterior and posterior surfaces have their highest degree of curvature and, therefore, the highest dioptric "power," or shortest focal length. When in this nearly spherical shape, the lens can focus images from near objects on the retina (Figure 5-9).

The suspensory ligaments attach to the periphery of the lens and extend radially to join the circular fibers of the ciliary muscle. When the ciliary muscle is fully contracted, the tension on the suspensory ligaments is reduced and the lens becomes more spherical; this is the mechanism of *accommodation* (see Figure 5-9).

When the ciliary muscle is relaxed, the suspensory ligaments pull the lens into a flatter contour. In this configuration, the lens has less dioptric power, or longer focal length, and focuses images on the retina from objects at a distance. The ciliary muscle is innervated by parasympathetic fibers; maximal relaxation of the muscle, with consequent flattening of the lens, can be achieved by the administration of eye drops that contain a muscarinic antagonist such as atropine (see Chapter 8). This technique is useful in clinical examination of the eye and in the determination of refractive errors.

The lens loses much of its elasticity with age, and, therefore, is less capable of assuming the more spherical shape. At some time during the fourth decade of life, most people begin to have difficulty focusing the images of near objects and need corrective lenses to replace some of the lost focusing power. This condition is called presbyopia (literally, "old eyes"). As it ages, the

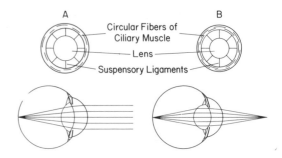

Figure 5-9. Accommodation. **A.** When the ciliary muscle is relaxed, the radially oriented suspensory ligaments pull the lens into a flatter shape, which permits parallel light rays from objects at a distance to be focused on the retina. **B.** When the ciliary muscle contracts, tension on the suspensory ligaments is reduced, and the elastic lens assumes a more spherical shape. Divergent light rays from near objects then can be focused on the retina.

lens also may become less transparent and develop the condition that is known as *cataract*.

Regulation of Light Intensity

IRIS

Just anterior to the lens is the *iris*, a ring-shaped sheet of muscle fibers and ligaments. The aperture in the center of the iris is the pupil, which changes in size to regulate the amount of light that enters the eye. The iris contains two physiologically separate networks of muscle fibers. The sphincter muscle, in which the fibers are arranged circumferentially, decreases the size of the pupil, or constricts it; the dilator muscle, in which the fibers are arranged radially, enlarges, or dilates, the pupil. The sphincter muscle is innervated by parasympathetic fibers, and the dilator muscle is innervated by sympathetic fibers. Pharmacological agents can dilate the pupil by either stimulating the dilator muscle or inhibiting the sphincter muscle. Thus, atropine not only paralyzes the ciliary muscle and prevents accommodation, but it also dilates the pupil; both actions facilitate the examination of the eye.

Under normal conditions, if a bright light is directed into the eye, the pupil *constricts* and reduces the amount of light that strikes the retina. This is called the *direct pupillary response*, which can be used to assess grossly the integrity of the visual afferent pathways and efferent pathways between the eye and the brainstem. The synapses for this pathway are located primarily within the midbrain portion of the brainstem. Interconnections between the two efferent nuclei at this level cause the contralateral pupil also to constrict; this is called the *consensual pupillary response.* By comparing the direct and consensual responses, one can obtain information that helps to localize lesions that disrupt these reflex pathways. For example, if a light is shone into the right eye and no pupillary response is obtained, the disruption could involve either afferent (optic nerve) fibers or efferent (oculomotor nerve) fibers. If afferent fibers from the right eye are disrupted, no pupillary response in either eye would be expected. If only efferent fibers to the right eye are affected, the consensual response still should occur in the left eye.

The pupils of the eyes also constrict when a person looks at a nearby object. In this situation, the constriction helps to increase the depth of field of the optical system (Figure 5-10). When focused on nearby objects, the eyes also *converge* (both eyes adduct, or deviate toward the midline) to make the image that is formed in each eye more nearly the same. An additional part of the convergence response is the reflex contraction of the ciliary muscles, accommodation (Figure 5-9), which increases the dioptric power of the lens. This constellation of responses—pupillary constriction, convergence, and accommodation—constitutes near synkinesis, or the *near response.* It involves connections between the brainstem and the occipital cortex in addition to those between the brainstem and the eyes.

Intraocular Fluids

The pupillary portion of the iris is in contact with the anterior capsule of the lens. The cavity bounded by the iris, anterior capsule, and cornea (the anterior chamber) is filled with a watery substance called the *aqueous humor.* This substance is produced in vascular portions of the ciliary body that lie adjacent to the ciliary muscle. The aqueous humor normally flows first into the posterior chamber, which is the ring-shaped cavity just behind the iris (see Figure 5-8), and then forward through the pupil into the anterior chamber. Aqueous humor is removed from the anterior chamber through channels located near the juncture of the cornea and the sclera (the region known as the *limbus*). These outflow channels connect with the venous circulation. If the outflow channels be-

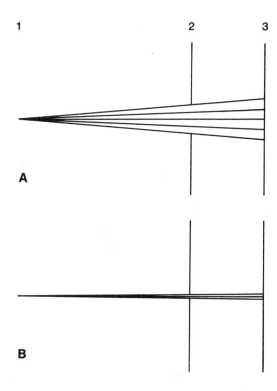

Figure 5-10.   Focusing effect of a small aperture. A point source of light in plane 1 enters the aperture in plane 2 and falls on the surface in plane 3. **A.** A large aperture admits a wide angle of light rays from the point source. **B.** A small aperture admits only those rays that are nearly parallel and, thus, produces a sharper image of the point source on the surface in plane 3. This effect is most marked for sources close to plane 2 because, at greater distances, the rays from the point source already are nearly parallel. The net effect of the small aperture is to increase the range over which the images of objects are in focus in plane 3; this is the principle that underlies the pinhole camera. Such a camera has enormous depth of field, with objects in focus from just in front of the camera to infinity, but the amount of light that enters the camera is very small, and long exposure times or very sensitive films must be used.

come blocked, so that the aqueous humor is not cleared as fast as it is produced, pressure builds up within the globe. This condition is known as *glaucoma,* and, if left untreated, can lead to blindness. Behind the lens lies the vitreous cavity, which is filled with a gelatinous, clear substance called the *vitreous humor.* Unlike the aqueous humor, the vitreous humor turns over little, if at all. Its main function appears to be to help retain the shape of the globe.

Refractive Errors

MYOPIA AND HYPEROPIA

If the globe is abnormally long or if the curvature is abnormally great, distant objects are focused ahead of the retina (Figure 5-11) and the images are blurred; however, nearby objects still can be focused adequately. This condition, known as *nearsightedness*, or *myopia*, can be corrected by placing a slightly concave (diverging) lens in the line of sight. This type of lens has negative dioptric power and may be called simply a minus lens. An abnormally short eyeball or an eyeball that has an abnormally flat cornea exhibits the opposite properties (Figure 5-12)—distant objects can be focused by utilizing the accommodative mechanism, but nearby objects are blurred. This condition, called *farsightedness*, or *hyperopia,* can be corrected by placing a convex (converging) lens in the line of sight. This type of lens has positive dioptric power and may be called simply a plus lens.

ASTIGMATISM

Astigmatism is another type of refractive error, in which objects are distorted regardless of their distance from the eyes. Astigmatism is caused by imperfect curvatures of the various refractive surfaces; it is caused most often by a nonspherical, or cylindrical, curvature of the surface of the cornea. Lenses that have a similar deviation from spherical can be ground to produce "cylindrical" correction. If the axis of the cylindrical lens is turned 90° to the axis of the cylindrical aberration in the corneal surface, the astigmatic error is corrected.

Retina

The light-sensing cells of the eye are located in the *retina*, a layer of tissue that develops embryologically from the CNS and lies on the inner surface of the choroid in contact with the vitreous body. The retina is attached to the choroid only at the *optic disk* (the region where the fibers of the optic nerve exit from the globe) and at the anterior, scalloped margin of the retina, called the *ora serrata*, where it joins the ciliary body. It is possible for the retina to float free from the choroid, or detach, but usually it is kept from doing so by the pressure of the vitreous humor.

The neural elements of the retina are placed in six major classifications: two types of photoreceptors, the *rods* and *cones;* two types of cells that propagate impulses sequentially toward the brain, the *bipolar* and *ganglion cells;* and two types of cells that integrate information from adjacent regions of the retina, the *horizontal* and *amacrine cells.* The somas and synaptic processes of these cells form distinct layers in the retina (Figure 5-13).

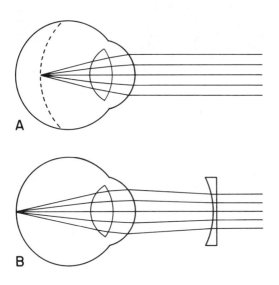

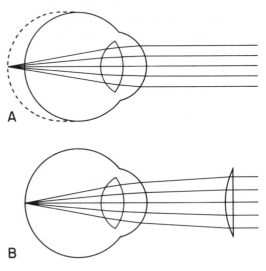

Figure 5-11.   Myopia. **A.** Light rays from distant objects focus in front of the retina. **B.** Correction by a concave lens, which causes light rays to diverge as they enter the eye.

Figure 5-12.   Hyperopia. **A.** Light rays from distant objects focus behind the retina. **B.** Correction by a convex lens, which causes light rays to converge as they enter the eye.

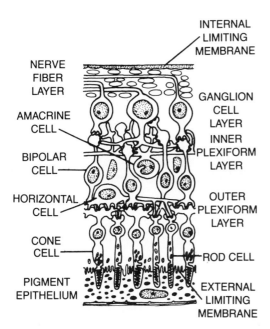

NERVE FIBER LAYER

INTERNAL LIMITING MEMBRANE

AMACRINE CELL

GANGLION CELL LAYER

INNER PLEXIFORM LAYER

BIPOLAR CELL

HORIZONTAL CELL

OUTER PLEXIFORM LAYER

CONE CELL

ROD CELL

PIGMENT EPITHELIUM

EXTERNAL LIMITING MEMBRANE

Figure 5-13.   The structure of the retina.

The ganglion cells, which constitute the "output stage" of the retina, are located in the most inner, or vitread (toward the vitreous humor), layer of the retina. Their long axons extend to the *lateral geniculate nucleus* (LGN), the thalamic relay station for vision.

In the vertebrate retina, light must pass not only through all of the refractive media of the eye (cornea, aqueous humor, lens, and vitreous humor) but also through the other cellular layers of the retina before it finally reaches the photoreceptors. In spite of scatter and the absorption of light rays in all of these tissues, the eye is able to discriminate fine details of patterns and to distinguish a large number of different wavelengths in the visible spectrum.

SENSITIVITY TO LIGHT

The two types of photoreceptors in the retina differ anatomically, physiologically, and functionally. The rods, cylindrical in shape, as their name implies (see Figure 5-13), are much more sensitive to light than the cones are. Overall, the retina is sensitive to an incredible range of light intensity, on the order of 11 log units (10^{11}). The rods alone account for the lower 2–3 log units of intensity; low levels of illumination, in which only the rods function, are referred to as the *scotopic range*. In very bright light, the *photopic* range, only the cones function, and they ac-

count for almost 5 log units of sensitivity. The latitudes of sensitivity of these two distinct cellular systems overlap considerably—both function over a range of about 3 log units. This intermediate range of illumination is referred to as the *mesopic range*.

In the particle theory of light, the smallest theoretical "packet" of light energy is the *quantum,* which is equivalent to the photon. Taking into account the amount of light that is reflected and absorbed by the ocular media, it has been determined that as few as six quanta of light can produce a visual sensation, and only one quantum is necessary to produce a measurable response in a single rod. Therefore, the retina approaches the theoretical upper limit of sensitivity to light.

VISUAL PIGMENTS

Rods contain a chemical pigment (a pigment absorbs light) called *rhodopsin*, which consists of opsin, a protein, linked with 11-*cis* retinal, an aldehyde of vitamin A. In the dark, rhodopsin has a reddish coloration (originally, it was called visual purple), but it loses its color when exposed to light. When the photopigment absorbs light, a series of chemical events occurs rapidly—the opsin-retinal bond is split, and *cis*-retinal is isomerized through several intermediate steps to *trans*-retinal. During this isomerization, the flow of ions across the photoreceptor membrane is altered, producing a receptor potential that stimulates the next element in the cellular chain, the bipolar cell. After its rapid conversion to *trans*-retinal, the pigment reconverts to *cis*-retinal relatively slowly. Because vitamin A is the source of the nonprotein portion of rhodopsin, severe depletion of vitamin A affects rod function adversely and causes a marked loss of vision at low levels of illumination, a condition known as *night blindness.*

The cones contain three different photopigments, which have absorption characteristics different from those of rhodopsin, but any given cone contains only one of these photopigments. The absorption spectra for the cone pigments overlap substantially, but the peaks differ slightly, so that one pigment is most sensitive to the short wavelengths of the visible spectrum (blue-violet), another pigment is most sensitive to the medium wavelengths (yellowish-green), and the third pigment is most sensitive to the longer wavelengths (yellow) (Figure 5-14). Because of their relative contributions to color

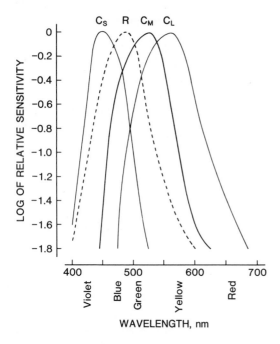

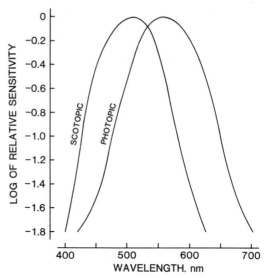

Figure 5-15. Change of the visible spectrum with change of the level of illumination (Purkinje shift).

Figure 5-14. Relative spectral sensitivities of the different types of photopigments, normalized to compensate for differences in absolute sensitivity. (C = cone; R = rod.)

vision, cones that have these types of pigments generally are called blue (B), green (G), and red (R), respectively.

Although the rods generally are not thought of as part of the system of color vision, under mesopic illumination (the middle range of intensity in which both rods and cones function), they do contribute to the perception of color. Because the peak spectral absorption of rods is around 500 nm, which corresponds to the portion of the electromagnetic spectrum that is perceived as bluish-green (see Figure 5-14), colors in that range appear to be brighter in medium (mesopic) light than in bright (photopic) light, when only the cones are functioning. This shift of spectral sensitivity toward the short wavelengths under low-light conditions is known as the *Purkinje shift* (Figure 5-15).

PHOTORECEPTOR POTENTIALS
If light is the effective stimulus for vision, the potentials generated by rods and cones are opposite to the potentials generated by effective stimuli for most receptor cells. The photoreceptors respond to an increase in light intensity by hyperpolarizing, rather than depolarizing, as other receptors do. A decrease in light intensity causes depolarization and the release of chemi-

cals (transmitters) that activate the bipolar and horizontal cells. Like the responses of other receptor cells, the response of the photoreceptor is graded, that is, it is proportional to the change in luminance.

NEURAL CONVERGENCE
The rods are more sensitive to light than the cones are, largely because of the way their neural connections are arranged. The rod system, or scotopic system, as it sometimes is called because of its role in night vision (from the Greek word, *skotos*, "darkness"), is characterized by neural convergence. In this type of cellular network, many cells synapse on the next cell in the chain. Thus, 100 or more rods might synapse with a single bipolar cell, and many bipolar cells synapse with a single ganglion cell. Such a network vastly increases the sensitivity of the system because low-amplitude receptor-potentials from several cells can summate to stimulate the next cell in the chain. This type of cellular network is common in the retina because the photoreceptors outnumber the ganglion cells by more than 100 to 1.

Although convergence enhances the sensitivity to light, it also decreases visual acuity, or the ability to distinguish detail. Obviously, if 100 or more photoreceptors send information to one ganglion cell, that ganglion cell is unable to determine which photoreceptors have been stimulated. Thus, two light sources cannot be distinguished from a single light source unless they are far enough apart to stimulate rods that converge on different ganglion cells.

DARK ADAPTATION

The sensitivity of the retina to light decreases significantly when the eye is exposed to bright light. Two different mechanisms are involved in this decrease of sensitivity; one is chemical and one is neural. The bleaching of rhodopsin by light, which decreases the amount of photopigment available to the rods, accounts for some of the loss. The cone system also contributes, through neural connections that inhibit rod function under conditions of light appropriate for cone function (bright). When the intensity of light is decreased, the rods gradually regain their former levels of sensitivity. Much of the sensitivity to light returns within a few minutes, as one can demonstrate by going from the sunny outdoors into a dark theater, but the restoration of full sensitivity (complete "dark adaptation") takes at least 20–30 minutes. If the eyes have been exposed to very bright light for an extended period, as they would be during a sunny day at the beach without sunglasses, full dark adaptation may require 24 hours or more, and, in some instances, the photoreceptors (both rods and cones) can be damaged permanently.

DISTRIBUTION OF RECEPTORS

Rods and cones are not distributed randomly throughout the retina, but rather each is concentrated in particular regions. Looking into the eye with an ophthalmoscope, one can see the pale-yellow optic disk, which is approximately 1.5 mm in diameter, and the various retinal arteries and veins that extend from the optic disk. About three disk diameters to the temporal side is a relatively avascular region that is about the same size as the disk and has a yellowish appearance. This region is called the *macula* (in older terminology, the macula lutea), and in its center is a small depression that is known as the *fovea* (also called the foveal pit, or fovea centralis). The concentration of cones is greatest in the fovea and is markedly lower in surrounding regions and on the periphery of the retina. Conversely, the fovea contains almost no rods, which are in highest concentration at a point almost 20° from the fovea. The optic disk,

the site at which all of the ganglion cell processes leave the globe to form the optic nerve, contains no photoreceptors and is insensitive to light; therefore, it produces a small blind spot in the visual field. The fovea is in the center of the visual axis; thus, when one looks at an object, the image falls on the fovea. This explains another phenomenon of night vision: because the fovea contains only cones, it essentially is a blind spot in dim light. To see a small object at night, one must direct the gaze slightly off center, so that the image falls on the more sensitive photoreceptors, the rods.

The cellular layers in the center of the fovea are different from the cellular layers in other regions of the retina. The cones are smaller in diameter and more rodlike in shape, and the associated bipolar cells are smaller (midget bipolars) than in other regions. In addition, the cellular processes slant outward from the foveal center, and the ganglion cell bodies with which the midget bipolars synapse are displaced outward. Because of these structural arrangements, the retina is thinner in the fovea than in its other areas, and a depression appears in the retinal surface. Because the photoreceptors are smaller, the retina can resolve finer images in this region. Because the retina is thinner and contains fewer cellular elements, light is scattered less in passing to the photoreceptors. This improves resolution in the region. Cones in this region tend to converge less, and some cones synapse 1 : 1 with bipolar cells. Elsewhere in the retina, the cones converge on the bipolar cells just as the rods do, although the ratios are smaller. Thus, the clarity of images formed even a few degrees from the visual axis is reduced markedly.

COMPARISON OF THE ROD
AND CONE SYSTEMS

The rods and the cones are two distinctly different classes of retinal receptor cells anatomically, chemically, and physiologically. Together with their associated transmission and processing cells, rods and cones form two distinctly different visual systems within the retina. The rod system functions primarily in low levels of light and provides a type of vision that is characterized by a relative lack of color discrimination and resolution of detail. The cone system operates in brighter light and provides a type of vision that is characterized by acuity and ability to distinguish colors.

Visual Acuity

Visual acuity is defined as the minimum separation that permits two sources of light to be perceived separately. This separation can be described by the visual angle—the angle subtended by the two sources with the eye as the center point. At a distance of 10 m, two sources 3 mm apart subtend an arc of 1/60 of a degree (1 minute). The normal eye can differentiate pinpoint sources of light that subtend an angle only about half as great, or approximately 30 seconds of arc. This is surprising when one considers that a foveal cone subtends an arc of about 40 seconds within the globe, so that visual acuity actually is better than would be expected from the size of the photoreceptors. This difference can be explained by the considerable amount of neural processing that is performed within the retina and at higher levels in the CNS (see the section entitled "Neural Processing in the Visual System" in this chapter).

Visual Pathways

The axons of the ganglion cells in the most vitread (toward the vitreous humor) portion of the retina extend all the way to the lateral geniculate nuclei (LGN) of the thalamus, the first relay station in the visual pathways. If one considers the visual field of each eye, that is, the space in which a point of light can elicit a visual sensation, the crossed representation that characterizes the somatosensory system (see the section entitled "Spinal Pathways" in this chapter) also is found in the visual system. The visual fields of the two eyes overlap considerably, providing the binocular vision that is used for depth perception (Figure 5-16). If a line is drawn along the optical axis of each eye, the visual field to the left of this line constitutes the left hemifield for each eye. Fibers from the parts of the retina that receive images from the left hemifield project to the right LGN and, subsequently, to the right visual cortex (Figure 5-17A). Fibers that serve the right hemifield project to the left hemisphere. Because the lens reverses the image on the retina, light that originates in the left hemifield strikes the right side of the interior of the globe, or the nasal retina of the left eye and the temporal retina of the right eye. For both of these two sets of fibers to reach the right hemisphere, those from the left eye must cross the midline (decussate), while those from the right eye do not cross. The opposite is true for the fibers that subserve the right field of view. Therefore, at the optic chiasm, fibers from

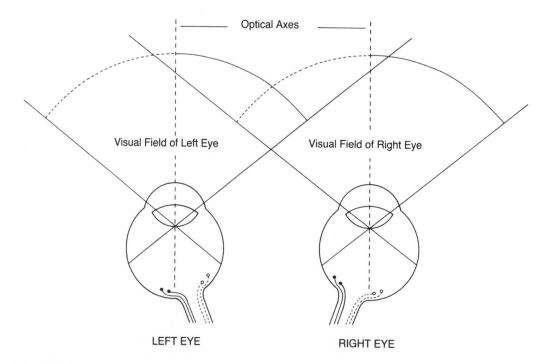

Figure 5-16. Visual fields of the eye.

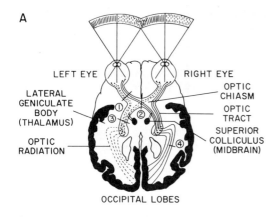

A

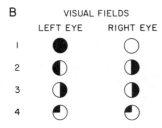

B

Figure 5-17. **A.** Neural pathways for vision. **B.** Defects of visual field that arise from lesions at sites indicated in **A.** Dark areas correspond to areas of blindness for each eye. **1.** Left optic nerve lesion. **2.** Bitemporal hemianopsia from interruption of fibers that cross in optic chiasm. **3.** Homonymous hemianopsia from lesion of left optic tract. **4.** Lesion of inferior portion of right optic radiations can produce quadrantic defect.

the nasal retina of each eye cross, and fibers from the temporal portion of each retina remain uncrossed. These fibers, called the *optic tracts* behind the chiasm, extend uninterrupted to each of the two lateral geniculate nuclei. Cells in each LGN send processes (the *optic radiations*) that loop outward and backward in the temporal and parietal lobes and synapse on cells in the visual cortex of the occipital lobes.

Lesions at various points along the visual pathways cause different defects of the visual fields (Figure 5-17B). One should remember that the term *visual field* refers to visual space and not to retinal topography. The visual field of a subject can be charted by presenting a brief test light at various points in the field and having the subject respond when he sees it.

Eye Movements and Their Control

Although the extraocular muscles and the associated neural network that functions to rotate the eyes constitute a motor system, it is involved so intimately with vision that it is considered in this chapter.

EXTRINSIC MUSCLES OF THE EYE

The six extraocular muscles (Figure 5-18) are organized as opposing pairs, extensors and flexors. The superior and inferior recti primarily turn the globe upward and downward, the medial and lateral recti primarily turn the globe

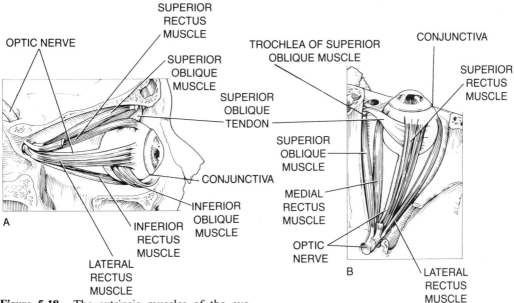

Figure 5-18. The extrinsic muscles of the eye viewed **A** from the side, and **B** from above.

toward the midline and laterally, and the superior and inferior obliques primarily turn the globe to keep the visual image upright throughout the range of eye movement. The superior oblique muscle is innervated separately by cranial nerve IV (trochlear), and the lateral rectus is innervated separately by cranial nerve VI (abducens). All of the other muscles are innervated by cranial nerve III (oculomotor).

The nuclei of cranial nerves III, IV, and VI are located in the brainstem at, or just caudal to, the superior colliculi. Connections within these regions provide the neural network for various ocular reflexes and the coordination of extraocular muscles to produce conjugate movements of the eyes. Voluntary and reflex movements of the eyes also are influenced by regions of the frontal cortex, the occipital cortex, and the pathways from the vestibular nuclei. The frontal and occipital regions of the cortex are responsible for two important aspects of visual fixation: saccadic movements and smooth pursuit movements. When fixating on different points in the visual field, the eyes move in rapid jerks called *saccades*. Regions of the frontal lobe, called the *frontal eye fields*, are involved in this type of eye movement. Maintaining fixation on a moving object is an example of *smooth-pursuit* eye movement, which requires integration of sensory data by centers in the visual association areas of the occipital cortex. Maintaining visual fixation as the head moves requires integration of sensory information from the vestibular system.

NYSTAGMUS

Vestibular-dependent eye movements consist of a combination of rapid, saccadic-type and slow, pursuit-type movements that make up the series of movements called *nystagmus*. Nystagmus represents an attempt by the visual system to retain and stabilize the visual image either when the head is turning (vestibular nystagmus) or when the head is stationary and the visual field is moving. The latter type of nystagmus occurs, for example, in a person who looks out the side window of a moving vehicle—the eyes move forward quickly to fix on a new spot in the visual field (saccadic component), then drift back, maintaining fixation (smooth-pursuit component). This type of nystagmus is called *optokinetic nystagmus* (OKN). The integrity of the pathways involved in OKN (retina, optic nerves, optic tracts, midbrain nuclei, and cra-

nial nerves III, IV, and VI) may be assessed grossly by moving a patterned strip of cloth or rotating a patterned drum in the field of vision of a subject and observing the associated OKN.

The types of nystagmus described above are normal physiological responses to changes in the environment. Nystagmus also may be spontaneous, but this is abnormal and usually indicates a lesion of the labyrinth, the vestibular nerve, or a pathway or nucleus in the brainstem.

DISORDERS OF EYE MOVEMENT

If the eyes do not fix on the same point in the visual field, binocular images do not fuse, and this causes "double vision," or *diplopia*. The failure of the eyes to move in unison (except in convergence, where both turn inward), called *strabismus*, may be a significant clinical finding. Strabismus may be caused by a lesion of the nuclei of cranial nerves III, IV, or VI or of the pathways that connect them. Strabismus also can be caused by lesions of the nerves that arise from those nuclei or by disorders of the eye muscles themselves.

If strabismus occurs early in life, the disparate images that are transmitted to the developing central visual centers may prevent the formation of normal synaptic connections. To reduce disparity, the image from one eye may be suppressed, and, if the condition is not corrected, vision in that eye may be impaired permanently.

Neural Processing in the Visual System

The retina contains two basic types of nerve networks: the radially oriented chain, which carries impulses to the brain (the photoreceptors, bipolar cells, and ganglion cells), and the circumferentially oriented network of horizontal and amacrine cells (see Figure 5-13). The horizontal and amacrine cells perform a considerable amount of the processing within the retina.

LATERAL INHIBITION

Lateral inhibition helps to sharpen the image on the retina (Figure 5-19). Lateral inhibition is not unique to the visual system; it also occurs in the somatosensory system, where it improves two-point discrimination. Stated simply, lateral inhibition involves the inhibition of neighboring cells by strongly stimulated receptor cells.

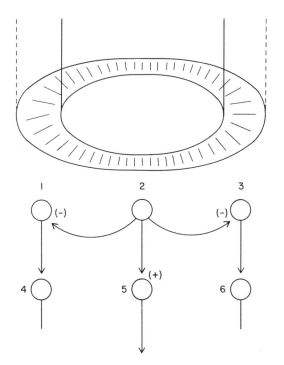

Figure 5-19. Lateral inhibition. Imperfectly focused spot of light falling on retina strongly stimulates only receptor *2*, which lies beneath the center of the spot. Receptors *1* and *3*, which lie beneath the less intense fringe, are stimulated weakly. Inhibitory collaterals from cell *2* to neighboring cells decrease net changes of potential in subsequent cells in chain, and only cell *5* responds. Mechanisms like this "sharpen" the image.

If the neighboring cells are stimulated less strongly, they do not stimulate the next cells in the chain, and this decreases the amount of information that must be processed at the next level. In this context, lateral inhibition functions like the contrast control on a television set.

Apparently, lateral inhibition, which is mediated by the amacrine cells, also occurs at the ganglion cell in the retina. This provides a second level of image processing. Recordings from microelectrodes inserted into single ganglion cells in the retina of an experimental animal reveal the net effect of the lateral processing system. Small spots of light of different shapes and colors can be directed onto the retina, producing a map that shows the region over which the stimulus causes a ganglion cell to respond. This region is called the *receptive field* for that cell. Most such cells display a *center-surround* organization. A small spot of light directed into the center of the receptive field of a cell elicits

one type of response, but if the same light is directed to the periphery of the receptive field, the cell responds in the opposite manner. For example, a given ganglion cell might respond to light directed into the center of its receptive field with an increased frequency of excitation, but if light is directed at the edge of its field, its frequency of excitation decreases. Such a cell is said to have an excitatory center with inhibitory surround, or, simply, an "on" center. Other cells have an opposite pattern of response; their rates of firing decrease in response to light in the center of a receptive field and increase if either a spot or a ring of light is directed onto the edge of the field. This type of cell is said to have an "off" center. Because of this center-surround arrangement, diffuse light is a relatively ineffective stimulus for the retina. Since the unpatterned light falls on both the center and the surround of the receptive field of a ganglion cell, it causes little change in the frequency of excitation, regardless of whether the cell has an on center or an off center.

ADAPTATION

Another important characteristic of retinal neurophysiology is rapid adaptation. The photoreceptors and other cells in the retina adapt very quickly, so that if the stimulus does not change, the perceived image fades almost immediately. To present a constantly changing stimulus to the photoreceptors and keep the image from fading, the eye makes small, continuous, nystagmoid movements, called *micronystagmus*. If the photoreceptors did not adapt rapidly, the blood vessels in the retina would be visible because their shadows always are present on the photoreceptor layer.

OPPONENT-RESPONSE ORGANIZATION

The previous discussion of information processing in the nervous system has shown how the amount of information a cell can transmit is increased if the cell has a resting frequency of excitation that is increased or decreased by summated excitatory and inhibitory input (see Chapter 3). The center-surround organization of the receptive field of retinal ganglion cells is an example of such neural circuitry. Light directed onto the center of the receptive field of an on-center cell increases the rate of firing, whereas the same light directed slightly away from the center decreases the rate of firing. This is an efficient arrangement because a single cell can indicate not only that light is falling onto its receptive field but also reveal something about the location and size of the stimulus. Ganglion cells that have overlapping receptive fields can convey considerable information about a stimulus through the integration of all of the excitatory and inhibitory influences acting on each cell. This *opponent-response* organization underlies the complex spatial processing that occurs both in the retina and at the next stage of processing, the lateral geniculate nucleus (LGN) of the thalamus.

COLOR VISION

Opponent-response organization also enables the ganglion cells of the retina and the cells of the LGN to transmit information about the wavelength of light that falls onto their receptive fields. Most ganglion cells in the primate retina respond differently to light of different wavelengths, which suggests that they are organized in an opponent-response manner and that the cones in their receptive fields have different pigments (see the section entitled "Visual Pigments" in this chapter). This is true also at the level of the LGN. Some of these spectrally sensitive cells increase their frequency of excitation when a red light is directed onto their receptive fields, and decrease their frequencies in response to a green light. Others act in an opposite manner, being excited by green light and inhibited by red. Still others respond in a similar manner to lights that normally are perceived as yellow and blue. This spectral opponent-response organization greatly enhances an individual's ability to discriminate light of different wavelengths, just as the spatial opponent-response organization of ganglion and LGN cells increases his perception of detail.

DEFECTS OF COLOR VISION

Abnormal color discrimination is a relatively common disorder that affects 8% of the male population and 0.4% of the female population. Disorders of color vision can arise from defects in one or more of the cone photopigments and may be either congenital (most are) or acquired (usually caused by the effects of toxins such as methanol). The various deficits of color vision are classified according to how many of the three cone pigments are either absent or deficient. *Trichromats* have color perception that

can be accounted for only by all three cone pigments; hence, people who have normal color vision are *normal trichromats*. A slight weakness in perceiving the red end of the spectrum because of a mild deficiency of one of the cone pigments is called anomalous red vision, or *protanomaly*, and a mild deficiency in green vision is *deuteranomaly*. *Dichromats* have only two cone pigments. People who are insensitive to deep red are *protanopes*, and individuals who are green-blind and confuse shades of red, green, and yellow are called *deuteranopes*. People who are insensitive to the extreme blue-violet end of the spectrum are called *tritanopes;* these individuals confuse shades of blue and green and, usually, orange and pink. Persons who have either no cone cells or cones with only one pigment are called *monochromats*. In this condition, there are no pairs of pigments to act as "opponents," so no discrimination of color is possible. *Rod monochromats,* who congenitally lack cones, also experience *photophobia* (fear of light). Their only photoreceptors, the rods, are highly sensitive to light because of the high degree of convergence in the rod system and because of the absence of inhibition of the rod system by the cone system in bright light (see the section entitled "Dark Adaptation" in this chapter). Rod monochromats lack visual acuity because of the convergence, and they experience nystagmus (see the section entitled "Nystagmus" in this chapter) because the fovea (which normally contains only cones) essentially is nonfunctional, and the eyes move constantly, attempting to compensate for the blind spot in the center of the retina.

Abnormal color vision also may be caused by lesions in the prethalamic visual pathways, which reflect the large proportion of fibers devoted to the central visual field, where the cones predominate.

VISUAL CORTEX

Although there is some topographic organization in the visual cortex, it is not the predominant characteristic. A stimulus presented to a discrete portion of the visual field excites cells in many distinct regions of the occipital cortex, scattered over a wide area. Thus, the visual cortex does not simply duplicate (neurophysiologically) the image on the retina. Anatomical studies have shown that the fibers from the LGN synapse primarily in the fourth layer of the occipital cortex. Other fibers carry information from this layer to the layers above and below, and after a few synapses, the information has been dispersed vertically through all layers in the immediate area of the incoming fiber. The lateral spread of this information is much more restricted, since it seldom extends more than a few millimeters. Fibers that originate in the visual cortex also carry information to other cortical regions and subcortical centers, including the LGN. These findings seem to imply that the primary visual cortex processes information in discrete, independent, cellular columns and does not integrate all of the information across the visual field. Some other region or regions must synthesize the data into a coherent visual perception.

Electrophysiological studies have shown that the receptive fields of the cells in the fourth layer of the visual cortex, the primary input stage, are organized in a circular, center-surround manner, like the layers of the lateral geniculate and ganglion cells. The cells outside the fourth layer have more complex stimulus-response characteristics. Some cells respond best to a line segment oriented at a specific angle; in some cells this line segment is a more effective stimulus if it is bright relative to its background, but in other cells the reverse is true. The simplest of these cells act as if they receive and integrate information from several center-surround cells, all of which are either on center or off center and have receptive fields that overlap along a straight line. Other cells, which represent a higher-order organization, respond best to line segments that have a particular orientation and move in a specific direction.

Even though many cells in the visual cortex appear to receive input from both eyes, if a microelectrode is advanced through the cortical layers along a line perpendicular to the surface, all of the cells in that column respond primarily to input from only one eye. Cells in an immediately adjacent column might respond mainly to input from the adjacent eye, but most cells clearly demonstrate such an ocular preference, or dominance. Since cells in this region are the first to receive binocular input (the LGN is organized into discrete layers that receive input from only one eye), one might assume that depth perception is represented here in some way. The mechanisms that underlie stereoscopic vision are not well understood, but several regions of the brain seem to be involved. Some regions deal with information about the degree of convergence of the eyes, and other regions are concerned with slight discrepancies between the images formed in each eye. It is clear also that the perception of color depends on cells in the visual cortex, at least to some extent, but most of our present knowledge of this region concerns its role in the processing of information about the orientation of items in space.

Electrophysiology of the Visual System

Like all neural tissue, the cells of the retina generate electrical responses when stimulated. Only the ganglion cells can generate action potentials; the other neural elements—photoreceptors and bipolar, amacrine, and horizontal cells—produce graded, nonpropagated potentials that are analogous to the potentials of dendrites. The electrical activity of neural elements in the retina forms the basis for several test procedures used in the clinical evaluation of the visual system, which are discussed briefly below.

ELECTRORETINOGRAM

When the illumination of the retina is either increased or decreased abruptly, a brief series of transient potentials can be recorded from an electrode placed on or near the eye. This recording, called the *electroretinogram*, or ERG, is used to aid in the diagnosis of retinal diseases (see Figure 5-21).

Most of our knowledge of the physiological events that underlie the ERG stems from research done by Granit in the 1930s. Granit showed that the series of flash-related potentials recorded from an electrode on the corneal surface actually represents a summation of at least three separate electrical events, or "processes" (Figure 5-20), that arise from different layers of cells. The initial corneal-negative potential recorded after a flash of light, called the *a-wave*, arises from the photoreceptors. More recent work with microelectrodes has shown that the process responsible for the next, corneal-positive, wave, the *b-wave*, probably lies within the radially oriented glial cells. The a- and b-waves are the waves that are most commonly incorporated into a clinical recording of the ERG (Figure 5-21) because their short latencies make them less susceptible to contamination from eye blinks and ocular rotation. For the clinical recording of the ERG, an electrode that consists of a silver, gold, or platinum wire embedded in

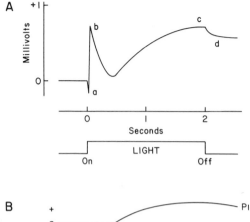

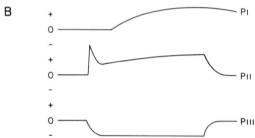

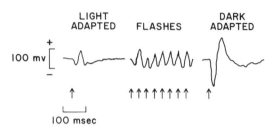

ELECTRORETINOGRAM

Figure 5-21. Normal electroretinogram (ERG) recorded from contact lens electrode; stimulus (indicated by arrows) is a brief flash of light. Light-adapted: ERG recorded with eyes adapted to bright background illumination (rods suppressed); flashes: ERG recorded to light flashing at rate of 30 per second—rods cannot recover quickly enough to respond to train of flashes; dark-adapted: ERG recorded with eyes adapted to the dark—rods contribute, which increases amplitude of response.

Figure 5-20. **A.** Electroretinogram (ERG) recorded from the eye of a cat, with initial negative wave (*a*) at onset of light followed by positive waves (*b* and *c*); light off is associated with negative wave (*d*). **B.** Granit's suggested retinal components that summate to produce ERG recorded from electrode at some distance from retina. *Process I* (PI), thought to arise in pigment epithelium, has a long latency and accounts primarily for the positive c-wave. *Process II* (PCII) is conceived of as being polyphasic and accounting primarily for the positive b-wave. *Process III* (PIII), thought to arise from photoreceptors, accounts primarily for the negative a-wave.

a contact lens usually is paired with a reference electrode placed at some relatively neutral site, such as the earlobe. Recordings generally are obtained under conditions that favor responses from either rod-related or cone-related cells; typically, to suppress rod function, the ERG is obtained initially in bright light, and then taken again after a period of dark adaptation that permits the rods to contribute to the response. Flickering stimuli also may be used to take advantage of the longer recovery period of the rods relative to that of the cones. Rods can respond to each flash in a series only at rates up to about 20 flashes per second. Therefore, stimuli delivered at the rate of 30 flashes per second yield a relatively rod-free response (see Figure 5-21). The ERG is used most commonly to aid

in the diagnosis of hereditary or acquired disorders of the retina, some of which affect rods and cones differently. However, the ERG also provides gross assessment of retinal function in an eye that, because of opacities caused by conditions such as cataract, cannot be examined ophthalmoscopically.

ELECTRO-OCULOGRAM

In the intact eye, the cornea is electrically positive to the posterior structures (*corneofundal,* or *standing, potential*). This potential, apparently generated in the region of the pigment epithelium of the retina, is affected by changes of illumination. However, the changes that the potential undergoes in response to light are extremely slow in comparison to the changes of potential measured in the ERG. After an abrupt increase or decrease of illumination, the standing potential oscillates with a period of about 20–30 minutes (Figure 5-22). The response of the standing potential to increases and decreases of illumination, called the *electro-oculogram,* or EOG, is the basis for a test of the integrity of the retinal pigment epithelium.

The EOG is recorded clinically by placing disk electrodes on the skin near the medial and lateral aspect of each eye; no potential is measured when the patient looks straight ahead. To generate a potential, the patient fixes his gaze alternately on two target lights; this causes the globe to rotate horizontally through a fixed arc.

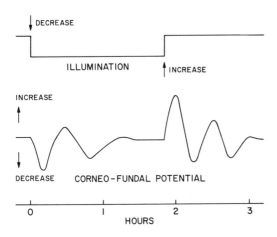

Figure 5-22. Fluctuations in the corneofundal potential (CFP), or standing potential, of the eye with changes in illumination.

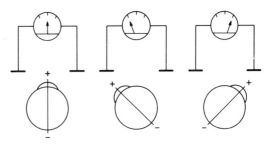

Figure 5-23. Recording of the electro-oculogram (EOG) either to monitor eye movements or to assess indirectly changes in the standing potential of the eye. As the corneally positive axis of the eye rotates closer to one or the other electrode, changes of potential are recorded.

This motion first brings the electrically positive cornea closer to one of the recording electrodes, and then, as the gaze is shifted, closer to the other electrode (Figure 5-23). The changes of potential that are generated in this way reflect the standing potential of the eye, and abnormalities of the standing potential in response to change of luminance can be detected by this indirect measurement. Although a clinical recording usually is intended to assess only the initial response to increasing and decreasing levels of light, because of the slowness of the response, the recording can take as long as 20–30 minutes.

Visually Evoked Cortical Potentials

Action potentials have been recorded in the optic nerves, optic tracts, and optic radiations, and responses have been demonstrated in the LGN, but only by invasive procedures. Potentials can be recorded noninvasively from the occipital cortex through electrodes placed on the scalp over the appropriate region. Although the changes of potential in response to visual stimulation are small and require computer processing to be extracted from the relatively large background electroencephalogram (see Chapter 7), the response of the visual cortex is used clinically to assess the integrity of the visual pathways. These responses, called *visually evoked potentials* (VEP), *visually evoked responses* (VER), or *visually evoked cortical potentials* (VECP), are used to detect subtle

changes in the function of the optic nerves and tracts caused by demyelinating diseases, tumors, or vascular disorders.

AUDITORY SYSTEM

The ear serves a dual purpose for the body. It functions as the sensory receptor for acoustic stimuli and provides information about the static position and movement of the head in space. The sensory cells of the auditory and vestibular systems are contained within the fluid-filled, membranous structures of the inner ear, which is embedded in the temporal bone. The stimulus for the sensory receptors of both systems (hair cells) is mechanical force, or displacement.

Major Divisions

The auditory system can be divided by anatomy and function into five sections: external ear, middle ear, inner ear or cochlea, auditory brainstem pathways, and primary auditory cortex of the temporal lobe.

EXTERNAL EAR

The external ear consists of the cartilaginous *pinna* and the *external auditory canal,* which leads to the *tympanic membrane,* or *eardrum* (Figure 5-24). Because of its mobility, the pinna serves mammals as a sound collector and source detector. In humans, the pinna does not rotate; however, it does aid in the localization of sound because the transmission characteristics of different pitches change with the direction of the sound relative to the pinna.

MIDDLE EAR

The middle ear is an air-filled cavity bounded laterally by the elastic tympanic membrane and medially by the *bony wall,* or *promontory,* of the temporal bone, which contains the inner ear (Figure 5-24). The resting air pressure of the normal middle ear is equal to the external atmospheric pressure; this equilibrium is maintained by opening of the *eustachian tube,* which courses from the middle ear cavity to the nasopharynx. The eustachian tube normally is closed, but it opens during yawning or swallowing.

Sound waves, or alternate compression and decompression of air, impinge on the tympanic membrane (TM) and cause it to vibrate. The *ossicular chain,* a set of three bones—the *malleus,* the *incus,* and the *stapes*—connects the tympanic membrane to the inner ear. Vibration of the TM causes the ossicular chain to vibrate. The footplate of the stapes rests in the *oval window,* a membranous area of the promontory. Movement of the ossicular chain causes the stapes to move in and out of the oval window.

The middle ear acts as an impedance-matching device between the air and the fluid-filled inner ear. The middle ear matches the low impedance of the air with the high impedence of the cochlea by concentrating the incident pressure from the large area of the TM (effective area about 43–55 mm^2) onto the small area of the oval window (about 3 mm^2). The ossicular chain contributes to this impedance matching by leverage, which decreases the amplitude of the vibration and, consequently, increases the vibrational force. The effective ratio of the area of the TM to the area of the oval window is about 14 : 1. The ratio of the displacement of the TM to the displacement of the oval window is approximately 1.3 : 1.

The muscles of the middle ear, the stapedius and the tensor tympani, support the ossicular chain in such a way that movement of the head imparts little motion to the chain. The stapedius muscle pulls the stapes footplate backward and into the oval window; the tensor tympani pulls the handle of the malleus inward. Contraction of either muscle decreases the effective conductance of low-frequency sound and protects the inner ear from damage; low-frequency sounds potentially are the most damaging to the cochlea. These muscles can contract (1) spontaneously, (2) in response to body movements, (3) in response to impending vocalization, (4) in response to contractions of the facial muscle (tensor tympani only), (5) in response to tactile stimulation of the ear canal, and (6) voluntarily.

In primates, the stapedius contracts reflexly to sound but the tensor tympani probably does not. Efferent impulses to the stapedius muscle travel along the facial nerve, and the reflex pathway probably goes no higher than the superior olivary complex of the brainstem.

The protective role of the muscles of the middle ear may be minimal. Their latency of response is 40–60 milliseconds, too long to per-

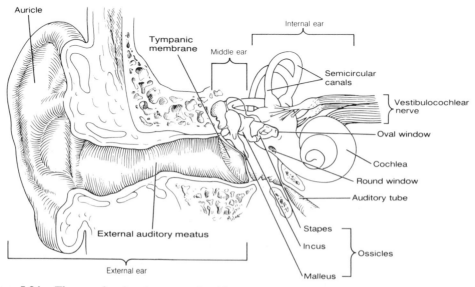

Figure 5-24.   The ear, showing the external, middle, and internal regions.

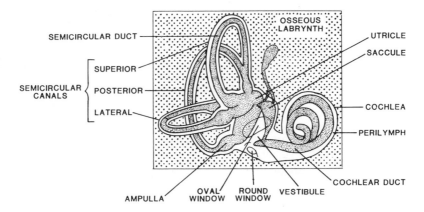

Figure 5-25. Structures of the inner ear. The membranous labyrinth (*shaded*) is filled with endolymph and separated from the osseous labyrinth by perilymph.

mit them to protect against brief, intense sounds. The most important function of the muscles of the middle ear may be to filter out low-frequency sounds from the body, especially the sounds of vocalization; for example, stutterers may have deficient prevocalization contraction.

INNER EAR

The inner ear can be divided into three areas: the *semicircular canals,* the *vestibule,* and the *cochlea* (Figure 5-25). The cochlea, a shell-shaped part of the bony labyrinth, spirals around a central bony core, the *modiolus.* The *membranous labyrinth*, which is the soft tissue structure of the inner ear, floats in *perilymph*, a fluid that has a low concentration of K^+ and a high concentration of Na^+. The membranous labyrinth contains two additional types of fluid—*endolymph,* a low-Na^+-high-K^+ fluid, and *cortilymph,* a fluid that is similar to perilymph in electrolyte content but different chemically from both perilymph and endolymph.

A cross-section of the cochlea in any of its spirals reveals three tunnels, or ducts: the *scala vestibuli,* the *scala media,* and the *scala tympani.* The upper duct, the scala vestibuli, extends from the oval window in the vestibule to the *helicotrema,* or peak of the modiolus. The lower duct, the scala tympani, extends from the round window to the helicotrema, where it is continuous with the scala vestibuli. These two ducts contain perilymph. The center duct, the scala media, or cochlear duct, is separated from the scala vestibuli by Reissner's membrane and from the scala tympani by the basilar membrane. The cochlear duct contains endolymph (Figure 5-26).

The *organ of Corti,* the primary sense organ of the auditory system, lies within the cochlear duct and rests on the basilar membrane. It consists of the sensory hair cells—one row of inner hair cells and three rows of outer hair cells—and supporting cells. The cilia of the outer hair cells extend upward, and the tallest of these cilia are embedded in the reticular lamina of the *tectorial membrane.* The cilia of the inner hair cells do not extend into the tectorial membrane (Figure 5-27).

The cochlea has two basic functions: (1) to transduce sound, or mechanical energy, into a form that stimulates the auditory nerve endings, and (2) to code, at least partially, the acoustic parameters of frequency and intensity.

Neural Pathways

Fibers of the cochlear division of cranial nerve VIII (auditory) run through the modiolus to synapse on the hair cells. Approximately 90% of the fibers of the auditory nerve connect with the outer hair cells, and the remainder of the fibers connect with the inner hair cells. In both the inner and outer portions one fiber contacts several hair cells, but the ratio of hair cells to fibers is smaller in the inner portion. The cell bodies of the nerve fibers are located in the spiral ganglion, and these primary neurons synapse in the cochlear nuclei at the pontomedullary junction of the brainstem.

The auditory pathway in the brainstem is complex. Above the level of the cochlear nuclei, most fibers cross to synapse within the contralateral superior olivary complex. Although most of the central auditory pathway is crossed, an uncrossed pathway also ascends from this area.

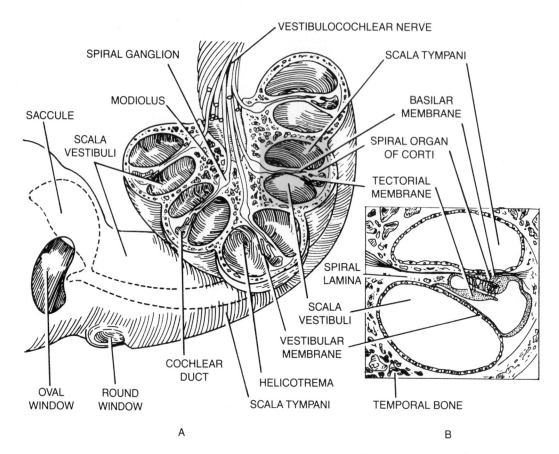

Figure 5-26.   **A.** Section through the cochlea. The scala tympani and scala vestibuli are continuous through the helicotrema. **B.** Magnified cross-section of one turn of the cochlea. The coch-lear duct is formed by the membranous laby-rinth and contains endolymph. The scala tym-pani and scala vestibuli contain perilymph.

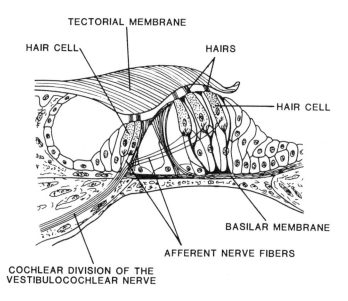

Figure 5-27.   Section of the spiral organ of Corti.

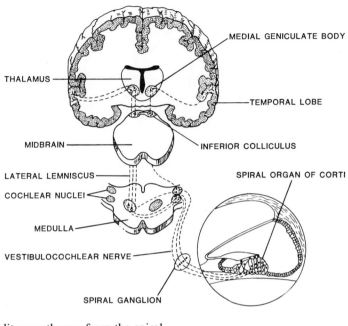

THALAMUS

MEDIAL GENICULATE BODY

TEMPORAL LOBE

MIDBRAIN

INFERIOR COLLICULUS

LATERAL LEMNISCUS

COCHLEAR NUCLEI

SPIRAL ORGAN OF CORTI

MEDULLA

VESTIBULOCOCHLEAR NERVE

SPIRAL GANGLION

Figure 5-28. Auditory pathways from the spiral organ of Corti through the central nervous system to the cortex of the temporal lobe of the brain.

Because the superior olivary complex receives input from both ears, binaural phenomena, such as the localization of sound, probably are mediated here. The inferior colliculi form the next major relay station; the pathways then ascend through the medial geniculate body of the thalamus and project to the auditory cortex of the temporal lobes (Figure 5-28).

Physiology of the Auditory System

Sound waves impinge on the tympanic membrane and cause it to vibrate; the motion is transmitted through the ossicular chain to the oval window. When the frequency of vibration is low, the changes of pressure in the scala vestibuli are compensated for by movement of perilymph through the helicotrema, causing the round window to bulge outward. Because the scala media is not displaced, no sound is perceived.

When the frequency of vibration is higher, the changes of pressure cannot be compensated for, and the scala media is displaced. The basilar membrane, on which the organ of Corti rests, is stiff but elastic. Vibration at the oval window causes a traveling wave to move in the basilar membrane, from base to apex, in about

3 milliseconds. A given frequency of stimulation displaces the basilar membrane maximally at a specific distance from the oval window. The amplitude drops quickly beyond the region of maximum displacement, and the wave travels no further. High-frequency sounds cause maximal displacement and terminate near the base of the cochlea, whereas vibrations produced by low-frequency sound waves travel farther along the basilar membrane (Figure 5-29).

The traveling wave deforms the basilar membrane, producing a shearing action between the reticular lamina and the tectorial membrane. The long cilia of the outer hair cells are attached to both membranes and, hence, are bent. The shorter cilia of the inner and outer hair cells may bend as fluid (cortilymph) is displaced because the two membranes move at different velocities. The movements of the cilia generate an electrical potential within the hair cells. When the basilar membrane moves upward, toward the scala vestibuli, the hair cells of the region depolarize and afferent impulses are generated within the cochlear division of cranial nerve VIII. When the basilar membrane moves downward, the cells hyperpolarize and the generation of afferent impulses ceases. The synapse between hair cell and cochlear nerve fiber is believed to be chemical, but the specific

CLINICAL CORRELATION
5.2   Presbycusis

CASE REPORT

The Patient: A 76-year-old male.

Principal Complaints: Progressive hearing loss and difficulty understanding speech.

History: The patient had noticed gradually increasing difficulty with his hearing and a great change in his ability to understand conversations in a background of noise. He had no history of dizziness, middle ear infections, head trauma, hypertension, or diabetes, and he was taking no medicines routinely.

Clinical Examination: Examination of the head and neck revealed no abnormality. No bruits (sounds caused by turbulent blood flow, due to vascular constriction or obstruction) were heard in the neck. Hearing tests showed a mild to moderate bilateral loss of the ability to hear high frequency sounds. His understanding of monosyllabic, phonetically balanced speech was consistent with the degree of hearing loss. His understanding of nonsense sentences embedded in a background story was poorer than his understanding of single words.

Comment: Presbycusis, the loss of hearing due to aging, is characterized by loss in the high frequency range. The ability to under-

stand simple spoken material is comparable to that of normal young people. When the pattern of speech is interrupted, the rate of speaking is changed, or background noise or unrelated speech interferes, older people do not comprehend as well as young people do. This difference of function may appear in persons as young as 40 to 50 years of age.

The pathophysiology of presbycusis is four-fold: peripheral, central, metabolic, and mechanical. Within the cochlea, the epithelial tissues—supporting cells, hair cells, and the basilar membrane—degenerate. Ganglion cells and nerve fibers are lost, initially in the basal cochlea and later throughout the cochlea. Centrally, fewer neurons are found at each successive level within the auditory pathways. The elasticity of the basilar and tectorial membranes changes, which causes mechanical differences between a young system and an old one. The stria vascularis degenerates, the walls of the capillaries in the stria thicken, and the nutrient supply to the cochlea is decreased. Since the stria vascularis participates in the formation of endolymph, the electrolyte balance of cochlear fluids also may be altered by increasing age.

Outcome: A moderate-gain, over-the-ear-style hearing aid was fitted to the patient, and his ability to hear was restored to normal.

---

neurotransmitter has not been identified. Electrical communication between hair cells also may exist.

Neural encoding of the parameters of sound is not understood completely, although at least two mechanisms are known to provide information about frequency. The relationship between frequency and space in the cochlea is maintained throughout the auditory system. At lower frequencies, the average, or collected, rate of firing of some neurons joins in phase with the frequency of a pure tone. Intensity is encoded

partially by the number of neurons excited and their rate of excitation; in addition, specialized cells within the auditory system may respond only to the onset of a signal or to a change of frequency or intensity of a signal.

Bioelectrical Potentials

Several bioelectrical events can be measured in the auditory system, and three electrical potentials have been identified within the cochlea: (1) the endocochlear potential, (2) the cochlear

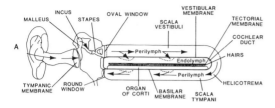

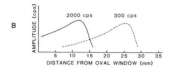

Figure 5-29. **A.** Transmission of sound waves in the cochlea. Compression of the perilymph inside the scala vestibuli is transmitted to the walls of the cochlear duct, causing the basilar membrane to vibrate. **B.** Maximum vibrations occur in one region of the basilar membrane, which, because of its width, has the same resonant frequency as the sound wave that causes the compression wave. Low-frequency sound waves cause maximum vibrations toward the wide, apical end of the basilar membrane. High-frequency waves have their maximum effect on the narrow end of the basilar membrane.

microphonic, and (3) the summating potential. Other potentials include the whole-nerve action potential, auditory brainstem response, middle-latency response, and slow, or cortical, response.

The auditory potentials are recorded best when the electrode array is close to the source. If an electrode is inserted into the fluid of the scala media, a constant potential of 90–115 mv, positive to the scala tympani, is registered. This is the *endocochlear potential,* which is generated across the hair-bearing ends of the hair cells. The *cochlear microphonic,* generated by acoustic stimulation, reproduces the waveform of the stimulating sound. Like other receptor potentials, the cochlear microphonic is graded and nonpropagated and has essentially no latency and no refractory period. The *summating potential* follows the envelope of the stimulating sound; thus, it is related to the intensity of a sound more than to its frequency.

By using computer averaging techniques, the summating potential, cochlear microphonic, and action potential of cranial nerve VIII may be recorded noninvasively from an electrode placed in the external auditory canal near the tympanic membrane. The relative amplitude of response and latency of onset and the presence or absence of these potentials may be used to identify dysfunctions within the cochlea or the primary auditory neurons.

The bioelectrical events measured from higher levels of the auditory system also are recorded by using computer averaging techniques. Several electrode arrays may be used, but the active electrode usually is scalp-mounted at the vertex. The *auditory brainstem response* (ABR) is a series of five or six waves that occur within 10 milliseconds after stimulation by an acoustic transient (click). The ABR is generated by successive activation of brainstem nuclei, from the primary auditory neurons and cochlear nuclei to the inferior colliculi of the midbrain. The *middle-latency response,* which has a latency of 20–50 milliseconds, is thought to represent activity of the midbrain and thalamic auditory relay centers (medial geniculate bodies). The *slow response,* which has a latency of approximately 150 milliseconds, is believed to be generated within the auditory-temporal cortex. Amplitude, latency, and configuration of these responses are used diagnostically to identify sites or levels of dysfunction within the auditory system.

Disease or injury to any portion of the auditory system may cause some loss in the ability to detect sound, understand speech, localize sound, or process complex acoustic stimuli. The type of dysfunction depends on the site of the lesion (Figure 5-30).

		SITE			
○ NONE					
◑ QUESTIONABLE					
◔ SLIGHT		PERIPHERAL		CENTRAL	
◕ MODERATE					
● SEVERE	MIDDLE EAR	COCHLEA	VIIIth NERVE	BRAIN STEM	TEMPORAL LOBE
LOSS OF SENSITIVITY	●	◕	◔	◑	○
DISTORTION	◑	●	◑	◑	○
ABNORMAL ADAPTATION	○	◔	●	◑	○
SPEECH PROCESSING	○	◔	◕	●	◕
EAR SYMPTOMS	SAME SIDE	SAME SIDE	SAME SIDE	OPPOSITE SIDE	OPPOSITE SIDE

Figure 5-30. Changes in auditory abilities caused by pathology at various levels of the auditory pathways. (Redrawn, with permission, from Jerger, J. (ed.). 1973. *Modern Developments in Audiology* (2nd ed.). New York: Academic Press, Inc.)

VESTIBULAR SYSTEM

Functional Anatomy

The membranous labyrinth of the vestibular system is housed in the temporal bone adjoining the auditory cochlea. The three *semicircular canals* open into the vestibule, which contains the *utricle* and the *saccule,* the sensory organs of the vestibular system. The semicircular canals, arranged at right angles to each other, form horizontal (lateral), anteriovertical (superior), and posteriovertical (posterior) canals (Figure 5-31A).

Functionally, the horizontal canal is horizontal; anatomically, the whole complex is tilted backward 30°. Each canal contains a semicircular duct with an expansion, the *ampulla,* adjacent to the utricle. The ampulla contains the sensory cells (cristae) for the canal with which it is associated (Figure 5-31B).

The saccule and utricle are membranous sacs that communicate with the semicircular canals. The saccule and utricle contain the sensory receptors (maculae) that detect changes in the position of the head (Figure 5-32). The vestibular ducts are continuous with the scala media through the saccule and endolymphatic duct.

Receptors

The receptor cells of the vestibular system are hair cells, similar to the hair cells of the cochlea (Figures 5-31 and 5-33). In the semicircular canal, the tuft of hair is embedded in an overlying gelatinous layer above the crista, which is called the *cupula.* The gelatinous layer of the macula is thinner than the cupula and contains crystals of calcium carbonate (*otoconia*).

Studies using the electron microscope (EM) have shown two types of hair cells in the maculae and cristae, similar to the inner and outer hair cells of the auditory system. Two types of cilia, kinocilia and stereocilia, also have been demonstrated by EM. Each hair cell has a single kinocilium associated with a bundle of 60–100 stereocilia. The kinocilium on each hair cell is located to one side of the bundle of stereocilia, and all of the hair cells in a given area tend to have their kinocilia on the same side of the bundle.

Neural Pathways

The vestibular system is served by the vestibular branch of cranial nerve VIII; the cell bodies of the primary neurons are contained within Scarpa's ganglion. The first-order neurons all synapse within the vestibular nuclear complex, below the floor of the fourth ventricle at the pontomedullary border.

The vestibular nuclear complex has four classical subdivisions: (1) the superior nucleus (Bechterew's), (2) the lateral nucleus (Deiters'), (3) the medial nucleus, and (4) the inferior nucleus. Most of the afferent nerves from the semicircular canal go to the superior and medial vestibular nuclei; both of these nuclei project to the oculomotor nuclei through the ascending medial longitudinal fasciculus. The otolith organs, especially the utricle, project primarily to the lateral vestibular nucleus, which then projects downward throughout the length of the

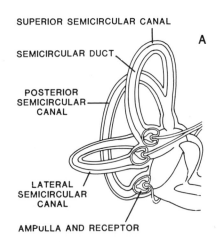

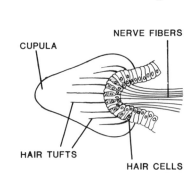

Figure 5-31. A. The semicircular canals and ducts. The ampullae of the ducts have been cut open to show the locations of the balance receptors (cristae) within them. **B.** Enlargement of a crista.

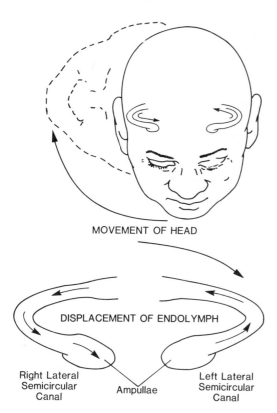

MOVEMENT OF HEAD

DISPLACEMENT OF ENDOLYMPH

Right Lateral
Semicircular
Canal   Ampullae   Left Lateral
Semicircular
Canal

Figure 5-32. Movement of endolymph in relation to the right and left lateral semicircular ducts, which are oriented horizontally. Because the endolymph lags momentarily, movement of the head toward the right increases the pressure on the cupula within the ampulla of the right horizontal duct and reduces the pressure on the cupula in the ampulla of the left horizontal duct. The different nerve messages from the two cristae produce a sensation of turning.

spinal cord through the lateral vestibulospinal tract. All vestibular organs project to the inferior nucleus, through which the most significant afferent and efferent connections of the vestibular system to the cerebellum are made. Apparently, some vestibular cortical tracts project through the ventroposteroinferior (VPI) nucleus in the thalamus to the somatosensory areas. Vestibular stimulation causes little conscious sensation, except through the secondary effects of nausea and vertigo or through reflex motor responses.

Physiology of the Vestibular System

Although the vestibular system generally is considered to regulate balance and equilibrium

in the body, it actually plays a relatively minor role in this function in most normal activities. The continuous resting discharge of the vestibular system provides an excitatory input (through the vestibular nuclei) into the motor centers associated with locomotion and the maintenance of posture. Loss of vision or proprioception causes much greater impairment of balance and equilibrium than loss of vestibular function does. The most significant disruption of balance and equilibrium occurs when the vestibular system is unbalanced by acute damage on only one side.

STIMULATION OF RECEPTORS

As in the cochlea, mechanical force is the effective stimulus. The semicircular canals register rotary acceleration through the different velocities of the cupula (tissue) and the endolymph (fluid). Rotation of the head causes the surrounding endolymph to move relative to the canal walls (see Figure 5-32). As the head begins to rotate, inertia delays the movement of the endolymph slightly, the fluid flows briefly in a direction opposite to the rotation, the crista in the duct is deformed, and the hair cells are bent. If the head rotates at a constant velocity, the flow of endolymph eventually ceases, and the crista no longer is deformed. When rotation slows, the momentum of the endolymph again produces relative movement that distorts the crista, but in the same direction as the movement of the head. Stimulation of the semicircular canal produces the sensation of turning or spinning. This provokes muscle reflexes of the eyes, neck, limbs, and vertebral column. If the canals are stimulated through injury, the sensation does not reflect movement of the body.

The otolithic system (saccule and utricle) reacts to linear acceleration. Tilting of the macular surfaces causes the dense otoconia to slide downward, carrying the gelatinous otolithic membrane and hair cell cilia with them (see Figure 5-33). Sensation from the otolithic system provides information about the position of the head in relation to the environment and signals changes of position. Reflexes from the otolithic system oppose the stimuli that cause them.

The afferent neurons from all parts of the vestibular system discharge spontaneously at rest, to some degree. The resting discharge, which may be regular or irregular, causes the system to be virtually without threshold. When the head is still, the activity is relatively constant. Movement may either increase or de-

CLINICAL CORRELATION

5.3   Endolymphatic Hydrops

CASE REPORT

The Patient: A 63-year-old male.

Principal Complaint: Periodic vertigo, nausea, and fluctuating loss of hearing.

History: The patient reported that he had experienced episodes of vertigo (dizziness), tinnitus (ringing of the ears), a feeling of pressure in the ears, and variable loss of hearing. These symptoms are consistent with either endolymphatic hydrops (accumulation of endolymph fluid) or acoustic neuroma (tumor).

Clinical Examination: Examination of the head and neck, tomograms (serial radiography) of the internal auditory canal (IAC), and CAT (computer-assisted tomograms) scan revealed no abnormality. Audiological evaluation showed a symmetrical, mild to moderate loss of hearing in the high-frequency range. Further audiological evaluation disclosed no evidence of dysfunction in the 8th nerve or the auditory pathway in the brainstem. Electronystagmography (ENG: recording of the movements of the eyeballs in nystagmus) showed changes that were consistent with an abnormality in the left vestibular apparatus. A diagnosis of left labyrinthitis (inflammation of the labyrinth of the inner ear), or endolymphatic hydrops, was reached.

Comment: Histopathological studies of endolymphatic hydrops show distension of the saccule and often also of the utricle. The abnormal expansion of the saccule due to increased volume of endolymph causes physical distortion and destruction of the membranous labyrinth, scala media, and organ of Corti.

Treatment: To decrease the fluid in the labyrinth, the patient was treated by salt restriction, diuretics, and temporary use of vasodilators.

Outcome: The patient returned after one year to report recent episodes of vertigo of increasing severity and frequency. He was incapacitated by nausea for as long as 48 hours after each episode. The loss of hearing in the left ear had progressed to moderate to severe. IAC films again were normal, and ENG showed progression of the changes found earlier.

Because of the unsuccessful management of dizziness by medical treatment, increasing loss of hearing, and the incapacitating degree of dizziness and nausea, the patient underwent an endolymphatic sac-to-mastoid shunt. The purpose of such surgery is to prevent abnormal accumulation of endolymph, and thereby to maintain normal fluid dynamics within the vestibular and auditory membranous labyrinths. The surgery was successful, and the patient's symptoms were relieved.

crease the resting frequency, enabling the vestibular system to function as a bidirectional sensor of dynamic or static displacement of the head.

When the cupula (of the semicircular canals) is in the resting position, it is most sensitive to deformation. Bending of the cupula changes the resting frequency. The extent of deviation determines the extent of change, while the direction of movement determines whether the change is an increase or a decrease. If the cilia deviate in the direction of the kinocilia, depolarization occurs, and the rate of spontaneous excitation increases. If an individual is immobile, even though in a deviated position, the frequency of the action potentials does not change, because the canals respond only to movement.

Resting potentials measured from the afferent nerves of the maculae of the otolithic system change with change of position. The actions of the saccule and utricle complement one an-

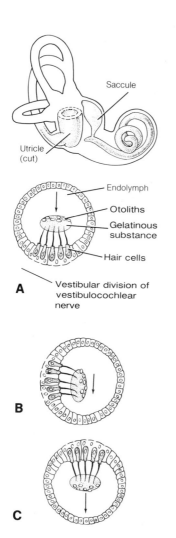

Figure 5-33. Stimulation of the balance receptors (maculae) within the utricle and saccule. The arrows indicate the direction of the force of gravity. **A.** A macula when the head is in an upright position. **B.** A macula when the head is in a horizontal position. **C.** A macula when the head is inverted.

other. The resting potential of the utricle is normal in the horizontal plane, whereas the resting potential of the saccule is normal in the saggital plane. Each position of the head is represented by a characteristic frequency of discharge that does not adapt if that position is held.

REFLEXES

Vestibular-mediated reflexes involve three muscular systems: (1) extrinsic oculomotor, (2) cervical, and (3) antigravity. The major output of

the semicircular canals, which sense rotation, goes to the extrinsic eye muscles and cervical muscles; these muscles compensate for rotation, whereas the otolith organ, which senses the position of the head, is connected primarily to the antigravity muscles. Extensive interconnection between the vestibular pathways and the cerebellum permits coordination of this sense of motor function.

The vestibulomotor reflexes are elicited when inputs from the left and right vestibular receptors or their central projections are unequal. The inputs can be unbalanced by an abnormality that involves one side more than the other—the reflex that results is termed *spontaneous*. Imbalance also can be produced by stimulating one or both receptors—the reflexes that result are termed *induced*.

Intense or prolonged vestibular stimulation produces a constellation of responses that includes head turning, falling or swaying, nystagmus, and vertigo (the sensation that one is spinning in space or that the external environment is spinning). The head turning, falling, past-pointing, and slow phase of nystagmus all are in the same direction—away from the ear that provides the greater sensory input.

NYSTAGMUS

One of the most important roles of the semicircular canals is to elicit eye movements that compensate for rotation of the head and facilitate visual fixation (see the sections on "Eye Movements and Their Control" and "Nystagmus" in this chapter). The eyes rotate in the direction that the endolymph moves. If the head rotates so extensively that the eyes cannot compensate totally for the rotation, nystagmus occurs—the eyes snap back rapidly, then move slowly in the original direction again. This is called *rotational nystagmus*. The slow movement is vestibular in origin; the fast movement is caused by central effects.

Increased neural activity from a horizontal canal causes the eyes to rotate away from the canal. Under physiological conditions, both right and left canals are stimulated simultaneously; however, because they are mirror images of one another, rotation in one direction causes the sensory input of one canal to increase and the sensory input of the other canal to decrease. The increased input from the one canal causes contraction of the lateral rectus in the contralateral eye and the medial rectus in the ipsilateral eye, which tends to rotate the eye away from that ear. Simultaneously, input from the opposite canal decreases; this decreases the resting tone in the lateral rectus of the contralateral eye and the medial rectus of the ipsilateral eye, which decreases the muscular opposition to the rotation. A lesion of one labyrinth or vestibular nerve disrupts this balance of neural activity and causes the disorders of eye movement that are seen clinically.

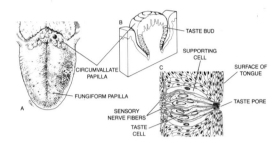

Figure 5-34. Locations of taste buds and structure of a taste bud.

GUSTATORY AND OLFACTORY SYSTEMS

Chemoreceptors

In general, all sensory systems in the body respond to chemicals because neurochemicals are involved in most forms of synaptic transmission. However, some receptors respond specifically to other types of chemicals. For example, the chemoreceptors located within the carotid bodies respond to changes in the P_{O_2}, P_{CO_2}, and pH of the blood and are involved in the reflex control of respiration. These receptors are discussed in Chapter 29. This chapter will consider only those systems that perceive chemicals in the external environment, that is, the gustatory (taste) and olfactory (smell) systems. These systems represent what may be phylogenetically the oldest of the sensory systems.

Gustatory System

RECEPTORS
The specialized sensory receptors for taste, called *taste buds,* are located in various regions of the nasopharynx but are found especially along the surface of the tongue (Figure 5-34). Each taste bud, which is approximately 0.03 mm in diameter, is composed of multiple taste cells that surround a small opening in the surface of the tongue, called a *taste pore.* Several microvilli, or taste hairs, project into the pore from each taste cell; presumably, these are the parts of the receptor cell that are sensitive to chemicals. The taste cells are replaced frequently because the life span of a single cell is only about 1 week.

The surface of the tongue is dotted by numerous papillae, which provide its somewhat rough texture. Many of these papillae, especially those along the tip, lateral margins, and posterior dorsal surface of the tongue, contain multiple taste buds. The papillae along the middorsal surface of the tongue contain very few taste buds.

PRIMARY TASTES
Classically, the sensations of taste are combinations of four fundamental, or primary, tastes: *salty, sweet, sour,* and *bitter.* Apparently, a single taste bud can respond to as many as three or four fundamental stimuli but is most sensitive to only one or two of them. The taste buds also are distributed topographically; those that are most sensitive to sweet and salty tastes are located near the tip of the tongue, those that are most sensitive to sour tastes are found along the lateral margins of the tongue, and those that are sensitive to bitter tastes are distributed primarily over the more posterior surfaces of the tongue (Figure 5-35). This topographic distribution of the different taste receptors is consistent with the seemingly ritualistic behavior of expert wine tasters: the tip of the tongue first is immersed in the wine, and then a small quantity of wine is allowed to enter the mouth and flow along the sides of the tongue; finally, the head is tilted back to permit the wine to bathe the most posterior portions of the tongue and adjacent tissue. This procedure elicits a sequence of sensations that enables the taster to categorize the wine by type and quality.

THRESHOLD OF TASTE
Any substance that is tasted must be soluble in water to enter the taste pore and reach the receptors. Although the sensitivity to different substances varies enormously, the bitter taste modality has the lowest threshold. This arrangement serves a protective function, since many naturally occurring toxins elicit a bitter taste. Quinine, for example, elicits a definitely

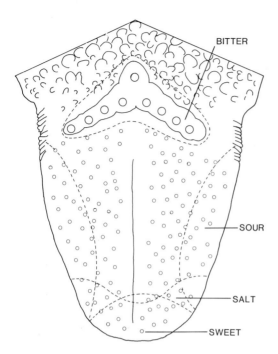

Figure 5-35. Areas of the tongue that are most sensitive to particular taste sensations.

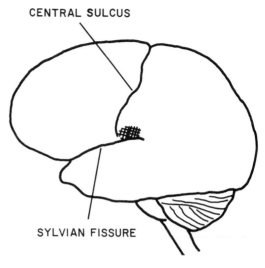

Figure 5-36. Cortical region (*cross-hatched*) that receives somatosensory information from the tongue and is believed to represent the major cortical projection for taste.

bitter sensation in solutions as dilute as 8×10^{-6} mol/liter, whereas a solution of sucrose must be at least 1000 times as concentrated to be perceived as sweet.

MECHANISM OF TASTE

The exact mechanism by which a water-soluble substance stimulates a taste receptor is not known. An important property of substances that elicit taste sensations is their molecular shape, and substances of similar configuration tend to elicit similar taste sensations. Presumably, these substances combine with a specific receptor in the microvilli of the taste cell and change the ionic conductance of that cell.

CORTICAL REPRESENTATION OF TASTE

Nerve fibers from the taste cells course to the brainstem in four different cranial nerves—the trigeminal, facial, glossopharyngeal, and vagus—and then form a fairly well defined tract that leads to the thalamus. From the thalamus, pathways project to a cortical region located near the junction of the central sulcus and the Sylvian fissure (Figure 5-36), an area close to, or

overlapping, the region that receives input from touch receptors in the tongue.

CONTRIBUTION OF SMELL TO TASTE

Some properties of other sensory systems also contribute to the perception of different tastes. The primary contributory sense is olfaction, and much of our perception of the taste of a food is caused by the action of volatile components of this food on the olfactory apparatus. This fact can be appreciated readily by blocking the nostrils and noticing how taste is affected, or by recalling how "tasteless" food became when one had a head cold. The somatosensory system also contributes to the quality of taste by encoding information about the temperature and the texture of food.

DISORDERS OF GUSTATION

The sense of taste may be assessed grossly by the application of substances of different taste categories to small regions of the tongue. The sense of taste is difficult to assess precisely because of the great interindividual differences, the marked role played by the olfactory apparatus in normal taste sensations, and the marked decrease in taste perception that occurs with increasing age.

Generally, when a specific deficit in taste can be determined, it is caused by interruption of the fibers of the facial and glossopharyngeal nerves, which carry taste information from the anterior two-thirds and posterior one-third of the tongue, respectively.

Olfactory System

RECEPTORS

The receptor mechanisms responsible for the sense of smell are similar to the receptor mechanisms responsible for taste; thus, we know little about them. Unlike the requirements for a substance to elicit a taste sensation, substances that stimulate the olfactory organ must be volatile, because molecules must be carried in the air to receptors called the *olfactory epithelium,* which are located in a specialized region of the nasal mucosa. To penetrate the mucus and react with the processes of the receptor cells, odorous substances must be lipid-soluble and at least slightly water-soluble.

The receptor cells are small, bipolar neurons that originate in the CNS; they have tiny, hairlike processes extending into the mucus that coats the lining of the nasal cavity. These neurons give rise to unmyelinated axons of very small diameter that traverse the olfactory epithelium and course through a perforated portion of the ethmoid bone called the *cribriform plate* (Figure 5-37). The olfactory bulbs lie just superior to the cribriform plate; the fibers synapse there, and second-order neurons project axons to the brain in the olfactory tracts, which lie just beneath the frontal lobes.

Primary categories of odors, like those of taste, probably exist, but there is no general agreement on the number of categories or their specific natures. Most likely, there are several specific types of olfactory receptors, each of which is most sensitive to substances of a certain molecular shape.

CORTICAL REPRESENTATION

Excitation that arises in the olfactory receptor cells apparently is processed to a considerable extent within the olfactory bulbs. The cellular architecture of these structures resembles the cellular architecture of the cerebral cortex, which has well-defined layers. The olfactory system, unlike every other sensory system, has no thalamic relay connections. Fibers in the

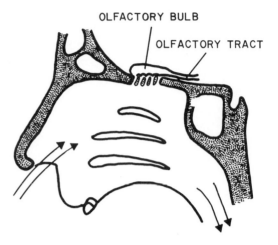

Figure 5-37. Relationship of olfactory apparatus to nasal cavity. Molecules carried by air flowing through the cavity contact the receptor cell processes in the olfactory epithelium that lines the upper portion of the cavity. Other processes of the receptor cells pass through tiny holes in the cribriform plate of the ethmoid bone and synapse with cells in the olfactory bulb.

olfactory tracts project primarily to the amygdala and other portions of the limbic system and to cortical regions in the temporal lobe. This arrangement is important clinically because epileptic seizures that originate in the temporal lobe may be characterized by olfactory hallucinations; that is, the perception of intense and usually unpleasant smells.

SENSITIVITY AND ADAPTATION

The olfactory system in humans is very sensitive: methyl mercaptan, the substance that is added to natural gas to give it a characteristic odor, can be detected in concentrations as low as 4×10^{-8} mg/liter of air. Nevertheless, the human olfactory system is not nearly as sensitive as the olfactory system of most animals. One of the primary characteristics of olfactory sensations is rapid adaptation. Even persistent, intense, pungent odors become almost unnoticeable after 1 or 2 minutes. This property apparently is due more to central mechanisms than to characteristics of the receptor cells.

DISORDERS OF OLFACTION

Clinically, the sense of smell is tested crudely by having the patient sniff the vapors of various common substances, for example, coffee grounds, using one nostril at a time. During such testing, it is important to eliminate factors, such as nasal congestion, that would obstruct the transmission of the odorous molecules to the olfactory epithelium.

Reduction of the sense of smell can occur either unilaterally (*hyposmia*) or bilaterally (*anosmia*). Cranial fractures that involve the cribriform lamina of the ethmoid bone, tumors and abscesses of the inferior aspects of the frontal lobe, and aneurysms of the internal ca-

rotid artery all can cause disorders of olfaction by interrupting fibers in the olfactory bulbs and tracts.

Although rare, specific deficits in sensations of smell can occur congenitally and are manifested by a lack of sensitivity to one of the primary odors. These deficits probably reflect the absence of a specific set of olfactory receptors and, therefore, are analogous to defects of color vision that are caused by the absence of a specific set of cones in the retina.

STUDY OUTLINE

CLASSIFICATION OF RECEPTOR CELLS

FUNCTIONAL   Summarized in text.

PHYSIOLOGICAL   Summarized in text.

RECEPTOR MECHANISMS

TRANSDUCER FUNCTION   To convert one form of energy to another.
  SPECIFICITY   Given receptor is most specific for particular stimulus.
  GENERATOR POTENTIALS   Stimulus causes graded, nonpropagated decrease of cellular potential.
  Initiates action potential in sensory nerve.

ADAPTATION   Rate of firing of sensory nerve decreases with time; property of receptor.
  Rapidly adapting or slowly adapting.

CUTANEOUS RECEPTORS   Specific for pressure, touch, pain, and temperature.
  PACINIAN CORPUSCLE   Quickly adapting mechanoreceptor; responds to vibration.
  Slippage of lamellae may permit adaptation.

MUSCLE RECEPTORS   Aid coordination of movement and regulation of muscle tone.
  PRESSURE-PAIN ENDINGS   In fascia.
  Unmyelinated nerve endings—pressure and pain.
  Pacinian corpuscles—pressure and vibration.
  TENDON ORGANS   Encode tension in tendons; slowly adapting.
  MUSCLE SPINDLES   Specialized fibers in skeletal muscles.
  Contractile, have motor nerves (γ-efferents).
  Excited by stretch of whole muscle or by own contraction.
  Convey information about length and rate of change of length of muscle.

JOINT RECEPTORS   Convey information about positions and movements of joints.
  Both slowly and rapidly adapting; innervated by both myelinated and unmyelinated fibers.

SOMATOSENSORY SYSTEM

TOUCH
  LIGHT TOUCH   Permits determination of surface characteristics—stereognosis.
  DEEP TOUCH   Detects object, but gives no information about object.

PAIN AND TEMPERATURE   Much of sensation of pain depends on central integration of information from varied types of receptors.
  GATE-CONTROL THEORY   Stimulation of pathways for light touch in painful area inhibits transmission of pain impulses in spinal cord—"closes the gate."
  REFERRED PAIN   Visceral pain is difficult to localize but is associated with pain in specific areas of skin.
  Pain impulses from internal organs may lower threshold for interneurons in cord, so that impulses from peripheral nerves that enter cord at same level produce painful sensation in skin—pain is "referred" to skin.
  PROJECTED PAIN   Stimulation anywhere along sensory tracts that carry pain fibers causes sensation of pain in receptor area; "projected" to periphery.
  Caused clinically by effects of trauma, tumor, or inflammation on sensory pathways; 'projection' helps to identify site of lesion.
  TEMPERATURE   Two populations of receptors: "cold," which respond to temperatures from 10–35 C, and "hot," which respond to temperatures from 25–45 C.

Both types respond in overlap range of 25–35 C.

Pain at temperature greater than 45 C.

VIBRATION AND JOINT POSITION   Vibration—test by use of tuning fork over bone.

Joint position—aids coordination of movements.

SPINAL PATHWAYS

LIGHT TOUCH, JOINT POSITION, AND VIBRATION Cell bodies in dorsal root ganglia, fibers in dorsal columns; cross in brainstem, connect with thalamus, and terminate in somesthetic receiving area of cortex.

PAIN AND TEMPERATURE Enter cord, cross, and ascend in ventrolateral columns.

DEEP TOUCH Two lateral columns; one is crossed and one is uncrossed.

DISORDERS OF SOMATOSENSORY SYSTEM   Irritation or destruction of sensory pathways causes pain or numbness, increased or decreased sensitivity, or loss of sensation.

BROWN–SÉQUARD SYNDROME Hemisection of cord—causes loss of pain and temperature sense on opposite side below lesion; vibration, touch, and position sense are lost on same side; paralysis on same side.

VISUAL SYSTEM

STRUCTURE AND FUNCTION   Sensitive to specific portion of electromagnetic spectrum.

Photoreceptors are embedded in light-absorbent epithelium.

Light is focused on retina; image is formed.

IMAGE FOCUSING

CORNEA Forms convex lens; provides most of focusing.

Remainder of focusing by crystalline lens.

CRYSTALLINE LENS In young person—elastic, nearly spherical.

Tension in suspensory ligaments flattens lens, decreases focal power.

Contraction of ciliary muscle decreases tension; permits lens to be more rounded, increases focal power.

With increasing age, lens becomes more fixed; permits less adjustment of focal power (presbyopia).

REGULATION OF LIGHT INTENSITY

IRIS Ring of muscle and ligaments in front of lens.

Determines size of opening—pupil.

Contraction of circular muscle decreases diameter of pupil; contraction of radial muscle increases diameter.

Circular muscle is innervated by parasympathetic system, radial by sympathetic; affected by pharmacological agents.

Pupil constricts in bright light, dilates in dark.

Near response—pupils constrict, eyes converge, focal power of lens increases.

INTRAOCULAR FLUIDS   Anterior chamber contains aqueous humor, formed by ciliary body; block of drainage increases pressure—glaucoma.

Vitreous cavity, behind lens, is filled with vitreous humor; little turnover.

REFRACTIVE ERRORS

MYOPIA AND HYPEROPIA Myopia (near-sightedness); focal power is too great or eyeball is too deep; distant objects are focused in front of retina; near vision is adequate; corrected with concave lens.

Hyperopia (farsightedness); focal power is too little or eyeball is too short; near objects are focused behind retina; distant vision is adequate; corrected with convex lens.

ASTIGMATISM Objects are not focused clearly at any distance; nonspherical curvature of refractive surfaces.

Corrected with appropriate lens.

RETINA   Contains light-sensing cells.

Attached only at optic disk and margin; can float free (detach); normally is held in place by vitreous humor.

Neural elements—photoreceptors (rods and cones); bipolar and ganglion cells, which propagate excitation toward brain; horizontal and amacrine cells, which integrate information from different parts of retina.

Light must pass through other cells to reach photoreceptors.

SENSITIVITY TO LIGHT Very wide range—about 10^{11}-fold.

Low levels of light, only rods function—scotopic range.

Very bright light, only cones function—photopic range.

Intermediate intensity of light, both rods and cones function—mesopic range.

VISUAL PIGMENTS Absorb light.

Rhodopsin ("visual purple"); colored in dark, bleached by light.

Chemical change stimulates bipolar cells, registering effect of light.

Insufficient rhodopsin (depends on vitamin A), decreased sensitivity to light (night blindness).

Three different cone pigments—one is most sensitive to short wavelengths (blue-violet), another is most sensitive to medium wavelengths (yellowish-green), the third is most sensitive to longer wavelengths (yellow).

Cones that have each type of pigment are called blue (B), green (G), and red (R), respectively.

In mesopic light, contribution of rods makes bluish-green colors appear brighter.

PHOTORECEPTOR POTENTIALS   Increase of light intensity hyperpolarizes receptor cells.

Decrease of light depolarizes receptor cells, causes release of transmitters that activate bipolar and horizontal cells.

Potentials are graded in proportion to change of light.

NEURAL CONVERGENCE   Many rods synapse with single bipolar cell; many bipolar cells synapse with single ganglion cell.

Increases sensitivity to light, but decreases acuity; rods cannot resolve fine detail.

DARK ADAPTATION   Sensitivity of retina decreases in bright light, increases in dim light or darkness.

Rhodopsin is bleached by light, decreases photopigment of rods.

Interneurons from cones inhibit rods in bright light.

When light decreases, much of sensitivity returns rapidly; remainder returns more slowly.

DISTRIBUTION OF RECEPTORS   Rods occur in all of retina except optic disk and fovea.

Optic disk, site at which ganglion cell processes leave to form optic nerve, contains no photoreceptors; is blind spot in visual field.

Fovea, center of visual axis, contains only cones; forms blind spot in dim light, when only rods are stimulated.

Cones in center of fovea are smaller than elsewhere; less convergence on bipolar cells.

Cell processes sweep outward, retina is thinner in fovea; less scattering of light, better resolution.

Clearest images are formed in line of visual axis.

COMPARISON OF ROD AND CONE SYSTEMS   Two different visual systems in retina.

Rod system functions mainly in low levels of light; provides sensitivity, but does not discriminate colors and cannot resolve fine detail.

Cone system operates in bright light, discriminates colors, and provides good resolution of detail.

VISUAL ACUITY   Minimum separation for two points to be perceived as separate.

Limited by size of photoreceptors, but enhanced by neural processing.

VISUAL PATHWAYS   Axons of ganglion cells extend to lateral geniculate nuclei (LGN) in optic tracts.

Left half of each eye projects to right LGN, and right half of each eye projects to left LGN.

Lens reverses image on retina; thus, fibers from each nasal half cross (in optic chiasm) and fibers from each temporal half do not cross.

Visual field refers to visual space, not retinal topography.

Visual fields overlap considerably; provides depth perception.

Axons from neurons of LGN form optic radiation, synapse on neurons of occipital cortex.

EYE MOVEMENTS AND THEIR CONTROL

EXTRINSIC MUSCLES OF THE EYE   Three opposing pairs of extensors and flexors.

Superior and inferior recti turn globe upward and downward; innervated by oculomotor nerve (cranial nerve III).

Medial and lateral recti turn globe toward midline and laterally; medial is innervated by oculomotor, lateral is innervated by abducens (cranial nerve VI).

Superior and inferior obliques turn globe to keep visual image upright through range of movements; superior is innervated by trochlear (cranial IV), inferior is innervated by oculomotor.

Connections from cranial nerves through superior colliculi of midbrain provide for reflex control and coordination.

Influenced by frontal cortex, occipital cortex, and vestibular nuclei.

Eyes move in rapid jerks to fix on different points in visual field.

Smooth-pursuit movement is used to follow moving object.

NYSTAGMUS   Attempt to stabilize image when either head or visual field is moving.

Rapid movement to new spot in visual field, then slow, pursuit movement to maintain image; normal response to changes in environment.

Lesions of vestibular apparatus or midbrain can produce spontaneous nystagmus.

DISORDERS OF EYE MOVEMENT   Diplopia ("double vision"); eyes do not fix on same spot in visual field; images do not fuse.

Strabismus; eyes do not move in unison; image from one eye may be suppressed.

NEURAL PROCESSING IN VISUAL SYSTEM   In retina, by horizontal and amacrine cells.

LATERAL INHIBITION   Inhibition of nearby cells by strongly stimulated receptor cells.

Sharpens retinal image.

Photoreceptor cells connected to single ganglion cell form receptive field of ganglion cell.

Center-surround organization—light in center of field has one effect; light at edge has opposite effect.

Some cells are stimulated (increase rate of firing) by light in center of field and inhibited by light at edge of field—excitatory center with inhibitory surround, or "on" center.

Other cells are inhibited by light in center and stimulated by light at edge—"off" center.

Effects increase contrast of images.

ADAPTATION   Photoreceptors adapt quickly to unchanging stimulus.

Small, rapid movements of eyes (micronystagmus) shift stimulus among receptors, prevent fading of image.

OPPONENT-RESPONSE ORGANIZATION
Center-surround arrangement permits single ganglion cell to provide information about location and size of light stimulus.

Cells that have overlapping fields integrate excitatory and inhibitory effects on each.

Opponent-response organization underlies spatial processing in retina and lateral geniculate nucleus (LGN).

COLOR VISION   Ganglion cells of retina and LGN respond differently to different wavelengths of light; caused by opponent-response organization and different photopigments.

DEFECTS OF COLOR VISION   Mostly congenital (inherited).

Normal trichromats have all three cone pigments.

Dichromats have only two cone pigments—e.g., protanopes are insensitive to red; deuteranopes (green blind) confuse shades of red, green, and yellow; tritanopes confuse shades of blue and green and of orange and pink.

Monochromats (rare) have no cone cells or have cones with only one pigment; cannot discriminate color.

Rod monochromats (no cone cells) are photophobic, lack visual acuity, and, because of large blind spot in fovea (normally filled by cones), have nystagmus.

Defects also are caused by lesions in neural pathways; color vision is affected because of large proportion of fibers that serve cones (relative lack of convergence).

VISUAL CORTEX   Topographic organization of images is not predominant.

Input is organized vertically, in columns; lateral spread is more restricted.

Primary visual cortex does not integrate information across visual field; other regions provide perception.

Cortical cells in given functional column respond to only one eye; adjacent column may respond only to other eye; may be beginning of binocular vision and depth perception.

ELECTROPHYSIOLOGY OF VISUAL SYSTEM   Ganglion cells form action potentials; other neural elements of retina produce graded, nonpropagated potentials.

ELECTRORETINOGRAM   Potentials are produced by change of light; recorded from electrode on or near eye.

Aids in diagnosis of disorders of retina.

By use of bright light to suppress rods, one can study cone-related defects.

By use of dim light to activate only rods, one can study rod-related defects.

ELECTRO-OCULOGRAM   Cornea is electrically positive to retinal area (standing potential).

Changes of illumination cause very slow, oscillatory changes of standing potential that permit assessment of retinal pigment epithelium.

Measured indirectly in clinical test.

VISUALLY EVOKED CORTICAL POTENTIALS   Recorded from scalp over occipital cortex.

Detect subtle changes in function of optic nerves and tracts.

AUDITORY SYSTEM   Ear serves both auditory and vestibular functions.

Stimulus for each system is mechanical force.

MAJOR DIVISIONS

EXTERNAL EAR   Pinna and external auditory canal.

MIDDLE EAR   Air-filled chamber between tympanic membrane and inner ear.

Opening to nasopharynx (eustachian tube) keeps chamber pressure equal to atmospheric.

Set of three small bones (ossicles)—malleus, incus, and stapes—connects tympanic membrane to membranous oval window of inner ear.

Energy of sound waves is transmitted through tympanic membrane and ossicles to oval window.

Leverage of ossicles and concentration of incident pressure of tympanic membrane on smaller oval window match low impedance of air to high impedance of fluid of inner ear.

Muscles support ossicles and filter out low-frequency body sounds.

INNER EAR   Cochlea, semicircular canals, and vestibule.

Cochlea spirals around horny core, the modiolus.

Three tunnels, or ducts, throughout spiral.

Scala vestibuli extends from oval window to peak, connects with scala tympani, which extends from round window to peak; both contain perilymph.

Cochlear duct, filled with endolymph, floats in perilymph.

Organ of Corti rests on basilar membrane within cochlear duct, contains hair cells, some are embedded in tectorial membrane.

Cochlea transduces sound energy into stimulus and encodes frequency and intensity.

NEURAL PATHWAYS   Hair cells are innervated by cochlear division of cranial nerve VIII (auditory).

Most fibers cross in brainstem but some do not.

Tracts connect at inferior colliculi in midbrain, ascend through medial geniculate body of thalamus, project to auditory cortex of temporal lobes.

PHYSIOLOGY OF AUDITORY SYSTEM
Sound waves cause tympanic membrane to vibrate, motion is transmitted through ossicular chain to oval window.

Low-frequency waves move perilymph through helicotrema, cause round window to oscillate; little pressure is generated, scala media is not displaced, and no sound is perceived.

Perilymph does not flow fast enough to compensate for higher frequencies; pressure waves are generated and scala media is displaced.

Wave travels in basilar membrane; given frequency causes maximum displacement at specific distance from oval window, then dies out quickly; the lower the frequency, the farther the wave travels.

Hair cells are bent by effects of traveling wave, generate electrical potential and stimulate afferent neurons.

Frequency is encoded mostly by site of stimulation, intensity is encoded by number of neurons excited and rate of excitation.

Special cells may respond to onset of stimulus or change of frequency or intensity.

BIOELECTRICAL POTENTIALS   Endocochlear potential—constant 90–115 mv positive to scala tympani; related to secretion of endolymph.

Cochlear microphonic, generated by hair cells, reproduces waveform of sound stimulus.

Summating potentials, generated by hair cells, are related to intensity of sound stimulus.

All can be recorded from external auditory canal, used to identify specific dysfunction.

Potentials are recorded from scalp by computer averaging techniques, used to identify dysfunction at different levels.

VESTIBULAR SYSTEM

FUNCTIONAL ANATOMY   Three semicircular canals, one in each plane; detect head movement.

Saccule and utricle in vestibule sense position of head.

RECEPTORS   Hair cells are embedded in overlying gelatinous layer.

In semicircular canals, cristae; in vestibule, maculae.

NEURAL PATHWAYS   Innervated by vestibular branch of cranial nerve VIII.

First synapse, vestibular nuclei in brainstem.

Most afferent nerves from semicircular canal go to superior and inferior vestibular nuclei, which project to oculomotor nuclei.

Utricle and saccule project mainly to lateral vestibular nucleus, then downward through length of spinal cord.

All vestibular organs project to inferior nucleus, then to cerebellum.

Some tracts project through thalamus to somatosensory areas; conscious sensation produced only through nausea and vertigo or through reflex motor responses.

PHYSIOLOGY OF VESTIBULAR SYSTEM
STIMULATION OF RECEPTORS   Mechanical force is transduced through bending of hair cells.

In utricle and saccule, gravity and linear acceleration displace membrane that contains otoliths.

Afferent nerves of ampulla are excited continuously when head is upright; rate increases with bend in one direction, decreases with bend in other direction; encodes direction and extent of head tilt and linear acceleration.

Rotation of head causes endolymph to move in semicircular canal, opposite direction of movement initially (inertia); hair cells bent.

During constant rotation, flow stops, cells are not bent.

When rotation stops, flow and bending in same direction as movement (momentum).

Canals sense direction and rate of angular acceleration and deceleration.

REFLEXES   Semicircular canals affect mostly eye muscles and cervical muscles—compensate for rotation.

Otolith organs affect mainly antigravity muscles; coordination through cerebellum.

Effects are elicited by imbalance of input from two sides.

Induced reflexes—by stimulating one or both receptors.

Spontaneous reflexes—by abnormality that affects one side more than the other.

Strong or prolonged stimulation causes head turning, falling, nystagmus, and vertigo.

Turning, falling, and slow phase of nystagmus away from side of greater sensory input.

NYSTAGMUS   Eyes move in direction endolymph of semicircular canals moves.

If rotation is extensive, eyes reach limit of movement, snap back, move again—rotational nystagmus.

Slow movement is caused by vestibular system; rapid movement is under central control.

Rotation stimulates canals on both sides, effects on eye movements are cooperative; lesion of one labyrinth or vestibular nerve disrupts balance and produces disorders seen clinically.

GUSTATORY AND OLFACTORY SYSTEMS

CHEMORECEPTORS   Gustatory and olfactory systems respond to chemicals in external environment.

GUSTATORY SYSTEM

RECEPTORS   Located on surface of tongue and in nasopharynx.

Taste buds—sensing cells around pore; microvilli project into pore from each cell.

Papillae contain multiple taste buds, mainly along tip, edges, and back of tongue.

PRIMARY TASTES   Salty, sweet, sour, and bitter.

Combinations form sensation of taste.

Single bud may respond to all tastes, but most buds are sensitive to one or two tastes.

Buds are most sensitive to sweet and salty near tip of tongue, to sour along edges, and to bitter mainly over back surfaces.

THRESHOLD OF TASTE   Substance tasted must be soluble in water to reach receptors.

Bitter has lowest threshold; many naturally occurring toxins taste bitter.

MECHANISM OF TASTE   Unknown; presumed related to chemical structures that combine with microvilli and change ionic conductance.

CORTICAL REPRESENTATION OF TASTE Afferent fibers in cranial nerves V, VII, IX, and X form tract to thalamus.

Project to cortex near junction of central sulcus and Sylvian fissure.

CONTRIBUTION OF SMELL TO TASTE Significant; caused by volatile components of food.

DISORDERS OF GUSTATION   Difficult to evaluate.

Assessed by applying substances of different tastes to small areas of tongue.

Usually caused by interruption of fibers in cranial nerves VII and IX.

OLFACTORY SYSTEM

RECEPTORS   In specialized region of nasal mucosa.

Substances must be volatile, lipid-soluble, and at least slightly water-soluble.

Small, bipolar neurons send hairlike processes into mucous coating of nasal cavity.

Project to olfactory bulbs, send neurons in olfactory tract to brain.

No standard classification of primary odors.

CORTICAL REPRESENTATION   In temporal lobes; much processing in olfactory bulbs.

SENSITIVITY AND ADAPTATION   Highly sensitive, rapidly adapting.

DISORDERS OF OLFACTION   Tested clinically by sniffing substances.

Trauma, tumors, abscesses, and aneurysms.

Genetic—rare; absence of specific receptors.

BIBLIOGRAPHY

Abrahamson, E.W., and Ostroy, S.E. (eds.). 1981. *Molecular Progress in Vision*. Stroudsburg, Pennsylvania: Hutchinson Ross.

Adrian, E.W. 1979. *Essentials of Ophthalmic Optics*. New York: Oxford University Press.

Amoore, J.E. 1965. Psychophysics of odor. *Cold Spring Harbor Symp. Quant. Biol.* 30:623.

Arden, G.B., Barrada, A., and Kelsey, J.H. 1962. New clinical test of retinal function based upon the standing potential of the eye. *Br. J. Ophthalmol.* 46:449.

Ary, L.B., Tremaine, M.J., and Monzingo, F.L. 1935. The numerical and topographical relation of taste buds to human circumvallate papillae throughout the life span. *Anat. Rec.* 64:9.

Barlow, H.B., Blakemore, C., and Pettigrew, J.D. 1967. The neural mechanism of binocular depth discrimination. *J. Physiol.* (London) 193:327.

Bizzi, E. 1974. The coordination of eye-head movements. *Sci. Am.* 231:100.

Bloemendal, H. 1977. The vertebrate eye lens. *Science* 197:127.

Brown, J.L., and Mueller, G. 1965. Brightness discrimination and brightness contrast. In *Vision and Visual Perception*. Edited by C.H. Grahan. New York: John Wiley and Sons.

Brown, K.T. 1968. The electroretinogram: Its components and their origins. *Vision Res.* 8:633.

Brown, P.K., and Wald, G. 1964. Visual pigments in single rods and cones of the human retina. *Science* 144:145.

Cauna, N. 1968. Light and electron microscopical structures of sensory end-organs in human skin. In *The Skin Senses*. Edited by D.R. Kenshale. Springfield, Illinois: Charles C. Thomas.

Cheney, P.D., and Preston, J.B. 1976. Classification and response characteristics of muscle spindle afferents in the primate. *J. Neurophysiol.* 39:1.

Cogan, D.G. 1965. *Neurology of the Ocular Muscles*. Springfield, Illinois: Charles C. Thomas.

Cogan, D.G. 1966. *Neurology of the Visual System*. Springfield, Illinois: Charles C. Thomas.

Davson, H. 1972. *The Physiology of the Eye* (3rd ed.). New York: Academic Press, Inc.

Daw, N.Y. 1973. Neurophysiology of color vision. *Physiol. Rev.* 53:271.

DeValois, R.L. 1973. Central mechanism of color vision. In *Handbook of Sensory Physiology*. Edited by R. Jung. New York: Springer-Verlag. Vol. 7/3A, p. 209.

Engström, H., and Wersäll, J. 1958. The ultrastructural organization of the organ of Corti and the vestibular sensory epithelia. *Exp. Cell. Res.* (Suppl. 5):460.

Gombrich, E.H. 1972. The visual image. *Sci. Am.* 227:1081.

Granit, R. 1933. The components of the retinal action potential in mammals and their relation to discharge in the optic nerve. *J. Physiol.* (London) 77:207.

Hubbell, W.L., and Bownds, M.D. 1979. Visual transduction in vertebrate photoreceptors. *Annu. Rev. Neurosci.* 2:17.

Hubel, D.H., and Wiesel, T.N. 1979. Brain mechanisms of vision. *Sci. Am.* 241:(3)150.

Hudspeth, A.J. 1983. The hair cells of the inner ear. *Sci. Am.* 248:(1)54.

Jerger, J. (ed.). 1973. *Modern Developments in Audiology* (2nd ed.). New York: Academic Press, Inc.

Kaneko, A. 1979. Physiology of the retina. *Annu. Rev. Neurosci.* 2:169.

Katsuki, Y., Norgren, R., and Sato, M. (eds.). 1981. *Brain Mechanisms of Sensation*. New York: John Wiley and Sons.

Kennedy, D. 1963. Inhibition in visual systems. *Sci. Am.* 209:1221.

Melzack, R., and Wall, P.D. 1966. Pain mechanisms: A new theory. *Science* 150:971.

Merskey, H. 1980. Some features of the history of the idea of pain. *Pain* 9:3.

Miller, E.F., Jr., Graybiel, A., and Kellog, R.S. 1966. Otolith organ activity within earth standard, one-half standard, and zero gravity environments. *Aerosp. Med.* 37:399.

Moulton, D.G., and Biedler, L.M. 1967. Structure and function in the peripheral olfactory system. *Physiol. Rev.* 47:1.

Nassau, K. 1980. The causes of color. *Sci. Am.* 243:(4)124.

Norrsell, U. 1980. Behavioral studies of the somatosensory system. *Physiol. Rev.* 60:327.

Oakley, B., and Benjamin, R.M. 1966. Neural mechanisms of taste. *Physiol. Rev.* 46:173.

O'Brien, D.F. 1982. The chemistry of vision. *Science* 218:961.

Ohloff, G., and Thomas, A.F. (eds.). 1971. *Gustation and Olfaction*. New York: Academic Press, Inc.

Parker, D.E. 1981. The vestibular apparatus. *Science* 243:118.

Raphan, T., and Cohen, B. 1978. Brainstem mechanisms for rapid and slow eye movements. *Annu. Rev. Physiol.* 40:527.

Regan, D., Beverly, K., and Cynader, M. 1979. The visual perception of motion in depth. *Sci. Am.* 241:(1)136.

Reinecke, R.D. 1978. *Strabismus*. New York: Grune & Stratton.

Roberts, M.H.T., and Llewelyn, M.B. 1982. The supraspinal control of pain. *Bioscience* 32:587.

Rodieck, R.W. 1972. Components of the electroretinogram: A reappraisal. *Vision Res.* 12:773.

Rodieck, R.W. 1979. Visual pathways. *Annu. Rev. Neurosci.* 2:193.

Rushton, W.A.H. 1962. Visual pigments in man. *Sci. Am.* 207:120.

Sato, T. 1980. Recent advances in the physiology of taste cells. *Prog. Neurobiol.* 14:25.

Scheich, O.C.H., and Schreiner, C. (eds.). 1979. *Hearing Mechanisms and Speech*. New York: Springer-Verlag.

Schepherd, G.M. 1972. Synaptic organization of the mammalian olfactory bulb. *Physiol. Rev.* 52:864.

Schlaer, S. 1937. The relation between visual acuity and illumination. *J. Gen. Physiol.* 21:165.

Schmidt, R.F. (ed.). 1981. *Fundamentals of Sensory Physiology* (2nd ed.). New York: Springer-Verlag.

Starr, A. 1974. Neurophysiological mechanisms of sound localization. *Fed. Proc.* 33:1911.

Syka, J., and Aitkin, L. 1981. *Neuronal Mechanisms of Hearing*. New York: Plenum Press.

Tasaki, I., Davis, H., and Eldredge, D.H. 1954. Exploration of cochlear potentials in guinea pigs with a microelectrode. *J. Acoust. Soc. Am.* 26:165.

Terenius, L. 1978. Endogenous peptides and analgesia. *Annu. Rev. Pharmacol. Toxicol.* 18:189.

Toates, F.M. 1972. Accommodation function of the human eye. *Physiol. Rev.* 52:828.

Toboas, J.V. (ed.). 1970. *Foundation of Modern Auditory Theory.* New York: Academic Press, Inc.

von Bekesy, G. 1960. *Experiments in Hearing.* New York: McGraw-Hill.

Wald, G., and Brown, P.K. 1965. Human color vision and color blindness. *Cold Spring Harbor Symp. Quant. Biol.* 30:345.

Wall, P.D. 1979. On the relation of injury to pain: The John J. Bonica lecture. *Pain* 6:253.

Wever, E.G., and Lawrence, M. 1954. *Physiological Acoustics.* Princeton: Princeton University Press.

Wilson, V.J., and Jones, G.M. 1979. *Mammalian Vestibular Physiology.* New York: Plenum Press.

Woolsey, C.N. (ed.). 1981. *Multiple Somatic Areas.* Clifton, New Jersey: Humana Press.

Zwislocki, J.J. 1981. Sound analysis in the ear: A history of discoveries. *Am. Sci.* 69:184.

6

Motor Systems

CHAPTER CONTENTS

GENERAL BACKGROUND

It is difficult, if not impossible, to consider the motor systems in isolation, because essentially all of their functions are related intimately to activity that occurs in sensory pathways. Indeed, this same problem arises when one attempts to study any of the various structures or neuronal networks of the brain in isolation. Because of the redundant circuitry and feedback pathways that characterize the organization of the brain, to study any portion in isolation is to create a highly artificial and nonphysiological situation. Nonetheless, much can be learned by such studies, and, artificial though they may be, one must understand how a system functions independently before one can begin to understand how it interrelates with other systems.

This discussion of the networks in the central nervous system (CNS) that take part in motor activity begins with a consideration of spinal reflexes and progresses through higher-order levels of processing. This traditional approach helps to provide a functional understanding of the hierarchical structure that characterizes the motor systems and virtually all other systems in the CNS.

SPINAL REFLEXES

In general, movements that are not under voluntary control and that consist of stereotyped muscular responses to specific sensory stimuli are called *reflexes*. This term, which comes from the word *reflection,* represents an attempt to describe the manner in which sensory input seems to be "reflected" onto the musculature without conscious action. Reflexes usually are categorized according to the minimum number of neurons that the underlying pathways contain.

Myotatic Reflexes

The simplest reflex arc that can be represented involves only two neurons—one sensory and one motor—hence, only one synapse. An example of such a monosynaptic reflex is the *knee jerk,* which belongs to a group of reflexes called *phasic stretch,* or *myotatic,* reflexes. If the tendon of the quadriceps femoris muscle is tapped briskly with a reflex hammer (a rubber-headed mallet) just below the patella (knee-cap), the quadriceps contracts, and the lower portion of the leg extends. Tapping the tendon in this manner stretches the quadriceps muscle briefly. The muscle spindle receptors of the quadriceps respond by sending a burst of impulses along the large-diameter group Ia afferent fibers (Figure 6-1). These fibers synapse directly onto the cell bodies of motoneurons located in the ventral gray matter of the spinal cord, and the afferent volley causes action potentials to be generated within the large α-motoneurons that arise from these cell bodies. The action potentials are propagated to the periphery, and the quadriceps muscle contracts. Because both the sensory and motor fibers involved in this reflex are large and propagate rapidly, and the pathway contains only one synapse to introduce delay, this type of reflex is one of the fastest in humans.

Other myotatic reflexes can be elicited by tapping the tendon of the biceps brachii, which produces flexion of the forearm, the tendon of the triceps brachii, which causes extension of the forearm, and the tendocalcaneous (Achilles) tendon, which produces plantar flexion of the foot.

Although only one synapse is imposed in the direct line of the reflex, other connections made in the spinal cord influence the reflex actions. If the quadriceps, for example, is to contract rapidly and extend the lower leg, the muscles that oppose it (flexors) must relax. This is accomplished through interneurons (short-axon cells in the gray matter of the cord) that inhibit the semitendinosus (flexor) muscle (Figure 6-1). Descending fibers from the brainstem and higher motor centers both excite and inhibit the myotatic reflexes, through synapses within the central gray matter and activity within the γ-efferent system. As the discussion of muscle receptors (Chapter 5) pointed out, γ-efferent fibers regulate the sensitivity of the muscle spindles by changing the length of the intrafusal fibers and altering the baseline firing rate of the spindles. Thus, increased γ-efferent output en-

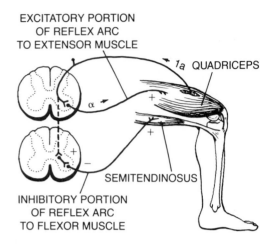

EXCITATORY PORTION
OF REFLEX ARC
TO EXTENSOR MUSCLE

Ia QUADRICEPS

SEMITENDINOSUS

INHIBITORY PORTION
OF REFLEX ARC
TO FLEXOR MUSCLE

Figure 6-1. The knee jerk reflex. Stretch of the quadriceps tendon causes stretch of intrafusal fibers, distortion of muscle spindles, and increased firing of Ia afferent fibers. The afferent fibers synapse directly on α-motoneurons to the extensor (quadriceps) muscle and, through an inhibitory interneuron, on the flexor (semitendinosus) muscle to produce a brief extension of the lower leg.

hances, or facilitates, the myotatic reflexes. Clinically, myotatic reflexes that are weak or difficult to elicit may be enhanced by having the patient attempt forcefully to pull his or her interlocked hands apart or perform some other "isometric" exercise. This procedure, which is called *Jendrassik's maneuver,* indicates that the γ-efferent system underlies the facilitation of the myotatic reflexes.

Polysynaptic Reflexes

Most reflexes involve at least three neurons and, thus, are *polysynaptic.* The withdrawal of a limb from a painful stimulus is an example of such a reflex. A stimulus that arises from a focal region of skin simultaneously excites flexors and inhibits extensors at several joints, so that the limb quickly withdraws from the potentially injurious stimulus. This is how one's hands can release an unexpectedly hot object before the sensation of pain, or even of heat, is felt. Such reflexes involve numerous synapses within the gray matter of the cord and implicate interneurons that carry impulses up and down the cord over several segments to activate the appropriate muscles.

Clinical Applications of Spinal Reflexes

The spinal reflexes usually are classified for clinical purposes as superficial, abnormal, or deep. The *superficial reflexes* are reflexes that are elicited by gentle stimulation of the skin. Examples are the *abdominal reflex,* in which the umbilicus moves toward the stimulus when the skin of the abdomen is stroked, and the *cremasteric reflex,* in which stroking of the inner aspect of the upper thigh in males produces contraction of the cremaster muscle and elevation of the testicle on that side. Another example is the *plantar reflex,* a complex response that involves various muscles around the great toe. The plantar reflex is elicited by drawing a blunt, pointed object, such as a key, across the lateral aspect of the plantar surface of the foot, from heel to toe. Normally, this action is accompanied by flexion of the toes. If the descending motor pathways are damaged, however, the plantar reflex is replaced by dorsiflexion of the great toe and fanning of the smaller toes (Babinski's sign). This is an example of an *abnormal reflex,* that is, a reflex that normally does not occur.

The myotatic, or tendon, reflexes are *deep reflexes.* Clinically important findings about these reflexes include greatly exaggerated (hyperactive) or diminished (hypoactive) responses to the reflex hammer. Because the briskness of the myotatic reflexes can vary among individuals, abnormalities are assessed most accurately by testing and comparing the same reflex on both sides of the body. Deep tendon reflexes are grossly exaggerated in some CNS disorders; for example, a single tap of the Achilles' tendon may produce repetitive ankle jerks (clonus) rather than the normal single contraction.

Testing the various spinal reflexes is an important part of the neurological examination that can provide information about the nature and location of pathology. Consider how the pathways involved in the knee jerk, for example, can be disrupted. First, the sensory receptors must function to encode the stretch of the muscle; second, the Ia afferent fibers must propagate the impulses to the spinal cord; third, the synaptic connections within the ventral gray matter must transmit properly for the reflex to continue and for the opposing muscles to be inhibited; fourth, the α-motoneurons must be intact to propagate excitation to the quadriceps. Finally, the myoneural junction must be sound and the contractile fibers of the quadriceps must be functional for the "twitch" to occur. Absence of this reflex does not tell one the precise location of a lesion, but it can be used to assign the lesion to a certain *level* in the nervous system.

MOTOR FUNCTIONS OF THE BRAINSTEM

The next highest "level" of motor system function resides in the medulla, pons, and midbrain of the brainstem. The nuclei of all twelve cranial nerves, all but three of which have motor components, are located in the brainstem. The *reticular formation,* a vast network of cell bodies and fibers within the white and gray matter of the brainstem, concentrated primarily in the central core, is important to all motor activity. It contains numerous small nuclei that are involved in motor functions; some of these nuclei, located primarily within the medulla, form an *inhibitory* system that projects to anterior horn cells and γ-afferent neurons, whereas other nuclei located somewhat higher in the brainstem form an *excitatory system.* Both groups project to the spinal cord through the *reticulospinal tracts,* although a major portion of the excitatory system arises in vestibular nuclei in the medulla and descends in the *vestibulospinal tracts.*

Other cellular networks in the medulla and the pons are responsible for the reflex actions that are involved in control of cardiac and respiratory functions. Farther up the brainstem, in the midbrain, are the *red nuclei,* which receive input from the cerebellum and send projections to other portions of the brainstem and the opposite side of the spinal cord (rubrospinal tracts). Fiber tracts that course through the brainstem on their way to spinal neurons also are important physiologically. These tracts consist of axons that originate in both cortical and subcortical centers in the cerebral hemispheres. These *corticospinal tracts* descend primarily in the fiber bundles that comprise the *pyramids,* which cross to the opposite side in the *pyramidal decussation.* The descending motor tracts outside the pyramids are termed *extrapyramidal.*

Motor Functions of the Cranial Nerves

The *oculomotor nerve* (CN III) controls all of the extrinsic muscles of the eye, except the superior oblique and lateral rectus. This nerve also carries the preganglionic parasympathetic fibers that originate in the Edinger–Westphal nucleus of the midbrain and terminate in the ciliary ganglion. Thus, the oculomotor nerve also is involved in the pupillary constriction that occurs in response to light and is part of the accommodation reflex (see Chapter 5). The *trochlear nerve* (CN IV) controls only the superior oblique muscle, and the *abducens nerve* (CN VI) controls only the lateral rectus. Although motor fibers in the *trigeminal nerve* (CN V) control primarily the muscles of mastication, they also supply some small muscles such as the tensor tympani in the ear. The *facial nerve* (CN VII) controls the superficial muscles of the face, which determine facial expression, and the orbicularis oculi, which close the eyelids. Although primarily sensory, some motor fibers in cranial nerve IX (glossopharyngeal) are involved in the production of saliva, and other motor fibers innervate striated muscles in the pharynx.

The *vagus nerve* (CN X) has multiple sensory and visceral motor functions in the thorax and abdomen and controls skeletal muscle in the soft palate, larynx, and pharynx. The *spinal accessory nerve* (CN XI) innervates the trapezius and sternocleidomastoid muscles, and thus is involved in rotating the head and shrugging the shoulders. The hypoglossal nerve (CN XII) innervates the skeletal muscles of the tongue.

Brainstem Reflexes

Interconnections between the nuclei of the cranial nerves and other structures within the brainstem underlie various reflexes of clinical and physiological importance. The pupillary reflexes, the oculomotor reflexes in accommodation, tracking, and vestibular function, and the acoustic reflexes all are discussed in Chapter 5. Fibers in cranial nerve V (trigeminal) carry sensory input from the cornea and synapse with interneurons in the brainstem. These interneurons, in turn, synapse bilaterally with the nuclei of cranial nerve VII (facial). This network is responsible for the *corneal reflex,* which consists of closure of both eyelids in response to a light touch of the cornea of either eye (tested with a wisp of cotton). Just as in the pupillary light reflex, the bilateral connections yield both direct and consensual responses (see Chapter 5), and the integrity of the sensory and motor components of the reflex can be judged separately. Interruption of motor fibers in the

facial nerve can cause facial paralysis; *Bell's palsy* is sudden paralysis of the facial muscles unilaterally, possibly caused by inflammation and compression of the nerve at the point at which it leaves the skull.

Touching the posterior wall of the pharynx elicits the *gag reflex,* which consists of elevation and constriction of the pharynx. Sensory input for this reflex is carried by fibers in cranial nerve IX, which synapse on cell bodies that give rise to efferent fibers in cranial nerve X. Both of these nerves also are involved in the *carotid sinus reflex,* which slows the heart rate in response to increased arterial blood pressure (see Chapter 15). The *vomiting reflex* also depends on structures in this region of the brainstem. The vagus nerve carries sensory input to centers in the medulla which, in sequence, close the glottis and inhibit inspiration, relax the gastroesophageal sphincter, and cause muscles in the anterior abdominal wall to contract and empty the stomach.

The medulla also contains centers for the automated control of respiration (see Chapter 29). Inspiration is mediated by fibers that arise from cells in the reticular formation and descend to the lower motoneurons of the phrenic and intercostal nerves. Expiration of air is due chiefly to the elastic properties of the lungs and the chest wall (see Chapter 28). When the lungs are inflated, stretch receptors in the bronchioles send impulses through the vagus trunks. These impulses inhibit the medullary respiratory center, and the expiration of air follows. The rhythm of respiration is controlled by additional input to the respiratory center from fibers that arise in the pons. This center also receives input from the carotid body, which detects alterations in the O_2 and CO_2 tensions of the blood and initiates appropriate respiratory changes (*carotid body reflex*).

THE CEREBELLUM

The cerebellum lies within the posterior fossa of the cranium, against the dorsal surface of the brainstem, separated from the ventral surface of the occipital lobes by a flat sheet of dura, the tentorium. The surface of the cerebellum is fissured, so that its appearance is similar to that of the cerebral cortex (Figure 6-2).

The cerebellum is divided into two large lateral portions, the *cerebellar hemispheres,* which connect near the midline with a ropy, or wormlike, structure called the *vermis.* The cerebellum is further subdivided along the anterior-posterior axis into the *anterior lobe, middle lobe,* and

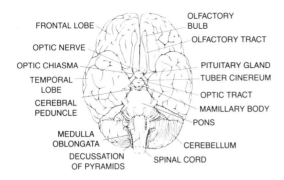

Figure 6-2. Ventral surface of brain showing relationships of medulla, pons, and cerebellum.

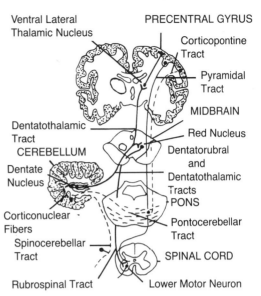

Figure 6-3. Major afferent and efferent pathways of the cerebellum.

posterior lobe. Three large, paired fiber bundles—the *superior, middle,* and *inferior cerebellar peduncles*—connect the cerebellum with the brainstem. Buried within the cerebellum are four paired nuclei; from the most medial to lateral, these nuclei are the *fastigial, globose, emboliform,* and *dentate nuclei.*

Functions of the Cerebellum

The cerebellum continuously processes input from tactile, auditory, vestibular, visual, and visceral sensory systems to provide the precise timing of muscular contractions that are essential to coordinated, smooth movements. One is not aware of the processing that takes place in the cerebellum, and stimulation of this structure elicits no perception. The absence of the cerebellum's influence is felt dramatically, however, when lesions interrupt its circuits. Movements become fragmented, rather than coordinated, and are clumsy and disorganized. This disruption of skilled movements, called *cerebellar ataxia,* cannot be compensated for by conscious effort.

Cerebellar Pathways

INPUT

The cerebellum is aided in its function as a "servocontrol" center by input from multiple sources (Figure 6-3). Activity in the sensorimotor cortex and descending pathways (pyramidal tracts) is monitored through connections with the pons (the *corticopontocerebellar tracts*). The corticopontocerebellar tract crosses the midline, so that the left cerebral hemisphere gives input to the right cerebellar hemisphere; the fibers enter the cerebellum through the middle cerebellar peduncle. Other input from higher centers is received through brainstem nuclei and the reticular formation. Feedback from skeletal muscles arrives through *spinocerebellar tracts,* primarily to the vermis. Vestibular information goes to the flocculonodular lobe.

OUTPUT

The primary outflow of the cerebellum is through fibers in the superior cerebellar peduncle that begin in the dentate, emboliform, and globose nuclei. Some of these fibers synapse in the *red nucleus* (of the midbrain). The red nucleus sends fibers to lower motor neurons in the spinal cord (*dentatorubrospinal tracts*); this pathway crosses the midline twice, so it is *uncrossed* at its termination. The dentate nucleus also sends fibers to the frontal (motor) cortex through the thalamus (*dentatothalamocortical tracts*), where it influences activity in the pyramidal tracts. Finally, the cerebellum sends fibers to both inhibitory and excitatory centers in the descending reticular system (*reticulospinal tracts*).

Lesions of the Cerebellum and Its Pathways

Because the pathways from the cerebellum to the cortex are crossed, and the pathways from the cerebral cortex to the spinal cord also are crossed, lesions on one side of the cerebellum affect muscles on the same side of the body. Similarly, the descending pathways to spinal motoneurons cross twice, so the effects of lesions there also are seen on the same side of the body.

Clinically, lesions of the cerebellar system may be evident in the execution of various types of movements. Ataxia may be manifest in alterations of gait, posture, hand-eye movements, and rapid, alternating movements. Even though all of the proprioceptive pathways may be intact, the patient staggers when walking, as if intoxicated. A lesion in one cerebellar hemisphere may cause the patient to fall toward the side of the lesion or, if asked to walk straight ahead with eyes closed, the patient might circle toward the side of the lesion. *Dysmetria,* the inability to "measure" movements, may be evident in the patient who cannot alternately touch his or her own nose and the examiner's fingertip, particularly if the examiner's fingertip moves. Attempts to perform such maneuvers are characterized by "overshooting" and coarse, oscillatory movements. This condition often is referred to as "intention tremor," although it is not a true tremor. Similarly uncoordinated movements of the diaphragm and other muscles involved in speech cause a condition known as "scanning" speech. The patient also may exhibit *dysdiadochokinesia,* which is the inability to perform alternating movements such as rapid pronation and supination of the hands or tapping with the fingers. *Ocular nystagmus,* a condition in which the eyes drift slowly in one direction and then snap back and drift again (see Chapter 5), may occur if fibers that connect with the vestibular system are involved. *Hypotonia,* or decreased muscle tone, also generally accompanies cerebellar lesions, and, as a consequence, tendon reflexes may be decreased markedly. This condition can be caused by decreased input to the γ-efferent fibers. Lesions of the cerebellum may not produce marked symptoms if they develop slowly and brain mechanisms are able to compensate; therefore, the effects are most pronounced in acute injury.

THE BASAL GANGLIA

Functional Anatomy

The basal ganglia are a collection of nuclei deep within the upper brainstem and forebrain. The caudate, globus pallidus, and putamen are al-

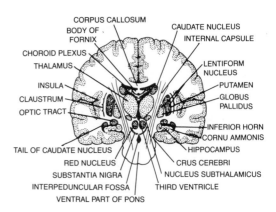

Figure 6-4.   A coronal section through the ventral pons and cerebral hemispheres showing the basal ganglia and related structures.

ways listed as parts of the basal ganglia; two other areas of the midbrain, the subthalamic nuclei and the substantia nigra, are included on a functional basis (Figure 6-4). The nuclei are grouped in several ways. The caudate, globus pallidus, and putamen constitute the corpus striatum, the globus pallidus and putamen comprise the lentiform nuclei, and the caudate and putamen form the neostriatum, or striatum (Figure 6-4). These structures, together with the cerebellum and all of the various connecting pathways, make up what generally is called the *extrapyramidal motor system.* This terminology persists from the earlier notion that the corticospinal and corticobulbar tracts (pyramids) constitute the major motor system.

Although the interconnections of the basal ganglia are complex, they are important to an understanding of the normal and pathological functions of this system (Figure 6-5). The major afferent pathways to the basal ganglia begin in the cerebral cortex, the intralaminar nuclei of the thalamus, and the substantia nigra of the midbrain. The pathways from the cortex receive input from both sides of the sensorimotor cortex and from the same side of other cortical regions. Most of the input to the basal ganglia from the rest of the brain arrives in the striatum (caudate nucleus and putamen). The primary efferent pathways of the basal ganglia run from the striatum to the substantia nigra (thus forming reciprocal connections between these two structures), and from the globus pallidus to the ventrolateral nucleus of the thalamus and the reticular formation of the brainstem. Other pathways connect with the superior colliculi in the midbrain.

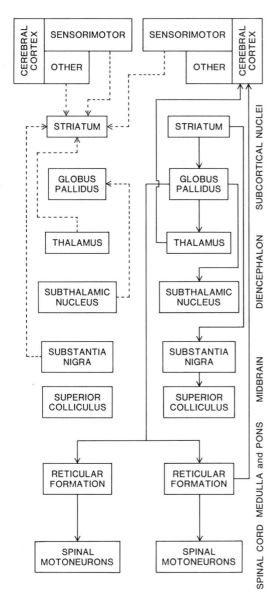

Figure 6-5. Major afferent (*dashed lines*) and efferent (*solid lines*) pathways of the basal ganglia and related structures.

Normal Functions

Although the basal ganglia and their related subcortical, diencephalic, and brainstem nuclei form an imperfectly understood system, conclusions may be reached about their general function. The symptoms of disorders that specifically affect the basal ganglia indicate that those structures are involved in the planning and monitoring of complex movements. The basal ganglia are concerned with relatively slow and sustained (postural and supporting) movements, rather than the fast, phasic movements with which the cerebellum is involved so intimately.

Dysfunctions

PARKINSONISM

Much of our knowledge of the function of the basal ganglia in humans comes from observations of patients who have *parkinsonism,* a disorder that involves degeneration of pigmented neurons in the substantia nigra—pigmented neurons are dopaminergic cells that terminate in the striatum. The major symptoms of this disorder, first described by James Parkinson in 1817, include tremor at rest (rhythmic, and involving primarily the thumb and forefinger—"pill-rolling"), rigidity (because of increased muscle tone), and akinesia, or paucity of movement. Patients who have this disorder move very slowly, generally exhibit a loss of dexterity, and have an impaired gait. They usually do not complain of sensory loss, however, and, as a rule, intellectual functions are unaffected.

The nigrostriatal pathways release dopamine as a transmitter and probably inhibit the excitation of other cells in the striatum. Removing the influence of these cells creates an imbalance in the basal ganglia network because other neurons, which release acetylcholine (ACh), γ-aminobutyric acid (GABA), or other neurotransmitters, remain active. The severity of the symptoms in parkinsonism directly reflects the degree of depletion of dopamine-containing cells in the substantia nigra, and many of the symptoms can be relieved by drugs that restore a balance of neurotransmitter substances by augmenting synthesis and release of dopamine, inhibiting the reuptake of dopamine, or suppressing the efficacy of the cholinergic pathway.

HUNTINGTON'S CHOREA

Another degenerative condition that affects the basal ganglia is *Huntington's chorea,* a hereditary disorder in which the first symptoms do not appear until patients are well into adulthood. This condition is characterized by the onset of abrupt and jerky involuntary movements (choreiform, or dancelike). Huntington's chorea is progressive and usually is fatal within 15 years of the onset of symptoms. The later stages of the disorder are associated with marked mental deterioration. The motor symptoms of Huntington's disease essentially are the opposite of the motor symptoms of parkinsonism

CLINICAL CORRELATION
6.1   Huntington's Chorea

CASE REPORT

The Patient: A 55-year-old man.

Principal Complaints: Involuntary movements, changes in cognitive ability, and personality changes.

History: The patient was a high school graduate who had worked in a petrochemical manufacturing plant, but had retired at the age of 52. His mother and older brother both had been diagnosed as having Huntington's disease; at the time of admission, his mother was deceased and his brother was in a nursing home. The patient's first symptoms, small involuntary movements of the hands, appeared 15 years earlier. At that time, the movements were not marked, and they had become prominent only in the past 5 years. The patient owned a single-engine airplane and continued to fly until just before admission. He had refused medication for his disorder, and had denied being handicapped in any way.

Clinical Examination: At the time of examination, the involuntary movements were pronounced, consisting of twisting, writhing motions of the hands, head, trunk, and feet, and occasional flailing motions of the arms and legs. These movements reportedly occurred almost constantly except during sleep, were purposeless in nature, and had a very abrupt, jerking quality. The patient's wife reported marked changes in the patient's personality during the past 6 months. On several occasions, he had been belligerent and abusive (verbally and physically) toward her and toward strangers. The wife also reported that

the patient's memory had become much worse recently. Neurological examination revealed no sensory deficits, no abnormalities of the cranial nerves, normal strength and muscle tone, and normal deep tendon reflexes (see the section entitled "Clinical Applications of Spinal Reflexes" in this chapter). CAT scans (computer-assisted tomograms [sectional radiography]) showed no intracranial mass, and the results of the remainder of the physical examination were within normal limits.

Comment: Chronic, progressive chorea (Huntington's disease) is a hereditary disorder; its inheritance pattern is autosomal dominant with complete penetrance, so that half of the children of an afflicted parent will develop the disease. Symptoms usually appear first in the fourth decade, unfortunately when the patient is well past the typical child-bearing years. Denial of the disease is common, even in well-educated people who are aware of the inheritance pattern and the risk of passing on the trait to their children. The disorder usually is rapidly progressive, and, in the later stages, dementia and profound personality changes typically occur, often with episodes of frankly psychotic behavior. Pathologically, neural degenerative changes are seen in the brain, primarily in the cortex and the caudate nucleus.

Outcome: The patient was treated with chlorpromazine, 25 mg, 3 times a day, and haloperidol, 2 mg, 3 times a day. Although these neuroleptic (tranquilizing) agents help to control the involuntary movements, the disease will continue to progress.

and are treated with drugs that tend to *block* excitation in the dopaminergic pathways.

MOTOR CORTEX

The cortical regions traditionally included in the motor system are the precentral gyrus, the

area just anterior to the precentral gyrus (premotor cortex), and the area just anterior to the premotor cortex (frontal eye fields) (Figure 6-6A). However, it is now generally held that, because of the abundance of sensory input to these regions, a clear demarcation between sensory and motor areas must be highly artificial. Nonetheless, the frontal lobe still is com-

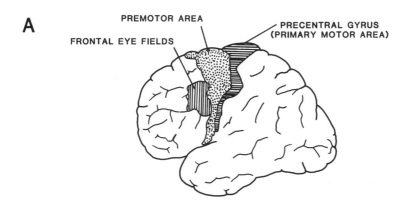

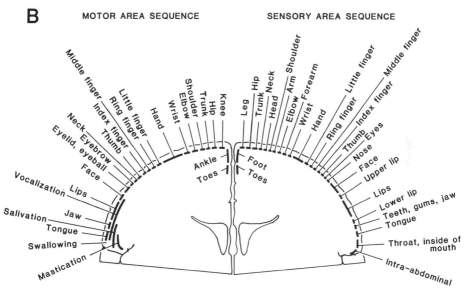

Figure 6-6. **A.** Lateral view of the left cerebral hemisphere showing the location of the primary motor area, premotor area, and frontal eye field. **B.** Frontal section of the cerebrum. Left half, through the precentral gyrus, shows the locations of neurons within the cerebral cortex that control voluntary movement of specific structures. Right half, through the postcentral gyrus, shows the locations of regions of the cerebral cortex that receive sensory nerve impulses from specific body structures.

monly regarded as a motor area, and the parietal lobe is considered sensory in function. It would be more accurate to refer to those regions near the central sulcus as the "sensorimotor" cortex.

Electrical stimulation of one side of the precentral gyrus produces isolated muscular contractions on the opposite side of the body. The cortical representation of motor functions in this region is disproportionate to the area of body served, just as it is for sensory functions in more posterior regions (Figure 6-6B). The degree of cortical representation is greatest in regions that require fine motor control—the hands, fingers, and tongue, for example. Stim-

ulation of the premotor cortex also may elicit movements, but the threshold for response is much higher, and the primary motor area (precentral gyrus) must be present for any response to occur. Thus, the premotor cortex is thought to represent a higher order, or integrative portion, of the motor system. Similarly, the frontal eye fields are believed to constitute a higher-order integrative center for coordinated movements of the eyes.

It is difficult, if not impossible, to identify discrete centers in the motor systems that are responsible for specific functions. It is not known, for example, where the sequence of neural events involved in a "voluntary" motor act begins. Electrodes inserted into various cortical and subcortical regions show that neurons in the basal ganglia can begin to fire before neurons in the primary motor cortex during volitional, or self-cued, movements. It has been suggested that the basal ganglia represent a high-order integrative system that involves attentional mechanisms. However, it is more likely that activity in the basal ganglia preceding activity in the primary motor cortex represents the "planning" of motor action—the preparation of certain motor pathways and muscles for the subsequent movements. The activity in the primary cortex probably represents the actual commands to the peripheral components. The conscious processes (decisions to act) that precede activity in both of these regions cannot be ascribed to a discrete region of the brain but more likely involve vast networks of neurons throughout the cerebrum, the bulk of which may lie in the frontal lobes.

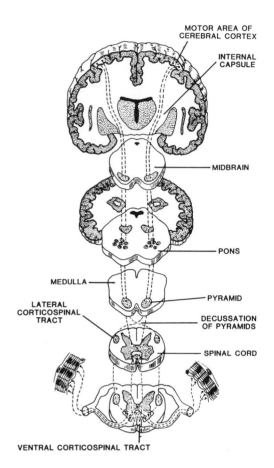

The Corticospinal Tracts

A portion of the fibers that arise from cells in the premotor cortex, precentral gyrus, and postcentral gyrus descend toward the spinal cord, come together in the internal capsule, and form discrete bundles in the upper brainstem. In the medulla these fibers form the pyramids, and at the junction of the medulla and the spinal cord, 80%–90% of these fibers cross the midline (the pyramidal decussation) to form the lateral corticospinal tracts (Figure 6-7). The remaining 10%–20% of the fibers descend on the same side in the ventral corticospinal tracts, not crossing the midline until they reach the level in the spinal cord at which they terminate. The corticospinal tracts primarily excite the lower motoneurons and are responsible for fine movements of the distal extremities. They are referred to commonly as the *pyramidal tracts*.

Figure 6-7. Pathways of the pyramidal tracts (lateral and ventral corticospinal tracts), which carry motor impulses to skeletal muscles.

crossed and uncrossed corticobulbar fibers. The corticobulbar tracts are involved in fine motor control of the head and neck muscles.

The Corticobulbar Tracts

Other fibers that begin in the precentral gyrus descend through the internal capsule to terminate on cranial nerve nuclei within the brainstem. With the exception of that portion of the motor nucleus of cranial nerve VII that is responsible for innervation of the lower facial muscles, which receive only crossed input, the motor nuclei of the cranial nerves receive both

The Corticoreticulospinal Tracts

Fibers of the corticoreticulospinal tracts, which originate in the motor cortex, intermingle with fibers of the corticospinal tracts to the level of the pons. Within the pons and medulla, the fibers course into the reticular formation on the opposite side and terminate on different sets of fibers that have either excitatory or inhibitory effects on the lower motoneurons in the spinal cord.

LESIONS OF THE MOTOR SYSTEM

Cerebral (Upper Motoneuron) Lesions

The most prevalent type of lesion that disrupts the higher motor centers is the cerebrovascular accident (CVA), commonly called a stroke. Such a lesion may be widespread, or it may be limited to a fairly small area (such as the internal capsule), where the density of motor fibers is high; hence, both pyramidal and extrapyramidal fibers usually are affected. Because most of the centers above the medulla have crossed representation, the symptoms appear on the side that is opposite the lesion. The muscles of the arms and legs are affected most and may be weak *(paresis)* or, in more severe disorders, paralyzed. The reflex pathways in the cord are intact; thus, myotatic reflexes still are present. In cerebral lesions, both excitatory and inhibitory influences to lower motoneurons are removed, but the effects of decreased inhibition predominate. The net effect may be exaggerated spinal reflexes (hyperactive stretch reflexes) and clonus (see "Clinical Applications of Spinal Reflexes" earlier in this chapter). Extrapyramidal excitatory influences on the γ-system may be intact, and muscle tone, especially in the antigravity muscles, may be greatly increased. This condition is known as *spasticity.* Abnormal reflexes, such as Babinski's sign, also may be present. Massive bilateral lesions or lesions that effectively transect the upper brainstem cause a marked increase in tone of the extensor muscles, called *decerebrate rigidity.*

Cerebral lesions rarely cause only motor symptoms, although these may be the most dramatic. Depending on the regions involved, sensory symptoms, language disorders, and cognitive deficits may be seen (see Chapter 7). In widespread cerebral disease, especially when the frontal lobes are involved, "regressive reflexes" also may develop. Like Babinski's sign, these reflex responses normally are seen in infants but disappear as the nervous system matures. Examples of regressive reflexes are the *snout reflex,* which consists of puckering or sucking movements of the mouth in response to stimulation of the perioral regions, and the *grasp reflex,* which consists of involuntary closure of the hand around an object drawn across the palmar surface. These reflexes also are called *release signs,* presumably because normal inhibitory influences have been removed.

Spinal Cord (Lower Motoneuron) Lesions

Because most of the corticospinal fibers cross at the junction of the medulla and the spinal cord, most of the motor symptoms that accompany unilateral spinal cord damage are seen on the same side as the lesion. Depending on which tracts are affected, myotatic reflexes may be either diminished or exaggerated, and abnormal reflexes (for example, Babinski's sign) may or may not be present. The level and extent of the lesion can be determined by correlating sensory and motor symptoms. The following findings accompany some classic lesions of the spinal cord.

Complete Transection of the Spinal Cord

If the spinal cord is transected above C4, the victim does not survive, because the pathways involved in spontaneous respiration have been interrupted. The symptoms that follow sudden transection below this level vary with time. Initially, all reflex activity is markedly suppressed, voluntary muscle control is gone, muscle tone is lacking (flaccid paralysis), all sensation is lost below the level of the lesion, and rectal and bladder reflexes are missing; this period of "spinal shock" may last for several weeks. The mechanisms that underlie this total disruption of spinal cord function are not well understood. After the initial phase, the myotatic reflexes begin to reappear; the reflexes that involve the distal muscles return first. Gradually, the visceral reflexes also reappear. With time, the myotatic reflexes become hyperactive and may produce *spasms* (sustained contractions) of the limb muscles—the flexors are affected first, followed by the extensors. If the transection occurred in the lower cervical or upper thoracic region, sexual reflexes return and, in the male, erection and ejaculation in response to cutaneous stimulation still are possible. The intense sensations of orgasm are not felt under these conditions, but patients who have high spinal cord lesions report that pleasant sensations accompany ejaculation.

CLINICAL CORRELATION
6.2   Multiple Sclerosis

CASE REPORT

The Patient: A 30-year-old woman.

Principal Complaint: Blurred vision in the left eye.

History: The patient reported the relatively rapid onset of blurring of vision in the left eye that had begun 3 weeks earlier. She recalled a similar episode that lasted for only a few days about 5 years earlier. She also recalled experiencing transient weakness of both legs once during the past 5 years, and several episodes of transient paresthesia (abnormal sensations) of similar duration that consisted primarily of tingling sensations in the hands and feet.

Clinical Examination: Visual acuity was found to be 20/20 in the right eye and 20/200 in the left. The pupillary light reflexes were normal in the right eye and slightly sluggish in the left. Ocular motility was normal, with no evidence of nystagmus. The pupils of both eyes constricted equally during convergence. Ophthalmoscopic examination revealed the fundi to be normal except for a slight pallor of the optic disk in the left eye. The visual fields were tested with a red test object; the left eye showed a central scotoma, whereas the right eye showed a slightly constricted field.

Comment: At this stage of the diagnostic evaluation, a disorder of the optic nerve was suspected. Various etiologies, including vascular disorders, tumors of the visual pathways or tissue adjacent to them, post-viral neuritis, and toxins, all were considered. The patient's history suggested other symptoms that could be caused by disease of the central nervous system (CNS). The multiplicity and transient nature of these symptoms are typical of a demyelinating disease, multiple sclerosis (MS). This is a relatively common disorder; estimates of its incidence in the United States range from 10–60 cases per 100,000 people. The first symptoms usually occur in the second or third decade of life, with no definite preponderence in either gender. The cause of MS is not known, but the disease is characterized by degeneration of the myelin sheaths of neurons in circumscribed regions of the CNS. The most common symptoms involve neurons in the spinal cord (weakness and parasthesias of upper and/or lower extremities), the cerebellum (ataxic gait, scanning speech, and tremor) and the visual system (blurred vision and double vision). The diagnosis of MS is made primarily by exclusion and is based heavily on the history, which suggests multiple sites of lesions and the occurrence of symptoms. The disease may have an immunological basis: the level of immunoglobulin G (IgG) in the cerebrospinal fluid is increased in most cases of MS. It is not increased in all cases, however, and similar increases in IgG are found in various other CNS disorders.

Treatment: Although many remedies have been tried, only ACTH (adrenocorticotropic hormone, see Chapter 60) has been shown to be effective in clinical trials. ACTH was given intravenously in a dose of 80 U/day (in a 500-ml solution of dextrose and saline) for 3 days, and then 40 U of ACTH gel was given intramuscularly every 12 hours for 7 days. After this initial series, the dose was decreased by 10 U every 3 days for 6 days, then continued at the rate of 20 U intramuscularly every other day for 1 month. Potassium chloride (60 mEq/day) was given to offset the loss of K^+ caused by the cortical steroids (see Chapter 60).

Outcome: The patient's symptoms were relieved temporarily, but the long-term course of the disease is unpredictable.

BROWN–SÉQUARD SYNDROME

After hemisection of the spinal cord (severing all ascending and descending tracts on one side of the midline), a characteristic set of symptoms develops. Below the lesion, spastic paralysis occurs on the same side because the descending pyramidal and extrapyramidal tracts have been interrupted. Damage of ventral horn cells (lower motoneurons) at the site of the transection causes flaccid paralysis at that level on the side of the lesion. Proprioception and stereognosis are lost on the same side below the lesion because the sensory pathways (ascending) do not cross until they reach the medulla (see Chapter 5). Sensations of pain and temperature are lost on the opposite side below the lesion because crossed pathways are disrupted. All tactile sensations may be lost on the same side at the level of the lesion because the dorsal roots are damaged.

CAUDA EQUINA SYNDROME

The spinal nerves that exit from the lower lumbar and sacral cord form a bundle called the *cauda equina* (literally, "horse tail"). Injury to these nerves causes pain or numbness in the lumbosacral region or the legs. Bladder symptoms and impotence also may occur, and, if the lesion is extensive, the legs may be paralyzed.

ANTERIOR SPINAL-ARTERY SYNDROME

Occlusion of the anterior spinal artery affects the ventral portions of the cord, causing partial paralysis (*paraparesis*) and loss of the sensations of pain and temperature but no loss of discriminative touch, vibration, or sense of joint-limb position, which are carried in the dorsal column.

TABES DORSALIS

Invasion of the CNS by syphilitic spirochetes causes the syndrome of *tabes dorsalis,* in which the dorsal columns and dorsal roots of the spinal nerves degenerate. Proprioception is lost, and the gait becomes unsteady (*ataxic*); because of the lack of sensory feedback, the feet slap the ground. To maintain balance, the subject may use visual cues, that is, look at the ground. In the early stages of the disease, irritation of the sensory fibers in the dorsal roots may cause severe pain in the legs and abdominal region. As degeneration continues, the pain subsides.

SYRINGOMYELIA

In syringomyelia, neural tissue in the area immediately surrounding the central canal of the spinal cord degenerates, primarily in the cervical region. Fibers that carry sensations of pain and temperature enter through the dorsal roots, cross the cord just ventral to the canal, and ascend in the lateral spinothalamic tracts. Interruption of these fibers in syringomyelia causes bilateral loss of pain and temperature sensation in the arms and hands; other senses and motor functions are retained because the more lateral tracts are not involved.

STUDY OUTLINE

GENERAL BACKGROUND Study of motor systems as separate from sensory systems artificial but necessary.

CNS is organized in levels of order based on complexity of processing.

SPINAL REFLEXES Stereotyped muscular responses to specific sensory stimuli; not under voluntary control.

MYOTATIC REFLEXES Simplest reflex—only two neurons (monosynaptic), but additional pathways are associated with it.

Example—knee jerk in response to slight stretch of patellar tendon.

Ia afferent fibers from muscle spindle, stimulated by stretch, excite cell bodies of α-motoneurons in cord; quadriceps muscle contracts.

Opposing muscles are relaxed through interneurons in cord.

Input from higher motor centers alters sensitivity of reflexes through muscle spindles and γ-efferent fibers.

POLYSYNAPTIC REFLEXES Three or more neurons are involved.

Example—withdrawal of limb from painful stimulus.

Stimulus causes simultaneous excitation of flexors and inhibition of extensors at several joints.

Synapses are made in cord, where interneurons connect to several segments needed to activate muscles involved.

CLINICAL APPLICATIONS OF SPINAL REFLEXES   Classified as superficial, abnormal, or deep.

Intensity of deep reflexes (e.g., myotatic) is affected by CNS disorders.

Integrity of reflex requires normal pathways and central connections.

Abnormal plantar reflex (Babinski's sign) is associated with damage to motor pathways.

MOTOR FUNCTIONS OF THE BRAINSTEM   Next highest level above spinal reflexes.

All cranial nerves originate in brainstem.

Reticular formation of medulla affects motor function by inhibitory and excitatory outputs through reticulospinal tracts.

Vestibular nuclei contribute to excitatory system through vestibulospinal tracts.

Reflex control of cardiovascular and respiratory system.

Red nuclei receive input from cerebellum, project to other parts of brainstem and to opposite side of spinal cord through rubrospinal tracts.

Corticospinal tracts cross in medulla.

MOTOR FUNCTIONS OF THE CRANIAL NERVES   Oculomotor nerve (CN III) controls most of extrinsic muscles of eye and mediates pupillary constriction in accommodation reflex.

Trochlear nerve (CN IV) controls superior oblique muscle.

Trigeminal nerve (CN V) controls muscles of mastication and some small specialized muscles.

Abducens nerve (CN VI) controls lateral rectus muscle.

Facial nerve (CN VII) controls facial expression through superficial muscles, and closing of eyelids through orbicularis oculi.

Glossopharyngeal nerve (CN IX) helps control production of saliva and action of some striated muscles in pharynx.

Vagus nerve (CN X) functions extensively in thorax and abdomen; controls skeletal muscle in soft palate, larynx, and pharynx.

Spinal accessory nerve controls muscles in neck and shoulders.

Hypoglossal nerve (CN XII) controls skeletal muscles of tongue.

BRAINSTEM REFLEXES   Important optic and acoustic reflexes discussed in Chapter 5.

Eye closure in response to touch of cornea (corneal reflex) mediated through trigeminal and facial nerves.

Bell's palsy—paralysis of facial muscles due to compression of facial nerve at point of exit from skull.

Sensory input of gag reflex through CN IX, motor function through CN X.

CN IX and CN X are involved in carotid sinus reflex.

Sensory input of vomiting reflex by vagus nerve; complex sequence of motor activity controlled through medullary centers.

Neural control of respiration in medulla and pons.

THE CEREBELLUM

FUNCTIONS OF THE CEREBELLUM Processes variety of sensory input, coordinates muscular contractions.

Cerebellar damage produces fragmented, disorganized, clumsy movements—ataxia.

CEREBELLAR PATHWAYS

INPUT   Activity in corticospinal tracts is monitored through corticopontocerebellar tracts.

Input from brainstem nuclei and reticular formation.

Feedback from skeletal muscles through spinocerebellar tracts.

Input from vestibular systems.

OUTPUT   Output to lower motor neurons through midbrain in dentatorubrospinal tracts.

Output to frontal (motor) cortex through thalamus; influences activity in pyramidal tracts.

Output to inhibitory and excitatory centers in descending reticular system.

LESIONS OF THE CEREBELLUM AND ITS PATHWAYS   Because of crossing and recrossing, lesions of cerebellum affect muscles on same side of body.

Ataxia—alterations of gait, posture, and movements.

Dysmetria—inability to measure movements.

Scanning speech—discoordination of muscles of speech.

Dysdiadochokinesia—inability to perform rapid, alternating movements.

Ocular nystagmus—fibers that connect to vestibular system are involved.

Decreased muscle tone and decreased tendon reflexes because of decreased input to γ-efferent fibers.

THE BASAL GANGLIA

FUNCTIONAL ANATOMY   Collection of nuclei deep within upper brainstem and forebrain.

With cerebellum and connecting pathways, form extrapyramidal system.

Major input from sensorimotor cortex, thalamus, and midbrain.

Primary output to midbrain, thalamus, and reticular formation of brainstem.

NORMAL FUNCTION   Disorders suggest involvement in planning and monitoring slow, sustained, complex postural and supportive movements.

DYSFUNCTIONS OF THE BASAL GANGLIA

PARKINSONISM   Tremor at rest, rigidity, slow movement, loss of dexterity.

Loss of dopaminergic neurons alters balance with cholinergic neurons—treated by augmenting dopaminergic pathways or suppressing cholinergic pathways.

HUNTINGTON'S CHOREA   Hereditary disease not manifest until adulthood.

Abrupt, jerky, involuntary movements.

Marked mental deterioration; death usually within 15 years of onset of symptoms.

Treated by blocking dopaminergic pathways.

MOTOR CORTEX   Precentral gyrus, premotor cortex, and frontal eye fields.

Not purely motor areas—because of large sensory input, really sensorimotor cortex.

Precentral gyrus is primary motor area; topical representation of body on opposite side.

Some areas are represented much more than others—for example, hands, fingers, and tongue, which require fine control, have much more cortical space than body trunk does.

Premotor cortex and frontal eye fields are higher integrative centers for coordinated movements.

Basal ganglia are involved in muscle activity associated with primary movement.

"Decision to act" cannot be ascribed to discrete region of brain—probably involves networks of neurons throughout cerebrum, perhaps most in frontal lobes.

THE CORTICOSPINAL TRACTS   Formed by fibers from cells in sensorimotor cortex that collect in upper brainstem; most cross at junction of medulla and cord, remainder cross in cord at level of termination.

Known commonly as "pyramidal" tracts.

Responsible for fine movements of extremities.

THE CORTICOBULBAR TRACTS   Begin in precentral gyrus and terminate on nuclei of cranial nerves in brainstem.

Nerves to lower facial muscles (CN VII) are crossed entirely; remainder are both crossed and uncrossed.

Mediate fine control of head and neck muscles.

THE CORTICORETICULOSPINAL TRACTS   Intermingle with corticospinal tracts down to pons, then go to reticular formation on opposite side.

Synapse with different fibers that either excite or inhibit lower motoneurons (spinal cord).

LESIONS OF THE MOTOR SYSTEM

CEREBRAL (UPPER MOTONEURON) LESIONS   Cerebrovascular accident (stroke) is most common.

Symptoms usually are on side opposite lesion because most centers above medulla receive crossed input.

Arm and leg muscles are weak or paralyzed, but myotatic reflexes still are present because spinal cord is intact.

Net decreased inhibition of lower motoneurons may cause hyperactive stretch reflexes and clonus.

If extrapyramidal system is intact, muscle tone of antigravity muscles may be increased (spasticity); massive damage may cause "decerebrate rigidity."

Sensory area usually also is involved, producing deficits of sensation, language, and cognition.

With widespread damage, "regressive reflexes" may appear, reflecting loss of normal inhibitory influences.

SPINAL CORD (LOWER MOTONEURON) LESIONS   Motor symptoms usually occur on same side as lesion because most corticospinal fibers cross at junction of medulla and cord.

Effects on reflexes depend on tracts affected.

Level and extent of lesion are determined by combination of symptoms observed and regions affected.

COMPLETE TRANSECTION OF THE CORD   Transection above C4 causes death, because neural respiratory control is interrupted.

For several weeks, reflexes are suppressed, muscles are paralyzed, sensation is lost, rectal and bladder reflexes are absent—"spinal shock."

Reflexes return gradually, may become hyperactive and produce spasms.

If transection is at upper thoracic or lower cervical level, sexual reflexes return.

BROWN–SÉQUARD SYNDROME   All tracts are severed on one side of cord.

Spastic paralysis on same side below lesion.

Flaccid paralysis on same side at level of lesion (damaged ventral horn cells).

Proprioception and stereognosis are lost on same side below lesion (tracts cross higher up).

Pain and temperature sense are lost on opposite side below lesion (crossed pathways are interrupted).

Tactile sensation is lost on same side at level of lesion (damage to dorsal roots).

CAUDA EQUINA SYNDROME   Spinal nerves from lower lumbar and sacral cord are injured.

Pain or numbness in lumbosacral region or legs; paralysis if damage is extensive.

Bladder symptoms and impotence may occur.

ANTERIOR SPINAL-ARTERY SYNDROME   Occlusion of vessel affects ventral parts of cord.

Partial paralysis and loss of pain and temperature sense.

No loss of touch or proprioception because those are carried in dorsal cord.

TABES DORSALIS   Degeneration of dorsal columns and roots caused by syphilis.

Proprioception is lost, gait is unsteady; ataxia.

Visual cues are needed to maintain balance.

Pain in early stages is caused by irritation of sensory fibers in dorsal roots.

SYRINGOMYELIA   Neural tissue around central canal degenerates, particularly in cervical region.

Loss of pain and temperature sense in arms and hands because fibers cross just in front of canal.

Other senses and motor function are not affected—tracts are more lateral.

BIBLIOGRAPHY

Allen, G.I., and Tsukahara, N. 1974. Cerebrocerebellar communication system. *Physiol. Rev.* 54:957.

Asanuma, A. 1975. Recent developments in the study of the columnar arrangement of neurons within the motor cortex. *Physiol. Rev.* 55:143.

Brooks, V.B. (ed.). 1981. *The Nervous System.* In *Handbook of Physiology.* Section 1. Motor Control. Volume II. Baltimore: Williams & Wilkins (American Physiological Society).

Bucy, P.C., and Fulton, J.F. 1933. Ipsilateral representation in the motor and premotor cortex of monkeys. *Brain* 56:318.

Calne, D.B. 1976. Developments in the treatment of parkinsonism. *N. Engl. J. Med.* 295:1433.

Carpenter, M.B. 1976. *Human Neuroanatomy* (7th ed.). Baltimore: Williams & Wilkins.

Darian-Smith, I., Johnson, K., and Goodwin, A. 1979. Posterior parietal cortex: Relations of unit activity to sensorimotor function. *Annu. Rev. Physiol.* 41:141.

Evarts, E.V. 1979. Brain mechanisms of movement. *Sci. Am.* 241(3):164.

Geschwind, N. 1975. The apraxias: Neural mechanisms of disorders of learned movement. *Am. Sci.* 63:188.

Granit, R. 1970. *The Basis of Motor Control.* New York: Academic Press.

Iversen, L.L. 1979. The chemistry of the brain. *Sci. Am.* 241(3):134.

Klawans, H.L.; Moses, H., III; Nausieda, P.A., et al. 1976. Treatment and prognosis of hemiballismus. *N. Engl. J. Med.* 295:1348.

Kostyuk, P.G., and Vasilenko, D. 1979. Spinal interneurons. *Annu. Rev. Physiol.* 41:115.

Liles, S.L., and Davis, G.D. 1969. Interrelation of caudate nucleus and thalamus in alteration of cortically induced movement. *J. Neurophysiol.* 32:564.

Llinás, R. 1974. Motor aspects of cerebellar control. *Physiologist* 17:19.

Massion, J. 1967. The mammalian red nucleus. *Physiol. Rev.* 47:383.

Matthews, P.B.C. 1964. Muscle spindles and their motor control. *Physiol. Rev.* 44:219.

Noback, C.R., and Demarest, R.J. 1969. *The Human Nervous System* (2nd ed.). New York: McGraw-Hill.

Perry, T.L., Hansen, S., and Kloster, M. 1973. Huntington's chorea: Deficiency of γ-aminobutyric acid in brain. *N. Engl. J. Med.* 288:337.

Purpura, D.P. 1976. Physiological organization of the basal ganglia. *Res. Publ. Assoc. Res. Nerv. Ment. Dis.* 55:91.

Renshaw, B. 1940. Activity in the simplest spinal reflex pathways. *J. Neurophysiol.* 3:373.

Skirboll, L.R., Grace, A.A., and Bunney, B.S. 1979. Dopamine auto- and postsynaptic receptors: Electrophysiological evidence for differential sensitivity of dopamine agonists. *Science* 206:80.

Stein, P.S.G. 1978. Motor systems with specific reference to the control of locomotion. *Annu. Rev. Neurosci.* 1:61.

Stein, R.B. 1974. Peripheral control of movement. *Physiol. Rev.* 54:215.

Talbot, R.E., and Humphrey, D.R., Eds. 1979. *Posture and Movement.* New York City: Raven Press.

Taylor, A., and Prochazka, A. 1981. *Muscle Receptors and Movement.* New York City: Oxford Univ. Press.

Trieschmann, R.B. 1979. *Spinal Cord Injuries.* New York City: Pergamon Press.

7

Integrative Systems

CHAPTER CONTENTS

GENERAL BACKGROUND

Mind vs. Brain

Throughout history, humans have sought to define the qualities that distinguish them from other animals. It has become apparent that the differences are primarily in the complexity of the higher-order processes of the brain, especially the processes that are related to linguistic functions and self-awareness. Although there has been some success in teaching rudimentary linguistic skills to chimpanzees, humans remain the only animals in which the study of the physiological and psychological essence of humans is possible. In this chapter, we will examine some of the higher-order processes in the central nervous system that analyze, synthesize, and integrate information from both the internal and external environment.

Localization of Function

The classical approach to the study of brain mechanisms has been to attempt to identify the functions subserved by specific aggregates of cells. Although the site-function approach had been suggested by the early anatomists and theorists, it was not formalized until 1861, when Paul Broca, a French anatomist, reported on the post mortem evaluation of a patient who had suffered from a disturbance of speech for years. Broca identified a lesion in the left frontal region and postulated that this area is specifically involved in the motor aspects of speech. A patient who has a lesion in this area cannot articulate words properly, although the muscles used in speech are not paralyzed, and he or she can understand what others say. Twelve years later, a German psychiatrist, Carl Wernicke, reported other cases in which lesions of the left temporal lobe produced specific losses related to the receptive aspects of speech. A patient who has a lesion in this area cannot understand what others say, although he or she can form and articulate words properly. Thus, lesions in two different areas can interfere with speech or cause aphasia by completely different means.

Organization of Higher Function

The reports by Broca and Wernicke were important because they represented the first scientific evidence for the localization of individual mental faculties to specific regions of the brain, and they suggested functional differences between the two hemispheres of the brain. With the exception of language functions, the search for correlations between specific sites and specific functions has not been rewarding. However, new diagnostic procedures, such as computer-assisted tomography (CAT scan), radioactively labeled glucose, positron-emission tomography (PET scan), and nuclear magnetic resonance (NMR) imaging may free us from the limitations of lesion studies and lend further impetus to the classical site-function approach.

Many neuroscientists reject the notion that distinct centers in the brain are responsible for specific functions. A.R. Luria, a Russian neuropsychologist, has suggested that mental processes depend on complex, interdependent systems composed of multiple sites and pathways. Luria postulated the existence of three basic functional systems in the brain. The first system, which regulates the background arousal state, or tone, of the cortex, consists mainly of the reticular activating system of the brainstem and its thalamocortical pathways. The second system, which receives, encodes, and stores sensory information, consists of the primary auditory, visual, and somatosensory receiving areas of the cortex and the "association" areas that surround them. The third system, which organizes conscious mental activity and "programs" motor output, consists primarily of the frontal lobes but also involves pathways that descend to the brainstem and provide a feedback loop for the regulation of cortical tone. The continuing debate between localizationists and those who embrace a more global, or "systems," theory of brain function is of more than academic interest. If centers are responsible for certain functions, their loss, through vascular disease, trauma, or tumors, should cause permanent impairment of those functions. However, if the brain is organized in a less

rigid, site-specific manner, it may recover some function after injury.

INVESTIGATIVE TECHNIQUES

Some of the techniques that are used to study higher cerebral function, and an overview of some of the topics with which the student should be familiar as they relate to both normal and altered mental functions, are presented here.

Electroencephalogram

The electroencephalogram (EEG), a graphic display of the electrical activity of the brain, popularly termed "brain waves," was first recorded in humans in the 1920s. The EEG is described by the frequency and amplitude of the electrical activity that is recorded from the scalp at any particular time. The frequency of the normal EEG ranges from 1 to 100 Hz, and the amplitude ranges from 5 to more than $100\,\mu v$. These parameters fluctuate continuously, especially during sleep and among different regions of the scalp (Figure 7-1). The dominant frequency in recordings obtained from the posterior portions of the head, that is, those regions that overlie the occipital lobes of the brain, is in the range of 8–11 Hz in a person who is awake but relaxed. This particular form of activity in the EEG, called the α-rhythm, is most prominent when the subject is relaxed, and his or her eyes are closed. Under the same conditions, recordings from the frontal region might contain

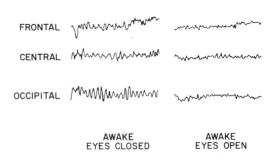

FRONTAL

CENTRAL

OCCIPITAL

AWAKE
EYES CLOSED

AWAKE
EYES OPEN

Figure 7-1.   EEG recorded from different areas of the scalp in an awake adult. When the subject is awake with eyes closed, a prominent, almost sinusoidal rhythm of 10–11 Hz—the α-rhythm—is evident over the occipital areas. When the eyes are opened or the person concentrates on a problem, the α-rhythm disappears and activity of higher frequencies (β) is more prominent.

very little α-rhythm but more activity of higher frequencies.

The activity recorded in the EEG arises primarily from the superficial layers of the cerebral cortex but is influenced by neural pathways from the thalamus and from other cortical regions. Clinically, the EEG is useful in the diagnosis of seizures, destructive and irritative lesions of the brain, and vascular and metabolic disorders that affect the brain. Analysis of the EEG has contributed greatly to our knowledge of the mechanisms of sleep and alterations of consciousness and to the confirmation of "brain death."

Sensory Evoked Potentials

Electrodes like those placed on the scalp to record the EEG also can detect electrical signals generated within the brain in response to various stimuli. These signals are much lower in amplitude than the background EEG and may be classed as either *exogenous* (elicited by external events) or *endogenous* (preceding a motor event or associated with some specific monitoring function of the brain).

A specialized form of computer known as a signal averager is essential to the recording of evoked potentials (EPs). The averager adds and obtains the mean of samples of electrical activity after repeated applications of a stimulus or before a motor event. The background EEG, which is random with respect to the stimulus, tends to cancel itself, whereas the EP, which is the same after each application of the stimulus, continues to add. After a predetermined number of samples has been taken, the summed signal is divided by the number of samples to yield an "average" response.

Sensory EPs are used clinically to identify or document defects of propagation in the auditory, somatosensory, or visual pathways. Potentials evoked by flashes of light or patterned stimuli (visual EPs, or VEPs), for example, often are used to document subtle disorders of the optic nerve. Figure 7-2 shows some VEPs that were recorded from a patient who had a demyelinating disease that affected one of the optic nerves. Propagation time in the visual pathways, as reflected by the latency between the presentation of the stimulus and the response of the occipital cortex, was normal when one eye was stimulated but prolonged when the other eye was stimulated.

Components of sensory EPs that occur after short latency (within about 75 milliseconds of

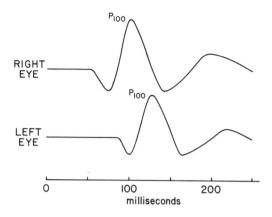

Figure 7-2. Visual evoked potentials (VEPs) in response to a patterned stimulus, recorded from a patient who had a lesion of the left optic nerve. The normal response recorded from the occipital scalp is a major positive wave, labeled above as P_{100}, that has a mean latency of 100 milliseconds. In this patient, the VEP recorded after stimulation of the right eye is normal, whereas the VEP recorded after stimulation of the left eye is delayed by about 25 milliseconds, which indicates a defect of propagation. Each trace represents an average of 256 samples.

the stimulus) generally are thought to represent input to the cortex from thalamic relay nuclei, whereas sensory EPs that occur after longer latency probably represent intracortical circuits or processing by higher-order integrative regions. When sound is the stimulus, EP components of very short latency (1–10 milliseconds) can be recorded after clicks presented through earphones. These components are assumed to arise from prethalamic portions of the auditory pathways, and measurements of these wavelets can be useful in detecting lesions that affect auditory pathways either in the periphery or in the brainstem. This particular type of auditory EP (Figure 7-3) is known as a *brainstem auditory evoked response* (BAER), or *auditory brainstem response* (ABR).

Blood Flow to the Brain

In the normal brain, increased activity in a specific region is associated with increased metabolism by neuronal and glial elements, which requires increased blood flow to that region (see Chapter 16). These factors underlie two relatively new investigative techniques that may help to explain some of the mechanism of "higher" cerebral functions.

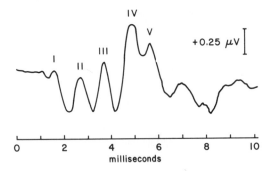

Figure 7-3. Brainstem auditory evoked response (BAER) recorded from a scalp electrode in response to clicks 80 dB above the normal hearing threshold (average response to 2048 clicks). The individual waves I–V arise from progressively higher levels in the auditory pathways. Wave I correlates with the action potential generated within the auditory nerve (cranial nerve VIII), and waves II–V arise from structures within the brainstem.

Blood flow to both gray and white matter of the cerebral hemispheres, the brainstem, and cerebellum may be measured noninvasively by having a subject inhale briefly a chemically inert radioactive gas (xenon). A helmet-shaped unit that contains multiple radiation detectors is placed over the head of the subject, and relative emissions from each region are used to measure the regional cerebral blood flow (rCBF). Specific patterns of change in the rCBF can be elicited in normal subjects either by stimuli or by specific types of mental activity. Counting aloud, for example, is associated with as much as a 40% increase in rCBF in the premotor (midfrontal) regions. Vascular disorders of the brain also affect the rCBF.

Although presently used only in animal research, isotopically labeled glucose is used to assess changes in metabolic activity of discrete cells or cellular aggregates. Labeled glucose is administered, and the relative uptake by cells in different areas of the brain is determined by radioautography. Because this method requires the removal of brain tissue, it holds more promise for investigators in the neurosciences than it does for clinicians.

HIGHER
CEREBRAL FUNCTIONS

Wakefulness and Sleep

Although humans have always been fascinated by the phenomenon of sleep, only during the past 50 years or so has some insight into this biological enigma been achieved. Various studies indicate that sleep is necessary for most vertebrates, but it is not clear what physiological purpose sleep serves. Our ability to recognize sleep in humans or animals and to distinguish its various stages depends to a large degree on the EEG.

REM AND SLOW-WAVE SLEEP

All vertebrates experience at least two distinctly different types, or stages, of sleep. In one of these stages the EEG activity resembles that of the alert, waking state and is accompanied by rapid, darting movements of the eyes; this stage has come to be called *rapid eye movement,* or *REM sleep.* The other stage can be referred to as *nonREM,* or *NREM,* sleep; it also commonly is called *slow-wave sleep* because, unlike that of the waking state and REM sleep, the EEG pattern of this stage contains predominantly low-frequency rhythms (Figure 7-4).

REM and slow-wave sleep differ not only in their EEG characteristics; they differ markedly in other ways also. A striking feature of REM sleep is a marked decrease of muscle tone; snoring usually occurs during this stage of sleep because the muscles of the pharynx are relaxed. The skeletal muscles also may twitch during REM sleep, which is consistent with dreaming at these times. Studies have shown that dreams may occur during both slow-wave and REM sleep, but the dreams that occur during REM sleep are usually more vivid, more emotionally charged, and more readily recalled. During slow-wave sleep, the physiological changes suggest a state of decreased activity—urinary output, salivation, lacrimation, intestinal motility, oxygen consumption, and carbon dioxide production all are diminished. Because of decreased sympathetic nervous system activity and increased parasympathetic activity during this stage, heart rate and blood pressure are reduced and the pupils of the eyes may constrict.

STAGES OF SLOW-WAVE SLEEP

In general, the stages of nonREM sleep are classified according to relative amounts of slow and fast EEG activity. Stage 1, which corresponds to a drowsy state, also called *transitional sleep,* is associated with decreased α-activity, increased θ-activity (4–7 Hz), and overall low amplitude of the EEG. Stage 2, a stage of true sleep, is associated with bursts of almost sinusoidal activity at 12–14 Hz ("sleep spindles") recorded from the frontoparietal regions. Some

AWAKE

EOG

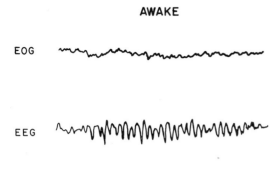

EEG

REM SLEEP

EOG

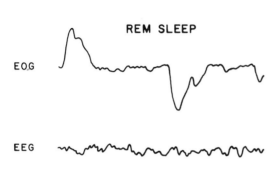

EEG

SLOW-WAVE SLEEP

EOG

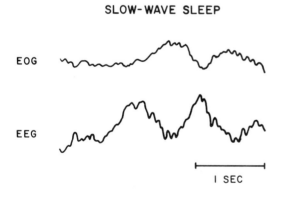

EEG

I SEC

Figure 7-4. The electrooculogram (EOG) and electroencephalogram (EEG) recorded from an awake person, during REM sleep, and during slow-wave sleep.

---

sleep spindles occur in stage 3, on a background of slow (1–2 Hz), high-voltage (Δ) waves. Sleep is of intermediate depth. The deepest nonREM sleep occurs in stage 4. In stage 4, the sleep spindles disappear, and the amount of high-voltage Δ-activity (1–3 Hz) increases in all regions.

PATTERNS OF SLEEP

The periods of REM sleep are not scattered randomly throughout a night's sleep but tend to

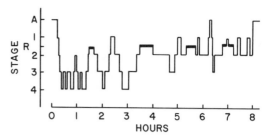

Figure 7-5. Chart of different stages of sleep throughout the night, defined by EEG criteria, showing the typical alternation between REM and slow-wave, or nonREM, sleep and the "cycling" between light and deep levels. A = awake; 1 and 2 = light nonREM sleep; 3 and 4 = deep nonREM sleep; R = REM sleep. The REM periods (*heavy black line*) occur fairly regularly with a periodicity of about 1.5 hours (courtesy of Dr. James D. Frost, Jr.).

---

occur fairly rhythmically at intervals that average about 90 minutes in adults. A typical 8-hour period of sleep is characterized by cyclic alternation between the lighter and the deeper stages of sleep (Figure 7-5).

NEED FOR SLEEP

Many theories have been proposed to explain why one sleeps, but little is known of the physiology underlying this state that characterizes almost one-third of our lives. Much evidence indicates that sleep serves a biological need; for example, evolution has not eradicated it. A person deprived of sleep on one night generally sleeps more the next night, exhibiting the "rebound" phenomenon. If sleep-study subjects are selectively deprived of REM sleep by being awakened whenever they begin to show the EEG characteristics of this stage. they spend a disproportionately large part of the next night's sleep in REM, which suggests a specific need for this subcategory of sleep.

NEUROPHYSIOLOGY OF SLEEP

At one time, sleep was thought to reflect a state of marked reduction in the processing of sensory information, or a state of "deafferentation." However, people who sleepwalk can navigate around objects, climb stairs, and perform other functions perfectly well, while they truly are asleep. Thus, one must conclude that the brain can process information during sleep.

Recent studies with animals suggest that two specific neural centers in the brainstem govern the occurrence of slow-wave and REM sleep.

These two centers not only are anatomically distinct, they also differ in their neurochemical functions. Serotonin, or 5-hydroxytryptamine, appears to be the neurotransmitter that is associated with the slow-wave sleep center, whereas norepinephrine and dopamine (the latter is a chemical precursor of norepinephrine) are implicated in REM sleep. The dopaminergic center may be part of a general arousal system, analogous to the first functional system described by Luria (see "Organization of Higher Function" earlier in this chapter), which fluctuates constantly. When one is awake, these fluctuations cause periodic changes in alertness, and when one is asleep, these fluctuations cause REM.

Disorders of Sleep

NARCOLEPSY

At least three recognized disorders of the sleep-wakefulness system are clinically significant. The most dramatic of these, *narcolepsy,* consists primarily of involuntary "attacks" of sleep that last about 15 minutes and may occur at almost any time during the day. These attacks can cause great embarrassment to the patient who suffers from them and are a genuine hazard for individuals who must drive an automobile or operate machinery. Studies have shown that the pattern of sleep in subjects who have narcolepsy differs significantly from the sleep patterns of normal subjects. Normal subjects do not experience REM until after the first appearance of slow-wave sleep; by contrast, narcoleptics usually begin sleep with REM. The EEG recorded during a daytime attack of narcolepsy also has the appearance of REM sleep. These findings suggest that narcolepsy represents the inability, in the waking state, to inhibit the circuit that is responsible for REM sleep.

INSOMNIA

Insomnia, which consists of difficulty in falling asleep and, usually, frequent awakening, is much more common than narcolepsy. Although many medications are available for individuals who suffer from this disturbance, virtually none of the sedatives and hypnotics produces sleep of normal quality. The proportion of REM and slow-wave sleep and the EEG patterns differ from those of normal sleep. The length of a "normal" night's sleep varies considerably among individuals; some people habitually sleep as little as 4 hours per night, and other people routinely sleep more than 9 hours. The reasons for these differences are unknown.

HYPERSOMNIA

Some individuals suffer from a disorder called hypersomnia; their sleep cycles and EEG patterns are normal, but these people may sleep as many as 15 hours or more per day.

Consciousness and Unconsciousness

The continuum of wakefulness-sleep is similar to the continuum of consciousness-unconsciousness. However, unlike sleep, which is defined best electrographically and reflects the functional state of higher cerebral centers, unconsciousness is determined behaviorally. Rating scales describe the relative level of consciousness of a subject by the response to particular stimuli and by the amount and kind of spontaneous activity that is displayed by the subject. Obviously, such measures depend on the integrity of the motor systems.

Learning and Memory

ELEMENTS OF THE LEARNING PROCESS

Although the learning process has been studied intensively, little is known about the neurophysiological mechanisms that underlie the storage and retrieval of information. Most investigators agree that learning is a multistage process that includes the encoding of sensory information, placement of this encoded information into short-term storage, and ultimately, consolidation of this information into long-term storage. A system for the retrieval of stored information also must exist.

NEURAL SUBSTRATES

Animal studies in which lesions are produced in various brain sites and observation of patients who have various diseases support some general comments about the processes of storage and retrieval of information. It is clear that information is not stored in any particular site in the brain, but that certain structures and pathways are implicated in the storage process; for example, the limbic and temporal lobes seem to be involved in both the storage and retrieval of information. Lesions involving pathways that connect the temporal lobes and the thalamus, or the thalamus and the inferior portions of the

CLINICAL CORRELATION
7.1   Depression (Pseudodementia)

CASE REPORT

The Patient: A 61-year-old man.

Principal Complaints: Loss of memory and inability to concentrate.

History: The patient had worked as a field engineer for a large construction company for more than 30 years, 25 of which were spent abroad. He has a master's degree in civil engineering. He was placed on long-term disability 2 years before admission because of chronic vertigo caused by a fungal infection of the ear. His wife had died of cancer 1 year earlier. During the past 8 months, the patient had noted a progressive decline in his ability to perform mathematical calculations, became irritable, and had difficulty finding the correct words to express himself. The patient admitted to fairly heavy consumption of alcohol throughout almost all of his adult life. He stated that since his wife's death, his alcohol consumption has increased to a fifth of whiskey every 2 or 3 days. The patient's only relatives were two cousins who lived nearby and visited him frequently.

Clinical Examination: At the time of admission, the patient was disoriented as to time and place, but had good recall of remote events. Slight tremor was evident in both hands. A CAT scan (computer-assisted tomography) revealed no abnormalities of the cerebral anatomy, and an electroencephalogram (EEG) also was within normal limits. The patient's condition improved during the first week of hospitalization. A neuropsychological examination at this time revealed that his short- and long-term memory were normal and his intellectual function was well above average. He was easily distracted, however, and demonstrated some difficulty with finding words. A personality screening inventory showed that he was anxious and depressed. The absence of specific neurological and cognitive deficits, specifically those related to memory; the normal laboratory findings; and his improvement while in the hospital argued against a degenerative neurological disorder. It was concluded that the patient's major complaints at the time of admission were due primarily to the acute effects of alcohol and secondarily to an underlying psychiatric disorder (depression). An interview with a family member revealed that the patient consumed at least twice as much alcohol as he had stated, and that his drinking often was binge-like.

Comment: The reduction in motivation and attentiveness associated with depression can produce many of the symptoms of organic brain syndromes. Unlike true dementias, however, the cognitive changes associated with depression generally have a definite onset and either do not progress, or progress unevenly. Although short-term memory always is impaired in the organic dementias, it usually is not found to be impaired in depression, when formal testing is employed. Another distinguishing feature is the degree of distress reported by the patient; depressed patients usually are very aware of their symptoms and are concerned by them, whereas patients who have organic dementia, especially individuals in the later stages of the disease, are unaware of their deficits and express little concern. When a history of long-term alcohol abuse is obtained, chronic alcoholic dementia (Korsakoff's syndrome) also must be considered. The main symptom of this disorder is a loss of short-term memory; this loss is due to pathological changes in the dorsomedial thalamus and its connections with the frontal and temporal lobes. In the case presented here, it is likely that true organic symptoms will develop if the patient continues to abuse alcohol, although at the time of testing there was no concrete evidence of organic change.

Outcome: The patient was discharged with the advice to seek counseling for his anxiety, depression, and alcoholism.

frontal lobes, can prevent the learning of new material, but material that already has been learned may not be affected.

The consolidation process, or the transfer of information from short-term to long-term storage, seems to be particularly susceptible to disruption. Trauma to the head, electroconvulsive therapy, seizures, and various drugs all can produce *amnesia* (loss of memory) for events that preceded the disruptive incident, presumably by interfering with permanent storage of the memory of the events. If only events that preceded the insult are forgotten, the condition is called *retrograde amnesia*. If the loss of memory extends to events after the incident, it is called *anterograde amnesia*. Depending on the type of insult, the amnesia may last for only a few hours, or it may be permanent.

Regardless of what neural networks are involved in storage and retrieval, at some point, either new synaptic connections are established or previously existing synapses are altered. Changes may include alterations in the protein molecules of the cell membranes, which modify the transfer of information at the junction. Both structural and functional changes probably underlie learning and memory.

The linguistic abilities of humans provide cerebral processing of a higher order, which makes the storage and retrieval of information distinctly different from those processes in lower animals. The use of a language subsystem means that perceptual events can be encoded in symbols, which can be compared quickly with the symbolic notations of other events. This more sophisticated and efficient form of processing depends on the neural networks that subserve language functions, and lesions that affect any portion of this network decrease intellectual performance.

Laterality of Function

Studies of patients who have brain lesions support the view that the language function is subserved by neural structures that reside primarily in only one of the two cerebral hemispheres (usually the left hemisphere). This is especially true for right-handed individuals, in more than 95% of whom the language functions are served by the left hemisphere. Surprisingly, the left hemisphere also controls most language functions in almost two-thirds of left-handed individuals. In some of the remainder, language functions are represented primarily in the right hemisphere, and, in others, it is represented in both hemispheres.

From the observation that language function resides in the left hemisphere in most individuals, and because most individuals are right-handed (a function that is also subserved by the left hemisphere), the concept of a dominant hemisphere evolved. However, this notion is overly simplistic and should not be taken to mean that one hemisphere always assumes an administrative, authoritarian role over the other hemisphere. Some functions are controlled primarily by the right hemisphere, regardless of handedness, so that the term *laterality of function* is more accurate than *dominance*. The functions of each hemisphere that are described below are for right-handed individuals; they may or may not be the same in left-handed individuals.

Functions of the Left Hemisphere

LANGUAGE

Many deficits of language (aphasias) are caused by lesions of the left hemisphere. As is summarized in Figure 7-6, distinct sets of aphasic symptoms correspond to the following four different sites of lesions:

1. The *expressive aphasia* described by Broca is characterized by marked impairment in speech and writing but no difficulty in understanding the speech of others or in reading. This form of aphasia arises from deep lesions, usually vascular, in the left frontal lobe.
2. The *receptive aphasia* described by Wernicke is associated with deficits that are related almost exclusively to the subject's understanding his or her own speech and the speech of others. Because of an inability to monitor his or her own speech adequately, the subject who has a lesion that involves the superior aspect

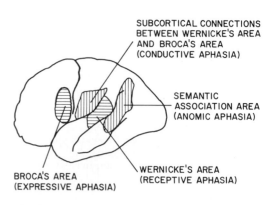

Figure 7-6.   Lesions of the left hemisphere that disturb language.

CLINICAL CORRELATION
7.2 Alzheimer's Disease (Presenile Dementia)

CASE REPORT

The Patient: A 61-year-old woman.

Principal Complaints: Loss of memory and disorientation.

History: The patient was reported by her sister to have shown a progressive decline in her mental capabilities over the past 5 years. Her family had attributed the mental changes to grief after the death of the patient's husband, but the increasing severity of the symptoms prompted them to seek medical evaluation. The family described the patient as very forgetful, and reported that she became confused and disoriented in places other than her home and the small food market that she and her husband had owned for years. The patient was no longer capable of handling the bookkeeping for the market, or of balancing her checkbook, although she had managed the market's finances for more than 30 years.

Clinical Examination: The patient was aware of her problems with memory and appeared concerned about the changes in her mental abilities. During an interview, she could not correctly state the current month, and although she correctly named the current president of the United States, she could not remember who preceded him. She had no difficulty with language, either receptive or expressive, no weakness of arms or legs, and no sensory deficits. Her gait was normal, and no abnormal movements were observed. Neuropsychological testing revealed a profound deficit in short-term memory, impaired visuospatial skills (manifested by the inability to duplicate three-dimensional constructions with blocks), and mild psychomotor slowing (decreased reaction time, decreased rate of finger-tapping). A standard adult-intelligence-test revealed that the patient's IQ was approximately 20 points lower than would be predicted by her performance in high school and her vocational history. Pertinent laboratory findings included a CAT scan consistent with mild, diffuse cerebral atrophy, an electroencephalogram (EEG) diffusely slow, with no focal abnormality, normal thyroid function tests, and a normal electrocardiogram (ECG) and blood pressure.

Comment: Clinically, dementia refers to a generalized diminution of mental abilities that consists mainly of memory loss, confusion and/or disorientation, personality changes, and generally slowed "mental processing." The term *dementia* usually is reserved for an irreversible condition; similar cognitive changes caused by reversible processes (such as drug effects, toxins, or hypoxia) are referred to as *delirium*.

Dementia can be caused by brain tumors, vascular disease, nutritional deficits, or hydrocephalus, and can accompany many specific neurological degenerative diseases. The most common cause, however, which accounts for about 40% of geriatric patients who have dementia, is Alzheimer's disease. Some of the pathological changes of Alzheimer's disease are found in normal, elderly individuals, but to a much lesser extent; hence, the disorder is generally thought to reflect an acceleration of the normal aging process of the cerebrum. Alzheimer's disease is not associated with arteriosclerosis. If the first symptoms arise after the age of 65 years, the disorder is called "senile dementia, Alzheimer type," although the distinction is arbitrary.

The diagnosis of Alzheimer's disease, except at autopsy, is made by exclusion, especially in the early stages. Other causes, especially those that are treatable, must be considered first. In the early stages, the dementia of Alzheimer's disease is almost indistinguishable from that of other disorders that have organic bases and from the dementia that is associated with depression (pseudodementia).

Outcome: Although there is no known effective treatment for Alzheimer's disease, the patient was given diazepam (valium), 2 mg, twice a day, to make her and her family more comfortable. Because of the progressive nature of the disorder, this patient probably will have to be placed in a special-care facility when the disease becomes more advanced.

of the left temporal lobe may have grossly disturbed speech. If the lesion is severe enough, the subject's speech may be almost unintelligible; however, he or she has no problem with articulation and the speech is fluent.

3. Lesions in the subcortical pathways that connect the areas described by Wernicke and Broca cause a *conductive aphasia*. Patients who have this disorder can understand what they hear and can speak fluently with no disturbances of articulation, but they have marked difficulty repeating words that are spoken to them. Unlike individuals who have receptive aphasia, however, patients with conductive aphasia are aware of their speech defects and attempt repeatedly to correct their verbal errors.

4. Another type of aphasia, characterized by a difficulty in naming objects, colors, and other qualities and elements, is called *anomic aphasia*. Although anomia may be caused by relatively small lesions near the junction of the temporal lobe and the occipital lobe, it also may occur after injury to almost any region of the brain. In "pure" anomia, other aspects of speech are relatively unaffected.

OTHER SYMBOLIC FUNCTIONS

Symbolic functions other than language also reside primarily in the left hemisphere. Lesions in this side of the brain can cause deficits in mathematical ability, called *acalculias*. For example, a patient who has this disorder might recognize the signs for addition, subtraction, multiplication, and division and be able to name them but be unable to use them, because their symbolic meanings have been lost.

SENSORIMOTOR FUNCTION

Although sensorimotor functions are considered in Chapters 5 and 6, it is appropriate to reemphasize here that the left hemisphere receives sensory input primarily from the right side of the body and controls most of the motor functions of the right side of the body.

Functions of
the Right Hemisphere

MUSICAL ABILITY

Although both hemispheres receive auditory input, the ability to appreciate pitch, reproduce musical sounds, appreciate the differences in timbre of different musical instruments, and differentiate and reproduce rhythmic sequences all seem to be properties of the right hemisphere, especially the temporal lobe. Thus, pa-

tients who have expressive aphasia caused by left frontal lesions have great difficulty with spoken language but usually still can sing.

SPATIAL ABILITIES

Tasks that require the perception of spatial relationships among objects, such as reproducing a design composed of blocks, are greatly disrupted by lesions of the right hemisphere, especially lesions that involve the parietal region. Such deficits also can cause acalculia, not through loss of the ability to interpret symbols, but because of an inability to distinguish the relationships among numbers. The number "312," for example, might be perceived as identical to "213" or "123." Similarly, a deficit in the ability to perceive the relationships among different elements can make a person unable to comprehend the meaning of a picture; the individual elements are perceived but cannot be integrated.

SENSORIMOTOR FUNCTION

Somatic sensation from the left side of the body, auditory input from the left ear, and information from the left visual field all go to the right hemisphere. Similarly, motor functions of the left side of the body are controlled by the right hemisphere.

Interhemispheric Transfer

Normally, one is not aware of the different capabilities of the two hemispheres. Pathways that connect the hemispheres, primarily the corpus callosum, transfer information readily from one hemisphere to the other, which makes the relative "talents" of each hemisphere available to both hands or both ears or eyes. Only when special test situations are employed or when pathology is present can differences between the hemispheres be appreciated.

Much of our knowledge about laterality of function comes from studies of patients who have naturally occurring lesions of the commissural pathways or lesions made surgically to control the propagation of epileptic seizures. Dramatic deficits of function caused by such lesions can be localized anatomically with considerable precision. A particular form of *amusia* (loss of musical abilities), for example, can be produced by a lesion of the corpus callosum. In this instance, the ability to read music, sing, distinguish pitch and timbre, and discriminate rhythmic patterns are retained, but the person loses the ability to manipulate a musical instrument with the right hand, although similar use of the left hand is retained. The condition is caused by interruption of the flow of impulses from the right temporal lobe, which is dominant for musical abilities, to the left hemisphere, which is dominant for control of the right hand. A similar type of deficit in writing can accompany a lesion in this location; because both hands are controlled by the left hemisphere, the ability to write with the left hand is lost, but the ability to write with the right hand is retained.

The current concept of hemispheric differences states that in the performance of different tasks or the analysis of specific types of information, one hemisphere or the other may be better adapted and "dominant" for the task. However, this does not mean that language, for example, depends totally on structures of the left hemisphere. Although the left hemisphere normally is dominant for language functions, the right hemisphere also contributes and can assume some of the functions of the left hemisphere if that side is disabled. Therefore, normal cerebral function is seen as an interplay of the two hemispheres, with one hemisphere playing a major role in linguistic, analytical, and intellectual functions, and the other hemisphere being involved principally in more aesthetic activities.

STUDY OUTLINE

GENERAL BACKGROUND

MIND VS. BRAIN   Human brain is characterized by complexity of higher-order processes.

LOCALIZATION OF FUNCTION   Attempts to identify functions subserved by specific groups of cells.

Broca's area—motor aspects of speech.
Wernicke's area—understanding speech.

ORGANIZATION OF HIGHER FUNCTION   Three systems.

Background arousal of cortex—reticular activating system of brainstem and thalamocortical pathways.

Receiving, encoding, and storing information—primary sensory receiving areas and association areas of cortex.

Conscious mental activity and motor output—frontal lobes and feedback loop to brainstem.

INVESTIGATIVE TECHNIQUES

ELECTROENCEPHALOGRAM   Record of electrical activity of brain recorded from scalp.

SENSORY EVOKED POTENTIALS   Responses of brain to stimuli; obtained from EEG by signal averaging.

BLOOD FLOW OF BRAIN   Local increases of blood flow are related to increases of metabolism elicited by stimuli.

HIGHER CEREBRAL FUNCTIONS

WAKEFULNESS AND SLEEP   Mostly studied by EEG.

REM AND SLOW-WAVE SLEEP   REM (rapid eye movement) sleep—physiological characteristics like those of wakefulness.

Slow-wave sleep—physiological changes typical of resting organism.

STAGES OF SLOW-WAVE SLEEP   Classified by EEG activity.

Stage 1—drowsy state; decreased α-activity, increased θ-activity, and low amplitude.

Stage 2—true sleep; bursts of nearly sinusoidal activity ("sleep spindles").

Stages 3 and 4—deepest nonREM sleep; in stage 4, sleep spindles disappear and Δ-activity increases.

PATTERNS OF SLEEP   Rhythmic alternation between light and deep stages.

NEED FOR SLEEP   Need exists but basis is not known.

REM sleep specifically seems needed.

NEUROPHYSIOLOGY OF SLEEP   Sleepwalking indicates brain functions while asleep.

Brainstem center is associated with slow-wave sleep; serotonin is transmitter.

Dopaminergic center is associated with REM sleep; may be part of fluctuating arousal system.

DISORDERS OF SLEEP

NARCOLEPSY   Involuntary periods of sleep during normal waking hours.

INSOMNIA   Difficulty going to sleep or remaining asleep.

HYPERSOMNIA   Excessive need for sleep.

CONSCIOUSNESS AND UNCONSCIOUSNESS   Similar to, but may not correlate with, wakefulness and sleep.

LEARNING AND MEMORY

ELEMENTS OF THE LEARNING PRO-CESS   Must include encoding, storage, and retrieval of information, but mechanism is not known.

NEURAL SUBSTRATES   Information is not stored at discrete sites, but structures and pathways in limbic and temporal lobes are involved.

Transfer from short-term to long-term storage is particularly susceptible to disruption—amnesia.

Synaptic connections are established or modified; proteins of membranes may be altered.

Use of language system (symbols) by humans greatly increases intellectual function.

LATERALITY OF FUNCTION   Left hemisphere controls language in most people, regardless of "handedness."

Particular function is controlled by one hemisphere or other, but neither hemisphere is entirely dominant.

FUNCTIONS OF LEFT HEMISPHERE

LANGUAGE   Deficits (aphasias) are caused by lesions of left hemisphere.

Impaired speech and writing, but can understand speech of others and read—deep lesions in left frontal lobe (Broca).

Impaired understanding of speech, including one's own—superior left temporal lobe (Wernicke).

Subject has difficulty repeating words spo-ken to him—subcortical lesion in pathways connecting areas described by Broca and Wernicke.

Difficulty in naming objects, colors, and so on (anomia)—small lesions near junction of temporal and occipital lobes, or in other regions.

OTHER SYMBOLIC FUNCTIONS   In left hemisphere in most people, regardless of "handedness"—e.g., mathematical ability.

SENSORIMOTOR FUNCTIONS   Primarily involves right side of body.

FUNCTIONS OF RIGHT HEMISPHERE

MUSICAL ABILITY   Subject who has aphasia because of a lesion in left frontal lobe still can sing.

SPATIAL ABILITIES   Subject who has lesion cannot reproduce designs or patterns.

SENSORIMOTOR FUNCTION   Primarily involves left side of body.

INTERHEMISPHERIC TRANSFER   Special capabilities controlled by either hemisphere normally are available to both sides of body.

Lesion of connecting tracts causes loss of special capability of one hemisphere by other side of body.

Specificities of hemispheres are not absolute, but left hemisphere normally is dominant in language and analytical and intellectual functions; right hemisphere is dominant in aesthetic activities.

Normal function reflects interplay of both hemispheres.

BIBLIOGRAPHY

Benson, D.F. 1979. *Aphasia, Alexia, and Agraphia.* Edinburgh: Churchill-Livingstone.

Bentley, D. 1978. Neural control of behavior. *Annu. Rev. Neurosci.* 1:35.

Buser, P. 1978. Higher function of the nervous system. *Annu. Rev. Physiol.* 38:217.

Cartwright, R.D. 1978. *A Primer on Sleep and Dreaming.* Reading, Massachusetts: Addison-Wesley.

Cotman, C.W., and McGaugh, J.L. 1979. *Behavioral Neuroscience.* New York: Academic Press.

Dimond, S.J. 1980. *Neuropsychology: A Textbook of Systems and Psychological Functions of the Human Brain.* Boston: Butterworths.

Dimond, S.J., and Blizard, D.A. 1977. Evolution and lateralization of the brain. *Ann. N.Y. Acad. Sci.* 299:1.

Fodor, J.A. 1981. The mind-body problem. *Sci. Am.* 244(1):114.

Gazzaniga, M.D. 1967. The split brain in man. *Sci. Am.* 217:24.

Geschwind, N. 1975. The apraxias: Neural mechanisms of disorders of learned movement. *Am. Sci.* 63:188.

Geschwind, N. 1979. Specialization of the human brain. *Sci. Am.* 241(3):180.

Gillin, J.C.; Mendelson, W.B.; Sitaram, N., et al. 1978. The neuropharmacology of sleep and wakefulness. *Annu. Rev. Pharmacol. Toxicol.* 18:563.

Goodglass, H. 1980. Disorders of naming following brain injury. *Am. Sci.* 68:647.

Gur, R.C.; Gur, R.E.; Obrist, W.D., et al. 1982. Sex and handedness in cerebral blood flow during rest and cognitive activity. *Science* 217:659.

Gur, R.C.; Packer, I.K.; Hungerbuhler, J.P., et al. 1980. Differences in the distribution of gray and white matter in human cerebral hemispheres. *Science* 207:1226.

Herron, J. (ed.). 1979. *Neurophysiology of Left-Handedness.* New York: Academic Press.

Hobson, J.A. 1969a. Sleep: Physiologic aspects. *N. Engl. J. Med.* 281:1343.

Hobson, J.A. 1969b. Sleep: Biochemical aspects. *N. Engl. J. Med.* 281:1468.

Horel, J.A. 1978. The neuroanatomy of amnesia. *Brain* 101:403.

Hubel, D.H. 1979. The brain. *Sci. Am.* 241(3):44.

Jouvet, M. 1967. Neurophysiology of the states of sleep. *Physiol. Rev.* 47:117.

Kety, S. 1979. Disorders of the human brain. *Sci. Am.* 241(3):202.

Kuschinsky, W., and Wahl, M. 1978. Local chemical and neurogenic regulation of cerebral vascular resistance. *Physiol. Rev.* 58:656.

Levinthal, C.F. 1979. *The Physiological Approach in Psychology.* Englewood Cliffs, New Jersey: Prentice-Hall.

Luria, A.R. 1973. *The Working Brain: An Introduction to Neuropsychology.* New York: Basic Books.

Morrison, A.R. 1983. A window on the sleeping brain. *Sci. Am.* 248(4):94.

Moskowitz, B.A. 1978. The acquisition of language. *Sci. Am.* 239:92.

Norrsel, U. 1980. Behavioral studies of the somatosensory system. *Physiol. Rev.* 60:327.

Olton, D.S. 1977. Spatial memory. *Sci. Am.* 236:82.

Pansky, B., and Allen, D.J. 1980. *Review of Neuroscience.* New York: Macmillan.

Peterson, L.R. 1966. Short-term memory. *Sci. Am.* 215:90.

Pribram, K.H. 1969. The neurophysiology of remembering. *Sci. Am.* 220:73.

Regan, D. 1979. Electrical responses evoked from the human brain. *Sci. Am.* 241(6):134.

Russell, I.S., and VanHoff, M.W. (eds.). 1978. *Structure and Function of Cerebral Commissures.* Baltimore: University Park Press.

Schmitt, F.O.; Worden, F.G.; Adelman, G., et al. 1981. *The Organization of the Cerebral Cortex.* Cambridge, Massachusetts: MIT Press.

Schneider, A.M., and Tarshis, B. 1979. *An Introduction to Physiological Psychology.* New York: Random House.

Sperry, R.W. 1974. Lateral specialization in the surgically separated hemisphere. In *The Neurosciences: Third Study Program.* Edited by F.O. Schmitt and F.G. Worden. Cambridge, Massachusetts: MIT Press.

Sperry, R. 1982. Some effects of disconnecting the cerebral hemispheres. *Science.* 217:1223.

8

Autonomic Nervous System

CHAPTER CONTENTS

GENERAL FUNCTIONS

The *autonomic nervous system* (ANS) helps to regulate respiration, circulation, digestion, metabolism and body temperature, the secretions of some endocrine glands, and some reproductive activities. The ANS coordinates a large number of vital body functions in concert with the central nervous system (CNS), from which it is inseparable.

Sympathetic Division

Although it is not essential to life, the sympathetic division of the ANS enhances the physiological reactions to stress. This system has been characterized as preparing the subject for "fight or flight." The sympathetic division of the ANS frequently is involved with the expenditure of energy; hence, it may be thought of as catabolic in nature. The sympathetic division was so named because it was believed to keep the organs aware of one another; that is, to transmit the *sympathies* or "feelings" of the organs.

Parasympathetic Division

As the name implies, the parasympathetic division functions alongside the sympathetic division. The parasympathetic division of the ANS generally is thought of as subserving anabolic and restorative functions, and it is essential for life.

142

GENERAL ORGANIZATION

Functional Classification

AFFERENT FIBERS

The *central nervous system* (CNS), composed of the brain and the spinal cord, interprets and integrates information received through somatic and visceral afferent nerves. The *somatic afferent fibers* are associated with receptors in the body wall and the extremities (e.g., in the skin, the skeletal muscles, the joints, and the bones). These afferent fibers carry information to the CNS about body position and movement and about the external environment. The *visceral afferent fibers* are associated with receptors in the internal organs, the blood vessels, smooth muscle, cardiac muscle, and glands. These afferent fibers transmit information to the CNS about the internal environment of the body (Figure 8-1).

EFFERENT FIBERS

Both somatic and autonomic efferent fibers originate in the CNS. The *somatic efferent fibers* go only to the skeletal muscles; the *autonomic efferent fibers* go to all other tissues of the body.

Functional Anatomy

The ANS is a motor division of the CNS that utilizes both somatic and visceral input. The involuntary control of the ANS made it appear autonomous to early investigators; hence, the name. The major autonomic reflex connections are made in the *medulla*. These reflex connec-

tions involve control of the heart and the blood vessels (cardiovascular control center), and neural control of the secretory and motor functions of the respiratory, gastrointestinal, and genitourinary systems. The *hypothalamus* provides the interface to autonomic, somatic, and endocrine functions. The hypothalamus integrates temperature control and is involved in the maintenance of the internal environment through the ANS and the releasing factors that integrate neural and endocrine regulation. The ANS is not controlled entirely by reflexes, however. The *cerebral cortex* can modify autonomic function, for example, by increasing blood flow to the skeletal muscles in anticipation of voluntary activity, and sexual activity and certain functions of the cardiovascular and gastrointestinal system are influenced by psychological conditioning. Because the ANS innervates smooth muscle, cardiac muscle, and glands, it has been called a *visceral motor system*.

The basic unit of the ANS is a chain of two neurons. The first neuron originates in the CNS and synapses with the second neuron in a *ganglion*, a group of nerve cell bodies that lie outside the CNS (Figure 8-2). The preganglionic axons are usually myelinated, whereas the postganglionic axons are not myelinated.

Many tissues are innervated by both the sympathetic and parasympathetic divisions of the ANS, but some tissues are innervated by only one of the divisions. The ANS may either stimulate or inhibit an effector tissue, depending on the tissue involved and the division that is acting. When an organ is innervated by both systems, the effects usually are opposite, although this is not invariable (see Table 8-2 for examples).

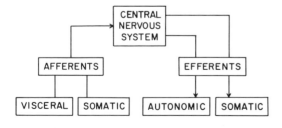

Figure 8-1.   Organization of the nervous system. Although the motor systems are separate anatomically and functionally, each is influenced by afferent activity from both somatic and visceral receptors.

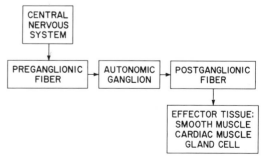

Figure 8-2.   The two-neuron chain of the autonomic nervous system.

SPECIFIC ORGANIZATION

Parasympathetic Division

FUNCTIONAL ANATOMY

The preganglionic neurons of the parasympathetic division of the ANS originate in the cranium and the sacrum. The preganglionic neurons exit through cranial nerves III, VII, IX, and X, and sacral nerves 2, 3, and 4, which join the pelvic nerves. This system is characterized by relatively long preganglionic fibers that synapse with relatively few postganglionic neurons outside the CNS. Most parasympathetic ganglia are located near, on the surface of, or within the effector organ or tissue (Figure 8-3). The structure and organization of this system predispose it to participate in relatively discrete, limited activity.

Chemical Transmission

The process of chemical transmission was discovered in the ANS. The effects of certain chemicals injected into experimental animals were similar to the effects produced by stimulation of the ANS. Eventually, it was shown that the effects of neural excitation are transmitted across the synapse to the effector site by special chemical compounds that are released at the nerve endings.

CHOLINERGIC TRANSMISSION

All preganglionic neurons of the ANS release *acetylcholine* (ACh), which excites the postganglionic neurons (Figure 8-4). The same effect can be produced experimentally by low doses of the alkaloid *nicotine;* hence, the action of ACh at the synapse is called *nicotinic.* All postganglionic neurons of the parasympathetic division transmit excitation to the effector site by also releasing ACh. The alkaloid *muscarine* produces effects similar to the effects of ACh at the parasympathetic effector sites. Thus, the action of ACh at the effector sites is called *muscarinic.*

Because of the effects these alkaloids produce and because certain chemical compounds block transmission specifically, it is thought that ACh reacts with three different receptors (Table 8-1).

ACh is an ester that is formed by the combination of choline and acetic acid (see Figure 8-4) in the terminal portion of the axon. The transmitter is stored in vesicles that are close to

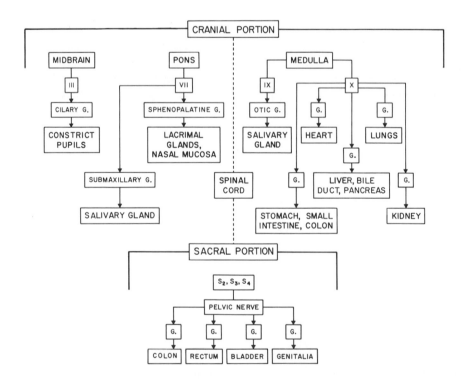

Figure 8-3. The parasympathetic division of the autonomic nervous system. The roman numerals refer to cranial nerves. G = ganglion; S2–4 refer to the sacral segments of the spinal cord.

TABLE 8-1
The sites of action of acetylcholine

Sites	Autonomic nervous system division	Receptor	Specific antagonist
All autonomic ganglia	Sympathetic and parasympathetic	Nicotinic	Tetraethylammonium
All parasympathetic effector sites	Parasympathetic	Muscarinic	Atropine
Sweat glands, blood vessels of skeletal muscle	Sympathetic	Muscarinic	Atropine
Somatic neuromuscular junctions	None	Nicotinic	Curare

or part of the plasma membrane. At the time of release, the vesicles become part of the presynaptic membrane and spill their contents into the synaptic cleft (Figure 8-5).

ACh is inactivated by the enzyme *cholinesterase,* which hydrolyzes ACh to choline and acetate. Inhibition of cholinesterase by specific chemical antagonists permits ACh to accumulate where it is released. Thus, inhibition of cholinesterase increases the magnitude and duration of the effect of ACh.

Sympathetic Division

FUNCTIONAL ANATOMY
The sympathetic division of the ANS is characterized by relatively short *preganglionic fibers* that synapse with a relatively large number of *postganglionic neurons* in ganglia outside the CNS. Sympathetic ganglia generally are not located close to the effector site, and the ratio of postganglionic neurons to preganglionic neurons is 20:1 or more. This arrangement increases the dispersion of the system and provides for massive discharge if that is required. Although the sympathetic division is involved in fine adjustments, it also has the capacity for large-scale responses.

The cell bodies of the *preganglionic neurons* lie in the intermediolateral cells of the spinal column from spinal segments T-1 (thoracic) through L-3 (lumbar). Myelinated fibers pass out of the cord through the ventral roots, leave the spinal nerves in the white rami, and join the paravertebral ganglionic chains (Figure 8-6), which run parallel to the spinal cord on each side, from C-1 (cervical) to S-3 (sacral). Neurons may synapse in the vertebral chain or pass through it and rejoin the spinal nerve through the gray rami. A neuron that synapses in the paravertebral ganglion may do so in the ganglion it enters first, or the neuron may pass up or down the chain before it forms a synapse. Those neurons that do not terminate in the paravertebral ganglia terminate in the prevertebral ganglia.

The neurons that have their cell bodies in the paravertebral chains send their *postganglionic fibers* through the gray rami into the spinal nerves for subsequent distribution to the body. The *prevertebral ganglia*—irregular masses that

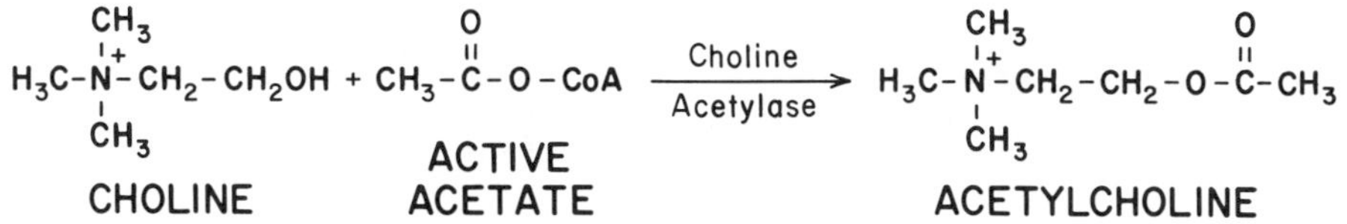

$$CH_3 \quad\quad\quad\quad\quad O$$
$$\underset{\underset{CH_3}{|}}{H_3C-\overset{+}{N}-}CH_2-CH_2OH + CH_3-\overset{O}{\overset{||}{C}}-O-CoA \xrightarrow[\text{Acetylase}]{\text{Choline}} \underset{\underset{CH_3}{|}}{H_3C-\overset{+}{N}-}CH_2-CH_2-O-\overset{O}{\overset{||}{C}}-CH_3$$

CHOLINE   ACTIVE   ACETYLCHOLINE
ACETATE

Figure 8-4.   The synthesis of acetylcholine.

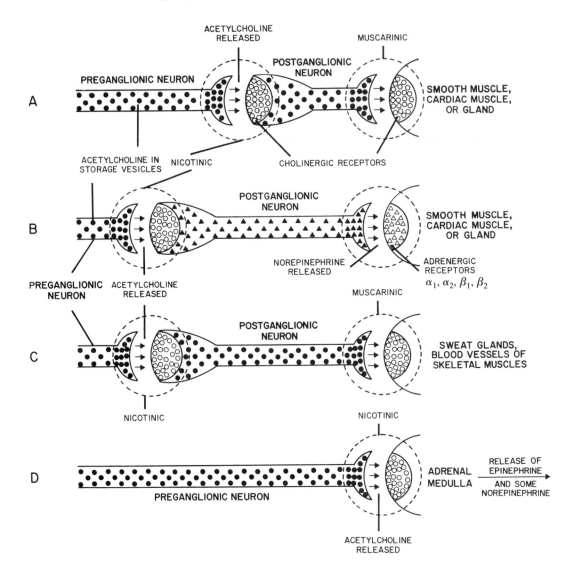

Figure 8-5. Three general arrangements of neurons and effector sites in the autonomic nervous system. **A.** Parasympathetic division. The relatively long preganglionic neuron is cholinergic, and the postsynaptic receptors are nicotinic; the relatively short postganglionic neuron is cholinergic, and the receptors on the effector organ are muscarinic. **B.** Sympathetic division: general. The relatively short preganglionic neuron is cholinergic, and the postsynaptic receptors are nicotinic; the relatively long postganglionic neuron is adrenergic, and the receptors on the effector organ are α_1, α_2, β_1, or β_2. **C.** Sympathetic division: special cases. The preganglionic neuron and the synapse are the same; the postganglionic neuron is cholinergic, and the receptors on the effector organ (sweat glands and blood vessels of the skeletal muscles) are muscarinic. **D.** The innervation of the adrenal medulla. The long preganglionic neuron, which is part of the sympathetic division, is cholinergic, and the receptors on the effector organ are nicotinic. There is no postganglionic neuron; functionally, the adrenal medulla behaves as if it were a postganglionic neuron that releases a large amount of transmitter into the circulation, rather than locally.

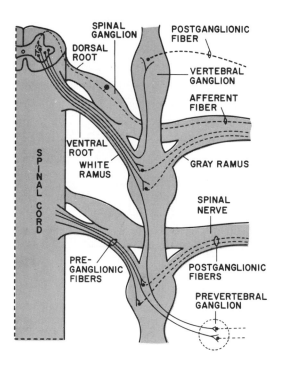

Figure 8-6. The paravertebral chain of ganglia and a prevertebral ganglion of the sympathetic division. See the text for further discussion. (Redrawn, with permission, from Strong, O.S., and Elwyn, A. *Human Neuroanatomy* (3rd ed.). © 1953, The Williams & Wilkins Co., Baltimore)

lie among the viscera in the neural plexuses that surround the aorta—are the celiac, superior mesenteric, aorticorenal, phrenic, and inferior mesenteric. The postganglionic neurons send their axons through visceral nerve trunks to the visceral organs. These fibers are joined by other postganglionic fibers, which originate in the paravertebral ganglia and pass through the prevertebral ganglia but form no junctions there.

CERVICAL GANGLIA

Although no sympathetic fibers leave the spinal cord above T-1, the paravertebral chain extends into the cervical area. This portion contains three cervical ganglia, presumed to have been formed by the fusion of eight ganglia that originally were segmented. The largest of these, the *superior cervical* ganglion, which is situated near vertebrae C-2 and C-3, sends postganglionic fibers up to the head and down to the neck and the upper thorax. The inferior cervical

ganglion, located approximately between C-7 and C-8, often fuses with the first thoracic ganglion to form the *stellate* ganglion, which sends postganglionic fibers to the heart. The middle cervical ganglion may lie near vertebra C-6, near the inferior cervical ganglion, or it may not exist. The remaining paravertebral ganglia are arranged segmentally (Figure 8-7).

ADRENERGIC TRANSMISSION

For a long time, physiologists believed that epinephrine was the adrenergic transmitter (Figure 8-8). However, the actions of epinephrine and the sympathetic nervous system were not always the same, and it was necessary to postulate secondary substances, or "sympathins," that were formed by some combination of epinephrine and receptor substances in the effector tissue. Sympathin E (excitatory) and sympathin I (inhibitory) provided early explanations for effects that are explained now by combinations of epinephrine, norepinephrine, and α and β receptors.

In the late 1940s, *norepinephrine*, a demethylated derivative of epinephrine, was found to be the *adrenergic neural transmitter* (Figure 8-9; see also Figure 8-5). Nevertheless, epinephrine is still an important component of sympathetic nervous system activity because it is released from accessory chromaffin tissue in or near certain effector organs, and it constitutes the majority of the catecholamine that is released from the adrenal medulla.

CONTEMPORARY RECEPTOR THEORY

In 1948, about the time that norepinephrine was discovered to be the adrenergic neurotransmitter, Ahlquist proposed that the adrenergic action at effector sites depended on the combination of the transmitter with specific receptors, which were designated α and β.

RECEPTOR SPECIFICITIES

On the basis of later structure-activity studies, the *β receptors* have been divided into β_1 receptors, which mediate increased heart rate and contractility and cause the release of renin from the kidneys, and β_2 receptors, which mediate most or all of the remaining effects that are attributed to β receptors. The α *receptors* also have been subdivided, on the basis of the type

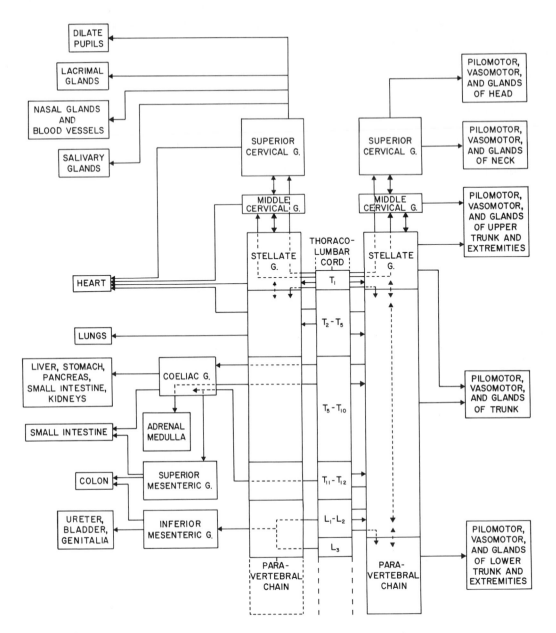

Figure 8-7. The sympathetic division. G = ganglia. The vertical arrows (dashes) in the paravertebral chain indicate that preganglionic axons run up and down from the point of entrance. The system is symmetrical; different information is provided on each side for the sake of clarity.

of action that is produced and the relative effects of specific agonists and antagonists. Most of the α receptors on effector cells belong to the α_1 group. α_2 receptors occur on ganglion cells and nerve terminals and are involved in feedback inhibition of the release of norepinephrine. α_2 receptors also occur on certain effector cells and on the blood platelets. Certain organs, such as the uterus and the brain, appear to contain a mixture of α_1 and α_2 receptors. In most instances, α_1 activity is associated with stimulation, and α_2 activity is associated with inhibition. Epinephrine stimulates all four types of receptors strongly; norepinephrine

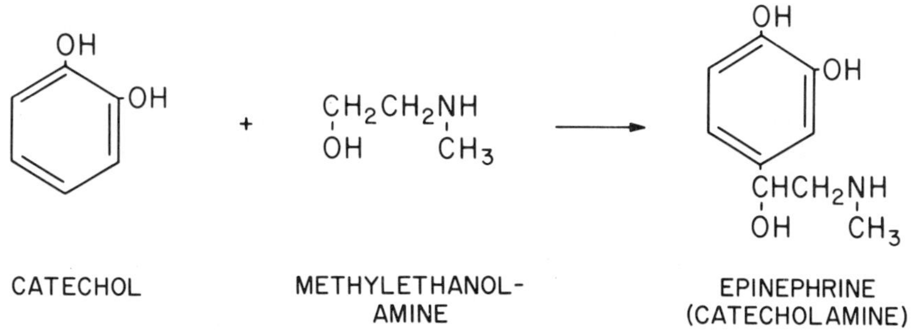

CATECHOL

METHYLETHANOL-AMINE

EPINEPHRINE
(CATECHOLAMINE)

Figure 8-8.   The structural components of epinephrine. (This is not the pathway of synthesis.)

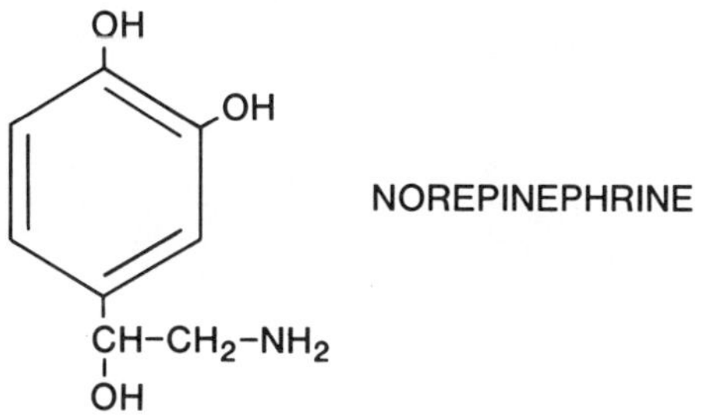

NOREPINEPHRINE

Figure 8-9.   Chemical structure of norepinephrine.

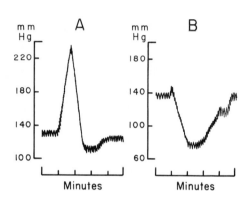

Figure 8-10.   **A.** Biphasic change of arterial blood pressure caused by the injection of a small dose of epinephrine. The initial increase is attributed to vasoconstriction and cardiac stimulation mediated through α receptors and β_1 receptors, respectively. The subsequent decrease of pressure is related to peripheral vasodilatation mediated through β_2-receptors. **B.** Effects of the same dose of epinephrine after the administration of a specific inhibitor of α receptors. This record demonstrates that the effects of β_2 stimulation were masked by the dominant effect of α_1 stimulation.

stimulates all α and β_1 receptors, but it stimulates certain β_2 receptors weakly or not at all. Thus, both epinephrine and norepinephrine stimulate the heart (β_1) and constrict certain blood vessels (α_1), but, of the two, only epinephrine dilates certain blood vessels (β_2). This combination of effects and certain other aspects of adrenergic receptors are illustrated in Figure 8-10.

Receptors initially were thought of as unchanging entities on cell membranes that receive hormonal or drug signals. However, the numbers and properties of the adrenergic receptors are changed, not only by their normal agonists, the *catecholamines,* but also by other hormones such as thyroxine, progesterone, cortisol, and prostaglandins. For instance, some tissues that are exposed continuously to catecholamines become less responsive. At least part of this phenomenon, called *desensitization,* or *tachyphylaxis,* is caused by alterations of receptors. Both α and β adrenergic receptors have been implicated in this kind of event. An example of another hormone affecting adrenergic receptors is provided by the actions of the thyroid hormones on the heart. In hyperthyroidism, the number of β receptors increases, and the heart becomes more sensitive to norepinephrine and epinephrine. In hypothyroidism, the number of β receptors and the sensitivity to sympathetic nervous system activity decrease. Although some results are conflicting, it appears that the number of α receptors in the heart changes reciprocally with the numbers of β receptors—decreasing in hypothyroidism and increasing in hypothyroidism. These results support the hypothesis that α and β receptors are interconvertible.

CLINICAL CORRELATION
8.1   Pheochromocytoma

CASE REPORT

The Patient: A 15-year-old boy.

Principal Complaints: Periodic headache, palpitations, and anxiety.

History: The patient had no medically relevant history aside from his current complaints.

Clinical Examination: The patient was somewhat small for his age, but aside from seeming nervous, appeared well. The arterial pressure at rest was 175/105 mm Hg (normal, 90–140/60–90 mm Hg), the heart rate was 120 beats/minute (normal, < 100 beats/minute), and the body temperature was 37.6 C. A systolic ejection murmur (see the section entitled "Murmurs" in Chapter 13) was heard along the left sternal border. The fasting blood glucose level was 125 mg/dl (normal, 70–110 mg/dl), the plasma epinephrine level was 6.5 μg/l, and the norepinephrine level was 1.1 μg/l (normal epinephrine and norepineph-

rine combined, 0.24 μg/l). In two consecutive 24-hour urine collections, total metanephrines (metabolites of catecholamines) were 63 mg and 56 mg, respectively (normal, 1.3 mg). Radiographs of the chest and the skull were normal, but an abdominal aortograph revealed hypertrophied branches of the left renal artery that supplied a highly vascular tumor, about 3 cm in the largest dimension, on or near the left adrenal gland. Both kidneys appeared normal, and tests for thyroid function were normal.

Treatment: Since the clinical evidence indicated pheochromocytoma (a tumor of the adrenal medulla, or one that functions like adrenal medullary tissue), preparation for surgery was begun. Because of the high renal perfusion pressure, patients who have hypertension caused by excessive release of intrinsic pressor agents, such as the catecholamines, have abnormally low plasma volumes, despite autoregulation. To decrease his arterial pressure and allow his plasma volume to

---

Most, if not all, β effects are mediated by stimulation of adenylate cyclase. Some α_2 effects may be mediated by inhibition of adenylate cyclase, but many α-related effects do not involve the adenylate cyclase system. Certain studies have shown that stimulating adenylate cyclase through β receptors or inhibiting adenylate cyclase through α receptors requires the presence of guanine nucleotides, such as *guanosine triphosphate* (GTP). Stimulation of muscarinic receptors by ACh modulates the GTP regulation; thus, activity of the cholinergic system can directly affect the activity of the adrenergic system in certain instances.

The actions of the transmitters at the sympathetic ganglia and the adrenergic neuroeffector site are modified by negative feedback of norepinephrine, by the actions of circulating epinephrine, and by the muscarinic actions of ACh (Figure 8-11).

Dopamine

Dopamine, the immediate precursor of norepinephrine in the chain of synthesis, differs from norepinephrine only in that it lacks the 1-hydroxy group (Figure 8-12). Dopamine is found in sympathetic nerves and the adrenal medulla and has been identified in areas in which norepinephrine does not occur.

ACTIONS ON THE HEART

Dopamine increases cardiac contractility and heart rate by stimulating β_1 receptors and by releasing norepinephrine from myocardial stores. These actions are blocked by β_1-receptor antagonists.

ACTIONS ON BLOOD VESSELS

In appropriate concentrations, dopamine dilates the renal, mesenteric, coronary, and cere-

increase, the patient initially was given phenoxybenzamine HCl, an adrenergic α-receptor antagonist, 10 mg orally every 12 hours, and the dose was increased gradually until the arterial pressure was near normal (125/80 mm Hg). The heart rate remained high, at 125 beats/minute. Because of the danger of postural hypotension,* the patient was kept in bed most of the time, except for supervised and controlled periods of exercise twice a day. After 9 days, the patient was considered to be ready for surgery. A tumor of the left adrenal gland was found. Examination of a frozen section revealed pheochromocytoma, and the tumor was removed.

Comment: More than half of all pheochromocytomas occur in one of the adrenal glands, and the remainder arise from accessory chromaffin tissue, usually along the aorta or its major branches. Because the adrenal medulla secretes mostly epinephrine, it is not surprising that this tumor also secreted much more epinephrine than norepinephrine. The symptoms relate to the cardiovascular and metabolic effects of epinephrine: the arterial pressure and heart rate are elevated, the metabolic rate is high, body temperature and fasting blood sugar are increased somewhat, sweating is common, and psychic effects—nervousness and anxiety—are apparent. Because of the high metabolic rate, growth may be somewhat retarded, as it was in this patient. The reduction of arterial pressure by phenoxybenzamine reflects the decrease of peripheral resistance after α-receptor antagonism; the persistence of the tachycardia reflects the continued stimulation of B_1 receptors in the heart. Although this patient did not report it, postural hypotension occurs frequently in individuals whose tumors secrete mostly epinephrine. This is attributed to the decreased blood volume and some loss of sympathetic reflex tone. The recurrence of pheochromocytoma in children is rare, and few of the tumors (about 6%) are malignant.

Outcome: The patient's recovery was uneventful. One month after the operation, the resting arterial pressure was 115/70 mm Hg and all symptoms of pheochromocytoma were gone. In a 24-hour urine collection, total metanephrines were 0.6 mg.

*When a subject stands up after he or she has been lying down, the force of gravity tends to cause blood to pool in the veins below the heart. Normally, this is offset by increased vascular tone in the venous system, elicited through the arterial baroreceptors. However, if the adrenergic α-receptors are blocked, reflex venoconstriction is prevented, the cardiac output decreases, and the arterial pressure decreases.

bral arterial beds of the anesthetized dog. These effects are not blocked by conventional β-receptor antagonists, which suggests the presence of dopamine receptors. When sufficiently large doses are given, dopamine causes net vasoconstriction that is blocked by conventional α-receptor antagonists.

PHYSIOLOGICAL ACTIONS

Dopamine is considered to have important effects on the CNS, where it serves as the principal transmitter in the extrapyramidal system. The participation of dopamine in physiological events in the cardiovascular system has not been demonstrated.

CLINICAL USES

Because of its renal and mesenteric vasodilating actions, dopamine has been recommended for selective use in the treatment of shock and cardiac failure that are refractory to digitalis and diuretics. The principal disadvantage is the occurrence of cardiac dysrhythmia.

Release of Stored Norepinephrine

Certain sympathomimetic drugs (e.g., ephedrine) do not interact directly with adrenergic receptors, but rather produce their effects by causing the release of norepinephrine from the sympathetic nerves that supply the effector organ. They produce effects that are similar to the effects of norepinephrine, but the onset is slower and the duration is longer. Tachyphylaxis occurs; that is, successive doses produce smaller effects as the stores of norepinephrine are depleted. Other sympathomimetic drugs

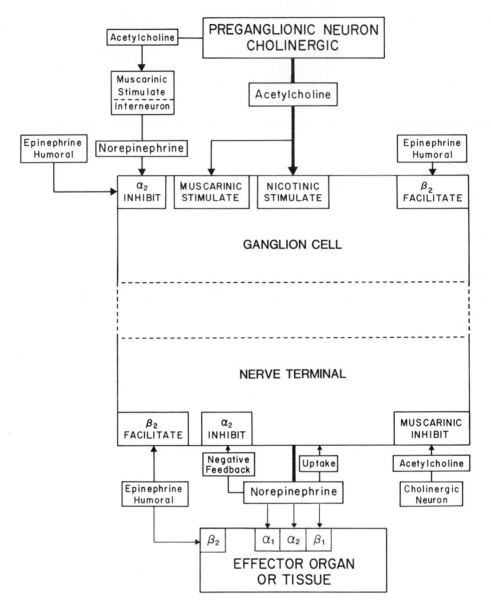

Figure 8-11. Sympathetic postganglionic adrenergic neuron and the adrenergic effector site. The transmitter at the ganglion (nicotinic) is acetylcholine; however, the magnitude of the effect is modified by other influences. Experimental evidence indicates that in many neurons the postganglionic receptor area also contains α_2, β_2, and muscarinic receptors. The α_2-receptors mediate inhibition of excitation of the postganglionic neuron, and the β_2 and muscarinic receptors enhance excitation. Norepinephrine, released by a postulated interneuron, reacts with the α_2-receptors; circulating epinephrine, released by the adrenal medulla, reacts with the α_2-receptors and the β_2 receptors. A branch of the preganglionic cholinergic neuron releases acetylcholine at the site of the muscarinic receptors. The effector organ contains α_1, α_2, β_1 and β_2 receptors, singly or in combination. The postganglionic nerve contains α_2 receptors that inhibit and β_2 receptors that facilitate the release of norepinephrine. Norepinephrine released by excitation of the preganglionic neuron (1) reacts with the receptors on the effector organ, (2) is taken up again by the nerve endings, and (3) reacts with α_2 receptors on the nerve endings. A cholinergic neuron in parallel releases acetylcholine at the site of the muscarinic receptors. Circulating epinephrine reacts with the β_2 receptors. This arrangement modulates and limits the rate of release of norepinephrine at the effector site, primarily by negative-feedback inhibition, but also permits amplification of the sympathetic response through the facilitative action of circulating epinephrine.

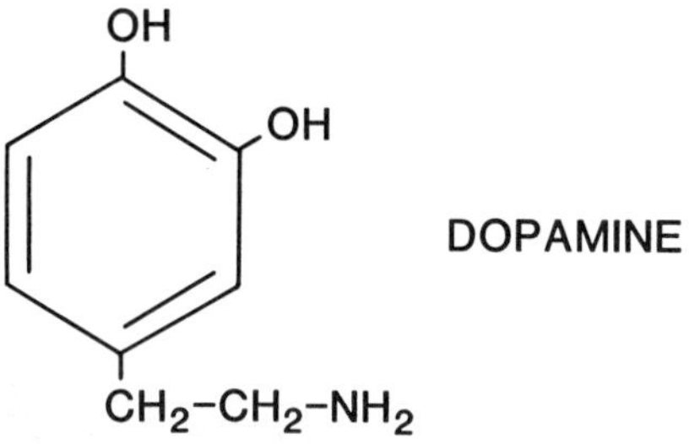

OH

OH

DOPAMINE

$CH_2-CH_2-NH_2$

Figure 8-12. Chemical structure of dopamine.

produce a combined effect that is mediated partly by the release of norepinephrine and partly by interaction with adrenergic receptors.

Denervation Sensitivity

When sympathetic effector organs are denervated, particularly by section of postganglionic neurons, they become unusually sensitive to circulating catecholamines. This phenomenon, called *supersensitivity,* reflects higher concentrations of catecholamine in contact with the receptors, and, possibly, increased numbers of receptors available. In normal function, only a small part of the norepinephrine that is released from the nerve is inactivated enzymatically. Monoamine oxidase (MAO) and catechol-O-methyltransferase (COMT), which are distributed throughout the body, metabolize norepinephrine, but the effect is not significant. Most of the norepinephrine that is liberated physiologically at adrenergic nerve endings is reabsorbed by the nerve. In addition, epinephrine and norepinephrine released from the adrenal medulla or injected into the bloodstream also are taken up by the post-ganglionic neurons. If this process is blocked, or if the nerve degenerates, the principal means of inactivating catecholamine is absent, and more transmitter reaches the postganglionic receptor.

Transmitter-Receptor Interaction

CONCENTRATION-EFFECT CURVE

The physiological effect is determined by the combination of neurotransmitter and receptor; because this is a reversible, equilibrium-seeking reaction, the law of mass action is applied. Thus, the rate of reaction is proportional to the product of the concentrations of the substances that react. The reactants are the transmitter (T) and the receptor (R):

$$T + R \rightleftharpoons TR$$

In a reversible reaction, two reactions proceed simultaneously as follows

$$I: T + R \rightarrow TR$$
$$II: T + R \leftarrow TR$$

At equilibrium, the rate of reaction I, V_1, equals the rate of reaction of II, V_2. Because the rate, V_1 or V_2, is proportional to the product of the concentrations of the reactants,

$$V_1 \simeq [T] \times [R],$$
$$V_2 \simeq [TR],$$
$$V_1 = K_1 \times [T] \times [R],$$
$$V_2 = K_2 \times [TR]$$

Therefore, because

$$V_1 = V_2$$

$$K_1 \times [T] \times [R] = K_2 \times [TR]$$

$$\frac{K_1}{K_2} = \frac{[TR]}{[T][R]}$$

$$\frac{K_1}{K_2} = K_{eq}$$

$$\frac{[TR]}{[T][R]} = K_{eq}$$

At equilibrium, the proportions of all the reactants, T, R, and TR, are related precisely, and any change in one reactant changes all the other reactants. Therefore, the magnitude of the physiological effect is proportional to the concentration of the transmitter that is released and the concentration of the receptor in the effector organ. This relationship is expressed in the concentration-effect curve (Figure 8-13).

ANTAGONISM

The magnitude of the effect is changed if the concentration of receptor available is decreased by the addition of a substance that competes for the receptor.

Let the substance be A

$$\frac{[AR]}{[A][R]} = K_{A_{eq}}$$

If A combines with the receptor but produces no effect, it is an *inhibitor,* or *antagonist.* If the combination is reversible, the substance is a *competitive antagonist.* The combination of the antagonist and the receptor decreases the number of receptors available to the transmitter. If more transmitter is released, it competes

TABLE 8-2
Actions of the autonomic nervous system on various organs and tissues

Effector organ or tissue	Receptor	Adrenergic effect	Cholinergic effect
Eye, iris			
Radial muscle	α	Contraction (mydriasis)	—
Sphincter muscle	α	—	Contraction (miosis)
Eye, ciliary muscle	β_2	Relaxation (slight)	Contraction
Lacrimal glands	—	—	Secretion
Nasopharyngeal glands	—	—	Secretion
Salivary glands	α	Secretion of ions and water	Secretion of ions and water
	β_2	Secretion of amylase	—
Heart			
SA node	β_1	Increase heart rate	Decrease heart rate
Atria	β_1	Increase contractility	Decrease contractility
AV junction	β_1	Increase automaticity and propagation velocity	Decrease automaticity and propagation velocity
Purkinje system	β_1	Increase automaticity and propagation velocity	—
Ventricles	β_1	Increase contractility	—
Arterioles			
Coronary	α, β_2	Constriction, dilatation	—
Skin	α, β_2	Constriction, dilatation	—
Mucosa	α	Constriction	—
Skeletal muscle	α, β_2	Constriction, dilatation	Dilatation
Cerebral	α	Constriction (slight)	—
Pulmonary	α, β_2	Constriction, dilatation	—
Mesenteric	α	Constriction	—
Renal	α, D*	Constriction, dilatation	—
Salivary glands	α	Constriction	Dilatation
Veins, systemic	α, β_2	Constriction, dilatation	—
Lung			
Bronchial muscle	β_2	Relaxation	Contraction
Bronchial glands	—	Inhibition (?)	Stimulation
Stomach			
Motility	β_2	Decrease	Increase
Sphincters	α	Contraction	Relaxation
Secretion	—	Inhibition (?)	Stimulation
Liver	β_2	Glycogenolysis	—
	α, β_2	Kalemotropic action	—
Gallbladder and ducts	—	Relaxation	Contraction
Pancreas			
Acini	α	Decreased secretion	Secretion
Islet cells	α, β_2	Decreased secretion, increased secretion	—
Intestine			
Motility	α_2, β_2	Decrease	Increase
Sphincters	α	Contraction	Relaxation
Secretion	—	Inhibition (?)	Stimulation
Adrenal medulla	—	—	Secretion of epinephrine and norepinephrine
Kidney	β_1	Secretion of renin	—
Ureter			
Motility	α	Increased	Increased *(Table continues)*

Effector organ or tissue	Receptor	Adrenergic effect	Cholinergic effect
Urinary bladder			
Detrusor	β_2	Relaxation	Contraction
Trigone and sphincter	α	Contraction	Relaxation
Sex organs, male	α	Ejaculation	Erection
Skin			
Pilomotor muscles	α	Contraction	—
Sweat glands	α	Localized secretion	Generalized secretion
Fat cells	α, β_2	Lipolysis	—
Pineal gland	β_2	Melatonin synthesis	—

*D = dopaminergic.

with the antagonist for the receptors, and the magnitude of the effect increases. Four reactions now are involved in the equilibrium.

$$\text{I. } T + R \rightarrow TR$$
$$\text{II. } T + R \leftarrow TR$$
$$\text{III. } A + R \rightarrow AR$$
$$\text{IV. } A + R \leftarrow AR$$

If the concentration of T increases, reaction I ($T + R \rightarrow TR$) increases, and the amount of R that is available for reaction III ($A + R \rightarrow AR$) decreases. The influence of the antagonist on the physiological effect is illustrated in Figure 8-14.

Atropine, tetraethylammonium, and *curare* antagonize ACh competitively (Table 8-1). *Propranolol* is a competitive antagonist of adrenergic β-receptors, and *phentolamine* is a competitive antagonist of adrenergic α-receptors. Relatively specific antagonists of β_1 and β_2 receptors also have been developed. The effectiveness of an antagonist depends on the affinity of the antagonist for the receptor relative to the affinity of the transmitter for the receptor.

ACTIONS OF THE AUTONOMIC NERVOUS SYSTEM ON VARIOUS ORGANS AND TISSUES

The actions of the autonomic nervous system on particular organs and systems are discussed in the appropriate chapters. Table 8-2 provides a summary of those actions.

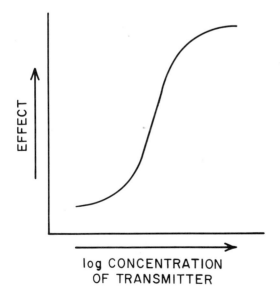

Figure 8-13.   The concentration-effect curve.

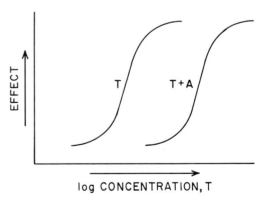

Figure 8-14. Displacement of the concentration-effect curve of a transmitter (T) by a competitive antagonist (T + A). Although the action of the transmitter at lower concentration is inhibited completely by the antagonist, full effect of the transmitter can be obtained, despite presence of the antagonist, if concentration is increased enough.

STUDY OUTLINE

GENERAL FUNCTIONS   Helps to regulate and coordinate most involuntary functions.

SYMPATHETIC   DIVISION   Enhances physiological reactions to stress.
  Energy-using, catabolic.
  Not essential for life.

PARASYMPATHETIC DIVISION   Restorative, anabolic.
  Essential for life.

GENERAL ORGANIZATION

FUNCTIONAL CLASSIFICATION

AFFERENT FIBERS   CNS receives information from both somatic and visceral afferent fibers.
  Somatic afferent fibers from body walls and extremities; information about body position and movement and external environment.
  Visceral afferent fibers from internal organs and tissues; information about internal environment.

EFFERENT FIBERS   Originate in CNS; somatic to skeletal muscles, autonomic to all other tissues.

FUNCTIONAL ANATOMY   Motor division of CNS; innervates involuntary organs, glands.
  Both somatic and visceral input.
  Reflex control.
  Major reflex connections are in medulla.
  Hypothalamus interfaces to autonomic, somatic, and endocrine functions.
  Cerebral cortex influences some autonomic functions.
  Two-neuron chain; synapse outside CNS.
  Preganglionic fiber is myelinated, postganglionic is not myelinated.

SPECIFIC ORGANIZATION

PARASYMPATHETIC DIVISION

FUNCTIONAL ANATOMY   Relatively short cranium and sacrum, exit through cranial nerves III, VII, IX, X, and sacral nerves 2–4.
  Relatively long preganglionic fibers; synapse with relatively few postganglionic neurons.
  Most ganglia are located on or near effector organ or tissue.
  Relatively discrete, limited activity.

CHEMICAL   TRANSMISSION   Discovered in ANS.
  Specific chemical compounds released by nerves at receptor sites transmit effects to organ or tissue.

CHOLINERGIC TRANSMISSION   All preganglionic neurons of ANS release acetylcholine (ACh); excites postganglionic neuron (nicotinic).
  All postganglionic neurons of parasympathetic division release ACh; excites effector organ or tissue (muscarinic).
  ACh is released by somatic motor nerves; excites skeletal muscle at neuromuscular junction (nicotinic).
  Three different blockers act specifically at cholinergic sites; ACh reacts with three different receptors.
  ACh is formed in nerve ending, inactivated by enzyme cholinesterase.
  Inhibition of cholinesterase prolongs magnitude and duration of ACh action.

SYMPATHETIC DIVISION

FUNCTIONAL ANATOMY   Relatively short preganglionic neurons synapse with relatively large number of postganglionic neurons.
  Ganglia are not located close to effector sites.
  Both discrete and widespread effects can be produced.
  Cell bodies in thoracic and lumbar spinal segments; preganglionic fibers exit in spinal nerves.
  Paravertebral ganglia are parallel to spinal cord, connected vertically; prevertebral ganglia among viscera.

CERVICAL GANGLIA   Formed by fusion of individual cervical ganglia.
  No preganglionic fibers in cervical neurons, but paravertebral ganglia extend above T-1.
  Superior cervical ganglion, level of C2–3; largest, supplies head, neck, and upper thorax.
  Middle cervical, near C-6; may be absent.
  Inferior cervical (stellate), near C7–8; may fuse with T-1; sends postganglionic fibers to heart.

ADRENERGIC TRANSMISSION   Norepinephrine is neural transmitter; epinephrine is released from accessory chromaffin tissue and adrenal medulla.

CONTEMPORARY RECEPTOR THEORY Adrenergic action depends on combination of transmitter with α or β receptor.

RECEPTOR SPECIFICITIES β receptors are subdivided; β_1—increased heart rate and contractility and secretion of renin by kidneys; β_2—remainder of β effects.
  α receptors are subdivided; α_1—most effector cells, stimulatory; α_2—ganglion cells and nerve terminals, inhibitory.
  Number of receptors is affected by catechol-

amines and other hormones; α and β may change reciprocally.

Most β effects and some α effects are mediated through adenylate cyclase.

Muscarinic receptors directly affect adrenergic receptors through GTP.

Epinephrine stimulates α_1, α_2, β_1, and β_2; norepinephrine stimulates α_1, α_2, and β_1.

Transmitter effects are modified by negative feedback, input of cholinergic (muscarinic) interneurons.

DOPAMINE   Immediate precursor of norepinephrine; found in adrenal medulla and some sympathetic nerves.

ACTION ON HEART   Stimulates β_1 receptors; causes release of norepinephrine from neurons; blocked by β_1-receptor antagonists.

ACTION ON BLOOD VESSELS   Dilatation in renal, mesenteric, coronary, and cerebral vascular beds, not blocked by β-receptor antagonists.

Large doses—vasoconstriction, blocked by α-receptor antagonists.

PHYSIOLOGICAL ACTION   Not demonstrated in cardiovascular system; may have CNS effects.

CLINICAL USES   For renal and mesenteric vasodilatation in shock.

In cardiac failure refractory to digitalis and diuretics.

RELEASE OF STORED NOREPINEPHRINE   By certain drugs—produces effects like norepinephrine.

Tachyphylaxis—successive doses produce smaller effects.

Some drugs combine release of norepinephrine and direct interaction with receptors.

DENERVATION SENSITIVITY   After denervation, effector organs are more sensitive to circulating catecholamines.

Normally, most locally released or circulating catecholamine is reabsorbed by nerves; if nerve degenerates, more catecholamine reaches receptors.

TRANSMITTER-RECEPTOR INTERACTION

CONCENTRATION-EFFECT CURVE   Free and bound transmitter equilibrium; proportion is determined by amount of transmitter, number of receptors, and tenacity of binding (affinity).

ANTAGONISM   Antagonist combines with receptor, prevents binding of transmitter, produces no effect; if reversible, competitive antagonism.

Specific antagonists for all ANS receptors are available.

ACTIONS OF THE AUTONOMIC NERVOUS SYSTEM ON VARIOUS ORGANS AND TISSUES   See Table 8-2 and appropriate chapters.

BIBLIOGRAPHY

Ahlquist, R.P. 1948. A study of the adrenotropic receptors. *Am. J. Physiol.* 153:586.

Cannon, W.B., and Rosenblueth, A. 1937. *Autonomic Neuro-Effector System.* New York: Macmillan.

Conti-Tronconi, B.M., and Raftery, M.A. 1982. The nicotinic cholinergic receptor: Correlation of molecular structure with functional properties. *Annu. Rev. Biochem.* 51:419.

Cryer, P.E. 1980. Physiology and pathophysiology of the human sympathoadrenal neuroendocrine system. *N. Engl. J. Med.* 303:436.

Elliott, K., and Lawrenson, G. 1981. Development of the autonomic nervous system. *CIBA Foundation Symposium 83.* Summit, New Jersey: CIBA Pharmaceutical.

Furchgott, R.F. 1967. The pharmacological differentiation of adrenergic receptors. *Ann. N.Y. Acad. Sci.* 139:553.

Goldberg, L.I. 1972. Cardiovascular and renal actions of dopamine: Potential clinical applications. *Pharmacol. Rev.* 24:1.

Goldberg, L.I.; Volkman, P.H.; and Kohli, J.D. 1978. A comparison of the vascular dopamine receptor with other dopamine receptors. *Annu. Rev. Pharmacol. Toxicol.* 18:57.

Gulbert, H.C., and Marsden, C.A. 1975. Catechol-O-methyltransferase: Pharmacological aspects and physiological role. *Pharmacol. Rev.* 27:135.

Haber, E., and Wrenn, S. 1976. Problems in identification of the beta-adrenergic receptor. *Physiol. Rev.* 56:317.

Hebb, C. 1972. Biosynthesis of acetylcholine in nervous tissue. *Physiol. Rev.* 52:918.

Hoffman, B.B., and Lefkowitz, R.J. 1980. Alpha-adrenergic receptor subtypes. *N. Engl. J. Med.* 302:1390.

Kunos, G. 1978. Adrenoceptors. *Annu. Rev. Pharmacol. Toxicol.* 18:291.

Lands, A.M.; Arnold, A.; McAuliff, J.P., et al. 1967. Differentiation of receptor system activated by sympathomimetic amines. *Nature* 214:597.

Langer, S.Z. 1980. Presynaptic regulation of the release of catecholamines. *Pharmacol. Rev.* 32:337.

Lee, C.M.; Javitch, J.A.; and Snyder, S.H. 1983. Recognition sites for norepinephrine uptake: Regulation by neurotransmitter. *Science* 220:626.

Mayer, S.E. 1980. Neurohumoral transmission and the autonomic nervous system. In *The Pharmacological Basis of Therapeutics* (6th ed.). Edited by A.G. Gilman, L.S. Goodman, and A. Gilman. New York: Macmillan.

Motulsky, H.J., and Insel, P.A. 1982. Adrenergic receptors in man: Direct identification, physiologic regulation, and clinical alterations. *N. Engl. J. Med.* 307:18.

Smith, A.D. 1972. Subcellular localization of noradrenaline in sympathetic neurons. *Pharmacol. Rev.* 24:435.

Starke, P. 1981. Presynaptic receptors. *Annu. Rev. Physiol.* 21:7.

Ungar, A., and Phillips, J.H. 1983. Regulation of the adrenal medulla. *Physiol. Rev.* 63:787.

Vanhoutte, P.M.; Verbeuren, T.J.; and Webb, R.C. 1981. Local modulation of the adrenergic neuroeffector interaction in the blood vessel wall. *Physiol. Rev.* 61:151.

Von Euler, U.S. 1956. *Noradrenaline.* Springfield, Illinois: Charles C. Thomas.

Watanabe, A.M.; Jones, L.R.; Manalan, A.S., et al. 1982. Cardiac autonomic receptors: Recent concepts from radiolabeled ligand-binding studies. *Circ. Res.* 50:161.

Westfall, T.C. 1977. Local regulation of adrenergic neurotransmission. *Physiol. Rev.* 57:659.

Wolfe, B.B.; Harden, T.K.; and Molinoff, P.B. 1977. In vitro study of β-adrenergic receptors. *Annu. Rev. Pharmacol. Toxicol.* 17:575.

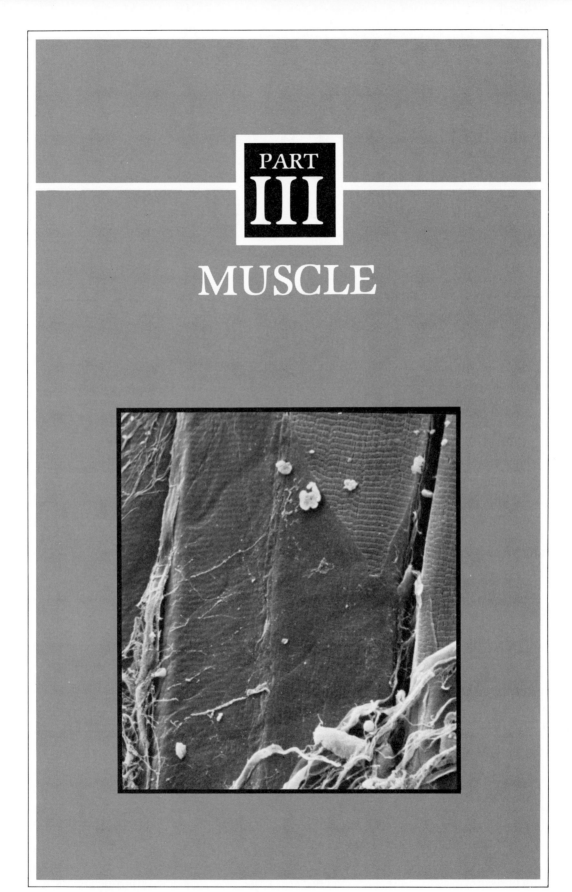

PART III

MUSCLE

Photomicrograph from *Tissues and Organs: A Text-Atlas of Scanning Electron Microscopy* by
Richard G. Kessel and Randy H. Kardon. W.H. Freeman and Company. © 1979.

9

Striated Muscle

CHAPTER CONTENTS

GENERAL COMMENTS

The best known property of striated muscle is contraction, through which the tissue develops tension and does work. Contraction may produce angular motion about a joint, complex motions such as movements of the tongue or the rotation of the arm about the shoulder, or the movement of gas or liquid in hollow organs such as the lungs and the heart. Work performed is defined as the exertion of a force through a distance ($W = f \times dX$) or of pressure throughout a volume ($W = P \times dV$).

Striated muscle may be divided into two general categories: *skeletal* and *cardiac*. The skeletal muscle of the human body ranges from 50% (newborn) to 40% (adult) of the total body mass. Therefore, as an aggregate, skeletal mus-cle may be thought of as the largest organ in the body. The mass of skeletal muscle makes it a large storehouse for both inorganic and organic matter; this storehouse is important in both health and disease.

STRUCTURE

Connective Tissue

In general, the skeletal muscles are surrounded by well-defined fascial layers. When the fascia extends inward and surrounds an individual muscle, it is called *epimysium* (Figure 9-1). The fascia also extends into the belly of the muscle as the *perimysium* and further divides the muscle into *fascicles*. The *endomysium* extends into

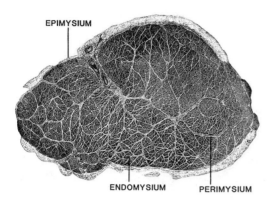

EPIMYSIUM

ENDOMYSIUM   PERIMYSIUM

Figure 9-1. Cross-section through a human sartorius muscle, showing the subdivision into bundles (fascicles) of various sizes. A layer of connective tissue (epimysium) surrounds the entire muscle and the individual fascicles (perimysium). Connective tissue then enters each fascicle and surrounds each muscle fiber (endomysium). (Reproduced, with permission, from W. Bloom and D.W. Fawcett. 1975. *A Textbook of Histology* (10th ed.). Philadelphia: W.B. Saunders Co.)

the fascicle to surround the individual muscle fibers; however, this connective tissue covering should not be confused with the membrane, or *sarcolemma*, of the individual fibers.

Microscopic Structure

The individual fibers of a muscle contain multiple nuclei, located adjacent to the cellular surface, and have a characteristic banding pattern of repeating dark and light zones. These cross striations, described by William Bowman in 1840, underlie the principal theory of striated muscle function that is held today. Bowman's description may be considered the beginning of the understanding of the structure of muscle. It is often forgotten that this great advance was preceded by technologic advances—the invention of the microscope and the development of techniques of tissue preparation for microtomy. Refinements of microscopy and tissue preparation continue today, and these advances are providing new knowledge of the microscopic and submicroscopic structure of muscle. A generalized schematic of the structure of striated muscle is given in Figure 9-2.

SARCOMERE
The repeated dark (anisotropic, A) and light (isotropic, I) bands in each fiber, which are in register with those of adjacent fibers, produce

the striated appearance of skeletal and cardiac muscle. Each muscle fiber is composed of many *sarcomeres* aligned in series. The *sarcomere*, the segment of muscle fiber found between two adjacent Z lines, consists of an A band sandwiched between the halves of two I bands. The sarcomere is the contractile unit of striated muscle, whereas the muscle fiber is the cellular unit.

Submicroscopic Structure
SARCOPLASMIC RETICULUM
The light microscope reveals that each skeletal muscle fiber consists of smaller units, which are termed *myofibrils*. Myofibrils essentially are cylindrical in shape, and each is composed of alternating light and dark bands, like the whole fiber. The electron microscope reveals an extensive membrane system surrounding each myofibril and, at certain points within the muscle fiber, contiguous to (but not continuous with) the surface membrane that covers each fiber. This internal membrane system is analogous to the endoplasmic reticulum in other cell types (see Chapter 2). In striated muscle of mature animals, including humans, the internal membrane system is called the *sarcoplasmic reticulum* (SR). The SR participates in the regulation of Ca^{++} in the sarcoplasm, which is important in the contractile process.

TRIAD
The relationship between the SR and the myofibrils within the muscle fiber should be understood. At each Z line, or at the edge of the A band, depending on the species, the internal membrane system forms two dilated structures, called *terminal cisternae,* separated by a smaller, more circular membrane component, called the T-tubule. These three units—the terminal cisternae of the SR and the transverse tubular (T-tubule) system—are called the *triad* (Figure 9-3). The T-tubule contains extracellular fluid, and the SR contains cellular fluid. The transverse tubular membrane system provides a means for external fluids and membrane structures to penetrate deeply into the core of each muscle fiber. When the muscle is excited physiologically, contraction is initiated by electrical activity conducted inward along the transverse tubule. Thus, the T-tubule of the triads provides the means for the synchronous activation of all of the sarcomeres within the muscle fiber. Depolarization during the action potential is thought to cause the release of Ca^{++} stored in

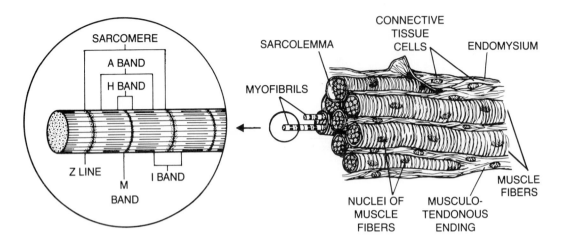

Figure 9-2. Schematic drawing of an aggregate of muscle fibers showing each fiber to be surrounded by both a connective tissue layer, the endomysium, and the plasma membrane, or sarcolemma. The inset shows the striated structure of each muscle fiber and gives the nomenclature for the striations. The location of the nuclei of the muscle fiber beneath the sarcolemma also is demonstrated.

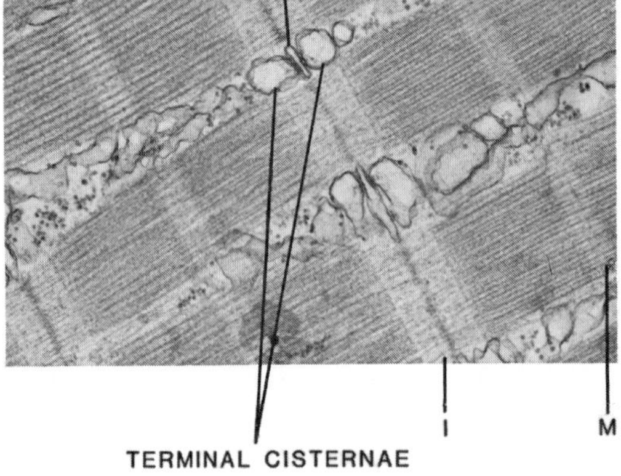

---

the terminal cistern, which initiates the contraction of the sarcomeres. A three-dimensional reconstruction of the SR, the T-tubule, and the myofibrils is given in Figure 9-4.

MOLECULAR STRUCTURE OF THE SARCOMERE

The sarcomere consists of an orderly array of *thick* (myosin) and *thin* (mostly actin) filaments. If the muscles are fixed at their normal rest length, the less dense thin filaments, predominantly in the I band, are found to connect with the Z line and extend into the A band. The thin filaments partially overlap the thick filaments. If a transverse section is made through a muscle fiber or myofibril, a double hexagonal array of thick and thin filaments is found. This orderly arrangement is shown schematically in Figures 9-5A–D.

THICK FILAMENTS

The thick filaments of the A band are composed of myosin molecules, which contain both light and heavy molecular components, termed *light meromyosin* and *heavy meromyosin*, respectively. The light component forms the body of the thick filaments, whereas the heavy component extends out from the thick filaments to form cross-bridges (Figures 9-5F–H). The molecular structure of the individual myosin molecules enables the heavy meromyosin cross-bridges to make contact with the thin filaments during the

Figure 9-3. Electron micrograph of frog skeletal muscle (× 25,100) showing the transverse tubule and the terminal cisternae, which together form the triad. Z = Z line; H = H band; A = A band; I = I band; M = M line. (Courtesy of Dr. Keith Porter.)

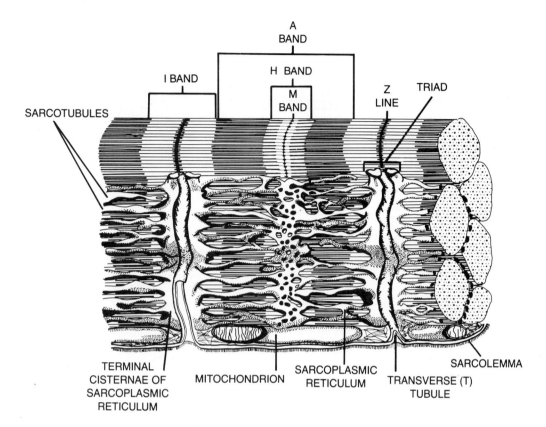

A
BAND

I BAND

H BAND

M
BAND

Z
LINE

TRIAD

SARCOTUBULES

TERMINAL
CISTERNAE OF
SARCOPLASMIC
RETICULUM

MITOCHONDRION

SARCOPLASMIC
RETICULUM

TRANSVERSE (T)
TUBULE

SARCOLEMMA

Figure 9-4.   Three-dimensional reconstruction of several myofibrils demonstrating the structural relationship of the various membrane systems to the myofibrils and their striations. The *sarcoplasmic reticulum* (SR), or inner membrane system, surrounds each myofibril. Near the Z line, the SR is dilated and contiguous with the *transverse* (T) tubule. These dilated portions of the SR (terminal cisternae) are connected by tubules that extend the length of the sarcomere. The T-tubule can be seen as an invagination of the sarcolemma. The juxta- position of the T-tubule with the cisternae of adjacent SR forms the triads (see Figure 9-3). This drawing shows muscle in which the triad appears over the Z line. (Redrawn, with permission, from W. Bloom and D.W. Fawcett. 1975. *A Textbook of Histology* (10th ed.). Philadelphia: W.B. Saunders Co. Modified/redrawn from L.D. Peachey. 1965. The sarcoplasmic reticulum and transverse tubules of the frog's sartorius. *J. Cell. Biol.* 25:222.)

contractile process. This arrangement appears to be possible because the head of the myosin molecule is flexible. It has been proposed that once the myosin head contacts the actin filaments, it pivots in such a manner that the actin filament is shifted toward the center of the sarcomere. This conceptualization of the contractile process is termed the *sliding filament theory* of muscle contraction. This mechanism is thought to operate in both skeletal and cardiac muscle, and, to some extent, in smooth muscle.

THIN FILAMENTS

The protein of the thin filaments occurs in two forms: globular, or G-actin, and fibrous, or F-actin. The G-actin binds Ca^{++} and adenosine triphosphate (ATP). ATP added to a solution of G-actin is split, and the monomers of G-actin polymerize to form F-actin. In the living state, the actin filaments are made of two F-actin strands coiled about each other, as depicted in Figure 9-5E. In addition, two other proteins, *tropomyosin* and *troponin,* are associated with the actin filaments. Tropomyosin, which makes up about 10% of the total contractile protein, is composed of two different kinds of polypeptide chains arranged in an α-helical configuration. Tropomyosin lies in the grooves formed by the two-stranded F-actin coils (Figure 9-5E). Troponin, the third protein of the thin filament, is found every 250 Å along the actin filament. This globular protein consists of three polypeptide subunits, termed *troponin-I, troponin-C,* and

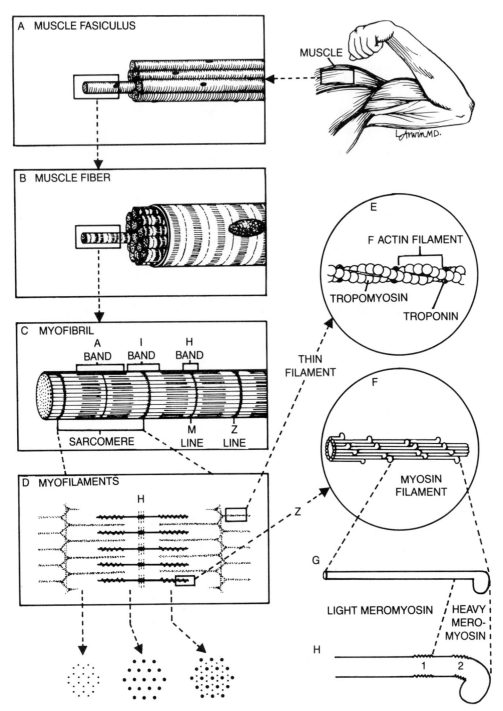

Figure 9-5. Skeletal muscle. **A.** Part of a fascicle from the deltoid muscle. **B.** A simple muscle fiber with striations. **C.** A single myofibril and its striated bands. **D.** The submicroscopic structure of a single sarcomere in longitudinal section. Transverse sections at the I and H bands and the overlap between actin and myosin filaments reveal the double hexagonal arrangements of filaments relative to each other. **E.** The thin filaments are shown to consist of actin monomers, tropomyosin, and troponin. **F–H.** The thick myosin filament and its subunits. The heavy meromyosin head is shown to have two flexible points (*1* and *2*) that are analogous to hinges. (Redrawn, with permission, from W. Bloom and D.W. Fawcett. 1975. *A Textbook of Histology* (10th ed.). Philadelphia: W.B. Saunders Co.)

troponin-T, and abbreviated as TN-I, TN-C, and TN-T (Figure 9-6). Ca^{++} binds to TN-C and induces a configurational change in the overall troponin complex such that TN-I, the inhibitory component, is moved away from the actin filament. In the most widely accepted model, this conformational change uncovers an "active" site on the actin filament. The head of the myosin cross-bridge can attach to this active site and initiate the contractile process.

MOLECULAR BASIS
OF CONTRACTION

Contractile Proteins

Four contractile proteins have been identified, and considerable quantitative data about them have been gathered (Table 9-1). However, much of this information has been obtained from studies that require the disruption of muscles by various extraction procedures. Investigators study the isolated components in the test tube and propose how these individual units operate in the living state. The geometric arrangement of the various proteins and the interactions among them appear to provide the organic structural matrix essential for contraction. In addition, other organic material (e.g., enzymes and ATP) and inorganic material (e.g., water and ions) provide the essential ingredients for the reversible processes of contraction and relaxation.

Excitation-Contraction Coupling

RELEASE OF Ca^{++}

The wave of depolarization that spreads over the surface of the muscle fibers (action potential) extends into the depths of each fiber by way of the T-tubular system. The current that flows after depolarization causes the release of Ca^{++} from the terminal cistern of the SR, which increases the concentration of Ca^{++}—[Ca^{++}]—within the sarcoplasm of the muscle fiber and initiates several events. The following is a summary of the effects of elevated [Ca^{++}] in the sarcoplasm, listed in the order in which they are believed to occur.

CHANGE OF CONFORMATION
IN THIN FILAMENT

Ca^{++} interacts with the troponin subunit C, which induces cooperative changes in the adjacent troponin subunits (T and I) of the tropomyosin molecule. These changes of conformation cause an active site on the actin molecule to be exposed, which allows the attachment of the myosin cross-bridges to that site (see Figure 9-6).

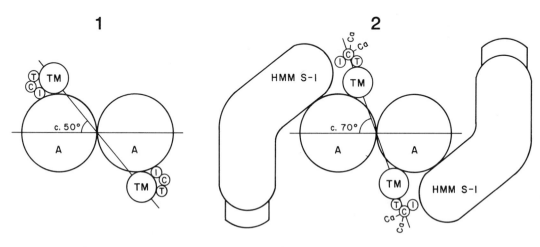

Figure 9-6. Relationship of the troponin subunits to tropomyosin and actin in the resting state (*1*) and to the heavy meromyosin S-I unit in the contracted state (*2*). In the resting state (*1*), the troponin-I subunit is attached to a specific actin subunit (*A*). When the muscle is excited (*2*), Ca^{++} interacts with the troponin-C subunit, causing a conformational change. The troponin-I subunit rotates away from the actin monomer and allows attachment of the heavy meromyosin (crossbridge) to the active sites on the myosin molecule. (Redrawn, with permission, from J.D. Potter and J. Gergely. 1974. *Biochemistry* 13:2702. Copyright 1974 American Chemical Society.)

TABLE 9-1
Contractile proteins of striated muscle

Protein	Location	Approximate molecular weight (daltons)	Role in contraction
Myosin	Thick filaments	480,000	Hydrolyze ATP and develop tension.
Two heavy chains Heavy meromyosin (HMM)	Thick filaments	240,000 105,000	Bind actin; ATPase activity
Three light chains Light meromyosin (LMM)	Thick filaments	25,000, 18,000, 17,000 75,000	Function unknown Form body of thick filaments
Actin	Thin filaments	42,000	Activate myosin ATPase activity; interact with myosin
Tropomyosin	Thin filaments	Two nonidentical chains of 34,000 each	Modulate actin-myosin interaction; chemical bond with troponin
Troponin	Thin filaments		
Troponin-T	Bonded to tropomyosin and troponin-C	37,000–41,000	Interact with troponin-C to bring about a structural change in tropomyosin that allows interaction of myosin and actin
Troponin-C	Bonded between troponin-T and troponin-I	18,000	Ca^{++} binding site that modulates "active" site on actin for interaction of myosin and actin
Troponin-I	Bonded to troponin-C; bond with actin that is postulated to vary as a function of Ca^{++} binding to troponin-C	21,000–28,000	Cooperative interaction with troponin-C when Ca^{++} binds to troponin-C

CHANGE OF CONFORMATION IN THICK FILAMENT

If [Ca^{++}] in the sarcoplasm is adequate, *heavy meromyosin* (HMM) swings toward the exposed binding sites on actin and away from the body of the thick filament, as if it were hinged. The hinge effect is thought to occur at the junction between heavy meromyosin and light meromyosin, which remains within the body of the thick filament. The association of HMM with sites on actin initiates the ATPase activity of myosin, which causes the splitting of ATP and a change of conformation in the HMM. Rotation about hinge point 2 (Figure 9-5H) changes the

angle between the HMM head and the long axis of the myosin molecule. This second change of conformation develops the force that causes the thin filaments to move along the thick filaments and, thus, to shorten the sarcomere.

The myosin molecule also is associated with proteins of low molecular weight, called "*light chains*" (Table 9-1). Skeletal muscle of one type (fast—see "Fast Muscles and Slow Muscles" in this chapter) is thought to contain three classes of light chains, as defined by their molecular weights. Another type of skeletal muscle (slow), cardiac muscle, and smooth muscle contain only two classes. The physiological role of these regulatory proteins in the contraction of striated muscle (skeletal and cardiac) is not known; however, the light chains are important in the regulation of myosin ATPase activity of smooth muscle (see Chapter 11).

Relaxation

Membrane vesicles, predominantly those of the SR, adsorb Ca^{++} and thereby permit the muscle to relax. The following scheme of relaxation is generally accepted:

1. After attachment of the cross-bridge, the affinity of the longitudinal SR for Ca^{++} increases; Ca^{++} diffuses from troponin and is either adsorbed to the structures or translocated to the lumen of the longitudinal SR.
2. Ca^{++} diffuses from the longitudinal portion of the SR to the terminal cistern. The movement of Ca^{++} into the SR greatly decreases the $[Ca^{++}]$ in the sarcoplasm; in addition, the mitochondria may take up Ca^{++}. Detachment of Ca^{++} from the active site on the troponin subunit permits the proteins to revert to their resting conformation. The cross-bridges detach and the sarcomere lengthens again.

PHENOMENOLOGY OF MUSCLE CONTRACTION

Motor Unit

In the intact organism, muscle fibers rarely, if ever, contract individually, because a single motoneuron innervates several muscle fibers. The group of muscle fibers innervated by a single neuron is termed a *motor unit* (Figure 9-7). When an adequate stimulus is applied to a single motoneuron, all of the muscle fibers in the motor unit contract.

If an electrode is placed across a nerve trunk (Figure 9-7) and a stimulus is applied with an intensity that allows only one motoneuron to be discharged, the muscle fibers innervated by that neuron will contract in an all-or-nothing fashion. As the intensity of the stimulus is increased, more and more motor units are recruited, until all of the muscle fibers innervated by the nerve trunk are activated. Measurements of the force of contraction of the muscles innervated by the nerve trunk show that the force increases as additional motor units are activated. After all of the units have been activated, further increase in intensity of the stimulus does not increase the force developed. The intensity of stimulus at which all motor units are recruited

is referred to as a *maximal stimulus.* Stimuli of higher intensity are referred to as *supramaximal.*

Similar results are obtained if an electrode is placed directly in contact with an isolated muscle. Theoretically, an applied stimulus may be so weak as to activate only one muscle fiber, and the force developed is very small. As the intensity of the stimulus is increased, more and more muscle fibers are activated, until all fibers respond to the stimulus. Further application of supramaximal stimuli does not cause greater force to develop.

Cycle of Contraction and Relaxation

LATENT PERIOD

The application of a brief maximal stimulus to a muscle causes contraction followed by relaxation, after a short delay (or latent period). During the latent period of about 3 milliseconds, the action potential is generated, the muscle lengthens slightly (latency relaxation), Ca^{++} is released from the terminal cisterns of the SR, and heat (latency heat) is produced. These events are associated with the phenomenon called *excitation-contraction coupling,* which initiates the contraction-relaxation cycle of striated muscle (Figure 9-8).

CONTRACTION

After the latent period, the contraction phase begins and continues until maximal tension has been developed; the time required is defined as the *contraction time.*

RELAXATION

The portion of the tension-time curve from the development of maximum force until the tension has returned to the resting level is the *relaxation time.* It is difficult to measure exactly because of the slow decrease of force during the latter part of the curve. The interval between the development of peak force and the decay of the force to one-half of the maximum value can be determined more accurately; this is the *half-relaxation* time. Figure 9-8 shows that the relaxation phase of the twitch is more than twice as long as the contraction phase. The significance of this fact is not well understood, but it is interesting that in most pathological states, the changes in relaxation time usually are much more dramatic than the changes in contraction time.

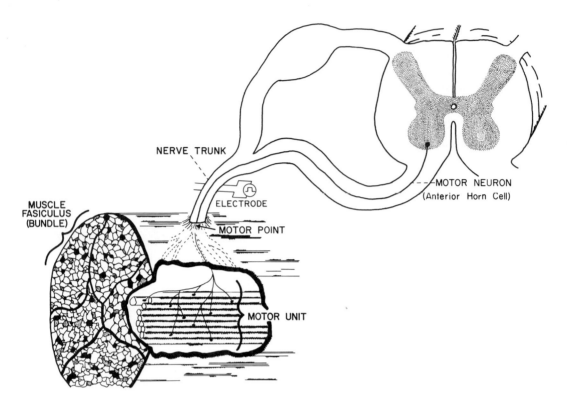

Figure 9-7. Single motoneuron passing through a spinal nerve and peripheral nerve trunk to a muscle. The axon branches and innervates more than one muscle fiber, forming a motor unit. Therefore, exciting a single motoneuron causes several muscle fibers to contract. The point at which the nerve trunk penetrates a muscle is called the motor point; it is sensitive to stimuli and may be used clinically to evaluate muscle function.

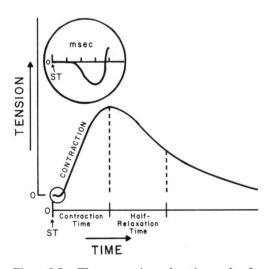

Figure 9-8. The contraction-relaxation cycle of a muscle. A maximal stimulus (ST) is applied at time zero. The latent period, which has a phase of lengthening, is shown in the inset. During this period, excitation is coupled with contraction. Relaxation begins after maximum tension is attained. The half-relaxation time is useful in the clinical evaluation of muscle function.

FAST MUSCLES AND SLOW MUSCLES

Skeletal muscles may be classified as either *fast* or *slow*, depending on the duration of the contraction-relaxation cycle (see Figure 9-18). The cycle is shorter in fast muscles than in slow muscles. Fast and slow muscles also differ in color (slow muscles are red and fast muscles are white) because of differences in myoglobin concentration. The breast muscles of avians that sustain long periods of flight (e.g., ducks) are red and slow, whereas the breast muscles of birds that cannot sustain long flight (e.g., domesticated chickens) are white and fast. These differences in mechanical properties are not limited to differences between species but are readily observed within species. In mammals, for example, the lateral rectus muscle, which participates in the control of eye movement, is a very fast muscle, with a contraction-relaxation cycle of about 30 milliseconds, whereas the soleus is one of the slowest muscles, with a contraction-relaxation cycle of about 3000 milliseconds. The contraction-relaxation cycles of a

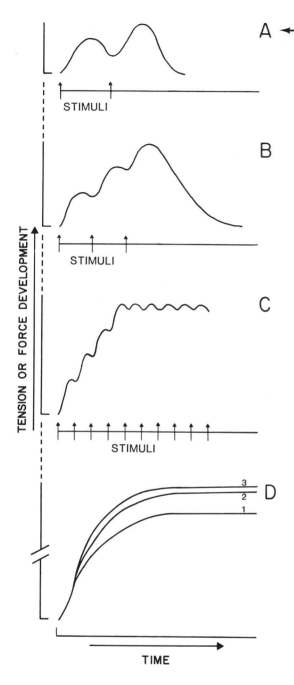

A ← **Figure 9-9.** A series of graphs that demonstrate the additive effect of subsequent stimuli on the development of tension in skeletal muscle. **A.** Two successive twitches are induced; the second, which occurs before the muscle has completely relaxed, sums with the first to produce more tension. **B.** The effect of a third stimulus is shown. **C.** More stimuli are applied, and the tension reaches an average maximum. Partial contraction and relaxation can be seen, however, and this phenomenon is called wave summation. **D.** Stimulation at higher frequencies produces a smooth curve of tension (tetanic stimulation, or tetanus). The stimuli are applied so frequently that the skeletal muscle does not relax. The curves depicted in *1*, *2*, and *3* show effects from lower to higher frequencies. Maximum frequency is obtained in *3*, and higher frequencies cause no greater tension.

high in red (slow) muscles. As one might expect, the mitochondrial ATPase activity of muscles of intermediate speed falls between that of the fast type and that of the slow type. The various types of muscle fiber also differ morphologically. The transverse tubular system is much more developed in fast fibers than in slow fibers. In addition, the mitochondrial content is less, the fiber diameter is greater, and the neuromuscular junction is larger in fast muscle fibers than in slow muscle fibers.

If the nerves that go to a fast muscle and the nerves that go to a slow muscle are cut and crossed (i.e., the nerve that goes to the fast muscle is connected to the nerve that goes to the slow muscle, and vice versa), the mechanical properties of the muscles are altered. The originally fast muscle, now supplied by the nerve of the slow muscle, behaves mechanically like a slow muscle. In corresponding fashion, the slow muscle that is supplied by the nerve of the fast muscle develops mechanical properties similar to those of the fast muscle. Moreover, the changes caused by cross-innervation are not limited to the mechanical properties: the fast muscle connected to the nerve of a slow muscle becomes histochemically similar to a slow muscle, and the slow muscle connected to the nerve of a fast muscle becomes histochemically similar to a fast muscle.

The differentiation of muscle cells into mechanically fast and slow types is discussed further in the section on the development of muscle (see "Postnatal Changes in Contractile Properties, Fast Muscles and Slow Muscles," in this chapter).

host of other muscles lie between these extremes. One example is the gastrocnemius muscle, which has a contraction-relaxation cycle of about 125 milliseconds. The gastrocnemius muscle also demonstrates that a mixture of red (slow) and white (fast) muscle fibers may exist within a single muscle.

Fast and slow muscles also differ histochemically; for example, mitochondrial ATPase activity is low in the white (fast) muscles but

CLINICAL CORRELATION
9.1 Skeletal Muscle Contracture During Sustained Activity

CASE REPORT

The Patient: A 25-year-old man.

Principal Complaint: Extreme muscle stiffness during exercise.

History: The patient's birth and development were normal. His earliest recollection of a disorder of movement was at 5 years of age, when he fell during a foot race because his muscles stiffened. Thereafter, he was aware that muscle stiffness occurred during vigorous exercise or sudden, rapid movements. Strenuous exercise caused painless stiffness within seconds, of such a magnitude that the exercise could not be continued. However, the stiffness disappeared after only a few seconds of rest. Despite his problem, the patient was able to carry out daily activities, provided he paced his movements. He could even play tennis and swim, if he were careful. He managed to qualify for the college wrestling team by using "brute strength," but when speed was required, he lost competitive matches. Cold temperatures led to the rapid occurrence of

stiffness, and the patient often noted clumsiness in his hands under these conditions. He had been accepted into military service, but subsequently was discharged because he could not perform "double time" marches. The patient denied weakness and had no history of myoglobinuria. He has no siblings, and no one in his known ancestry had a similar condition.

Physical Examination: At examination, the patient appeared healthy and was well developed. Abnormal findings were limited to the skeletal muscles. Under gross examination, the muscles were normal in contour, tone, and strength, but a progressive lengthening of the relaxation time was observed during vigorous exercise. After 10 to 15 seconds of repetitive contraction with maximal effort, the arm muscles became paralyzed in a contracted state. This was recognizable grossly, and after 5 to 15 seconds of rest, the muscles relaxed again, and exercise could be resumed. The momentary "contracture" was painless unless the patient continued his efforts to contract the shortened muscles. This phenomenon was

SUMMATION AND TETANUS

If a second maximal stimulus is applied during the relaxation phase of a twitch, a second contraction-relaxation cycle is initiated (Figure 9-9A), and the maximum force developed in the second cycle is greater than that in the first. Thus, the two contractions *summate*. If the frequency of stimulation is increased (segments A–D of Figure 9-9), the forces continue to sum until a maximum force is attained. In segment D of Figure 9-9, the individual contraction-relaxation cycles fuse to produce a single smooth curve, called *tetanus*. The contraction of skeletal muscle can summate to the point of fusion because the refractory period, the time during which the tissue does not respond to a second stimulus, is short relative to the contraction time. Thus, the muscle can be re-excited before it relaxes. By comparison, car-

diac muscle has a very long refractory period, and its contractions do not summate.

Types of Muscle Contraction

Although the contraction and relaxation of muscle can be studied in vivo, the bulk of our understanding of the mechanics of these events has come from studies in vitro, which allow the investigator to isolate the events of contraction and relaxation. Most widely used is the isolated sartorius muscle of the frog, in which the fibers extend through the entire length of the muscle. Such a preparation decreases the number of variables that might obscure the observation of contraction-relaxation events.

In vivo or in vitro, single muscles or muscle groups can develop tension that may or may not perform work (i.e., displace a weight through a distance). If a muscle develops tension but does

identified in muscles of the limbs, the face, and the jaws. There were no fasciculation, symptoms of myotonia, incoordination, or disturbance of gait. The muscle-stretch reflexes appeared normal, and passive movements did not induce the persistent shortening in any muscles. Electrical studies using external electrodes showed that the nerve propagation velocities were normal, and the muscle responded normally to either single or repetitive excitation. During the contracture induced by exercise, no electrical activity could be detected in the muscle.

A muscle (needle) biopsy was performed to provide tissue for study. Examination of samples by both light and electron micrography disclosed no abnormal morphology. Biochemical analysis revealed a normal concentration of ATP and normal total phosphorylase activity; however, the fraction of active phosphorylase (that is, without added AMPase) was unusually high (89%, compared with 30% in control tissues). A sample of muscle was homogenized, and microsomes were obtained from it by ultracentrifugation. The uptake of calcium by the microsomes, measured using ^{45}Ca, was significantly less than that of control tissues. The microsomal ATPase activity was normal relative to the controls.

Comment: The biochemical studies suggest a defect in the uptake of Ca^{++} by the sarcoplasmic reticulum (SR). Apparently, Ca^{++} accumulates in the sarcoplasm during repeated contractions until contracture is produced. The condition is made worse by cold, which further decreases the rate of uptake of Ca^{++} by the SR. The increased concentration of Ca^{++} in the sarcoplasm also may account for the unusually high ratio of active phosphorylase to inactive phosphorylase because Ca^{++} activates phosphorylase-b kinase, which converts inactive phosphorylase to active phosphorylase. Active phosphorylase promotes glycolysis and the production of lactate, which may explain the high concentration of lactate in the venous blood, even when the patient was at rest. However, the occurrence of contracture does not appear to be related directly to any abnormality of glycolysis. At present, the defect that causes the abnormal function of the SR is not known. Although the uptake of Ca^{++} by the SR depends on the splitting of ATP, this patient's Mg-ATPase activity was normal. Other ATPase activity was not measured.

Outcome: The patient's condition has not progressed, and despite the lack of any useful therapy, he lives a reasonably normal life. He accepts his limitations and avoids muscular activity that is rapid or prolonged enough to induce contracture.

not shorten, the contraction is *isometric*. If the muscle is allowed to shorten, the contraction is *isotonic*.

ISOTONIC CONTRACTION

Isotonic contraction of muscle may be studied under two conditions (Figures 9-10B and C): (1) preloaded, in which a load acts on the muscle before contraction, and (2) afterloaded, in which an additional load is lifted when the muscle contracts. Tension applied to a resting muscle constitutes preload: examples are restlength in skeletal muscle and ventricular end-diastolic volume in cardiac muscle (see "Stroke Volume, Preload" in Chapter 15). Examples of afterload are contraction of the ventricular myocardium during the ejection phase of the cardiac cycle and execution of the "snatch" in weight lifting.

ISOMETRIC CONTRACTION

A schematic depiction of the experimental measurement of isometric contraction is given in Figure 9-10D. It should be emphasized that in the isotonic, afterloaded condition, the muscle contracts isometrically until the force developed equals the load against which the muscle is working (Figure 9-11B).

Mechanical Model

According to the most widely accepted model, striated muscle is the mechanical equivalent of a contractile element in series with an elastic element (Figure 9-11). Another elastic element, in parallel with the contractile and series elastic elements, is almost completely relaxed when the muscle is at rest length. Connective tissue and other inert structural components, which are stretched to some extent when a muscle con-

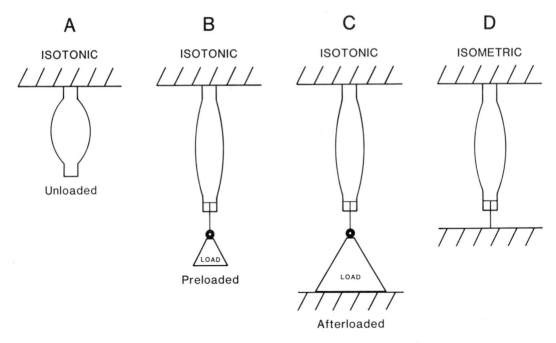

A	B	C	D
ISOTONIC	ISOTONIC	ISOTONIC	ISOMETRIC
Unloaded	Preloaded		

Afterloaded

Figure 9-10. Contraction of muscle under different conditions. **A.** Unloaded. If a muscle is not stretched by an initial load (preload), it contracts passively to about 70% of its optimum length, or rest-length in the body, and develops little or no tension when excited. **B.** Isotonic, preloaded. The muscle is stretched initially by a limited load and allowed to shorten when it is excited. **C.** Isotonic, afterloaded. Most of the load is supported, but the height of the support is arranged so that the muscle is stretched; thus, the muscle is preloaded. The muscle does not experience the main load until it begins to contract, and it must develop tension equal to the load before it shortens externally and lifts the load. After the load is lifted, the tension remains unchanged (isotonic). **D.** Isometric. The muscle is fixed so that it develops tension but does not shorten externally. The muscle develops the maximum tension of which it is capable, depending on its initial length and contractile state.

tracts against a force, provide the elastic properties of muscle. The mechanical analogue of skeletal muscle shown in Figure 9-11 has been adopted as a representation of the mechanics of cardiac muscle also.

ACTIVE STATE

After an adequate stimulus has been applied, the sarcomeres shorten rapidly (*active state*), and external tension develops. In a moderately fast skeletal muscle, the active state lasts for approximately 10 milliseconds at room temperature. If another stimulus is applied in less than 10 milliseconds, the active state persists, and external tension continues to develop. If stimuli are applied continuously at intervals equal to or less than the duration of the active state, external tension develops as a smooth curve (tetanus; see "Summation and Tetanus" in this chapter) to its maximum possible value (Figure 9-12).

The failure of the muscle to develop maximum tension during a twitch is explained by the transmission of the action of the contractile element through the series elastic element within the muscle. If the muscle is stretched between the occurrence of the action potential and the development of external tension, however, the mechanical force of the contractile element is transmitted fully.

Relationships Among Force, Length, and Velocity

LENGTH-TENSION

In the animal body, skeletal muscles are stretched between their tendons of origin and insertion, which causes a small, steady, resting tension, or preload. If a muscle is removed from the body of an animal and arranged so that the force of contraction can be measured, the force developed during excitation (active tension) varies as a function of the initial length of the muscle, up to a maximum P_0 at length L_0 (Figure 9-13). When the muscle is stretched beyond this optimum length, the active tension that is developed begins to decline. These dif-

MECHANICAL MODELING OF MUSCLE

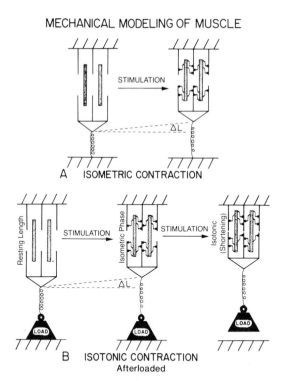

Figure 9-11. A mechanical model of contraction that consists of a contractile element in series with an elastic element. **A.** Isometric contraction. The muscle shortens internally as the elastic element is stretched, but it does not shorten externally. **B.** Isotonic contraction, afterloaded. Isometric phase—the contractile element shortens and the elastic element stretches until the tension in the muscle equals the load. Isotonic phase—the muscle shortens externally, and the load is lifted, but no more tension develops.

ferences of active tension coincide with differing amounts of overlap of the actin and myosin filaments, which suggests an optimal degree of overlap for optimal contraction.

FORCE-VELOCITY

The initial velocity of shortening, the maximum force developed, and the extent of shortening all are related. In general, the lighter the load on a muscle, the faster it develops tension (Figure 9-14) and the more it shortens (Figure 9-15). As the load is increased, the initial velocity of shortening and the amount of shortening decrease. When the load is equal to the maximum force the muscle can develop, the muscle does not shorten (isometric contraction). The maximum velocity of shortening is attained at resting length L_0. If the muscle is stretched beyond L_0, or allowed to be less than L_0, the velocity of shortening is less.

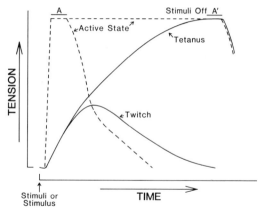

Figure 9-12. Twitch and tetanus in skeletal muscle. An effective stimulus causes the onset of the active state, but the series elastic component stretches (see Figure 9-11), and the full tension of the contractile element is not transmitted through the muscle. If only one stimulus is applied (twitch), the active state begins to decay after a short time (*A*), and the tension develops in the muscle only until it reaches the declining value of the contractile element (*dashed line*). If the muscle is stimulated repeatedly after intervals equal to or less than the duration of the active state, the tension-time curves of the contractile element and the whole muscle coincide (tetanus). When the tetanic stimulation is stopped, the maximal tension remains for a short time (*A'*), and this interval during which maximum tension persists is defined as the *duration of the active state.*

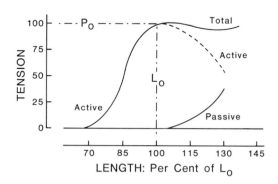

Figure 9-13. The length-tension relationship. As the muscle is stretched, the tension developed during excitation increases to a maximum (P_0) and then declines. Subtraction of the passive component from the curve of total tension reveals the active tension developed at lengths greater than L_0 (*dashed line*). (Redrawn, with permission, from R.M. Dowben. 1980. Contractility, with special reference to skeletal muscle. In *Medical Physiology* (14th ed.). Edited by V.B. Mountcastle. St. Louis: C.V. Mosby Co. Courtesy, K.L. Zierler.)

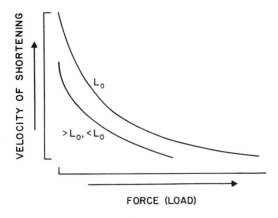

Figure 9-14. The force-velocity relationship. If the initial velocity of muscle shortening is plotted against a range of loads applied to a muscle, a smooth, monotonically decreasing curve is obtained. The velocity at any load is maximum at L_0 and decreases at lengths less or greater than L_0.

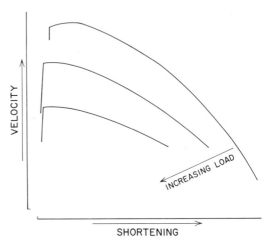

Figure 9-15. Effects of afterload on velocity and amount of shortening of skeletal muscle. When the initial length is held constant, the muscle shortens less as the load increases. (From K.L. Zierler. 1974. Mechanism of muscle contraction and its energetics. In *Medical Physiology* (13th ed.). Edited by V.B. Mountcastle. St. Louis: C.V. Mosby Co. Traced from unpublished photographic records obtained by A.S. Bahler.)

DEVELOPMENT OF MUSCLE

Skeletal Muscle

MYOBLASTS

The structure and function of immature muscle cells (*myoblasts*) and immature muscle fibers (*fused myoblasts*) change dramatically during formation and maturation. These structural changes, which appear to be caused primarily by changes in the organic matter (primarily protein), in turn are associated with dynamic changes in the inorganic matter (primarily water and monovalent ions). The structural evolution of the skeletal muscle fiber and the changes in organic and inorganic matter result in the differentiation of skeletal muscle into the fast type and the slow type (see "Fast Muscles and Slow Muscles" in this chapter).

MUSCLE FIBERS

With few exceptions, the cells that ultimately form skeletal muscle fibers (*myoblasts*) arise from embryonic mesoderm. The myoblasts destined to form an integral part of a given fiber divide and align much as individual railroad cars connect to a locomotive (Figure 9-16). These individual cells, each containing its own nucleus, then fuse. Part of the membrane of each cell appears to dissolve, producing a long, tubelike structure that contains all of the original cellular nuclei. These nuclei remain aligned and located in the center of the tubelike

cell. This particular phase of development of a muscle fiber is called the *myotube* stage. Further maturation of the skeletal muscle fiber leads to the formation of the contractile proteins and their aggregation into individual myofibrils, the development of the internal membrane system, and the peripheral migration of the nuclei. These events end with a skeletal muscle fiber that possesses all of the structural and functional characteristics presented earlier in this chapter.

SATELLITE CELLS

The satellite cell depicted in Figure 9-16 is thought to have the potential of dividing and ultimately forming a new muscle fiber. This cell, considered to be an inactive myoblast, may be activated if the muscle hypertrophies or cells are injured. During early postnatal development, satellite cells comprise a large fraction of the muscle. As the muscle matures, the number of satellite cells decreases, and, in the mature muscle, satellite cells comprise less than 1% of the tissue. Although hypertrophy involves primarily an increase in diameter of individual fibers caused by increased protein synthesis, the satellite cells represent the potential for formation of new muscle fibers.

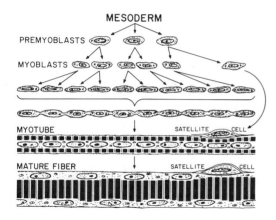

Figure 9-16. Development of muscle. Premyoblasts that arise from mesodermal tissues differentiate into myoblasts, which aggregate in linear chains. Later, the membranes of the myoblasts that are destined to become a muscle fiber appear to fuse, forming a myotube that has striations and in which all nuclei are located in the center. Some of the myoblasts form satellite cells that may be activated later to form new fibers. (Redrawn, with permission, from A. Mauro et al., eds. 1970. *Regeneration of Striated Muscle, and Myogenesis.* Amsterdam: Excerpta Medica.)

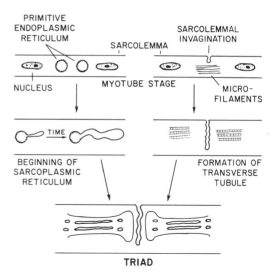

Figure 9-17. Origin of the internal membranous systems of skeletal muscle early in embryonic development. The transverse tubular system develops as invaginations from the sarcolemma. The sarcoplasmic reticulum arises from primitive, ribosomally studded (rough) endoplasmic reticulum. Ultimately, these two independently developed structures come together with the contractile proteins to form individual myofibrils. The terminal cisternae of the sarcoplasmic reticulum become contiguous, but not continuous, with the T-tubular systems. The triads are located over the myofibrillar I bands or at the ends of the A bands, depending on the species of animal studied.

INTERNAL MEMBRANE SYSTEMS

Skeletal muscle has two internal membrane systems: the *transverse tubule* (T-tubule) *system* necessary for the transfer of excitation inward, and the *longitudinal* (sarcoplasmic reticulum) *system*, which serves as a storehouse for adsorbed calcium (see "Submicroscopic Structure" in this chapter). During early embryonic development, perhaps during the myotube stage, invaginations of the sarcolemma form and penetrate deep within the muscle fiber proper. These invaginations form the T-tubular system, which is contiguous to, but not continuous with, the terminal cisterns of the sarcoplasmic reticulum.

Early in the formation of skeletal muscle fibers, a ribosomally studded membrane structure (see Chapter 2), called the primitive, or rough, *endoplasmic reticulum* (ER), appears within the myoplasm (Figure 9-17). This structure is thought to originate from the protein-synthesizing machinery of the cellular nuclei. As development continues, this structure gives rise to smooth, membranelike extensions that have no ribosomal particles. These structures develop into large membrane sacs. Soon only the membrane sacs develop, and the rough ER structures disappear. Next, the sacs migrate

toward, and ultimately lie adjacent to, the sarcolemmal invaginations. This longitudinal membrane system, which originates in the rough ER, surrounds the filamentous systems that are forming and that ultimately become the myofibrils. The mechanisms that underlie these events are not known; however, the structural consequences are the formation of myofibrils surrounded by a sarcoplasmic reticulum, and the periodic occurrence of transverse tubules between two terminal cisterns. This arrangement is repeated throughout the length of the individual myofibrils.

INORGANIC MATTER

The events that involve changes in organic matter also are associated with dramatic changes in inorganic matter. The immature state is characterized by high concentrations of water, Na^+, and K^+ in the muscle tissue. When the proliferative activity of the immature muscle appears to be highest, the tissue contains more Na$^+$ than K$^+$, and the tissue content of water may be as high as 90% of the total mass. On the other hand, the mature muscle is characterized by a higher content of K$^+$ than Na$^+$, and the tissue content of water is 75% of the total mass (see Chapter 36).

Postnatal Changes in Contractile Properties

FAST MUSCLES AND SLOW MUSCLES

In most mammalian species, skeletal muscle usually differentiates into the fast type or the slow type (see "Fast Muscles and Slow Muscles"

in this chapter) during early postnatal life. At birth, both types of muscle have similar contraction-relaxation times, but, by the end of the first week of postnatal development, the two types are clearly distinguishable (Figure 9-18). The contraction time and half-relaxation time both decrease during postnatal development, but the decreases are much greater in the fast muscles. The amount of force that can be developed by each type of muscle is about the same at birth and increases about 25 times by 140 days of postnatal life. These changes in contractile properties occur during the time that the large changes in inorganic matter also occur.

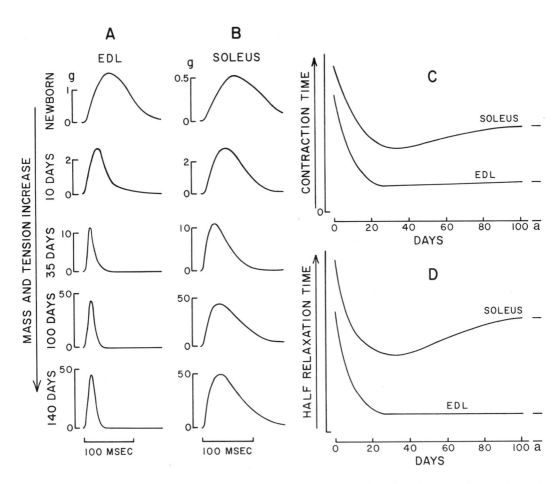

Figure 9-18. Time relations of single isometric contractions of *extensor digitorium longus* (EDL) and soleus muscles at various times during development. **A** and **B.** Representative tension-time curves taken at several ages. **C** and **D.** Times for contraction and half-relaxation of EDL and soleus muscles plotted against the age. The portions of the curves above *a* on the abscissae are for muscles from animals aged 140 days or more. (Redrawn, with permission, from R. Close. 1964. Dynamic properties of fast and slow skeletal muscles of the rat during development. *J. Physiol.* 173:74.)

STUDY OUTLINE

GENERAL COMMENTS   Contraction—develops tension, does work.

Two types—skeletal and cardiac.

STRUCTURE

CONNECTIVE TISSUE   Fascia.

Epimysium surrounds entire muscle.

Perimysium divides muscle into fascicles.

Endomysium surrounds individual muscle fibers.

MICROSCOPIC STRUCTURE   Multiple nuclei and cross-striations.

SARCOMERE   Basic contractile unit.

Between two Z lines; consists of the A band between two halves of I bands.

Muscle fiber is composed of many sarcomeres in series.

SUBMICROSCOPIC STRUCTURE

SARCOPLASMIC RETICULUM   Muscle fiber contains myofibrils, is surrounded by membrane system (sarcoplasmic reticulum).

TRIAD: Two terminal cisterns of sarcoplasmic reticulum and transverse tubular system.

External fluids and membrane structures penetrate deeply into muscle fiber.

Contraction is initiated by action potential propagated inward along transverse tubule.

Synchronous activation of all sarcomeres within muscle fiber.

MOLECULAR STRUCTURE OF SARCOMERE   Orderly array of thick (myosin) and thin (actin) filaments.

Thin filaments connect with Z line, extend into A band, overlap thick filaments.

Double hexagonal array in cross-section.

THICK FILAMENTS   Myosin molecule contains light meromyosin (body of thick filaments) and heavy meromyosin (cross-bridges).

Cross-bridges contact thin filaments, pivot to make filaments slide.

THIN FILAMENTS   Globular G-actin binds Ca^{++} and ATP, forms fibrous F-actin.

Tropomyosin is associated with F-actin strands.

Troponin (TN)—subunits TN-I, TN-C, TN-A.

TN-C binds Ca^{++} to initiate contraction.

MOLECULAR BASIS OF CONTRACTION

CONTRACTILE PROTEINS   Four identified—myosin, actin, tropomyosin, and troponin.

Enzymes, ATP, water, ions are also needed for contraction and relaxation.

EXCITATION-CONTRACTION COUPLING

RELEASE OF Ca^{++}   Depolarization extends into fibers through T-tubules.

Ca^{++} is released from terminal cistern of SR.

CHANGE OF CONFORMATION IN THIN FILAMENT   TN-C binds Ca^{++}, causes change in conformation of troponin complex—active site on actin filament is exposed to allow attachment of cross-bridges.

CHANGE OF CONFORMATION IN THICK FILAMENT   With activation of ATPase, heavy meromyosin cross-bridges attach to thin filament.

"Hinged" heads develop force, slide filaments; sarcomere shortens.

RELAXATION Ca^{++} is taken up by SR, cross-bridges detach, and sarcomere lengthens again.

PHENOMENOLOGY OF MUSCLE CONTRACTION

MOTOR UNIT   Single motoneuron innervates several to many muscle fibers; all contract at once.

Force increases as additional motor units are activated.

CYCLE OF CONTRACTION AND RELAXATION

LATENT PERIOD   Interval between stimulus and contraction; action potential is formed, Ca^{++} is released, and so on.

CONTRACTION   From beginning to development of maximum tension.

RELAXATION   From peak tension to resting value; slower process than contraction.

FAST MUSCLES AND SLOW MUSCLES   Slow muscles, red (due to myoglobin); have longer cycles; examples: breast muscle of duck, soleus of mammals.

Fast muscles, white; have shorter cycles; examples: breast muscle of chicken, lateral rectus of mammals.

Example of muscle of intermediate speed: gastrocnemius.

Differ also in histochemistry and morphology.

Crossing nerves can convert fast to slow and slow to fast; histochemical properties also change.

SUMMATION AND TETANUS   If second stimulus is applied during relaxation, contractions summate.

If stimulus is repeated frequently enough, contractions fuse.

If frequency is great enough, smooth curve of tension is formed (tetanus, maximal force of muscle).

TYPES OF MUSCLE CONTRACTION
Studied in isolated tissues; isotonic and isometric.

ISOTONIC CONTRACTION   Muscle shortens.

Preloaded (load on muscle before contraction); example: ventricular end-diastolic pressure.

Afterloaded (more load added after contraction begins); example: ventricular myocardium during ejection phase.

ISOMETRIC CONTRACTION   Muscle develops tension, does not shorten.

All muscles contract isometrically until developed tension equals load.

MECHANICAL MODEL   Contractile element in series with elastic element; another elastic element is in parallel.

Connective tissue and other noncontractile elements provide elasticity.

ACTIVE STATE   Contractile element (sliding filaments of sarcomere) shortens.

Persists for about 10 milliseconds in skeletal muscle at room temperature.

Maintained by repeated stimuli, maximal tension of muscle developed at tetanus.

In single twitch, or less than tetanus, some shortening of contractile element is absorbed by stretch of series elastic element.

Stretch series elastic, transmits full force of contraction.

RELATIONSHIPS AMONG FORCE, LENGTH, AND VELOCITY
LENGTH-TENSION   Muscle stretched be-

fore contraction develops more tension, up to limit.

May be related to overlap of actin and myosin in filaments.

FORCE-VELOCITY   Velocity and amount of shortening are related inversely to load.

Maximum velocity with no load; no shortening if load equals maximum tension developed (isometric).

DEVELOPMENT OF MUSCLE

SKELETAL MUSCLE
MYOBLASTS   Immature muscle cells; differentiate into fast type and slow type.

MUSCLE FIBERS   Myoblasts divide and align, eventually form tubelike structure.

Contractile proteins aggregate into myofibrils.

Internal membrane system develops.

SATELLITE CELLS   Inactive myoblasts with potential to form new muscle fibers.

Activated during hypertrophy or by injury.

Numerous during early postnatal development, decrease with maturation.

INTERNAL MEMBRANE SYSTEM   Transverse tubule develops from sarcolemmal invagination.

Sarcoplasmic reticulum forms from rough endoplasmic reticulum.

INORGANIC MATTER   High concentration of Na^+, K^+, and H_2O in immature muscle; cells contain more Na^+ than K^+.

In mature muscle, H_2O is less, and cells contain more K^+ than Na^+.

POSTNATAL CHANGES IN CONTRACTILE PROPERTIES
FAST AND SLOW MUSCLES   Differentiate early in postnatal life.

BIBLIOGRAPHY

Bahler, A.S. 1967. Series elastic component of mammalian skeletal muscle. *Am. J. Physiol.* 213:1560.

Bahler, A.S.; Fales, J.T.; and Zierler, K.L. 1968. The dynamic properties of mammalian skeletal muscle. *J. Gen. Physiol.* 51:369.

Bastholm, E. 1950. The history of muscle physiology. *Acta Historica Scientiarum Naturalium Et Medicinalium.* Volume 7. Copenhagen: Bibliotheca Universitatis.

Bessman, S.P., and Geiger, P.J. 1981. Transport of energy in muscle: The phosphoryl-creatine shuttle. *Science* 211:448.

Bloom, W., and Fawcett, D.W. 1975. *A Textbook of Histology* (10th ed). Philadelphia: Saunders.

Bourne, G.H. 1972–1973. *The Structure and Function of Muscle.* 4 volumes. New York: Academic Press.

Bowman, W. 1840. On the minute structure and movements of voluntary muscle. *Phil. Trans. R. Soc.* 130:457.

Church, J.C.T. 1970. A model for myogenesis using the concept of the satellite cell segment. In *Regeneration of Striated Muscle, and Myogenesis.* Edited by A. Mauro, S.A. Shafig, and A.T. Milhorot. Amsterdam: Excerpta Medica.

Close, R. 1964. Dynamic properties of fast and slow skeletal muscles of the rat during development. *J. Physiol.* 173:74.

Dowben, R.W., and Shay, J.W. (eds.). 1982. *Cell and Muscle Motility.* New York: Plenum.

Ebashi, S.; Maruyama, K; and Endo, M. 1980. *Muscle Contraction: Its Regulatory Mechanisms.* New York: Springer-Verlag.

Eccles, J.C., and Sherrington, C.S. 1930. Numbers and contraction values of individual motor-units examined in some muscles of the limb. *Proc. R. Soc. Lond.* 106:326.

Edge, M.B. 1970. Development of apposed sarcoplasmic reticulum at the T-system and sarcolemma and the change in orientation of triads in rat skeletal muscle. *Dev. Biol.* 23:634.

Ernst, E. 1963. *Biophysics of the Striated Muscle.* Budapest: Akademiai Kiado.

Ezerman, E.G., and Ishikawa, H. 1967. Differentiation of the sarcoplasmic reticulum and T-system in developing chick skeletal muscle in vitro. *J. Cell Biol.* 35:405.

Fischman, D.A. 1970. The synthesis and assembly of myofibrils in embryonic muscle. *Curr. Top. Dev. Biol.* 5:235.

Fulton, J.F. 1926. *Muscular Contraction and the Reflex Control of Movement.* Baltimore: Williams & Wilkins.

Hazlewood, C.F., and Nichols, B.L. 1969. Changes in muscle sodium, potassium, chloride, water, and voltage during maturation in the rat: An experimental and theoretical study. *Johns Hopkins Med. J.* 125:119.

Hill, A.V. 1950. Development of the active state of muscle during the latent period. *Proc. R. Soc. Lond.* 137:320.

Hill, A.V. 1953. The mechanics of active muscle. *Proc. R. Soc. Lond.* 141:104.

Huxley, H.E. 1973. Molecular basis of contraction in cross-striated muscles. In *The Structure and Function of Muscle.* Edited by G.H. Bourne. Volume I. New York: Academic Press.

Ishikawa, H. 1968. Formation of elaborate networks of T-system tubules in cultured skeletal muscle with special reference to the T-system formation. *J. Cell Biol.* 38:51.

Jewell, B.R., and Wilkie, D.R. 1958. An analysis of the mechanical components in frog's striated muscle. *J. Physiol.* 143:515.

Jolesz, F., and Sreter, F.A. 1981. Development, innervation, and activity-pattern induced changes in skeletal muscle. *Annu. Rev. Physiol.* 43:531.

Lipton, B.H., and Schultz, E. 1979. Developmental fate of skeletal muscle satellite cells. *Science* 205:1292.

Martonosi, A. 1982. The development of sarcoplasmic reticulum membranes. *Annu. Rev. Physiol.* 44:337.

Ontell, M., and Dunn, R.F. 1978. Neonatal muscle growth: A quantitative study. *Am. J. Anat.* 152:539.

Peachey, L.D. 1965. The sarcoplasmic reticulum and transverse tubules of the frog's sartorius. *J. Cell Biol.* 25:209.

Phillips, C.A., and Petrofsky, J.S. (eds.). 1983. *Mechanisms of Skeletal and Cardiac Muscle.* Springfield, Illinois: Charles C. Thomas.

Pollack, G.H. 1983. The cross-bridge theory. *Physiol. Rev.* 63:1049.

Porter, K.R., and Palade, G.E. 1957. Studies on the endoplasmic reticulum. III. Its form and distribution in striated muscle cells. *J. Biophys. Biochem. Cytol.* 3:269.

Rosse, C., and Clawson, D.K. 1980. *The Musculoskeletal System in Health and Disease.* Hagerstown, Maryland: Harper & Row.

Sandow, A. 1944. General properties of latency-relaxation. *J. Cell. Comp. Physiol.* 24:221.

Sandow, A. 1965. Excitation-contraction coupling in skeletal muscle. *Pharmacol. Rev.* 17:265.

Schaefer, H., and Gopfert, H. 1937. Aktiönsstrom und Optisches verhalten des froschmuskels in ihrer zeitlichen beziehung zurzuckung. *Pflügers Arch.* 238:684.

Schiaffino, S., and Margreth, A. 1969. Coordinated development of the sarcoplasmic reticulum and T-system during postnatal differentiations of rat skeletal muscle. *J. Cell Biol.* 41:855.

Wilkie, D.R. 1949. Relation between force and velocity in human muscle. *J. Physiol.* 110:249.

Wilkie, D.R. 1956. Measurement of the series elastic component at various times during a single muscle twitch. *J. Physiol.* 134:527.

Wilkie, D.R. 1956. The mechanical properties of muscle. *Br. Med. Bull.* 12:177.

10

Neuromuscular Junction

CHAPTER CONTENTS

FUNCTIONAL ANATOMY

Motoneuron

The large myelinated nerve fibers that originate from the anterior horns of the spinal cord innervate skeletal muscle cells; the axon that originates from the cell body of a given *motoneuron* branches many times. In the adult mammal, each branch innervates one muscle cell and each muscle cell is innervated by only one branch of an axon. In newborn mammals, however, the innervation is different, in that a muscle cell is innervated by branches of axons from more than one motoneuron. Trophic factors released by the muscle cell and the inability of the motoneuron to maintain connections with many muscle cells may cause the loss of multi-innervated muscle cells during maturation.

Motor Unit

The axon and the muscle cells innervated by its branches make up the *motor unit*. The size of the motor unit, that is, the number of muscle cells innervated by a given axon, determines the degree of muscle control. For example, where fine motor control exists, such as in the muscles

of the eye, as few as 13 muscle cells are innervated by a given axon. However, in the head of the gastrocnemius, as many as 1700 muscle cells are innervated by the branches of a single axon.

Neuromuscular Junction

As the branch of an axon approaches the muscle cell, it loses its myelin sheath and comes to lie in an invagination of the muscle membrane (Figure 10-1). The nerve ending and the specialized area of the muscle membrane underlying it is called the *neuromuscular,* or *myoneural, junction.* The specialized area of the muscle membrane that lies directly below the end of the axon is called the motor end-plate. Because most adult mammalian muscles are innervated by a single axon, each muscle cell has only one motor end-plate, usually located in the middle of the muscle cell.

MOTOR END-PLATE

The end-plate region of the muscle membrane and the portion of the muscle cell directly below the end-plate are highly specialized. The membrane has many folds, and the sarcoplasm beneath it contains abundant mitochondria. The depression in the muscle cell in which the nerve

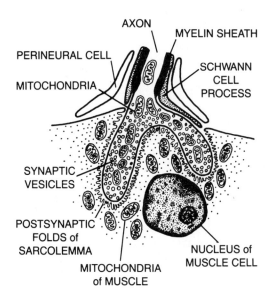

Figure 10-1. Relationship between the axon terminal, the terminal Schwann cell, and the postsynaptic folds of the sarcolemma. (Redrawn, with permission, from R.E.M. Bowden and L.W. Duchen. 1976. *Handbook of Experimental Pharmacology,* Vol. 42, E. Zamis, ed. New York: Springer Verlag.)

ending lies is called the *synaptic gutter* or *trough.* The depth, shape, and size of the trough depend on the animal species and the particular muscle. The gutter tends to be deeper in mammalian muscles and more complex in muscles of the fast twitch type.

ACETYLCHOLINE

The axon terminal that lies within the synaptic gutter contains many mitochondria, has no myelin sheath, and contains many membrane-bound vesicles (see Figure 10-1). The vesicles contain the neurotransmitter *acetylcholine* (ACh), which is synthesized and packaged in the axon terminal. In response to an action potential, the vesicles migrate to the end of the axon terminal, fuse with the axon membrane, and discharge their contents into the synaptic gutter. The membranes of empty vesicles may be recycled to the interior of the axon terminal, where they are loaded with ACh again.

The ACh that is released into the synaptic gutter is degraded by the enzyme *acetylcholine esterase,* which is located within the gutter and on the motor end-plate. The acetylcholine esterase rapidly degrades the ACh that is released by a single action potential; consequently, the concentration of ACh within the synaptic gutter

is high for only 2–3 milliseconds. This is long enough to depolarize the motor end-plate temporarily, yet not long enough to keep the motor end-plate depolarized continuously, and, hence, refractory to further stimulation.

TRANSMISSION OF INFORMATION

Prejunctional Events

QUANTAL RELEASE OF ACETYLCHOLINE

Because each vesicle in the axon terminal constitutes a package, or *quantum,* of ACh molecules, the release of ACh in such discrete packages has been termed the *quantal theory* of ACh release. It has been estimated that one vesicle contains 2000 to 10,000 molecules of ACh; thus, one quantum represents this number of ACh molecules. A single action potential in the motoneuron may release as many as 100–300 quanta of ACh. A single quantum cannot depolarize the motor end-plate enough to produce an action potential, but it does produce a small depolarization of the motor end-plate, called a *miniature end-plate potential.* Because an action potential in the motoneuron releases enough quanta of ACh to depolarize the motor end-plate maximally, there is always one action potential in the muscle cell per action potential in the motoneuron.

CALCIUM IONS

Calcium ions are required for the release of ACh. It is thought that the action potential in the motoneuron permits the entry of Ca^{++} into the nerve ending, or at least into the axon terminal, which causes migration of the vesicles and the subsequent release of ACh into the synaptic cleft.

Postjunctional Events

SENSITIVITY TO ACETYLCHOLINE

The sensitivity of the muscle cell to ACh is greatest at the motor end-plate and falls off rapidly on all sides. The entire surface of the muscle cell of neonates is sensitive to ACh, and sensitivity is limited to the area of the neuromuscular junction only after maturation. The reduction in the area of sensitivity probably is related to the innervation of the muscle. This concept is supported by the observation that

CLINICAL CORRELATION

10.1   Myasthenia Gravis

CASE REPORT

The Patient: A 34-year-old woman.

Principal Complaint: Muscle weakness.

History: About 2 months before the current admission, the patient began to notice episodes of diplopia (double vision), ptosis (drooping of the eyelids), difficulty chewing and swallowing, and generalized weakness. The severity of the symptoms increased with activity, decreased with rest, and varied with time. About 1 month before the current admission, she experienced a particularly severe episode of muscular weakness, during which she was unable to walk. The patient was seen by a physician, who suspected that she had myasthenia gravis. She was given 0.5 mg of neostigmine methylsulfate intramuscularly, which inhibits cholinesterase, thereby prolonging the action of the ACh that is released at synapses and effector sites. Her condition temporarily improved. Another severe attack resulted in her present admission.

Clinical Examination: The patient was dyspneic (breathing with difficulty). She had bilateral ptosis, some loss of ability to move her eyes and turn her head, inability to close her mouth completely, and weakness of the arms and legs. Repeated attempts to open her eyes widely or to clench her teeth produced greater fatigue. Because of the fatigue of the respiratory muscles, an endotracheal tube was inserted and mechanical respiration was provided.

Treatment: Neostigmine methylsulfate was administered intravenously in increments of 0.125 mg/5 min until a satisfactory response was obtained (indicated by strength of hand-grip). The patient was extubated and neostigmine bromide was given orally in increments of 7.5 mg until a satisfactory response was obtained. Pyridostigmine bromide, which also inhibits cholinesterase and prolongs the action of the ACh that is released at synapses and effector sites, in sustained release tablets (6–8 hours' duration), was used at night.

Comment: The muscular weakness of myasthenia gravis is caused by inadequate transmission of excitation at the neuromuscular junction. The condition appears to reflect an autoimmune response that decreases the number of ACh receptors. The destructive immune reaction also alters the ultrastructure of the synaptic cleft. Exacerbations and remissions occur frequently, sometimes in response to such variables as upper respiratory tract infection, loss of sleep, intake of alcohol, and menstruation. Antireceptor antibody has been identified in patients who have myasthenia gravis.

Drugs that inhibit cholinesterase benefit the patient by decreasing the rate of destruction of endogenous ACh. Presumably, a larger number of receptors, over a greater area of the motor end-plate, thereby are exposed to concentrations of ACh that are adequate for stimulation. The fluctuations in the myasthenic condition require that patients learn to modify the dosage schedule as their needs change.

Outcome: The patient was stabilized on neostigmine bromide by day and sustained-release pyridostigmine bromide at night. Her condition has not increased in severity, but the prognosis (probable outcome) with myasthenia gravis is uncertain.

denervation of adult muscle makes the entire surface of the muscle cell sensitive to ACh.

DEPOLARIZATION

The ACh that is released from the axon terminal into the synaptic gutter depolarizes the motor end-plate by increasing the permeability of the membrane to various cations, primarily Na^+ and K^+. The mechanism by which ACh causes these increases in ionic conductance is not known. *Depolarization* of the motor end-plate causes current to flow in adjacent portions of the muscle cell, which produces a propagated action potential.

SUMMARY

The events at the neuromuscular junction can be summarized as follows. An action potential in the motoneuron releases enough ACh to depolarize the motor end-plate. This depolarization in turn produces an action potential in the muscle cell membrane, which causes the muscle to contract.

STUDY OUTLINE

FUNCTIONAL ANATOMY

MOTONEURON   Muscle cell innervated by only one branch of a motoneuron.

MOTOR UNIT   The muscle cells innervated by a given motoneuron.

NEUROMUSCULAR JUNCTION   Specialized area of nerve and muscle interaction.

MOTOR END-PLATE   Specialized area of muscle cell directly below nerve ending.

ACETYLCHOLINE   Chemical transmitter released by motor nerve, degraded by acetylcholine esterase in synaptic cleft or on motor end-plate.

TRANSMISSION OF INFORMATION

PREJUNCTIONAL EVENTS

QUANTAL RELEASE OF ACETYLCHOLINE   Acetylcholine (ACh) is released in vesicles; each is a "quantum."

Depolarizes end-plate, produces action potential in muscle.

CALCIUM IONS   Required for ACh release.

POSTJUNCTIONAL EVENTS

SENSITIVITY TO ACETYLCHOLINE   Greatest at motor end-plate.

DEPOLARIZATION   Due to increased permeability of end-plate.

Causes current that produces action potential in muscle.

SUMMARY   Action potential in motoneuron → release of ACh at neuromuscular junction → end-plate depolarized → current → depolarized muscle → action potential in muscle.

BIBLIOGRAPHY

Aidley, D.J. 1971. *The Physiology of Excitable Cells.* New York: Cambridge University Press.

Bowden, R.E.M., and Duchen, L.W. 1976. The anatomy and pathology of the neuromuscular junction. In *Neuromuscular Junction.* Edited by E. Zaimis. New York: Springer-Verlag.

Drachman, D.B. 1978. Myasthenia gravis. *N. Engl. J. Med.* 298:136.

Fambrough, D.M. 1979. Control of acetylcholine receptors in skeletal muscle. *Physiol. Rev.* 59:165.

Gage, P.W. 1976. Generation of end-plate potentials. *Physiol. Rev.* 56:177.

Peper, K.; Bradley, R.J.; and Dreyer, F. 1982. The acetylcholine receptor at the neuromuscular junction. *Physiol. Rev.* 62:1271.

11

Physiology of Smooth Muscle

CHAPTER CONTENTS

STRUCTURE AND FUNCTION

Contraction

Smooth muscle cells surround hollow organs such as the uterus, stomach, intestine, bladder, and blood vessels. Unlike skeletal muscle cells, which insert through tendons to bones, smooth muscle cells attach to a matrix of the connective tissues, collagen and elastin. The function of most smooth muscle is to change the volume of the organ it surrounds, by *contraction* or relaxation. However, it is important to realize that the smooth muscle cell also has other functions, which can affect its contractile properties.

Synthesis

A second function of smooth muscle cells is synthesis, which encompasses the synthesis of additional cells (hyperplasia), the synthesis of intracellular proteins such as actomyosin, and the synthesis of the connective tissue proteins, collagen and elastin.

Secretion

Because the connective tissue proteins are found in the extracellular space, a third function of smooth muscle is secretion.

Neural and Humoral Influences

The contractile activity of the smooth muscle cell is influenced by the *autonomic nervous system* and *humoral substances* that circulate in the blood. The means by which contractile activity is changed will be discussed later. The synthetic activity of the smooth muscle cell also may be subject to the same influences. One example is the effect of *estrogen* on the immature uterus; at puberty, plasma estrogen levels increase and stimulate the synthesis of more uterine smooth muscle cells. Another example involves the arterial wall. Injury to the endothelial lining of a vessel, such as the damage that is caused by abnormally high arterial blood pressure (hypertension), allows factors associated with the platelets of the blood to increase the net production of collagen and elastin by smooth muscle cells and to modify the ability of the cells to handle fats (atherosclerosis). In the example of the uterus, changes in synthesis support normal contractile function; however, in the blood vessel wall abnormal changes in synthesis can alter contractile function. In general, the balance between the various functions of the smooth muscle cells defines whether the cells and the organ walls that they form operate normally.

COMPARISON OF SMOOTH MUSCLE WITH SKELETAL MUSCLE

The objective of the discussion that follows is to explain the responses of the whole tissue in terms of its cellular and subcellular properties. The characteristics of smooth muscle that essentially are the same as those of skeletal muscle are noted but not discussed, and the reader is encouraged to review the appropriate material in the section on skeletal muscle, if necessary. The characteristics of smooth muscle that differ from those of skeletal muscle are discussed.

Mechanical Characteristics

The mechanical properties of a muscle usually are described in terms of the relationships of force-velocity, active-length–tension, and passive-length–tension. Qualitatively, these relationships are the same for smooth muscle as they are for skeletal muscle. Quantitatively, they differ in the values for V_{max} and P_0 of the force-velocity curve. In general, smooth muscle

has a much lower maximum velocity of shortening (V_{max}), yet, in some cases, it can develop as much maximum isometric force (P_0) as skeletal muscle does. The observation that smooth muscle exhibits an active-length–tension relationship similar to that of skeletal muscle supports the sliding-filament model of force development.

Structural Characteristics

Even though smooth muscle exhibits mechanical properties similar to those of skeletal muscle, smooth muscle is different structurally. In skeletal muscle, the individual cell spans the whole length of the muscle, and the ends of the cells attach to tendonous material. In addition, most skeletal muscle cells are arranged parallel to each other. Smooth muscle cells are short (50–200 μm) compared to skeletal muscle cells (up to 300,000 μm). A single muscle cell is not long enough to reach all the way around an organ; thus, the cells are bound together by strands of collagen and elastin. Evidence suggests that there are few cell-to-cell mechanical connections, and so the contractile force generated by a given cell must be transmitted throughout the organ wall by connection between the cell and the connective tissue matrix. Unlike skeletal muscle, smooth muscle cells are not always arranged parallel to each other throughout the organ. Such nonparallel arrangement occurs in the aorta. The tunica media of the aorta consists of alternating layers of elastin and smooth muscle cells surrounded by collagen. The smooth muscle cells in each layer are oriented at a different angle relative to adjacent layers. Because smooth muscle cells are embedded in a matrix of connective tissue and are not always parallel to one another, it is difficult to extrapolate from the mechanical characteristics of the whole organ wall to those of the individual smooth muscle cells that make up the wall.

Organization of Filaments

Not only does the arrangement of smooth muscle cells within an organ wall differ from that of skeletal muscle, but the arrangement of the contractile filaments within the cell also differs. Although the mechanical characteristics of an active-length–tension relationship in smooth muscle are consistent with the sliding-filament model of contraction, morphological data do not support this model for smooth muscle as clearly as they do for skeletal muscle.

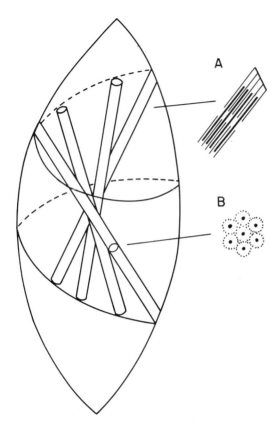

thin filaments attach at electron-dense areas along the cell membrane. The protein that comprises these dense areas is α-actinin, which also is a constituent of the Z band in skeletal muscle. Therefore, these dense membrane areas can be thought of as the Z bands for smooth muscle.

The third difference between smooth muscle and skeletal muscle is that the thick filaments and the thin filaments are arranged at an angle in smooth muscle cells, rather than parallel to the long axis of the cell as they are in skeletal muscle. This means that the filaments develop force at an angle to the long axis of the cell. These various features are illustrated diagrammatically in Figure 11-1.

Attachments

Evidence that the contractile filaments exert force on the cell membrane comes from scanning electron micrographs of individual smooth muscle cells of the frog stomach. In the relaxed state, the cell membrane appears smooth (Fig-

Figure 11-1. Arrangement of contractile filaments in smooth muscle. Bundles of thick and thin filaments are represented as cylinders. **A.** The arrangement of filaments when a longitudinal section of the cylinder is viewed. **B.** A cross-section of a cylinder. Note that the filament bundles course diagonally through the cell and insert at specific areas on the cell membrane. (From J.V. Small. 1977. *Excitation-Contraction Coupling in Smooth Muscle.* Originally published by Elsevier/North Holland).

For a variety of technical reasons, it has been possible only recently to visualize clearly both thick and thin contractile filaments in electron micrographs of smooth muscle. Recent micrographs reveal several interesting characteristics of smooth muscle contractile filaments.

The first difference is that the ratio of thin filaments to thick filaments is 16 to 1, whereas in skeletal muscle the ratio is 6 to 1. Thin filaments tend to surround thick filaments as they do in skeletal muscles; however, there is no morphological evidence to suggest that the filaments move relative to each other during contraction and relaxation.

The second difference is that there are no Z bands and, therefore, no easily identifiable sarcomeres. Instead of attaching to Z bands, the

A

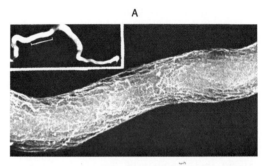

B

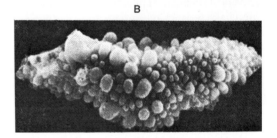

Figure 11-2. Scanning electron micrographs of (A) relaxed (× 5780, inset × 580) and (B) contracted isolated smooth muscle cells from frog stomach (× 1496). Note the large number of membrane invaginations in the contracted muscle. These invaginations correspond to areas of cell membrane where the contractile filaments appear to insert. (From F.S. Fay, et al. 1976. *Physiology of Smooth Muscle*, E. Bülbring, ed. New York: Raven Press.)

ure 11-2A); when the cell contracts, the membrane becomes contorted (Figure 11-2B) by many invaginations. At the base of each invagination is a dense area of membrane in which thin filaments end. Therefore, activation of the contractile proteins may lead to the pulling in of these discrete membrane areas. Such invaginations of the cell membrane probably do not occur normally, because the cells are attached to the connective tissue matrix.

Protein Composition and Organization

The protein composition and organization of the thick and the thin filaments of smooth muscle and skeletal muscle are similar in that the major protein of the thin filament is actin and the major protein of the thick filament is myosin; however, there are differences. Although the molar ratio of tropomyosin to actin in the thin filament of smooth muscle is the same as it is in the thin filament of skeletal muscle, the third constituent of the thin filament in skeletal muscle, troponin, has been difficult to demonstrate in smooth muscle, and, therefore, it is thought to be absent. The interaction of troponin and calcium forms the basis for regulating the ATPase activity of actomyosin in skeletal muscle; hence, the supposed absence of troponin from smooth muscle implies that the regulation of this enzyme in smooth muscle is different. The molecular basis for this regulation is discussed later.

The difficulty of visualizing thick filaments in smooth muscle cells has led to controversy about the organization of myosin molecules in the thick filament. Electron micrographs of smooth muscle cells demonstrate thick filaments that have tapered ends and a helical arrangement of myosin molecules but no central bare zone. The bare zone in skeletal muscle is thought to represent that area of the thick filament in which the orientation of the myosin molecules has changed and the filaments have end-to-end polarity (Figure 11-3A). The absence of this bare zone in thick filaments of smooth muscle cells raises the question of how polarity occurs. One possible explanation is supported by in vitro studies that demonstrate filaments formed by myosin molecules oriented in opposite directions on opposite sides (Figure 11-3B). This results in "face-polarized" filaments rather than "end-to-end" polarized filaments.

Direct chemical analyses indicate that smooth muscle cells have an actin-to-myosin

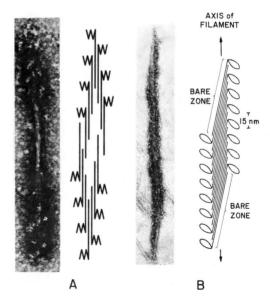

Figure 11-3. **A.** Myosin isolated from skeletal muscle forms filaments with a central bare zone and end-to-end polarity. **B.** Myosin isolated from smooth muscle forms filaments with a bare zone at each end and side-to-side polarity. (From H.E. Huxley. The mechanism of muscular contraction. Copyright © 1965 by Scientific American, Inc. All rights reserved, and from R. Craig and J. Megerman. 1977. Assembly of smooth muscle myosin into side-polar filaments. *J. Cell. Biol.* 75:992.)

molar ratio of 31 to 1, compared to a ratio of 3 to 1 in skeletal muscle. These analyses, which agree with estimates of filament content based on electron micrographs, mean that each gram of smooth muscle cell may have twice as much actin and only one-fourth as much myosin as is found in skeletal muscle. The smaller amount of myosin in smooth muscle raises the question of how tissue that contains smooth muscle can develop as much force as it does. The answer is not known, but it may involve the structural organization of the cells, the contractile filaments within the cells, or a combination of the two.

BIOCHEMICAL CHARACTERISTICS

Actin and Myosin

The biochemical characteristics of contractile proteins in smooth muscles and skeletal muscles are similar in some ways and different in other ways. The actin and myosin of smooth muscle are chemically distinct from the actin and myosin of skeletal muscle. In addition, the enzymatic activity of the actomyosin that is isolated from smooth muscle is much slower than that from skeletal muscle. The lower maximum rate of splitting ATP explains, in part, why the maximum velocity of shortening is slower in smooth muscle than in skeletal muscle.

Light Chain Proteins

Because the identification of troponin in smooth muscle has been difficult, alternative explanations for the regulation of actomyosin ATPase activity have been sought. The most generally accepted mechanism of regulation involves a protein that is associated with the myosin molecule of the thick filament. In all of the muscle tissues that have been studied, the globular end of the myosin molecule is associated with a group of proteins called "light chain proteins." In skeletal muscle, each myosin molecule has three classes of light chains, based on their molecular weight, while smooth muscle has two classes of light chains. One of these light chains, which has a molecular weight of 20,000 daltons, is implicated in the regulation of actomyosin ATPase activity in smooth muscle.

Calcium and Calmodulin

Actomyosin ATPase is activated by an increase in the intracellular concentration of calcium, $[Ca^{++}]$, in both skeletal and smooth muscle; however, in smooth muscle, Ca^{++} binds to a cytoplasmic protein called *calmodulin,* which is part of a much larger protein called *light chain kinase* (Figure 11-4). The binding of Ca^{++} ac-

tivates the kinase, which enables calmodulin to catalyze the phosphorylation of the light chain of myosin referred to above. As more Ca^{++} binds to calmodulin, more kinase is activated, more myosin light chains are phosphorylated, and the actomyosin ATPase activity increases. When the $[Ca^{++}]$ is decreased to the extent that the light chain kinase no longer is active, actomyosin ATPase is inactivated, and the muscle relaxes. This inactivation permits another cytoplasmic enzyme, light chain phosphatase, to remove the phosphate from the light chain and thereby to inactivate actomyosin. It is not known whether the activity of the light chain phosphatase changes during contraction and relaxation. In summary, the enzyme activity of smooth muscle actomyosin is determined at any moment by the balance of activities of light chain kinase and light chain phosphatase, which is regulated by the $[Ca^{++}]$.

This type of regulation is interesting for several reasons. First, the range of $[Ca^{++}]$ over which the light chain kinase is regulated is identical to the range of $[Ca^{++}]$ over which troponin is regulated in skeletal muscle. This similarity suggests that the affinities of calmodulin and troponin for Ca^{++} are similar; however, the proteins are distinct. Second, the type of regulation found in smooth muscle is intrinsically slower than that found in skeletal muscle because the former involves an enzymatic phosphorylation, while the latter involves the physical reorientation of molecules. This slow-

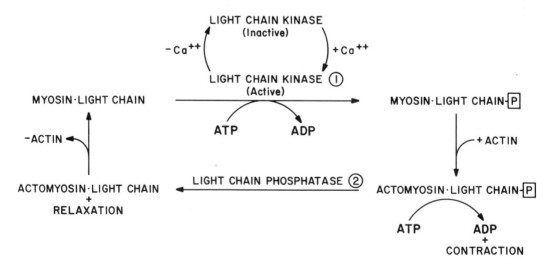

Figure 11-4.   If the activity of light chain kinase (**1**) is greater than the activity of light chain phos- phatase (**2**), contraction results; if the reverse is true, relaxation results.

ness of activation of actomyosin may explain, in part, the relatively longer delay between stimulation and contractile response in smooth muscle. Third, this type of regulation is not unique to smooth muscle but also is characteristic of actomyosins isolated from cell membranes and invertebrate muscles. In fact, it may be the basic form of regulation from which that found in skeletal and cardiac muscles evolved. Myosins of skeletal and cardiac muscles have light chains, but they do not function in a regulatory capacity, as the myosins in smooth muscle do. In this respect, therefore, they may be remnants of evolution.

REGULATION OF CONTRACTION

Calcium

The intracellular $[Ca^{++}]$ indirectly controls the enzyme activity of actomyosin and, thereby, the magnitude of contraction. Smooth muscle, unlike skeletal muscle, does not have a well developed sarcoplasmic reticulum and transverse tubular system. For this reason, a variety of sources of Ca^{++} have been suggested (Figure 11-5). Intracellular vesicular structures have been observed by electron microscopy in some smooth muscles. These structures are located close to the cell surface and, therefore, may be affected by changes in cellular potential or by humoral agents that act on the cell membrane. Because the number of these vesicular structures varies greatly from one muscle to another, other sources of Ca^{++}, such as mitochondria and the extracellular fluid, have been suggested. Mitochondria from a variety of muscle and nonmuscle tissues take up Ca^{++}; however, it is not clear whether they can release Ca^{++} under physiological conditions and whether the rates of release and uptake are compatible with the rates of contraction and relaxation.

The extracellular fluid also could supply Ca^{++} for the contractile process. In the relaxed state, a large electrochemical gradient favors the movement of Ca^{++} into the cell, and Ca^{++} is thought to carry the depolarizing current during the action potential. The Ca^{++} that is thus transported could be responsible for contraction. Because the cell is not always contracted, the permeability of the cell to Ca^{++} must be low, and the cell must have some way to maintain a low intracellular $[Ca^{++}]$. Systems of active transport have been identified and proposed to transport Ca^{++} directly out of the cell or to be linked to the movement of Na^+ into

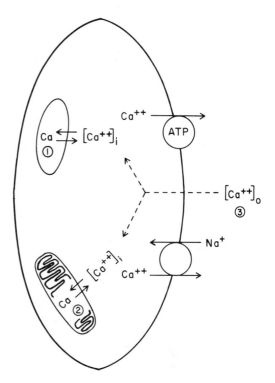

Figure 11-5. Sources of calcium in smooth muscle for activation of the contractile proteins. **1.** Intracellular stores within intracellular vesicular structures. **2.** Intracellular stores within mitochondria. **3.** Extracellular stores.

the cell down its electrochemical gradient (see Figure 11-5). In summary, neither the specific source of Ca^{++} for the activation of actomyosin in a given smooth muscle nor the specific source of Ca^{++} that is released by a given form of stimulation is known, and this is an important area for future research.

Cellular Potential

Whatever its source, Ca^{++} can be released for activation in a variety of ways. As with skeletal muscle, a decrease of the *cellular potential* causes contraction of the cell. Some smooth muscle, such as that which lines the gastrointestinal tract, undergoes rhythmic changes in potential called *slow waves*. Periodically, bursts of action potentials arise from the slow waves and cause contraction. Smooth muscle cells with this type of rhythmic activity also have intercellular connections that facilitate transmission of the changing potential between cells and thereby coordinate the contractile response. Because such smooth muscle cells function together, they have been classified as *single-unit smooth muscles.* Other types of smooth muscle cells do not exhibit rhythmic electrical and contractile activity and do not have many functional intercellular connections. One example of this type of smooth muscle is that which is found in the walls of many blood vessels. In such muscle cells, the potential changes in graded fashion, rather than forming action potentials, and the graded depolarization is associated with graded contractions. Because each muscle cell functions independently, this type of smooth muscle has been termed *multi-unit.*

Neural Effects

Whether the smooth muscle is of the single-unit or multi-unit type, its contractile activity can be modified at any moment by extrinsic factors such as the level of autonomic neural activity or the concentrations of humoral agents. Smooth muscle is innervated by both the parasympathetic and sympathetic divisions of the autonomic nervous system. Unlike skeletal muscle, in which the motor nerve ends at a specific location on a single muscle cell, smooth muscle does not have a single specialized area on which a neurotransmitter acts. Instead, receptors for various neurotransmitters are located over the entire surface of the cell. In addition, transmitter is not released from a single specialized nerve ending of the autonomic nerve but, rather, from areas all along the axon. Finally, not every smooth muscle cell is located directly adjacent to a site of neurotransmitter release. In the single-unit type of smooth muscle, an effect of the neurotransmitter on the cellular potential can be conveyed to cells distant from the site of transmitter release by the intercellular electrical connections. However, in the multi-unit type of smooth muscle, spread of the influence of the neurotransmitter depends on diffusion. Anything that changes the diffusion distance, such as a change in the amount of connective tissue, will change the effectiveness of a given level of autonomic nerve stimulation.

The parasympathetic neurotransmitter, acetylcholine (ACh), and the sympathetic neurotransmitter, norepinephrine, initiate their effects by interacting with discrete areas of the cell surface called *receptors.* The transmitters cause different effects, depending on the type of smooth muscle cell they contact. The contractility of the gastrointestinal smooth muscle is inhibited by norepinephrine but stimulated by ACh. The opposite is true for vascular smooth muscle. The bases of these differences involve the location of the receptor in the tissue and the nature of the process initiated by activating the receptor.

Humoral Effects

Smooth muscle also is sensitive to a variety of blood-borne agents. These substances include epinephrine, angiotensin, bradykinin, prostaglandin, K^+, oxygen, carbon dioxide, and H^+. Sensitivity to such agents causes the contractile activity of the smooth muscle cell to be modified according to local tissue needs, independent of changes mediated through the autonomic nervous system.

METABOLISM

Adenosine Triphosphate

Smooth muscle, like skeletal muscle, uses adenosine triphosphate (ATP) as an immediate source of energy for contraction. The ATP content of smooth muscle is similar to that of skeletal muscle; that is, 1–3 $\mu M/g$. However, smooth muscle does not possess a pool of high-energy phosphate analogous to the pool of creatine phosphate that is found in skeletal muscle. This means that the short-term energy supply is very limited in smooth muscle, and the cell depends on the synthesis of ATP from various substrates to meet the requirements for contraction. Several characteristics of smooth muscle make possible this obligatory link between the supply of ATP and the demand for it.

Substrates

One characteristic of smooth muscle is that it uses a wide variety of substrates, including carbohydrates, fats, and metabolic intermediates of the Krebs cycle. Some smooth muscles can produce sufficient ATP for contraction anaerobically, and, even when sufficient oxygen is available, the production of lactic acid still is high. A second characteristic of smooth muscle is that the velocity of shortening is slow, and, therefore, the rate at which ATP must be made available for the contractile process is low.

Contractile Efficiency

Smooth muscle is a more economical contractile machine than skeletal muscle. Smooth muscle may develop as much maximum tension as skeletal muscle does, but the metabolic cost of maintaining the tension is much less. During the maintenance of force, the rate of consumption of ATP doubles in smooth muscle, but it increases 50–200 times in skeletal muscle, even though the same level of force is achieved. For this reason, smooth muscle is ideally suited for the long-term maintenance of tension. The molecular explanation for this high efficiency is unknown, but it may involve a "latch" mechanism in which the cross-bridge remains in the attached position longer, thereby reducing the cycling rate and the rate of consumption of ATP.

STUDY OUTLINE

STRUCTURE AND FUNCTION

CONTRACTION   Primary   function   of smooth muscle.

SYNTHESIS   Additional cells, intracellular proteins, connective tissue proteins (collagen and elastin).

SECRETION   Connective tissue proteins.

NEURAL AND HUMORAL INFLUENCES Affect contractility and synthesis.

COMPARISON OF SMOOTH MUSCLE WITH SKELETAL MUSCLE

MECHANICAL CHARACTERISTICS Qualitatively similar to mechanical characteristics of skeletal muscle; maximum velocity of shortening (V_{max}), and, in some cases, maximum active development of tension, (P_0), less.

STRUCTURAL CHARACTERISTICS Connective tissue matrix links smooth muscle cells, which may not be parallel to one another.

ORGANIZATION OF FILAMENTS   Thin and thick filaments are contained in smooth muscle; thin-to-thick filament ratio is much higher in smooth muscle than in skeletal muscle.

No Z bands in smooth muscle; no definite sarcomeres.

Thin filaments attach to Z band protein α-actinin, located in discrete patches on cell membrane.

Thin and thick filaments are arranged at angle relative to long axis of cell.

ATTACHMENTS   During contraction in isolated smooth muscle cells, membrane invaginates at discrete locations corresponding to insertion points of thin filaments.

PROTEIN COMPOSITION AND ORGANIZATION   Thin filaments are made up of actin; thick filaments are composed of myosin.

Tropomyosin is present in thin filament; troponin is absent.

Myosin molecules may be arranged in thick filament of smooth muscle so as to impart functional "polarity" to "faces" rather than to ends of filament as in skeletal muscle.

About twice as much actin and one-fourth as much myosin per gram of tissue as in skeletal muscle.

BIOCHEMICAL CHARACTERISTICS

ACTIN AND MYOSIN   Smooth muscle myosin is chemically distinct from skeletal muscle myosin.

LIGHT CHAIN PROTEINS   Two classes of light chains in smooth muscle myosin; one is involved with regulation of ATPase activity.

CALCIUM AND CALMODULIN   Intracellular [Ca^{++}] regulates activity of actomyosin ATPase through interaction with calmodulin and subsequent phosphorylation of one of myosin light chains.

REGULATION OF CONTRACTION

CALCIUM   Magnitude of contraction is controlled by intracellular [Ca^{++}]; it is not known whether the cell membrane, intracellular membrane structures, or both, are involved.

CELLULAR POTENTIAL   Decrease causes contraction.

"Single unit"—slow waves are formed rhythmically, bursts of action potentials from slow waves cause contraction (gastrointestinal muscle).

"Multi-unit"—graded depolarization produces graded contraction; no action potentials are formed (blood vessels).

NEURAL EFFECTS   Autonomic nervous system modulates contractile activity of smooth muscle.

HUMORAL EFFECTS   Many blood-borne agents also modulate contractile activity of smooth muscle; provide local control of function.

192 Part III. Muscle

METABOLISM

ADENOSINE TRIPHOSPHATE Smooth muscle uses ATP for contraction; limited short-term energy stores require tight link between metabolism and contraction.

SUBSTRATES Smooth muscle can use wide variety of substrates for synthesis of ATP.

CONTRACTILE EFFICIENCY Smooth muscles may generate as much force as skeletal muscle, yet consume much less energy.

BIBLIOGRAPHY

Bohr, D.F., Somlyo, A.P., and Sparks, H.V., Jr. (eds.). 1980. The cardiovascular system. In *Handbook of Physiology*. Section 2. Vascular smooth muscle. Volume II. Baltimore: Williams & Wilkins. (American Physiological Society).

Bulbring, E., and Shuba, M.F. (eds.). 1976. *Physiology of Smooth Muscle*. New York: Raven Press.

Dowben, R.W., and Shay, J.W. (eds.). 1982. *Cell and Muscle Motility*. Volume 2. New York: Plenum.

Hartshorne, D.J., and Siemankowski, R.F. 1981. Regulation of smooth muscle actomyosin. *Annu. Rev. Physiol.* 43:519.

Murphy, R.A. 1979. Filament organization and contractile function in vertebrate smooth muscle. *Annu. Rev. Physiol.* 41:737.

Stephens, N.L. (ed.). 1977. *The Biochemistry of Smooth Muscle*. Baltimore: University Park Press.

PART
IV

CARDIOVASCULAR PHYSIOLOGY

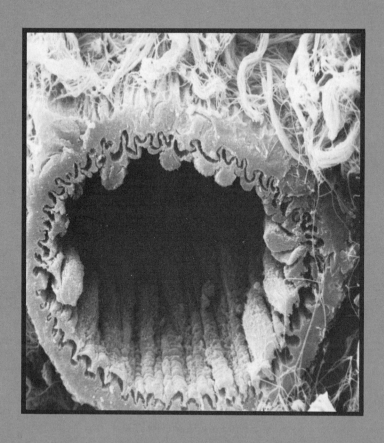

12

General Aspects
of the Circulation

CHAPTER CONTENTS

CIRCULATORY SYSTEM

The unicellular organism exists in a relatively simple system. It takes the nutrition that it needs from its immediate environment and excretes its waste products into the same environment. If the volume of the environment is very large compared to the volume of the unicellular organism, the supplies of nutrient are not depleted, and the environment is not polluted.

In the human body, each individual cell functions like a unicellular organism; it takes the nutrition it needs from its immediate envir-

onment and excretes its waste products into the same environment. The environment in which all cells, except the surface cells, live is enclosed within the body, and, although this environment is small relative to the mass of the cells it serves, it is adequate because it exchanges materials and energy with the larger, external environment in which the whole body moves. The body provides for this exchange by causing blood to circulate continuously between the two environments. The blood circulatory system also provides a means of exchanging materials and energy among individual cells, for the human body functions as an integrated "society" of cells.

Although the ultimate function of the blood circulatory system is the *exchange* that is carried out at the cellular level, which provides for the metabolism of the cells of the body and helps to integrate the activities of the body, this is not the only legitimate interest of the physiologist and the physician, who also must be concerned with understanding and maintaining the gross components of the system that supports this exchange function. The gross components of the system are the *heart,* a pump that generates the force to make the blood flow, the *arteries,* a series of tubes through which blood flows from the heart to all parts of the body, the *capillaries,* which provide close contact between the blood and the internal environment in which the cells live, and the *veins,* a series of tubes through which blood flows from all parts of the body back to the heart.

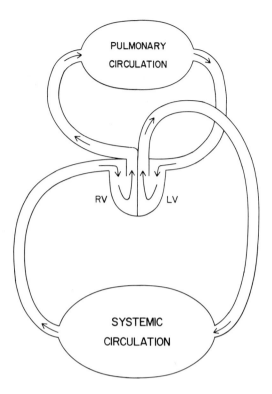

Figure 12-1. The systemic circulation and the pulmonary circulation are arranged in series. RV = Right ventricle; LV = Left ventricle. Arrows indicate the directions in which blood flows.

Heart

The heart consists of two "pumps" (the right and left sides of the heart) connected in series: the output of one becomes the input of the other (Figure 12-1). Blood that returns from the *systemic* circulation, which supplies the metabolic needs of most of the body, enters the right side of the heart, is pumped through the *pulmonary* circulation (the lungs), and returns to the left side of the heart, which pumps it through the systemic circulation again. Because the pulmonary circulation differs from the systemic circulation in several important ways, it will be considered in detail in a later chapter. The remainder of this chapter deals specifically with the systemic circulation.

Blood Vessels

ARRANGEMENT

The blood vessels are connected sequentially, that is, the blood flows successively from one type of vessel to another and completes a circuit from the heart to the tissues and back to the heart. All of the blood that circulates through the body leaves the heart through a single large artery and is distributed to all of the tissues through the branches that leave the major vessels. Each branch is smaller than the vessel from which it arises, and each branch gives off other branches until the smallest vessels, the capillaries, are formed.

Blood leaves the capillaries through vessels that join other vessels; each vessel is larger than any one of the vessels that join to form it. Ultimately, the blood returns again to the heart, flowing last through the largest veins in the body.

When two arteries are formed by branching, the total cross-sectional area is increased, and when two veins join to form one vein, the cross-sectional area is decreased. Therefore, as the blood flows through the arteries and their successive branches, the mean velocity of flow decreases and reaches its lowest value in the capillaries. As the blood flows through the veins, which join to form fewer vessels, the velocity of flow increases again (Figures 12-2 and 12-3). If the cross-sectional area of an artery and of the vein to which it corresponds were the same, the velocity of flow in each would be the same; however, any artery is slightly smaller than its corresponding vein. Thus, the velocity of flow is slightly greater in the artery. For example, the mean velocity of flow in the descending aorta exceeds that in the inferior vena

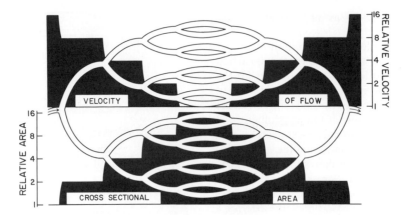

Figure 12-2. The relationship between the cross-sectional area and the velocity of flow in a system of tubes. In the diagram, the cross-sectional area doubles at each division of the tubes, from the left to the center, and halves at each junction, from the center to the right. Because the volume that flows in a unit of time is the same throughout the system, the velocity of flow is halved at each division and doubled at each junction. Although the changes do not occur in such a regular fashion in the vascular system, the cross-sectional area and the mean velocity of flow are related inversely, as shown here.

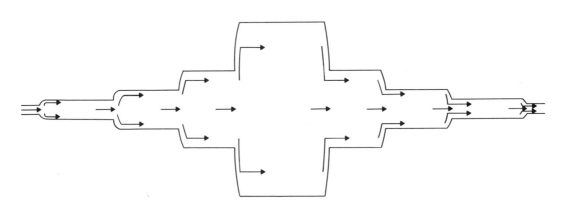

Figure 12-3. The changes of cross-sectional area that affect the velocity of flow in the system that was diagrammed in Figure 12-2. (Arrows indicate the direction of flow.) As the cross-sectional area increases, from the left to the center, fluid must flow laterally as well as forward to fill the increased volume; therefore, the mean velocity forward must decrease. As the cross-sectional area decreases, from the center to the right, fluid must flow inward again as the volume of the tube diminishes, and the mean velocity forward must increase.

cava, although the two vessels carry almost the same volume of blood in a unit of time.

BLOOD PRESSURE

MEASUREMENT.   Blood pressure is high in the arteries because the heart forces blood into the arteries rapidly, through a large orifice, and the blood runs out of the arteries more slowly, through many small vessels (arterioles). If a tube were connected to an artery and held vertically, blood would flow upward into it; however, the height to which the blood would flow is limited by the earth's gravity, which acts on the mass of the blood to produce *weight*. When the blood flows as high as it will go, the force of its weight on each unit of area of the column it forms is equal to the force of the arterial pressure; therefore, the measure of any pressure is how high it can raise a column of fluid. The denser the fluid (hence the heavier per unit volume), the smaller the distance it will rise before it is stopped by its own weight. Mercury is the densest liquid; it is used commonly to measure pressure because most pressures will not make it rise beyond convenient heights in a tube. Mercury is about 13.6 times as dense as blood; therefore, a force that would cause blood to flow upward in a tube to a height of 136 cm would cause mercury to rise to only 10 cm, yet the weights of the two columns per cross-sectional area would be the same (Figure 12-4). Arterial blood pressure is expressed in *millimeters of mercury*, thus, a pressure of 10 cm Hg would be expressed as 100 mm Hg.

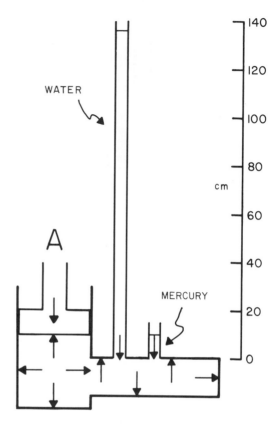

Figure 12-4. Measurement of fluid pressure. In the diagram, the piston, A, applies force against the fluid in the chamber, and the pressure thus generated is exerted in all directions (as the arrows indicate). If the fluid can enter a pipe that is open to the atmosphere, it will rise until the weight of the fluid in the pipe stops the upward flow. Therefore, the height of the column of fluid, which is proportional to the weight of the column of fluid, indicates the pressure in the chamber. If the fluid in the pipe is water, it will rise to a greater height than mercury would. In the diagram, the pressure is equal to the weight of a column of water 136 cm high, or to a column of mercury 10 cm (100 mm) high. In a system that connects with the atmosphere, as this one does, the atmospheric pressure (that is, the weight of the column of air above the column of fluid) is applied uniformly throughout, and the pressure indicated is that in excess of atmospheric pressure; therefore, atmospheric pressure is the reference, or zero value.

PRESSURE GRADIENT.   Blood flows in the vascular system along a *gradient* of pressure, from one end of a vessel, where a certain pressure exists, to the other end, where the pressure is less. It is important to understand that the absolute value of blood pressure at any point in a vessel does not determine the flow of blood within the vessel; only the *difference* of pressure makes the blood flow. In the arteries, blood flows freely, and only a small difference of pressure between the aorta and the ends of the small arteries causes blood to flow rapidly (Figure 12-5).

In the arterioles and the capillaries, the resistance to flow is high, and a large difference of pressure is required to make blood flow through these vessels (Figure 12-5). After the blood enters the veins, it flows freely again, and a small pressure gradient, similar to that in the arteries, causes the blood to flow rapidly from the smallest vein to the heart.

BLOOD VOLUME

The human body contains about 5 liters of blood; variations in volume depend on body size. About 80%–90% of the blood is in the systemic circulation, and the rest is in the pulmonary circulation. At any time, about 75% of the blood in the systemic circulation is in the veins, about 20% is in the arteries, and about 5% is in the capillaries. The volume of the ve-

nous system is subject to the greatest variation; for example, if blood is lost by hemorrhage, the difference of blood volume is accommodated by a decrease of venous vascular volume.

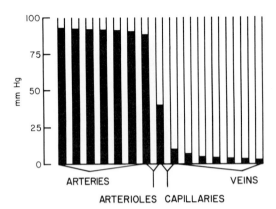

Figure 12-5. Mean pressure at different points in the systemic circulation. Mean arterial pressure is high and declines very little as the blood flows through the arteries. The mean pressure decreases as the blood flows through the arterioles and the capillaries; it declines very little more as the blood flows through the veins.

STRUCTURE-FUNCTION RELATIONSHIPS

Arteries

STRUCTURE

The arteries have tough, strong walls that are composed of elastic connective tissue, fibrous connective tissue, and smooth muscle; the walls are lined by endothelial cells.

FUNCTIONS

The arteries serve as (1) reservoirs of pressure during each cycle, (2) reservoirs of volume during each cycle, and (3) low-resistance conduits.

VOLUME-PRESSURE RELATIONSHIP

Because the arteries are compliant, they expand when blood is forced into them by the heart. The arteries also are elastic; this means that they oppose distention and will return to their previous volume when the blood that was forced into them has run out again. Suppose the arteries formed a closed system like the one illustrated in Figure 12-6A. In this diagram, fluid is forced into the system by the piston at the left, and the system expands from volume a to volume b. As the volume increases, the pressure also increases. This relationship between volume and pressure is illustrated in Figure 12-6B, which shows the volume and the pressure at point a and the linear increase of vol-

ume and pressure at point b. In an elastic system such as the arteries, neither volume nor pressure can be changed without the other being changed. Figure 12-6C shows how both pressure and volume increase in the hypothetical, closed system as the fluid is injected, and then remain constant.

Now, suppose that a small outlet is placed in the system (Figure 12-6D) in such a way that fluid runs out, although more slowly than it runs in. As fluid is pushed into the system by the piston, the volume a begins to increase; but, since fluid also is running out, the volume increases only to b'; it decreases again when inflow stops and outflow continues. The changes of volume and pressure now resemble those seen in Figure 12-6E. During injection, fluid flows in faster than it flows out, yet the rate of outflow increases as the volume and the pressure in the system increase. When the inflow stops, the outflow continues, and volume and pressure decline at a decreasing rate. If the piston withdraws and begins to inject again when the volume reaches c, (which is the same as a), a second sequence identical to the first is seen (Figure 12-6E).

The heart and the arteries form a system like that shown in Figure 12-6D, and the regular, pulsatile increase and decrease of arterial blood pressure are like that shown in Figure 12-6E.

DIASTOLIC PUMP

The elastic arteries form, in effect, an auxiliary pump that functions during the period of *diastole* (when the heart is being filled). The volume of blood that is stored in the arteries during the period of *systole* (when the heart is ejecting blood) and the energy that is stored in the arteries when their elastic walls are stretched, are given back to the circulation when the heart relaxes. Thus, before the blood reaches the tissues, the arteries have converted the intermittent flow of blood that the heart generates into a continuous flow (Figure 12-7).

CONDUIT

The arteries also function as low-resistance channels to carry blood from the heart to all of the tissues. Thus, no tissue is very far from an adequate supply of blood, regardless of how far it is from the heart. When it is necessary for the velocity of flow to increase, as it is when the body is performing work and the tissues must have more blood, the smooth muscles in the

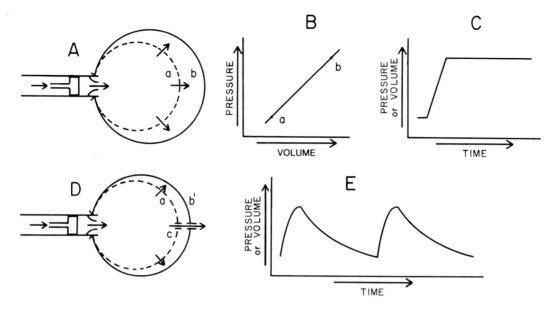

Figure 12-6. Volume-pressure relationships in model systems. The volume-pressure relationship of the arteries is analogous to that in an elastic system into which fluid flows intermittently and rapidly, and out of which fluid flows continuously and less rapidly. See text for discussion.

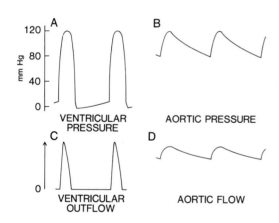

Figure 12-7. Pressures and flow in the left ventricle and the aorta. The compliant, elastic arteries convert the intermittent pressure and outflow of the heart (**A** and **C**) into continuous pressure and flow (**B** and **D**).

walls of the arteries contract, and the compliance (distensibility) of the arteries is decreased. Under these conditions, the arteries expand less when the heart forces blood into them; therefore, some of the blood that would expand the arteries during systole in the resting body is forced to flow on, toward the tissues, and the mean velocity of flow is increased. This change of conditions does not prevent the arteries from converting the intermittent outflow of the heart into continuous flow because the arteries do retain a fair degree of compliance.

Moreover, the rate of the heartbeat increases, which decreases the interval between periods of ejection and helps to keep the flow continuous. The fibrous connective tissue does not stretch easily; therefore, it strengthens the walls of the arteries and limits their expansion when arterial pressure is high.

Arterioles and Precapillary Sphincters

STRUCTURE
The walls of the arterioles and precapillary sphincters are thick, relative to the size of the vessels, and are composed mostly of smooth muscle; they contain relatively little elastic tissue or fibrous connective tissue.

FUNCTIONS
The arterioles and the precapillary sphincters are located at the ends of most arteries, where they act as "variable resistors," or "stopcocks," to control the flow of blood into the vascular beds. They provide most of what is called the *peripheral resistance*, which makes possible (1) the maintenance of arterial pressure, (2) opposition to the effects of gravity on the flow

of blood in the arteries, and (3) selective flow to vascular beds.

MAINTENANCE OF CENTRAL ARTERIAL PRESSURE

Arterial blood pressure is generated by a combination of the flow of blood into the arteries (cardiac output) and the resistance to the flow of blood out of the arteries (peripheral resistance). This relationship is expressed in the equation

$$P = \dot{Q}R$$

in which P is pressure, $\dot{Q}$ is the rate of flow, and R is the resistance to flow.

COUNTERING EFFECTS OF GRAVITY

When a person is standing, the force of gravity aids the flow of blood into the arteries and the vascular beds below the heart and opposes the flow of blood into the arteries and the vascular beds above the heart. Therefore, increase of vascular resistance in the areas below the heart, which prevents accumulation of the blood in those areas and helps to ensure perfusion of the tissues above the heart, is essential.

SELECTIVE PERFUSION

The volume of blood that the body contains and the ability of the cardiovascular system to circulate the blood are not adequate to supply all of the organs and systems at a high level at the same time. Therefore, the blood supply to some systems must be curtailed when other systems increase their activity. An example of this reciprocal arrangement is the reduction of renal and mesenteric blood flow during periods of physical exertion, when the skeletal muscles must have greater blood flow. Although some of the resistance vessels must be constricted at all times to maintain the central arterial pressure and to direct the flow of blood, other resistance vessels always will be relatively dilated to permit selective, appropriate perfusion of vascular beds (Figure 12-8). Thus, restricting the flow in some vascular beds makes the adequate perfusion of other vascular beds possible.

Origin of Vascular Resistance

LAMINAR FLOW

Because like molecules are held together by cohesive forces, a homogeneous fluid subjected to a gradient of pressure in a tube is displaced as

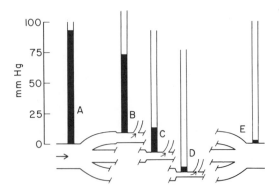

Figure 12-8. How an individual arteriole can permit more or less blood to flow into the vascular bed that it supplies. **A.** Arterial pressure. **B.** Pressure in a relatively dilated arteriole; blood is made available under considerable pressure and can fill the vascular bed rapidly. **C** and **D.** Blood under less pressure is available to vascular beds when the arterioles that supply them are constricted. **E.** Venous system. Although mean resistance is high in the arterioles and mean pressure declines more in the arterioles as a class of vessels than it does elsewhere, their location at the ends of the arteries and their function as "stopcocks" permit the arterioles not only to maintain central arterial pressure but also to utilize the pressure (and the flow that the pressure produces) to perfuse vascular beds selectively.

a unit. The layer of fluid that touches the wall, however, is held by adhesive forces and does not move. The force of the pressure causes molecular layers, or laminae, of the fluid near the wall to separate and to slide over each other (*laminar flow*). The layers accelerate as they are formed farther from the wall, but the gradient of velocity decreases, until a maximum velocity is reached at some distance from the wall (Figure 12-9). The friction between the laminae forms the basis of resistance to flow.

RELATION TO SIZE OF VESSEL

Although blood is not a homogeneous fluid, it flows in laminae, and the resistance to its flow occurs between the laminae. In large blood vessels, a considerable part of the flowing blood moves with very little internal friction (Figure 12-9), and a zone near the wall is affected most by the friction of laminar flow (Figure 12-10). This flow of fluid at a distance away from the wall of the vessel, where the internal friction is low, accounts for the low resistance to the flow of blood in the arteries and the veins (see Figure

PRESSURE GRADIENT

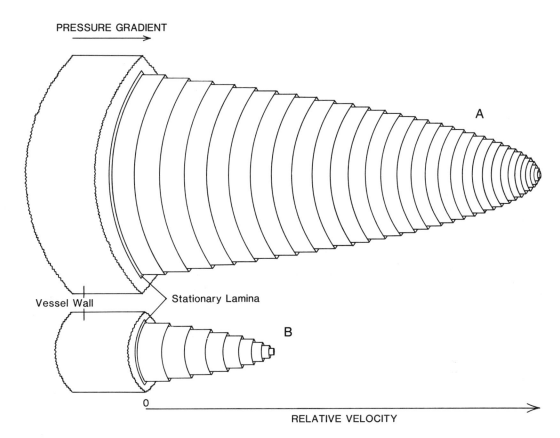

Figure 12-9.   Laminar flow and how it determines resistance to flow in blood vessels. As blood is displaced by a pressure gradient, it begins to move as a mass. However, the layer (lamina) nearest the wall does not move, and the next lamina must slide over it. Friction between the two laminae slows the moving one, the next one slides over it, and so on. This internal fluid friction is the basis of the vascular resistance. As the laminae occur farther from the wall, the distance they move apart decreases as the maximum velocity is approached. Thus, the internal fluid friction decreases. The velocity is maximum at the center and decreases to zero at the wall. In a large vessel, **A**, the proportion of the relatively low-resistance core to the relatively high-resistance periphery is greater than in a small vessel, **B**. Thus, the resistance decreases as the size of the vessel increases.

12-5). In small vessels such as the arterioles, the radius of the vessel is less than that of the zone of greatest resistance (Figure 12-10); thus, the resistance to flow in the vessel is high (see Figure 12-5).

VARIABLES THAT CONTRIBUTE TO RESISTANCE

In a system of fluid flowing in small tubes, in which all of the flow is laminar and subject to internal friction, the flow ($\dot{Q}$) is proportional to the driving force (the difference of pressure, P_1-P_2, or ΔP) and inversely proportional to the resistance (R). Therefore,

$$\dot{Q} \simeq \frac{\Delta P}{R}$$

POISEUILLE'S EQUATION

The factors that contribute to the resistance can be identified, and, in simple systems, measured. Because the friction that must be overcome to produce flow arises from the sliding of the laminae over each other, the resistance is related directly to the viscosity of the fluid, which reflects the cohesive forces that act between laminae. In addition, the resistance is related to the distance through which the laminae move, hence, to the length of the tube. Therefore,

$$R \simeq \eta l$$

where η is the viscosity of the fluid, and l is the length of the tube.

The force that is required to produce flow

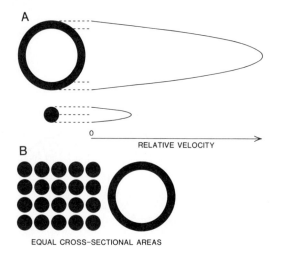

RELATIVE VELOCITY

EQUAL CROSS-SECTIONAL AREAS

Figure 12-10. Comparison of internal fluid friction in a single large vessel to that in a number of small vessels. **A.** The zone of greatest internal fluid friction near the wall occupies a relatively small part of the total cross-sectional area of a large vessel, such as the aorta, leaving a relatively large central zone of low-friction flow. In a small vessel, such as an arteriole, the width of the zone of greatest internal fluid friction equals the radius; hence, all of the blood flows in the high-friction peripheral zone. **B.** The large circle represents the cross-section of a large blood vessel such as the aorta; the dark band depicts the zone of high friction flow near the wall, and the open area in the center portrays the low-friction zone. The filled circles represent a group of small vessels; the zone of high friction occupies the entire cross-section of each vessel, and there is no zone of low-friction flow. The cross-sectional area of the large vessel equals the total cross-sectional area of all of the small vessels. This diagram illustrates the reason why, as the blood flows from a few large vessels into many vessels, vascular resistance increases, despite the increase of total cross-sectional area.

---

decreases as the distance away from the lamina that adheres to the wall increases; therefore, resistance must be related in some way to the size of the tube. Although it is not intuitively obvious, the relationship is to the fourth power of the radius:

$$R \simeq \frac{1}{\pi r^4}$$

Combining all factors that relate to resistance, we have

$$R \simeq \frac{\eta l}{\pi r^4}$$

To make the relationship mathematically precise, the numerical constant 8 is included, and the more complex term for resistance is substituted in the expression that relates flow, pressure, and resistance. The result is *Poiseuille's equation*

$$\dot{Q} = \frac{\Delta P}{R} = \frac{\Delta P \pi r^4}{8 \eta l}$$

which describes quantitatively the continuous flow of homogeneous fluid in small, rigid tubes.

Although the vascular system differs in several ways from the simple model, the principles are the same: the pressure gradient, the size of the vessel, the viscosity of the fluid, and the length of the vessel determine the rate of flow. All of these variables can change in the vascular system, yet the only variable that is controlled physiologically is the size of the lumen of the vessel; it is altered by contraction or relaxation of the smooth muscle in the walls. Because the rate of flow varies with the fourth power of the radius, flow in a particular vessel can be changed greatly by changing the radius only slightly. For example, changing the radius by a factor of 2 (doubling it or halving it) changes the flow by a factor of 16. Most of the controlled change of vessel size occurs in the relatively muscular arterioles and precapillary sphincters; the resistance to flow in these vessels constitutes the bulk of the peripheral vascular resistance, and control of it gives control of the distribution of blood flow in the body.

Calculation of Vascular Resistance

Because the variables that make up the vascular resistance are difficult to measure, resistance is not stated as a primary unit but is expressed as a ratio of the difference of pressure that is imposed and the flow that is produced:

$$R = \frac{\Delta P}{\dot{Q}} = \frac{\text{Units of pressure}}{\text{Units of flow}} \left(\text{usually } \frac{\text{mm Hg}}{\text{ml/sec}} \right)$$

TOTAL PERIPHERAL RESISTANCE

The systemic circulation begins in the aorta and ends in the right atrium. To calculate the resistance in the system, one must know the pressure gradient (the difference between mean aortic pressure and mean right atrial pressure) and the rate of flow (the cardiac output).

Ideal central arterial pressure is 120/80 mm Hg, that is, the highest level to which the arterial pressure rises during the ejection of blood by the heart is 120 mm Hg (*systolic pressure*), and the lowest level to which arterial pressure falls before the next beat is 80 mm Hg (*diastolic pressure*). These two extreme values do not reveal much about *mean arterial pressure*, which is an average of the pressures at every point during the cardiac cycle, not merely of the highest value and the lowest value (Figure 12-11). As a useful approximation, one can estimate mean arterial pressure by adding one-third of the pulse pressure (the difference between systolic pressure and diastolic pressure) to the diastolic pressure. Thus, approximate mean arterial pressure might be

$$80 \text{ mm Hg} + \left(\frac{120 - 80}{3}\right) \text{mm Hg} = 93 \text{ mm Hg}$$

A reasonable value for the mean right atria pressure is 3 mm Hg; therefore, the total pressure gradient that moves blood in the body at rest is about

$$93 \text{ mm Hg} - 3 \text{ mm Hg} = 90 \text{ mm Hg}$$

A reasonable value for the total blood flow through the systemic circulation of a resting adult human in a unit of time (that is, the *cardiac output*) is 5 liters/min, or about 83 ml/sec.
Thus,

Total peripheral resistance

$$= \frac{\text{Mean aortic pressure} - \text{Mean right atrial pressure}}{\text{Cardiac output}}$$

and, in a typical adult human at rest,

$$R = \frac{\Delta P}{\dot{Q}} = \frac{90 \text{ mm Hg}}{5 \text{ liters/min}} = 18 \text{ mm Hg/liter/min}$$

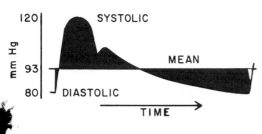

Figure 12-11.   Mean arterial pressure. Mean arterial pressure is derived by integrating a large number of points on the curve of pressure obtained during the cardiac cycle. Therefore, the area between the mean and the portion of the curve above the mean equals the area between the mean and the portion of the curve below the mean.

or

$$\frac{90 \text{ mm Hg}}{83 \text{ ml/sec}} = 1.1 \text{ mm Hg/ml/sec}$$

COMBINING RESISTANCES

The total peripheral resistance is the sum of the individual resistances in each of the local vascular beds of the body, which are arranged in parallel. When resistances in parallel are combined, the total resistance is less than the resistance of any of the components because the gradient of pressure for all is about the same as the gradient of pressure for each, but the total flow is greater than the flow of any one (Figure 12-12). Thus, the resistance R is related inversely to the flow $\dot{Q}$: $1/R \simeq \dot{Q}$.

Suppose that the resistances of three individual vascular beds R_1, R_2, and R_3 are 2 mm Hg/(ml/sec), 10 mm Hg/(ml/sec), and 25 mm (Hg/(ml/sec), respectively, and ΔP is the same for each of them. If one begins with the relationship $\dot{Q} \simeq \Delta P/R$, and ΔP is constant, then

$$\dot{Q} \simeq \frac{1}{R} \text{ and } \dot{Q}_t \simeq \frac{1}{R_1} + \frac{1}{R_2} + \frac{1}{R_3} \simeq \frac{1}{R_t}$$

where $\dot{Q}_t$ is the combined flow in the three vascular beds and R_t is the combined resistance to flow. Thus, the reciprocal of the total resistance is equal to the sum of the reciprocals of the individual resistances. By substituting the val-

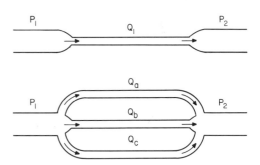

Figure 12-12.   Why the total resistance to flow decreases when resistances are added in parallel. The difference between P_1 and P_2 (that is, the gradient of pressure) is the same in both sets of tubes. The resistance to flow in each narrow tube is about the same; however, the total volume that flows in a unit of time is about three times as great in the combination of $\dot{Q}_a$, $\dot{Q}_b$, and $\dot{Q}_c$ as it is in $\dot{Q}_1$. Therefore, the resistance, which is derived from $(P_1 - P_2)/\dot{Q}$, is about three times as great in $\dot{Q}_1$ as it is in the combination of $\dot{Q}_a$, $\dot{Q}_b$, and $\dot{Q}_c$.

ues that were given earlier, one obtains

$$\frac{1}{R_t} = \frac{1}{\frac{2 \text{ mm Hg}}{\text{ml/sec}}} + \frac{1}{\frac{10 \text{ mm Hg}}{\text{ml/sec}}} + \frac{1}{\frac{25 \text{ mm Hg}}{\text{ml/sec}}}$$

$$= \frac{0.5}{\frac{\text{mm Hg}}{\text{ml/sec}}} + \frac{0.1}{\frac{\text{mm Hg}}{\text{ml/sec}}} + \frac{0.04}{\frac{\text{mm Hg}}{\text{ml/sec}}}$$

$$= \frac{0.64}{\frac{\text{mm Hg}}{\text{ml/scc}}}$$

and

$$R_t = \frac{1}{\frac{0.64}{\frac{\text{mm Hg}}{\text{ml/sec}}}} = 1.6 \text{ mm Hg/(ml/sec)}$$

which is less than the smallest of the individual resistances.

Viscosity of Blood

AXIAL FLOW

If the temperature is kept constant, the viscosity of a homogeneous fluid, such as water, always is the same, regardless of the size of the tube or the velocity of flow. Particles suspended in a homogeneous fluid, however, add to the friction between laminae and increase the viscosity. If the diameter of the tube is less than about 0.5 mm, some of the increase of viscosity that is due to the suspended particles is offset. This effect is attributed to the tendency of the suspended particles—red cells, if the suspension is blood—to move toward the center of the stream in a process called *axial flow*, leaving a cell-free zone near the wall. As the size of the vessel decreases, the relative magnitude of the cell-free layer and the reduction of viscosity increase up to a limit.

At very low velocities of flow in vessels of less than about 0.5 mm diameter, the viscosity of the blood begins to increase again. This effect is attributed to movement of the red cells back toward the walls of the vessels as the velocity decreases. In clinical situations associated with decreased tissue perfusion, such as hypovolemic shock, decrease of velocity causes increase of viscosity, which in turn causes further decrease of velocity and further impairment of tissue perfusion.

EFFECT OF HEMATOCRIT

The viscosity of blood is related directly to the concentration (volume percent) of red cells, which is called the *hematocrit*. The viscosity of the plasma relative to the viscosity of water is between 1.5 and 2, and, at the normal hematocrit of about 45%, the relative viscosity of blood is only about 3 (Figure 12-13). If the hematocrit increases to more than 60%–65%, the viscosity increases proportionately much more, and the consequent increase of peripheral resistance begins to impair the effectiveness of the circulation. The general term for such a high concentration of red cells in the blood is *polycythemia*. It may represent a compensatory reaction of the body to inadequate oxygenation of the blood, or it may be caused by an abnormality of the system that controls the concentration of red cells in the blood.

Capillaries

STRUCTURE

A capillary is composed of a single layer of endothelial cells. Its inner diameter is about the same as the largest dimension of a red blood cell, about 10 μm. Although the length of a typical capillary may vary considerably, a mean value of about 1 mm is usual. Therefore, because the mean velocity of flow of blood in a capillary is about 1 mm/sec, a single red cell

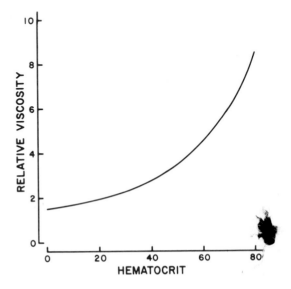

Figure 12-13. Viscosity of the blood is related directly to the concentration of red cells in the blood.

remains in a systemic capillary for approximately 1 sec.

Most capillaries do not branch from arterioles, but arise from smaller vessels called *metarterioles,* or *terminal arterioles.* The *precapillary sphincter* is a cuff of smooth muscle that surrounds the capillary at its origin (Figure 12-14). The flow of blood through the capillary is controlled by the precapillary sphincter; at any time, a given sphincter either will be completely open or completely closed; hence, blood either will flow through a given capillary or it will not. The rate of flow in the vascular bed is determined by the number of precapillary sphincters open at one time.

The capillaries may branch or join other capillaries and then terminate in the *venules.* In some tissues, blood can flow from the arterioles to the venules through *preferential channels,* which bypass the capillaries. Because such flow does not permit exchange of materials with the tissues, it is called *nonnutrient flow,* in distinction to the flow through the capillaries, which is considered to be *nutrient flow.* Capillaries also may arise from, and terminate on, the preferential channel.

FUNCTIONS

The systemic capillaries provide intimate contact between the circulating blood and the extracellular fluid, which comprises the environment of the cells. The thin walls of the cap-

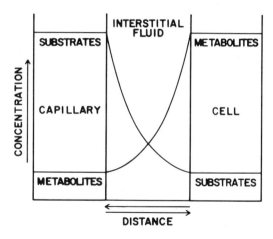

Figure 12-15. Materials in solution move from the capillary to the cell and from the cell to the capillary, down chemical activity gradients. The larger the gradient, the higher the rate of transfer. There is no active transport between the capillary fluid and the interstitial fluid.

illaries permit the rapid exchange of substrates, metabolites, and special products, such as hormones, between the blood and the tissues. Water moves easily across the capillary wall, but other elements of the blood, such as the red blood cells and the plasma proteins, do not leave the capillaries readily. Larger bodies, such as white blood cells, probably move through spaces between the endothelial cells of the capillary wall by a process that is similar to amoeboid movement. Dissolved substances move by diffusion down chemical activity gradients (Figure 12-15). Diffusion is a very rapid process at molecular dimensions; however, it is a very slow process at gross dimensions. Therefore, for the circulation to be effective, every cell must be close to a capillary.

Fluid Exchange

COLLOIDAL OSMOTIC PRESSURE

The capillary blood pressure, or *hydrostatic pressure,* tends to force fluid through the capillary walls and out of the vessel. If this movement were not opposed, all of the water in the blood would filter into the tissue spaces. Another force, however, tends to move water from the intercellular space into the capillaries, and hence, to hold water in the capillary against the hydrostatic pressure (Figure 12-16). This force is derived from a special case of osmosis (see "Osmosis" in Chapter 1 and "Water" in

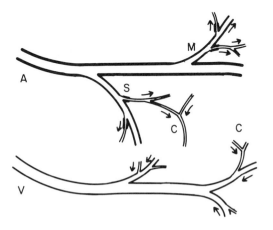

Figure 12-14. The capillaries originate at the metarteriole and terminate at the venule. A = arteriole; M = metarteriole; S = precapillary sphincter; C = capillary; V = venule. The arrows indicate the direction of flow.

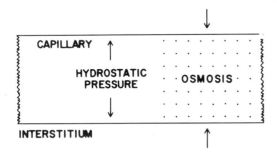

Figure 12-16. Capillary hydrostatic pressure and plasma colloidal osmotic pressure are opposing forces; the arrows indicate the directions that each force tends to move the plasma water. The dots represent the proteins that form a colloidal solution in the plasma and dilute the plasma water.

Chapter 2), which occurs because the plasma water is diluted by the proteins that are dissolved in it. The water in the interstitial space contains a much smaller concentration of protein; therefore, its chemical activity is higher than the chemical activity of the plasma water, and a chemical activity gradient drives it into the capillary.

The force of osmosis (*osmotic pressure*) can be evaluated by measuring the height to which it will cause water to flow in a tube against the force of gravity. It must be emphasized that the osmotic movement of water across the capillary wall is not the same as that which causes red blood cells to swell. For osmosis to occur, some barrier must limit the movement of the dissolved particles that dilute the water. In red blood cells, the surface membrane limits the movement of crystalloidal particles such as sodium, chloride, and potassium, and these particles dilute the intracellular water; the capillary wall does not prevent the movement of such small particles. The capillary wall limits the movement of the plasma proteins, and the dilution of the plasma water by these colloidal particles is responsible for the force called *colloidal osmotic pressure*, or *oncotic pressure*.

HYDROSTATIC PRESSURE VS. PLASMA ONCOTIC PRESSURE

The balance of water between the vascular fluid and the extravascular fluid is determined by the balance between the net hydrostatic pressure and the net colloidal osmotic pressure (Figure 12-16). In a person in a horizontal position, the force of gravity is not a factor, and the blood

pressure is about 40 mm Hg in the metarteriole (that is, at the beginning of the capillary), and about 10 mm Hg in the venule (that is, at the end of the capillary). Therefore, a pressure gradient of about 30 mm Hg causes the blood to flow through the capillary when the precapillary sphincter is dilated and the capillary is open. The mean blood pressure in an open capillary is about 25 mm Hg (relative to atmospheric pressure). This force, which drives fluid out of the vessel, is augmented by the pressure of the tissue fluid, which is about 7 mm Hg less than atmospheric pressure, that is, −7 mm Hg. Therefore, in an open capillary, the net hydrostatic pressure gradient from the capillary to the tissues is 32 mm Hg (Figure 12-17).

The colloidal osmotic pressure of the plasma is about 28 mm Hg, and this value is offset in part by a colloidal osmotic pressure of about 4 mm Hg in the tissue fluid, leaving a net inward force of 24 mm Hg. (A small osmotic force is generated in the tissue water because the capillary wall is not completely impermeable to the plasma proteins, and the interstitial water is diluted slightly by the proteins that leak out of the capillary.) In the typical open capillary, the net hydrostatic pressure of 32 mm Hg (Figure 12-17) exceeds the net colloidal osmotic pressure of 24 mm Hg, and plasma water is filtered through the capillary wall by a net hydrostatic pressure of 8 mm Hg.

When the precapillary sphincter contracts, the capillary is closed at the metarteriolar end but open at the venular end, forming a cul-de-sac. The hydrostatic pressure of the capillary decreases to equal that of the venule (10 mm Hg), and the addition of the subatmospheric tissue pressure (−7 mm Hg) yields a net hydrostatic pressure of 17 mm Hg. Therefore, in the typical closed capillary (Figure 12-17), the net colloidal osmotic pressure of 24 mm Hg exceeds the net hydrostatic pressure of 17 mm Hg, and interstitial water is absorbed into the capillary by a net colloidal osmotic pressure gradient of 7 mm Hg.

According to the model of the capillary system described above and illustrated in Figure 12-17, plasma water is filtered into the extracellular space when a capillary is open, and interstitial water is absorbed into the plasma water when the capillary is closed. The balance between filtration and absorption depends on how many capillaries are open and how many capillaries are closed at one time. When the metabolic rate of a tissue increases (e.g., when skeletal muscles do work), the number of sphincters open at one time increases, and the

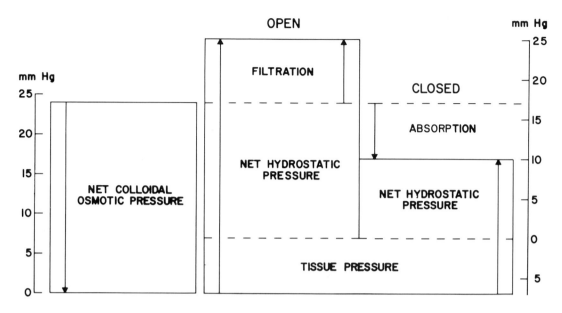

Figure 12-17. Balance of the opposing forces that act on the plasma water in the capillaries. (Arrow directed downward indicates a force acting to move water into the capillary; arrow directed upward indicates a force acting to move water out of the capillary.) When the precapillary sphincter is open, plasma water is filtered; when the sphincter is closed, interstitial water is absorbed. Absorption into the closed capillary is limited, however, because the gradient of colloidal osmotic pressure decreases as interstitial water enters the vessel.

rate of transudation of fluid from the capillaries into the interstitial space increases. If the rate of filtration exceeds the rate of absorption, the excess extracellular fluid is absorbed by the lymphatic system (see Figure 12-19).

FACTORS THAT AFFECT FLUID BALANCE

Several factors can alter the balance between the vascular fluid and the extravascular fluid; for example, if the venous pressure increases, the capillary pressure also increases, and, if the capillary pressure is great enough, vascular fluid enters the interstitial space, regardless of whether the capillary is open or closed. When a person stands, for example, the force of gravity increases the venous pressure in the feet; hence, the capillary pressure and the rate of movement of fluid from the capillary to the intercellular space increase. If the rate of capillary transudation is great enough, the capacity of the lymphatic system to take up fluid is exceeded, and fluid accumulates in the tissues. This condition is called *edema*; it occurs, for example, in people who have congestive heart failure or venous obstruction. The excess fluid in the extracellular space causes the tissues to swell, and the tissue pressure may equal or exceed the atmospheric

pressure (Figure 12-18). Extracellular fluid also accumulates if the lymphatic channels are blocked. This condition will be discussed further in the section entitled "Lymphatic System" that follows.

Other conditions in which fluid filters excessively from the capillaries include the following:

1. Capillary pressure is increased because of arteriolar dilatation (e.g., in inflammatory conditions such as those caused by bacterial infections and insect bites). Hydrostatic pressure exceeds colloidal osmotic pressure by more than it does normally.
2. Capillary permeability is increased (e.g., in inflammatory conditions or circulatory shock). Colloidal osmotic pressure decreases as the barrier to the movement of the plasma proteins is lowered; the proteins move into the extracellular space and dilute the extracellular water. The colloidal osmotic pressure is reduced to less than its normal value.
3. Colloidal osmotic pressure is low because the concentration of the plasma proteins is low (e.g., in liver disease).

Filtration decreases and absorption increases when capillary pressure is low; for example, in the condition of arterial hypotension due to the loss of blood.

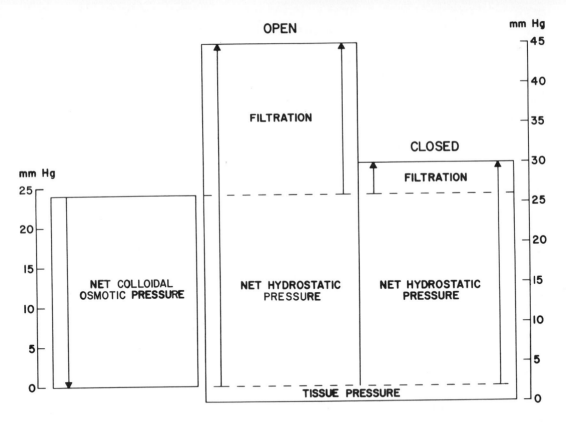

Figure 12-18. Effects of high venous pressure on capillary hydrostatic pressure and, hence, on fluid balance between the capillaries and the interstitial space. The conventions are the same as those of Figure 12-17. As net hydrostatic pressure exceeds net colloidal osmotic pressure, plasma water is filtered from both open capillaries and closed capillaries (open at the venular end). Note that the tissue pressure is positive (that is, greater than atmospheric pressure).

Lymphatic System

The *lymphatic system* is a special vascular system that drains the interstitial spaces. It returns capillary filtrate to the bloodstream and, at the same time, removes particles that cannot be absorbed into the blood capillaries. The lymph capillaries are closed at the ends (Figure 12-19), but, if the tissues become inflamed, the capillaries may develop openings that permit the uptake of larger particles.

The contribution of the lymphatic system is essential to the maintenance of the balance between vascular fluid and extravascular fluid. The rate of formation of lymph in humans is about 4–5 liters/day, and it is proportional to the number of capillaries that are being perfused. By evacuating the extracellular space, the lymphatic system develops and maintains the subatmospheric tissue pressure.

A small amount of protein, mainly albumin, leaks from the plasma through the capillary wall. These protein molecules cannot be reabsorbed by the blood capillaries, and, if they were allowed to accumulate in the tissue spaces,

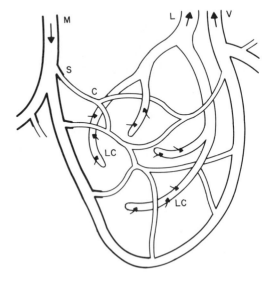

Figure 12-19. Location of the lymphatic capillaries relative to the blood capillaries. M = metarteriole; S = precapillary sphincter; C = blood capillary; V = venule; LC = lymph capillary; L = lymphatic vessel. Arrows indicate the direction of flow.

they would dilute the interstitial water and counteract the colloidal osmotic pressure of the plasma. The lymph capillaries are more permeable than the blood capillaries, and they can take up the molecules of albumin and return them to the plasma. The value of this function is illustrated by certain tropical diseases; for example, in elephantiasis, in which parasites block the lymph channels, edema of enormous proportions is produced. The swelling of a leg until it resembles that of an elephant gives the condition its common name.

The lymphatic capillaries anastomose to form larger vessels that run in the sheaths with the arteries and the veins and, eventually, drain into the subclavian veins in the thorax. In the larger lymph vessels, endothelial flaps occur periodically, oriented to form valves similar to those in the veins (see Figure 12-24). Because of these valves, if the lymph vessel is compressed, the lymph flows in only one direction. The flow of lymph is maintained by intermittent compression of the vessels by skeletal muscles, by the pulsatile expansion of the artery contained in the same sheath, and by the spontaneous contraction of smooth muscle in the walls of the lymphatic vessels. The junction of the lymphatic system with the venous system in the thorax, which is subjected to subatmospheric pressure (see "Effects of Intrathoracic Pressure on Blood Flow" in Chapter 17), also provides an aid to flow.

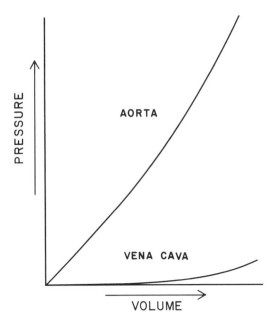

Figure 12-20. Compliance of the vena cava, and of veins as a class of vessels, is much greater than that of the aorta and of arteries as a class of vessel.

it also depends on the occurrence of relatively low pressure in the large veins. Normally, these vessels are somewhat flattened or elliptical in shape, and very little increase of pressure is required to round them out and increase their volume.

Veins

STRUCTURE
Compared with the arteries, the veins are thin-walled, fibrous, and muscular; a given vein is slightly larger than the artery that lies in the same sheath with it. The veins are more compliant than the arteries, but they are less elastic; that is, they do not return as readily to their previous form after they have been distended.

FUNCTIONS
The veins serve as a volume reservoir and as low-resistance conduits.

VOLUME-PRESSURE RELATIONSHIP
The veins can accommodate relatively large changes in volume by relatively small changes in pressure (Figure 12-20). This property depends partly on the compliance of the veins, but

VENOUS TONE
The capacity of the venous system can be decreased by the contraction of smooth muscle in the walls of the veins and the venous reservoirs, such as those in the skin and the liver. The volume of the venous system normally is at an intermediate level, and the smooth muscle always is partially contracted; thus, a certain *venous tone* is maintained. If the venous tone is increased, the venous pressure increases or the venous volume decreases; if the venous tone is decreased, venous pressure decreases or the venous volume increases.

Effects of Gravity on Vascular Pressures

The values of blood pressure that were discussed earlier in this chapter are measured in a person who is reclining, in whom all of the long axis of the body is in the horizontal plane. These pressures are generated by the contraction of the heart and the flow of blood against vascular resistance; the effect of gravity is negligible in these measurements. In the erect person, however, blood vessels form vertical columns that are greatly affected by the force of gravity.

EFFECTS ABOVE THE HEART

Because the flow of blood originates at the heart, the effect of gravity on the vascular system begins at the level of the heart, and the effect differs, depending on whether the pressure is measured below the heart or above the heart. Because the weight of the column of blood is a force that always is directed downward, all pressures decrease with distance above the heart and increase with distance below the heart (Figure 12-21). Therefore, at some distance above the heart, arterial pressure will be zero, and blood will flow no higher. If we take the mean arterial pressure at the level of the heart to be 90 mm Hg, mean arterial pressure will be zero at a point about 120 cm above the heart. Fortunately, the head of the average person is not more than about 30 cm above the heart, so that when the person is erect, a mean arterial pressure of about 65 mm Hg is available to perfuse the brain.

Since venous pressure at the level of the heart essentially is zero, venous pressure in the head must be negative, that is, subatmospheric. As the blood leaves the rigid cranium, however, the thin-walled veins collapse because the pressure outside the veins (atmospheric pressure) exceeds the pressure in the veins, and the pressure in the jugular vein is zero. One can easily see the effect of gravity on the superficial veins of the arms (Figure 12-22). If the arm is permitted to hang downward, the veins are seen to distend because the weight of the blood in the vessels adds to the venous pressure. Then, as the arm is raised slowly, the veins shrink and disappear at about the level of the heart. If the arm is held extended above the head, grooves, or indentions, appear where the distended veins were seen before. Thus, because of the subatmospheric pressure in the lumen, the veins collapse, and the skin is pushed inward by the pressure of the atmosphere. If the vein were punctured by an open needle, the atmospheric pressure would push air into the bloodstream. This event should be avoided, of course, but the same effect can be utilized to decrease or prevent bleeding from wounds, if the bleeding site can be placed above the heart.

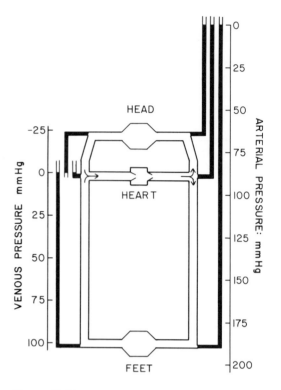

Figure 12-21. Arterial and venous pressures at the levels of the heart, the head, and the feet in a person who is standing still. The bars on each side of the diagram depict manometers that register the pressures. Note that the *difference* between mean arterial pressure and mean venous pressure is 90 mm Hg when the pressures are compared at the same level on each side (regardless of the actual values on each side). Thus, at the heart, arterial pressure is 90 mm Hg and venous pressure is 0 mm Hg; at the head, arterial pressure is 65 mm Hg and venous pressure is −25 mm Hg; at the feet, arterial pressure is 190 mm Hg and venous pressure is 100 mm Hg. Because it is the same on each side, neither adding to nor subtracting from the absolute value, the pressure due to gravity does not affect the flow of blood, and only the difference of pressure provides a gradient of energy that causes blood to flow.

EFFECTS BELOW THE HEART

In both arteries and veins, the blood pressure increases with distance below the heart. The effects on the veins are of greater consequence, however, because of the greater distensibility of the veins. If no compensatory mechanisms were available, the weight of the blood would distend the relatively thin-walled veins so much that the blood would pool in the legs and the abdomen,

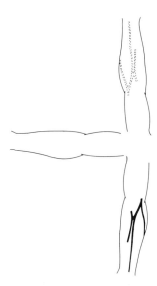

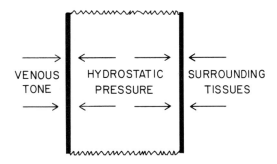

Figure 12-23.   Contraction of the smooth muscles in the walls of the veins, which produces venous tone, and the mass of the surrounding tissues oppose the dilatation of the veins by the venous blood pressure.

Figure 12-22.   When the arm is held downward, the superficial veins are distended and can be seen in most subjects. When the arm is held horizontally, the veins disappear. When the arm is held above the head, slight depressions appear where the distended veins were seen.

and no blood from the lower parts of the body would reach the heart. This does not occur because the veins are supported by the tissues that surround them (the fibrous sheaths, skeletal muscles, and viscera) and by the smooth muscle in the vascular walls (Figure 12-23).

Venous tone (the sustained partial contraction of the smooth muscle) is controlled by the central nervous system and mediated through the sympathetic division of the autonomic nervous system.

Venous drainage of the tissues also is aided by extensive communication among the veins, which permits shunting of blood through other vessels if obstruction occurs or backpressure develops. Thus, most vascular beds do not depend entirely on the functioning of only one vein.

The medium and large veins contain valves that interrupt the long columns of blood and direct the flow of blood in the proper direction when the vessels are compressed (Figure 12-24). Unless a person stands absolutely still, contraction of the skeletal muscles of the legs will compress the deep veins and aid the flow of blood toward the heart. This important mechanism has been called the *muscle pump*.

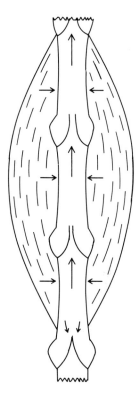

Figure 12-24.   Compression of veins by the contraction of the surrounding skeletal muscle, and the orientation by the venous valves of the force thus generated, constitute the "muscle pump."

Effects of Gravity on Blood Flow

In a person standing quietly, the weight of the column of blood in the veins and arteries adds to the vascular pressures. Thus, depending on the height of the person, arterial pressure in the feet may be 180–190 mm Hg, and venous pressure may be as much as 100 mm Hg (see Figure 12-21). These values alone might seem to indicate that arterial blood must flow against a pressure gradient of 90 mm Hg at the heart to 185 mm Hg at the feet, and that venous blood is subjected to an enormous gradient of 100 mm Hg at the feet to 0 mm Hg at the heart; however, these figures are misleading. The blood pressure in a systemic vessel always is referred to the atmospheric pressure. Therefore, this blood pressure is the transmural pressure (the difference of pressure across the vessel wall), and it represents only the force tending to drive blood from the vessel to the atmosphere. Transmural pressure is important if the vessel is punctured and blood flows out of the vessel; however, taken alone, it is not relevant to the flow of blood within the vessel. The driving force that causes blood to flow is the difference of pressure between two points after the effect of gravity has been taken into account. Usually, this is done by taking both measurements at the same level in the gravitational field. In the diagram shown in Figure 12-21, the difference between arterial pressure and venous pressure at any level is about 90 mm Hg, which is the force that makes the blood flow.

The circulatory system may be visualized as two U-tubes, one above the heart, one below the heart, and each open to the heart (Figure 12-25). The force of gravity is applied equally to both sides of each tube, its propulsive effects are cancelled, and the gradient of pressure that causes blood to flow is not affected by the upright position of the body, provided that the vessels do not collapse or become overly distended.

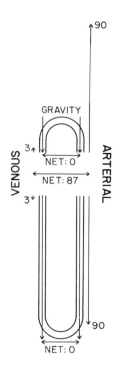

Figure 12-25. The circulatory system in an erect person is represented by two U-tubes, one turned upward and one turned downward. Because the force of gravity is exactly the same on each side of the tubes, the net difference of pressure caused by gravity in each tube is zero. The force that makes the blood flow is the difference between the arterial pressure and the venous pressure. In this example, the heart generates a mean arterial pressure of 90 mm Hg, and mean venous pressure at the level of the heart is 3 mm Hg, providing a gradient of 87 mm Hg that is not affected by gravity.

Effects of Transmural Pressure on Blood Vessels

DILATATION

The walls of the arteries are sufficiently thick and strong that the transmural pressure added by gravity distends them very little. Because they are thin-walled and compliant, the veins are affected strongly by distending forces and tend to enlarge permanently if they are dilated persistently. The veins of some people are particularly distensible; if the dilatation is too great, the cusps of the venous valves do not meet in the center, and the valves are incompetent. This increases the length of the hydrostatic column, increases venous pressure, and promotes further dilatation. Such dilated veins are called *varicose* veins. The superficial veins of the legs are most susceptible to this effect because they are not supported as well as the deeper veins are.

Persistent dilatation is caused or aggravated by circumstances that require a person to stand much of the time with little movement, by garments that fit tightly about the waist, pelvis, and upper thighs, and by pregnancy. Persistent dilatation of the veins of the legs may be prevented or alleviated by leg exercises such as walking or running; by deliberate, rhythmic tightening and relaxing of the leg muscles when one must stand still; and by elevation of the feet and legs.

CLINICAL CORRELATION
12.1   Variation of Serum Cholesterol with Posture

CASE REPORT

Patient: A 32-year-old woman.

Clinical Complaints: Borderline arterial hypertension with familial hypercholesterolemia.

History: The patient has been receiving treatment for borderline systemic arterial hypertension for 11 years. The therapeutic agent (hydrochlorathiazide, a diuretic agent) has controlled the hypertension (most recent reading, 115/80 mm Hg), but 5 years ago, her serum cholesterol level began to increase. She has been under treatment for this condition since then, using a resin (cholestyramine) that combines with the bile acids in the intestine to form an insoluble complex that is excreted in the feces. Because cholesterol is the precursor of the bile acids, it must be diverted to replace the bile acids that are excreted, and the concentration of cholesterol in the plasma decreases. The patient has a complete physical examination once a year, and, in addition, her serum cholesterol is checked every 6 months. Perusal of her record to determine whether her therapeutic regimen is optimal revealed that her cholesterol level, after overnight fasting, always is higher at the 6-month checkup than it is when measured as part of the annual examination. The venous blood samples have been taken by the same laboratory technician during the 5 years that she has been treated for hypercholesterolemia, and the same commercial laboratory has made all of the determinations, using the same method each time.

Solution: After reflecting on factors that might contribute to the regular variation, the technician recalled that for the annual checkup, blood always was drawn while the patient was lying down, after blood pressure had been taken several times and an ECG recorded. In the 6-month checkup, however, only serum cholesterol was measured. On this occasion, the patient arrives at the laboratory, sits in a chair, and the blood is drawn immediately. Because there are reports in the literature that certain values, including serum cholesterol, can vary with posture,* a study of the effects of posture in this patient was done. First, blood was taken while the patient was sitting, shortly after entering the laboratory. Then she reclined for 30 minutes, and another sample was taken. The last sample was taken after she had been standing again for 10 minutes. The results were: control, upright: serum cholesterol, 230 mg/dl; hematocrit, 44%; blood glucose, 86%. After 30 minutes of reclining: serum cholesterol, 185 mg/dl; hematocrit, 39%; blood glucose, 87%. After 10 minutes of standing: serum cholesterol, 220 mg/dl; hematocrit, 41%; blood glucose, 85%.

Comment: These data are consistent with the movement of fluid out of the vascular system, through the capillaries, into the extracellular space and lymphatic channels, producing relative hemoconcentration while the subject is standing, and back into the vascular system while the subject is reclining, producing relative hemodilution. These changes are caused by the effects of gravity on the tissues below the heart. The changes of hematocrit confirm the changes of plasma volume. The cholesterol remains in the blood because it is bound to large molecules of lipoprotein that do not pass through capillary walls. Thus, the concentration of cholesterol changes inversely with the plasma volume. The blood glucose level does not change, because glucose passes through the capillary wall in solution, hence is distributed evenly between the plasma and the interstitial fluid. Since this study was done, blood samples always are taken after the patient has been sitting for at least 20 minutes, and much more consistent results are obtained.

*Ian, M.H., Wilmhurst, E.G., Gleason, R.E., et al. 1973. Effect of posture on serum lipids. *N. Eng. J. Med.* 289:416.

CAPILLARY TRANSUDATION

When venous pressure in the legs is high, the capillary pressure of the legs and feet also must be high (see Figure 12-21). Venous pressures greater than about 25–30 mm Hg force fluid out of the capillaries continuously (see Figure 12-18). Therefore, the feet, even of healthy people, usually swell during periods of prolonged standing.

WALL TENSION—
THE LAW OF LAPLACE

In a cylinder, such as a blood vessel, the tension in the curved walls is given by the expression

$$T = Pr$$

in which T is the tension, P is the pressure, and r is the radius (see "Wall Tension, Law of Laplace" in Chapter 1). Therefore, at any internal pressure, the wall tension depends on the size of the vessel (Figure 12-26). This relationship explains how a capillary can withstand a pressure of 100 mm Hg (see Figure 12-21); its radius is so small that very little tension in the walls is needed to prevent dilatation. Suppose that the pressure in an aorta with a radius of 1.5 cm also is 100 mm Hg. Because the pressure is the same in both vessels, the wall tension of each depends on the radius of each; therefore,

$$\frac{T_A}{T_C} \simeq \frac{r_A}{r_C} = \frac{1.5 \text{ cm}}{0.0005 \text{ cm}} = \frac{3000}{1}$$

where T_A is the tension in the wall of the aorta, T_C is the tension in the wall of the capillary, r_A is the radius of the aorta, and r_C is the radius of the capillary. Thus, because of its very small size, the capillary needs to withstand only 1/3000 as much tension as the aorta does at any given pressure, and no problem of dilatation or rupture of capillaries is encountered.

The law of Laplace also helps to explain why the veins are so susceptible to dilatation and

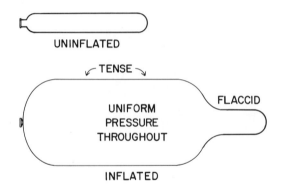

Figure 12-26.   Relationship between radius and tension in the wall of a vessel. The diagrams depict a balloon that is empty and then is partially inflated. Although the pressure is the same in all parts of the balloon, the tension in the walls that have been stretched is considerably greater than the tension in the unstretched portion.

why dilatation once begun, tends to progress. Suppose that a vein in the foot has a radius (r_V) of 1 mm and is subjected to 100 mm Hg of pressure; the tension in the wall of the vein (T_V) relative to that in the wall of a capillary (T_C) subjected to the same pressure would be

$$\frac{T_V}{T_C} \simeq \frac{r_V}{r_C} = \frac{0.1 \text{ cm}}{0.0005 \text{ cm}} = \frac{200}{1}$$

Therefore, because the vein is larger, its walls are subjected to much greater tension than the walls of the capillary are, and the vein is dilated. This increases the tension, which is proportional to the radius, and the vein may be dilated further. The fibrous components of the vein resist further dilatation, but, eventually, the vein will lose some of its elasticity and remain somewhat dilated, even at lower pressures. Thus, if the vein is stretched persistently, it will dilate progressively, and it never can return to its former, smaller size.

STUDY OUTLINE

CIRCULATORY SYSTEM

HEART   Two pumps in series.

BLOOD VESSELS

ARRANGEMENT   Blood goes from heart to tissues through arteries, returns to heart through veins.

As arteries divide, total cross-sectional area increases; velocity of flow decreases.

Total cross-sectional area of capillaries is far greater than that of arteries or veins.

Blood flows most slowly in capillaries.

Veins join to form fewer vessels, total cross-sectional area decreases, and velocity of flow increases.

BLOOD PRESSURE

Measurement   Height to which blood will flow upward against gravity.

Height of equal weight of column of mercury is used for convenience.

Unit of measurement is millimeter of mercury (mm Hg).

Pressure Gradient   Difference of pressure makes blood flow.

Small difference from heart to end of arteries; blood flows freely, resistance is low.

Large difference from beginning of arterioles to end of capillaries; resistance is high.

Small difference from beginning of veins to heart; resistance is low.

BLOOD VOLUME   About 5 liters; 80%–90% in systemic circulation, 10%–20% in pulmonary circulation.

Seventy-five percent of systemic blood is in veins, 20% in arteries, 5% in capillaries.

Volume of veins is most variable.

STRUCTURE-FUNCTION RELATIONSHIPS

ARTERIES

STRUCTURE   Tough, strong; fibrous, elastic, muscular; lined by endothelium.

FUNCTIONS   Pressure reservoir during each cycle.

Volume reservoir during each cycle.

Low-resistance conduit.

VOLUME-PRESSURE RELATIONSHIP
Compliant—expanded by blood from heart.

Elastic—contract as blood runs into arterioles.

DIASTOLIC PUMP   Blood is stored during systole and runs off during diastole.

Intermittent flow out of heart; continuous flow out of arteries.

CONDUIT   Low resistance, high velocity.

Contraction of smooth muscle decreases compliance; increases pressure gradient and velocity of flow.

Fibrous connective tissue adds strength.

ARTERIOLES AND PRECAPILLARY SPHINCTERS

STRUCTURE   Thick, muscular walls.

FUNCTION   Variable resistors.

MAINTENANCE OF CENTRAL ARTERIAL PRESSURE   Flow × resistance.

COUNTERING EFFECTS OF GRAVITY
Prevent overperfusion below heart; aid perfusion above heart.

SELECTIVE PERFUSION   Restrict in some beds to increase in others.

ORIGIN OF VASCULAR RESISTANCE

LAMINAR FLOW   Friction between layers of fluid.

RELATION TO SIZE OF VESSEL   Laminae near wall affected most by friction—proportionally greater area in smaller vessels.

VARIABLES THAT CONTRIBUTE TO RESISTANCE

POISEUILLE'S EQUATION   Pressure gradient, size of vessel, viscosity of blood, and length of vessel determine flow.

Size of vessel (arterioles and sphincters) is controlled physiologically; resistance is proportional to fourth power of radius.

CALCULATION OF VASCULAR RESISTANCE   Pressure gradient divided by rate of flow.

TOTAL PERIPHERAL RESISTANCE
Cardiac output divided by aortic pressure minus right atrial pressure.

COMBINING RESISTANCES   Add reciprocals; sum of individual resistances is less than any single resistance.

VISCOSITY OF BLOOD   Increased by suspended particles (red cells).

AXIAL FLOW   Cell-free zone forms near walls of vessels; viscosity decreases in small vessels, increases at low rates of flow.

EFFECT OF HEMATOCRIT   Viscosity increases with hematocrit.

CAPILLARIES

STRUCTURE   Single layer of endothelial cells; about 10 μm in diameter; average length is 1 mm.

Arise from metarterioles; may branch or join other capillaries; terminate in venules.

Flow is controlled by precapillary sphincters; either open or closed.

FUNCTIONS Permit exchange between blood and interstitial fluid.

Water exchanges easily, red cells and plasma proteins do not.

Dissolved substances diffuse down gradients of chemical activity.

FLUID EXCHANGE

COLLOIDAL OSMOTIC PRESSURE
Plasma proteins decrease chemical activity of plasma water; water enters capillary down activity gradient (osmosis).

Capillary walls restrict movement of plasma proteins.

HYDROSTATIC PRESSURE VS. PLASMA ONCOTIC PRESSURE
Balance determines whether water leaves capillary or enters it.

In open capillary, hydrostatic pressure exceeds colloidal osmotic pressure; fluid leaves vessel.

In closed capillary, colloidal osmotic pressure exceeds hydrostatic pressure; fluid enters vessel from interstitium.

Balance depends on how many capillary sphincters are open and how many are closed.

Excess extracellular fluid is absorbed by lymphatic system.

FACTORS THAT AFFECT FLUID BALANCE Increased capillary pressure because of gravity (prolonged standing); increased venous pressure (cardiac failure or venous obstruction); arteriolar dilatation (inflammation).

Increased capillary permeability (inflammation or circulatory shock).

Decreased colloidal osmotic pressure (increased capillary permeability: inflammation, shock); decreased plasma proteins (liver disease).

Decreased capillary pressure (arterial hypotension).

LYMPHATIC SYSTEM Drains interstitial fluid into venous system.

Removes excess fluid and protein that leaks out.

Maintains subatmospheric interstitial pressure.

VEINS

STRUCTURE Thin-walled, fibrous, muscular; more compliant and less elastic than arteries.

FUNCTIONS Volume reservoir and low-resistance conduits.

VOLUME-PRESSURE RELATIONSHIP
Veins can accommodate relatively large change of volume with relatively small change of pressure.

VENOUS TONE Affects capacity (volume) and pressure; normally held at intermediate level.

EFFECTS OF GRAVITY ON VASCULAR PRESSURES

EFFECTS ABOVE THE HEART All pressures are decreased; venous pressure is equal to atmospheric (zero); veins collapse.

EFFECTS BELOW THE HEART All pressures are increased; veins are affected most; integrity of circulation depends on support of veins.

Venous tone—contraction of smooth muscle under sympathetic nervous system influence.

Venous anastomoses—a vein may drain another vein that is distended.

Muscle pump—compression of veins by contracting skeletal muscles; valves in veins direct flow toward heart.

EFFECTS OF GRAVITY ON BLOOD FLOW Relatively small if collapse or overdistention of vessels is prevented; driving force is difference of pressure between points at same level.

EFFECTS OF TRANSMURAL PRESSURE ON BLOOD VESSELS

DILATATION Veins suffer permanent enlargement and develop incompetent valves; become varicose.

CAPILLARY TRANSUDATION Swelling of feet, edema.

WALL TENSION—THE LAW OF LAPLACE Tension = pressure × radius.

Capillaries withstand high pressure because radius is small.

Aorta needs thick, tough wall because pressure is high and radius is large.

Dilatation of veins tends to progress because radius increases.

BIBLIOGRAPHY

Brace, R.A. 1981. Progress toward resolving the controversy of positive versus negative interstitial fluid pressure. *Circ. Res.* 49:281.

Bundgaard, M. 1980. Transport pathways in capillaries—in search of pores. *Annu. Rev. Physiol.* 42:325.

Burton, A.C. 1944. Relation of structure to function of the tissues of the wall of blood vessels. *Physiol. Rev.* 34:619.

Burton, A.C. 1972. *Physiology and Biophysics of the Circulation* (2nd ed.). Chicago: Year Book.

Cokelet, G.R. 1980. Rheology and hemodynamics. *Annu. Rev. Physiol.* 42:311.

Cromer, A.H. 1977. *Physics for the Life Sciences* (2nd ed.). New York: McGraw-Hill.

Fahraeus, R., and Lindquist, T. 1931. The viscosity of the blood in narrow capillary tubes. *Am. J. Physiol.* 96:562.

Gore, R.W., and McDonagh, P.F. 1980. Fluid exchange across single capillaries. *Annu. Rev. Physiol.* 42:337.

Green, H.D. 1944. Physical principles. In *Medical Physics.* Volume 1. Edited by O. Glasser. Chicago: Year Book.

Guyton, A.C., Granger, H.J., and Taylor, A.E. 1971. Interstitial fluid pressure. *Physiol. Rev.* 51:527.

Hargans, A.R. (ed.). 1981. *Tissue Fluid Pressure and Composition.* Baltimore: Williams & Wilkins.

Kaley, G., and Altura, B.M. (eds.). 1977. *Microcirculation.* Baltimore: University Park Press.

LaBarbera, M., and Vogel, S. 1982. The design of fluid transport systems in organisms. *Am. Sci.* 70:54.

Merrill, E.W. 1969. Rheology of blood. *Physiol. Rev.* 49:863.

Milnor, W.R. 1982. *Hemodynamics.* Baltimore: Williams & Wilkins.

Rushmer, R.F. 1976. *Cardiovascular Dynamics* (4th ed.). Philadelphia: Saunders.

Taylor, A.E. 1981. Capillary fluid filtration: Starling forces and lymph flow. *Circ. Res.* 49:281.

Whittaker, S.R.F., and Winton, F.R. 1933. The apparent viscosity of blood flowing in the isolated hindlimb of the dog, and its variation with corpuscular concentration. *J. Physiol.* (London) 78:339.

13

The Cardiac Cycle

CHAPTER CONTENTS

GENERAL BACKGROUND

The heart functions as two pumps connected in series. The pump situated to the right and anterior in the chest, the *right ventricle*, forces blood through the lungs and into the left ventricle; the pump located to the left and posterior in the chest, the *left ventricle*, forces blood through the systemic circulation and into the right ventricle (Figure 13-1). Not all of the force that makes the blood flow comes from contraction of the heart—small, but important, contributions to blood flow are made by the skeletal muscle pump and the respiratory pump. Nevertheless, the bulk of the flow of blood is generated by the heart.

EVENTS OF THE CARDIAC CYCLE

Both ventricles function as intermittent pumps that stop pumping to fill and stop filling to pump. The system by which the heart is excited and made to contract is arranged so that both

pumps fill at the same time and empty at the same time. The period during which the ventricles fill is called *diastole*, and the period during which the ventricles empty, or pump, is called *systole*; together, they make up the *cardiac cycle*, which is the repeating unit of cardiac function. These two major periods are subdivided to permit detailed analysis of the cardiac cycle (Figure 13-2).

Atrial Contraction

The cardiac *pacemaker,* the group of heart cells that initiates the cardiac cycle, is located at the junction of the right atrium and the superior vena cava (sinoatrial node); therefore, it begins activation of the right atrium first. Excitation is propagated throughout both atria, and the P wave of the electrocardiogram (ECG) is produced; atrial contraction follows (Figure 13-2, phase A).

Contraction of the atria increases both right and left atrial pressures. Because the atrioventricular valves, which guard the openings of the atria into the ventricles, are open and there are

218

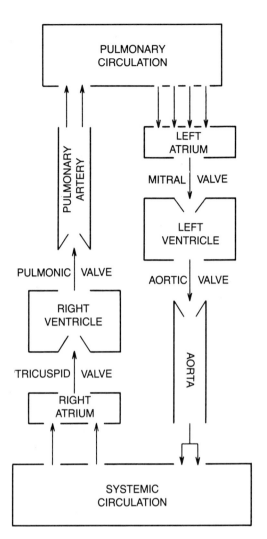

Figure 13-1. Circulation through the heart. (Arrows indicate the direction of flow.)

atria, which are acting merely as conduits to connect the veins and the ventricles. Thus, when the atria contract, the ventricles are nearly full and have little need for the pump function of the atria. The situation is different when the cardiac output is increased, as it is when a person exercises, for example; the heart rate is increased, the duration of the cardiac cycle is decreased, and the duration of diastole is decreased. Because there is less time for the heart to fill by venous inflow alone, the contraction of the atria can contribute significantly to the filling of the ventricles.

The atria perform another function that is important regardless of whether the heart rate is fast or slow. The blood that is pushed into the ventricles by atrial contraction distends the ventricles slightly; the walls of the ventricles then rebound elastically, and the pressure wave thus generated helps to float the atrioventricular (AV) valves into a position to be closed when the ventricles contract. The vibration associated with atrial contraction normally is not perceived as sound, but it can be recorded. Sometimes it is heard, however, and then it is called the *fourth heart sound.*

The pulmonic valve and the aortic valve are closed, and blood is flowing from the elastic reservoir of the central arteries into the vascular beds; hence, the pressures in the pulmonary artery and the aorta are declining. This phase, the last part of the larger period of ventricular diastole, ends with the beginning of ventricular contraction.

no valves between the atria and the veins, *pressure waves* are sent forward into each ventricle, and backward into the veins. The pressure wave produced in the systemic veins by the contraction of the right atrium can be recorded easily; it is the *a* wave of the jugular venous pulse (Figure 13-3). At this time, blood still is flowing in the large veins, toward the atria, and its momentum keeps it flowing despite the opposing atrial pressure wave. The atrial pressure wave aids flow from the atria into the ventricles, although the effect is slight in the slowly beating heart of the normal person at rest. In this circumstance, the period of diastole is relatively long, and the ventricles fill almost entirely with blood that flows from the large veins through the relaxed

Ventricular Isovolumic Contraction

Ventricular isovolumic contraction marks the beginning of ventricular systole (Figure 13-2, phase B). It lasts about 15 msec in the right ventricle and about 40 msec in the left ventricle. Ventricular contraction begins near the peak of the R wave of the ECG and develops rapidly; in each ventricle, blood forced back toward the atrium closes the atrioventricular valve. Vibration associated with this movement and with the arrest of the mass of ventricular blood against the taut tricuspid and mitral valves is perceived as the initial components of the first heart sound.

Supporting strands (*chordae tendineae*) connect from the edges of the valve leaflets to muscular pillars (the *papillary muscles*) that project from the walls of the ventricles. These

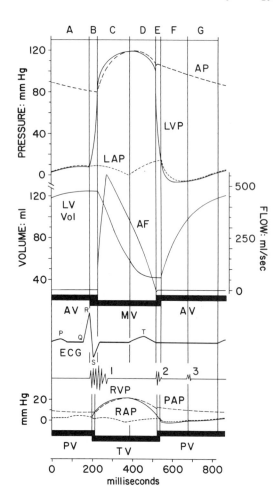

Figure 13-2. Some of the most important events of the cardiac cycle. Phases: A = atrial contraction; B = ventricular isovolumic contraction; C = rapid ventricular ejection; D = decreased ventricular ejection; E = isovolumic relaxation; F = rapid ventricular filling; G = diastasis. Other designations: AP = aortic pressure; LVP = left ventricular pressure; LAP = left atrial pressure; LV Vol = left ventricular volume; AF = aortic flow; AV = aortic valve; MV = mitral valve; PV = pulmonic valve; TV = tricuspid valve (a solid bar above the designation means that the valve is closed); ECG = electrocardiogram; P, Q, R, S, T = component waves of the ECG; 1, 2, 3 = heart sounds; RVP = right ventricular pressure; PAP = pulmonary arterial pressure; RAP = right atrial pressure.

fibers keep the valves from turning back into the atria. The papillary muscles contract very soon after the beginning of ventricular excitation and provide additional support to the chordae. The valves bulge into the atria somewhat, and the atrial pressures increase slightly,

producing a venous pressure wave that can be detected in the jugular venous pulse as the *c* wave (Figure 13-3).

Because the pulmonic and aortic valves are closed, the volumes of the ventricles do not change, but the pressure in each ventricle increases rapidly. Thus, potential energy is stored in the blood in the ventricles. The longer duration of this phase in the left ventricle is consistent with the higher pressure that must be developed.

The pressures in the pulmonary artery and the aorta still are decreasing and will reach their lowest values (*diastolic pressure*) at the end of this phase.

Rapid Ventricular Ejection

Ejection begins with the opening of the aortic and pulmonic valves when the pressure within the ventricle exceeds the pressure in the artery (Figure 13-2, phase C). As the ventricular pressure increases rapidly, the valves open abruptly, and blood is expelled from the heart in projectile fashion.

Left ventricular volume and rate of ejection are illustrated in Figure 13-2. Left ventricular ejection, which also is aortic flow, reaches a maximum in about 50–100 milliseconds and begins to decline. The bulk of the transfer of blood from the ventricle to the aorta occurs during the phase of rapid ejection; in the cycle represented in Figure 13-2, for example, 80% of the stroke volume (the volume ejected with each beat of the heart) flowed during this phase. The ability of the heart to do most of its work early in systole is very important because the heart rate increases when the cardiac output increases physiologically, and the duration of systole thus is shortened.

When the pulmonic and aortic valves open, the blood that is ejected encounters a stationary mass of blood in each great artery. (This is to be expected because the blood left at the base of the artery after the last closure of the valve could not flow away without causing the artery to collapse.) Some of the inflowing blood is arrested during this encounter, and its kinetic energy is transformed into potential energy; thus, the volume and the pressure in the artery are increased, and the arterial blood flow is accelerated. The rapid expansion of the elastic pulmonary artery and aorta creates vibration that, on auscultation, is perceived as a continuation of the *first heart sound*. As the peak velocity in the great arteries is approached, the flow becomes turbulent, and the final component of the first heart sound is heard.

Because the tricuspid and mitral valves remain closed during this phase, the atria serve as reservoirs for venous inflow. Despite the increase of volume that occurs, the pressure in both atria declines temporarily during this phase. This decline is related to a reduction of thoracic blood volume that occurs because of the decrease of left ventricular volume. Thus, the efflux of blood from the thorax through the arterial system facilitates the influx of blood into the thorax through the venous system.

During the phase of rapid ventricular ejection, ventricular pressure exceeds arterial pressure, and the flow of blood in the pulmonary artery and the aorta is accelerated. Because the pulmonary artery and the aorta both are large vessels, the zone of laminar flow near their walls is small relative to their total cross-sectional areas. Hence, the resistance to flow is slight, and acceleration is accomplished primarily by overcoming the inertia of the mass of blood. Therefore, once the blood is set in motion, it tends to continue to flow because of its momentum.

The ventricles empty rapidly, and the ventricular myocardium completes most of its contraction during this phase. Just as energy was put into the blood to make it flow, energy must be taken from the blood to make it stop flowing. The decreasing rate of aortic flow after the peak is reached (Figure 13-2, phase C) represents a loss of kinetic energy, and the continued increase of pressure in the pulmonary artery and the aorta reflects the transformation of at least a part of that kinetic energy into potential energy. Thus, energy imparted into the blood initially by the contraction of the ventricle is stored in the elastic walls of the large arteries early in systole and given back to keep the blood flowing during diastole. When left ventricular pressure and aortic pressure become equal, the ventricle no longer is transferring energy to the blood, and the phase of rapid ventricular ejection is concluded.

Decreased Ventricular Ejection

The beginning of the phase of decreased ejection is marked by the decrease of left ventricular pressure to less than aortic pressure (Figure 13-2, phase D). Blood still is flowing into the aorta, utilizing the momentum imparted by the early, rapid contraction of the ventricle. The decline of aortic pressure is delayed as the elastic walls of the aorta continue to absorb the energy that must be removed to complete the deceleration of ventricular outflow and permit the aortic valve to close. When ejection ceases, the gradient of pressure from the aorta to the ventricle begins to accelerate flow from the aorta back to the ventricle, and the aortic valve closes. A similar series of events occurs with the pulmonary artery, right ventricle, and pulmonic valve. The arrest of backward flow in the aorta and the pulmonary artery by the valves produces vibration that is perceived as the *second heart sound.*

Because the rate of outflow of blood from the thorax through the aorta decreases and the atria continue to be filled by blood flowing in through the systemic veins and the pulmonary veins, atrial pressures increase during this phase.

The occurrence of the T wave of the ECG indicates that the ventricles are repolarizing. Closure of the aortic and pulmonic valves marks the end of the phase of decreased ventricular ejection and the end of the period of systole.

Isovolumic Relaxation

After the aortic and pulmonic valves close, the ventricular pressures decrease rapidly as the ventricular myocardium relaxes, but the volumes of the ventricles do not change. The pressure in the aorta rebounds after the slight fall associated with closure of the aortic valve and produces the *dicrotic notch.* The great arteries now are isolated from further input, and the pressures in them decline steadily. This phase ends as the pressure in each ventricle decreases to less than that in the corresponding atrium and the AV valves open.

Rapid Ventricular Filling

During contraction of the ventricles, with shortening of the muscle fibers and decrease of the ventricular dimensions, some tension develops in the connective tissue that binds the layers of muscle together; during relaxation, release of this tension aids the expansion of the ventricular volumes. This effect is greatest in the thick-walled left ventricle, where the pressure may decrease to a value that is several mm Hg less than atmospheric pressure. Thus, very early in diastole, the gradient of pressure between the atria and the ventricles is increased, and filling of the ventricles is augmented.

The orifices of the AV valves are large, the atria and the great veins are well filled, and the relaxed ventricles are highly compliant. Therefore, a very small gradient of pressure is adequate to accelerate the flow of blood into the ventricles. As the ventricles expand, their compliances decrease, and the mass of blood that had been accelerated is arrested. The vibration that is produced is perceived by auscultation as the *third heart sound*.

In the heart of a person at rest, most of the filling of the ventricles occurs early in diastole, during the phase of rapid filling. This arrangement is important because, when the cardiac output increases physiologically, the heart rate increases, and the duration of diastole is shortened.

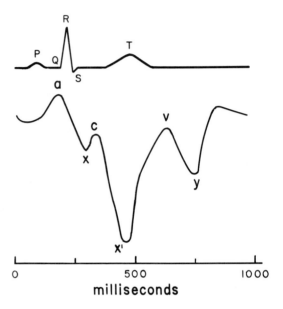

Figure 13-3. Jugular venous pulses. The transducer was held over the jugular vein, against the skin of the neck; hence, the pulses are not calibrated. The electrocardiogram is shown to permit relation of the venous pressure waves to the phases of the cardiac cycle. *a*: contraction of right atrium; *x*: relaxation of atrium; *c*: closure of tricuspid valve and isovolumic contraction of right ventricle; *x′*: reduction of thoracic volume during rapid ventricular ejection; *v*: filling of great veins and right atrium during ventricular systole; *y*: rapid filling of right ventricle.

Diastasis

Diastasis is a phase of relative inactivity. Blood is flowing under the impetus of the pressures in the elastic arteries, and the ventricles are filling slowly; the atria and the large veins have delivered the blood they had stored during systole and now are filling again as blood flows in from the periphery. There is no electrical activity in the heart, and no sounds are heard. This phase constitutes "reserve time" that can be used for more frequent repetition of the cardiac cycle; therefore, its duration is variable, depending on the heart rate. It is terminated by the P wave of the ECG, which begins another cycle.

VENOUS PRESSURE WAVES

Certain of the events of the cardiac cycle cause variations of pressure in the systemic veins that can be recorded easily by an appropriate transducer (device that records pulse waves) placed over the external jugular vein (Figure 13-3). Certain abnormalities of the rhythm and the contractility of the heart can be detected by study of these waves.

The *a* wave is caused by the contraction of the right atrium; the *x* wave is caused by the subsequent relaxation of the atrium. The *c* wave is related to the pressure wave that closes the tricuspid valve and to the abrupt bulging of the valve into the atria during isovolumetric contraction of the ventricle. The wave designated *x′*

is caused by the rapid expulsion of blood from the thorax, through the aorta, during approximately the first half of systole. Reduction of the volume of fluid contained in the thorax decreases intrathoracic pressure. Thus, right atrial pressure decreases, and the jugular vein empties into the right atrium, producing the *x′* wave. The *v* wave reflects the filling of the atrium and the great veins during systole, when the tricuspid valve is closed. The *y* wave reflects the decrease of jugular venous volume as the large veins and the right atrium relinquish their contents during rapid filling of the ventricle.

VALVE MOTIONS
AND HEART SOUNDS

The *first heart sound* is rather complex and prolonged because it involves the closure of the mitral and tricuspid valves, the opening of the aortic and pulmonic valves, and the beginning of ejection into the aorta and the pulmonary

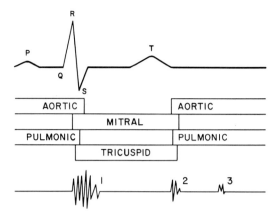

Figure 13-4. Movements of the valves. A labeled box indicates that the valve is closed; an open space indicates that the valve is open. The electrocardiogram is shown to permit reference to the cardiac cycle. The heart sounds (1, 2, 3) are shown to permit relation to the motions of the valves. The overlapping of the boxes (above sounds 1 and 2) indicates the periods of isovolumic contraction and isovolumic relaxation of each ventricle. Note that the period of right ventricular ejection exceeds the period of left ventricular ejection. The difference shown here probably is minimal. Increase of the right ventricular stroke volume would move the closure of the pulmonic valve to the right and cause splitting of the second heart sound.

---

artery. None of the valve motions begins at the same time as another; the mitral valve closes first, followed by closure of the tricuspid valve, opening of the pulmonic valve, and opening of the aortic valve (Figure 13-4). Thus, events in the right ventricle occur *between* events in the left ventricle.

The *second heart sound* involves the closures of the aortic and pulmonic valves. The aortic valve closes first, but the interval between that event and the closure of the pulmonic valve varies normally during the cycle of respiration. At the end of quiet expiration, the two events occur only a few milliseconds apart (Figure 13-4); however, during inspiration, the sound has two distinct components and is said to be "split." The second heart sound is split by any condition that prolongs the right ventricular ejection time and delays the closure of the pulmonic valve. Splitting during inspiration is caused by an increase of right ventricular stroke volume; the reason for the increase of stroke volume will be discussed in Chapter 17, in the section entitled "Effects of Intrathoracic Pressure on Blood Flow."

The intensity of any component of the first heart sound is increased by stronger, more rapid contraction of the ventricles, which sets up more vibration. The intensity of the second heart sound is increased by abnormally high pressure in either of the great arteries, which increases the force of the backward flow that closes the valve. The intensity of the third heart sound is heightened by an increase of the stroke volume of either ventricle, which increases the rate of rapid ventricular filling.

MURMURS

Murmurs are abnormal sounds caused by turbulence in rapidly flowing blood. Virtually all blood flow normally is silent because of the formation of laminae that slide smoothly over one another; however, discrete laminae persist only up to certain velocities. At a critical velocity, the laminae begin to break up, and some flow at right angles to the mainstream occurs, tending to form eddies and vortices (see also "Turbulent Flow" in Chapter 1).

The critical velocity for turbulent flow in straight tubes of constant radius varies with the viscosity of the fluid; thus,

$$V_c \simeq \eta$$

where V_c is the critical velocity, and η is the viscosity of the fluid. The critical velocity varies inversely with the density of the fluid and the radius of the tube; thus,

$$V_c \simeq \frac{1}{\rho r}$$

where ρ is the density of the fluid, and r is the radius of the tube. Putting these together,

$$V_c \simeq \frac{\eta}{\rho r}$$

A constant called *Reynolds's number* (Re) is factored in to produce the equation:

$$V_c = Re \frac{\eta}{\rho r}$$

Re is about 1000 for blood flowing in straight tubes.

Turbulence may occur in any condition that causes a velocity of flow greater than the critical velocity; it is more likely to occur in large vessels (such as the aorta, the pulmonary artery, and the venae cavae) in which the rate of flow is high and the critical velocity is less than in small vessels. Turbulence occurs normally in the pul-

CLINICAL CORRELATION
13.1   Aortic Stenosis and Replacement
of the Aortic Valve

CASE REPORT

The Patient: A 53-year-old man.

Principal Complaint: Fatigue and chest pain during exertion.

History: At the age of 31 years, a heart murmur was detected during a routine physical examination for an insurance policy. Medical surveillance of the problem was not maintained. About a year before the present admission, the patient noted chest pain during exertion. The condition has progressed, with fatigue and chest pain during even slight exertion, and on one occasion, the patient temporarily lost consciousness.

Clinical Examination: The patient appeared chronically ill. His arterial pressure was 95/80 mm Hg (normal, 90–140/60–90 mm Hg), his heart rate was 85 beats/min (normal, 60–100 beats/min), and his respiratory rate was 21 breaths/min (normal, 13–19 breaths/min). The arterial pulse was decreased in volume, and the upstroke was prolonged. The ECG suggested left ventricular hypertrophy (see Chapter 19), but no evidence of myocardial infarction was found. A chest radiograph confirmed that the heart was enlarged and the lungs were clear. Calcification was indicated in the region of the aortic valve. A soft systolic thrill and a harsh ejection murmur were heard, with maximal intensity at the apex of the heart. There were no other clinically significant findings.

Clinical Course: Digoxin (which increases cardiac contractility) was administered, and cardiac catheterization was performed. Coronary angiography (injection of contrast medium and observation under the fluroscope) revealed no significantly decreased coronary flow. The aortic pressure was 90/50, and the upstroke time of the arterial pulse was 0.25 seconds (normal, 0.05–0.1 second). The orifice of the aortic valve could not be penetrated. On the following day, the chest was opened and the aortic valve was examined; it was heavily calcified, and only a pinhole-sized orifice existed. The defective valve was excised, and a prosthetic aortic valve was installed.

Outcome: The patient recovered without event, and was discharged 3 weeks after admission, on a regimen of digoxin and warfarin (an anticoagulant). At a followup examination 6 weeks after the operation, the patient felt well, the arterial pressure was 115/75 mm Hg, and no cardiac murmur was heard. The digoxin and warfarin were discontinued, and the patient was continued on aspirin (inhibits the aggregation of platelets), 150 mg twice a day.

monary artery and the aorta as the peak velocity of ventricular ejection is reached; thus, it is a normal component of the first heart sound. It always occurs in the great arteries when the cardiac output is increased, as it is in exercise; the enhanced fourth component of the first heart sound heard under these conditions is called the *innocent murmur.* Turbulence also occurs in the inferior vena cava, but the sound is slight (*venous hum*) and the vessel is deep, so that no murmur usually is heard.

Murmurs are produced by the high velocity of flow through constrictions of large vessels, as in coarctation of the aorta, and by the high velocity of blood flow through abnormal openings, such as a patent ductus arteriosus. Murmurs also are caused by obstruction in the outflow tracts of the ventricles or by valves that are partially fused (and thus do not open wide) or are incompetent (and thus they leak when they are closed). Examples of the latter include stenosis of the pulmonic valve, which causes blood to be ejected at high velocity through a narrow opening, and insufficiency of the mitral valve, which permits blood to be squirted backward when the left ventricle contracts.

STUDY OUTLINE

EVENTS OF THE CARDIAC CYCLE   The entire cycle consists of *systole* (the ventricles contract) and *diastole* (the ventricles relax).

ATRIAL CONTRACTION   Pacemaker in the sinoatrial node initiates activity; excitation propagates through atria; P wave of ECG.

Contraction increases atrial pressure, sends wave forward into ventricles, backward into veins (*a* wave).

Contributes little to ventricular filling at low heart rates; contributes significantly at high heart rates, when ventricular filling time is decreased.

Rebound of pressure wave helps to position the atrioventricular (AV) valves for closure.

VENTRICULAR ISOVOLUMIC CONTRACTION   Beginning of ventricular systole.

Begins near peak of R wave of ECG.

Ventricular pressures (right and left) increase rapidly; volumes do not change. Potential energy is stored in blood of ventricles.

Flow toward atria closes AV valves; arrest produces vibration, a component of first heart sound.

Chordae tendineae and papillary muscles support valves; bulging produces *c* wave of venous pressure.

Pressures in pulmonary artery and aorta still are decreasing.

RAPID VENTRICULAR EJECTION   Begins with opening of pulmonic and aortic valves.

Pressure increases rapidly, valves open abruptly, blood is ejected rapidly.

Most of stroke volume is ejected early; important when heart rate increases—cycle length decreases, and duration of systole decreases.

Blood flowing rapidly from ventricles encounters stationary blood in each great artery, vibration produces a component of first heart sound; arterial blood flow is accelerated; turbulence develops at peak rate of flow, producing last component of first heart sound.

Atria are filling from venous inflow; atrial pressure decreases temporarily as volume of thorax decreases temporarily—rate of blood flow out of thorax through aorta exceeds rate of flow into thorax through venae cavae.

Ventricular pressure exceeds arterial pressure early in cycle.

Decreasing velocity represents transformation of kinetic energy to potential energy; arterial pressure increases.

Phase concludes when ventricular pressure and arterial pressure become equal.

DECREASED VENTRICULAR EJECTION   Begins with decrease of left ventricular pressure below arterial pressure.

Flow continues because of momentum of mass of blood.

Atrial pressure is increasing.

T wave of ECG indicates ventricles are repolarizing.

When ejection ceases, slight backflow closes pulmonic and aortic valves; arrest of backflow produces vibration—second heart sound.

Closure of valves marks end of systole.

ISOVOLUMIC RELAXATION   Ventricles relax, ventricular pressure decreases rapidly, ventricular volume does not change.

Aortic and pulmonary arterial pressures decline steadily.

RAPID VENTRICULAR FILLING   Begins as atrial pressure exceeds ventricular pressure and AV valves open.

Ventricular filling is aided as ventricles spring open in early relaxation; ventricular pressure decreases, increasing atrioventricular pressure gradient.

Blood accumulated in great veins and atria during systole flows rapidly through wide AV orifices.

Completion of filling and arrest of moving columns of blood produces vibration—third heart sound.

Most of filling occurs early in diastole; important when heart rate increases, and duration of diastole decreases.

DIASTASIS   Phase of relative inactivity late in diastole; essentially "reserve time" at resting heart rates; can be used when heart rate increases and period of diastole decreases.

VENOUS PRESSURE WAVES   Recorded in jugular vein.

a wave = contraction of right atrium.

x wave = relaxation of atrium.

c wave = closure and bulging of tricuspid valve.

x' wave = rapid expulsion of blood from thorax through aorta; decreased volume and pressure in chest.

v wave = filling of atria and veins during ventricular systole.

y wave = decrease of venous volume and pressure as ventricle fills.

VALVE MOTIONS AND HEART SOUNDS First sound—closure of tricuspid and mitral valves, opening of pulmonic and aortic valves, beginning of ejection.

Second sound—closure of pulmonic and aortic valves.

Third sound—completion of rapid ventricular filling.

Split sounds—asynchronous closure of pulmonic and aortic valves.

Intensity of sounds. First sound is related to force and rapidity of contraction; second sound is related to level of arterial pressure; third sound is related to stroke volume (rate of filling).

MURMURS Sounds caused by turbulence in rapidly flowing blood; at a critical velocity, laminar flow breaks up.

Critical velocity is proportional to viscosity of blood and inversely proportional to size of vessel.

Innocent murmur in pulmonary artery and aorta at peak of ejection, particularly during increased cardiac output; enhanced fourth component of first sound.

Murmurs caused by high velocity of blood flow through constrictions of large vessels, through obstructed valves or outflow tracts, and through abnormal openings (such as an interventricular septal defect).

BIBLIOGRAPHY

Brecher, G.A. 1956. Experimental evidence of ventricular diastolic suction. *Circ. Res.* 4:513.

Coulter, N.A., Jr., and Pappenheimer, J.R. 1949. Development of turbulence in flowing blood. *Am. J. Physiol.* 159:483.

Hartman, H. 1960. The jugular venous tracing. *Am. Heart J.* 59:698.

Little, R.C.; Hilton, J.G.; and Schaeffler, R.D. 1954. The first sound in normal and ectopic ventricular contraction—mechanisms of closure of the AV valves. *Circ. Res.* 2:48.

Luisida, A.A. 1982. *The Heart Sounds.* New York: Praeger.

Luisida, A.A., and MacCanon, D.M. 1972. The phases of the cardiac cycle. *Am. Heart J.* 83:705.

Mitchell, J.H.; Gupta, D.N.; and Payne, R.M. 1965. Influence of atrial systole on effective ventricular stroke volume. *Circ. Res.* 17:11.

Noble, M.I.M. 1968. The contribution of blood momentum to left ventricular ejection in the dog. *Circ. Res.* 23:663.

Noble, M.I.M. 1979. *The Cardiac Cycle.* Oxford: Blackwell.

Rushmer, R.F. 1976. *Cardiovascular Dynamics* (4th ed.). Philadelphia: Saunders.

Sabbah, H.N., and Stein, P.D. 1981. Negative diastolic pressure in the intact right heart: Evidence of diastolic suction. *Circ. Res.* 49:108.

Spencer, M.P., and Greiss, F.C. 1962. Dynamics of ventricular ejection. *Circ. Res.* 10:274.

Measurement of Cardiac Output

The cardiac output is the total amount of blood that the left ventricle pumps in some specified period of time; hence, it is a *rate* of pumping blood, rather than a total volume pumped. The cardiac output can be measured by a number of methods, and some of them will be discussed in this chapter. All of the methods are indirect because any direct measurement would alter the function being measured.

VARIATIONS OF THE DILUTION PRINCIPLE

The concentration of a solute in a solvent may be expressed by

$$C = \frac{W}{V}$$

where C is the concentration of the solute in the solution, expressed as weight in volume, W is the weight of the solute added to the solvent, and V is the volume of the solvent to which the solute was added. By rearranging the terms, we can solve for the volume,

$$V = \frac{W}{C},$$

and substituting appropriate units

$$ml = \frac{g}{g/ml}$$

Thus, if the amount of solute that was added to make the solution is known, and the concentration of the solute that was produced, after uniform distribution, can be determined, the volume of the solution can be calculated (Figure 14-1A). The solute is an *indicator* that has been diluted by the volume to which it was added.

Fick Method

This method, a classic in physiology, treats the uptake of oxygen by the blood as the addition of an indicator solute (oxygen) to a solvent (blood) to form a solution (oxygenated blood). It differs from the simple addition of a certain quantity of indicator to a fixed volume all at once in that the indicator is added continuously,

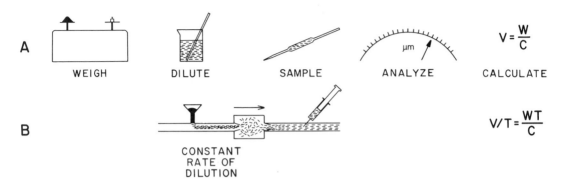

Figure 14-1. The indicator-dilution principle. **A.** A known quantity of a substance (one that can be identified and measured; hence, serves as an *indicator*) is dissolved in an unknown volume of a solvent. A uniform solution is obtained, a sample is taken, and the volume is calculated according to the formula given (V is the volume of the solution, W is the quantity of the indicator added, and C is the concentration of the indicator in the solution formed). **B.** An indicator substance is dissolved at a known, constant rate into a stream of solvent flowing at a constant rate. A uniform solution is obtained, a sample is taken, and the volume that flowed during a unit of time is calculated according to the formula given (V/T is the volume that flowed during a unit of time [rate of flow], W/T is the quantity of indicator [solute] added during a unit of time [rate of dilution], and C is the concentration of the indicator in the solution formed).

at a constant rate, to a stream of the solvent that is flowing at a constant velocity. The solution is produced continuously, at a constant rate, and the volume that is measured flows during a unit of time; hence, a rate of flow is being measured (Figure 14-1B). The basic formula becomes

$$V/T = \frac{W/T}{C}$$

where T is a unit of time (Figure 14-1B). By substituting the appropriate units, we obtain

$$ml/min = \frac{g/min}{g/ml}$$

Because the venous blood returning to the heart still contains oxygen, one cannot determine how much oxygen was added to the blood merely by measuring the oxygen content of the arterial blood; the oxygen content of the venous blood also must be measured, and the difference between the two is the amount that was added. The data are rate of uptake of oxygen, 250 ml/min (W); concentration of oxygen in venous blood, 14 volumes percent (14 ml of oxygen, measured at standard temperature and pressure, per 100 ml of blood); concentration of oxygen in arterial blood, 19 volumes percent; arteriovenous oxygen difference, which is the average increase of oxygen concentration of the blood, 5 volumes percent (C).

$$V/T = \frac{W/T}{C} = \frac{250 \text{ ml } O_2/min}{5 \text{ ml } O_2/100 \text{ ml blood}}$$
$$= 5000 \text{ ml blood}$$

Each 100-ml quantum of blood that passed through the lungs in 1 minute was given a 5-ml quantum of oxygen. A total of 250 ml of oxygen was added; 250 ml of oxygen yields 50 such 5-ml quanta of oxygen. Thus, each 5-ml quantum of oxygen represents 100 ml of blood, and $50 \times 100 = 5000$, which is the number of milliliters of blood passing through the lungs each minute. The average pulmonary blood flow normally equals the average cardiac output.

OBTAINING DATA

Because the theory underlying this method requires that the solute be added at a constant rate to the solvent, which is flowing at a constant rate, all of the measurements must be made at steady state. To be at steady state, the subject must be at rest.

The rate of oxygen consumption is measured by arranging for the subject to breathe from a spirometer that contains air and a CO_2 adsorbent. Thus, the decreasing volume of the spirometer reflects the uptake of oxygen by the subject. The rate of uptake must be constant during the period of measurement because it is represented in the calculation by a mean value.

ARTERIOVENOUS OXYGEN DIFFERENCE

Since all systemic arterial blood is the same, the concentration of oxygen in the arterial blood may be determined in a sample taken from any artery that can be reached conveniently. Not all venous blood is the same, however. The blood flowing in the veins from one organ may contain a residual amount of oxygen that is different from the amount of oxygen contained in the blood draining from another organ because of different rates of metabolism and different functions of the organs. For example, blood in a renal vein may contain 17.5% oxygen, whereas the blood coming from the brain may contain 12% oxygen, and blood in the portal vein may contain 14.5% oxygen. Because of laminar flow and streaming, the blood coming from the various sources is not mixed well, and a sample taken from one vein or even at one level of the vena cava may be different from a sample taken from another vein or at another level. It has been determined that the most peripheral site from which truly representative venous blood can be obtained is the pulmonary artery; blood in this vessel has been mixed by the swirling of ventricular filling and the turbulence of ejection. It can be taken by a catheter placed in a vein of an arm or a leg and passed through the vena cava, the right atrium, the right ventricle, and into the pulmonary artery. Although this is a routine procedure in the catheterization laboratory, it is not one to be undertaken casually elsewhere.

The principal disadvantage of the Fick method is that cardiac output during exercise cannot be measured because of the requirement of steady state and the relatively long period needed to measure accurately the uptake of oxygen. It has the advantage of being relatively accurate ($\pm$ 10%) when done properly, but it is a difficult procedure; its main value may be its use as a prototype for other dilution procedures and for the modifications of the basic method that are described below.

EVALUATION OF SHUNTS

The right atrium and the left atrium share a common wall, the atrial septum; the right ventricle and the left ventricle also share a common wall, the ventricular septum. Because of congenital errors of development, one or both of these septa are incomplete in some subjects. In addition, a vessel that connects the pulmo- nary artery and the aorta of the fetus, the ductus arteriosus, which normally closes shortly after the birth of the infant, may remain open, or patent. In these conditions, blood flows, or *shunts*, between the cardiac chambers or between the great arteries, and pulmonary blood flow and cardiac output are not identical. Although the Fick method in its proper form does not provide a valid measurement of cardiac output under these conditions, the principle on which it is based can be used to estimate the relative magnitudes of the shunts.

Suppose that the concentration of oxygen in the systemic arterial blood and the rate of uptake of oxygen are the same as given earlier, 19% and 250 ml/min, respectively, but the concentration of oxygen in the pulmonary arterial blood is 16% (rather than 14%). The arteriovenous oxygen difference is 3%, and the cardiac output appears to be

$$V/T = \frac{W/T}{C} = \frac{250 \text{ ml O}_2/\text{min}}{3 \text{ ml O}_2/100 \text{ ml blood}}$$

$$= \frac{8333 \text{ ml blood}}{\text{min}}$$

This probably is a true measure of pulmonary blood flow; however, it probably is not a true measure of the cardiac output because additional samples obtained by placing the catheter at several sites in the venae cavae reveal no area in which the blood contains as much as 16% oxygen. This combination of data indicates that the pulmonary arterial blood is not providing a representative sample of mixed venous blood and that oxygen is being added to the blood somewhere between the venae cavae and the pulmonary artery. The most likely possibility is left-to-right shunting between the atria or the ventricles, that is, an *atrial septal defect* (ASD) or a *ventricular septal defect* (VSD). Thus, oxygen is being increased in the venous blood by the addition of fully oxygenated blood coming from the left atrium or the left ventricle (Figure 14-2).

Cardiac output can be estimated in these circumstances by taking several samples of venous blood (e.g., from the superior vena cava, the inferior vena cava, and the atriocaval junction) and averaging the oxygen content. Suppose that the mean concentration of oxygen in the venous blood is 14%; the cardiac output is estimated to be 5000 ml/min. Although pulmonary blood flow and cardiac output are not

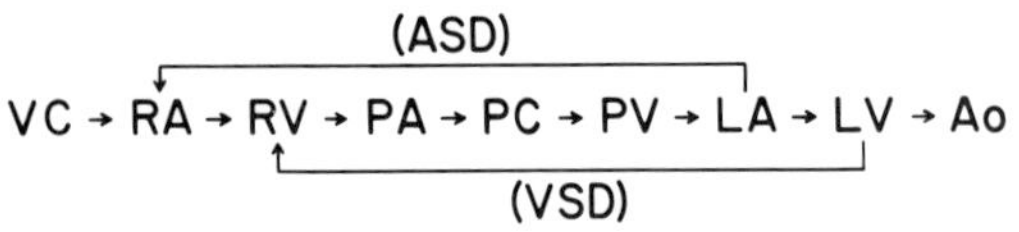

$$\overset{\text{(ASD)}}{\text{VC} \rightarrow \text{RA} \rightarrow \text{RV} \rightarrow \text{PA} \rightarrow \text{PC} \rightarrow \text{PV} \rightarrow \text{LA} \rightarrow \text{LV} \rightarrow \text{Ao}}\underset{\text{(VSD)}}{}$$

Figure 14-2. Flow of blood in a heart that has an *atrial septal defect* (ASD) and a *ventricular septal defect* (VSD). VC = venae cavae; RA = right atrium; RV = right ventricle; PA = pulmonary artery; PC = pulmonary capillaries; PV = pulmonary veins; LA = left atrium; LV = left ventricle; Ao = aorta. Arrows indicate the direction of flow.

---

the same, and the Fick method in its best form cannot be used to measure the cardiac output, the data can be used to estimate the magnitude of the shunt. Because the pulmonary blood flow was 8333 ml/min, and systemic blood flow (the cardiac output) was 5000 ml/min, the difference must represent the volume of blood that was recirculated through the lungs during each minute (Figure 14-3).

It is customary to evaluate an intracardiac shunt as the *ratio* of pulmonary blood flow, Q_p, to systemic blood flow, Q_s, as follows.

$$\frac{Q_p}{Q_s} = \frac{8333 \text{ ml/min}}{5000 \text{ ml/min}} = \frac{1.7}{1} = 1.7$$

This ratio often is spoken of erroneously as indicating a "1.7-to-1 shunt." The correct statement is that the pulmonary blood flow is 1.7 times the systemic flow.

The relative magnitude of the shunt may be estimated without knowing the absolute value of either the cardiac output or the shunt, because the ratio, Q_p/Q_s, can be approximated without establishing either Q_p or Q_s. This procedure does not require measurement of the uptake of oxygen. The higher the rate of blood flow through either the pulmonary circulation or the systemic circulation, the more a given amount of oxygen is diluted. Thus, Q_p is inversely proportional to the difference between the pulmonary arterial concentration of oxygen and the systemic arterial concentration of oxygen, that is, to the dilution of the oxygen added to the blood in the lungs as follows.

$$Q_p \simeq \frac{1}{\text{Systemic arterial } [O_2] - \text{Pulmonary arterial } [O_2]}$$

Systemic blood flow is inversely proportional to the dilution of oxygen added between the vena cava and the systemic arteries.

$$Q_s \simeq \frac{1}{\text{Systemic arterial } [O_2] - \text{Vena caval } [O_2]}$$

The ratio is:

$$\frac{Q_p}{Q_s} = \frac{\dfrac{1}{\text{Systemic arterial } [O_2] - \text{Pulmonary artery } [O_2]}}{\dfrac{1}{\text{Systemic arterial } [O_2] - \text{Vena caval } [O_2]}}$$

$$= \frac{\text{Systemic arterial } O_2 - \text{Vena caval } O_2}{\text{Systemic arterial } [O_2] - \text{Pulmonary arterial } [O_2]}$$

Thus, using the data from above,

$$\frac{Q_p}{Q_s} = \frac{19 \text{ vol } \% - 14 \text{ vol } \%}{19 \text{ vol } \% - 16 \text{ vol } \%} = \frac{5}{3} = 1.7$$

A convenient approximation is used by cardiologists; the ratio, Q_p/Q_s, is calculated by using oxygen *saturation*, rather than oxygen *concentration*. This is permissible because the fractional part of the hemoglobin that is combined with oxygen is directly proportional to the amount of oxygen that the blood contains. Blood that contains the maximum amount of oxygen its hemoglobin can bind is said to be fully (or 100%) saturated. The advantage of this procedure is that data obtained quickly and easily during catheterization studies can be used. The formula is as follows.

$$\frac{Q_p}{Q_s} = \frac{\text{Systemic arterial } O_2 \text{ sat.} - \text{Vena caval } O_2 \text{ sat.}}{\text{Systemic arterial } O_2 \text{ sat.} - \text{Pulmonary arterial sat.}}$$

Suppose that the oxygen saturations associated with the oxygen concentrations used

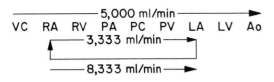

$$\xrightarrow{\text{5,000 ml/min}}$$
$$\text{VC} \quad \text{RA} \quad \text{RV} \quad \text{PA} \quad \text{PC} \quad \text{PV} \quad \text{LA} \quad \text{LV} \quad \text{Ao}$$
$$\xrightarrow{\text{3,333 ml/min}}$$
$$\xrightarrow{\text{8,333 ml/min}}$$

Figure 14-3. Pathways and rates of blood flow in a heart that has an atrial septal defect. The key to the symbols used is the same as in Figure 14-2. The cardiac output of 5000 ml/min is the rate at which the blood flows through the heart and into the systemic circulation. In addition, blood flows from the left atrium, through the septal defect, and into the right atrium, at the rate of 3333 ml/min. The rate of blood flow in the circuit of the shunt is equal to the sum of the normal flow and the shunt flow; therefore, blood flows into the right atrium, into the right ventricle, through the lungs, and into the left atrium at the rate of 8333 ml/min.

previously were: systemic arterial, 98%; vena caval, 70%; pulmonary arterial, 82%. Then,

$$\frac{Q_p}{Q_s} = \frac{98\% - 70\%}{98\% - 82\%} = \frac{1.7}{1} = 1.7$$

Rapid-Injection Indicator Dilution

In another method, called the *rapid-injection indicator method*, the indicator (solute) is injected rapidly into a vein, and the entire amount passes through the heart during the period of measurement. Because the indicator is not distributed uniformly, the entire volume of solution in which it is contained must be sampled, either frequently or continuously, to permit calculation of the mean concentration of the indicator. This is feasible because the period of measurement is short—usually less than 30 seconds. Because the concentration of the indicator is determined by the rate of flow of the solvent, the time factor appears in the denominator (Figure 14-4).

In a sample calculation, data are as follows: 2.5 mg of indicator dye was injected, and an average concentration of 1 μg/ml was determined during a collection period of 30 seconds.

$$V/T \; \frac{W}{CT} = \frac{2500 \; \mu g}{1 \; \mu g/ml \times 0.5 \; min}$$

$$= 5000 \; ml/min$$

To determine the average concentration of the indicator, several samples are taken at short intervals, and the points are plotted against time, or blood is withdrawn continuously through an indicator cell and a continuous curve is plotted. Because all of the solvent that contains indicator must be sampled to determine the average concentration accurately and to establish the time required for all of the indicator to pass through the heart, sampling should continue until the concentration of solute has decreased to zero; however, a complication appears here. Some of the indicator is recirculated; that is, it goes through a capillary bed and returns to the heart with the venous blood before all of the indicator has passed through the heart the first time (Figure 14-5). Examples of vascular beds that might be involved in this early recirculation are those of the coronary circulation (the heart) and the bronchial circulation (the nonrespiratory tissues of

the lungs). The technique for determining the concentration of the indicator that would have been measured if recirculation had not occurred and the time at which all of the indicator has passed through the heart the first time is explained in Figures 14-4 and 14-5. Modern data processors may be used to provide direct read-out of cardiac output; nevertheless, it is important for both the physiologist and the physician to understand the principles on which the measurements are based.

The advantage of the rapid-injection method of indicator dilution is the speed with which a determination can be made; this is possible because the achievement and maintenance of steady state are not required. The recirculation of the indicator through short pathways before the first circulation is complete constitutes a disadvantage; however, very early appearance of the indicator can be used to detect small shunts.

INDICATORS USED

Variously colored dyes have been used, and a particular one, called *indocyanine green*, is used the most. In recent years, *heat* has been used as an indicator to be diluted; a volume of cold saline is injected, and the resulting change in temperature is taken to be proportional to the concentration of the indicator. A hypertonic solution of *sodium chloride* (NaCl) also may be used as an indicator; the change of electrical conductivity of the blood, a property related to the concentration of ions in the blood, is measured to assess the concentration of the indicator.

CATHETER-TIP FLOWMETER

The *catheter-tip flowmeter* is useful in the cardiac catheterization laboratory. The techniques of modern semiconductor electronics are used to mount an instrument in a catheter that can be passed, in the usual manner, through a vein in the arm or the leg to rest eventually in the pulmonary artery or the aorta. The underlying principle is that a conductor (blood) moving in the field of a magnet induces an electrical current proportional to the velocity of the movement. Hence, the instrument is a velocity meter, and, to calculate the rate of flow, the cross-sectional area of the vessel in which the velocity is measured must be known. Fortunately, this in-

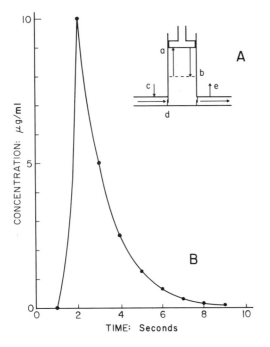

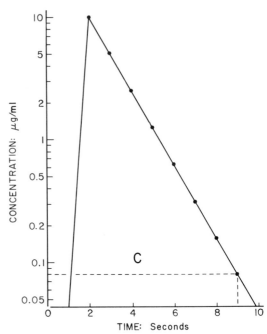

Figure 14-4. An ideal system that illustrates how the rapid-injection technique of indicator dilution is used to measure cardiac output. **A.** A pump contains 100 ml of fluid when it is filled (*a*), and ejects 50 ml, which is one-half of its capacity, with each stroke (*b*). The rate of pumping is one stroke per second. Now, suppose that 1000 μg of an indicator is injected rapidly (*c*) near the intake valve of the pump (*d*), and all of it is taken into the pump at once. The mean concentration of indicator in the pump becomes 1000 μg/100 ml, or 10 μg/ml; assume that swirling of the fluid during the filling of the pump causes the indicator to mix uniformly. The next stroke ejects a volume of 50 ml; a sample is taken (*e*) and found to contain 10 μg/ml of indicator. On its next intake, the pump takes in 50 ml of fluid that contains no indicator; the fluid mixes with the 50 ml of residual solution that contains 10 μg/ml of indicator. The new concentration, after mixing, is 5 μg/ml; the next sample taken after the stroke of the pump shows 5 μg/ml of indicator in the outflow tube. It is apparent that during each stroke the pump will eject one-half of the indicator it contains; the remainder will be diluted by the next intake of the pump, and the concentration of indicator measured in each sample will be one-half that of the preceding sample; **B.** The concentration of indicator decreases exponentially; a graph of it plotted on a semilo-

garithmic scale will form a straight line **(C).** This technique permits one to extrapolate to the time base the descending curve of the concentration of indicator. Although the logarithmic scale has no 0, and, theoretically, the indicator never will wash out completely, the concentration becomes insignificantly small. In practice, the time at which the concentration of fluid has decreased to about 1% of the maximum value is used to establish the duration of the collection period. In this example, the indicator was injected at 0 seconds and appeared in the outflow at 1 second. If the period of collection ended at 9 seconds, the last data point given in **B**, the duration of the period of collection was 8 seconds, and the mean concentration of indicator during the period, obtained by integration, was 2.5 μg/ml. Therefore, by substituting in the formula one finds the following:

$$V/T = \frac{W}{CT} = \frac{1000 \ \mu g}{2.5 \ \mu g/ml \times 8 \ sec}$$

$$= 50 \ ml/sec, \ or \ 3000 \ ml/min$$

Although the measurement of the cardiac output in an actual circulatory system is not so simple, the same principles apply, and they serve to justify the use of the technique (see Figure 14-5).

formation can be obtained by placing a calibrated grid in the field of the fluoroscope that is used to observe the catheter. Because the method provides an instantaneous measure of

the velocity of blood flow, it can be used to record any change of velocity, which is proportional to flow, even if the rate of blood flow were not determined.

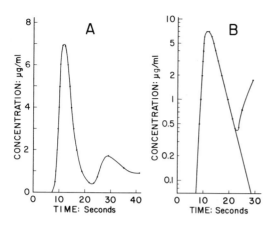

Figure 14-5. **A.** A curve obtained by the rapid-injection technique of indicator dilution. **B.** The way the data are replotted on a semilogarithmic scale to determine the end of the first circulation and permit calculation of the average concentration of indicator during the first circulation. Note the second increase of concentration in **A**, beginning at about 23 seconds, caused by recirculation of the indicator. The exponential portion of the curve forms a straight line in **B**; the remainder of the line is extrapolated to a baseline drawn at the concentration of 0.07 μg/ml, which is 1% of the highest concentration ($7\mu g/ml$). The duration of the period of first circulation is obtained from this baseline, and the average concentration of the indicator during that period is found by integrating the entire curve.

NONINVASIVE METHODS

Impedance Plethysmography

In *impedance plethysmography*. electrodes are placed on the chest, and a low-intensity, high-frequency alternating current is passed through the thorax in a path that includes the heart. The conductivity of the pathway, measured between surface electrodes, is altered as blood enters and leaves the heart. The impedance, which is the inverse of conductivity, decreases as the heart fills and increases as the heart empties. The advantages of this method are that it is noninvasive, can be carried out quickly and easily, and provides a beat-by-beat reflection of the cardiac output. The disadvantage is that the signal is affected by a number of factors other than the cardiac output; hence, it cannot be calibrated for the individual subject, and only *change* of cardiac output can be measured.

Echocardiography

In another method, called *echocardiography,* ultrasonic vibration is directed toward the heart by means of a special transducer placed in contact with the chest wall. Echoes returning from structures of different density are filtered and recorded to form images of the structures. To avoid the dense material of the ribs, the transducer is placed between the ribs, usually in the third, fourth, or fifth intercostal space at the left sternal border. The transducer can be tilted through an arc in any direction, which permits it to scan all of the heart. An excellent knowledge of the anatomy of the heart is required to interpret the results.

Although the technique is used most often to study the motions of the cardiac valves and to identify structural abnormalities of the heart, the cardiac stroke volume can be calculated by using the dimensions of the right ventricle at the end of diastole and at the end of systole. The cardiac output can be found by multiplying the stroke volume by the heart rate. The advantage of the method is that it is noninvasive. The disadvantage is that only limited accuracy is possible in calculating the volume of the ventricle from ventricular dimensions.

Radionuclide Angiography

Radioactive materials injected into the blood and allowed to mix may be used to register an image of the ventricle in one or more planes. The stroke volume can be calculated from the difference between the end-diastolic volume and the end-systolic volume and the cardiac output obtained from the product of stroke volume and heart rate. The advantage of the method is that it is relatively nontraumatic; the disadvantage is that the result obtained by calculating the stroke volume from the area in only one or two planes is relatively inaccurate.

A newer method, which requires the use of a computer, is based on the dilution principle. The stroke volume is computed from the difference between the radioactivity in the ventricle at the end of diastole and at the end of systole. A dilution constant ([counts/unit of plasma]/unit of time) is determined from a sample of blood. The advantage of the method is that it does not depend on assumptions about the geometry of the ventricle. The disadvantages are that rather expensive, sophisticated equipment is required, and certain simplifying assumptions still must be made.*

CARDIAC INDEX

To permit comparison of the cardiac output of a particular subject with the cardiac output of other subjects and to establish normal values, the cardiac output of the resting subject is related to the body surface area. The result that is obtained, called the *cardiac index*, is expressed as liters per minute per square meter. This is a reasonable thing to do, because the rate of metabolism is related to the body surface area, and the cardiac output is related to the rate of metabolism. The cardiac index increases rapidly after the birth of the infant, reaches a peak at about 2 years of age, and declines exponentially throughout the remainder of life (Figure 14-6).

*Examples: the concentration of administered radioactive material remained constant and the single cardiac cycle measured was a true representative of the other cycles.

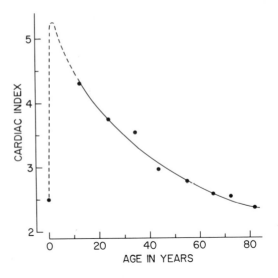

Figure 14-6. A graph of the cardiac index, in liters per minute per square meter, from birth to advanced age. The solid line, covering the period from 12 years to 82 years of age, is based on measurements of cardiac index reported in the literature; however, no comparable data were available for the period from birth to 12 years. The dashed line is based on measurements of cardiac index in newborn infants (age 0) and measurements of basal metabolic rate in children from 1 year to 12 years of age; the cardiac index in assumed to be related closely to the metabolic rate.

STUDY OUTLINE

VARIATIONS OF THE DILUTION PRINCIPLE   An unknown volume can be determined by dispersing in it a known amount of solute (indicator), sampling the solution that results, and solving for V (volume) in the equation $V = W/C$, where W is the weight of indicator added, and C is the concentration of indicator in the solution.

FICK METHOD   Oxygen, added to the blood through the lungs, is the indicator.

As the solute is added continuously to a stream of solvent (blood), the rate of formation of solution defines a rate of flow: $V/T = (W/T)/C$.

OBTAINING DATA   Subject must be in steady state; hence, at rest.

ARTERIOVENOUS   OXYGEN   DIFFERENCE   Mixed arterial blood from any systemic artery.

Mixed venous blood taken from pulmonary artery by catheter.

EVALUATION OF SHUNTS   Pulmonary blood flow must equal systemic blood flow if cardiac output is measured.

If intracardiac shunts exist, pulmonary flow exceeds systemic flow (cardiac output).

Systemic flow can be measured, less accurately, by using vena caval blood.

The amount by which pulmonary flow exceeds systemic flow reflects the magnitude of the shunt.

The ratio of pulmonary flow to systemic flow and, hence, the magnitude of a shunt, can be estimated roughly by using percent saturation rather than oxygen content.

RAPID-INJECTION INDICATOR DILUTION   The indicator is injected rapidly, and the entire amount passes through the heart during the period of measurement.

To obtain the average concentration of indicator, and the duration of passage, a time-concentration curve must be plotted.

As the indicator begins to recirculate before all of it has passed through once, the descending part of the curve is obtained by extrapolation.

Advantages of the method—relatively short duration; cardiac output can be measured during and after exercise in nonsteady state.

INDICATORS USED   Dyes, heat, NaCl.

CATHETER-TIP FLOWMETER   Requires cardiac catheterization.

Velocity of flow is measured; diameter of aorta (or pulmonary artery) must be determined to calculate rate of flow.

NONINVASIVE METHODS

IMPEDANCE PLETHYSMOGRAPHY

Low-intensity, high-frequency alternating current is passed through the thorax.

Impedance changes inversely with volume of heart.

Changes of cardiac output are measured, not absolute values.

ECHOCARDIOGRAPHY   Ultrasonic vibration directed toward heart; echoes are used to construct image.

Assumptions are made about geometry of heart; stroke volume is calculated by formula.

Cardiac output—product of heart rate × stroke volume.

RADIONUCLIDE ANGIOGRAPHY   Radioactive materials are used to form image of heart, or stroke volume is determined by dilution of indicator.

Cardiac output—product of heart rate × stroke volume.

CARDIAC INDEX   Cardiac output is related to body surface area: liters per minute per square meter; permits comparison.

Increases from birth, reaches peak at about 2 years of age, declines thereafter.

BIBLIOGRAPHY

Brandfonbrener, M.; Landowne, M.; and Shock, N.W. 1955. Changes in cardiac output with age. *Circulation* 12:557.

Brotmacher, L., and Fleming, P. 1957. Cardiac output and vascular pressures in normal children and adults. *Guy's Hosp. Rep.* 106:268.

Carr, K.W.; Ergler, R.L.; Forsythe, J.R., et al. 1979. Measurement of left ventricular ejection fraction by mechanical cross-section echocardiography. *Circulation* 59:1196.

Eaton, L.W.; Maugham, W.L.; Shoukas, A.A., et al. 1979. Accurate volume determination in the isolated ejecting canine left ventricle by two-dimensional echocardiography. *Circulation* 60:320.

Feigenbaum, H.; Zaky, A.; and Nasser, W.K. 1967. Use of ultrasound to measure left ventricular stroke volume. *Circulation* 35:1092.

Fox, I.J.; Brooker, L.Q.S.; Heseltine, D.W., et al. 1957. A tricarbocyanine dye for continuous recording of dilution curves in whole blood independent of variation in blood oxygen saturation. *Proc. Staff Meet. Mayo Clin.* 32:478.

Geddes, L.A., and Baker, L.E. 1975. 2nd Ed. *Principles of Applied Biomedical Instrumentation.* New York: Wiley.

Guyton, A.C. 1963. *Cardiac Output and Its Regulation.* Philadelphia: Saunders. pp. 1–124.

Massie, B.M.; Kramer, B.L.; Gertz, E.W., et al. 1982. Radionuclide measurement of left ventricular volume: Comparison of geometric and counts-based methods. *Circulation* 65:725.

Morganroth, J., Parisi, A.F., and Pohost, G.M. (eds.). 1983. *Noninvasive Cardiac Imaging.* Chicago: Year Book.

Prec, K.J., and Cassels, D.E. 1955. Dye dilution curves and cardiac output in newborn infants. *Circulation* 11:789.

Slutsky, R.; Karliner, J.; Ricci, D., et al. 1979. Left ventricular volumes by gated equilibrium radionuclide angiography: A new method. *Circulation* 60:556.

Weisel, R.D.; Berger, R.L.; and Hechtman, H.B. 1975. Measurement of cardiac output by thermodilution. *N. Engl. J. Med.* 292:682.

15

Control of the
Cardiac Output

CHAPTER CONTENTS

COMPONENTS OF CARDIAC OUTPUT

Heart Rate

The frequency of beating of the heart (*heart rate*) is controlled through the actions of the *autonomic nervous system* (ANS). Efferent activity that passes through the parasympathetic nerves to the sinoatrial node, which is the pacemaker of the heart, decreases the heart rate; efferent activity that passes through the sympathetic nerves to the sinoatrial node increases the heart rate. Both divisions of the ANS are tonically (continuously) active in a person at rest; however, the net effect is inhibitory, and if all input of the ANS to the heart is blocked, the heart rate increases. When physiological demands require that the cardiac output be increased, the heart rate is increased by inhibition of the parasympathetic input and activation of the sympathetic input to the heart (Figure 15-1).

Stroke Volume

The *stroke volume* is the difference between the volume of the ventricle at the end of diastole (*filling*) and the volume of the ventricle at the end of systole (*emptying*) (Figure 15-2). The volume to which the ventricle fills is determined by the ventricular filling pressure and the compliance of the ventricle. The filling pressure of the right ventricle is the *right atrial pressure*, and the filling pressure of the left ventricle is the *left atrial pressure;* the atrial pressures are kept relatively constant in the normal heart by the venous tone and the mechanisms of venous support (see "Effects Below the Heart" in Chapter 12); however, beat-to-beat variations do occur.

PRELOAD
The ventricular pressure at the end of diastole, which distends the relaxed ventricle, constitutes

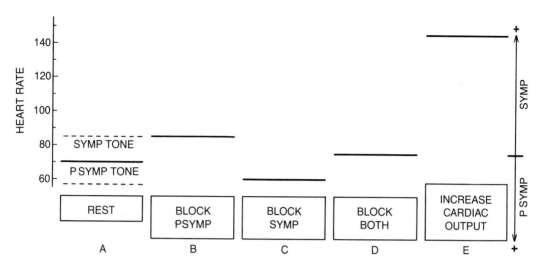

Figure 15-1. Effects of the autonomic nervous system (ANS) on the heart rate. The arrows at the right show that sympathetic nervous system activity increases the heart rate and parasympathetic activity decreases the heart rate. **A.** The heart rate of the subject at rest (*solid line*). The sympathetic nervous system and the parasympathetic nervous system both are active (tone). Each dashed line indicates the heart rate that would prevail if only one of the systems were functioning. **B.** The heart rate would increase if the parasympathetic input to the heart were blocked. **C.** The heart rate would decrease if the sympathetic input to the heart were blocked. **D.** If both systems were blocked, the heart rate would increase. Thus, the parasympathetic tone is slightly dominant in the resting subject. **E.** The heart rate is increased by the action of the sympathetic nervous system.

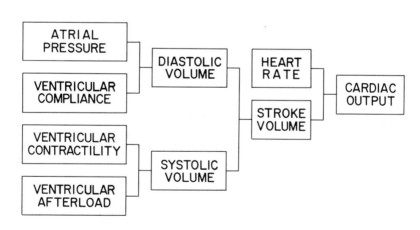

Figure 15-2. Factors that determine cardiac output.

the *preload* for the ventricle (see "Types of Muscle Contraction" in Chapter 9). The preload stretches the *myocardium* and, within limits, increases the rate at which the muscle develops tension and shortens when it is excited, and the maximum tension that it can develop (Figures 15-3 and 15-4). The normal ventricle is highly compliant, and a change of filling pressure changes the end-diastolic volume. Hence, the ventricle is conditioned automatically to eject the stroke volume.

The compliance of the relatively thin-walled right ventricle is greater than that of the relatively thick-walled left ventricle, and the difference between right atrial pressure and left atrial pressure is due primarily to the difference between the compliances of the ventricles.

The end-systolic volume, the volume that remains in the ventricle after ejection has stopped, is determined by the *contractility* of the ventricle and the afterload against which the ventricle must contract.

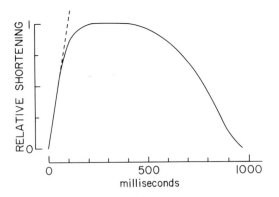

Figure 15-3.   The normal time course of the contraction and relaxation of the cardiac muscle. A relative shortening of 1 is the maximum for the preload and the afterload to which the muscle was subjected. The earliest shortening is the most rapid (*dashed line*), and it is used to compare the rates of contraction or development of tension under different conditions.

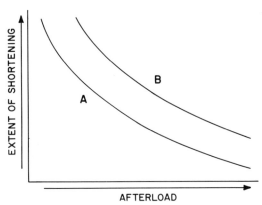

Figure 15-5.   Relationship between afterload and maximal shortening of cardiac muscle. The muscle shortens less as the afterload increases and more as the afterload decreases. **A.** Control curve. **B.** Effect of sympathetic nervous system stimulation.

CONTRACTILITY

Contractility is a measure of the amount of tension the contracting myocardium can develop, and, more importantly, the *rate of development* of tension. The end-systolic volume is affected by the contractility of the myocardium because the contractility determines how much the muscle fibers shorten against a given load (Figure 15-5).

AFTERLOAD

The *afterload* is the tension the myocardium must develop; it is determined by the arterial pressure and the end-diastolic volume of the ventricle. To produce pressure in the ventricle, the muscle in the curved wall must direct force laterally (Figure 15-6), and to eject blood, the ventricle must generate a pressure greater than the arterial pressure. If the end-diastolic volume increases, the radius increases, the curvature of the ventricle decreases, and the tension in the myocardium during contraction must increase merely to produce the same pressure; if the volume of the ventricle decreases, the curvature of the muscle increases, and less tension is required to produce the same pressure (Figure 15-7). Although the afterload increases with the end-diastolic volume, the preload also increases; therefore, within physiological limits, the heart adapts to the work load intrinsically. As the ventricle empties, and the radius decreases, the afterload decreases; hence, the heart has a mechanical advantage that aids in emptying.

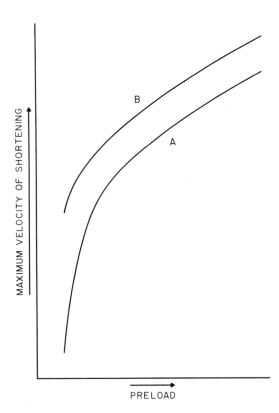

Figure 15-4.   Relationships between preload and maximum velocity of shortening of cardiac muscle. As the preload on the muscle is increased, within limits, the maximum velocity of shortening increases. **A.** Control curve. **B.** Effect of sympathetic nervous system stimulation.

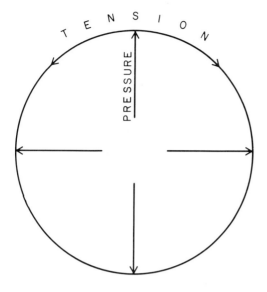

Figure 15-6. Relationship between pressure and tension in a hollow organ. The diagram represents the cross-section of a cylinder or of a sphere. The tension in the wall, which is represented by the arc, is directed tangentially to the pressure within and must produce a lateral force equal to that of the pressure. In a single plane, with an infinitely thin wall, the relationship is $T = Pr$, where T is the wall tension, P is the pressure, and r is the radius of the circle to which the arc is related.

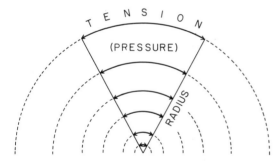

Figure 15-7. Relationship between radius and tension in a single plane. The magnitude of the wall tension is reflected in the length of the arc. The relationship is $T = Pr$ (see Figure 15-6). If the pressure is held constant, the change of tension is equal to the change of radius.

EJECTION FRACTION

The ventricle does not eject all of the blood it contains; the portion ejected is expressed by the *ejection fraction,* the stroke volume divided by the end-diastolic volume. The end-diastolic volume of the normal ventricle is about 70 to 80 ml/m^2, and the normal ejection fraction of the resting heart is about 60%–75%. The ejection fraction is increased by factors that increase contractility (e.g., sympathetic nervous system activity) or decrease afterload (e.g., decreased peripheral resistance); it is decreased by factors that decrease contractility (e.g., cardiac disease) or increase afterload (e.g., arterial hypertension or obstructive valvular disease).

COMPONENTS OF VENTRICULAR CONTRACTION

The two ventricles share a common wall, the intraventricular septum; however, the septum conforms far more closely to the dimensions and the geometry of the left ventricle than to those of the right ventricle (Figure 15-8). In the cross-section of the ventricles near the base of the heart, the left ventricle appears to form a cylinder with relatively thick walls, and the right ventricle appears to form another cylinder of larger diameter appended to the left ventricle. Because of the bulging of the interventricular septum into the right ventricle, much of the potential area of the right ventricle is occupied by the left ventricle. Each ventricle contracts by shortening along the longitudinal axis and by reducing the diameter of the cylinder (see Figure 15-8). The right ventricle forms a

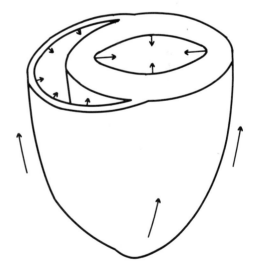

Figure 15-8. The shapes of the ventricles. The ventricular septum conforms to the geometry of the left ventricle, causing the right ventricular chamber to form a crescent. The arrows show how the dimensions of the ventricles change during contraction.

relatively narrow chamber between two broad surfaces; its action is comparable to that of a bellows. Because it represents a portion of a cylinder of large diameter, it has less mechanical advantage; however, a relatively small contraction displaces a relatively large volume of blood. This characteristic makes the right ventricle very effective for producing a high-volume, low-pressure output.

The left ventricle appears to be adapted to generating high pressure. The walls are thick, and the full-circular cross-section in the horizontal dimension provides a cylinder with a relatively small radius; hence, it has a greater mechanical advantage and operates under conditions that are more nearly optimal for the generation of force laterally (see Figure 15-6).

PHYSIOLOGICAL CONTROL OF CARDIAC OUTPUT

When the metabolic needs of the body change, the output of the heart is altered primarily by change in the heart rate; the stroke volume is kept relatively constant by appropriate adjustment of the rates of ventricular filling and emptying.

Effect of Body Position on Stroke Volume

In the past, some confusion has arisen because the stroke volume of the resting subject was measured in some studies in subjects who were lying down, and in other studies in subjects who were standing; the results were compared with the stroke volumes in active subjects.

The stroke volume is relatively large in the subject who is lying down; in the subject who is standing, the stroke volume decreases (Figure 15-9). This change of stroke volume is related to the effects of gravity on the cardiovascular system—primarily on the veins—and the adjustments that are made to them. Although the veins are supported and venous tone is increased, the compensation is not complete, and the ventricles fill less completely. The consequences include decreased stroke volume, increased heart rate, decreased cardiac output, and increased peripheral resistance (in the vascular beds below the heart). These effects are caused by increased sympathetic nervous system activity; the decrease of cardiac output reflects decreased renal and mesenteric perfusion. If the subject then exercises, the stroke

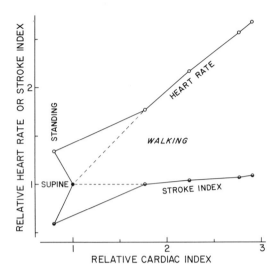

Figure 15-9. Relative contributions of heart rate and stroke volume (*stroke index*) to increase of cardiac output (*cardiac index*) during exercise. Data were obtained from normal human subjects. The cardiac output was measured by the technique of indicator (dye) dilution. All data are related to the corresponding values in the resting, supine subjects. When the subjects stood, the heart rate increased and the cardiac output and the left ventricular stroke volume decreased. As the subjects exercised by walking up a treadmill, the stroke volume increased to the resting value and then remained almost constant; the cardiac output and the heart rate increased almost proportionately. The value of the heart rate and the stroke volume obtained while the subjects were supine and resting are related also to those obtained while the subjects exercised (*dashed lines*).

volume increases again to about the level at which it was at rest; however, it increases little more as the cardiac output is increased further by heavier exercise (see Figure 15-9).

The effects on end-diastolic ventricular volume and end-systolic ventricular volume are illustrated in Figure 15-10. In the standing subject, increased cardiac contractility causes the ventricular myocardial fibers to shorten further and, hence, to decrease the end-systolic volume. As the heart rate increases, and the cardiac output remains unchanged, the stroke volume decreases, owing entirely to decreased end-diastolic volume (less complete filling). When the subject begins to exercise, the flow of blood to the muscles increases, and the cardiac output must increase to maintain the central arterial pressure. As part of the means by which the cardiac output increases, the cardiac con-

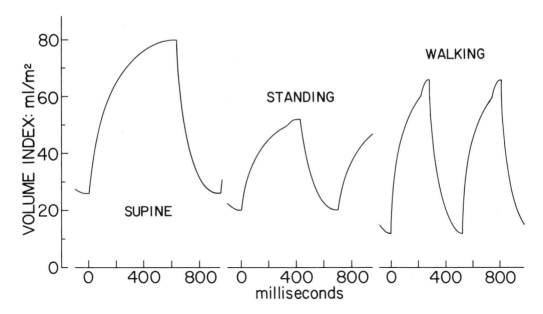

Figure 15-10. Changes of end-diastolic ventricular volume, end-systolic ventricular volume, and cardiac cycle length during activities like those represented in Figure 15-9.

tractility increases further and the end-systolic volume decreases further. The contraction of the skeletal muscles (the "muscle pump") and the respiratory movements of the thorax (the "lung pump") contribute to the filling of the ventricles, and the end-diastolic volume is restored partially (see "Effects of Intrathoracic Pressure on Blood Flow" in Chapter 17). Thus, relative to the values obtained in the subject at rest, the volume of the ventricle at the end of diastole is less and the stroke volume is about the same. Further increase of the cardiac output is related almost entirely to the increase of heart rate (Figure 15-10; see also Figure 15-9).

Coordinated Cardiovascular Response

It should be emphasized that the increased heart rate is part of a coordinated cardiovascular response; if the filling of the ventricles during diastole were not maintained, the stroke volume would not be maintained and the cardiac output would not be increased. The extra blood that is required to increase the venous inflow to the heart initially is made available by the contraction of the venous reservoirs under the skin and in the viscera (supports filling of the right ventricle), and of the pulmonary vessels (supports filling of the left ventricle). The increased cardiac output, which becomes ar-

terial flow, soon reaches the venous side and contributes to the filling of the ventricles. Thus, only a temporary priming effect is needed to increase the cardiac output.

The perfusion of some vascular beds increases when the cardiac output increases, and some additional volume is needed to fill these beds. This need is met partly by the decreased perfusion of some other vascular beds and partly by the contraction of systemic venous and pulmonary vascular reservoirs. It should be emphasized, however, that the increased cardiac output reflects almost entirely increased *velocity* of flow, rather than increased *volume* flowing. For example, the increase of cardiac output from 5 ml/min to 15 ml/min requires the mean velocity of blood flow from the heart to be increased threefold. Therefore, the heart functions as an impulse producer, or *accelerator of the rate of flow of blood.*

Adjustment of Cardiac Function to Cycle Length

VENTRICLES

The heart is an intermittent pump; when the heart rate increases, the duration of the cardiac cycle decreases. The period of ventricular diastole is shortened directly, simply because it is the interval between the beats; however, the period of ventricular systole shortens also, as an intrinsic response of the myocardium. As the heart rate increases, the stroke volume remains about the same or increases slightly (see Figure 15-9); therefore, the same or a slightly greater volume of blood must enter the heart during a shorter interval, and it also must be ejected during a shorter interval.

The heart is adapted to function during reduced cycle length in two ways. First, at resting heart rates, ventricular filling is nearly complete early in diastole (the phase of rapid ventricular filling), and most of the stroke volume is ejected early in systole (the phase of rapid ventricular ejection) (see Figure 13-2). Thus, there is reserve time in both diastole and systole that can be used when the cardiac cycle must be repeated more frequently. Second, during physiological increases of cardiac output, when the cycle length is shortened, the ventricles fill more rapidly and empty more rapidly, requiring less time during each cycle. The rate of ventricular filling is greater because the velocity of flow of venous blood is greater. In addition, sympathetic nervous system activity, which accompanies physiological increases of cardiac output, increases the rate at which all of the mechanical events of the cardiac cycle are carried out. Increased cardiac contractility is the prime effect; that is, the cardiac muscle develops tension and shortens more rapidly, and the blood is ejected more rapidly. This increased acceleration is of the utmost importance because the cardiac output can be increased only by increasing the mean velocity at which the blood flows. Sympathetic nervous system activity also increases the rate of relaxation of the ventricles, decreases the intraventricular pressure at the beginning of diastole, and increases the compliance of the ventricles; all of these effects help to increase the rate at which the ventricles fill during diastole.

ATRIA

When the heart rate is slow, as it is in the normal subject at rest, the ventricles fill almost entirely by passive inflow of blood from the veins, and the principal contribution of the *atria* is to help position the AV valves (see "Atrial Contraction" in Chapter 13). When the cardiac cycle is shortened, however, atrial contraction aids ventricular filling significantly, and this function also is enhanced by the increased contractility that is caused by sympathetic nervous system activity.

Length-Tension Relationship

All muscle has the general property of increasing the rate at which it develops tension and shortens during activity, as its resting length (preload) is increased, within limits (see Figure 15-4). This property can be demonstrated in the intact heart by increasing the intraventricular pressure, which increases the volume of the ventricle and stretches the ventricular muscle fibers; because of the increased fiber length, the ventricle can eject the larger volume. This intrinsic ability of cardiac muscle to adapt immediately to a changing load is utilized physiologically to permit each ventricle to adjust to specific variations of preload or afterload that each may encounter independently of the other.

ABNORMAL VOLUME LOAD

The volume load of the right ventricle is increased by an *atrial septal defect* (ASD), which permits some of the blood returning from the lungs to be shunted back to the right ventricle, rather than being sent directly to the left ventricle (Figure 15-11). Suppose, for example, that half of the blood from the pulmonary veins goes through the defect into the right atrium and, thence, into the right ventricle. As the metabolic needs of the body must be supplied, the volume of blood that flows from the pulmonary veins into the left atrium and, thence, to the left ventricle equals the normal cardiac output, and the right ventricle also must pump this volume in addition to an equal volume that is shunted. The extra blood that enters the right ventricle during each cycle distends it (increases the preload), and the stroke volume of the right ventricle is twice as great as that of the left ventricle. Thus, the right ventricle can pump twice as much blood as the left ventricle, even though the rate of beating of the two ventricles

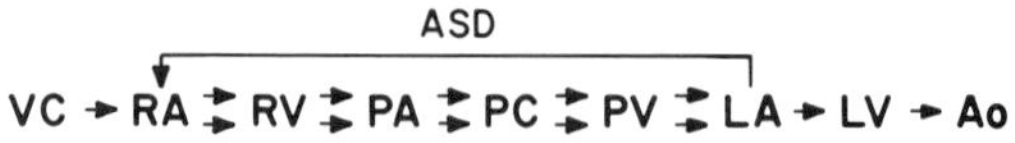

ASD

VC → RA ⇵ RV ⇵ PA ⇵ PC ⇵ PV ⇵ LA → LV → Ao

Figure 15-11. The normal sequence of blood flow through the heart and the lungs, and the pathway through which some of the blood recirculates in a subject who has an *atrial septal defect* (ASD). The arrows indicate the direction of blood flow. Two arrows indicate that the pathway carries both the normal flow of blood, which constitutes the cardiac output, and the blood that is being recirculated.

is the same, and each ventricle is subjected to the same level of sympathetic nervous system activity.

ABNORMAL PRESSURE LOAD

If the outflow tract of the left ventricle is obstructed, for example, by a stenotic aortic valve, the left ventricle must generate more pressure than it normally does to eject the normal volume per stroke; yet, the demands of the body for perfusion must be satisfied. The rate of beating and the sympathetic nervous system input are the same for each ventricle. Because of the added afterload, the left ventricle cannot attain the normal ejection fraction, and the end-diastolic volume increases; hence, the preload for the next stroke is increased. Because of the increased preload, the ventricle can generate more tension; if the resistance to outflow is not too great, a normal volume will be ejected with each beat.

Through intrinsic adaptation, one ventricle can respond quickly to an increased work load independently of the other ventricle, which has only a normal work load. If an added pressure load persists, however, the myocardium undergoes *hypertrophy*. The mass of the individual fiber increases, increasing the mass of the myocardium, so that sufficient tension can be generated without increased preload, and the diastolic volume returns to normal.

SHIFTS OF BLOOD VOLUME

Even in normal circumstances, the outputs of the two ventricles differ temporarily. When a subject reclines, some blood is transferred from the systemic circulation into the pulmonary circulation, and the output of the right ventricle exceeds the output of the left ventricle while the transfer is occurring. When the subject stands, the effect of gravity causes the transfer of blood back to the abdomen and the lower limbs, and the output of the left ventricle exceeds the output of the right ventricle during the period of the transfer. Even during each cycle of respiration, a small amount of blood is transferred back and forth between the systemic circulation and the pulmonary circulation; hence, it is improbable that the stroke volumes of the right ventricle and the left ventricle ever are exactly the same. The function of the length-tension relationship to bring the outputs of the two ventricles back into balance is essential; if the

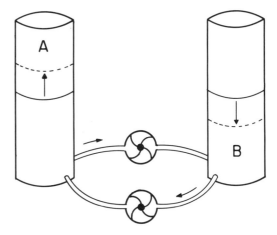

Figure 15-12.   The consequences of imbalance in two pumps connected in series. In the diagram, one pump moves fluid from *A* to *B*, and the other moves fluid from *B* to *A*. If the outputs of the two pumps were exactly equal, the volume of fluid in each reservoir would remain the same. However, if the output of one pump (in this illustration, the one that supplies *A*) exceeded that of the other pump continuously, fluid would be transferred continuously from *B* to *A*, the volume of fluid contained by *A* would increase, and the volume contained by *B* would decrease.

stroke volumes were fixed, even a slight difference would have disastrous consequences because the blood would accumulate in one of the circulations at the expense of the other (Figure 15-12).

INTERACTIONS BETWEEN EXTRINSIC EFFECTS AND INTRINSIC EFFECTS

The effects of the *sympathetic nervous system* (extrinsic effects) and of changes of preload (intrinsic effects) are complementary, because they function simultaneously, and each contributes in a unique fashion. When the combined function of both ventricles is needed, as it is when the cardiac output is increased in response to the metabolic needs of the body, the action of the sympathetic nervous system is appropriate because the same rate of beating and the same level of contractility are applied to both ventricles simultaneously. In addition, the increases of rate and contractility both are part of a coordinated response that includes adjustments of venous tone and arteriolar tone that provide for the control of ventricular filling pressure and the redistribution of arterial blood

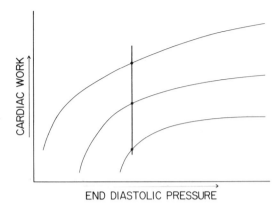

Figure 15-13. Effect of the level of cardiac contractility on the relationship between end-diastolic pressure and cardiac work. Each curve, from the bottom one to the top one, represents an increased level of sympathetic nervous system input to the heart. The heavy vertical line indicates the normal means of changing the ability of the heart to do work without change of end-diastolic pressure, by increase of sympathetic nervous system activity. At a given level of sympathetic nervous system activity, changes of the work load in either ventricle alone are accommodated by individual changes of preload.

flow to active tissues. When the function of one ventricle must be adjusted independently of the other, to meet acute, varying demands on the individual ventricle and to balance the mean outputs of both ventricles, the *intrinsic length-tension relationship* must be used. Finally, the ability of cardiac muscle to increase its contractility intrinsically, through increased fiber length, provides a backup system that assures cardiac function when adrenergic stimulation alone is inadequate (Figure 15-13).

Relation of Cardiac Output to Central Arterial Pressure

The blood that perfuses the tissues of the body flows from the elastic (central) arteries, where it has been placed under pressure by the action of the heart. Pressure develops in the large arteries because blood flows freely into them; because of the resistance at the ends of the arteries, blood does not flow out at the same mean rate until a certain mean pressure has developed (Figure 15-14). The bulk of the resistance to flow from the arteries is in the *arterioles* and the *precapillary sphincters* (Figure 15-15); if these resistance vessels dilate or constrict, flow through them changes, and arterial pressure

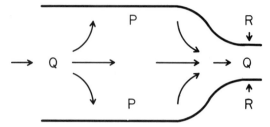

Figure 15-14. The relationships among blood flow, arterial pressure, and peripheral resistance. Blood flows into the arteries freely, but, because of the resistance to flow through the arterioles (*peripheral resistance*), blood does not flow out of the arteries at the same rate until a certain level of pressure has developed. Thus, the flow of blood from the arteries into the tissues, driven by a sustained level of arterial pressure, is determined by the peripheral resistance.

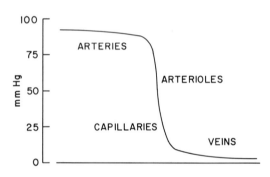

Figure 15-15. The pattern of mean pressure to which the blood is subjected as it moves through the systemic circulation.

changes unless flow into the arteries (*cardiac output*) also changes appropriately. The relationships are as follows:

$$P \simeq \dot{Q}(\uparrow\downarrow) \times R(\uparrow\downarrow)$$

where P is the mean central arterial pressure, $\dot{Q}$ is the cardiac output, and R is the total peripheral resistance. The arrows indicate that both cardiac output and peripheral resistance may be varied.

MONITORING CARDIAC OUTPUT
The demand for cardiac output is determined primarily by the metabolic needs of the body, and changes in this demand are communicated through the effects of changes of peripheral resistance on the *central arterial pressure*. Most tissues appear to *autoregulate,* or to determine their own blood flow by intrinsic regulation of

their own vascular resistance. If one is given the relationship $P \simeq \dot{Q}R$, and P is held constant, then $\dot{Q}$ varies inversely with R.

The central arterial pressure is monitored closely and the resources of the circulation are utilized to support it. These resources include the adjustments of the circulating blood volume, the venous and the arteriolar tone, and the contractility and the frequency of beating of the heart. Therefore, the system that controls the central arterial pressure also controls the cardiac output.

Other factors, which do not change quickly enough to be related to the metabolic needs of the body, affect the peripheral resistance, and, hence, the arterial pressure, during periods of weeks, months, or years. These factors, which involve the kidneys, are very important in the origin of arterial hypertension (abnormally high arterial pressure) and will be considered in the chapter on arterial hypertension.

Cardiovascular Control System

SENSOR

Arterial pressure is sensed by *mechanoreceptors* located in the walls of certain arteries (Figure 15-16), principally in the arch of the aorta and in the bifurcation of the common carotid arteries (the carotid sinuses), but also at other areas in between.

The carotid sinuses have been studied the most because of their accessibility to experimental control. Cross-perfusion techniques have been used to control the pressure in the carotid sinuses and to record the effects that changes of pressure in these sensing areas have on the heart and the systemic circulation (Figure 15-17). When the pressure in the isolated carotid sinus is increased, the heart rate and the systemic arterial pressure decrease, and when the pressure in the isolated carotid sinus is decreased, the heart rate and the systemic arterial pressure increase. These changes, which occur in the heart and the systemic circulation, are interpreted as being those which, in the intact circulation, would counter the deviations from normal pressure detected by the carotid *pressoreceptors*.

CHARACTERISTICS OF BARORECEPTORS

The arterial *baroreceptor* is a stretch receptor that is sensitive to the absolute level of arterial pressure and to change of arterial pressure.

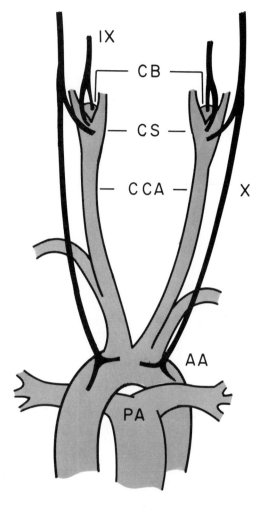

Figure 15-16. Location of the principal arterial baroreceptor areas in the human, and the sensory nerves that supply them. AA = aortic arch; CS = carotid sinuses; CCA = common carotid arteries; IX = carotid sinus branch of cranial nerve IX (*glossopharyngeal*); X = aortic branch of cranial nerve X (*vagus*); CB = carotid bodies; PA = pulmonary artery.

Figure 15-18 represents the recording simultaneously of the pressure in the carotid artery and the electrical activity of a single fiber teased from the carotid sinus nerve. In column A, the arterial pulse wave is shown; after a control recording, the pressure was decreased by bleeding the animal. The action potentials of the nerve have been redrawn and positioned along the pressure curves to emphasize the levels of pressure at which they occurred. In column B, a steady pressure equal to the mean pressure of each pulse is shown; it was obtained by isolating the carotid sinus and setting the steady perfusion pressure with a leveling bulb.

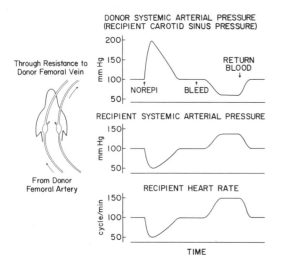

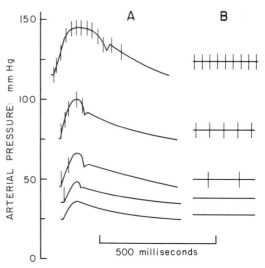

Figure 15-17. Effects of changes of arterial pressure in the carotid sinus on the heart rate and systemic arterial pressure. The diagram represents the head of a dog (*recipient*). The carotid sinuses are isolated and perfused from the systemic arteries of a donor dog. Thus, the blood pressure in the carotid sinuses of the recipient is the same as that in the systemic arteries of the donor. When the systemic arterial pressure of the donor animal and, hence, the carotid sinus pressure of the recipient animal, is changed, the systemic arterial pressure and the heart rate of the recipient animal change in the opposite direction. The changes of arterial pressure and heart rate in the recipient animal are interpreted to reflect the compensatory responses to the changes of pressure that were sensed in the carotid sinuses.

Figure 15-18. Effects of constant pressure and changing pressure on the response of the carotid sinus baroreceptor. The figure represents the systemic arterial pressure and the action potentials from a single fiber that was teased from one carotid sinus nerve of a cat. The pulsatile pressure during one cardiac cycle is represented in **A**. The action potentials have been redrawn along the pressure traces to illustrate better the relationship between the level of arterial pressure and the occurrence of the action potential. The relationship between steady arterial pressure and the occurrence of action potentials is illustrated in *B*. The steady pressure in each trace in *B* is the same as the mean arterial pressure in the corresponding pulsatile trace in *A*. The arterial pressure was decreased in the successive cycles.

In the two highest pulse waves, when the pressure is rising, the frequency of impulses is greater than that recorded at the steady mean pressure, even at values less than the mean. When the pressure is falling, the frequency of the impulses decreases; firing stops at levels higher than those at which it began when the pressure was rising and higher than the steady mean pressure. In the next two traces, impulses appear on the rising phase only, and in the last trace, no impulse appears. Thus, the frequency of impulses increases as the mean pressure increases, and the sensitivity of the receptor is increased by rising pressure and decreased by falling pressure.

INTEGRATOR

A cardiovascular control center has been identified and localized in the brain stem, in the medulla, in the floor of the fourth ventricle. It is a tonically active system that is inhibited by the input of the baroreceptors through cranial nerve IX, which innervates the carotid sinus, and cranial nerve X, which innervates the aortic arch. When the sensory input from the baroreceptors decreases, as it does when the arterial pressure decreases, the sympathetic nervous system outflow to the heart and the blood vessels increases, and the parasympathetic outflow to the heart decreases. These changes of ANS activity would oppose a fall of arterial pressure. When the sensory input from the baroreceptors increases, as it does when the arterial pressure increases, the sympathetic outflow to the heart and the blood vessels decreases, and the parasympathetic outflow to the heart increases. These changes of ANS activity would oppose a rise of arterial pressure.

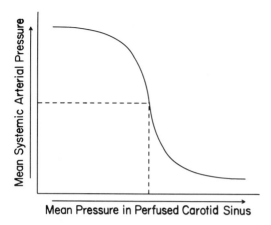

Figure 15-19. The reciprocal relationship between the pressure in the isolated, perfused carotid sinus and the systemic arterial blood pressure. The change of systemic arterial pressure opposite in direction to that of the perfused carotid sinus is interpreted to reflect the compensatory response that tends to keep the arterial pressure constant. The position of the normal arterial pressure on the curve also is shown (*dashed lines*).

In experimental animals, the baroreceptors operate effectively in a range of arterial pressure of about 150 mm Hg. When the pressure in the isolated, perfused carotid sinuses is about 200 mm Hg, the inhibitory input of the baroreceptors to the cardiovascular control center is maximal, and when the perfusion pressure is only about 50 mm Hg, the baroreceptors provide no inhibitory input. This reciprocal relationship is plotted in Figure 15-19; it shows that the baroreceptor is most sensitive in a middle range of pressures. Thus, it is able to oppose deviation of arterial pressure either above or below the normal value.

CENTRAL MODIFICATION

The function of the cardiovascular control system, as it has been studied in the resting subject, is modified by higher central nervous system activity in the exercising subject. The level of activity of the sympathetic nervous system is increased, and the sensitivity of the baroreceptors is decreased. One manifestation of this change is that the heart rate is permitted to increase, regardless of whether the mean arterial pressure increases or remains about the same. Under these conditions, there is little need for a system to prevent the arterial pressure from falling too low. Thus, the decreased sensitivity of the baroreceptors is appropriate. The baroreceptors still do function, however,

and high mean arterial pressure, such as that which may be experienced in certain isometric exercises, decreases the upper limit to which the heart rate will increase.

OTHER INFLUENCES

The medullary control center also is subjected to sensory input from a variety of other receptors. Pressoreceptors have been identified in the lungs, the mesentery, and the heart. *Chemoreceptors* in the carotid bodies (see Figure 15-16) and the aortic bodies, although much more important in the control of respiration, can be shown, under experimentally controlled conditions, to affect the arterial pressure. In addition, sensory inputs from *stretch receptors* in the lungs and from painful stimulation of the skin and the viscera impinge on the medullary control center. Although these other influences exist, and they can be demonstrated under special conditions, they are subordinate to the sino-aortic baroreceptor system in normal physiological function.

EFFECTOR: THE AUTONOMIC NERVOUS SYSTEM

The central arterial pressure is generated by a combination of the cardiac output and the peripheral resistance. If either of these variables is changed, the other must be changed in the opposite direction to compensate. The cardiac output is varied through the actions of the ANS on the veins and the heart. Ventricular filling is adjusted by altering the ventricular compliance, the venous tone, and the volumes of the venous reservoirs; the function of the heart is modulated by changing the heart rate and the cardiac contractility. The peripheral resistance is altered by selective variation of the diameters of the arterioles and the precapillary sphincters. The arterioles are controlled by sympathetic nervous system activity; the precapillary sphincters appear to be controlled intrinsically, that is, autoregulated by the tissues (Figure 15-20).

The perfusion of a vascular bed is determined by the arterial pressure and the resistance to flow in the arterioles and the precapillary sphincters that lead to the bed. Dilatation of the resistance vessels increases the flow of blood to the area and tends to decrease the central arterial pressure. The arterial pressure may be kept up by a compensatory vasoconstriction in some other tissue, by an increase of the cardiac output, or by a combination of both

CLINICAL CORRELATION
15.1   Carotid Sinus Nerve Stimulation

CASE REPORT

The Patient: A 49-year-old woman.

Principal Complaint: Frequently recurring tachycardia.

History: About a year before the current admission, the patient began to have episodes of rapid heart rate two or three times a week. As the frequency of the attacks increased, medical help was sought, and paroxysmal supraventricular tachycardia was diagnosed on the basis of ECGs. The patient was taught how to stop the dysrhythmia by manual pressure on the carotid sinuses (massaging the neck), by carrying out the Valsalva maneuver (see "Valsalva Maneuver" in Chapter 17), by initiating the diving reflex,* or by intramuscular self-injection of a pressor agent (methoxamine, an adrenergic α-receptor agonist, which increases systemic arterial pressure through peripheral arteriolar constriction. The increased pressure elicits vagal activity reflexly). However, these procedures gradually became less effective. Several antidysrhythmic agents were tried, alone or in combination, but none of them consistently decreased the frequency of the episodes of tachycardia.

Clinical Examination: The patient appeared healthy. Her arterial pressure was 115/70 mm Hg (normal, 90–140/60–90 mm Hg), her pulse rate was 65 beats/min (normal, 60–100 beats/min), and no cardiac abnormalities were found. Her blood chemistry was normal, and her thyroid function was within normal limits. No dysrhythmia occurred during the examination. The cause of the dysrhythmia was not established.

Treatment: A radiofrequency-controlled carotid sinus nerve stimulator was implanted. A transverse incision was made below the clavicle on each side and a receiver was placed in a pocket fashioned beneath the lower flap of the incision. The carotid sinus nerve bundle on each side was located through an incision in the neck. A tunnel that connected the neck incision with the infraclavicular incision was made on each side. The bipolar platinum electrodes were pulled through the tunnel and attached to each carotid sinus nerve by means of a silicone jacket. Stimuli were generated at a frequency of 5 Hz by an external, battery-powered radiofrequency generator and transmitted by an induction coil placed on the skin directly over the receiving unit. The patient could control the unit by pressing and releasing an on-off switch.

Outcome: During the first week after the operation, episodes of supraventricular tachycardia could be terminated by use of the stimulator only after the arterial pressure had been increased by a pressor agent (phenylephrine, an adrenergic α-receptor agonist) injected intravenously. During the second postoperative week, however, and thereafter, paroxysmal attacks could be stopped by the stimulator alone. Test use of the stimulator during periods of normal sinus rhythm decreased heart rate and arterial pressure markedly. The unit now has been used successfully for more than 2 years, and it is expected to remain functional indefinitely.

---

*When the face is immersed in water, a reflex is elicited to slow the heart rate, stop respiration, and constrict blood vessels in the kidneys, splanchnic area, and skeletal muscles.

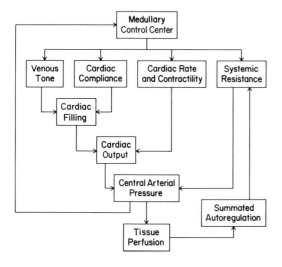

Figure 15-20. Diagrammatic illustration of (1) the factors involved in the control of the central arterial pressure, (2) the relationship of cardiac output, systemic resistance, and central arterial pressure to tissue perfusion, and (3) the combined control of the systemic resistance by neural input and tissue autoregulation.

means. The rate of perfusion of the tissues ultimately is limited by the cardiac output that can be generated; however, as long as the decrease of peripheral resistance can be matched by an increase of cardiac output, the maintenance of the arterial pressure assures adequate perfusion of the tissues.

The normal physiological state permits the peripheral resistance to be varied widely—to be increased or decreased, generally or selectively—as the needs of the tissues for perfusion dictate. Under certain conditions, however, this normal flexibility is lost; because the system is unable to compensate in the normal way for a decrease of peripheral resistance (by increasing the cardiac output), selective reduction of specific resistances, which would tend to increase the rates of perfusion of various tissues, cannot be permitted. Under these conditions, in which the cardiac output is limited abnormally, the maximum peripheral resistance is required merely to keep the central arterial pressure from falling. The best example of this is hemorrhagic shock, which is caused by an acute loss of blood; because the cardiac output is low, the peripheral resistance must be increased to keep up the arterial pressure. In this situation, maintenance of the central arterial pressure does not assure adequate perfusion of all the tissues because the arterial pressure is maintained by increasing the peripheral resistance, rather than by increasing the cardiac output. In fact, the generalized arteriolar constriction that prevails threatens the integrity of many of the vascular beds of the body. The organs that escape the deprivation and receive the benefit of the maintenance of the central arterial pressure are the heart and the brain. Their perfusion is not reduced by the generalized vasoconstriction because it is not limited normally by the arterioles; the blood supply of these organs comes more directly from the large arteries. This arrangement is appropriate to the location of the sensors of the arterial pressure—the baroreceptors—adjacent to the heart and the brain. Therefore, the generalized arteriolar constriction that maintains the central arterial pressure when the cardiac output is limited restricts the perfusion of all other vascular beds but tends to assure the perfusion of the heart and the brain. Thus, the system of general circulatory control functions as if only the heart and the brain are indispensable.

STUDY OUTLINE

COMPONENTS OF CARDIAC OUTPUT

HEART RATE   Controlled through the autonomic nervous system (ANS).

Decreased by parasympathetic activity, increased by sympathetic activity; both systems are tonically active.

In physiological increase of heart rate, parasympathetic input is inhibited and sympathetic input is activated.

STROKE VOLUME   Difference between volume of ventricle at end of filling (diastole) and end of emptying (systole).

Filling is determined by gradient of pressure (atrium to ventricle) and ventricular compliance.

Atrial pressures are kept relatively constant by venous inflow.

PRELOAD   Ventricular pressure at end of diastole.

Stretches myocardium, increases rate of development and magnitude of tension and shortening.

Automatically conditions ventricle to eject stroke volume.

Volume at end of systole is determined by contractility and afterload.

CONTRACTILITY   Rate of development and maximum tension developed.

Determines how much the muscle fibers shorten against a given load.

AFTERLOAD   Tension that ventricular myocardium must develop.

Determined by arterial pressure and end-diastolic volume.

Tension = pressure × radius.

EJECTION FRACTION   Proportion of end-diastolic volume ejected.

Normal is about 60%–75%.

Increases with increased contractility, decreased afterload.

Decreases with decreased contractility, increased afterload.

COMPONENTS OF VENTRICULAR CONTRACTION   Left ventricle is cylindrical in cross-section, right ventricle like half of larger cylinder appended.

Both shorten in longitudinal axis and decrease diameter of cylinder.

Right ventricle is adapted to eject volume against low pressure.

Left ventricle is adapted to generate high pressure.

PHYSIOLOGICAL CONTROL OF CARDIAC OUTPUT   Mainly by change of heart rate; stroke volume changes much less.

EFFECT OF BODY POSITION ON STROKE VOLUME   Stroke volume is large in reclining subject, decreases when subject stands; end-diastolic volume decreases.

Effects of gravity on ventricular filling lead to vasoconstriction and increased heart rate.

With exercise, stroke volume returns quickly to resting value because of more complete emptying.

Further increase of cardiac output is related almost entirely to increase of heart rate.

COORDINATED CARDIOVASCULAR RESPONSE   Enhanced ventricular filling maintains stroke volume as heart rate increases.

Increased venous tone, contraction of venous reservoirs, muscle pump, and lung pump.

Increased perfusion of some vascular beds is aided by decreased perfusion of others.

Increased cardiac output is gained by increased velocity of flow.

Heart functions as accelerator of blood flow.

ADJUSTMENT OF CARDIAC FUNCTION TO CYCLE LENGTH

VENTRICLES   As heart rate increases, cycle length decreases; durations of both diastole and systole are shortened.

At rest, ventricular filling and emptying is mostly in early phases of diastole and systole.

Ventricles fill and empty more rapidly when cardiac output, hence, heart rate, increases.

Increased contractility, increased compliance, increased velocity of venous and arterial blood flow.

ATRIA   Atrial contraction aids ventricular filling at higher heart rates.

Atrial contractility is increased by sympathetic nervous system activity.

LENGTH-TENSION   RELATIONSHIP
Rate at which myocardium develops tension and shortens increases with resting length (preload), within limits.

Permits each ventricle to adjust independently to different preload or afterload.

ABNORMAL VOLUME LOAD   Example is atrial septal defect (ASD).

Blood recirculates from left atrium to right atrium.

Normal cardiac output is maintained.

Right ventricular stroke volume exceeds left ventricular stroke volume because of increased preload.

ABNORMAL PRESSURE LOAD   Example is aortic obstruction.

Increased afterload decreases left ventricular ejection fraction.

Residual volume added to normal filling increases preload.

Stroke volume returns to normal if obstruction is not too great.

If pressure load persists, ventricle hypertrophies, and diastolic volume may return to normal.

SHIFTS OF BLOOD VOLUME   With changes of posture and during each respiratory cycle, blood is transferred between systemic and pulmonary circulation.

Stroke volumes are adjusted by length-tension property.

INTERACTIONS BETWEEN EXTRINSIC EFFECTS AND INTRINSIC EFFECTS
Extrinsic effects (sympathetic nervous system) when cardiac output increases in response to metabolic needs.

Increases of cardiac rate and contractility coordinated with adjustments of venous and arteriolar tone.

Intrinsic effects (length-tension) when function of one ventricle must be adjusted independently of the other.

Provides backup for extrinsic system.

RELATION OF CARDIAC OUTPUT TO CENTRAL ARTERIAL PRESSURE

Central arterial pressure = cardiac output × peripheral resistance.

If peripheral resistance changes but arterial pressure remains constant, cardiac output must change oppositely.

MONITORING CARDIAC OUTPUT Cardiac output is determined mainly by metabolic needs of body.

Tissues autoregulate; decrease of resistance and increase of flow tends to decrease arterial pressure.

Central arterial pressure is monitored; heart and circulation are adjusted to maintain it.

CARDIOVASCULAR CONTROL SYSTEM

SENSOR Mechanoreceptors (or baroreceptors) in walls of aortic arch and carotid sinuses.

Stretch of baroreceptors by increased arterial pressure causes pressure to be decreased again.

A system that opposes deviation from a set value.

CHARACTERISTICS OF BARORECEPTORS Sensitive to absolute level of pressure and change of pressure.

INTEGRATOR Cardiovascular control center in medulla.

Tonically active, inhibited by input of baroreceptors.

Decreased inhibition—increased arterial pressure, heart rate, cardiac contractility.

Increased inhibition—decreased arterial pressure, heart rate, cardiac contractility.

CENTRAL MODIFICATION During exercise, baroreceptor sensitivity decreases and heart rate is permitted to increase.

OTHER INFLUENCES Input from chemoreceptors and baroreceptors from other areas subordinate to carotid sinus-aortic arch system.

EFFECTOR Autonomic nervous system—affects heart (rate of contractility), veins (volume and tone), and arterioles (peripheral resistance).

Normally, decrease of peripheral resistance is matched by increase of cardiac output; maintenance of arterial pressure assures tissue perfusion.

If output is limited, as in hemorrhagic shock, decrease of resistance is overridden, and arterial pressure is maintained by decreasing perfusion of skin, viscera, muscles.

Perfusion of heart and brain is related directly to maintenance of arterial pressure.

BIBLIOGRAPHY

Badeer, H. 1963. Contractile tension in the myocardium. *Am. Heart J.* 66:432.

Bevegard, B.S., and Shepherd, J.T. 1967. Regulation of the circulation during exercise in man. *Physiol. Rev.* 47:178.

Burton, A. 1972. *Physiology and Biophysics of the Circulation* (2nd ed.). Chicago: Year Book.

Heymans, C., and Neil, E. 1958. *Reflexogenic Areas of the Cardiovascular System.* Boston: Little, Brown.

Kroner, P.I. 1971. Intergrative neural cardiovascular control. *Physiol. Rev.* 51:312.

Ludbrook, J. 1983. Reflex control of blood pressure during exercise. *Annu. Rev. Physiol.* 45:155.

Mahler, F.; Covell, J.W.; and Ross, J., Jr. 1975. Systolic pressure-diameter relations in the normal conscious dog. *Cardiovasc. Res.* 9:447.

McGregor, M. 1979. Pulsus paradoxus. *N. Engl. J. Med.* 301:480.

Melcher, A., and Donald, D.E. 1981. Maintained ability of carotid baroreflex to regulate arterial pressure during exercise. *Am. J. Physiol.* 241:H838.

Nixon, J.V.; Murray, R.G.; Leonard, P.D., et al. 1982. Effect of large variations in preload on left ventricular performance characteristics in normal subjects. *Circulation* 65:698.

Phillips, C.A., and Petrofsky, J.S. (eds.). 1983. *Mechanics of Skeletal and Cardiac Muscle.* Springfield, Illinois: Charles C. Thomas.

Rushmer, R.F. 1976. *Cardiovascular Dynamics* (4th ed.). Philadelphia: Saunders.

Sonnenblick, E.H. 1964. Series eleastic and contractile elements in heart muscle: Changes in muscle length. *Am. J. Physiol.* 207:1330.

Sonnenblick, E.H. 1965. Instantaneous force-velocity-length determinants in the contraction of heart muscle. *Circ. Res.* 16:441.

Wang, Y.; Marshall, R.J.; and Shepherd, J.T. 1963. The effect of changes in posture and of graded exercise on stroke volume in man. *J. Clin. Invest.* 39:1051.

Yin, F.C.P., 1981. Ventricular wall stress. *Circ. Res.* 49:829.

16

The Circulations of Special Regions

CHAPTER CONTENTS

CIRCULATORY CONTROL

The circulation must carry blood to different tissues that have widely varying needs for perfusion. The flow of blood to certain tissues, such as the skin and the kidneys, is related largely to special functions of those organs. In most other tissues, the rate of blood flow is related closely to the rate of metabolism. The circulation must supply blood to tissues that have low rates of metabolism all of the time, to tissues that have moderate to high rates of metabolism all of the time, and to other tissues that have low rates of metabolism when they are resting but which may increase their activity manyfold. Tissues that never need large amounts of blood contain relatively few capillaries; those that continuously or periodically need relatively high rates of blood flow have dense capillary beds. In any tissue, the rate of perfusion at any given time is determined by the number of capillaries that are open.

The control of blood flow to the tissues is vested in the *muscular arterioles* and the *precapillary sphincters*. The lumen of the vessel is decreased by the contraction and increased by the relaxation of the smooth muscle that encircles it. In these small vessels, a relatively small change in the caliber of the lumen produces a relatively large change of flow because the resistance is related to the fourth power of the radius (see the Poiseuille equation in Chapter 12).

MECHANISMS OF CONTROL

Local Control

Most tissues determine their own rates of perfusion by mechanisms that act within the tissues and are not affected directly by the autonomic nervous system. The general term for this type of control is *autoregulation;* it is defined as the tendency of some vascular beds to keep their blood flow relatively constant despite changes of perfusion pressure (Figure 16-1), and the intrinsic ability of other vascular beds to change their blood flow despite relatively constant perfusion pressure. Thus, autoregulation may increase flow, decrease flow, or keep flow constant.

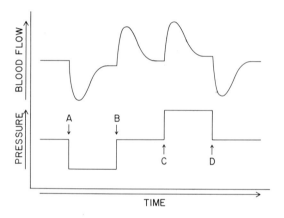

Figure 16-1. Autoregulation in a tissue subjected to varying perfusion pressures not related to the needs of the tissue. At *A*, a decrease of pressure is accompanied by an immediate decrease of blood flow. Although the lower pressure is maintained, the rate of flow returns gradually toward the original value; however, the compensation is not complete. When the pressure is returned to the original value, at *B*, the rate of flow increases to more than the original value, then returns gradually to the control value. These maneuvers indicate that when the pressure fell, the resistance vessels dilated, the resistance was decreased, and the blood flow was restored nearly to normal despite the continued low pressure. When the pressure was increased again, the rate of flow temporarily was high, but it returned to the original value as the resistance increased again. The maneuvers at *C* and *D* illustrate the effects of the corresponding changes of pressure in the opposite direction; each change of pressure is accompanied by a change of resistance that tends to restore the rate of blood flow to the original value.

METABOLIC THEORY

If the artery that supplies a certain tissue is occluded briefly and then released, the rate of flow of blood into the tissue increases rapidly, temporarily exceeds the control value, and then returns gradually to normal (Figure 16-2). The effect, called *reactive hyperemia*, has been taken to indicate that some product of metabolism that has vasodilator activity and normally is kept at a low concentration by the flow of blood through the tissue accumulates during the period of occlusion and causes the resistance vessels to dilate when the flow of blood is permitted to resume. As the substance is washed out, the normal vascular tone returns and the rate of blood flow decreases to normal again. A related possibility is that some substrate normally carried by the blood, and which supports constriction, is depleted during the period of occlusion. Either of these hypotheses is consistent with an attractive model that would serve to match the rate of blood flow with the metabolic needs of the tissues (Figure 16-3). Several products of metabolism and at least one substrate, each of which normally is present in the tissues, could account, at least in part, for reactive hyperemia. Among the substances that might accumulate in the tissue are K^+, H^+, CO_2, adenosine, histamine, and certain of the prostaglandins. It does not appear that any one of these substances alone can account for autoregulation; it is possible that all of them contribute to some extent to the overall effect.

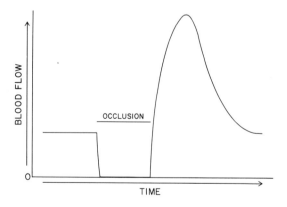

Figure 16-2. Reactive hyperemia. A control level of blood flow to a tissue (e.g., skeletal muscle) is established; then, the vessel is occluded for about 1 minute. When the vessel is opened again, the rate of blood flow increases rapidly, reaches a peak that is greater than the control rate, and then returns gradually to normal.

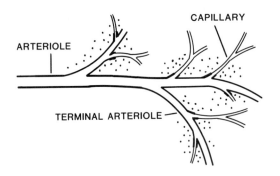

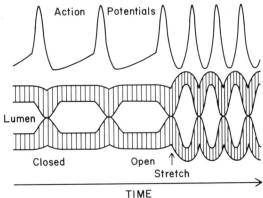

Figure 16-3. Metabolic hypothesis of autoregulation of blood flow. The cuffs at the origin of the capillaries represent the precapillary sphincters. The dots represent either metabolites that are produced by the surrounding tissue and cause the sphincters to dilate or a substrate that is used by the tissue and causes the sphincters to contract. Dilatation would be proportional to the concentration of the metabolite and inversely proportional to the concentration of the substrate. In either event, the rate of blood flow would be matched to the metabolism of the tissue.

Oxygen might be thought of as a vasoconstrictor material in the sense that the degree of contraction of smooth muscle in the precapillary sphincters might be related to the oxygen content of the immediate environment. This is a particularly attractive model of a self-regulating system that would relate blood flow to metabolism; however, it, also, cannot be the only metabolic factor that operates, because the rate of consumption of oxygen and the rate of flow of blood are not related closely in all tissues at all times. Nevertheless, in many tissues, the rate of metabolism, the rate of blood flow, and the rate of oxygen consumption are related approximately, and it is likely that oxygen is an important determinant of tissue blood flow in general.

MYOGENIC THEORY

Under appropriate conditions, the smooth muscle of the precapillary sphincters reacts to distention, such as would be caused by an increase of arteriolar pressure, with increased contraction. This mechanism cannot be thought of as one that would maintain an increased *tone* in response to an increase of perfusion pressure, because the contraction of the muscle would remove the stretch that was the stimulus to contract. Instead, the frequency of complete closure of individual precapillary sphincters is increased and, hence, the mean resistance of the vascular bed is increased (Figure 16-4).

Figure 16-4. Myogenic autoregulation. The top tracing shows the regular occurrence of action potentials in the smooth muscle of the precapillary sphincter, and the lower strip represents the regular closing and opening of the sphincter related to the activity of the smooth muscle. Note that stretch of the sphincter, which would be caused by an increased perfusion pressure, increases the frequency of the cycle of closing and opening. Thus, although the vessel is dilated more when it is open, it also is closed more frequently, the mean cross-sectional area of the lumen is decreased, the resistance to flow through the vessel is decreased, and the rate of flow is kept approximately the same, despite the increase of perfusion pressure.

When the perfusion pressure increases and the vessel is distended, the tension in the wall increases, according to the law of Laplace. Thus,

$$T = Pr$$

where T is the wall tension, P is the pressure, and r is the radius of the vessel. Because the smooth muscle already is rhythmically active, producing the regular sequence of opening and closing called *vasomotion*, the increased tension increases the basic frequency of contraction. When the muscle contracts, the wall tension increases and exceeds the product of the pressure and the radius of the lumen. Thus,

$$T > Pr$$

The pressure is not increased by the constriction of the precapillary sphincter, because other channels also are connected in parallel to the source of the pressure, the arterial system. Thus, with the pressure constant and the radius decreasing, the constriction of the vessel becomes a cascading effect, and the vessel closes completely. When the smooth muscle relaxes again, the tension decreases drastically ($Pr > T$), and the vessel dilates. As the radius increases, the product of $P \times r$ increases further, and the vessel continues to dilate. The stretch of the muscle initiates another action potential, which in turn initiates another cycle of closing and opening. Through this mechanism, the average time that the sphincters are open is decreased, the resistance of the tissue to flow is increased, and the rate of perfusion is kept relatively constant despite the increase of perfusion pressure. Thus, the *myogenic theory* provides a model for the means by which any tissue can offset the variation of perfusion that would be produced by changes of arterial pressure unrelated to the needs of the tissues.

Neural Control

The functions of the medullary cardiovascular control center to counter the effects of gravity and to maintain central arterial pressure within limits by controlling heart rate and contractility, venous tone, and arteriolar resistance were described in Chapters 12 and 15. Under normal physiological conditions, in which blood volume and cardiac function are adequate, maintaining the central arterial pressure also provides the means for satisfying the locally determined needs of the tissues for perfusion. All of the tissues cannot be supplied maximally all of the time, however. Certain activities that require extensive organ function are undertaken reciprocally; for example, strenuous muscular exercise and digestion-absorption-excretion. Thus, mesenteric and renal perfusion are decreased by neurally mediated vasoconstriction during skeletal muscle activity. Certain priorities for the allocation of blood flow exist. If the circulating blood volume is decreased (e.g., by hemorrhage or dehydration) or if the cardiac output is curtailed by cardiac insufficiency, neurally mediated vasoconstriction may supersede the local autoregulatory controls and decrease the perfusion of certain tissues. Thus, for the most part, the neural mechanisms are used to integrate regional vascular control with overall body function, rather than to regulate local tissue perfusion.

SYMPATHETIC VASOCONSTRICTION

The *sympathetic nervous system* provides the most important neural mechanism of vasomotor control; it is applied to all of the arterioles,

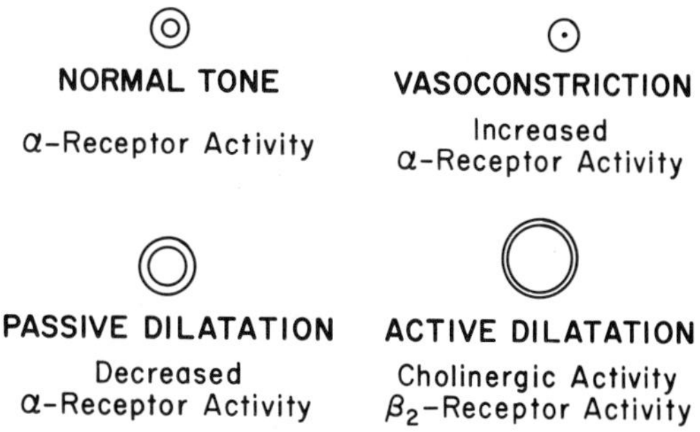

NORMAL TONE
α-Receptor Activity

VASOCONSTRICTION
Increased
α-Receptor Activity

PASSIVE DILATATION
Decreased
α-Receptor Activity

ACTIVE DILATATION
Cholinergic Activity
β_2-Receptor Activity

Figure 16-5.   Circles represent the cross-sections of arterioles.

and it is mediated through the combination of norepinephrine with α-receptors at the effector sites on the smooth muscle. The arterioles usually are maintained in a state of partial contraction, or *tone*, and a considerable range of vessel diameters is possible, subject to control, between maximum constriction and passive dilatation (Figure 16-5).

PASSIVE VASODILATATION

The amount of neurally mediated tone in a vascular bed is estimated by the increased flow of blood that occurs when sympathetic vasoconstriction in an area is abolished experimentally by surgical resection of the nerves or by the use of specific α-receptor inhibitors (see Figure 16-5). The arterioles dilate passively because the blood pressure distends the walls when the smooth muscle relaxes; however, the dilatation is not maximal. For example, blocking the sympathetic tone in the vascular bed of skeletal muscle may increase local blood flow by two or three times, but the performance of muscular work may increase flow by an additional four or five times.

SYMPATHETIC VASODILATATION

The specific effect of the transmitter released at the receptor site or into the circulating blood by sympathetic nervous system activity depends on the presence of hypothetical receptors in the smooth muscle of the arterioles. Certain arterioles possess at least two types of receptors and may be either constricted or dilatated. When both types of receptors are stimulated simultaneously, the constrictor effect usually dominates, and net vasoconstriction occurs. The vasodilator effect, which is mediated through

β_2-receptors, can be demonstrated after the α-receptors have been blocked by a specifically acting drug. In addition, certain postganglionic nerves of the sympathetic division of the autonomic nervous system release acetylcholine at effector sites and thereby produce arteriolar vasodilatation.

Norepinephrine and epinephrine both possess the configuration to stimulate α-receptors; however, epinephrine also stimulates β_2-receptors, whereas norepinephrine does not. Most investigators believe that the sympathetic adrenergic nerves release only norepinephrine; therefore, they conclude that the β_2-receptors are stimulated by epinephrine released from the adrenal medulla and carried in the circulating blood. One should be reminded, parenthetically, that both epinephrine and norepinephrine stimulate β_1-receptors, which occur in the heart. Sympathetically mediated vasodilatation may be seen in the skin, the oral mucous membrane, the coronary system, the gastrointestinal tract, and, particularly, in skeletal muscle.

PARASYMPATHETIC VASODILATATION

Parasympathetic nervous system activity produces vasodilatation only in localized sites and in relation to highly specialized functions. These sites include the erectile tissues, the salivary glands, and some glands of the gastrointestinal system.

CORONARY CIRCULATION

Functional Anatomy

The ventricles are supplied from two main arterial trunks that arise from the aortic sinus just above the semilunar valves. Broadening of the stream at this point aids the laterally directed flow into the coronary system (Figure 16-6). A system of end-arteries is formed; there is little functional exchange between them, so that a given area of the myocardium depends mostly on a single arterial source and is deprived of its blood supply if the artery is occluded.

Factors that Affect Coronary Flow

AORTIC PRESSURE
The driving force for coronary flow is the central arterial pressure; thus, the heart depends on its own ability to generate pressure. The greatest coronary flow occurs during

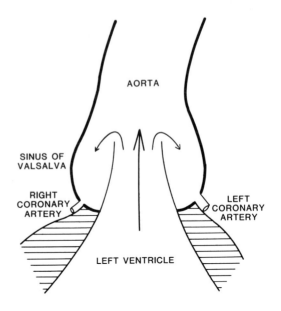

Figure 16-6.   How the aortic sinus (Valsalva) favors flow into the coronary arteries. The arrows show the directions of flow of blood through the open aortic valve.

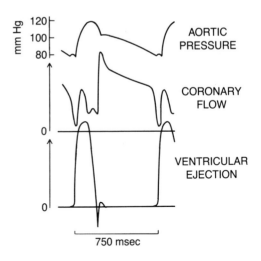

Figure 16-7.   Changes of coronary flow during the cardiac cycle. The data were obtained from conscious dogs in which devices to sense pressure and flow had been implanted chronically. Aortic pressure was measured by an indwelling transducer, coronary flow by an electromagnetic flow probe implanted on the left main coronary artery, and ventricular ejection by an electromagnetic flow probe implanted at the base of the aorta. (Redrawn, with permission, from Gregg, D.E., and Fisher, L.C. 1963. Blood supply to the heart. In *Handbook of Physiology*. Section 2. The Cardiovascular System. Volume II. Edited by W.F. Hamilton and P. Dow. Baltimore: Williams & Wilkins [American Physiological Society].)

diastole, and the rate of flow parallels the arterial pressure during that period (Figure 16-7). Coronary flow decreases during systole and may almost cease during the period of ventricular isovolumic contraction, when the tension of the contracting myocardium nearly occludes the coronary arteries. This effect is most pronounced in the endocardial layers of the left ventricle, which are compressed between the outer layers of muscle and the blood that is contained within the ventricle.

CARDIAC METABOLISM

The most important determinant of coronary blood flow is metabolic need. The metabolism of the heart is almost entirely aerobic; although some anaerobic metabolism can be demonstrated, it is not an important factor. The relationship of the coronary flow to the consumption of oxygen by the heart is illustrated in Figure 16-8. The rate of extraction of oxygen

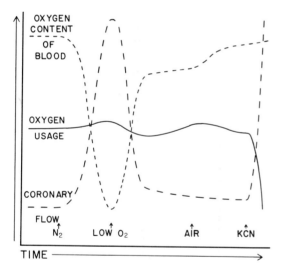

Figure 16-8. Relationship of the coronary flow to the use of oxygen by the heart. The data were obtained from an isolated-heart preparation. Note that when the oxygen content of the blood is decreased, the coronary flow increases sufficiently to keep the oxygen consumption approximately constant. The experiment was terminated by the administration of cyanide, which blocks the use of oxygen by the tissues. Although the oxygen content of the blood was normal at that time, the rate of coronary flow increased precipitously; hence, the coronary flow is related to the use of oxygen and not to the amount of oxygen in the blood. (Redrawn with permission from Hilton, R., and Eicholtz, F.J. 1925. The influence of chemical factors on the coronary circulation. *J. Physiol.* 59: 413.)

from the blood normally is high; therefore, when the heart needs additional oxygen, it is provided mostly by increased flow through the coronary system.

NEURAL MECHANISMS

Stimulation of β_1-receptors increases the rate of coronary flow; however, because autonomic nervous system activity also affects the metabolism of the heart, by affecting the heart rate and contractility, neural effects directly on the coronary vessels have been difficult to determine. Blockade of the α-receptors of the heart increases further the coronary flow that accompanies sympathetic stimulation of the heart. Therefore, it appears that adrenergic α-receptors mediate constriction of the coronary arteries; however, this vasoconstriction is overshadowed by vasodilatation mediated through β-receptors and by the effects of metabolism on the coronary flow. Parasympathetic stimulation has been shown experimentally to produce a small increase of coronary flow, but the physiological significance of this effect also is small compared with that of metabolism.

SKELETAL MUSCLE

Metabolic Control

The rate of blood flow in the vascular beds of the skeletal muscles varies widely between rest and activity; the rate of perfusion is determined by a combination of *neural control* and *local chemical autoregulation*. The resistance is high in resting muscle because many precapillary sphincters are closed in the absence of active vasodilatation, and the arterioles are constricted because of adrenergic α-receptor activity (see Figure 16-5).

Sympathetic Vasodilatation

The arterioles of the skeletal muscles possess both β_2 and cholinergic receptors. Because norepinephrine does not stimulate these β_2-receptors, it is assumed that *vasodilatation* through this mechanism is accomplished by epinephrine carried by the circulating blood. The cholinergic receptors are stimulated by acetylcholine released from cholinergic postganglionic fibers of the sympathetic nervous system. The neurally mediated vasodilatation is originated by action of the central nervous system on the autonomic centers of the hypothalamus. Blood flow is increased in the thoroughfare channels (Figure 16-9) but not in the cap-

CLINICAL CORRELATION
16.1   Coronary Artery Bypass

CASE REPORT

The Patient: A 59-year-old man.

Principal Complaints: Chest pain and dyspnea.

History: The patient began to experience occasional chest pain 10 years before the present admission; angina pectoris was diagnosed at that time, and glyceryl trinitrate (which decreases left ventricular afterload and dilates coronary arteries) was prescribed. Since then, the pain has occurred more frequently, and the treatment with glyceryl trinitrate or other coronary vasodilators has become less effective. Dyspnea (sensation of difficult breathing) and orthopnea (discomfort when lying down—must sleep propped up) have developed.

Clinical Examination: On examination, no evidence of acute myocardial infarction (dead tissue caused by inadequate blood flow) was found. However, coronary angiography (fluoroscopy of contrast material injected through a catheter into each coronary artery) showed that the right coronary artery was completely occluded about 1 cm from its origin, and both the left anterior descending and left circumflex coronary arteries were about 80% occluded in their initial portions. The right coronary artery was supplied by collaterals that had developed from the left coronary system. All of the major vessels also were diffusely atherosclerotic (vascular lining had thickened), and the contractility of the left ventricle was decreased considerably. Right ventricular pressure was within the normal range (systolic, 12–28 mm Hg, end-diastolic, 0–5 mm Hg), but left ventricular pressure was 105 mm Hg systolic and 21 mm Hg diastolic (normal systolic, 90–140 mm Hg, normal end-diastolic, 3–12 mm Hg).

Treatment: Because the patient was essentially an invalid, suffering anginal pain with even minimal exertion, he was evaluated for a coronary artery bypass. The laboratory results were favorable, and digoxin (increases cardiac contractility), hydrochlorathiazide (diuretic), and isosorbide dinitrate (coronary vasodilator) were administered. Saphenous vein bypass grafts were placed on the right coronary artery and the left anterior descending coronary artery. After the grafts were in place, flow through each was within the range of normal for each of the arteries affected.

Outcome: The patient's recovery was uneventful, and he was discharged from the hospital. The long-term benefit of his surgery remains to be evaluated.

Comment: Coronary bypass surgery is recommended* when intensive medical treatment does not provide an acceptable quality of life. Although the procedure has been shown to increase myocardial perfusion and to improve myocardial function, severe impairment of left ventricular function, as this patient had, decreases the probability of long-term survival. One of the main hazards of long-term survival has been occlusion of the graft; however, for all patients who have undergone the surgery, an average of 85%–90% of the grafts have remained open for at least 1 year. This patient will need to remain in the care of a cardiologist and to undergo further evaluation if adverse symptoms develop.

*National Institutes of Health consensus-development conference statement. 1981. *N. Engl. J. Med.* 304:680.

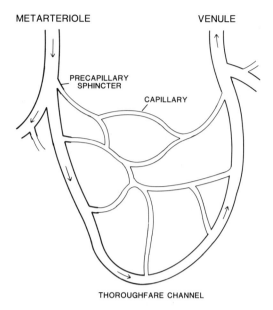

METARTERIOLE   VENULE

PRECAPILLARY
SPHINCTER

CAPILLARY

THOROUGHFARE CHANNEL

Figure 16-9.   Arrangement of thoroughfare channel, precapillary sphincter, and capillary in skeletal muscle. The arrows indicate the directions of blood flow.

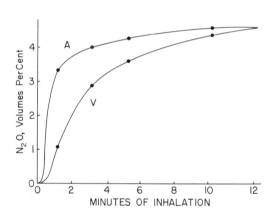

Figure 16-10.   The nitrous oxide method of estimating the rate of blood flow through the brain. The subject inhales a mixture of N_2O and air. The initial large difference between the arterial (A) concentration of N_2O and the venous (V) concentration reflects the initial rapid uptake of N_2O by the brain. When the AV difference is negligible, the brain is saturated with N_2O. The mean rate of uptake during the period of breathing is given by the mean AV difference during the period, and the concentration of N_2O in the brain is assumed to be the same as that of the blood. (Redrawn, with permission, from Kety, S.S., and Schmidt, C.F. 1948. The nitrous oxide method for the quantitative determination of cerebral blood flow in man: theory, procedure, and normal values. *J. Clin. Invest.* 27:476.)

illaries, which still are guarded by the precapillary sphincters. This nonnutritive flow of blood can be elicited by the manipulation of an inactive limb or the expectation of activity. For example, in dogs that have been trained to exercise on a treadmill, and in which devices to measure blood flow have been implanted chronically, blood flow to the skeletal muscles begins as the preparations for running are made, even though the animal is standing motionless. This observation is interpreted to show the existence of a system that makes arterial blood more readily available for perfusion of the capillaries when the muscles begin to work, when the precapillary sphincters are dilated in response to the accumulation of vasodilator metabolites or the reduction of oxygen tension locally. Because of the great rapidity with which skeletal muscles can attain a very high rate of metabolism, this system serves the useful function of providing for a high rate of nutritive blood flow very rapidly. However, the final determinant of the rate of nutritive flow is the number of the precapillary sphincters that are open at any time; this is related closely to the rate of metabolism of the tissue.

BRAIN

The metabolic rate of the brain is high, and the rate of blood flow of the brain is high; it is about 20% of the cardiac output of the person at rest. The overall metabolic rate of the brain is relatively constant; hence, the perfusion of the brain also must be relatively constant, and failure of the cerebral circulation for as little as 10 seconds causes unconsciousness. Blood reaches the brain through the two internal carotid arteries and the two vertebral arteries; these four vessels all communicate through the circle of Willis, at the base of the brain. This arrangement decreases the dependence of any part of the brain on any one artery.

Measurement

OVERALL
An adaptation of the Fick method is used to measure total blood flow to the brain; nitrous oxide (N_2O), taken up by the brain, is the indicator. The amount of N_2O taken up is determined by measuring the arteriovenous (AV) difference (Figure 16-10), using any convenient artery and the internal jugular vein for sampling. The subject breathes a mixture that con-

tains 15% N_2O, 21% O_2, and 64% N_2. The rate of uptake of N_2O is rapid at first; however, after about 10–14 minutes, the AV difference is negligible, and N_2O is in equilibrium between the blood and the brain. Fortunately, the blood-brain distribution of N_2O is approximately 1:1, so that the concentration of N_2O in the brain is equal to that in the blood. The formula is as follows:

Brain blood flow

$$= \frac{\text{Average rate of uptake of } N_2O \text{ by the brain}}{\text{Average AV difference of } N_2O}$$

Example: at equilibrium, the concentration of N_2O in the venous blood is 4.2 ml/100 ml of blood; thus, the concentration of N_2O in the brain is 4.2 ml/100 g of brain. The mean AV difference of N_2O for 12 minutes is 0.65 ml of N_2O/100 ml of blood.

Brain blood flow

$$= \frac{4.2 \text{ ml of } N_2O/100 \text{ g of brain}}{0.65 \text{ ml of } N_2O \times 12 \text{ min}/100 \text{ ml of blood}}$$

$$= \frac{54 \text{ ml of blood}/100 \text{ g of brain}}{\text{min}}$$

Thus, a brain that weighs 1360 g receives 734 ml of blood per minute; this is about 15%–20% of the cardiac output in a person at rest.

REGIONAL

Although the N_2O method indicates that overall blood flow to the brain does not vary, localized increases of metabolic activity cause localized increases of blood flow. These variations have been detected by more sensitive methods of measurement that have been developed more recently. One method uses a device that holds multiple radiation sensors. The device is placed on the head of a subject who then breathes xenon, a chemically inert radioactive gas. The level of radioactive emission is proportional to the blood flow in each area of the brain. Regional blood flow can be altered by the application of stimuli or the performance of specific tasks, such as problem-solving or speaking. This method also can detect vascular disorders.

Another method, which is applied experimentally, uses isotopically labeled glucose to measure changes of metabolism locally; the relative uptake of glucose by different parts of the brain is determined by radioautography. Because brain tissue must be removed and slices prepared, the use of this method is limited to studies with animals.

Control

AUTOREGULATION

The overall rate of blood flow to the brain is relatively constant, normally, at arterial pressures that vary from 60 to 150 mm Hg. Thus, it depends merely on the maintenance of a minimal central arterial pressure.

NEURAL EFFECTS

Sympathetic nervous system activity can be shown to produce some vasoconstriction; however, this effect probably is relatively unimportant physiologically. Vasodilator nerves that go to the cerebrum have been demonstrated experimentally, but their physiological function is not known.

BLOOD GASES: OXYGEN

The blood flow to the brain is relatively insensitive to changes of concentration of oxygen in the air that is breathed. For example, in one series of experiments, breathing 100% oxygen decreased blood flow to the brain by about 15%, and breathing 10% oxygen increased the flow by about 35%. In neither case was the consumption of oxygen by the brain changed.

BLOOD GASES: CARBON DIOXIDE

In the study mentioned in the preceding section, voluntary hyperventilation, which decreased the concentration of CO_2 in the blood, decreased the blood flow to the brain by about 35%; inhalation of air that contained 5% CO_2 increased blood flow by about 45%. These relatively small changes of blood flow in response to changes of CO_2 that are far beyond the normal physiological range are consistent with the relationship of brain blood flow to the overall constant rate of brain metabolism. Some evidence indicates that the metabolic factor that mediates cerebral autoregulation is the concentration of H^+ in the local environment of the small arteries of the cerebral circulation.

MEDULLARY ISCHEMIA

If the cerebral perfusion pressure is decreased below about 40 mm Hg, a powerful sympathetically mediated increase of systemic arterial pressure is elicited. This effect has been shown experimentally to be related to ischemia of the brain stem; it is considered to be a primitive protective reflex.

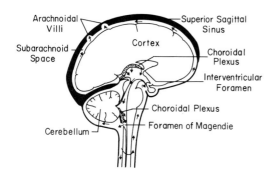

Figure 16-11. Saggital section of the brain; formation, circulation, and reabsorption of the cerebrospinal fluid. The fluid is formed in the choroidal plexuses, circulates through the subarachnoid spaces of the brain and the spinal cord, and is absorbed through the arachnoid villi into the venous sinuses.

Cerebrospinal Fluid

A special compartment of *extracellular fluid* fills the ventricles of the brain and the subarachnoid spaces that surround the brain and the spinal cord (Figure 16-11). It floats the brain and the spinal cord and cushions them hydraulically. These functions are exceedingly important because the brain is too heavy and too soft to support itself, and it can be damaged severely by trauma. In addition, the *cerebrospinal fluid* (CSF) performs the lymphatic functions of the central nervous system.

CIRCULATION

The CSF is secreted into the ventricles by the choroidal plexuses (see Figure 16-11) at the rate of about 500 ml/day. Because the volume of fluid formed in a day is about four times the total volume of fluid contained, the CSF is renewed, on the average, about four times a day. The circulation of fluid is from the two lateral cerebral ventricles through the third ventricle to the fourth ventricle, where it communicates with the subarachnoid spaces (Figure 16-12; see also Figure 16-11). It is reabsorbed into the venous sinuses through the arachnoid villi (Figure 16-13). If the circulation of the CSF is blocked in any of the narrow passages during infancy, before the bony plates of the skull have united, the pressure rises and the head enlarges enormously; the condition is called *hydrocephalus.* If the block occurs during adulthood, after the size of the skull has been fixed, the cerebrospinal fluid pressure increases and the

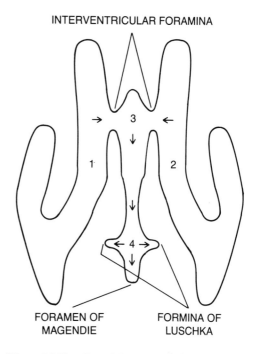

Figure 16-12. Ventricles of the brain as viewed in outline from above. Lateral ventricles *1* and *2* lie within the cerebrum; the third ventricle is in the midbrain, and the fourth ventricle is in the medulla. The arrows indicate the directions in which the cerebrospinal fluid flows. The fluid enters the subarachnoid spaces through the foramen of Magendie and the foramina of Luschka.

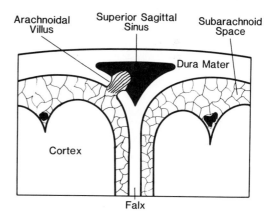

Figure 16-13. Cross-section of the brain at the junction of the two cerebral hemispheres illustrates the mechanism of the return of the cerebrospinal fluid to the blood. The fluid flows from the subarachnoid space through the arachnoid villi, which consists of thin-walled channels that perform the function of a valve. (Redrawn, with permission, from Carpenter, M.B. 1976. *Human Neuroanatomy* (7th ed.). Baltimore: Williams & Wilkins.)

brain is compressed. CSF pressure normally is about 15 cm of water (about 11 mm Hg); it is measured when the subject is in the recumbent position to avoid the effects of gravity that would be imposed if the subject were upright. If the CSF pressure exceeds about 35 mm Hg, it begins to interfere with the blood supply of the brain, and the systemic arterial pressure rises as a result of medullary ischemia.

BLOOD-BRAIN BARRIER

Many substances that are dissolved in the plasma do not move freely from the capillaries to the extracellular fluid in the central nervous system. This distinct feature is demonstrated when certain dyes, injected intravenously, stain all of the tissues of the body except those of the central nervous system. The barrier is formed by the tight junctions of the capillaries in the central nervous system. Some substances do pass easily; for example, water, oxygen, CO_2, and lipid-soluble substances, such as ethanol. The inorganic ions Na^+, K^+, and Cl^- pass somewhat more slowly, and the concentrations of these ions in the CSF are different from their concentrations in the plasma. Some drugs, both inorganic and organic, establish effective concentrations in the central nervous system and others do not; this factor must be considered when drug therapy is planned.

SKIN

The flow of blood to the skin is related primarily to the control of the temperature of the body. Heat is produced continuously as a result of metabolism and must be dissipated continuously. The body can lose heat only where it comes into contact with the external environment, which is mostly at the surface of the body. Most of the heat is produced by cells that are located beneath the surface, and much of the heat is brought by the blood into the vessels of the skin, from which it can move into the environment. (See also Chapter 66.)

General Control

NEURAL

The core of the body, which consists of the trunk and the head and contains the vital organs, is maintained at a mean temperature of about 37 C; the limbs and the skin are permitted to be much cooler. The temperature of the core is sensed at the hypothalamus, from the temperature of the blood that perfuses that part of

the brain. Extensive arteriovenous shunts in the skin are constricted by sympathetic nervous system activity (α-receptor stimulation) when the rate of loss of heat from the body must be decreased, and permitted to dilate passively (reduction of α-receptor stimulation) when the rate of loss of heat must be increased. This is the principal means of controlling the rate of loss of heat from the body.

ACTIVE VASODILATATION

The flushing of the skin of the face, shoulders, and chest associated with anger or embarrassment appears to be mediated actively; however, neither the transmitters nor the receptors that may be involved have been identified.

LOCALIZED NEURAL EFFECTS

When an area of skin is cooled or heated locally, vasoconstriction increases or decreases appropriately in the affected area. If the area includes a hand or foot, the effect is seen in the other hand or foot also. For example, the vessels of a hand placed in cold water constrict, and the effect can be shown not to depend on any change of temperature of the blood because it also occurs in the other hand, even if the arteries that supply the cooled hand are occluded.

COLD-INDUCED VASODILATATION

If the temperature of the skin falls to near 0 C, the initial vasoconstriction eventually will be relieved temporarily, and alternating periods of vasoconstriction and vasodilatation may ensue. The effect is to keep the skin from freezing or to delay its freezing if the depth of temperature is extreme, yet to keep the loss of core temperature minimal. The mechanism of this effect is not known, but some evidence indicates that the local release of prostaglandins may be involved.

NUTRITIVE FLOW

The skin also contains capillaries that provide for the exchange of substrates and metabolites between the tissue and the blood, and the sphincters that control the flow in these capillaries are controlled locally. The rate of metabolism of the skin is not high, however, and the rate of nutritive flow is not great. In addition, the skin obtains much of its oxygen directly from the air. Fortunately, this fact has become well known, and a practical consequence is the use of lightweight, porous adhesive bandages that permit the diffusion of oxygen, instead of the heavy, solid bandages used in the past.

STUDY OUTLINE

CIRCULATORY CONTROL Widely varying needs for perfusion.

Perfusion is related to special functions in some tissues, to metabolic needs in others.

Density of capillaries is related to need for perfusion.

Perfusion is controlled by arterioles and precapillary sphincters.

MECHANISMS OF CONTROL

LOCAL CONTROL   Autoregulation, intrinsic control of blood flow in a tissue.

METABOLIC THEORY Reactive hyperemia, higher rate of blood flow after a period of occlusion.

Vasodilator metabolite or vasoconstrictor substrate.

Probably several different metabolites contribute.

Oxygen may be vasoconstrictor.

MYOGENIC THEORY Precapillary sphincters are either completely open or completely closed.

Frequency of regular closing and opening (vasomotion) is increased by stretch caused by increased pressure.

Average time sphincters are closed increases; hence, resistance increases as pressure increases, increase of flow is prevented.

NEURAL CONTROL   Normally, maintaining arterial pressure provides for perfusion of tissues.

Not all tissues can be perfused maximally all of the time.

Perfusion must be decreased in some tissues to provide it in others.

If blood volume or cardiac contractility is decreased, neurally mediated vasoconstriction decreases perfusion of certain tissues.

Neural control is used mostly to integrate regional vascular control with overall body function.

SYMPATHETIC VASOCONSTRICTION Mediated through α-receptors, applied to all systemic arterioles.

Maintained in intermediate state; arteriolar tone.

PASSIVE VASODILATATION Caused by hydrostatic pressure when vasoconstriction is removed.

SYMPATHETIC VASODILATATION Mediated by epinephrine acting at β_2-receptors or acetylcholine from sympathetic cholinergic neurons.

PARASYMPATHETIC VASODILATATION Only in localized sites related to specialized functions.

CORONARY CIRCULATION

FUNCTIONAL ANATOMY   Supplied by central arterial pressure from base of aorta.

Little exchange; a given area of myocardium depends mostly on a single arterial source.

FACTORS THAT AFFECT CORONARY FLOW

AORTIC PRESSURE Heart depends on its own ability to generate pressure for perfusion.

Most of flow is during diastole, when myocardium is relaxed.

CARDIAC METABOLISM Most important factor in determining coronary blood flow is related to oxygen consumption; metabolism of heart is almost entirely aerobic.

Rate of extraction of oxygen is high; to get more oxygen, rate of perfusion must increase.

NEURAL MECHANISMS β_1-receptor stimulation increases coronary flow.

α-receptor stimulation decreases coronary flow.

Metabolic effects outweigh neural effects.

SKELETAL MUSCLE Resistance is high at rest; arterioles are constricted by α-receptor stimulation, precapillary sphincters are constricted due to lack of active (metabolic) vasodilatation.

METABOLIC CONTROL   Principal determinant of blood flow.

SYMPATHETIC VASODILATATION   Arterioles are dilated through β_2-receptors and cholinergic receptors.

Thoroughfare channels are dilated through sympathetic cholinergic neurons; makes high rate of flow available to capillaries.

Capillary sphincters are opened by vasodilator metabolites.

BRAIN Blood flow is about 20% of cardiac output, relatively constant; interconnection of arteries decreases dependence on any one vessel.

MEASUREMENT

OVERALL Adaptation of Fick method using N_2O.

REGIONAL Distribution of radioactive gas, xenon.

CONTROL

AUTOREGULATION Relatively constant, depends on arterial pressure.

NEURAL EFFECTS   Some (but not important) physiological control.

BLOOD GASES: OXYGEN Blood flow is relatively insensitive to it.

BLOOD GASES: CARBON DIOXIDE Affected by relatively large changes; not a fine control.

Effect may be mediated through $[H^+]$ in small arteries of cerebral circulation.

MEDULLARY ISCHEMIA Decreased perfusion of brainstem causes strong, sympathetically mediated increase of systemic arterial pressure; may be a primitive protective reflex.

CEREBROSPINAL FLUID   A special compartment of extracellular fluid.

Floats and cushions brain and spinal cord.

Provides lymphatic drainage of central nervous system.

CIRCULATION   Secreted into lateral ventricles by choroidal plexuses.

Circulates through third and fourth ventricles and around spinal cord.

Reabsorbed into venous sinuses through arachnoid villi.

Block in infants causes hydrocephalus; block in adolescents and adults causes increased fluid pressure.

BLOOD-BRAIN BARRIER Certain substances do not pass readily from capillaries into extracellular fluid of brain; body constituents do, some drugs do not.

SKIN   Related primarily to control of body temperature.

GENERAL CONTROL

NEURAL Core of body is maintained at about 37 C; limbs and skin are cooler.

Temperature of blood is sensed by hypothalamus.

Skin circulation is controlled through sympathetic nervous system.

a-v̄ anastomosis constricted through α-receptors, dilated passively.

Body loses heat from warm blood to environment.

ACTIVE VASODILATATION Flushing associated with anger or embarrassment; transmitters and receptors are not known.

LOCALIZED NEURAL EFFECTS Cooling or heating locally causes vasoconstriction or vasodilatation, respectively.

Cooling or heating one hand or foot also affects other hand or foot.

COLD-INDUCED VASODILATATION If skin is cooled near freezing, periodic vasodilatation occurs.

Protects skin against freezing.

May be mediated by prostaglandins released locally.

NUTRITIVE FLOW Nutritive blood flow controlled by autoregulation.

Much of oxygen is obtained from air.

BIBLIOGRAPHY

Abboud, F.M., and Heistad, D.D. (chairmen). 1981. Regulation of the cerebral circulation (symposium). *Fed. Proc.* 40:2296.

Berne, R.M. 1964. Metabolic regulation of blood flow. *Circ. Res. (Suppl.* 1) 15:261.

Betz, E. 1972. Cerebral blood flow: Its measurement and regulation. *Physiol. Rev.* 52:595.

Cohen, R.A., and Coffman, J.D. 1981. β-adrenergic vasodilator mechanism in the finger. *Circ. Res.* 49:1196.

Coleridge, H.M., and Coleridge, J.C.G. 1980. Cardiovascular afferents involved in regulation of peripheral vessels. *Annu. Rev. Physiol.* 42:413.

Donald, D.E., and Shepherd, J.T. 1980. Autonomic regulation of the peripheral circulation. *Annu. Rev. Physiol.* 42:429.

Duling, B.R., and Klitzman, B. 1980. Local control of microvascular function: Role in tissue oxygen supply. *Annu. Rev. Physiol.* 42:373.

Feigen, L.P. 1981. Actions of prostaglandins in peripheral vascular beds. *Fed. Proc.* 40:1987.

Feigl, E.O. 1983. Coronary physiology. *Physiol. Rev.* 63:1.

Folkow, B. 1955. Nervous control of blood vessels. *Physiol. Rev.* 35:629.

Folkow, B. 1964. Description of the myogenic hypothesis. *Circ. Res. (Suppl.* 1) 15:279.

Franz, D. 1979. The effect of indomethacin on cold-induced vasodilation in the domestic feline. *Fed. Proc.* 38:1055.

Friedman, P.L.; Brown, E.J., Jr.; Gunther, S., et al. 1981. Coronary vasoconstrictor effect of indomethacin in patients with coronary-artery disease. *N. Engl. J. Med.* 305:1171.

Granger, D.N., and Kvietys, P.R. 1981. The splanchnic circulation: Intrinsic regulation. *Annu. Rev. Physiol.* 43:409.

Green, H.D., and Rapela, C.E. 1964. Blood flow in passive vascular beds. *Circ. Res.* 15:1.

Gregg, D.E., and Fisher, L.C. 1963. Blood supply to the heart. In *Handbook of Physiology.* Section 2. The Cardiovascular System. Volume II. Edited by W.F. Hamilton and P. Dow. Baltimore: Williams & Wilkins (American Physiological Society). p. 1517.

Guyton, A.C.; Ross, O.M.; Carrier, O., Jr., et al. 1964 Evidence for tissue oxygen demand as a major factor causing autoregulation. *Circ. Res.* 15:1.

Guyton, A.C.; Granger, H.J.; and Coleman, T.G. 1971. Autoregulation of the total systemic circulation and its relation to control of cardiac output and arterial pressure. *Circ. Res.* 28:1093.

Hilton, R., and Eichholtz, F.J. 1925. The influence of chemical factors on the coronary circulation. *J. Physiol.* (London) 59:413.

Kalsner, S. (ed.). 1982. *The Coronary Artery.* New York: Oxford University Press.

Keatinge, W.R., and Harman, W.C. 1979. *Local Mechanisms Controlling Blood Vessels.* New York: Academic Press.

Kety, S.S., and Schmidt, C.F. 1948. The nitrous oxide method for the quantitative determination of cerebral blood flow in man. Theory, procedure, and normal values. *J. Clin. Invest.* 27:476.

Kontos, H.A. 1981. Regulation of the cerebral circulation. *Annu. Rev. Physiol.* 43:397.

Kuschinsky, W., and Wahl, M. 1978. Local chemical and neurogenic regulation of cerebral vascular resistance. *Physiol. Rev.* 58:656.

Lindgren, P. and Uvnäs, B. 1955. Vasoconstrictor inhibition and vasodilator activation—two functionally separate vasodilator mechanisms in the skeletal muscles. *Acta. Physiol. Scand.* 33:108.

Mohrman, D.E., and Feigl, E.O. 1978. Competition between sympathetic vasoconstriction and metabolic vasodilatation in the canine coronary circulation. *Circ. Res.* 42:70.

Nicoll, P.A. 1964. Structure and function of minute vessels in autoregulation. *Circ. Res. (Suppl.* 1) 15:245.

Olsson, R.A. 1981. Local factors regulating cardiac and skeletal muscle blood flow. *Annu. Rev. Physiol.* 43:385.

Pitt, B.; Elliot, E.C.; and Gregg, D.E. 1967. Adrenergic receptor activity in the coronary arteries of the unanesthetized dog. *Circ. Res.* 21:75.

Rosell, S. 1980. Neuronal control of microvessels. *Annu. Rev. Physiol.* 42:409.

Stone, L.H. 1983. Control of coronary circulation during exercise. *Annu. Rev. Physiol.* 45:213.

Uvnäs, B. 1960. Sympathetic vasodilator system and blood flow. *Physiol. Rev. (Suppl.* 4) 40:69.

Wiedman, M.P.; Tuma, R.F.; and Magrowitz, H.N. 1981. *An Introduction to Microcirculation.* New York: Academic Press.

17

Dynamics of the Pulmonary Circulation

CHAPTER CONTENTS

The pulmonary circulation will be considered in this chapter only to the extent that it is involved in general circulatory function and control. The specific relationships between the pulmonary circulation and respiratory function will be covered in the section on respiratory physiology (Chapter 30).

FUNCTIONAL ANATOMY

Arteries

The *pulmonary artery* is larger than the aorta, and its wall is thinner. The main pulmonary artery divides into right and left branches that divide further, after only short distances, into smaller branches and, eventually, into capillaries. The arteries are elastic and contain some smooth muscle; however, there are no muscular arterioles and sphincters that correspond to

those in the systemic circulation. Vascular control is exerted by the small arteries and veins.

Capillaries

The *capillary beds* surround the *alveoli* (air sacs) of the lungs. The dynamics of fluid exchange are the same, in principle, as those that are discussed in Chapter 12; however, the rate of exchange in the pulmonary circulation is less than that in the systemic circulation because the pulmonary capillary blood pressure (typical mean, about 8 mm Hg), which is the driving force, is less than the systemic capillary blood pressure (typical mean, about 25 mm Hg). In addition, the *alveolar pressure* is equal to atmospheric pressure, instead of being subatmospheric as most systemic tissue pressures are; thus, the transmural pressure gradient is not augmented.

Pulmonary Arterial Wedge Pressure

The pulmonary circulation terminates at the junction of the pulmonary veins and the left atrium. In most adults, the left atrium cannot be reached by catheter, except retrograde, through a systemic artery. To estimate left atrial pressure, a catheter is advanced through the pulmonary artery until it wedges in a small branch (Figure 17-1). The catheter occludes the vessel and connects hydraulically through the capillary bed to the pulmonary vein. The pressure that is actually measured is the pulmonary venous pressure at the first confluence. Because the resistance normally is low in the pulmonary veins, pulmonary venous pressure exceeds left atrial pressure only slightly; thus, a reasonably good estimate of left atrial pressure is obtained.

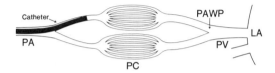

Figure 17-1. Measurement of pulmonary arterial wedge pressure (*PAWP*). The catheter, which enters the body through a vein in the right arm or the right groin, passes through the right atrium, the right ventricle, and the pulmonary artery (*PA*) into a small arterial branch, where it is wedged. The flow of blood is stopped in the vessels distal to the tip of the catheter, so that a stationary column of fluid extends forward to the first junction of the pulmonary veins (*PV*). Thus, the catheter functionally is extended through the pulmonary capillary bed (*PC*), and the pulmonary arterial wedge pressure is measured at the site indicated by the arrow. LA = left atrium.

DIFFERENCES BETWEEN PULMONARY CIRCULATION AND SYSTEMIC CIRCULATION

The two ventricles pump blood at the same rate, but the two circulations perform different functions and have different properties (Figure 17-2).

Vascular Resistances and Pressures

The pulmonary vascular resistance is much lower than the systemic vascular resistance; hence, the pulmonary arterial pressure is much lower than the systemic arterial pressure. Normal systolic pressure in the pulmonary artery is

about 22 mm Hg, and normal diastolic pressure is about 8 mm Hg. Normal mean pulmonary arterial pressure is about 13 mm Hg, and normal mean left atrial pressure is about 7 mm Hg; thus, the total pressure gradient across the normal pulmonary circulation is about 6 mm Hg. If one uses a typical cardiac output of 5 liters/min, which is about 83 ml/sec.

$$R = \frac{\Delta P}{\dot{Q}} = \frac{6 \text{ mm Hg}}{83 \text{ ml/sec}}$$

$$= 0.07 \text{ mm Hg/(ml/sec)}$$

where R is vascular resistance, ΔP is the difference of pressure, and $\dot{Q}$ is the rate of blood flow. In contrast, the typical net driving force in the systemic circulation (mean aortic pressure

PULMONARY CIRCULATION	SYSTEMIC CIRCULATION
Low Resistance	High Resistance
Low Pressure	High Pressure
Serves One Tissue	Serves Many Tissues
Small Blood Volume	Large Blood Volume
Short Hydrostatic Columns	Long Hydrostatic Columns

Figure 17-2. The major differences between the pulmonary circulation and the systemic circulation.

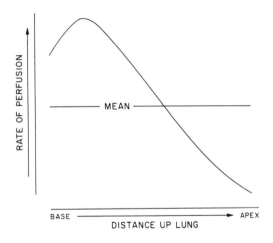

Figure 17-3. The different rates of perfusion of the lungs at different levels in the resting, upright human. The mean value would be obtained if all areas of the lungs were perfused equally. Note that the middle and basal portions of the lungs receive the most blood, and the apex receives the least blood. (Redrawn, with permission, from J.M.B. Hughes, et al. 1968. Effect of lung volume on the distribution of pulmonary blood flow in man. *Resp. Physiol.* 4:63.)

minus mean right atrial pressure) is 90 mm Hg, and the resistance is 1.1 mm Hg/(ml/sec). Therefore, in the resting subject, the vascular resistance of the pulmonary circulation is only about 1/15 that of the systemic circulation.

BASIS OF LOW PULMONARY VASCULAR RESISTANCE

The principal basis of the *low pulmonary vascular resistance* is the absence of a sustained vascular tone; hence, the pulmonary vascular system effectively is passively dilated. In addition, the pulmonary arteries are large, short, and distensible relative to the systemic arteries.

Effects of Gravity

The force of the earth's gravity aids the flow of blood into the middle and basal portions of the lungs, which lie below the pulmonary artery, and opposes the flow of blood into the apical portions of the lungs, which lie above the pulmonary artery (Figure 17-3). The vessels that receive the larger volume of blood are distended and their resistance to flow is decreased even

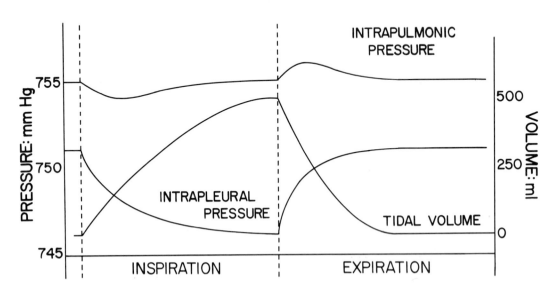

Figure 17-4. The levels of the intrapulmonic pressure, to which the pulmonary capillaries are exposed, and the intrapleural pressure, to which the remainder of the pulmonary blood vessels are

exposed, during the respiratory cycle of inspiration and expiration. The tidal volume, which is the amount of air moved into and out of the lungs with each breath, also is shown.

further, whereas the vessels that receive the lesser volume of blood are not filled completely and may be partially collapsed (see Figure 30-4). Thus, a low-resistance pathway through the pulmonary circulation is formed, and the normal pulmonary circulation effectively has unused vascular capacity.

EFFECTS OF ALVEOLAR PRESSURE

Because only a relatively low pulmonary arterial pressure develops, the level to which it can cause blood to flow upward, against the force of gravity, is not very high. If the systolic pressure of the pulmonary artery is 22 mm Hg (equivalent to about 30 cm of blood) and the diastolic pressure of the pulmonary artery is 8 mm Hg (equivalent to about 11 cm of blood), one can calculate that blood will flow to a level of about 30 cm above the pulmonary artery at the most and about 11 cm at the least. This should be adequate to perfuse all of the lungs all of the time; however, another factor also is involved. Because the blood pressure in the vessels above the pulmonary artery reaches only very low levels relative to atmospheric pressure, external forces that affect the transmural pressure gradient may determine whether the vessels are open or collapsed completely. Most of the pulmonary blood vessels are subjected to a distending force because of the subatmospheric intrapleural pressure; however, the pulmonary capillaries are exposed to the pressure of the atmosphere, through the alveoli. During expiration, alveolar pressure increases temporarily (Figure 17-4); therefore, the flow of blood in much of the apical region may cease, temporarily, during each cycle of respiration.

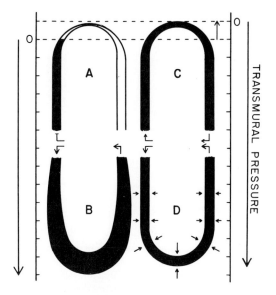

Figure 17-5. How fluid flows preferentially in a set of U-tubes, one of which is upright and one of which is inverted, when the tubes are compliant and the perfusion pressure, which is common to both of them, is relatively low. The pressure relative to the atmosphere is 0 at the top of the column in *A* and maximum at the bottom of the column in *B*. The tube in *B* is distended by the difference of pressure across the wall. In *A*, the pressure generated is inadequate to push the fluid to the top of the tube. In *C* and *D*, the rate of flow of fluid into the system has been increased; the walls of the tube in *D* have been supported (*arrows*) so that they are not distended. As a consequence, the pressure generated is adequate to cause the fluid to flow through the upper portion of the tube in *C* and down the other side. The level of pressure had to be increased only slightly (arrow between the two 0 levels) to engage the additional channel of flow.

Effects of Increased Cardiac Output

When the cardiac output increases, the rate of blood flow through the lungs increases far more than the pulmonary arterial pressure increases; therefore, pulmonary vascular resistance decreases. The pulmonary arteries are relatively large, short, and distensible, and these properties do contribute to the physical capacity of the pulmonary circulation to accept a higher rate of blood flow with relatively little additional driving force; however, the most important factor is the utilization of the relatively unused vascular capacity of the upper regions of the lungs. The undistended or even partially collapsed vessels in these areas can be perfused at a much higher rate merely by the addition of enough driving force to raise the blood a few centimeters against the force of gravity (Figure 17-5). After the blood has perfused the capillaries in these apical regions, it flows freely through the pulmonary veins to the left atrium, driven by the force of gravity.

Although the vasoconstriction that is necessary to divert some of the blood flow to the apical regions increases the resistance to flow in the middle and basal vessels, the total resistance is decreased by the utilization of the apical vessels. In addition, the decrease of pulmonary

CLINICAL CORRELATION
17.1   Pulmonary Hypertension

CASE REPORT

The Patient: A 54-year-old woman.

Principal Complaints: Fatigue and dyspnea.

History: The patient was well until about 6 months before admission, when she began to develop fatigue and dyspnea on exertion. She had been active for many years, playing golf, hiking, and jogging.

Clinical Examination: At the time of examination, the patient was unable to complete a stress test, and signs of peripheral edema were evident (e.g., swelling of the feet and ankles). Cardiac catherization revealed a resting pulmonary arterial pressure of 115/28 mm Hg (normal systolic, 12–28 mm Hg, normal diastolic 3–13 mm Hg), with a mean of 57 mm Hg (normal, 6–18 mm Hg). The right ventricular pressure was 115/18 mm Hg (normal systolic, 12–28 mm Hg, normal end-diastolic, 0–5 mm Hg), the mean right atrial

pressure was 8 mm Hg (normal, 0–5 mm Hg), and the pulmonary arterial wedge pressure (see "Pulmonary Arterial Wedge Pressure" in this chapter) was 7 mm Hg (normal, 3–11 mm Hg). The second heart sound was widely split (see "Valve Motions and Heart Sounds" in Chapter 13) and fixed (i.e., did not change with respiration). This finding is consistent with prolonged right ventricular ejection time caused by increased resistance. The ECG showed sinus rhythm and a heart rate of 92 beats/min (normal, 60–100 beats/min). Signs of right ventricular "strain" (Chapter 19) were seen in the ECG: tall, peaked P waves, increased R waves and depressed S-T segments in the right precordial leads, and right axis deviation (+120°) in the frontal plane (normal, –30° to +110°). Chest radiographs showed that the heart was within the range of normal size.

Treatment: The combination of normal pulmonary artery wedge pressure, which reflects left atrial pressure, and high pulmonary ar-

vascular capacity increases the volume of blood in the systemic circulation, and together with the decrease of pulmonary arterial compliance, aids the acceleration of the blood.

EFFECTS OF INTRATHORACIC PRESSURE ON BLOOD FLOW

Normal Respiration

In the normal subject, because of the elastic recoil of the lungs, the pressure within the thorax is about 4 mm Hg less than atmospheric pressure (see Figure 17-4). The subatmospheric pressure is applied to all of the structures that lie between the pleural linings; this includes all of the pulmonary blood vessels, except the capillaries. As the volume of the thorax expands during normal *inspiration,* the intrapleural

pressure decreases further to about 8 mm Hg subatmospheric (Figure 17-6; see also Figure 17-4). The aortic, pulmonary arterial, and vena caval pressures decrease immediately because the vessels dilate when the pressure outside decreases. The cardiac output and the systemic arterial pressure decrease because of the temporary increase of pulmonary vascular capacity. As the gradient of pressure between the systemic veins outside the thorax and those inside the thorax increases, the rate of flow of blood into the venae cavae increases, and the output of the right ventricle increases. In the latter part of inspiration, the pulmonary arterial and aortic pressures and the cardiac output begin to level off as the increased rate of flow of blood into the thorax begins to fill the expanded capacity of the pulmonary system. During *expiration,* the intrapleural pressure and

(CLINICAL CORRELATION continued)

tery pressure indicates high vascular resistance within the pulmonary circulation, rather than any abnormality of the mitral valve or the left ventricle. Pulmonary vasodilator drugs were administered without providing substantial relief. Because of the right ventricular failure, digitalis (digoxin) and a diuretic (furosemide) were begun. Some improvement was seen initially, but her condition worsened during the next 6 weeks. She was found to be hypoxemic and in respiratory alkalosis, with an arterial P_{O_2} of 51 mm Hg (normal, 75–100 mm Hg), P_{CO_2} of 26 mm Hg (normal, 35–45 mm Hg), and pH of 7.55 (normal, 7.35–7.45), while breathing room air. At this time, she was hospitalized and given supplemental oxygen to breathe. A lung scan using [99]technetium revealed numerous defects consistent with the presence of emboli throughout the lungs. Heparin (an anticoagulant) was injected (15,000 u, intravenously) followed by intravenous infusion at the rate of 1,500 u/hr. The thrombin time (a measure of the rate of clotting) was kept to no more than one to two times the control value (12 seconds) for 48 hours, during which the patient improved steadily. Heparin therapy was withdrawn gradually and the patient was sta-

bilized on warfarin (an anticoagulant that can be taken orally).

Comment: An important function of the lungs is to trap occasional emboli, which might lodge in the heart, brain, or kidney if permitted to reach the systemic circulation. Thromboemboli (trapped blood clots) usually dissolve in a few days, through the action of the normal mechanisms of the body. In this patient, however, emboli were formed so frequently that another function of the pulmonary circulation, to transfer blood from the systemic veins to the left ventricle, was being compromised. As more small vessels were occluded, the pulmonary vascular resistance increased, and the work of the heart increased. If the process had continued, the right ventricle eventually would have been unable to pump enough blood through the lungs to supply the needs of the body, and the patient would have died.

Outcome: Although the cause of the abnormal clotting has not been determined, the patient has continued on anticoagulant therapy, her pulmonary vasculature has virtually cleared, and she has been able to resume her active lifestyle.

---

the rate of flow of blood into the pulmonary circulation return to the previous level, and the cardiac output and the systemic arterial pressure increase as the pulmonary vascular capac-

ity decreases again. Thus, the cardiac output and the systemic arterial pressure fluctuate with *respiration,* reflecting the cyclic changes of the rate of flow of blood into and out of the thorax. This effect of respiration on the flow of blood has been termed "the respiratory pump," and it may contribute significantly to the circulation of the blood during periods of physical exertion (Figure 17-7).

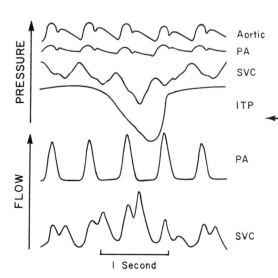

Figure 17-6.   Effects of changes of intrathoracic pressure during the normal respiratory cycle on vascular pressures and blood flow in the thorax. From the top downward: aortic pressure; PA = pulmonary arterial pressure; SVC = superior vena caval pressure; ITP = intrathoracic pressure; PA = pulmonary arterial blood flow; SVC = superior vena caval blood flow. The intrathoracic pressure decreases during inspiration and increases during expiration. (Redrawn, with permission, from G.A. Brecher. 1956. *Venous Return.* New York: Grune & Stratton.)

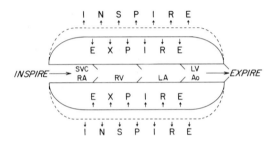

Figure 17-7. The respiratory pump. During inspiration, the volume of the thorax increases and filling of the blood vessels of the thorax is aided; during expiration, the volume of the thorax decreases again and emptying of the vessels is favored. Because of the cardiac valves and the momentum of the flowing blood, the action of the pump is directed forward. This mechanism makes an even larger contribution during strenuous exercise, when the rate and the depth of breathing are increased. SVC = superior vena cava; RA = right atrium; RV = right ventricle; LA = left atrium; LV = left ventricle; Ao = aorta.

Valsalva Maneuver

In the *Valsalva maneuver,* one attempts forcibly to exhale while the glottis is closed and the diaphragm is fixed; thus, intrathoracic pressure increases. The cardiac output and the systemic arterial blood pressure increase temporarily, as blood is forced from the thorax. The heart rate slows reflexly. The high intrathoracic pressure prevents the entry of blood into the thorax, and systemic venous pressure increases; if the condition is maintained, the cardiac output is curtailed and the systemic arterial pressure falls. The heart rate increases reflexly. When the intrathoracic pressure is released, the cardiac output and the systemic arterial pressure remain low and may continue to decrease until the pulmonary vascular capacity has been refilled. When the cardiac output resumes, the systemic arterial pressure increases and temporarily exceeds normal because of the reflex systemic vasoconstriction that developed during the period of hypotension.

The Valsalva maneuver, which is used physiologically during defecation and in the pre-

lude to a cough, is dangerous for subjects who have weakened or damaged veins (e.g., varicosities or venous obstruction and high venous pressure, such as in cirrhosis of the liver). It is used intentionally in several diagnostic procedures; for example, to alter the intensity of cardiac murmurs by altering the rate of flow of blood into and out of the heart.

EFFECTS OF HYPOXIA

When the oxygen content of the alveoli or the systemic blood is decreased, the small pulmonary arteries that lead to the capillaries constrict, the pulmonary vascular resistance increases, and the right ventricular and pulmonary arterial pressures increase. The mechanism of the response to *hypoxia* in the alveoli has not been determined. The effect of systemic hypoxemia is mediated, at least in part, through stimulation of chemoreceptors in the carotid and aortic bodies (see Figure 15-16).

Patients who have inadequate respiratory function and healthy people who live at high altitudes, where the concentration of oxygen in the air is relatively low, have abnormally high pulmonary vascular resistance. The severity of the condition is increased in patients who live at high altitudes, and sometimes these individuals must move to lower altitudes. Breathing air that has a high content of oxygen decreases the pulmonary vascular resistance in these patients; the administration of oxygen is used as a diagnostic test to determine whether high pulmonary resistance in a particular patient is caused by hypoxia or is due to primary pulmonary vascular disease.

Although an increase of pulmonary vascular resistance in response to inadequate concentrations of oxygen in the lungs or the blood appears to be paradoxical, it may reflect a protective response that improves the delivery of oxygen to the blood by increasing the pulmonary arterial pressure and increasing blood flow to the underperfused portions of the lungs.

STUDY OUTLINE

FUNCTIONAL ANATOMY

ARTERIES   Pulmonary artery is slightly larger and thinner-walled than aorta.

No muscular arterioles and precapillary sphincters as in systemic circulation.

Vascular control is exerted by small arteries and veins.

CAPILLARIES   Surround alveoli (air sacs).

Rate of fluid exchange is less than in systemic circulation.

Pulmonary capillary pressure is lower than systemic capillary pressure, and alveolar pressure is higher (atmospheric) than systemic interstitial fluid pressure.

PULMONARY ARTERIAL WEDGE PRESSURE   Estimate of left atrial pressure.

DIFFERENCES BETWEEN PULMONARY CIRCULATION AND SYSTEMIC CIRCULATION

VASCULAR RESISTANCES AND PRESSURES   Lower in pulmonary circulation.

BASIS OF LOW PULMONARY VASCULAR RESISTANCE   Low vascular tone; relatively large, short, distensible arteries.

EFFECTS OF GRAVITY   Aids blood flow below main pulmonary artery; opposes it above.

Lower vessels are distended, resistance decreased further; upper vessels are not filled completely, may be collapsed.

Normal pulmonary circulation has unused vascular capacity.

EFFECTS OF ALVEOLAR PRESSURE Equal to atmospheric pressure, may collapse pulmonary capillaries in apical area.

EFFECT OF INCREASED CARDIAC OUTPUT   Pulmonary vascular resistance decreases, due mostly to increased flow in underperfused area.

EFFECTS OF INTRATHORACIC PRESSURE ON BLOOD FLOW

NORMAL RESPIRATION   Intrathoracic pressure decreases during inspiration; thoracic vessels dilate, pressures decrease.

Blood flow into thorax increases along pressure gradient.

Intrathoracic pressure increases again during expiration; thoracic vascular pressures increase, cardiac output increases.

The respiratory aid to cardiac output constitutes the "respiratory pump."

VALSALVA MANEUVER   Attempted exhalation against closed glottis and fixed diaphragm; intrathoracic pressure increases.

Cardiac output and systemic arterial pressure increase temporarily; heart rate slows reflexly.

Venous inflow to thorax is prevented, cardiac output decreases, arterial pressure decreases; heart rate increases reflexly.

When intrathoracic pressure is released, pulmonary vascular capacity refills and cardiac output resumes; reflex vasoconstriction increases systemic arterial pressure temporarily.

Used physiologically during defecation, coughing, childbirth.

EFFECTS OF HYPOXIA   Small arteries constrict, pulmonary vascular resistance increases.

Caused partly by stimulation of peripheral chemoreceptors.

Occurs at high altitudes or with inadequate respiratory function.

Increases perfusion of underperfused apical portions of lungs.

BIBLIOGRAPHY

Brecher, G.A. 1956. *Venous Return.* New York: Grune & Stratton.

Bromberger-Barnea, B. 1981. Mechanical effects of inspiration on heart function: A review. *Fed. Proc.* 40:2172.

Buda, A.J.; Pinsky, M.R.; Ingels, N.B., et al. 1979. Effect of intrathoracic pressure on left ventricular performance. *N. Engl. J. Med.* 301:453.

Heistad, D.D., and Abboud, F.M. 1980. Circulatory adjustments to hypoxia. *Circulation* 61:463.

Hughes, J.M.B.; Glazier, J.B.; Maloney, J.E., et al. 1968. Effect of lung volume on the distribution of pulmonary blood flow in man. *Resp. Physiol.* 4:58.

Jardin, F.; Farcot, J.-C.; Boisante, L., et al. 1981. Influence of positive end-expiratory pressure on left ventricular performance. *N. Engl. J. Med.* 304:387.

Rushmer, R.F. 1976. *Cardiovascular Dynamics* (4th ed.). Philadelphia: Saunders.

18

Electrical Activity of the Heart

CHAPTER CONTENTS

The most distinguishing characteristic of the heart is its repetitive, rhythmic activity, which begins very early in the development of the embryo and continues throughout the life of the animal.

PACEMAKER

The electrical activity of the heart begins in the *sinoatrial* (SA) node, which is located at the junction of the superior vena cava and the right atrium. In humans, the SA node is a vestigial remnant of the *sinus venosus,* which persists in certain other animals. The hearts of amphibians and reptiles, for example, have all three chambers—the sinus venosus, the atrium, and the ventricles—and the principal pacemaker occurs in the sinus.

Electrophysiological Characteristics

The cells of the SA node depolarize spontaneously to form action potentials (Figure 18-1). The individual cell does not have a resting potential; as soon as it repolarizes to a maximum value, it begins to depolarize again. When the potential reaches the threshold level, the cell is excited, and its activity is propagated to adjacent cells. A number of cells in the same area depolarize almost at the same rate and are excited almost at the same time.

LATENT PACEMAKERS
Other cells, in certain other parts of the heart, also depolarize spontaneously but more slowly than the cells of the SA node do; hence, their potentials normally do not reach threshold

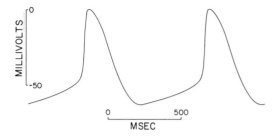

Figure 18-1. Pacemaker action potentials recorded from single cells of the *sinoatrial* (SA) node; the diastolic potential blends smoothly into the action potential. The slowly rising action potential and the absence of a reversal potential, or overshoot, is characteristic of the SA node. It is related partly to the slow depolarization during diastole, which permits inactivation of the "fast" Na⁺ channels, and partly to the predominance of "slow" channels, which carry mainly Ca⁺⁺, in the SA node.

spontaneously, and they are excited by propagated activity that originates in the SA node (Figure 18-2). Such cells, called *latent pacemakers,* occur in the internodal tracts of the atrium, in the AV junctional area, in the bundle of His, and in the Purkinje (specialized ventricular propagating) system. A gradient of *pacemaker potentiality* (rate of slow diastolic depolarization) occurs in the order: SA node > internodal tracts > AV junction > bundle of His > Purkinje system. The latent pacemakers can provide for continued rhythmic excitation of the heart if the dominant pacemaker should be stopped or slowed excessively.

PACEMAKER SUPPRESSION
The intrinsic rate of slow depolarization of a pacemaker cell is decreased when the cell is excited by activity propagated to it from a faster pacemaker. When the slower pacemaker is released from the dominance of the faster pacemaker, the intrinsic rate of slow depolarization increases progressively until its characteristic value is reached (Figure 18-3). If the dominant pacemaker is slowed sufficiently, the latent pacemaker cells will depolarize to threshold and initiate excitation (see Figure 18-6). Ectopic beats, which may be caused by latent pacemakers, occur in everyone, and they occur more frequently in people who have slow heart rates, for example, trained athletes.

The atrial and ventricular myocardial cells do not undergo spontaneous excitation; these cells have stable diastolic potentials, and they

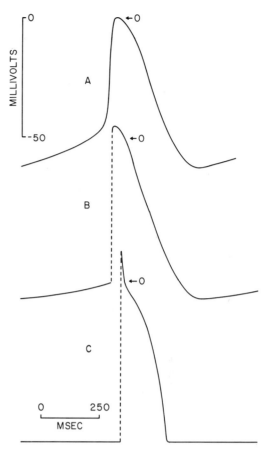

Figure 18-2. Diastolic and action potentials recorded from single cells of the SA node, *A* and *B,* and the atrial myocardium, *C.* **A.** The potential has the characteristics of the dominant pacemaker (see Figure 18-1). **B.** The potential has the characteristics of a latent pacemaker. Compared with the potential of the dominant pacemaker, the rate of slow depolarization during diastole is less, the onset of the action potential is abrupt, the rate of rise of the action potential is greater, and there is an overshoot. **C.** The potential is constant during diastole; compared with the record taken from the SA node, the diastolic potential, rate of onset and rise of the action potential, and the overshoot all are greater.

remain at rest until they are excited by activity propagated from a pacemaking area. Therefore, only a relatively few, specialized, cells of the heart normally exhibit spontaneous activity.

PACEMAKER CONTROL
The characteristics of the pacemaker potential that might be affected to permit control of the heart include (1) the rate of slow depolarization

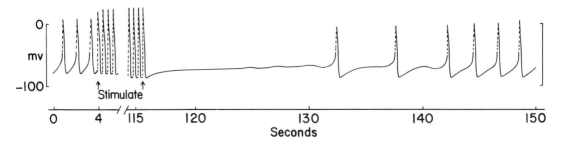

Figure 18-3. Suppression of spontaneous depolarization in a canine cardiac Purkinje cell by the action of a dominant pacemaker, and the gradual resumption of spontaneous activity after the faster pacemaker is stopped. The beginning of the trace shows the intrinsic frequency of the cell, which was 47 cycles/min. Beginning at the first arrow, the cell was driven at a frequency of 130 cycles/min by propagated excitation that originated at the site of an external pacemaker. The drive was stopped after about 112 seconds (*second arrow*), and the cell was allowed to resume its spontaneous depolarization. The first cycle after the period of suppression always is the longest, and the frequency increases progressively back to the original value. The degree of suppression depends on how much the intrinsic frequency of the dominant pacemaker exceeds that of the latent pacemaker and how long the faster pacemaker has controlled the slower one.

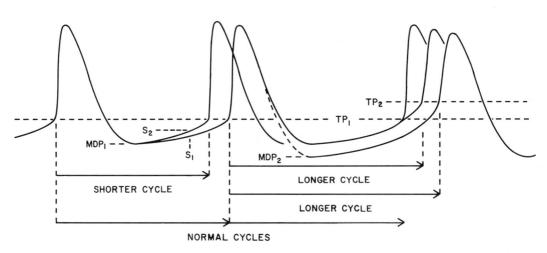

Figure 18-4. Characteristics of the pacemaker potential through which the frequency of excitation of the pacemaker cell might be controlled. *S:* the slope (*rate*) of slow depolarization during diastole; *TP:* the threshold potential; *MDP:* the maximum diastolic potential. S_1: the diastolic potential intersects the threshold at the end of a cycle of "normal" length. S_2: the rate of slow depolarization is greater; the diastolic potential intersects the threshold potential sooner, the cycle is shorter, and the frequency is greater. If the rate of depolarization were decreased to less than that of S_1, the frequency would be less. TP_1: the action potential begins and the "normal" cycle is terminated. TP_2: the potential at which the action potential begins is decreased; the cell must depolarize further, the cycle length is increased and the frequency is decreased. MDP_1: slow depolarization begins at this level, and a cycle of "normal" length is produced. MDP_2: the maximum diastolic potential is greater; if the rate of slow depolarization is not changed, the cycle will be longer and the frequency will be decreased.

during diastole, (2) the maximum diastolic potential, and (3) the threshold, or critical, potential (Figure 18-4). The heart rate is controlled through the actions of the autonomic nervous system on one or more of these factors.

AUTONOMIC EFFECTS

Parasympathetic activity decreases the frequency of excitation of the pacemaker by decreasing the rate of slow depolarization during diastole and by increasing the maximum

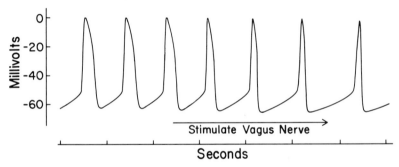

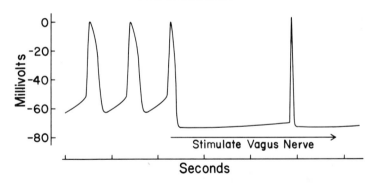

Figure 18-5. Effects of the parasympathetic nervous system on the pacemaker potential of a cell of the SA node. The maximum diastolic potential is increased, and the rate of slow diastolic depolarization is decreased; both of these effects increase the cycle length, and the frequency of excitation is decreased. The threshold potential is not affected. The effects are mediated by acetylcholine, which is released from the parasympathetic nerve endings at the effector sites. Acetylcholine increases the permeability of the cell specifically to K^+. The increased efflux of K^+ down an electrochemical gradient increases the electrical negativity of the cell; hence, the maximum diastolic potential is increased, and the rate of slow depolarization is decreased. The duration of the action potential is decreased because the increased efflux of K^+ hastens repolarization; however, the effect is not related to the slowing of the heart rate. The height of the action potential also is decreased slightly, but this effect is related to the decreased rate of slow depolarization during diastole, which permits inactivation of the relatively limited population of "fast" Na^+ channels.

Figure 18-6. Emergence of latent pacemaker activity when the dominant pacemaker of the SA node is arrested, in this instance, by strong parasympathetic nervous system activity. The cell is hyperpolarized, and the slow depolarization during diastole virtually is abolished. The action potential that occurs during the period of vagal stimulation was caused by propagated excitation that originated in a latent pacemaker in another part of the heart. The abrupt onset of the action potential is the principal indication that the cell was not excited spontaneously.

diastolic potential (Figures 18-5 and 18-6). The threshold potential is not affected. Sympathetic activity increases the frequency of excitation of the pacemaker by increasing the rate of slow depolarization during diastole (Figure 18-7). Neither the maximum diastolic potential nor the threshold potential is affected.

PROPAGATION

Action Potential

When the pacemaker cells depolarize to a certain critical, or threshold, value, they become highly permeable to Na^+ and Ca^{++}; these posi-

tive ions, which are present in the extracellular fluid, flow into the negatively charged interiors of the cell and depolarize the cells completely, and the rising phase of the *action potential* is formed. The potential difference causes current to flow into the adjacent cells, and action potentials are formed there, also. Excitation is propagated in the heart in this way, from cell to cell (Figure 18-8).

Margin of Safety

The action potential is the sign of excitation, and it also reflects the electromotive force that serves to stimulate adjacent cells. The velocity

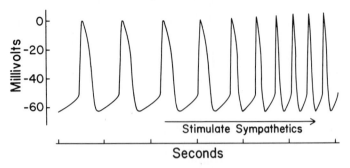

Figure 18-7. Effects of the sympathetic nervous system on the pacemaker potentials of a cell of the SA node. The rate of slow depolarization during diastole is increased; thus, the cycle length is decreased and the frequency of excitation is increased. The maximum diastolic potential and the threshold potential are not affected. The effect is mediated by norepinephrine, which is released from the nerve endings at the effector sites, and by epinephrine, which is released from the adrenal medulla and carried by the circulating blood; both substances act on adrenergic β_1-receptors of the heart. A specific component of K^+ permeability, which normally decreases slowly during diastole and brings about the slow depolarization, now decreases rapidly. Thus, the efflux of K^+ decreases, the rate of slow diastolic depolarization increases, and the frequency of excitation increases. The increase of the magnitude of the action potential and the decrease of the duration of the action potential are related directly to the decrease of cycle length, rather than to the stimulation of β_1-receptors.

of propagation varies directly with the magnitude of the electrical current that flows and the rate of depolarization (rise of the action potential). Small, slowly rising action potentials produce relatively slow propagation with a small margin of safety. (The *margin of safety* is expressed as the ratio of the electrical current that flows during the action potential to the minimum current that is required to excite the adjacent cells.) Propagation through the SA node, which produces small, slowly rising action potentials, is slow and can be blocked easily.

ATRIAL MYOCARDIUM

The cellular potential of the *atrial myocardium* is stable and constant during diastole. It is larger than that of the SA node; the action potential rises sharply (see Figure 18-2) and excitation is propagated with a greater margin of safety. The velocity of propagation in the atrium is about 1 m/sec.

Special Atrial Pathways

Excitation is propagated through the myocardial cells of the right atrium in radial fashion; however, excitation of the left atrium and the AV junction is aided by propagation through special atrial pathways (Figure 18-9). The cells of these pathways produce larger action potentials and propagate excitation faster than the cells of ordinary atrial myocardium do.

INTERATRIAL TRACT

The *interatrial tract* (Bachmann's bundle) extends from the SA node into the left atrium. Because most of the left atrium lies farther from the SA node than the right atrium does, this system helps to synchronize the contractions of the two atria. It is especially important in larger animals, such as cows and horses.

INTERNODAL TRACTS

Three different pathways connect the SA node and the AV junction. In addition to their special characteristics of propagation, many cells in these tracts also serve as latent pacemakers. Apparently, these tracts are not like insulated cables that propagate excitation from the SA node to the AV junction without functional contact with the right atrium. Rather, they have special properties that enable them to continue to function under adverse conditions that block propagation in ordinary atrial myocardium. For example, when the concentration of K^+ in the extracellular fluid is increased to about 8–10 mEq/liter, the atrial myocardium is inexcitable, yet the SA node, the AV junction, and the ventricles continue to function. Excitation is propagated from the SA node to the AV junction through the *internodal tracts,* and if these

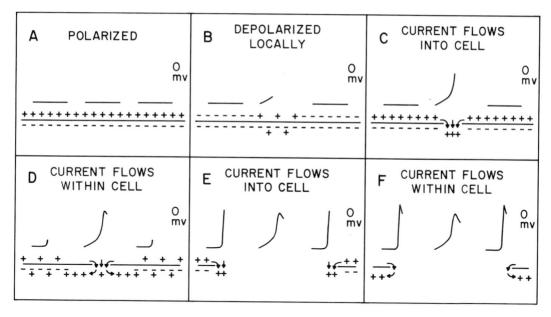

Figure 18-8. Initiation and propagation of excitation. **A.** A fully polarized, resting tissue. The horizontal lines represent the instantaneous cellular potential in three contiguous areas; the cell membrane is represented as a charged condenser. **B.** Spontaneous depolarization begins at one site; a small net influx of positive charges, which might be either Na^+ or Ca^{++}, decreases the cellular potential locally. **C.** The cellular potential in the localized area decreases to the threshold; the permeability of the membrane to Na^+ or Ca^{++} increases greatly (indicated by the absence of the line that represents the membrane). A current appears, carried by the cations down an electrochemical gradient, and the cellular potential decreases regeneratively. **D.** The current that flowed into the cell in C now flows through the cell, neutralizes the negative charges (cellular anions) stored at the inner surface of the membrane (as in a capacitor), and the adjacent areas are depolarized. The adjacent areas represent other cells, connected through low-resistance pathways so that current spreads from cell to cell. The rate of rapid depolarization in these cells is greater than in the pacemaker cell. **E.** The cellular potential of the adjacent cells decreases to the threshold; the permeability of the membrane to Na^+ or Ca^{++} increases greatly, as indicated by the absence of the lines that represent the membrane. The rapid influx of cations depolarizes the cell and produces the rising phase of the action potential. **F.** The electrical current that flows into and through the cell depolarizes additional adjacent cells, and the excitation spreads, as the process is repeated again and again, until all of the tissue has been excited. The process of repolarization, which involves the return of the normal low-permeability of the cell to Na^+ and Ca^{++} and an efflux of K^+ that carries enough positive charges to repolarize the membrane, is not shown.

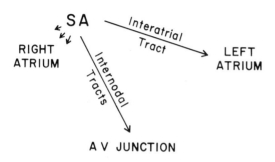

Figure 18-9. Functional arrangements of the special atrial pathways.

tracts did not exist, the normal cardiac pacemaker would be isolated from the remainder of the heart.

Autonomic Effects

Parasympathetic activity, which releases acetylcholine at the effector site, shortens the duration of the action potential of the atrial cell (Figure 18-10) and, hence, decreases the refractory period. This effect is important in the genesis of atrial arrhythmia, but its functional value is not apparent. Sympathetic activity does not affect the electrical properties of the atrial myocardium directly.

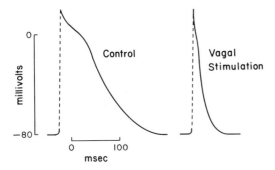

Figure 18-10. Effect of parasympathetic nervous system activity on the action potential of the atrial myocardial cell. Acetylcholine, which is released at the neuroeffector site, increases the permeability of the cell specifically to K$^+$, and the increased efflux of K$^+$ along an electrochemical gradient hastens repolarization.

ATRIOVENTRICULAR JUNCTION

Characteristics

The junction between the atria and the ventricles has been associated for a long time with the interval between the completion of atrial excitation and the beginning of ventricular excitation, but the mechanism of the AV delay was not determined until techniques for recording the electrical potentials of single cells were developed.

SITE OF DELAY

A narrow strip of very small junctional fibers is formed by extensive branching of the atrial fibers; the small fibers then coalesce to join the AV node (Figure 18-11). These junctional fibers propagate excitation at a velocity as low as 0.05 m/sec (Figure 18-12); physiologists had not known previously that propagation could proceed this slowly in the heart.

MARGIN OF SAFETY

The AV junction has a lower margin of safety and is blocked more easily than the atria and the ventricles are. The small atrionodal fibers have a low diastolic potential, and they produce small, slowly rising action potentials (Figure 18-13). Because of the relatively small amount of electrical current that flows during the excitation of one of the small fibers, the combined actions of several small fibers are required to excite one of the larger nodal fibers. Under certain

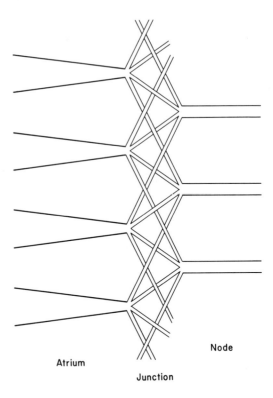

Figure 18-11. The band of very small fibers that branch extensively and connect the atrium and the AV node. (Redrawn, with permission, from B.F. Hoffman and P.F. Cranefield. 1960. *Electrophysiology of the Heart.* New York: McGraw-Hill.)

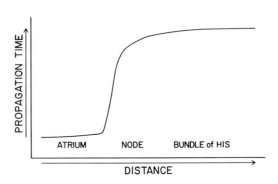

Figure 18-12. Relative time required for excitation to propagate from a site in the right atrium to successive points between the atrium and the ventricle in the region of the AV node and the bundle of His. The intervals between the arrival of excitation at one electrode that remained at a fixed site in the right atrium and another electrode that was moved sequentially from the atrium to the bundle of His were determined. (Adapted, with permission, from the data of B.F. Hoffman, A. Paes de Carvalho, W.C. de Mello, et al. 1959. Electrical activity of single fibers of the atrioventricular node. *Circ. Res.* 7:15.)

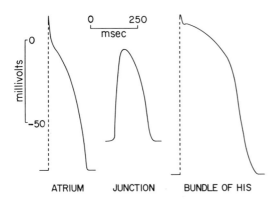

Figure 18-13. Comparison of the action potential of an atrionodal-junctional cell with that of an atrial cell and a cell of the bundle of His. The small, slowly developing action potential reflects the relatively small flow of current responsible for the slow rate of propagation and the small margin of safety in the junctional cells. Parasympathetic nervous system activity decreases the rate of rise and the magnitude of the action potential even further; hence, the flow of current necessary for propagation to continue is decreased further, and propagation is slower or may fail. Sympathetic nervous system activity increases the rate of development of the action potential and aids propagation in the junctional area.

---

conditions, such as an abnormally high frequency of excitation, reflexly mediated parasympathetic nervous system activity, or localized ischemia, some of the small fibers may not recover in time to be reexcited after the regular interval, and propagation may fail temporarily (AV block).

Autonomic Effects

Parasympathetic activity tends to stabilize the resting potential. The increased efflux of K^+ supports the negative cellular potential, and the cell is excited less readily. Propagation is slowed and blocked if the effect is great enough. Experimental studies have shown that the parasympathetic influence on electrical activity does not extend past the AV node and that the bundle of His is not affected directly.

Sympathetic activity facilitates AV propagation; the velocity of propagation is increased, and AV block may be reversed. Hence, the margin of safety is increased. The sympathetic effect is due largely to the increased influx of Ca^{++} through the slow channels. Thus, the influx of positive charges needed to depolarize the cell and form the action potential is enhanced.

PURKINJE SYSTEM

Distribution

The *Purkinje system* of the heart is a network of specialized cardiac tissue that continues from the bundle of His. It forms a right bundle branch, which goes to the right ventricle, and a left bundle branch, which goes to the left ventricle. In addition, the left bundle branch divides into anterior and posterior hemibranches. The Purkinje fibers are distributed along the endocardium, and finer branches penetrate the myocardium.

Velocity of Propagation

The Purkinje system propagates excitation at a velocity of 5 to 10 m/sec, which is about 5 to 10 times the velocity of propagation in the ventricular myocardium. Because of its high velocity of propagation, the Purkinje system causes all of the myocardium to be excited within a short enough period to make each ventricle contract synchronously and, hence, to function effectively as a pump. The function of the Purkinje system is essential to the function of the ventricles. If it is inactivated, excitation must be propagated through the ventricular myocardium; however, propagation proceeds so slowly in the myocardium that the first muscle to be excited contracts before all of the ventricular mass has been activated. Hence, instead of generating a uniform, high pressure that causes blood to be ejected, it merely transfers blood within the ventricle in a peristaltic fashion; the heart is ineffective as a pump, and the subject does not survive.

Spontaneous Excitation

The *Purkinje cells* have latent pacemaker activity; however, this property normally is not manifested unless the frequency of the dominant pacemaker is slowed, so that suppression of the latent pacemaker is relieved (Figure 18-3), or the latent pacemaker escapes the suppression because its intrinsic frequency is increased by sympathetic nervous system activity or by certain drugs, such as digitalis.

AUTONOMIC EFFECTS

Sympathetic nervous system activity increases the rate of slow depolarization of the Purkinje cells during diastole, and thereby increases the chance that premature ventricular contractions

CLINICAL CORRELATION
18.1   Complete AV Block

CASE REPORT

The Patient: A 41-year-old woman was admitted while undergoing cardiopulmonary resuscitation. She had been found unconscious on the floor of her office at her place of work. No pulse or respiration had been detected; cardiopulmonary resuscitation was begun and was continued en route to the hospital and in the emergency room. However, she could not be resuscitated and was pronounced dead.

History: At the age of 10 years, the patient was noted to have a heart murmur and "skipped beats." There was no history of rheumatic fever or diphtheria, which might have damaged the valves or the specialized propagating system of the heart. The pulse rate was 65 beats/min (normal, 60–100 beats/min), and the arterial pressure was 115/60 mm Hg (normal, 90–140/60–90 mm Hg). The ECG showed a normal atrial rhythm of 78 beats/min, with second-degree atrioventricular (AV) block (Wenckebach phenomenon, see Figure 19-35). The second heart sound was loud, and a systolic murmur was heard. The heart appeared normal on a chest radiograph. Periodic reexamination revealed persistence of the systolic murmur and a ratio of atrial beats to ventricular beats as high as 2:1. At the age of 16 years, her resting pulse rate was found to be 44 beats/min, increasing to 58 beats/min during exercise. The blood pressure was 110/85 mm Hg, and a systolic murmur, consistent with the large stroke volume made necessary by the slow ventricular rate, was heard. The ECG re-

vealed complete heart block (see Figure 19-37), with an atrial rate of 95 beats/min and a ventricular rate of 44 beats/min at rest. A similar pattern was seen at age 26. At age 30, the arterial pressure was 145/80 mm Hg, and the pulse rate was 42 beats/min. A systolic murmur was heard. At age 35, the arterial pressure was 185/70, and the pulse rate was 41 beats/min. The development of systolic arterial hypertension was not related to her dysrhythmia, and no evidence of impending cardiac failure was seen. An echocardiogram showed that the cardiac valves were normal, and the left ventricular ejection fraction (ratio of stroke volume to end-diastolic volume) was greater than normal, because of the large stroke volume engendered by the slow ventricular rate. The ECG showed that complete heart block persisted. At age 41, the patient collapsed and died, as described above.

Diagnosis: At autopsy, a benign mesothelioma of the atrioventricular node was discovered.

Comment: Although this small, benign, cystic lesion does not grow and may produce no symptoms, it can replace the node entirely, which it did in this case. The condition occurs most frequently in females and usually is seen first during the first or second decade of life or during pregnancy. This suggests that estrogen may be involved in the growth of the tumor. Patients who have AV block caused by mesothelioma often die suddenly. Cases that have been monitored show ventricular tachycardia proceeding to ventricular fibrillation.

will occur. The results of many experimental studies have indicated that the ventricles, both myocardium and Purkinje system, are not influenced directly by the parasympathetic nervous system. Some studies of isolated cardiac tissues have shown that acetylcholine placed in the solution that bathes the tissues decreases the rate of slow depolarization of cardiac Purkinje cells, but there is no indication that the parasympathetic nervous system is a significant avenue of control of the electrical activity of the Purkinje system.

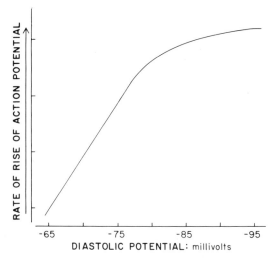

Figure 18-14. Relationship between the rate of rapid depolarization that forms the action potential of a canine cardiac Purkinje cell and the level of the cellular (diastolic) potential from which the action potential originates. The diastolic potential was set by a voltage-clamp technique; the rate of rise of the action potential usually is expressed in volts per second. In a particular tissue, the velocity of propagation is related directly to the rate of development of the action potential. (Redrawn, with permission, from S. Weidmann. 1955. The effect of cardiac membrane potential on the rapid availability of the sodium-carrying system. *J. Physiol.* (London) 127:217.)

The relative lack of inhibition of latent pacemaker activity of the ventricles by the autonomic nervous system can be demonstrated in the student laboratory. If an appropriate dose of epinephrine is injected into a dog intravenously, the mean arterial pressure increases, and the heart rate decreases because of baroreceptor function, and then increases again as ventricular ectopic beats appear. In this classical experiment, the latent pacemakers of the ventricles are relieved of suppression by the dominant pacemaker while being stimulated by the circulating epinephrine. The epinephrine also reaches the SA nodal pacemaker and the latent pacemaker cells of the atrionodal tracts and the AV junction; however, its effect at those sites is opposed by the strong inhibitory action of the parasympathetic nervous system. Because the ventricular pacemakers are stimulated by epinephrine but not subjected to any significant inhibition, ventricular ectopic beats appear.

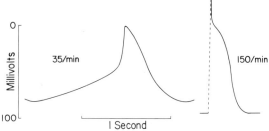

Figure 18-15. A pacemaker action potential recorded from a canine cardiac Purkinje cell at an intrinsic frequency of 35 cycles/min, and the action potential recorded from the same cell driven for 2 minutes at a frequency of 150 cycles/min by excitation propagated from an external pacemaker. The pacemaker action potential resembles that of the SA node; in addition, the velocity of propagation is slow and the margin of safety is small, as in the SA node. When the external pacemaker was begun, the spontaneous depolarization was suppressed, as shown in Figure 18-3; the diastolic potential increased, an overshoot developed, and, consistent with the large action potential, the velocity of propagation increased. The function of the Purkinje system to propagate excitation rapidly to the ventricular myocardium is impaired seriously when the cellular potential is decreased by spontaneous depolarization.

EFFECTS ON PROPAGATION

The high velocity of propagation of the cardiac Purkinje system depends on the maintenance of the relatively large diastolic potential. If, for any reason, spontaneous subthreshold depolarization of the Purkinje cells in some area of the heart is not suppressed or is enhanced, the action potential generated in that area is smaller and develops more slowly than normal (Figures 18-14 and 18-15). As a consequence, the velocity of propagation and the margin of safety are decreased. When these conditions occur, the effectiveness of the heart as a pump is impaired because of the decreased synchrony of the contraction, and, in addition, the probability of dysrhythmia is increased greatly. The latter situation will be considered more fully in the section on cardiac dysrhythmia.

Duration of Action Potential

When the heart rate increases, the duration of the cardiac action potential decreases. This fundamental property of all cardiac tissues is

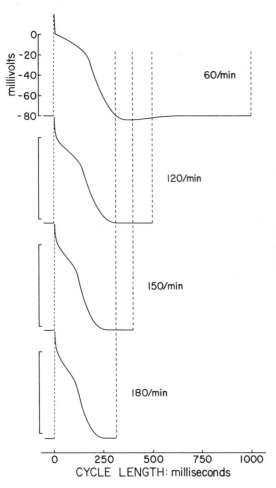

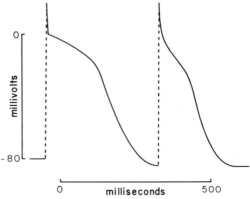

Figure 18-17.   Shortening of the action potential of a cardiac Purkinje cell after a single short cycle (simulating a premature ventricular contraction).

Figure 18-16.   Relationship between the length of the cardiac cycle and the duration of the cardiac action potential. The records presented here were taken from a canine Purkinje cell, but the property illustrated is shared by all cardiac tissues: as the heart rate increases, and the length of the cycle decreases, the duration of the action potential decreases. The *dashed lines,* which in each trace represent the beginning of the next action potential, are extended in the three lower traces to facilitate comparison among the records.

VENTRICULAR MYOCARDIUM

Propagation

The cellular potential of the ventricular myocardium remains constant during diastole. Excitation is brought to the myocardium through the fine branches of the Purkinje system and propagated locally throughout the myocardial cells at a velocity of about 1 m/sec. The action potential is slightly smaller than that of the Purkinje system, but it is propagated with a relatively high margin of safety.

Effect of Frequency of Excitation

The duration of the ventricular action potential is determined by the duration of the cardiac cycle (see Figures 18-16 and 18-17). By means of this important property, the duration of mechanical systole also is adjusted to match the duration of the cardiac cycle; hence, the diastolic interval, during which the ventricles must relax and fill again, is conserved when the heart rate increases.

illustrated with action potentials of the Purkinje system in Figures 18-16 and 18-17. The duration of a particular action potential is related closely to the interval by which it follows the completion of the preceding action potential. The interval may be determined by the heart rate (see Figure 18-16) or by the occurrence of premature ventricular excitation (see Figure 18-17).

STUDY OUTLINE

PACEMAKER Located in sinoatrial (SA) node.

ELECTROPHYSIOLOGICAL CHARACTERISTICS Spontaneous rhythmic depolarization.

LATENT PACEMAKERS Other cells depolarize spontaneously but more slowly.
Located in specialized tissues.

PACEMAKER SUPPRESSION Spontaneous depolarization is inhibited by imposed higher frequency.

PACEMAKER CONTROL Through rate of slow depolarization, maximum diastolic potential, or threshold potential.

AUTONOMIC EFFECTS Parasympathetic activity decreases frequency of excitation by decreasing maximum diastolic potential and rate of slow depolarization.
Sympathetic activity increases frequency of excitation by increasing rate of slow depolarization.

PROPAGATION

ACTION POTENTIAL At threshold potential, Na^+ and Ca^{++} flow into pacemaker cells and cause rapid depolarization.
Excitation propagated cell to cell by flow of current into negatively charged interiors.

MARGIN OF SAFETY Ratio of current that flows to minimum current that is needed for excitation.
Action potential reflects electromotive force that stimulates adjacent cells.
Rate of onset and magnitude of action potential varies with magnitude of current flow.
Velocity of propagation varies with rate of onset and size of action potential.
Propagation through SA node is slow and easily blocked.

ATRIAL MYOCARDIUM Action potential is larger than that of SA node; no diastolic depolarization.
Greater margin of safety; velocity of propagation is about 1 m/sec.

SPECIAL ATRIAL PATHWAYS Produce larger action potentials and propagate faster than ordinary atrial myocardium.

INTERATRIAL TRACT SA node to left atrium; faster propagation helps to synchronize contraction of atria.

INTERNODAL TRACTS SA node to AV junction; more resistant to block than ordinary myocardium.

AUTONOMIC EFFECTS Parasympathetic—shortens duration of atrial action potential.

Sympathetic—no significant direct effect.

ATRIOVENTRICULAR JUNCTION

CHARACTERISTICS Delays excitation of ventricles; vulnerable to block.

SITE OF DELAY Very slow propagation in strip of small atrionodal junctional fibers.

MARGIN OF SAFETY Smaller than that of atria or ventricles.
High frequency of excitation, parasympathetic input, or localized ischemia may cause block.
Sympathetic input increases margin of safety, opposes block.

AUTONOMIC EFFECTS Parasympathetic—slows propagation, can produce block; stabilizes diastolic potential, opposes depolarization; increased efflux of K^+.
Sympathetic—speeds propagation, may reverse block; increased influx of Ca^{++}.

PURKINJE SYSTEM

DISTRIBUTION Right and left bundle branches, continuation of bundle of His; finer branches penetrate myocardium.

VELOCITY OF PROPAGATION Much faster than in ventricular myocardium; synchronizes ventricular contraction.

SPONTANEOUS EXCITATION Occurs if frequency of dominant pacemaker decreases or intrinsic frequency of latent pacemaker increases.

AUTONOMIC EFFECTS Sympathetic activity increases slow diastolic depolarization; increases probability of premature ventricular contraction.
Direct parasympathetic effect is not significant.

EFFECTS ON PROPAGATION Partially depolarized cells produce small action potential, propagate slowly.
Increases probability of dysrhythmia.

DURATION OF ACTION POTENTIAL Related directly to preceding cycle length.

VENTRICULAR MYOCARDIUM

PROPAGATION About 1 m/sec, large margin of safety; no slow diastolic depolarization.

EFFECT OF FREQUENCY OF EXCITATION Duration of action potential is related to length of preceding cycle.
Intrinsic means of adjusting duration of mechanical systole to duration of cardiac cycle.

BIBLIOGRAPHY

Brown, H.F. 1982. Electrophysiology of the sinoatrial node. *Physiol. Rev.* 62:505.

Carpenter, D.O. 1982. *Cellular Pacemakers*. Volume 1. *Mechanisms of Pacemaker Generation*. New York: Wiley.

Coraboeuf, E. 1978. Ionic basis of electrical activity in cardiac tissues. *Am. J. Physiol.: Heart Circ. Physiol.* 3:H101.

Hoffman, B.F., and Cranefield, P.F. 1960. *Electrophysiology of the Heart*. New York: McGraw-Hill.

Hoffman, B.F.; Paes de Carvalho, A.; de Mello, W.C., et al. 1959. Electrical activity of single fibers of the atrioventricular node. *Circ. Res.* 7:11.

Hogan, P.M., and David, L.D. 1968. Evidence for specialized fibers in the canine right atrium. *Circ. Res.* 23:387.

Hutter, O.F., and Trautwein, W. 1956. Vagal and sympathetic effects on the pacemaker fibers in the sinus venosus of the heart. *J. Gen. Physiol.* 39:715.

James, T.N. 1963. The connecting pathways between the sinus node and the AV node and between the right and left atrium in the human heart. *Am. Heart J.* 66:498.

Kohlhardt, M.; Figulla, H.R.; and Tripathi, O. 1976. The slow membrane channel as the predominant mediator of the excitation process of the sinoatrial pacemaker cell. *Basic Res. Cardiol.* 71:17.

Little, R.C. (ed.). 1980. *Physiology of Atrial Pacemakers and Conductive Tissues*. Mount Kisco, New York: Futura.

Lu, H.S.; Lange, G.; and Brooks, C.M. 1965. Factors controlling pacemaker action in cells of the sinoatrial node. *Circ. Res.* 17:460.

McDonald, T.F. 1982. The slow inward current in the heart. *Annu. Rev. Physiol.* 62:505.

Noble, D. 1979. *The Initiation of the Heartbeat*. (2nd ed.). Oxford: Clarendon Press.

Reuter, H., and Scholz, H. 1977. The regulation of the calcium conductance of cardiac muscle by adrenaline. *J. Physiol.* (London) 264:49.

Ruzyllo, W., and Vick, R.L. 1974. Cellular resting and diastolic potentials in canine cardiac Purkinje cells: effects of external [K] and repetitive excitation. *J. Molec. Cell. Cardiol.* 6:27.

Tawara, S. 1906. *Das Reizleitungssystem der Saügetierherzens*. Jena, Germany: Gustav Fisher Verslagsbuchhandlung.

Trautwein, W.; Kuffler, S.W.; and Edwards, C. 1956. Changes in membrane characteristics of heart muscle during inhibition. *J. Gen. Physiol.* 40:135.

Vassalle, M., and Hoffman, B.F. 1965. The spread of sinus activation during potassium administration. *Circ. Res.* 17:285.

Vick, R.L. 1969. Suppression of latent cardiac pacemaker: Relation to slow diastolic depolarization. *Am. J. Physiol.* 217:451.

Vick, R.L. 1971. Action potential duration in canine Purkinje tissue: Effects of preceding excitation. *J. Electrocardiol.* 4:104.

Wagner, M.L.; Lazzara, R.; Weiss, R.M., et al. 1965. Specialized conduction fibers in the interatrial band. *Circ. Res.* 18:502.

Weidmann, S. 1955. The effect of the cardiac membrane potential on the rapid availability of the sodium-carrying system. *J. Physiol.* (London) 127:213.

The Electrocardiogram

CHAPTER CONTENTS

The electrocardiogram (ECG) is a record of the heart's electrical activity recorded from the surface of the body. There are other sources of electrical potential in the body, such as the skeletal muscles; however, the potential difference generated by the heart is one of the largest, and if the subject remains motionless, the electrocardiogram can be recorded with relatively little interference from other sources.

The modern electrocardiogram was originated by Einthoven, a Dutch physiologist. He developed the string galvanometer, an instru-

ment that responded quickly enough to record the rapid changes of potential generated by the heart. Electronic instruments now have replaced the string galvanometer.

LEAD SYSTEMS

Bipolar Limb Leads

The conventions of the electrocardiogram were designated by Einthoven, who used the bipolar limbs leads (Figure 19-1). The limb leads record

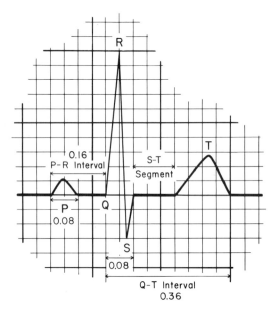

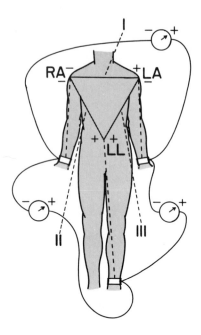

Figure 19-1. Conventions that govern the recording of the electrocardiogram and the designation of its principal components. The paper speed is 25 mm/s, the calibration of the scale of potential is 1 mv/cm, and the lines of the grid are 1 mm apart. Hence, each line represents 0.04 s (or 40 ms) horizontally, and 0.1 mv vertically. The P-R interval, which normally is isopotential, is taken as the reference, or baseline. Any trace above the baseline is positive, and any trace below the baseline is negative. P: Excitation of the atria; QRS: Excitation of the ventricles; T: Repolarization of the ventricles. (The repolarization wave of the atria is too small to be seen at conventional amplification. In addition, the atria repolarize while the ventricles are being excited; hence, no record of atrial repolarization could be obtained, as it would be masked by the QRS complex.) P-R Interval: the time that elapses between the beginning of the excitation of the atria and the beginning of the excitation of the ventricles. (Thus, it includes the time required for excitation to propagate through the atrioventricular junction.) Q-T Interval: The beginning of the excitation of the ventricles to the end of the repolarization of the ventricles; ST segment; The period between the completion of the excitation of the ventricles and the beginning of the repolarization of the ventricles; normally, no significant potential difference is recorded during this time. The numbers represent typical values that are easy to remember. Because of biological variation, there is a range of normal values for each wave or interval, rather than a single value. The range of normal also is affected by specific conditions such as the age and heart rate of the subject.

Figure 19-2. Placements of the electrodes to form the standard limb leads. Lead I is obtained by recording the potential difference between the right arm, RA, and the left arm, LA. Lead II is formed by the electrode on the RA and the electrode on the left leg, LL. Lead III is formed between LA and LL. The connections between the electrodes and the amplifier are arranged so that an upward (+) deflection is recorded from a given lead when the relative electrical potentials of the electrodes are as shown: Lead I, RA −, LA +; Lead II, RA−, LL +; Lead III, LA−, LL+. A downward (−) deflection is recorded when the relative electrical potentials in each lead are the opposite of that shown. The axes of the leads are drawn to form Einthoven's triangle.

---

the heart's electrical activity in the frontal plane of the body (Figure 19-2). Although the electrodes are placed on the wrists and on one ankle, the potential differences recorded at each of those sites are the same as those that could be recorded at the junction of the limb with the trunk; hence, the limb is acting merely as a conductor of electricity. This system of electrodes is treated as though it forms a triangle, called *Einthoven's triangle*, with the heart in the center.

Unipolar Leads

The unipolar leads are used to obtain more localized, more specific information about the

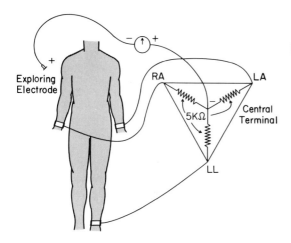

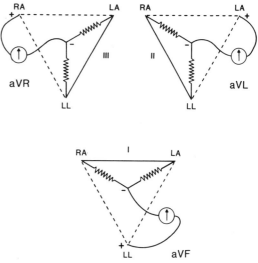

Figure 19-3.   Placements of the electrodes, and the resistances that are included to form the central terminal ("indifferent electrode") and the exploring electrode. The connections between the electrodes and the amplifier are arranged so that when the exploring electrode is electrically positive relative to the indifferent electrode, as shown in the figure, an upward (+) deflection is recorded.

Figure 19-4.   Placements of the electrodes to record from the augmented limb leads, aVR, aVL, and aVF. An upward (+) deflection is recorded when the exploring electrode is electrically positive relative to the "indifferent electrode," as shown in the figure. This system records special aspects of the ECG in the frontal plane.

heart's electrical activity in more than one plane. An arrangement that approaches an indifferent electrode is formed by connecting the three standard limb leads through 5000-ohm resistors to a center post, the *central terminal.* The resistors are used to cancel any small differences of electrical resistance that may exist among the electrodes on the wrists and the ankle. A unipolar "exploring" electrode completes the system (Figure 19-3). The designation of each standardized position in which the exploring electrode is placed is preceded by the capital letter "V."

UNIPOLAR LIMB LEADS
In the unipolar limb leads, the exploring electrode is placed on the right arm, VR, the left arm, VL, and the left leg, VF ("foot"). The results obtained from this configuration generally are not satisfactory: very small deflections are obtained, probably because the placement of both the exploring electrode and one branch of the central terminal at the same site removes any potential difference between those two electrodes. The unaugmented unipolar limb leads are primarily of historical interest, because they constitute a transitional phase in the

development of the augmented limb leads, which are used widely.

AUGMENTED LIMB LEADS
To increase the magnitude of the signal, the potential difference is taken between the exploring electrode, which is placed on one limb, and the other two limb electrodes, which are connected together (Figure 19-4). The leads are: aVR, in which the exploring electrode is connected to the right arm, and the left arm and left leg are connected together to form the "indifferent" electrode; aVL, in which the exploring electrode is placed on the left arm, and the RA and LA electrodes are connected appropriately; aVF, in which the exploring electrode is placed on the left leg ("foot"), and RA and LA are connected together.

PRECORDIAL LEADS
The precordial leads record the electrical activity of the heart in the horizontal plane. The exploring electrode is placed in various standardized positions across the chest wall (Figure 19-5), and the potential difference between it and the central terminal is recorded.

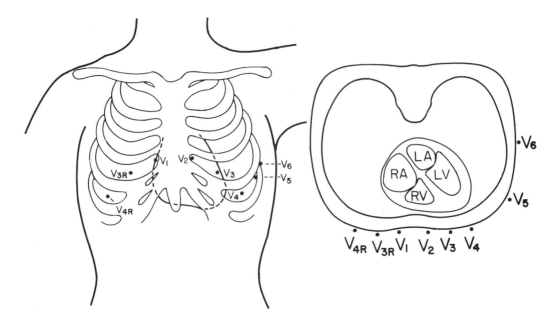

Figure 19-5. Placements of the precordial leads that are used most commonly, relative to the ribs (left) and the heart in the horizontal plane (right). The system of electrodes illustrated in Figure 19-3 is used. V_1: in the fourth interspace at the right border of the sternum; V_2: in the fourth interspace at the left border of the sternum; V_3: midway on a line between V_2 and V_4; V_4: in the fifth left interspace at the anterior clavicular line; V_5: in the fifth left interspace at the anterior axillary line; V_6: in the fifth left interspace at the mid-axillary line; V_3R: midway on a line between V_1 and V_4R; V_4R: in the fifth right interspace at the anterior axillary line.

BASIS OF
THE ELECTROCARDIOGRAM

Volume Conductor

The body is considered to be a volume conductor of electricity, like a tank of saline solution, which conducts electricity in all three dimensions. When a source of electrical potential difference (a battery) is connected by appropriate electrodes to such a solution of electrolyte, the positive ions flow toward the cathode, which is the electrically negative electrode, and the negative ions flow toward the anode, which is the electrically positive electrode (Figure 19-6). An electrical potential difference, which can be measured along each line of current, represents the driving force. More electrical charges flow in a straight line between the two electrodes than in any other pathway; however, some charges flow in each of the three dimensions. The amount of electrical current, and hence the magnitude of the potential difference, diminishes in proportion to the square of the distance from the source. The body is an irregular and inhomogenous volume conductor,

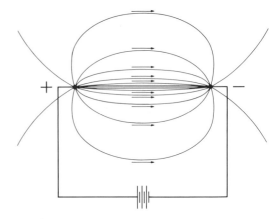

Figure 19-6. Leads from the poles of a battery immersed in a tank of saline solution; the lines represent the electrical current. Although the electricity flows in both directions—the negative ions to the anode and the positive ions to the cathode—it is conventional to follow the flow of the positive ions; the arrows indicate that direction of flow. The density of the current is greatest in the solution that lies directly between the electrodes; as the electricity flows in the more circular pathways, the distance between the lines increases exponentially, because the current must fill the solution in all three dimensions.

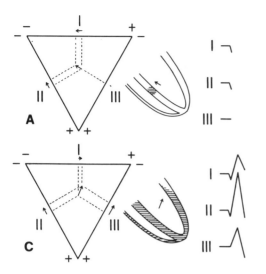

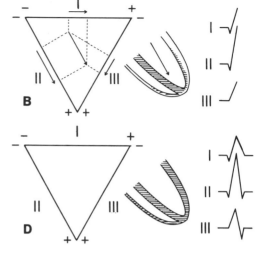

Figure 19-7. Reflection of the vector of the cardiac ventricles in the traces obtained from each standard limb lead. **A.** The first depolarization occurs in the interventricular septum; the potential difference associated with the electrical current at one instant is represented by a vector that points upward and to the left in the frontal plane. The vector is reproduced in the center of Einthoven's triangle, and perpendicular lines are drawn to the axis of each lead. The potential difference in each lead is determined by the length of the vector projected to each lead. When the vector is exactly parallel to the axis of a lead, its full magnitude is registered and the largest deflection occurs in that lead. When the vector is exactly perpendicular to the axis of a lead, no potential difference is recorded from that lead. The polarity of the electrodes (the sign of the potential difference between them) is determined by the direction of the vector. At the time represented in A, the vector points in the negative direction in both leads I and II; hence, the recording pen of each of these leads is deflected downward. The vector is perpendicular to the axis of lead III; hence, there is no potential difference between LA and LL, and the recording pen of lead III shows no deflection. **B.** Excitation has spread through the septum and along the endocardium of the apex of the heart. Although current flows in many directions simultaneously in the irregularly shaped ventricles, it can be represented by a single summated vector that is larger than it was in A and points downward and to the left in the frontal plane. The vector is reproduced within Einthoven's triangle, and its orientation with respect to each lead is determined by the dashed lines, which are perpendicular to each lead. The arrow along each axis shows the magnitude and direction of the vector relative to each lead. The vector is positive in all three leads; hence, the recording pen of each lead is deflected upward. The vector appears largest in lead II and about equal in leads I and III. **C.** All of the ventricular tissue is depolarized except the basal portion of the left ventricle, toward which the small summated vector points. The vector is negative in leads II and III and slightly positive in lead I. **D.** All of the ventricular myocardium is depolarized and no electricity is flowing; therefore, there is no vector, and all of the pens have returned to the (isopotential) baseline. In a similar fashion, vectors for the excitation of the atria and the repolarization of the ventricles are formed, grow, change direction, and recede, to produce the P wave and the T wave.

but the electrocardiogram can be interpreted in terms of a simple, uniform volume conductor.

Source of Current

As the heart depolarizes, a source of potential difference is formed, with the depolarized area negative to the polarized area. The boundary of the depolarized tissue and the polarized tissue may be thought of as lying between the poles of a battery; electrical charges flow through it, and measurable electrical potential differences exist along the lines of flow. As a wave of excitation travels through the heart, the magnitude and the direction of the current change, depending on the sequence of activation of the irregularly shaped structure. Because each line of current has both *magnitude* and *direction,* this line can be considered as a *vector.* The entire current can be treated as a mean, or summated vector. The magnitude of the potential difference recorded is greatest when the summated vector is exactly parallel to the axis of a bipolar lead, or exactly perpendicular to a unipolar lead. Figure 19-7 shows how each bipolar lead constructs the time course of the vector as "seen" from its own perspective.

INFORMATION CONTAINED IN THE ELECTROCARDIOGRAM

Mean Electrical Axis

Because the magnitude of the current is related to the mass of the tissue, the ECG contains information about the shape and position of the heart and the relative sizes of its component structures. The mean electrical axis in the frontal plane is obtained by plotting the net deflection in each of the standard limb leads, using the triaxial reference system (Figures 19-8 and 19-9). The normal axis of the ventricles is +60°, and the range of normal extends from −30° to +110°. An axis that lies between −30° and −90° constitutes *left axis deviation,* and an axis in the range of +110° to +180° constitutes *right axis deviation* (Figure 19-10).

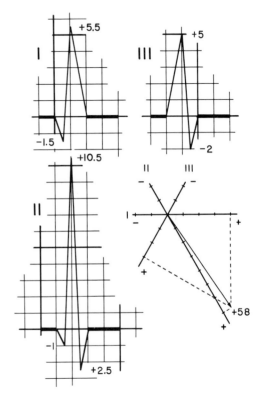

Figure 19-9. Use of the triaxial reference system to determine the mean electrical axis in the frontal plane. The QRS complexes illustrated were recorded simultaneously. In lead I, the Q wave is −1.5 mm, and the R wave is +5.5 mm; therefore, the net deflection is +4 mm. This value is plotted on the axis for lead I. In lead III, the R wave is +5 mm, and the S wave is −2 mm; the net deflection is +3 mm. This value is plotted on the axis for lead III. Perpendicular lines are drawn from each axis, and the mean electrical axis of the ventricles, which also is the principal instantaneous vector of the ventricles, is constructed. Only leads I and III are needed to construct the axis; lead II is the algebraic sum of leads I and III (Einthoven's rule). To test this, one can determine the net deflection in lead II: The Q wave is −1 mm, the R wave is +10.5 mm, and the S wave is −2.5 mm. The sum of these values is +7 mm, which is the same as the sum of leads I and III.

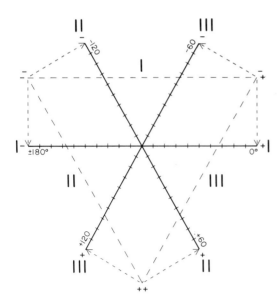

Figure 19-8. The triaxial reference system related to Einthoven's triangle represented in figure by dashed lines. To form the triaxial system, the axis of each lead is moved toward the center (dashed arrows), so that each remains parallel to its former position and all three intersect the center point of the triangle. The axes now form sextants. The axis of lead I runs from 0° to ± 180°; below it is 0° to +180° and above it is 0° to −180°. Each mark on the axes represents one mm on the ECG paper. To the right of the center point and downward is positive; to the left of the center point and upward is negative.

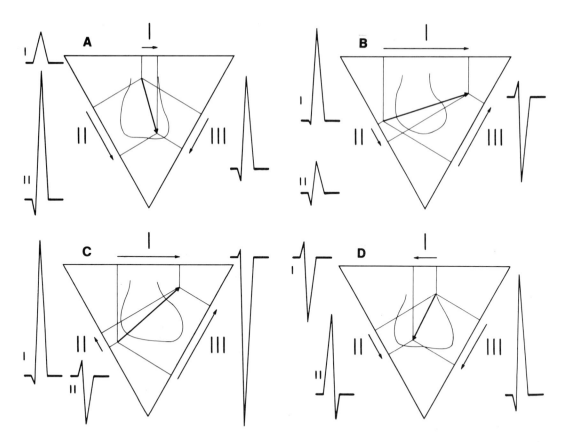

Figure 19-10. Four variations of the mean electrical axis in the frontal plane. The QRS complexes recorded from leads I, II, and III are represented; the principal vector is plotted within Einthoven's triangle and projected to the axes of the standard limb leads. **A** and **B** represent divergence of the axis within the range of normal due to the position of the heart. **C** and **D** represent deviation of the axis outside the range of normal due to increases of the mass of the ventricular myocardium. **A.** A slightly vertical heart; the axis is +75°. **B.** A horizontal heart; the axis is −18°. **C.** Left ventricular hypertrophy; the axis is −41°. **D.** Right ventricular hypertrophy; the axis is +118°.

VECTORCARDIOGRAM

Instead of recording the increase and subsequent decrease of the cardiac vector in time, to produce the waves of the standard ECG, one can record directly the changing magnitude and direction of the vector. A cathode-ray oscilloscope is used; one electrode is connected to the horizontal input, and the other is connected to the vertical input.

This system records a loop that depends on the sign and the magnitude of the potential difference between the electrodes (Figure 19-11). The vector loop can be recorded in each of the three planes (Figure 19-12) and viewed stereoscopically to obtain three-dimensional visualization of atrial and ventricular activation (P and QRS) and ventricular repolarization (T). The information obtained from the vectorcardiogram is limited, however, and the vectorcardiogram serves as a supplement to the standard electrocardiogram rather than as a primary tool.

Indications of Hypertrophy

CANCELLATION

If the mass of the cardiac muscle increases, more electrical current appears at the surface of the body, where the ECG leads are placed; however, larger potential differences may or may not be recorded. The heart is fairly symmetrical, so that during excitation some current flows simultaneously in opposite directions. These opposing currents produce differences of potential of opposite sign, and each cancels the effects of the other on the ECG. Thus, hypertrophy is indicated most clearly

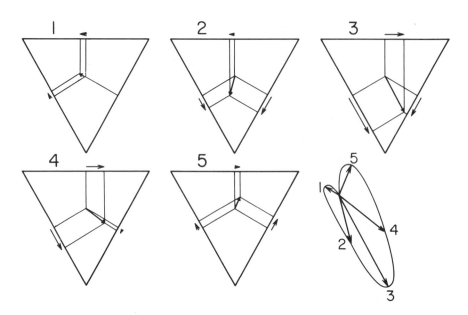

Figure 19-11. The directly recorded vector of the cardiac ventricles in the frontal plane. The vector is shown in five stages; first, projected within Einthoven's triangle, and then as points in a vector loop. Only the line formed by the tip of the vector actually is recorded. In a standard ECG, 1 would form the Q wave, 3 would form the R wave, and 5 would form the S wave.

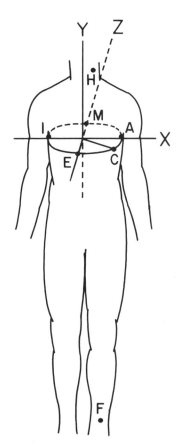

Figure 19-12. Placement of the electrodes to record the vector in each plane of the body, according to the method of Frank (1956). Five electrodes, A, C, E, I, and M, are placed at the level of the fifth interspace in the subject who is sitting, and at the level of the fourth interspace in the subject who is reclining. A is at the left mid-axillary line, and E is at the center of the sternum; these two electrodes form a 90° angle, one to the other. C is placed at a 45° angle to A and E. I is at the right mid-axillary line, and M is at the center of the spine. Two additional electrodes are used: H is on the back of the neck, and F is in the standard position on the left leg. To record in the frontal plane (X-Y), the potential difference between I and a combination of A and C is taken. To record in the horizontal plane (X-Z), the potential difference between a combination of C, E, and I and a combination of A and M is taken. To record in the saggital plane (Y-Z), the potential difference between H and a combination of M and E is taken.

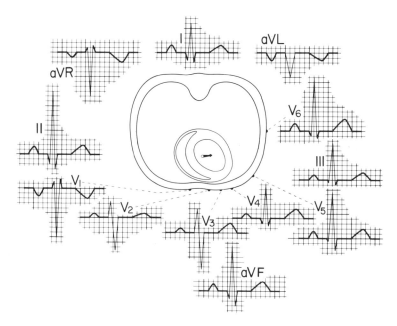

Figure 19-13. Diagrammatic illustration of the ventricles in the horizontal plane and the recording of the ECG from a 12-lead array. The principal vector of the ventricles during excitation, which points downward and to the left (in the subject), has been constructed; however, the entire loop of the vector, particularly in the horizontal plane, should be kept in mind as the records are interpreted.

In the normal heart, leads I, II, and III are positive; by using the triaxial reference system, one finds the principal axis in the frontal plane to be +65°. In the unipolar leads, the exploring electrode is positive; therefore, when the vector points toward a particular lead, the deflection is positive (upward), and when the vector points away from the lead, the deflection is negative (downward). All of the deflections normally are

negative in aVR (which nearly is a mirror-image of lead I), may be negative to nearly isoelectric in aVL, and are positive in aVF.

In the precordial leads, V_1, which is closest to the right ventricle, sees approximately opposite that which V_6, which is nearest to the left ventricle, sees. In V_1, P and T are negative, and S is the only wave or the dominant one. In V_6, P and T are positive, and R is the only wave or the dominant one. *These conditions hold because the vector of the ventricles is dominated by the electrical events of the left ventricle.*

The "transitional" leads, in which both R and S appear prominently because these leads see the vector both coming and going, usually are V_2 and V_3, but this can vary, depending on the exact location of the axis in the range of normal (−30° to +110°).

when only one chamber is involved, and significant deviation of the mean electrical axis can be detected.

TWELVE-LEAD ARRAY
The best results are obtained by using a 12-lead array, which consists of the three standard bipolar limb leads, the three augmented limb leads, and six unipolar precordial leads. This system detects the vector from a variety of positions in both the frontal plane and the horizontal plane, and therefore helps to define the vector more accurately. The recordings ob-

tained from a normal heart by using this system are illustrated in Figure 19-13.

LEFT VENTRICULAR HYPERTROPHY
Figure 19-14 illustrates left axis deviation due to left ventricular hypertrophy. Note that the normal dominance of the ECG by the left ventricle is enhanced. A pattern called "ventricular strain" also occurs. This pattern consists of discordant T waves (directed opposite to the QRS complex) and depressed ST segments; however, the S waves and R waves are not abnor-

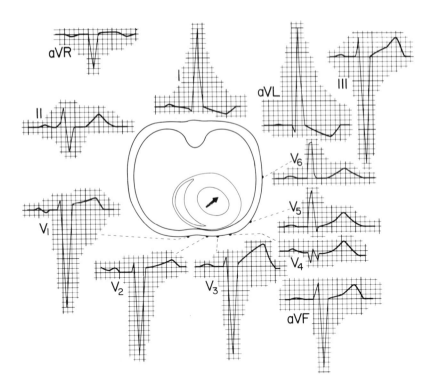

Figure 19-14. Left ventricular hypertrophy. The ventricles are illustrated in the horizontal plane; the ECG is recorded from a 12-lead array. The principal vector of the ventricles during excitation, which points upward, to the back, and to the left (in the subject), has been constructed; however, the entire loop of the vector should be kept in mind as the records are interpreted.

Lead II is nearly isoelectric, but slightly negative; lead I is strongly positive, and lead III is strongly negative. The mean axis in the frontal plane is about −45°. aVL is positive; aVR and aVF are negative.

Leads V_1 through V_3 are strongly negative (large S waves). The ventricular activation time, which is the time from the beginning of the principal deflection to the peak, is increased in V_5 and V_6. This increase represents the additional time required for excitation to propagate through the thicker mass of muscle. The T wave is inverted ("discordant"), and the ST segment is depressed in leads I and aVL, which are related closely to the left ventricle. The changes are correlated empirically; they do not rest on a sound theoretical base.

mally large. This pattern cannot be explained; it is associated with myocardial overload, such as that imposed by systemic arterial hypertension that has not yet caused hypertrophy. It should be emphasized that electrocardiographic data can only suggest mechanical or anatomical abnormalities; other factors also can affect the ECG, and all of the available evidence must be correlated before a conclusion can be justified.

RIGHT VENTRICULAR HYPERTROPHY

Figure 19-15 illustrates right axis deviation due to right ventricular hypertrophy. Note that the right ventricle contributes to the ECG more than it normally does. A pattern of right ventricular "strain" also occurs; this pattern con-

sists of discordant T waves and depressed ST segments; however, the R wave is not dominant in the right chest leads, and no significant S waves appear in the left chest leads. This pattern is associated with conditions, such as mitral stenosis, that impose abnormal work loads on the right ventricle, but have not yet caused hypertrophy.

Injury Potential

MYOCARDIAL INFARCTION

When an area of myocardium is infarcted, electricity flows between the injured tissue and the healthy tissue that surrounds it. This abnormal current is reflected as an injury potential in the ECG; the current appears only during diastole, although its effect, which is deviation

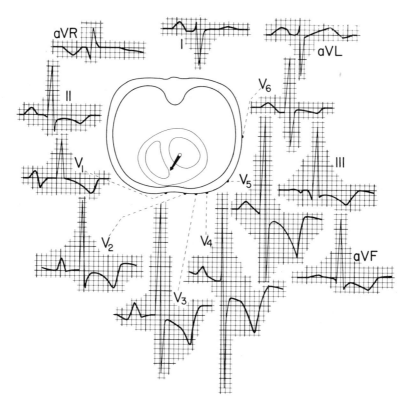

Figure 19-15. Right ventricular hypertrophy. The ventricles are illustrated in the horizontal plane; the ECG is recorded from a 12-lead array. The principal vector of the ventricles during excitation, which points downward, forward, and to the right (in the subject) has been constructed; however, the entire loop of the vector should be kept in mind as the records are interpreted.

Lead I is negative, and leads II and III are positive; the mean axis in the frontal plane is about +120°. aVL is negative, aVR is nearly isoelectric but slightly positive, and aVF is positive.

R is greater than S in V$_1$ through V$_3$, which are the leads associated most closely with the right ventricle, and significant S waves also appear in V$_5$ and V$_6$. The T waves are discordant in all of the leads. The ST segments are depressed in all of the leads except aVR, aVL, I and V$_6$; this abnormality is variable in right ventricular hypertrophy, but it almost always occurs in the right chest leads.

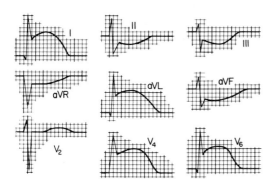

Figure 19-16. Deviation of the ST segment caused by a recent myocardial infarct. The magnitude and direction of the shift depend on the spatial relationship of each lead to the area that is infarcted.

of the ST segment, is seen during systole (Figure 19-16). This apparent contradiction is explained in the following way. The reference line of the ECG is the trace made during diastole, between the end of the T wave and the beginning of the P wave. Normally, this line is isoelectric; no electricity flows while it is being recorded. When the injury current appears, however, this baseline is not isoelectric, but is displaced in a direction that depends on the location of the injury and the lead being recorded. Under this condition the current of injury occurs during diastole, when the injured tissue is depolarized and the normal tissue is polarized, and it disappears during systole, when the normal tissue also is depolarized. The operator of the electrocardiograph adjusts the position of the pen to the "isoelectric" segment, and in doing so, enters a

CLINICAL CORRELATION

19.1   Electrocardiographic Manifestations of Myocardial Infarction

CASE REPORT

The Patient: A 53-year-old man.

Reason for Admission: Chest pain and syncope (fainting).

History: The patient had a history of diabetes mellitus and stable angina pectoris.

Clinical Examination: At admission, the patient was in acute distress, pale, perspiring, and short of breath. He complained of "crushing" chest pain that radiated into his left shoulder and arm. His arterial pressure was 90/50 mm Hg (normal, 90–140/60–90 mm Hg), his heart rate was 34/minute (normal 60–100/minute), and his respiratory rate was 22/minute (normal, 13–17/minute). An ECG confirmed the bradycardia and revealed atrioventricular (A-V) block with occasional A-V dissociation. The ST segment was elevated in leads II, III, and aVF, and reciprocally depressed in leads I, aVL, and V_1–V_3 (Figure 1). Unfortunately, no previous record was available for comparison. Morphine sulfate was given (4 mg, intravenously) to miti-

gate pain and relieve anxiety, followed by atropine sulfate (1 mg, intravenously), to offset the vagomimetic effects of morphine on heart rate and A-V propagation. Another ECG, taken 3 hours later, indicated more advanced A-V block and occasional A-V junctional escape beats. At this time, a transvenous demand pacemaker was implanted. The elevation of the ST segment in certain leads and depression in others, described above, persisted. Twelve hours after admission, an accelerated junctional rhythm appeared, at a rate of 105/minute, and Q waves were seen in leads III and aVF (Figure 2). The changes of ST segment seen earlier were more marked; in addition, elevated ST segments and inverted T waves appeared in leads V_5 and V_6. Lidocaine HCl was administered, 1 mg/kg, i.v., followed by 0.5 mg/kg 30 minutes later, to control dysrhythmia.

Comment: The changing pattern of the ECG in this case suggests an acute myocardial infarct with growth of the ischemic area. The altered ST segments and T waves appear first, reflecting the current of injury. As the

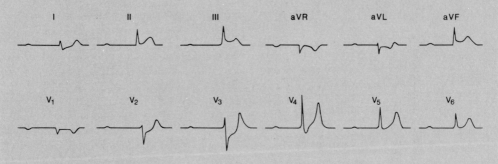

Figure 1.   ECG at time of admission.

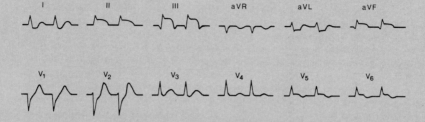

Figure 2. ECG 12 hours after admission.

dominance of the ECG by the left ventricle diminishes, Q waves appear and R waves diminish in the left chest leads, and R waves appear in the right chest leads.

More than half of the individuals who suffer acute myocardial infarction die within one hour of the event, usually because of ventricular fibrillation. Bradydysrhythmia (dysrhythmic and slow heart rate) and profound hypotension, related to cardiogenic shock, contribute to the fatal result.

The development of myocardial ischemia and infarction in this patient undoubtedly was affected by his pre-existing diabetes mellitus, which predisposes to atherosclerosis.

Outcome: The patient was discharged from the coronary care unit two weeks after admission. His recovery was uneventful, and he was referred to the cardiac rehabilitation center for exercise evaluation and the development of an exercise program. Six months later, the electrocardiogram showed first-degree block (prolonged PR interval) but no second-degree block and no dysrhythmia. The Q waves in leads III, aVF, V_5, and V_6, the diminished R waves in leads I, III, aVF, and V_4-V_6, and the R waves in V_1 and V_2 persisted, but the changes of ST segment and T wave were gone (Figure 3).

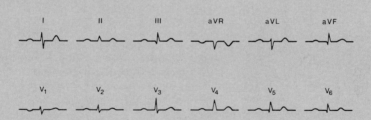

Figure 3. ECG 6 months after discharge.

potential difference equal in magnitude and opposite of sign to the injury potential (Figure 19-17). When the injury potential disappears during the ST segment, the balancing potential that was added during diastole is unopposed and appears as a displacement of the ST segment. In fact, the TP segment has shifted, but that cannot be detected, because the TP segment is used as the reference.

According to ECG convention, the vector points from depolarized tissue to polarized tissue. Therefore, the vector that represents the injury potential points from the injury toward healthy tissue; however, the shift of the ST segment represents the vector of the balancing potential and is opposite in direction to that of the injury potential. Thus, the "apparent vector" of the injury potential points toward the injury.

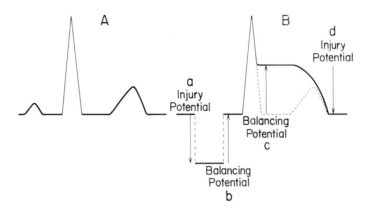

Figure 19-17. The apparent shift of the ST segment reflects the potential added through the instrument to balance the injury potential. **A.** A normal sequence of P, QRS, and T. **B. a.** The injury potential appears and shifts the baseline during diastole. **b.** The balancing potential is added to re-position the baseline. **c.** The injury potential disappears during systole, leaving the balancing potential unopposed. **d.** The injury potential returns as the myocardium repolarizes. The remainder of the normal QRS complex and the T wave (dashed lines) are provided for comparison.

MYOCARDITIS AND PERICARDITIS

Inflammation of the pericardium or of the subepicardial layer of muscle also produces an injury potential that appears in the ECG.

Other Alterations of ST Segment or T Wave

MYOCARDIAL ISCHEMIA

In a person who has atherosclerotic heart disease, the coronary arteries are partially occluded, and the capacity of the coronary flow to satisfy the heart's metabolic demands is abnormally limited. If the limitation of the coronary flow is not too great, the metabolic needs of the heart can be met satisfactorily when the person is resting, but the perfusion of the heart may be inadequate when the person exercises. In such a person, an ECG taken immediately after an exercise test shows the characteristic signs of left ventricular ischemia; these signs are depression of the ST segment in leads V_3 through V_6, and alterations of the T wave (Figure 19-18). The causes of these changes are not known for certain, but some abnormal electrical current must be involved.

DIGITALIS

Digitalis is used widely in the treatment of cardiac failure and certain arrhythmias. It produces a characteristic pattern in the ECG, as illustrated in Figure 19-19.

Myocardial Infarction

When the infarct is fresh, ischemic tissues cause an injury current (see Figure 19-16). After the infarct is healed and nonexcitable scar tissue has replaced excitable myocardium, the injury current disappears and the effects on the ECG can be related to the absence of active tissue (Figure 19-20). Normally, the left ventricle dominates the ECG, and its potential cancels much of that which might be recorded from the right ventricle. Myocardial infarcts, which usually involve the left ventricle and the septum, decrease the contribution of the left ventricle and thereby increase the contribution of the right ventricle. A thorough knowledge of the locations of the coronary arteries helps one to assess the damage that may have been done to the heart.

A small infarct may produce only minor symptoms, and the ECG may be helpful to establish that an infarct has occurred. A "control" ECG, taken when the subject is healthy, aids in the assessment of subtle changes that may occur later.

Atrioventricular Block

Partial or complete atrioventricular (A-V) block may occur if myocardial ischemia due to arteriosclerotic heart disease or myocardial infarction involves the A-V junctional area. This topic will be developed more fully in the section on cardiac dysrhythmia.

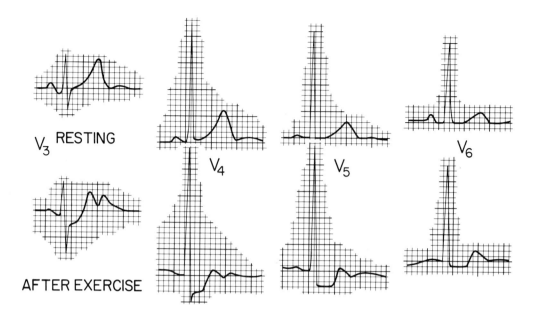

Figure 19-18.   The effects of myocardial ischemia on the ECG recorded from the left precordial leads. **Upper panel:** The control ECG taken when the subject was resting. **Lower panel:** The ECG taken after an exercise test. Note the depression of the ST segment and the alteration of the T wave in all four leads.

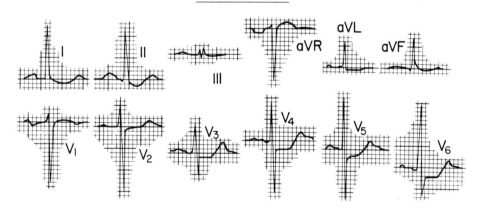

Figure 19-19.   The effects of digitalis that are seen in the electrocardiogram. The characteristic changes are a rounded depression of the ST segment in most leads and shortening of the Q-T interval. Because the ECG reflects mainly the electrical activity of the left ventricle, the ST segment is elevated in V_1 and aVR. The T wave may be altered by the shift of ST. This pattern is not a sign of toxicity; it accompanies the therapeutic effect of digitalis and may be used to confirm that digitalis is reaching the heart. In this figure, the changes of the P waves reflect mitral stenosis; they are not a part of the usual effect of digitalis.

Bundle-Branch Block

IDENTIFICATION

The QRS complex is altered if the specialized propagating tissues have been damaged. Interruption of the cardiac Purkinje system by myocardial infarction or other causes forces the spread of excitation in the ventricles to detour through slowly propagating myocardial pathways; this detour causes abnormal sequences of excitation and abnormal configurations of the QRS, which may be prolonged, slurred, and notched. Thus, the principal axis in the frontal plane cannot be determined by the usual relatively simple method, and the precordial leads provide the most precise basis for diagnosis.

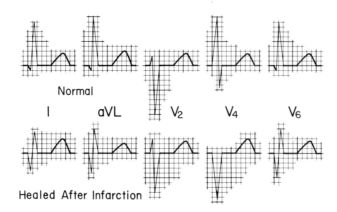

Figure 19-20. The effects of a myocardial infarct in the left ventricle after the damaged tissue has been replaced by scar tissue. Only selected leads that are affected the most are shown. The deep Q waves in leads I, aVL, and V_6, the increased R wave in V_2, and the S wave in V_4 all represent potentials from the right ventricle that normally are cancelled by larger potentials from the left ventricle.

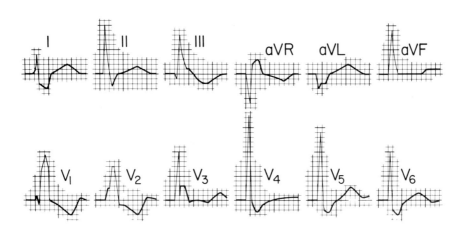

Figure 19-21. Right bundle-branch block. The underlying event is the delayed activation of the right ventricle, which permits the emergence of potentials from the right ventricle that normally would be cancelled by the larger potentials from the left ventricle. The delayed activation is reflected in the RSR′ pattern in V_1 and the depressed ST segments in the left chest leads. The prolonged ventricular activation times in V_1, V_2, and V_3 reflect the abnormal pathway that was followed.

RIGHT BUNDLE-BRANCH BLOCK AND LEFT BUNDLE-BRANCH BLOCK

When propagation is blocked in the right bundle-branch, R waves appear in the right chest leads because of the delayed activation. These usually are preceded by Q waves that reflect excitation of the left ventricle; S waves or depressed ST segments follow the usual R waves in the left chest leads (Figure 19-21).

When the left bundle-branch is blocked, the delayed activation of the left ventricle enhances the dominance of the ECG by the left ventricle; this enhancement produces prominent S waves in the right chest leads and wide, slurred R waves, which are not followed by S waves, in the left chest leads (Figure 19-22).

Bundle-branch block can be produced by conditions other than atherosclerotic heart disease and myocardial infarction: cardiac surgery that involves ventriculotomy, for example.

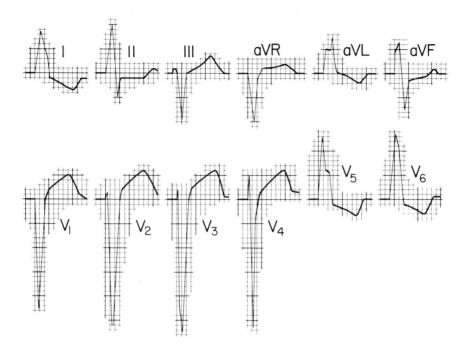

Figure 19-22. Left bundle-branch block. The underlying event is the delayed activation of the left ventricle, which makes more pronounced the usual dominance of the ECG by the left ventricle.

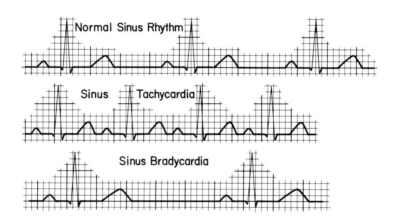

Figure 19-23. Normal sinus rhythm, at a frequency of 71 beats/min; sinus tachycardia, at a frequency of 125 beats/min; and sinus bradycardia, at a frequency of 50 beats/min.

DYSRHYTHMIA

Normal Sinus Rhythm

The normal heart beat originates in the sino-atrial node; hence, the normal activity of the heart is called "normal sinus rhythm." In the normal ECG, each beat produces a P wave that is followed, after an interval, by QRS and T waves. The normal heart rate for adults falls within a range between 60 to 100 beats/min (Figure 19-23). The normal rate for children is greater.

Sinus Tachycardia

In sinus tachycardia, the ECG is normal, but the resting heart rate exceeds 100 beats/min in adults (Figure 19-23).

Sinus Bradycardia

The ECG is normal in sinus bradycardia, but the resting heart rate is less than 60 beats/min in adults (Figure 19-23).

Sinus Arrhythmia

Sinus arrhythmia is a pattern in which normal sinus rhythm alternates with periods of faster or slower rates that are correlated to respiration (Figure 19-24). The changing rate reflects the degree of inhibition mediated through the parasympathetic nervous system This effect is strong in infants and children, is present in young adults, but decreases with age. It is enhanced by athletic conditioning.

Sinus Arrest

The sinoatrial node may fail to initiate impulses temporarily, because of external pressure on the carotid sinuses, excess parasympathetic tone ("vagotonia"), the effects of cardiac surgery, or drug toxicity (for example, digitalis). Any of several courses may follow (Figure 19-25): normal activity of the sinus node may resume, or latent pacemakers may initiate activity, temporarily or continuously, in the atrionodal junctional area (junctional rhythm) or in the specialized propagating system of the ventricle (idioventricular rhythm).

Sinoatrial Block

The SA node may initiate activity that is not propagated into the atrium. If the block is intermittent, whole cycles may drop out, and the prevailing cycle may be two or more times as long as normal. If the block is complete, the consequences are not distinguishable from those of sinus arrest.

Premature Excitation

PREMATURE ATRIAL BEATS

Excitation may be initiated prematurely in the SA node or from an ectopic site in the atrionodal pathways. If the beat is very much premature, A-V nodal block may occur and a ventricular cycle may be dropped, but this is not common. The SA node may or may not be reset. If activity is propagated through the SA node, the short (premature) cycle will be followed by a cycle of normal length as sinus rhythm resumes (Figure 19-26). If excitation is blocked at the atriosinus junction, the SA node maintains its rhythm and the short cycle is followed by a cycle of greater than normal length (Figure 19-27).

PREMATURE JUNCTIONAL CONTRACTIONS

As a rule, the QRS complexes that follow latent pacemaker activity in the A-V junction are normal, because excitation is propagated over the normal ventricular pathway. P waves may or may not be identifiable, as the atria may be excited before, during, or after the QRS complex, depending on the site of origin and the extent of retrograde propagation. If excitation is not propagated into the SA node, there will be a compensatory pause (a cycle longer than normal follows a cycle shorter than normal; the combined length of the two cycles is equal to that of two normal cycles) (Figure 19-28).

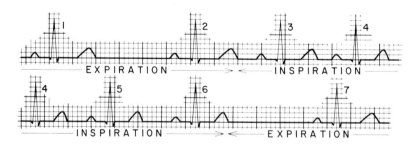

Figure 19-24. Sinus arrhythmia. The record is continuous; beat number 4 is repeated in the second panel to permit accurate evaluation of the length of the cycle that precedes it and of the cycle that follows it. The heart rate increases with inspiration and decreases with expiration. The lowest frequency in a single cycle, which occurs between numbers 1 and 2 and 6 and 7, is 50 beats/min, and the highest frequency, which occurs between numbers 3 and 4 and 4 and 5, is 94 beats/min. Because of sinus arrhythmia, the durations of the cardiac cycles in a normal series usually are not of identical length.

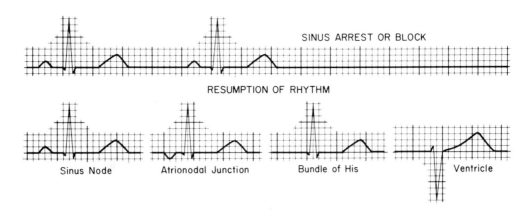

Figure 19-25.   Various rhythms that may follow sinus arrest or sinoatrial block. Note the inverted P wave and the shortened P-R interval that ac- company junctional rhythm, and the absence of the P wave when excitation originates distal to the atrioventricular junction.

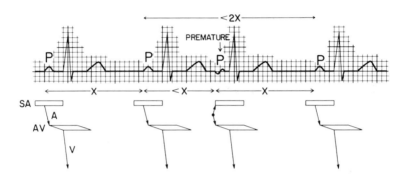

Figure 19-26.   Premature atrial excitation. The biphasic P wave and the shortened P-R interval indicate that the latent pacemaker was located in the atrionodal tracts, between the SA node and the A-V junction. In the diagram drawn below the ECG, the boxes that follow "SA" and "AV" indi- cate the duration of refractoriness of the SA node and the A-V junction, respectively; the lines and arrows connected to the boxes indicate propaga- tion through the atrium (A) and the ventricles (V); "X" is the duration of a normal cycle in the SA node. The premature beat causes the atrial and ventricular cycles to be less than normal ($<$X); the dot indicates the origin of the premature beat between the SA node and the A-V junction, and the arrows indicate the propagation of excitation in both directions. As the SA node is excited by the propagated activity, it is "reset" (its cells begin to depolarize again), and a cycle of normal length (X) follows. Thus, the combined length of the prema- ture cycle and the normal cycle that follows is less than that of two normal cycles ($<$ 2X).

PREMATURE VENTRICULAR CONTRACTIONS (PVC)

PVCs normally originate in some part of the specialized ventricular propagating system, or, in abnormal circumstances, in the damaged tissue around a myocardial infarct. The QRS complex is wide, slurred, or notched (Fig- ure 19-29); this configuration reflects the ab- normal pathway through which excitation is propagated in the ventricle. There is a com- pensatory pause, because activity propagated from the sinus node is blocked at the atrionodal junction or early in the ventricle, and the sinus node is not reset (Figure 19-29). Usually the T wave is opposite in direction to the main deflection of the QRS complex (discordant).

PULSE DEFICIT

Often the premature contraction is ineffective, or comes so soon after a normal beat that the ventricle has not filled enough to provide any blood for ejection, and no pulse is felt. Con- versely, after a compensatory pulse the ventri- cle fills more and the pulse usually is stronger than normal.

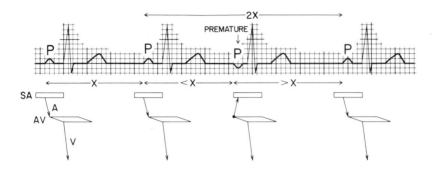

Figure 19-27.   Premature excitation of low atrial or high junctional origin. The conventions of the diagram below the ECG are explained in Figure 19-26. The premature beat terminates a cycle that is shorter than normal ($< X$); the atria are excited in a retrograde direction. By the time excitation is propagated back to the SA node, the pacemaker cells have depolarized spontaneously, the sinus pacemaker is not reset, and the next cycle follows after a normal interval (X); however, because the atria and the ventricles were excited prematurely, the length of the next cycle is greater than normal ($> X$). Thus, the combined length of the premature cycle and the cycle that follows is equal to that of two normal cycles ($2X$).

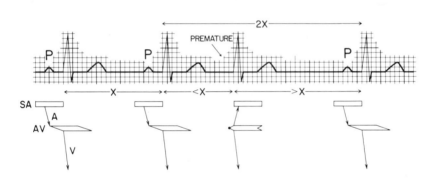

Figure 19-28.   Premature junctional excitation. The absence of a P wave indicates either that the atria were not excited, or that the atria were excited at about the time that the ventricles were excited and the P wave was masked by the QRS complex. The conventions of the diagram below the ECG are explained in Figure 19-26. The SA node depolarized spontaneously, rather than being excited by the premature activity; therefore, it retained its normal rhythm and initiated excitation after a normal interval. Because the atria and the ventricles were excited prematurely, the length of the next cycle is greater than normal, thus constituting a compensatory pause, and the combined length of the premature cycle and the cycle that follows is equal to that of two normal cycles.

VENTRICULAR EXTRASYSTOLES

Ventricular extrasystoles are uncommon; each is truly an *extra* beat; the basic rhythm is undisturbed (Figure 19-30). Sometimes the term extrasystole is applied incorrectly to include all premature ventricular contractions.

BIGEMINY

Beats may occur in pairs (Figure 19-31); the most frequent combination is a sinus beat followed by a premature nodal or ventricular beat. A pulse deficit is common, as the premature contraction usually is ineffective. The premature beat is followed by a compensatory pause.

MULTIFOCAL PREMATURE VENTRICULAR CONTRACTIONS

Multifocal PVCs are identified by at least two premature ventricular contractions of different origin (Figure 19-32).

PAROXYSMAL TACHYCARDIA

Paroxysmal tachycardia is characterized by the appearance of a rapid succession of impulses that begins abruptly and ends abruptly (Figure 19-33). The focus may reside in the atria (paroxysmal atrial tachycardia), the A-V junction (paroxysmal junctional tachycardia), or the ventricles (paroxysmal ventricular tachycardia).

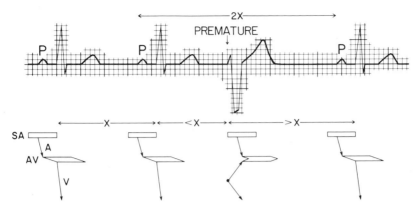

Figure 19-29.   Premature ventricular excitation. As the diagram indicates, the premature activity begins at some point in one of the ventricles and propagates by an abnormal pathway through both ventricles and back to the ventriculo-atrial junc- tion. Retrograde propagation may occur; how- ever, the atrium usually is excited in a normal way, and excitation is extinguished in the A-V junc- tional area.

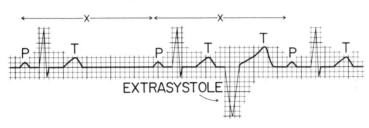

Figure 19-30.   A premature ventricular contrac- tion that also is an extrasystole because the basic rhythm is not altered significantly. This dysrhyth- mia can occur only at slow heart rates; a basic rate of 53 beats/min is shown here. Although the P to P interval is not changed, the first P-R interval after the extrasystole is increased slightly because of the effect of the previous excitation on the A-V junction.

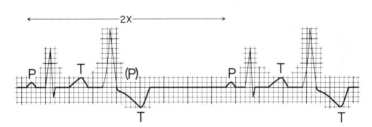

Figure 19-31.   Bigeminy. The sinus node usually discharges regularly, but propagation from the atrium to the ventricle is blocked at the atrionodal junction (the P wave is lost in the QRS complex or the T wave of the premature beat). Thus, a com- pensatory pause occurs invariably, and a pulse deficit occurs usually.

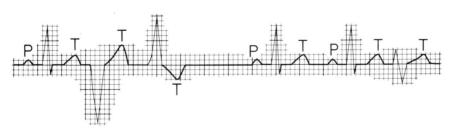

Figure 19-32.   Multifocal premature ventricular contractions from three different foci. The missing P waves are lost in the abnormal QRS and T complexes.

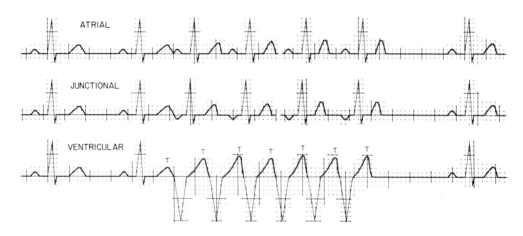

Figure 19-33. Paroxysmal tachycardia of three different origins. The duration of the paroxysm can vary greatly. The records of the atrial tachy-cardia and the junctional tachycardia are interrupted; the record of the ventricular tachycardia is continuous.

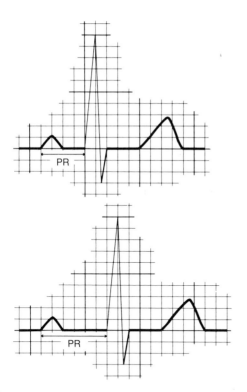

Figure 19-34. Upper record: normal ECG. Lower record: first-degree A-V block (prolonged P-R interval).

Atrioventricular Block

FIRST DEGREE
In first degree block, the P-R interval is prolonged; usually it is greater than 0.2 seconds (Figure 19-34).

SECOND DEGREE
Second degree block is incomplete block, and beats are dropped periodically. In one type, which is called the Wenckebach phenomenon, the P-R interval increases progressively until a ventricular beat is missed, then the cycle is repeated (Figure 19-35). In the other type, ventricular beats are dropped regularly; the ratio of P waves to QRS complexes is 2:1, 3:1, and so on (Figure 19-36).

THIRD DEGREE
Third degree block is complete A-V dissociation (Figure 19-37); the atria and the ventricles function separately, and ventricular activity depends on idioventricular pacemakers. The block may not be continuous; it may occur intermittently and abruptly (Stokes–Adams syndrome). If latent pacemakers do not take over when the block occurs, death is inevitable. In some cases, latent pacemakers take up the rhythmic excitation of the ventricles, but the intrinsic frequency is so slow that the cardiac output is not adequate to support normal function, and an artificial pacemaker must be attached to the ventricles.

HIS-BUNDLE ELECTROGRAM
The electrical activity of the bundle of His can be recorded discretely by placing the tip of an electrode catheter under the septal leaflet of the tricuspid valve (Figure 19-38). Comparison of the *a-H* and *H-V* intervals permits further analysis of A-V block. For example, increased

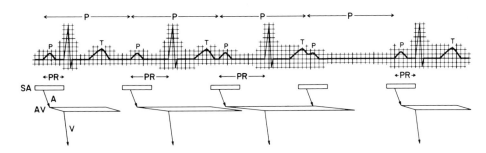

Figure 19-35. Second degree A-V block of the Wenckebach type. The conventions of the diagram below the ECG are explained in Figure 19-26. The P-R interval and the A-V refractory period increase until propagation through the A-V junction fails. After the complete block, which permits more time for the A-V junction to recover, the P-R interval again is shorter, and the progressive prolongation that leads to complete block and subsequent recovery begins again.

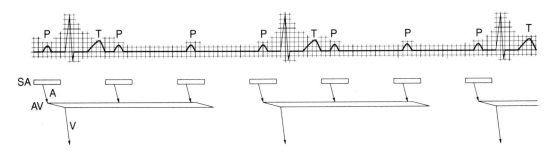

Figure 19-36. Second-degree A-V block. Since three P waves are recorded for each QRS complex, the block is 3:1.

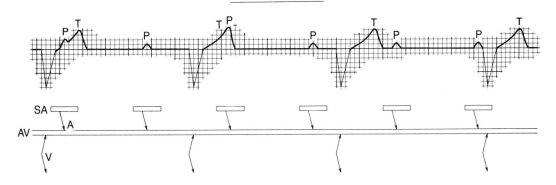

Figure 19-37. Complete A-V dissociation. The P waves and QRS complexes are unrelated.

parasympathetic nervous system input to the A-V junctional area, which is caused experimentally by stimulating the vagus nerve, prolongs the P-R interval and produces complete block if the effect is great enough. In this circumstance, the *a–H* interval is increased, but the *H–V* interval is not changed. The effects of other conditions (such as atherosclerotic heart disease and surgical intervention) on A-V propagation can be studied in humans, in the catheterization laboratory.

Atrial Flutter

Flutter consists of regular, rapid atrial activity at rates of approximately 200–400 beats/min. Second degree A-V block occurs, usually with ratios of 2:1 or 4:1; the ventricular activity usually is regular (Figure 19-39).

RE-ENTRY EXCITATION

Experimentally, excitation can be made to propagate in one direction in a ring of muscle (Fig-

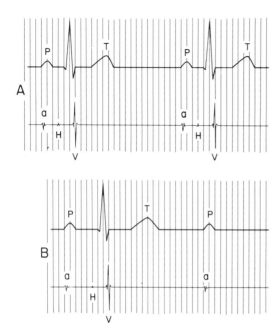

Figure 19-38. Simultaneous recording of the ECG and the electrogram of the His bundle in a dog. **A.** Control record. a: the atrial electrogram; H: the His-bundle electrogram; V: the ventricular electrogram. **B.** Vagal stimulation. In the first complex, the P-R interval is increased; the a to H interval is increased, and the magnitude of H is decreased, but the H to V interval is unchanged. In the second complex, complete A-V block occurs; only the P wave and the atrial electrogram are recorded.

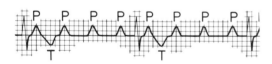

Figure 19-39. Atrial flutter at a rate of 250 beats per minute; the block is 4:1.

ure 19-40) and to travel continuously around the circle, provided that the tissue recovers excitability before the circuit is completed. Excitation continues as long as the length of the pathway exceeds the product of the velocity of propagation and the refractory period. For example, suppose that the length of the circus in Figure 19-40 were 9.6 cm, the velocity of propagation 40 cm/s, and the refractory period 0.2 s. The product of the velocity and the refractory period is 8 cm; this means that the filled portion of the ring, which represents tissue that has been excited and has not yet recovered excitability, is

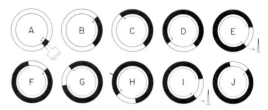

Figure 19-40. Production of circus motion (re-entry excitation) in a ring of excitable tissue. In **A,** a stimulus is applied. Excitation begins at the cathode (the negative pole of the battery) and proceeds in both directions; however, it is blocked at the anode (the positive pole of the battery). Excitation then proceeds in only one direction, as indicated by the arrow within the circle. The filled area represents tissue that has been excited and is refractory to re-excitation. Excitation proceeds around the circus at a velocity characteristic of the tissue and the experimental conditions (**B, C,** and **D**). By the time the wave of excitation reaches the point at which it began, in **E,** the tissue has recovered excitability and propagation continues around the ring again (**F** through **J**). An action potential is recorded each time the circuit is completed (**E** and **I**).

8 cm long, and the open portion of the ring, which represents tissue that has recovered and can be excited again, is 1.6 cm long. Thus, at any time, a portion of the tissue will have recovered excitability and the persistence of an *excitable gap* will be assured. If the excitable gap is closed, excitation is extinguished. The gap could be closed by decreasing the length of the pathway, increasing the velocity of propagation, or increasing the refractory period. The gap could be increased by increasing the length of the pathway, decreasing the velocity of propagation, or decreasing the refractory period.

According to the theory of re-entry excitation, activity is propagated continuously through some path in the atrium, and the body of the atrium is re-excited each time a circuit is completed. Experimentally, flutter can be modeled by lifting and clamping one auricular appendage, forming an obstacle around which excitation can be made to propagate. It has been proposed that in spontaneously-occurring atrial flutter, excitation could move in such a fashion around the junction of the vena cavae with the right atrium.

Certain findings, both experimental and clinical, can be explained best by reference to re-entry excitation. First, parasympathetic nervous system activity, which slows the spontaneous pacemaker of the heart, increases the rate

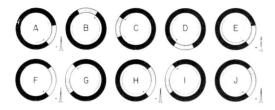

Figure 19-41. The model of circus motion that probably relates most closely to the production of atrial flutter. Excitation has been initiated by the method shown in Figure 19-40. **A** through **E:** The filled portion of each ring represents tissue that has been excited and is *absolutely refractory* to re-excitation. An action potential is recorded each time the circuit is completed (**A** and **E**). The lined portion of each ring represents tissue that has become excitable again, but which still is *relatively refractory.* Relatively refractory tissue propagates excitation less rapidly than normal tissue does. Because of the limited length of the pathway, the duration of the absolutely refractory period, and the normal velocity of propagation in the atrium, it is likely that during re-entry excitation the wavefront proceeds continuously in relatively refractory tissue, and the velocity of propagation in the circuit is less than that of the atrial myocardium under normal conditions. **F** through **J:** The refractory period has been decreased; fully recovered tissue now is available in the circus path, and the velocity of propagation has increased. The circuit is completed more frequently, and three action potentials now are produced (**F, H,** and **J**) during a period that provided for only two action potentials (**A** and **E**) under the previous conditions. In the atrium, parasympathetic nervous system activity decreases the refractory period of the myocardium.

---

of atrial flutter. This effect can be related to the shortening of the refractory period of the atrial myocardium, which increases the velocity of propagation in the circus, increases the frequency of completion of the circus, and thereby increases the frequency of excitation (Figure 19-41). If the flutter depended on spontaneous depolarization, parasympathetic activity would decrease the rate (see Figure 18-5). Second, experimental flutter can be produced more readily and persists longer in an animal, such as the cow, that has relatively large atria, than in an animal, such as the dog, that has relatively small atria. This relationship probably reflects the length of the pathway that is available. Finally, drugs that increase the refractory period of the atrium, such as quinidine, oppose flutter.

Fibrillation

ATRIAL FIBRILLATION

Atrial fibrillation consists of rapid, irregular activity in which P waves are not recognizable, and the ventricular cycles are irregular (Figure 19-42). The latter activity reflects the effect of partial A-V block that occurs because excitation appears at the junction much more frequently than the junctional tissue can recover and accept it. The A-V junction is not homogeneous, and activity that enters it either may propagate all of the way through, or fail at various levels, leaving different segments of the junctional tissue in different stages of refractoriness; consequently, the effective refractory period is variable and irregular. By this means, the A-V junction protects the ventricles from the high-frequency atrial excitation.

Atrial fibrillation occurs often in the dilated atria associated with disease or structural defects of the A-V valves, and it is a toxic manifestation of digitalis, which, because it shortens the atrial refractory period, may convert atrial flutter to atrial fibrillation. Although it decreases the effectiveness of the heart as a pump, partly because of the irregularity of ventricular function it causes and partly because it renders the atria ineffective mechanically, atrial fibrillation is not a fatal dysrhythmia and may persist for many years.

VENTRICULAR FIBRILLATION

Ventricular fibrillation is characterized by completely irregular electrical activity of the ventricles (Figure 19-43). If this condition is left unattended, it is quickly and invariably fatal in the human, because fibrillating ventricles do not pump blood. When the appropriate equipment is available, fibrillation can be reversed easily by the application of enough electrical current to depolarize all of the ventricular tissue at once; this permits synchronous activity to begin again.

BASIS OF FIBRILLATION

Fibrillation generally is considered to reflect re-entry excitation; however, the total irregularity of the arrhythmia makes dependence on a single parent circus unlikely. It is probable that excitation wanders randomly through different pathways; that islands of excitable tissue appear and disappear, and that wave fronts join and then separate again, always limited by the

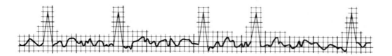

Figure 19-42.   Atrial fibrillation. The main characteristics are the complete irregularity of the electrical activity of the atria and of the intervals between QRS complexes (ventricular excitation).

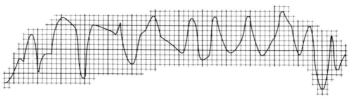

Figure 19-43.   Ventricular fibrillation. The principal characteristic is the absolute irregularity of the electrical activity of the ventricles.

length of the pathway available at the moment, the velocity of propagation, and the refractory period. In such a system, recovery from fibrillation depends on the statistical chance that all of the wavelets will fall into phase, and all of the tissue will be either excitable or refractory at the same time. As this model suggests, the spontaneous recovery from fibrillation of a relatively large heart, such as that of the human, is very unlikely.

STUDY OUTLINE

LEAD SYSTEMS   Record the electrical activity of the heart from the surface of the body.

BIPOLAR LIMB LEADS   Record in the frontal plane.
  Lead I: Right arm, left arm (RA, LA).
  Lead II. Right arm, left leg (RA, LL).
  Lead III. Left arm, left leg (LA, LL).
  Form Einthoven's triangle.

UNIPOLAR LEADS   Exploring electrode combined with "indifferent" electrode.
  UNIPOLAR LIMB LEADS   Indifferent electrode ("central terminal") formed by connecting all three standard limb leads.
  Exploring electrode placed successively on RA, LA, LL.
  Small signal because of cancellation.
  AUGMENTED LIMB LEADS   Indifferent electrode formed by two limb components opposite exploring electrode.
  aVR: Exploring electrode on RA, indifferent electrode formed by LA and LL.
  aVL: Exploring electrode on LA, indifferent electrode formed by RA and LL.
  aVF: Exploring electrode on LL (LF), indifferent electrode formed by RA and LA.
  PRECORDIAL LEADS   Record in horizontal plane.
  Exploring electrode placed in various standard positions, central terminal forms indifferent electrode.

BASIS OF THE ELECTROCARDIOGRAM

VOLUME CONDUCTOR   Current flows in three dimensions.
  Electrical potential difference develops parallel to each line of current.
  Current density and potential difference diminish with square of distance from source.
  Body treated as volume conductor.

SOURCE OF CURRENT   Depolarizing heart generates electrical current.
  Potential difference exists along lines of flow.
  Magnitude and direction of flow change as excitation proceeds, can be expressed as summated vector.
  Potential recorded is greatest when summated vector exactly parallel to bipolar lead or perpendicular to unipolar lead.
  Each lead constructs time course of vector as seen from own perspective.

INFORMATION CONTAINED IN ELECTROCARDIOGRAM

MEAN ELECTRICAL AXIS   In frontal plane.

Vector related to mass of tissue; provides information about size, shape, and position of heart.

Mean axis (of vector) obtained from net deflection of each limb lead.

Normal axis $+60°$, range $-30°$ to $+110°$.

Left axis deviation $-30°$ to $-90°$, right axis deviation $+110°$ to $+180°$.

VECTORCARDIOGRAM Direct recording of waxing and waning of mean vector.

INDICATIONS OF HYPERTROPHY

CANCELLATION Larger muscle mass produces more current.

Much current in opposite directions, cancelling effect on mean vector.

Hypertrophy most apparent when only one ventricle involved.

TWELVE-LEAD ARRAY Bipolar limb leads, augmented limb leads, and precordial leads.

Represent vector in frontal and horizontal planes.

LEFT VENTRICULAR HYPERTROPHY Left axis deviation (in frontal plane).

Large positive deflections in left precordial leads, large negative deflections in right precordial leads.

Normal dominance of ECG by left ventricle exaggerated.

RIGHT VENTRICULAR HYPERTROPHY Right axis deviation (in frontal plane).

Positive deflections in right precordial leads.

More influence of right ventricle on ECG than normal.

INJURY POTENTIAL

MYOCARDIAL INFARCTION Infarcted tissue remains depolarized, current flows between injured and healthy tissues.

MYOCARDITIS AND PERICARDITIS Inflammation of pericardium or of subepicardial layer of myocardium.

OTHER ALTERATIONS OF ST SEGMENT OR T WAVE

MYOCARDIAL ISCHEMIA Depression of ST segment and inverted or biphasic T waves in left precordial leads.

DIGITALIS Depression of ST segment in left chest leads, elevation in right chest leads, and shortening of the Q-T interval.

MYOCARDIAL INFARCTION Fresh infarct causes injury potential.

After infarct heals, effect on ECG related to absence of left ventricular tissue.

Relative contribution of right ventricle increased.

Q waves and decreased R waves in left chest leads, R waves appear in right chest leads.

ATRIOVENTRICULAR BLOCK Due to myocardial ischemia or infarct in A-V junctional area.

BUNDLE-BRANCH BLOCK Produced by myocardial disease or cardiac surgery.

IDENTIFICATION QRS complex altered if Purkinje system damaged.

Spread of excitation partly through slower-propagating myocardium.

QRS prolonged, slurred, or notched.

RIGHT BUNDLE-BRANCH BLOCK Excitation of right ventricle delayed, not masked as usual by left ventricular excitation.

R waves appear in right chest leads, S waves or depressed ST segments follow R in left chest leads.

LEFT BUNDLE-BRANCH BLOCK Normal dominance by left ventricular excitation enhanced.

Prominant S waves in right chest leads, slurred R waves and no S waves in left chest leads.

DYSRHYTHMIA

NORMAL SINUS RHYTHM P, QRS, and T in regular, normal sequence.

Rate between 60 and 100 beats/min in adults.

Faster in children, varies with age.

SINUS TACHYCARDIA ECG normal, rate > 100/min in adults.

SINUS BRADYCARDIA ECG normal, rate < 60/min in adults.

SINUS ARRHYTHMIA Normal sinus rhythm. Characterized by increase of rate during inspiration and decrease of rate during expiration.

SINUS ARREST Failure of SA node to initiate impulses.

SINOATRIAL BLOCK Failure of propagation at junction of SA node with atrium.

PREMATURE EXCITATION

PREMATURE ATRIAL BEATS Originate in SA node or atrionodal pathways.

PREMATURE JUNCTIONAL CONTRACTIONS P wave often masked by QRS.

Usually produce normal QRS.

Compensatory pause if excitation not propagated into SA node: short cycle followed by long cycle.

PREMATURE VENTRICULAR CONTRACTIONS Originate in Purkinje system or in damaged tissue (ischemia or infarct).

Abnormal QRS, reflecting abnormal pathway.

Compensatory pause (SA node not reset, short cycle followed by long cycle).

Usually, T wave directed opposite to QRS (discordant).

PULSE DEFICIT Premature contraction ineffective, no blood ejected; next stroke volume larger, pulse stronger.

VENTRICULAR EXTRASYSTOLES Interpolated, or extra, beats.

BIGEMINY Coupled beats, usually sinus with premature.

MULTIFOCAL PREMATURE VENTRICULAR CONTRACTIONS At least two premature ventricular contractions of different origin.

PAROXYSMAL TACHYCARDIA Rapid succession of impulses begins abruptly, ends abruptly; may originate in atria, A-V junction, or ventricles.

ATRIOVENTRICULAR BLOCK

FIRST DEGREE Prolonged P-R interval.

SECOND DEGREE Incomplete block; beats dropped periodically.

Wenckebach type: P-R interval increases until beat dropped, then cycle repeated.

Regular: 2:1, 3:1, etc.

THIRD DEGREE Complete A-V dissociation.

HIS-BUNDLE ELECTROGRAM Local recording of His-bundle activity.

ATRIAL FLUTTER Regular, rapid atrial activity, 200–400 beats/min.

Second degree A-V block.

RE-ENTRY EXCITATION Continuous propagation, as excited tissue recovers and is excited again.

Will continue as long as length of pathway exceeds product of velocity of propagation and refractory period.

To cause atrial flutter, excitation travels in circuitous path, atrium is re-excited each time circuit is completed.

Excitation propagated in relatively refractory tissue; decreasing refractory period provides more-nearly recovered tissue, increases velocity of propagation.

Stimulation of vagus nerves increases rate of flutter by decreasing refractory period of atrial myocardium.

FIBRILLATION

ATRIAL FIBRILLATION Rapid, irregular activity; P waves not recognizable.

Ventricular cycles irregular, reflecting irregular partial A-V block; ventricles protected by block.

Ventricles less effective, but dysrhythmia can be tolerated.

VENTRICULAR FIBRILLATION Apparently random electrical activity.

In the human, invariably fatal if not attended, as fibrillating ventricles pump no blood.

Reversed by depolarizing all of ventricular tissue at once with applied current.

BASIS OF FIBRILLATION Probably irregular, random, re-entry excitation, limited at any instant by length of pathway available, velocity of propagation, and refractory period.

Recovery depends on chance that all tissue will be either excitable or refractory at same time.

Mass of tissue (length of pathway) an important factor.

BIBLIOGRAPHY

Allessi, M.A., Bonke, F.I.M., and Schopman, F.J.G. 1977. Circus movement in rabbit atrial muscle as a mechanism for tachycardia. III. The "leading circle" concept: a new model of circus movement in cardiac tissue without the involvement of an anatomical obstacle. *Circ. Res.* 41:9.

Burger, H.C. 1968. *Heart and Vector. Physical Basis of Electrocardiography.* Eindhoven (The Netherlands): Philips.

Chung, E.K., 1980. *Electrocardiography: Practical applications with vectorial principles.* New York City: Harper and Row.

Damato, A.M., Gallagher, J.J., and Lau, S.H. 1972. Application of His bundle recordings in diagnosis of conduction disorders. *Progr. Cardiovasc. Dis.* 14:601.

Frank, E. 1956. An accurate, clinically practical system for spatial vectorcardiography. *Circulation* 13:737.

Goldberger, E. 1953. *Unipolar Lead Electrocardiography and Vector-cardiography.* Philadelphia: Lea and Febiger.

Goldman, M.H. 1976. *Principles of Clinical Electrocardiography.* 9th ed., Los Altos, California: Lange.

Jones, K.M., and Ochs, G.M. 1982. *Interpretation of the electrocardiogram: A review for health professionals.* Norwalk, Conn.: Appleton-Century-Crofts.

Kastor, J.A., Horowitz, L.N., Harken, A.H., et al. 1981. Clinical electrophysiology of ventricular tachycardia. *N. Engl. J. Med.* 304:1004.

Lewis, T. 1925. *The Mechanism and Graphic Registration of the Heart Beat.* 3rd ed., London: Shaw and Sons.

Mines, G.R. 1913. On dynamic equilibrium in the heart. *J. Physiol.,* London. 46:349.

Moe, G.K. 1962. On the multiple wavelet hypothesis of atrial fibrillation. *Arch. internat. Pharmacodyn.* 140:183.

Moe, G.K. and Abildskov, J.A. 1959. Atrial fibrillation as a self-sustaining arrhythmia independent of focal discharge. *Amer. Heart J.* 58:59.

Wilson, F.N., Johnston, F.D., Macleod, A.G., and Barker, P.S. 1934. Electrocardiograms that represent the potential variations of a single electrode. *Amer. Heart J.* 9:447.

Wilson, F.N., Kossman, C.E., Burch, G.E., et al. 1954. Report of committee on electrocardiography, American Heart Association: Recommendations for standardization of electrocardiographic and vectorcardiographic leads. *Circulation* 10:564.

20

Fetal and Neonatal Circulation

CHAPTER CONTENTS

CHARACTERISTICS OF THE FETAL CIRCULATION

Differences Between Fetal and Postnatal Circulation

The circulation of the fetus differs in several important ways from that of the infant after birth. First, the *fetal circulation* does not provide direct contact between the internal environment and the external environment. The lungs of the fetus are collapsed and filled with fluid, and the digestive tract is inactive. Gases are exchanged, nutritional materials are acquired, and materials that are not needed are excreted through the placenta, and the basic functions of respiration, digestion, and elimination are carried out by the mother. Second, both sides of the fetal heart supply blood to the systemic circulation; hence, they work largely in parallel, rather than in series. The pulmonary vascular resistance is higher than the systemic vascular resistance, and shunts between the atria and between the great arteries permit most of the blood to bypass the lungs. Finally, by postpartum standards, the fetus exists in relatively hypoxic conditions.

Route of Fetal Circulation

Blood passes from the *placenta,* where it has exchanged materials with the maternal blood, through the *umbilical veins* to the *fetus* (Figure 20-1). About half of the blood that flows from the placenta perfuses the *liver* and then enters the *inferior vena cava* (IVC); the other half enters the *vena cava* directly, through the *ductus venosus.* Most of the blood carried by the inferior vena cava passes through the *foramen ovale,* which forms a right-to-left valve, into the *left atrium,* the *left ventricle,* and the *systemic circulation;* only a small portion enters the *right ventricle* and the *pulmonary artery.* Most of the blood carried by the *superior vena cava* (SVC)

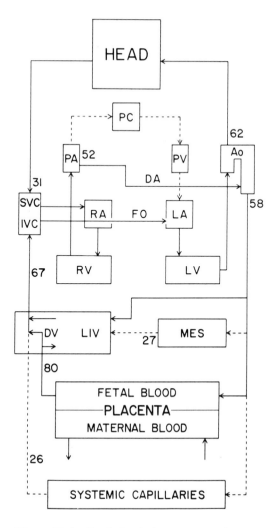

Figure 20-1 Fetal circulation. *PC* = pulmonary capillaries; *PA* = pulmonary artery; *PV* = pulmonary veins; *Ao* = aorta; *DA* = ductus arteriosus; *SVC* = superior vena cava; *IVC* = inferior vena cava; *RA* = right atrium; *FO* = foramen ovale; *LA* = left atrium; *RV* = right ventricle; *LV*=left ventricle; *DV*=ductus venosus; *LIV*= liver; *MES* = mesentery. *Arrows* indicate the direction of blood flow. *Dashed lines* indicate that the rate of flow in the fetus is relatively less than it will be in normal extrauterine life. The numbers indicate, at the point where each occurs, the relative saturation (percent) of the blood with oxygen. (From Dawes, G.S.; Mott, J.C.; and Widdicombe, J.G. 1954. The foetal circulation in the lamb. *J. Physiol.* (London) 126:563.)

enters the *right atrium*, the *right ventricle*, and the *pulmonary artery*; the drainage of the *coronary sinus* also goes to the *right ventricle*. Some of the blood that flows in the *pulmonary artery* goes through the *lungs*, but most of it bypasses

the lungs, flowing through the *ductus arteriosus* into the *aorta*. Most of the combined output of the *right ventricle* and the *left ventricle* enters the *systemic circulation*; hence, the two ventricles function essentially in parallel.

Oxygenation of Fetal Blood

The blood that leaves the lungs of the normal adult is about 95% to 98% saturated with oxygen. To reach the fetal blood, oxygen must diffuse from the maternal blood in the placenta; in the fetal lamb, the *placental venous blood* is only about 80% saturated (see Figure 20-1). After the placental venous blood has mixed with blood from the lower limbs and the liver, the blood that will perfuse the fetus is about 67% saturated with oxygen. This is approximately the saturation of the mixed venous blood returning to the lungs to be oxygenated in the normal person. The lowest saturation in the fetal circulation occurs in the blood from the lower inferior vena cava (26% in the fetal lamb); blood in the superior vena cava, which comes mostly from the head, is only 31% saturated.

The relatively hypoxic state of the fetus is made tenable by the adaptation of the cellular enzymes to low oxygen tension and by the special properties of the fetal hemoglobin that permit it to deliver oxygen to the tissues despite the relatively low saturation (see section entitled "Fetal Hemoglobin" in Chapter 31). These special properties are lost within a few days after birth.

The brain of the human fetus is large relative to the rest of the body, and its supply of oxygen is very important. The fetal brain is perfused with the most highly saturated blood available, because of the relative separation of the blood in the right atrium so that most of the output of the left ventricle is supplied by the inferior vena cava. The output of the right ventricle, which is less saturated, enters the aorta beyond the origin of the arteries that supply the brain.

CHANGES AT BIRTH

Pulmonary Ventilation

In the fetus, the lungs are collapsed because of the recoil of the elastic tissue; the pulmonary blood vessels are compressed and the pulmonary vascular resistance is relatively high. Because the alternate channel for the output of the right ventricle, the systemic circulation by way of the ductus arteriosus, also offers relatively high resistance to flow, the pulmonary arterial pressure is approximately equal to the aortic pressure. When the lungs expand, the relatively compliant pulmonary blood vessels are dilated by the pulmonary blood pressure, and the pulmonary vascular resistance decreases. The output of the right ventricle flows preferentially into the pulmonary circulation, and the pulmonary arterial pressure decreases. Because the aortic pressure then exceeds the pulmonary arterial pressure, the direction of flow in the ductus arteriosus reverses, and blood flows from the aorta into the pulmonary circulation. During the first few hours of extrauterine life, the left-to-right shunt may comprise 30% to 50% of the output of the left ventricle; hence, the output of the left ventricle exceeds the output of the right ventricle.

CLOSURE OF FORAMEN OVALE

Because of the decrease of pulmonary arterial pressure, the right ventricular end-diastolic pressure decreases, right atrial pressure decreases, and the valve of the *foramen ovale* closes.

Removing the Placental Circulation

The placenta forms a low-resistance shunt in the systemic circulation of the fetus; hence, when the cord is tied, the systemic vascular resistance and the systemic arterial pressure increase temporarily.

Closure of the Ductus Arteriosus

Flow through the ductus, from the aorta into the pulmonary artery, normally decreases within 1 to 2 hours after birth and continues to decrease slowly for about 9 to 12 hours. A small, slitlike lumen persists until about 18 days after birth, at which time the channel normally is closed permanently.

CONGENITAL HEART DEFECTS

The development of the heart in the human embryo is a very complex process, and occasionally certain defects occur. Four of the most common ones, which also serve to illustrate the

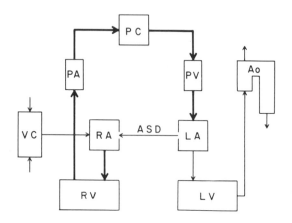

Figure 20-2. The effects of an atrial septal defect (*ASD*) on blood flow in the heart and lungs. *PC* = pulmonary capillaries; *PA* = pulmonary artery; *PV* = pulmonary veins; *Ao* = aorta; *VC* = vena cavae; *RA* = right atrium; *LA* = left atrium; *RV* = right ventricle; *LV* = left ventricle. *Arrows* show the route of blood flow. *Heavy lines* indicate the high rate of flow in the vessels through which blood is recirculating. The rate of flow from the left atrium to the left ventricle and from the left ventricle into the aorta is normal, and the rate of flow from the vena cavae into the right atrium is normal. The rate of flow through the right atrium includes both the normal flow from the vena cavae and the blood recirculated from the left atrium. The high rate of flow continues from the right atrium into the right ventricle, from the right ventricle through the pulmonary circulation, and back to the left atrium again.

adaptive capacities of the circulation, are discussed briefly in this section.

Atrial Septal Defect

FUNCTIONAL EFFECTS

Normally, the mean left atrial pressure exceeds the mean right atrial pressure by about 5 mm Hg; thus, if an opening persists in the interatrial septum, oxygenated blood flows from the left atrium to the right atrium and is recirculated needlessly through the lungs (Figure 20-2). Autoregulation in the systemic circulation, supported by the circulatory reflexes, keeps the output of the left ventricle at normal levels; because of the shunt, the output of the right ventricle may be two to four times that of the left ventricle. The exact magnitude of the shunt is related to the size of the defect in the septum and the gradient of pressure between the left atrium and the right atrium. The gradient does not change during a physiological increase of

CLINICAL CORRELATION
20.1   Atrial Septal Defect

CASE REPORT

The Patient: A 13-year-old boy.

Reason for Admission: A cardiac murmur.

History: The patient was well and had no cardiac symptoms; a murmur had been heard during a routine physical examination for summer camp.

Clinical Examination: The first heart sound was normal, with some enhancement of the component related to tricuspid closure. A midsystolic pulmonary ejection murmur was heard, and the second sound was widely split and did not move with respiration. A mid-diastolic rumbling murmur was heard at the lower left sternal border. The ECG showed right axis deviation (+ 120°) in the frontal plane and prominent R waves and discordant T waves in the right precordial leads; these findings indicate right ventricular hypertrophy. X-ray films of the chest revealed enlargement of the right atrium and ventricle, dilatation of the main pulmonary artery and the major branches, and evidence of abnormally large pulmonary blood flow ("vascular markings"). Echocardiographic examination revealed normal cardiac valves and confirmed the increased right ventricular volume. At cardiac catheterization, an atrial septal defect (ASD) of the secundum* type was suggested by the ready passage of the catheter across the atrial septum, from right to left, at the midseptal level. However, in about 35% of the patients at this age, the catheter may be passed through the system from right to left because of incomplete seal of the foramen ovale ("probe patency"). Measurement of relative oxygen content in the superior vena cava, mid cava, inferior cava, right atrium, right ventricle, and pulmonary artery revealed increased saturation in the right atrium compared to the vena cava. Thus, oxygenated blood was reaching the right atrium, a condition consistent with ASD. The ratio of pulmonary blood flow (Qp) to systemic blood flow (Qs) was calculated to be 3:1 (see Chapter 14, "Evaluation of Shunts"). Injection of contrast medium into the left atrium, under fluoroscopic observation, provided visual evidence of the left-to-right shunt. No other defect was found.

Treatment: The defect was closed in surgery, using a Dacron patch.

Comment: A left-to-right shunt was indicated by the characteristics of the heart sounds. Enhancement of the tricuspid closure component and the ejection murmur associated with the first sound, and the wide and fixed splitting of the second sound, are consistent with large and prolonged right ventricular ejection. Normally, the amount of splitting of the second sound varies with respiration, increasing during inspiration, when blood flow into the thorax is enhanced, and decreasing during expiration, when blood flow into the thorax decreases. The magnitude of the shunt largely prevented the changes with respiration. The mid-diastolic murmur is consistent with the large volume of right ventricular filling. Right ventricular dilatation and hypertrophy, and dilatation of the pulmonary vessels, also are consistent with the large volume of pulmonary blood flow. The definitive diagnosis was made from the data obtained during cardiac catheterization.

Outcome: The patient recovered without incident. He is completely active again and has returned to school.

---

*Part of the ostium secundum (an opening in the interatrial septum) is left uncovered because the septum secundum is incomplete.

the cardiac output; therefore, the rate of flow through the septal defect does not increase during exercise, whereas the systemic output does, and the relative magnitude of the shunt decreases. Thus, children who have this defect usually tolerate exercise well.

LONG-TERM EFFECTS

If the shunt is allowed to persist, the *pulmonary blood vessels* may be damaged because of the high rate of blood flow, and irreversible *pulmonary hypertension* may develop as the walls of the vessels thicken and become less compliant. If fluid accumulates in the lung tissues, the defense of the lungs against infectious agents that are inhaled may be compromised, and *pneumonia* may develop. *Right ventricular failure* eventually may occur as a result of the large work load.

Ventricular Septal Defect

Ventricular septal defects occur most frequently in the membranous portion of the interventricular septum, just below the roots of the aorta and the pulmonary artery (Figure 20-3). During development, this is the interventricular foramen; it is the last portion of the septum to be filled in. Ventricular septal defects also can occur in the more muscular areas of the septum.

FUNCTIONAL EFFECTS

Because the blood pressure is higher in the left ventricle than in the right ventricle, blood shunts from left to right, and more in systole, when the difference of pressure is greatest, than in diastole, when the difference is less. If the defect is as large as the orifice of the aortic valve, the pressure of the left ventricle is transmitted undiminished to the right ventricle, and the magnitude of the shunt depends on the relative resistances in the two circulations. The resistance of the systemic circulation, as set by autoregulation, largely determines the cardiac output; with the support of the circulatory reflexes, a normal cardiac output may be obtained. As the vascular resistance in the pulmonary circulation normally is very low relative to that in the systemic circulation, the magnitude of the shunt can be very great.

LONG-TERM EFFECTS

If the high rate of flow is permitted to continue for as little time as 1 year, the *pulmonary blood*

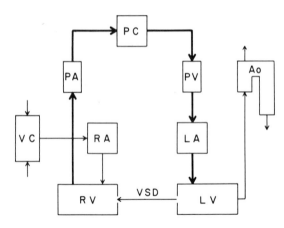

Figure 20-3. Effects of a ventricular septal defect (*VSD*) on blood flow in the heart and lungs. *PC* = pulmonary capillaries; *PA* = pulmonary artery; *PV* = pulmonary veins; *Ao* = aorta; *VC* = vena cavae; *RA* = right atrium; *LA* = left atrium; *RV* = right ventricle; *LV* = left ventricle. *Arrows* show the route of blood flow. *Heavy lines* indicate the high rate of flow in the vessels through which blood is recirculating. The rate of flow from the left ventricle into the aorta is normal, and the rate of flow from the vena cavae to the right atrium and from the right atrium to the right ventricle is normal. The output of the left ventricle also includes the blood that flows through the defect into the right ventricle; the output of the right ventricle includes the blood that passes through the defect, in addition to that which flows from the right atrium. The high rate of flow continues from the right ventricle, through the pulmonary circulation and back to the left ventricle again.

vessels usually are damaged and irreversible *pulmonary hypertension* develops. The imposition of a volume load on the left ventricle, in addition to the pressure load that it has already, leads to *left ventricular failure*, accompanied by increased *left atrial pressure, pulmonary congestion*, and *pneumonia*.

Patent Ductus Arteriosus

Sometimes, for reasons that are not understood fully, the *ductus arteriosus* fails to close completely, and it provides a conduit between the aorta and the pulmonary artery.

FUNCTIONAL EFFECTS

Because the pressure is higher in the systemic circulation, blood flows from the aorta into the pulmonary artery and recirculates through the lungs (Figure 20-4). The gradient of pressure may be as high as 100 mm Hg during systole

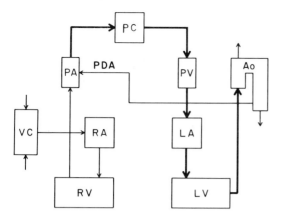

Figure 20-4. Effects of a patent ductus arteriosus (*PDA*) on blood flow in the heart and lungs. *PC* = pulmonary capillaries; *PA* = pulmonary artery; *PV* = pulmonary veins; *Ao* = aorta; *VC* = vena cavae; *RA* = right atrium; *LA* = left atrium; *RV* = right ventricle; *LV* = left ventricle. *Arrows* show the route of blood flow. *Heavy lines* indicate the high rate of flow in the vessels through which blood is recirculating. The rate of flow from the vena cavae, through the right atrium and the right ventricle, and into the pulmonary artery is normal, and the rate of flow through the aorta into the systemic circulation is normal. The flow from the lungs into the left atrium and the left ventricle, and the output of the left ventricle, includes the blood that is recirculated in addition to the normal output of the left ventricle.

---

and about 70 mm Hg during diastole (these are the differences between the aortic pressure and the pulmonary arterial pressure at the systolic and diastolic levels, respectively). Because of autoregulation and the circulatory reflexes, if the demand is not too great, the output of the left ventricle will be increased enough to maintain a normal rate of flow to the systemic circulation, in addition to the blood diverted back into the lungs. The stroke volume of the left ventricle is increased, because the left ventricle must support an additional volume load. The significance of the effect depends on the size of the shunt. A small ductus may have so little effect that it is not detected for a long time, whereas a large ductus causes the systemic arterial pressure to fall more rapidly than normal during diastole, and the systemic arterial pulse pressure increases.

LONG-TERM EFFECTS

The dangers of the patent ductus arteriosus arise from the effects of the work load imposed

on the left ventricle and the high rate of flow imposed on the pulmonary blood vessels and the ductus. If the ductus is large and the condition is left unattended, it can lead to *left ventricular hypertrophy* and, ultimately, *left ventricular failure and pulmonary congestion.* Irreversible *pulmonary hypertension* may develop if the pulmonary vessels are damaged and become thickened and rigid. *Bacterial endocarditis* is a constant threat, because the high rate of flow through the ductus may abrade and roughen the walls, providing a site for bacteria to lodge and grow.

Tetralogy of Fallot

Tetralogy of Fallot, as the name implies, has four main features: (a) the aorta is placed over the interventricular septum (*overriding aorta*), (b) the ventricular septum is incomplete (*ventricular septum defect*), (c) the pulmonary outflow tract is partially occluded (*pulmonary stenosis*), and (d) the right ventricle is hypertrophied. All of the lesions are related; the latter

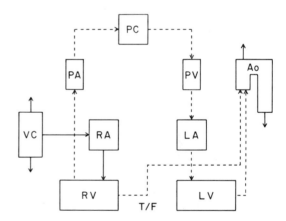

Figure 20-5. Effects of tetralogy of Fallot (*T/F*) on blood flow in the heart and lungs. *PC* = pulmonary capillaries; *PA* = pulmonary artery; *PV* = pulmonary veins; *Ao* = aorta; *VC* = vena cavae; *RA* = right atrium; *LA* = left atrium: *RV* = right ventricle; *LV* = left ventricle. *Arrows* show the route of blood flow. *Dashed lines* indicate that the rate of flow is less than normal. The rate of flow into the right atrium from the vena cavae is normal, and the rate of flow through the aorta into the systemic circulation is normal. The blood flow is divided at the right ventricular outflow, so that part of it follows the normal path through the lungs, back to the left ventricle, and then to the aorta, and part of it goes directly into the aorta.

three must follow from the first. The displacement of the aorta is the primary event. Once this has occurred, the ventricular septum cannot be complete, the pulmonary outflow tract is crowded, and, because of the high resistance in the pulmonary outflow tract, the right ventricular pressure is high, and the right ventricle undergoes hypertrophy.

FUNCTIONAL EFFECTS

The pulmonary stenosis impedes the flow of blood into the pulmonary artery, and the ventricular septum defect and the rightwardly placed aorta permit part of the output of the right ventricle to go directly to the systemic circulation (Figure 20-5). Hence, the right ventricular pressure increases to equal the left ventricular pressure, the blood tends to bypass the lungs, and the systemic blood is only partly oxygenated. The arterial blood contains increased amounts of reduced hemoglobin, which produces cyanosis; hence, the appellation "blue baby." The volume of blood that flows to the lungs is determined by the resistance of the pulmonary outflow tract relative to the resistance of the systemic circulation.

STUDY OUTLINE

CHARACTERISTICS OF THE FETAL CIRCULATION

DIFFERENCES BETWEEN FETAL AND POSTNATAL CIRCULATION   In fetal circulation, all exchange with environment is through maternal circulation.

Pulmonary resistance is high, intracardiac shunts exist; ventricles work largely in parallel.

Fetus exists in relative hypoxia.

ROUTE OF THE FETAL CIRCULATION In placenta, exchange of materials with maternal circulation.

Umbilical veins to liver, partial bypass through ductus venosus.

Most IVC blood shunts through foramen ovale to left atrium, left ventricle, systemic circulation.

Most SVC blood enters right atrium, right ventricle, and pulmonary artery; from pulmonary artery, most blood shunts through ductus arteriosus to descending aorta.

OXYGENATION OF FETAL BLOOD   Placental venous blood, exchanging with maternal blood, is about 80% saturated with oxygen.

After mixing with IVC blood, it is about 67% saturated.

Blood from SVC (head) and lower IVC only about 25% to 30% saturated.

Fetal hemoglobin delivers oxygen at relatively low saturation.

The most highly saturated blood flows to head, providing greatly needed oxygenation of brain.

CHANGES AT BIRTH

PULMONARY VENTILATION   Fetal lungs collapsed, blood vessels compressed, pulmonary vascular resistance high; output of pulmonary artery shunts to aorta through ductus arteriosus.

When lungs expand, pulmonary vascular resistance decreases, blood flows through lungs, pulmonary arterial pressure decreases.

Direction of flow reverses in ductus arteriosus.

CLOSURE OF FORAMEN OVALE   Right atrial pressure decreases to less than left atrial pressure, valve of foramen ovale closes.

REMOVING THE PLACENTAL CIRCULATION   Resistance to flow through placenta low; tying cord increases systemic resistance and systemic arterial pressure.

CLOSURE OF DUCTUS ARTERIOSUS Mostly closed after about 12 hours, completely after about 18 days.

CONGENITAL HEART DEFECTS

ATRIAL SEPTAL DEFECT   Left-to-right atrial shunt; oxygenated blood recirculated through lungs.

FUNCTIONAL EFFECTS   Output of left ventricle (cardiac output) normal; output of right ventricle increased.

Rate of shunt determined by size of defect and gradient of pressure.

Shunt not affected by physiological increase of cardiac output; subject tolerates exercise well.

LONG-TERM EFFECTS   Not common.

Pulmonary vascular damage and irreversible pulmonary hypertension.

Pneumonia, because of fluid collection in lungs.

Right ventricular failure, because of large work load.

VENTRICULAR SEPTAL DEFECT   Most frequently in membranous portion of septum.

FUNCTIONAL EFFECTS Blood shunts from left ventricle to right ventricle, more during systole, less during diastole; right ventricular pressure increased.

Cardiac output normal; total left ventricular output includes shunt.

Shunt can be large because of low pulmonary vascular resistance.

LONG-TERM EFFECTS   After as little time as 1 year, pulmonary vessels damaged and irreversible pulmonary hypertension develops.

Left ventricular failure because of volume load.

Pulmonary congestion and pneumonia.

PATENT DUCTUS ARTERIOSUS   Persistent conduit between aorta and pulmonary artery.

FUNCTIONAL EFFECTS   Blood flows from aorta to pulmonary artery, down pressure gradient.

Output of left ventricle increases to keep systemic perfusion normal; shunted blood recirculates through lungs.

Large ductus increases systemic arterial pulse pressure.

LONG-TERM EFFECTS   Left ventricular hypertrophy and failure; pulmonary congestion.

Irreversible pulmonary hypertension.

Bacterial endocarditis.

TETRALOGY OF FALLOT: Four interrelated defects.

Aorta placed over ventricular septum.

Ventricular septal defect.

Pulmonary outflow occlusion.

Right ventricular hypertrophy.

FUNCTIONAL EFFECTS   Right ventricular outflow shunted to aorta, lungs partially bypassed.

Systemic blood only partly oxygenated; cyanosis ("blue baby").

Perfusion of lungs determined by pulmonic resistance relative to systemic resistance.

BIBLIOGRAPHY

Becker, A.E.; Loosekoot, T.G.; Marceletti, C., et al. 1981. *Paediatric cardiology.* New York: Churchill Livingstone.

Bloor, C.M., and Liebon, A.A. 1980. *The pulmonary and bronchial circulations in congenital heart disease.* New York: Plenum.

Dawes, G.S.; Mott, J.C.; and Widdicombe, J.G. 1954. The foetal circulation in the lamb. *J. Physiol.* (London) 126:563.

Heymann, M.A., Iwamoto, H.S., and Rudolph, A.M. 1981. Factors affecting changes in the neonatal systemic circulation. *Annu. Rev. Physiol.* 43:371.

Kieth, J.D., Rowe, R.D., and Vlad, P., editors. 1978. *Heart disease in infancy and childhood.* New York: Macmillan.

Rashkind, W.J., editor. 1982. *Congenital heart disease.* Stroudsburg, Pa.: Hutchinson Press.

Roberts, W.C., editor. 1979. *Congenital heart disease in adults.* Philadelphia: F.A. Davis.

Rudolph, A.M. 1979. Fetal and neonatal pulmonary circulation. *Annu. Rev. Physiol.* 41:383.

21

Arterial Pressure and Systemic Arterial Hypertension

CHAPTER CONTENTS

INDIRECT MEASUREMENT

The arterial pressure of the human subject is *measured indirectly*, by measuring the pressure in a cuff placed around an arm and inflated. If the dimensions of the cuff relative to those of the arm are appropriate, the pressure in the cuff is transmitted to the artery (Figure 21-1). The pressure in the cuff is increased until the artery is occluded continuously; the pressure in the cuff is greater than that in the artery at all phases of the cardiac cycle. The pressure in the cuff then is decreased slowly; when the artery opens briefly only at its highest pressure, the pressure in the cuff and that in the artery at the peak of systole are about the same; this value is

called the *systolic pressure* (Figure 21-2). When the pressure in the cuff is decreased until the artery is occluded only at its lowest pressure and open continuously after a further slight decrease of cuff pressure, the pressure in the cuff is about equal to that in the artery at the lowest point in diastole. This value is called the *diastolic pressure* (Figure 21-2).

Identifying Pressures by Evaluating Sounds

SYSTOLIC PRESSURE
After the cuff has been inflated until the artery is occluded, the pressure in the cuff is released

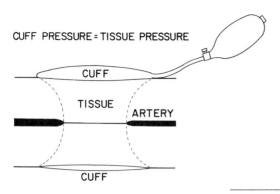

CUFF PRESSURE = TISSUE PRESSURE

Figure 21-1. Use of the cuff in the indirect measurement of arterial pressure. The pressure in the cuff is indicated by a manometer (not shown). The cuff is inflated, and the pressure in it is transmitted to the tissue of the limb and to the artery (*area within the dashed lines*). If the cuff pressure exceeds the arterial pressure, the artery is occluded. If the artery is just open or just closed, the pressure in the cuff is the same as that in the artery and can be read as the arterial pressure.

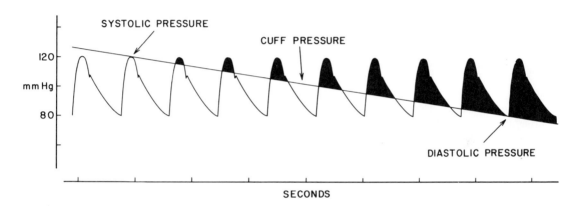

Figure 21-2. Estimation of the systolic pressure and the diastolic pressure by the indirect method. The cuff pressure that will be required to occlude the artery is estimated, and the cuff is inflated rapidly. The cuff pressure then is decreased slowly; when it is equal to the highest pressure reached in the artery during the cardiac cycle (indicated by the first intermittent opening of the artery), the systolic pressure is read. The cuff pressure is decreased further; when it is equal to the lowest pressure reached at any time during the cardiac cycle (indicated when the artery first remains open at all times during the cardiac cycle), the diastolic pressure is read.

slowly until blood flows through, intermittently, at the peak of each pulse. The periodic opening of the artery is verified by the use of a stethoscope placed over the artery just distal to the cuff. An intermittent, sharp, tapping sound is heard; this is the point of the *systolic pressure,* and it is identified easily.

DIASTOLIC PRESSURE
The pressure in the cuff is lowered continuously until a level is reached at which the sounds diminish abruptly. The flow is continuous because the pressure in the artery exceeds the pressure in the cuff at all times during the cycle; some sound still is heard, as partial compression of the artery produces turbulence. This is the *diastolic pressure,* and it is more difficult than systolic pressure to assess with confidence.

ARTERIAL PULSE

The ejection of blood by the left ventricle produces a stretch of the arterial wall that travels down the elastic arteries as a "pulse wave" (*arterial pulse*). In general, the pulse wave represents the stroke volume and the compliance of the arteries (i.e., the volume-pressure relationship, $D = dV/dP$) (Figure 21-3).

Pulse Contours

CHANGES IN CONTOUR
The pulse pressure increases as it moves through the long elastic arteries. The mean pressure decreases slightly between the aorta and the femoral artery; however, the systolic pressure increases and the diastolic pressure

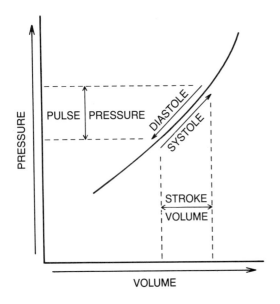

Figure 21-3. Change of pressure in the arteries with change of volume. The volume and the pressure both increase during systole, when the ventricle ejects blood into the artery, and decrease during diastole, as the blood flows out of the arteries through the peripheral resistance. Because the arteries are elastic and distended, neither variable can change without changing the other. The relationship is curvilinear, because the walls of the arteries are not homogeneous (see Chapter 12). The slope of the curve is an indication of the compliance of the arteries. If the compliance increases, the pulse pressure that accompanies a given stroke volume decreases; if the compliance decreases, the pulse pressure increases.

decreases (Figure 21-4). These changes probably can be related to the lesser compliance of the smaller arteries.

EFFECTS OF DISEASE:
AORTIC STENOSIS

If the leaflets of the aortic valve are fused together (stenosed) or if the left ventricular outflow tract is restricted so that only a narrow orifice is provided for the efflux of blood from the left ventricle, ejection is slowed and prolonged, and the pulse is low and broad (see Figure 21-4).

ARTERIOSCLEROSIS

Arteriosclerosis causes "hardening of the arteries," in which the compliance of the arteries is less than normal; therefore, the arterial pressure increases sharply during systole and

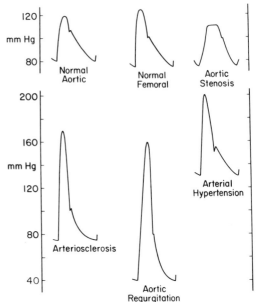

Figure 21-4. Normal aortic pulse, normal femoral arterial pulse, and aortic pulses characteristic of four abnormal conditions.

declines rapidly during diastole (see Figures 21-3 and 21-4). The pulse pressure is large, as the systolic pressure is much higher than normal, and the diastolic pressure is slightly lower than normal.

AORTIC INSUFFICIENCY

If the aortic valve does not produce a tight seal when it closes during diastole (*aortic insufficiency*), blood flows backward ("regurgitates") into the left ventricle, as well as forward into the aorta. Because the needs of the tissues must be satisfied, the net cardiac output must be normal; therefore, the stroke volume must be larger than normal. This adjustment is made intrinsically, because the blood that leaks back increases the preload of the ventricle (see Chapter 15). Because of the large stroke volume, the arterial systolic pressure is abnormally high, and because of the backflow of blood from the aorta, the arterial diastolic pressure is abnormally low (see Figure 21-4). Two disadvantages to the circulation ensue from this condition: (a) the large residual volume of the ventricle interferes with the filling of the ventricle during diastole, and (b) the extra work that must be performed decreases the reserve capacity of the heart (see Chapter 22).

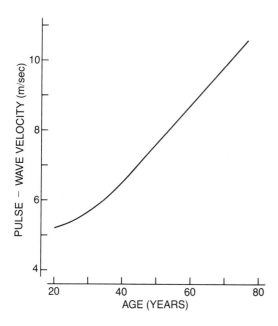

Figure 21-5. Relationship between age of the subject and the velocity of propagation of the pulse wave in the human aorta. (Redrawn, with permission, from P. Hallock. 1934. *Arch. Intern. Med.* 54:786. Copyright, 1934, American Medical Association.)

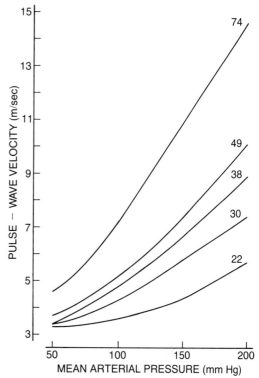

Figure 21-6. Relationship between the mean pressure and the pulse-wave velocity in the aorta of human subjects of different ages. The number beside each curve is the mean age of a group of subjects; the ages of the groups do not overlap. In a given age group, increasing arterial pressure increases the wall tension and causes the pulse wave to be propagated at a faster rate. The curves of increasing age show the effect of increased arteriosclerosis added to that of arterial pressure. (Redrawn, with permission, from A.L. King. 1947. *J. Appl. Physics* 18:598.)

ARTERIAL HYPERTENSION

In most cases of systemic *arterial hypertension*, the primary condition is the high diastolic pressure, which occurs because the peripheral resistance is high (see Figure 21-4). The systolic pressure also must be high, since the arterial pulse begins with the diastolic pressure. The pulse pressure, which is the difference between the diastolic pressure and the systolic pressure, is greater than normal simply because of the lesser compliance of the arteries at the higher pressure (see Figure 21-3). The pulse is increased even further if arteriosclerosis accompanies the hypertension and decreases the compliance further.

Velocity of Propagation

CHANGES WITH AGE

The mean velocity at which a wave of distention moves through the arterial system increases with the age of the subject in the population at large (Figure 21-5). This effect is related to the extent of arteriosclerosis and the mean arterial pressure, both of which increase with age; the less compliant, more tense arterial wall propa-

gates the pulse wave more rapidly. The influences of these factors separately are shown in Figure 21-6.

HYPERTENSION, OR ABNORMALLY HIGH ARTERIAL BLOOD PRESSURE

Determination of Normal

IDEAL NORMAL

The typical example of normal arterial blood pressure is "120/80 mm Hg," which means that the systolic pressure is 120 mm Hg and the diastolic pressure is 80 mm Hg. These values, typical of healthy young people, also might be considered ideal for adult persons of any age. There is considerable uncertainty, however, about the distinction between normal arterial pressure and hypertension.

STATISTICAL NORMAL

If the arterial pressure of a large number of subjects is measured, the values obtained are distributed about a mean value (Figure 21-7). The data can be analyzed according to conventional statistical methods, and certain values can be designated as being significantly greater or less than the mean. In a large population, approximately 96% of the readings of arterial pressure will fall within two standard deviations above the mean and two standard deviations below the mean of the entire group. The individual values that differ from the mean by more than two standard deviations may be considered not to belong to the same population, or to be significantly different from the rest of the population, and, hence, to be abnormal. In the general population, arterial pressure increases with age; therefore, one might determine the mean value in a population of subjects all of whom are of the same age, and those individuals whose arterial pressure is significantly greater than the mean for the group may be said to be hypertensive (Figure 21-8). It is apparent that these statistical criteria permit no value judgments to be made, and as a person grows older, if his arterial pressure increases by no more than a certain amount, he is not considered to have hypertension. For example, a person who is 50 years old might have arterial blood pressure readings of 160 mm Hg systolic

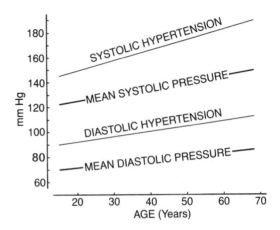

Figure 21-8.   Progression of arterial pressure with increasing age in a large population of human subjects. The mean systolic pressure and the mean diastolic pressure both increase; the systolic pressure increases at a greater rate than the diastolic pressure does; hence, the mean pulse pressure increases. The levels considered to be abnormally high are approximately two standard deviations above the corresponding mean.

---

and 90 mm Hg diastolic and still be considered "normal" (see Figure 21-8). Although these criteria have been thought to be adequate in the past, they are coming to be thought less so; a blood pressure reading of 160/90 probably should not be considered acceptable for a person of any age.

ORIGINS OF HYPERTENSION

The factors that determine the *systemic arterial blood pressure* are the *cardiac output* and the *total peripheral resistance:* Pressure = Flow × Resistance. In most cases of systemic arterial hypertension, the cardiac output is normal and the peripheral resistance is high.

Hypertension Caused by Specific Disease Processes

KIDNEY DYSFUNCTION

The systemic arterial blood pressure is elevated in a wide variety of *renal diseases* that decrease the renal blood flow or the functional renal mass. Conditions in which the rate of blood flow to the kidney is decreased include *atherosclerosis,* in which the lumina of the systemic arteries are narrowed by thickening of the intimal lining, and localized *constriction of the aorta or of the renal arteries.*

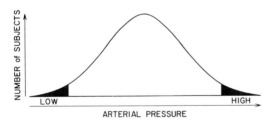

Figure 21-7.   Distribution of the readings of arterial blood pressure in a large human population. The exact values depend on the age of the group, but the shape of the curve is the same for all groups. Those values that are considered high or low bear some specified relationship to the mean and the variation of the population about the mean; for example, they might be more than two standard deviations from the mean.

POSSIBLE MECHANISMS: RENIN-ANGIOTENSIN SYSTEM

There appears to be a pressure-sensing mechanism in the *juxtaglomerular cells* (see Chapter 32), which causes the release of a proteolytic enzyme, *renin*, when the renal blood flow is reduced. Renin acts on a specific globulin of the plasma to produce a peptide, *angiotensin I*, which then is converted to *angiotensin II*, a vasoconstrictor. Angiotensin II acts on the systemic arterioles to increase the peripheral vascular resistance. Constriction of the renal arterioles is prevented by prostaglandin E_2, a vasodilator released locally in the kidney. In addition, angiotensin II causes the adrenal cortex to release *aldosterone*, a hormone that promotes the retention of salt and water by the kidneys. Renin also is released, by sympathetic nervous system activity that stimulates adrenergic β-receptors in the juxtaglomerular cells.

UNKNOWN SUBSTANCES

The systemic arterial pressure also may be increased by other metabolites or substances that may be retained or produced as a consequence of decreased renal function.

RENAL VASCULAR DAMAGE

Hypertension caused by any means may damage the *renal blood vessels* and thereby cause the renal mechanisms to be involved. Thus, there may be additive effects that make therapy more difficult. It is important to realize that because of its effects on the kidney and other organ systems, hypertension can be a progressive disease.

DYSFUNCTION OF ADRENAL GLANDS: PHEOCHROMOCYTOMA

Pheochromocytoma is a tumor of the *chromaffin cells,* in the *adrenal medulla* or associated with sympathetic ganglia, that secretes *catecholamines*. The systemic arterial pressure is increased because the heart rate, the cardiac output, and the peripheral resistance are increased (see Clinical Correlation 8.1, pp. 150–151).

ADRENOCORTICAL TUMOR: CUSHING'S SYNDROME

Hypertension is the principal cardiovascular effect of *adrenocortical tumors,* which cause the release of large amounts of corticosteroid hormones (see Chapter 60). The mechanism is not clear, but sodium retention and increased extracellular fluid volume are implicated. In addition, cortical hormones increase the sensitivity of the systemic arterioles to norepinephrine and epinephrine.

TOXEMIA OF PREGNANCY

The effects of *toxemia of pregnancy* may be related to increased secretion of adrenocortical hormones or to effects of the placental hormones similar to those of the mineralocorticoids; in either circumstance, fluid is retained and edema and hypertension develop. Renal lesions, which suggest the possibility of an immunological or allergic response, also occur.

COARCTATION OF THE AORTA

Coarctation of the aorta is a congenital malformation in which the aorta is constricted at its junction with the *ductus arteriosus*; thus, the blood that flows to the distal parts of the body must overcome an abnormal resistance. The perfusion of the distal parts usually is normal, partly because an extensive system of collateral vessels develops from arteries central to the lesion, and partly because a large gradient of pressure is generated across the constriction. The *arterial pressure* central to the constriction is abnormally high, despite the fact that the baroreceptors of the aortic arch and the carotid sinuses are located within the area of hypertension. The following *sequence of adaptation* probably occurs: the kidneys, through the renin-angiotensin system, cause the retention of Na^+ and water, which increases the blood volume and the cardiac output; the tissues central to the constriction increase their vascular resistance by autoregulation; the aortic pressure increases until enough blood flows past the constriction and through the developing collaterals to satisfy the needs of the kidneys. The cardiac output returns to normal, and the central arterial pressure remains high. The baroreceptors of the aortic arch and the carotid sinuses adapt to the high pressure. Thus, it is clear that, in the long run, the kidney is the dominant factor in the determination of the systemic arterial pressure.

CARDIOVASCULAR DISEASE: GENERALIZED ATHEROSCLEROSIS

In the condition of *atherosclerosis*, the *intima* of the arteries is thickened and the *elastic laminae* degenerate; the *lumen* is decreased and resistance to blood flow appears in the medium

CLINICAL CORRELATION
21.1   Hypertension

CASE REPORT

The Patient: A 27-year-old man.

Reason for Admission: Systemic arterial hypertension, discovered on physical examination.

History: The patient had been discovered to have mild hypertension six years ago. Recently he had experienced fatigue, dyspnea during exercise, and headaches.

Clinical Examination: At admission, the patient appeared well. The heart was of normal size, and the rhythm was regular, but a systolic murmur was heard. The arterial pressure was elevated in the brachial artery, but not in the posterior tibial artery. An arteriogram indicated coarctation of the aorta, and the femoral pulse was delayed relative to the radial pulse. The ECG revealed a normal rhythm at a rate of 72/min, and the axis in the frontal plane (see Chapter 19, "Information Contained in the Electrocardiogram") was normal. Catheterization disclosed that right atrial, right ventricular, pulmonary arterial, left atrial, and left ventricular end-diastolic pressures were normal. Pressure in the aortic arch was 150/90 mm Hg (normal, 90–140/60–90 mm Hg); differences of 45 mm Hg in peak pressure and 25 mm Hg in mean pressure were found across a length of vessel that was irregularly narrowed, beginning at the aortic isthmus.

Comment: Constriction of the aorta as seen in this case usually gives rise to extensive collateral circulation that effectively bypasses the lesion. If the coarctation develops early in life, dilated intercostal arteries usually cause "rib-notching" (grooves, or notches, in the ribs). Neither this nor other signs of the enlargement of collateral vessels were seen. Thus, it appeared that the lesion was not congenital and probably had occurred in young adult life. The systolic murmur that usually is heard reflects the decrease of the vessel size and the consequent increase of velocity of blood flow (see Ch. 12) in the aorta and any collaterals that develop.

Treatment: A thoracotomy was performed (the chest was opened), and the aorta was found to be obstructed by thickening of the wall in a 6.5 cm segment distal to the origin of the subclavian artery. The partially occluded segment was bypassed, using a prosthetic graft. Samples from the aorta at the sites of anastomosis revealed an arteritis consistent with Takayasu's aortitis. Its cause is not known; it may be an immune disease, or it may be releated to infection.

Outcome: After the surgery, arterial pressures in the arms and legs were about equal, in the range of 130/80 mm Hg. Although corticosteroids (see Chapter 60, "Lymphoid Tissue and Elements of Blood") help to alleviate the symptoms of the aortitis, the disease is likely to recur or progress.

and small arteries. *Ischemia* of the kidneys causes hypertension.

Primary, or Essential, Hypertension

About 90% of the cases of hypertension are *primary hypertension*. The origin of the condition cannot be attributed to any specific lesion; the renal function is normal at the outset; however,

one never should forget that *hypertension of any cause eventually damages the kidney*.

A condition of *labile hypertension* has been described, and attributed to a *hyperkinetic circulation*. The increase of pressure is caused by inappropriately high cardiac output in response to stressful circumstances. The peripheral resistance is normal initially, but it increases because the cardiac output is more than is needed and the tissues autoregulate their

perfusion. A *genetic predisposition* to inadequate renal function, which permits the fluid
volume of the body to increase and thereby
leads to inappropriate cardiac output, also has
been proposed.

Consequences of Primary Hypertension

VASCULAR DAMAGE

In *primary hypertension,* the most serious harm
is done to the *renal vessels;* however, the *retinal
arteries* also are threatened and vision may be
impaired. Generalized *arteriosclerosis,* which
involves the replacement of the elastic tissue by
collagen, is accelerated by high arterial blood
pressure. The small elastic arteries are eroded
and weakened; thrombi may form in the fractured walls or the vessels may rupture. Cerebral
hemorrhage may occur.

CARDIAC DAMAGE

Continuously high systemic arterial pressure
increases the afterload against which the left
ventricle must empty (see Chapter 15), and the
ventricle undergoes hypertrophy. The mass of
the muscle increases, and this adaptation enables the ventricle to meet the added work
load; however, if the overload persists, the *myocardium* eventually is damaged. *Myocardial
ischemia* occurs, frequently accompanied by
pain (*angina pectoris*) and followed eventually
by *cardiac failure* (see Chapter 22).

RESETTING THE BARORECEPTORS

If the mean arterial pressure remains elevated
long enough, the *baroreceptors* of the aortic arch
and the carotid sinuses adapt and maintain the
new level (Figure 21-9). This can occur after
only a few days, and it may be another factor in
the gradual progression of hypertension. It has
been proposed that intrinsically abnormal setting of the baroreceptors may account for some
cases of essential hypertension; however, it is
more likely that other systems, which do not
adapt so readily, determine the level of the arterial pressure in the long term.

MALIGNANT HYPERTENSION

Malignant hypertension is a progressive condition in which the arterial pressure rises rapidly
and death occurs within a few months from
vascular rupture, cardiac failure, or degenerative renal disease.

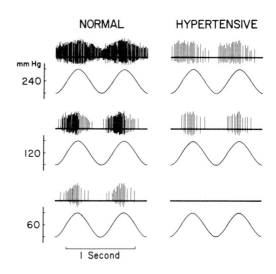

Figure 21-9. Decreased sensitivity of the carotid
sinus baroreceptor in a hypertensive dog compared to that in a normal dog. One carotid sinus
was isolated and connected to a pressure bottle,
which permitted control of the carotid sinus pressure. Electrical activity was recorded from the
carotid sinus nerve. The pressure at the left indicates the mean carotid sinus pressure; the pressure
waves vary by 50 mm Hg from trough to peak.
(Redrawn, with permission, from J.W. McCubbin,
J.H. Green, and I.H. Page. 1956. Baroreceptor
Function in Chronic Renal Hypertension. *Circ.
Res.* 4:208.)

Relation of Hypertension to Diet

SALT

Studies of intake and excretion indicate that in
the general population, most people consume
far more sodium chloride (*salt*) than they need.
Excessive intake of sodium may predispose to
hypertension, and it makes existing hypertension worse. The effect may be related to expansion of the extracellular fluid volume, to edema
of the walls of small arteries and arterioles, or to
increased sensitivity of arterioles to sympathetic
constrictor activity. The addition of salt to food
reflects an acquired taste, and it appears that to
acquire a taste for less salt would be wise.

FATS

There is a strong statistical correlation between
hypertension and *excess body weight;* therefore,
to the extent that the high caloric value of *fat* in
the diet increases the probability of obesity, the
intake of fat should be controlled carefully. In
addition, considerable evidence links the blood

levels of saturated fats and cholesterol with *degenerative artery disease*, and foods that contain large quantities of those substances should be avoided.

Psychosocial Stimuli

The tensions, anxieties, and hostilities associated with modern life may predispose to *hypertension*. Experimentally, animals forced into crowded, threatening, or strongly competitive environments develop cardiovascular disease and hypertension. Worldwide survey studies show that people who are adapted to secure, traditional cultures are less subject to hypertension than are those who are experiencing *psychological stress* in the form of technological, social, political, or religious change. It has been proposed that higher nervous system input, acting on the defense alarm mechanism of the hypothalamus, causes repeated increases of arterial pressure, the consequences

of which eventually sustain hypertension. Thus, hypertension may be considered a disease of civilization.

Heredity

The complex mechanisms that underlie hypertension likely are too varied to be attributed to a single gene. It has been proposed that the level of an individual's arterial pressure is *inherited polygenetically,* and environmental factors determine whether it will increase with age. Statistically, hypertensive people transmit the condition to their offspring. If one parent has hypertension, approximately half of the children also will have hypertension. If both parents have hypertension, the chances of an offspring also having hypertension approach certainty. However, the role of the environment cannot be ignored, even here, for the child shares with the family his early environment as well as his genes.

STUDY OUTLINE

INDIRECT MEASUREMENT Pressure in cuff around arm can be equated to arterial pressure at certain times of the cardiac cycle.

Pressure that barely occludes artery at highest pressure of cycle is *systolic pressure*.

Pressure that barely occludes artery at lowest pressure of cycle is *diastolic pressure*.

IDENTIFYING PRESSURES BY EVALUATING SOUNDS

SYSTOLIC PRESSURE Intermittent, sharp, tapping sound heard when previously occluded artery opens at peak of pressure.

DIASTOLIC PRESSURE Sound diminishes as artery previously occluded at lowest level of pressure remains open during entire cycle.

ARTERIAL PULSE Stretch of arterial wall that travels down elastic arteries as "pulse wave."

PULSE CONTOURS

CHANGES IN CONTOUR Pulse pressure increases from aorta to periphery.

EFFECTS OF DISEASE: AORTIC STENOSIS Ejection slowed and prolonged, pulse low and broad.

ARTERIOSCLEROSIS Compliance is decreased, pulse is increased.

AORTIC INSUFFICIENCY Blood leaks back during diastole.

Large stroke volume, large pulse pressure.

End-systolic pressure and end-diastolic pressure increased.

Added work load on heart.

ARTERIAL HYPERTENSION Primary condition is increased diastolic pressure due to increased peripheral resistance.

Systolic pressure must increase; sum of diastolic pressure and pulse pressure.

Pulse pressure increased; decreased compliance of arteries as pressure increases.

Arteriosclerosis decreases compliance further.

VELOCITY OF PROPAGATION Related to decreased arterial compliance.

CHANGES WITH AGE Increases with arteriosclerosis.

Increases with mean arterial pressure.

HYPERTENSION, OR ABNORMALLY HIGH ARTERIAL BLOOD PRESSURE

DETERMINATION OF NORMAL

IDEAL NORMAL Systolic pressure 120 mm Hg, diastolic 80 mm Hg (120/80).

STATISTICAL NORMAL Within some

specified range above and below mean value of population; increases with age.

ORIGINS OF HYPERTENSION   Usually, cardiac output normal and systemic vascular resistance high.

HYPERTENSION CAUSED BY SPECIFIC DISEASE PROCESSES

KIDNEY DYSFUNCTION   Decreased renal blood flow or renal mass.

POSSIBLE MECHANISMS: RENIN-ANGIOTENSIN SYSTEM   Renin (enzyme) released by kidneys; acts on plasma globulin to produce angiotensin I (peptide), converted to angiotensin II (constricts systemic arterioles).

Renin released because of renal ischemia, sympathetic nervous system input to kidneys.

UNKNOWN SUBSTANCES   Retained or produced as result of decreased renal function.

RENAL VASCULAR DAMAGE   Hypertension from any cause can damage renal blood vessels, make hypertension progressive.

DYSFUNCTION OF ADRENAL GLANDS: PHEOCHROMOCYTOMA   Tumor of chromaffin cells, secretes catecholamines.

ADRENOCORTICAL TUMOR: CUSHING'S SYNDROME   Mineralocorticoid action of excess adrenal steroids.

TOXEMIA OF PREGNANCY   May be related to increased secretion of cortical hormones, to mineralocorticoid effect of placental hormones, or to immunological lesions of kidneys.

COARCTATION OF THE AORTA   Constriction of descending aorta; abnormally high arterial pressure develops central to constriction.

CARDIOVASCULAR DISEASE: GENERALIZED ATHEROSCLEROSIS   Intima of arteries thickens, lumen decreases, resistance to blood flow appears; renal ischemia causes hypertension.

PRIMARY, OR ESSENTIAL, HYPERTENSION   About 90% of cases.

Hyperkinetic circulation: cardiac output too great, tissues autoregulate, resistance increases.

Fluid volume increases, causes inappropriate cardiac output, because of inherently inadequate renal function.

CONSEQUENCES OF PRIMARY HYPERTENSION

VASCULAR DAMAGE   Damage of renal vessels most serious; generalized arteriosclerosis accelerated.

CARDIAC DAMAGE   Increased afterload causes hypertrophy, cardiac failure.

RESETTING BARORECEPTORS   Baroreceptors adapt in a few days, support higher pressure; leads to progression of hypertension.

MALIGNANT HYPERTENSION   (without treatment) Arterial hypertension progresses rapidly, leads to death in a few months.

RELATION OF HYPERTENSION TO DIET

SALT   Excess intake predisposes to hypertension.

FATS   High caloric value increases probability of obesity.

Hypertension often associated with obesity.

Saturated fats and cholesterol associated with degenerative artery disease.

PSYCHOSOCIAL STIMULI   Repeated increases of arterial pressure caused by stress, tension, hostility eventually may sustain hypertension.

HEREDITY   Predisposition for hypertension transmitted to offspring; probably a combination of genetics and environment.

BIBLIOGRAPHY

Bohr, D.F., and Sitrin, M. 1970. Regulation of vascular smooth muscle contraction: changes in experimental hypertension. *Circ. Res.* 27:(Suppl. II) II-83.

Brenner, B.M., and Stein, J.H. 1981. *Hypertension.* New York City: Churchill-Livingstone.

Brody, M.J.; Haywood, J.R.; and Touw, K.B. 1980. Neural mechanisms in hypertension. *Annu. Rev. Physiol.* 42:441.

Chobanian, A.V. 1982. Hypertension. *Clin. Symp.* 34:3.

Cohn, J., editor. 1977. Hypertension: experimental and clinical studies. *Circ. Res.* 40 (Suppl. 1).

Coleman, T.G.; Granger, H.J.; and Guyton, A.C. 1971. Whole-body circulatory autoregulation with hypertension. *Circ. Res.* 28:(Suppl. II) II-76.

Dawber, T.R. 1980. *The Framingham study: the epidemiology of arteriosclerotic disease.* Cambridge, Mass: Harvard University Press.

Dorward, P.K.; Andresen, M.C.; Burke, S. L., et al 1982. Rapid resetting of the aortic baroreceptors in the rabbit and its implications for short-term and longer-term reflex control. *Circ. Res.* 50:428.

Dworkin, B.R.; Filewich, B.J.; Miller, N.E., et al. 1979. Baroreceptor activation reduces reactivity to noxious stimulation: implication for hypertension. *Science* 205:1299.

Folkow, B. 1982. Physiological aspects of primary hypertension. *Physiol. Rev.* 62:347.

Freeman, T.M., and Gregg, O.W., editors. 1982. Sodium intake: dietary concern. St. Paul, Minn.: American Assoc. Cereal Chemists.

Fregly, M.J., and Kare, M.R. 1982. *The role of salt in cardiovascular hypertension.* New York: Academic Press.

Frolich, E.D. 1982. Hemodynamic factors in the pathogenesis and maintenance of hypertension. *Fed. Proc.* 41:2400.

Frolich, E.D.; Vlado, J.K.; Tarazi, R.C., et al. 1970. Physiological comparison of labile and essential hypertension. *Circ. Res.* 27:(Suppl. II) II-55.

Grundy, S.M., et al. 1982. Rationale of the diet-heart statement of the American Heart Association: report of Nutrition Committee. *Circulation* 65:839A.

Guyton, A.C. 1980. *Arterial pressure and hypertension.* Philadelphia: Saunders.

Hallock, P. 1934. Arterial elasticity in man in relation to age as evaluated by pulse wave velocity method. *Arch. Intern. Med.* 54:770.

Henry, J.P., and Cassel, J.C. 1969. Psychosocial factors in essential hypertension: recent epidemiologic and animal experimental evidence. *Am. J. Epidemiol.* 90:171.

Hunt, J.C., editor. 1973. Hypertension in man and the experimental animal. *Circ. Res.* 32 (Suppl. I).

Kaplan, H.R., chairman. 1981. Hypertension and antihypertensive drugs (Symposism). *Fed. Proc.* 40:2250.

King, A.L. 1947. Pressure-volume relation for cylindrical tubes with elastomeric walls: the human aorta. *J. Appl. Physics.* 18:598.

Li, J.K-J.; Melbin, J.; Riffle, R.A., et al. 1981. Pulse wave propagation. *Circ. Res.* 49:442.

Master, A.M.; Garfield, C.C.; and Walters, M.B. 1952. *Normal blood pressure and hypertension.* Philadelphia: Lea & Febiger.

McCubbin, J.W.; Green, J.H.; and Page, I.H. 1956. Baroreceptor function in chronic renal hypertension. *Circ. Res.* 4:205.

O'Malley, K., and O'Brien, E., 1980. Management of hypertension in the elderly. *N. Engl. J. Med.* 302:1397.

Onesti, G., and Kim, K.E. 1981. *Hypertension in the young and the old.* New York: Grune & Stratton.

Rushmer, R.F. 1976. *Cardiovascular dynamics.* 4th ed. Philadelphia: Saunders.

Sleight, P.O., editor. 1981. *Arterial baroreceptors and hypertension.* New York: Oxford University Press.

Sparrow, D.; Garvey, A.J.; Rosner, B., et al. 1982. Factors in predicting blood pressure change. *Circ.* 65:789.

Tuck, M.L.; Sowers, J.; Dornfeld, L., et al. 1981. The effect of weight reduction on blood pressure, plasma renin activity, and plasma aldosterone levels in obese patients. *N. Engl. J. Med.* 304:930.

Wood, J., editor. 1967. Renin mechanisms and hypertension. *Circ. Res.* 21:(Suppl. 2).

22

Cardiac Failure

CHAPTER CONTENTS

CARDIAC RESERVE

The manifestation of cardiac failure is low cardiac output in relation to the needs of the body. Whether failure occurs depends on what is required of the heart—a subject may do well if he is relatively inactive but may be unable to exercise strenuously. A person uses his *cardiac reserve* when he increases his activity; therefore, cardiac failure may be defined as *diminution of the cardiac reserve.* The subject in cardiac failure will have used a portion of his cardiac reserve for normal function and will have less of it left to meet added demand. If the demand is limited and the heart can meet it, the subject is *compensated.* If the demand is not met, he is *decompensated.*

Venous Oxygen Reserve

Active tissues obtain more oxygen by extracting some of the oxygen that remains in the venous blood in the resting state. Even in the healthy person, increased cardiac output is paralleled by increased arteriovenous oxygen difference (Figure 22-1). Together, the cardiac output and the oxygen that can be extracted from it constitute the cardiac reserve.

Fully saturated arterial blood contains about 19 ml of oxygen per 100 ml of blood and, in the resting state, venous blood still contains about 14 ml of oxygen per 100 ml. This is the oxygen content of mixed venous blood, which comes from tissues that have high, or potentially high, rates of oxygen consumption, such as the heart

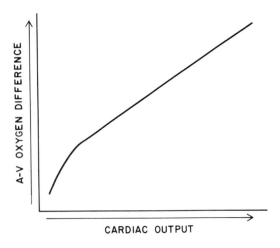

Figure 22-1.   More of the oxygen content is taken from the arterial blood as the cardiac output increases to meet increased metabolic needs of the tissues. This change occurs because the rate of flow increases in active tissues, which extract a larger fraction of oxygen from the blood, and decreases in less active tissues.

and the skeletal muscles, as well as from tissues that extract oxygen at low rates, such as the skin and the kidney. During exertion, vasoconstriction diverts blood from the skin, the kidneys, and the gastrointestinal tract and makes it available to supply oxygen to the active muscles (Figure 22-2).

Heart Rate

The heart rate is the most labile component of the cardiac reserve; it also is the factor that is called on most readily. As a component of cardiac output, the normal heart rate of about 70 beats per minute may be increased to an effective upper limit of 150–180 beats per minute. However, the physiological increase of heart rate is not an isolated event; it occurs always as part of a coordinated cardiovascular response that is mediated by the autonomic nervous system.

Stroke Volume

SYSTOLIC RESERVE

The normal heart ejects only about two-thirds of its volume in one stroke, and it can respond to a need for increased cardiac output by further emptying. This adjustment is used less than the heart rate in responding to increased demand;

however, a physiological increase of cardiac output is accompanied by a slight, progressive increase of the stroke volume, which is accomplished mostly by decreasing the end-systolic volume of the ventricle (see Figure 15-10). Increase in stroke volume is mediated by the sympathetic nervous system, and it is correlated with appropriate adjustments of vascular tone to maintain the venous input. The ejection fraction (the ratio of stroke volume to end-diastolic volume) is increased because the stroke volume is increased and the end-diastolic volume is decreased (see Figure 15-10).

DIASTOLIC RESERVE

Additional stroke volume can be gained by increasing the diastolic volume; this adjustment is not related to the physiological increase of cardiac output, in which the diastolic volume diminishes. An increase in diastolic volume is a component of the intrinsic system of cardiac adaptation; its physiological function is to balance the outputs of the two ventricles (see Figure 15-12). In certain pathophysiological conditions, it is used to accommodate intracardiac shunts or to provide an immediate response to increased outflow resistance (vasoconstriction or obstruction).

TYPES OF CARDIAC FAILURE

High-Output Failure

In high-output failure, the demand for blood flow is so great that the heart is unable to meet the needs of the body without abnormal use of the cardiac reserve. The increased demand is caused by a condition that usually can be identified and corrected, such as anemia, vitamin deficiency, or thyrotoxicosis. Although this category of failure meets the definition of heart failure, it usually is distinguished from low-output failure. Nevertheless, it does illustrate further that cardiac failure is a chronic state in which *the heart is the limiting factor in determining the cardiac output.*

Low-Output Failure

Low-output failure usually is caused by coronary artery disease or by conditions that chronically increase the preload or the afterload of the heart, such as valvular disease, arterial hypertension, or congenital cardiac defects. Low-

CLINICAL CORRELATION
22.1   High-Output Cardiac Failure

CASE REPORT

The Patient: A 42-year-old male.

Principal Complaint: Difficult breathing (dyspnea).

History: The patient was a chronic alcoholic. For several months, his diet has consisted of chips and snacks ("junk food") and about 1.5 liters/day of vodka. Recently, he had experienced pain in the feet and legs, general weakness, and occasional nausea and vomiting. Two days before admission, he developed dyspnea, orthopnea, and nocturnal sweating.

Clinical Examination: At admission, the patient appeared acutely ill, anxious, and in mild respiratory stress. His blood pressure was 100/60 mm Hg at rest (normal, 90–140/60–90 mm Hg), his pulse rate was 140 beats/min (normal, < 100 beats/min), and his temperature was 36.2 C. The jugular vein was distended. The lungs were clear by auscultation; there was a strong systolic murmur and an early diastolic murmur. Sounds ("bruits") were audible over the femoral arteries, which indicates a high velocity of blood flow (see "Murmurs" in Chapter 13). The ECG showed sinus tachycardia; a chest radiograph revealed mild pulmonary venous congestion and increased heart size compared with a film taken a year earlier. Arterial blood pH was 7.06 (normal, 7.35–7.45), P_{O_2} was 92 mm Hg (normal, 75–100 mm Hg), and P_{CO_2} was 12 mm Hg (normal, 35–45 mm Hg). The serum lactate concentration was 22 mEq/liter (normal, 0.6–1.8 mEq/liter). The pH and P_{CO_2} indicate metabolic acidosis, and the lactate indicates, specifically, lactic acidosis. Cardiac catheterization revealed a cardiac output of 23 liters/min (13 liters/min/m²), measured by the Fick oxygen method (normal, 2.5–4.2 liters/min/m²). The arteriovenous oxygen difference was 1.5 ml of O_2/100 ml of blood) (normal, 3–5 ml of O_2/100 ml of blood), which indicates car-

diac output in excess of tissue needs. Mean aortic pressure was 68 mm Hg (normal, 70–105 mm Hg), and the mean right atrial pressure was 22 mm Hg (normal, 0–8 mm Hg). Thus, systemic vascular resistance was 0.12 mm Hg/ml/sec (160 dyne cm^{-2}/cm^{3}sec^{-1}), which is about one-tenth of normal. Mean pulmonary arterial pressure was 28 mm Hg (normal, 9–16 mm Hg), and the mean pulmonary arterial wedge pressure, which is taken to represent mean left atrial pressure (see "Pulmonary Arterial Wedge Pressure" in Chapter 17), was 23 mm Hg (normal, 3–15 mm Hg). Thus, pulmonary vascular resistance was 0.013 mm Hg/ml/sec (17 dyne cm^{-2}/cm^{3}sec^{-1}), which is about one-fifth of normal. The high cardiac output appears to be related to low vascular resistance. Right ventricular end-diastolic pressure was 21 mm Hg (normal, 0–8 mm Hg), and left ventricular end-diastolic pressure was 23 mm Hg (normal, 3–12 mm Hg). These values, and the patient's respiratory symptoms, indicate high-output cardiac failure. The patient's nutritional history, the low systemic vascular resistance, biventricular cardiac failure, and lactic acidosis all suggest beriberi (thiamine deficiency) as the cause.

Treatment: The patient was treated initially with digoxin (a cardiac glycoside, which increases the contractility of the heart), thiamine, and bicarbonate. Improvement was rapid, and only thiamine and other vitamins were given after the first day. Because the failure was not caused by a cardiac lesion, digoxin was not needed, and correction of the metabolic defect enabled the homeostatic mechanisms of the body to correct the acidosis. The cause of the peripheral vasodilation, which precipitated the failure, is not known, but the condition was corrected by administration of thiamine.

Outcome: Within 2 weeks, the patient's hemodynamic indices were normal, and he has continued to be well, receiving only thiamine as treatment.

output failure will serve as the prototype for cardiac failure in the remainder of this chapter.

CONSEQUENCES OF COMPENSATION (FIGURE 22-2)

Mild heart disease may produce no symptoms until the appropriate stress is encountered; then it may be "corrected," or compensated, by the use of the cardiac reserve. If the stress is too great, it will cause "decompensation," which means that the cardiac reserve is inadequate to meet the demand for more cardiac output.

Effects Related Directly to Sympathetic Nervous System Activity

REFLEX ARTERIOLAR CONSTRICTION: REDISTRIBUTION OF CARDIAC OUTPUT

Compensation restricts the flow of blood to most organs, but some are affected much more than others (Figure 22-4). Blood flow to the skin of the hands, the face, and the head decreases; these areas become cold, and because of the slow rate of flow, may be cyanotic. The rate of blood flow to the mesentery and the kidneys decreases markedly. Perfusion of the heart and the brain is affected little, and the rate of oxygen consumption by these vital organs does not decrease. Skeletal muscles are perfused because of metabolically induced autoregulation, but

the demand must be strong, and fatigue limits activity.

TACHYCARDIA
The increased heart rate reflects the use of the cardiac reserve.

CARDIAC CONTRACTILITY
Although ventricular contractility may be augmented by sympathetic nervous system activity, it still is less than normal (Figure 22-3). The capacity of the myocardium to develop tension more rapidly and to contract more forcefully in response to demand is decreased markedly.

INCREASED CENTRAL VENOUS PRESSURE
Increased venous tone increases the filling pressure of the heart. This effect is a part of the sympathetically mediated drive to increase the cardiac output. Increased diastolic filling pressure recruits the length-tension property of the heart, which is a component of the intrinsic cardiac adaptation; however, the capacity of the failing myocardium to respond to this stimulus is less than normal (Figure 22-5).

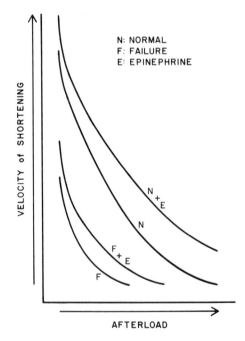

Figure 22-3.   Impaired contractility of the failing heart compared with the normal heart. The increase of contractility is smaller in the failing heart than in the normal heart.

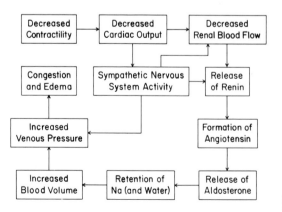

Figure 22-2.   Causes and consequences of cardiac compensation.

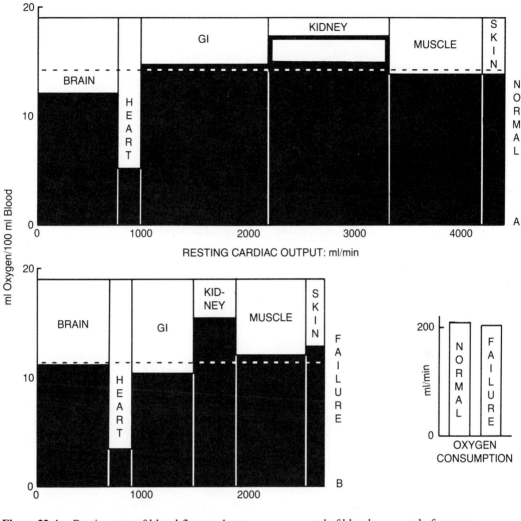

Figure 22-4. Resting rate of blood flow and resting arteriovenous oxygen difference in the various tissues in a healthy subject and in one who has cardiac failure. The rates of flow in each tissue are added to give the cardiac output in each case. The concentration of oxygen in the arterial blood is 19 ml/100 ml of blood. The light portion of each bar indicates the amount of oxygen that is extracted from each 100 ml of arterial blood, and the dark area of each bar shows the amount of oxygen that remains in each 100 ml of venous blood. The dashed line in each graph gives the concentration of oxygen in the mixed venous blood. In each bar, the product of the rate of blood flow and the rate of extraction of oxygen gives the amount of oxygen that is consumed by each tissue in one minute:

$$\frac{\text{ml of blood}}{\text{min}} \times \frac{\text{ml of oxygen}}{100 \text{ ml of blood}}$$

$$= \frac{\text{ml of oxygen}}{\text{min}}$$

Although the resting cardiac output is decreased in the subject who has heart failure (because of blood flow redistribution in the gastrointestinal tract and the kidney and the increased rate of extraction in all tissues), the mean rate of oxygen consumption is not significantly different. It is important to understand, however, that this equality exists only when the subject is resting; the subject who has cardiac failure would be able to engage in only very limited activity because virtually all of his or her cardiac reserve has been used up.

RELEASE OF RENIN
Renin is released (see below) in part through activation of adrenergic beta-receptors located in the kidney.

Effects Related Indirectly to Sympathetic Nervous System Activity

INCREASED BLOOD VOLUME
Because of the low cardiac output and the vasoconstriction that characterize cardiac failure, renal blood flow is reduced and redistributed within the kidney, and the excretion of salt and water is curtailed. Impaired renal function leads to retention of fluid and increased blood volume.

RELEASE OF ALDOSTERONE
A sensory system in the juxtaglomerular apparatus of the kidney senses the distention of the afferent arterioles; if the perfusion of the kidneys decreases, renin is released into the circulation. Renin, an enzyme, acts on a specific globulin of the plasma to produce angiotensin I, a peptide; angiotensin I is converted to angiotensin II in the lungs and the kidneys. Angiotensin II causes the adrenal cortex to release aldosterone, which promotes the reabsorption of sodium in the distal renal tubules; the retention of sodium leads to the retention of water. Angiotensin, a vasoconstrictor, also may contribute to the redistribution of the cardiac output. It appears to increase the afterload of the left ventricle in cases of cardiac failure, since administration of a drug that inhibits the converting enzyme, and thereby opposes the formation of angiotensin, increases the cardiac index; decreases the pulmonary wedge pressure, the mean systemic arterial pressure, and the heart rate; and improves renal and hepatic function. Aldosterone is inactivated by the liver; if the function of the liver is impaired by the inadequate circulation, aldosterone may accumulate and its effects may be intensified.

INCREASED HEART SIZE
The increased blood volume enhances the action of the increased venous tone to augment the diastolic filling pressure and hence the diastolic volume of the heart. The length-tension property of the myocardium may help to maintain the stroke volume; however, the capacity of the heart to utilize this intrinsic pro-

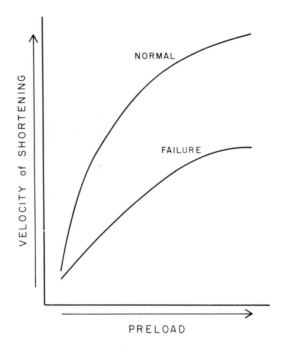

Figure 22-5.   Velocity of shortening in a failing heart is affected less than that of a normal heart by an increase of preload.

perty is impaired (see Figure 22-5). The ejection fraction is less than normal because the end-diastolic volume increases and the stroke volume remains small.

EDEMA
When the venous pressure increases, the capillary pressure also increases. If the mean capillary pressure exceeds the mean plasma oncotic pressure (see Figure 12-18), fluid accumulates in the interstitial space. Fluid accumulates first in the tissues of the dependent parts (ankles, feet, and legs) because the force of gravity also increases the capillary pressure. In the pulmonary circulation, fluid may accumulate in the interstitial space of the lungs. If the edema is mild, it may decrease when the subject rests. In the systemic circulation, edema forms during the day, when the subject is upright and more active, and is reabsorbed during the night, when the subject is reclining and the effect of gravity on the dependent limbs is less. The rate of urine formation increases at night, as fluid is reabsorbed from the tissues. In the pulmonary circulation, edema may be a more serious problem when the subject is reclining, because an additional volume of blood is transferred into the vessels of the lungs. When the subject is upright,

the volume of blood is transferred back to the systemic circulation in the lower parts of the body under the influence of gravity. If the failure is more severe, fluid forms in the potential serous spaces (for example, ascites in the peritoneal cavity), and the liver, spleen, kidneys, and lungs may be congested. To a certain extent, edema is self-limiting, because the collection of fluid in the interstitial space increases the interstitial fluid pressure and decreases the transcapillary pressure gradient. Experimentally, edema is associated with tissue-fluid pressure that equals or slightly exceeds atmospheric pressure (see Chapter 12).

Signs and Symptoms of Cardiac Failure

The clinical syndrome of cardiac failure is related to inadequate circulation and the consequences of compensation. Fatigue and weakness are caused by inadequate circulation. Cold, pale skin and tachycardia reflect the continuous activity of the sympathetic nervous system. Venous engorgement is caused by high central venous pressure and increased blood volume. The swollen liver and peritoneal cavity, congested lungs, and peripheral edema reflect high capillary hydrostatic pressure.

UNILATERAL FAILURE

Up to this point, the discussion of cardiac failure has not distinguished between the ventricles involved; it is not unusual for only one ventricle to fail at a time.

Right Ventricular Failure

The right ventricle is adapted to be a volume pump (see Figure 15-8), and it rarely fails as a result of a volume load alone; however, pulmonary hypertension may develop in response to excessive pulmonary blood flow. Thus, in many cases of congenital malformation of the heart in which blood recirculates through the pulmonary circuit, cardiac failure is caused by the chronic pressure load that develops secondarily. The ultimate cause of the hypertension is not clear, but the immediate cause is increased pulmonary vascular resistance, as the small pulmonary arteries become thickened and noncompliant and the lumina diminish.

The most common cause of failure of the right ventricle is prior failure of the left ventricle. The high pulmonary venous pressure that develops adds to the afterload of the right ventricle. Other conditions that cause chronic pressure loading and failure of the right ventricle include stenosis of the mitral or pulmonic valve, subvalvular obstruction of the outflow tract of the right ventricle, and primary lung disease that includes pulmonary hypertension. The signs and symptoms of right ventricular failure are those of systemic venous congestion and peripheral edema.

Left Ventricular Failure

The immediate danger in left ventricular failure is pulmonary congestion. The increased blood volume and increased left ventricular diastolic pressure, which are the consequences of compensation, as described earlier, add to the pressures in the pulmonary circulation. The gradient of mean pressure from the pulmonary artery to the atrium is so small (about 6 mm Hg; see Chapter 17) that virtually any increase of left ventricular filling pressure affects the pulmonary vascular pressures significantly. If the mean capillary pressure exceeds the plasma oncotic pressure, fluid moves out of the capillaries into the alveolar spaces.

DYSPNEA (FIGURE 22-6)
Dyspnea is characterized by shortness of breath and rapid, shallow breathing. The major factors that contribute to it are reflexes initiated in the lungs by vascular distention, and the increased rigidity of the lungs caused by the excess fluid, which increases the work of breathing. Apparently, shallow breathing requires less work. Fluid in the interstitial space and the alveoli impairs the uptake of oxygen and contributes to the condition; however, chronic dyspnea can occur in the absence of serious hypoxemia.

ORTHOPNEA
When the body is erect, some blood is shifted from the pulmonary circulation to the lower extremities under the influence of gravity; when the subject lies down, some blood is transferred back to the pulmonary vessels and the air space is reduced. If the subject already has pulmonary congestion, the increase of pulmonary blood volume makes it worse, and he will be more comfortable sitting up or propped up in bed than lying down.

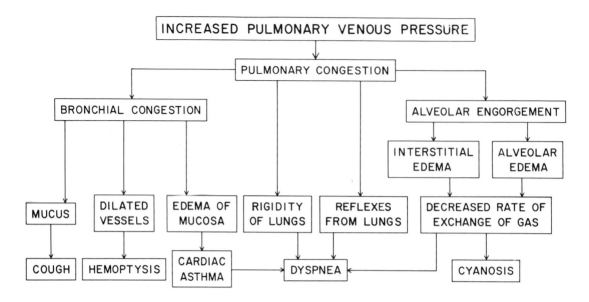

Figure 22-6.   Effects of pulmonary congestion caused by left ventricular failure.

BRONCHIAL CONGESTION

Most of the bronchial capillaries drain into the pulmonary veins; therefore, increased pulmonary venous pressure causes congestion of the bronchial vessels, which produces edema of the mucosal membranes and reduces the caliber of the airways. The increased airway resistance ("cardiac asthma") contributes to dyspnea. The congested mucosa causes a productive cough, as excess mucus is produced, and the sputum may be tinged with blood from ruptured mucosal capillaries.

EVENTS LEADING TO FAILURE

Any increased work load increases the metabolic activity of the heart, but normally the demand is temporary and discontinuous, because periods of activity are interspersed with periods of rest. Continuously high demand, such as that imposed by high vascular resistance, obstructive lesions, or shunts, leads to compensatory hypertrophy and eventually to exhaustion. Thus, the effects of continuous use of the cardiac reserve in cardiac compensation may be likened to those of continuous physical activity without rest.

Meerson (1969) has proposed the following scheme to account for the progression from myocardial overload to cardiac failure.

Stage 1: Damage. Because of the high afterload, the myocardial wall tension increases and the adrenergic drive is continuous; the consumption of oxygen per unit of muscle increases and the stores of substrates are depleted.

Stage 2: Hypertrophy and relatively stable hyperfunction. The consumption of oxygen per unit of muscle returns to normal as the muscle mass increases to match the load; the use of substrates appears to be normal.

Stage 3: Progressive cardiosclerosis and gradual exhaustion. Despite the appearance of stability, the myocardium has deteriorated. Decreased are: the synthesis of proteins and nucleic acids, the rate of renewal of the contractile (muscle) and energy-producing (mitochondria) structures, the myocardial ATPase activity, the myocardial content of creatinine, ATP, and catecholamines, and myocardial contractility (see Figure 22-4).

TREATMENT OF CARDIAC FAILURE

This section is not intended to provide instruction in the medical therapy of cardiac failure; it is included because the effective treatment is consistent with the pathophysiology believed to underlie the disease.

Digitalis

Digitalis increases the contractility of the myocardium (Figure 22-7) and thereby decreases the inappropriate use of the cardiac reserve. As

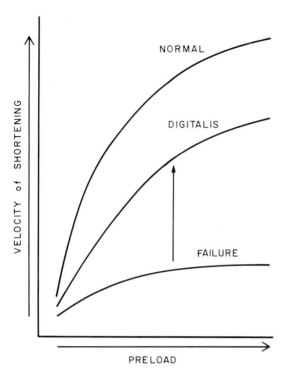

Figure 22-7. Increased contractility of the failing myocardium under the influence of digitalis; the velocity of shortening at any preload is increased.

a result of the improved hemodynamics and the decrease of sympathetic nervous system activity, renal function increases and the symptoms of failure usually are relieved. Because of its apparent renal effect, digitalis once was regarded as a diuretic.

Diuretics

The use of a diuretic in addition to digitalis decreases the reabsorption of salt and water and makes the therapy more effective; sometimes a diuretic alone is adequate. In other cases, restriction of salt and water in the diet may be all that is needed. Impaired renal function and the retention of salt and water may be thought of as side effects, or indirect and undesirable consequences, of compensation. If the side effects are controlled, the patient may tolerate the reduction of cardiac reserve.

Venesection (Bleeding)

Reduction of the blood volume by bleeding is an emergency procedure. Like the diuretics, it reduces venous pressure; however, certain effective diuretic agents can mobilize fluid quickly when given intravenously, and it is likely that bleeding seldom is needed.

TREATMENT AFTER MYOCARDIAL INFARCTION

When the mass of working myocardium is decreased, an agent that increases the contractility of the undamaged portion is needed. Isoproterenol, dopamine, or glucagon may be lifesaving. In addition, using vasodilator drugs to reduce the afterload against which the left ventricle must contract has proved to be helpful.

STUDY OUTLINE

CARDIAC RESERVE   Reserve capacity to deliver oxygen to the tissues.

Cardiac failure—Diminution of cardiac reserve.

Compensated failure—Reserve diminished, but limited demand for cardiac output can be met.

Decompensated failure—Demand for cardiac output cannot be met.

VENOUS OXYGEN RESERVE   Oxygen left in venous blood returning to heart.

Certain organs extract smaller fraction of oxygen from blood than others do.

During exertion, vasoconstriction diverts blood to supply oxygen to active muscles.

In cardiac failure, venous oxygen reserve used at rest.

HEART RATE   Most readily used component of cardiac reserve; part of coordinated cardiovascular response.

STROKE VOLUME

SYSTOLIC RESERVE   Volume left in heart after completing ejection in resting state; utilized by increasing ejection fraction.

DIASTOLIC RESERVE   Additional ejection gained by greater filling—part of intrinsic system of cardiac adaptation.

TYPES OF CARDIAC FAILURE

HIGH-OUTPUT FAILURE   Heart unable to meet demand because demand is so great.

LOW-OUTPUT FAILURE   Heart unable to meet normal demand.

CONSEQUENCES OF COMPENSATION
Cardiac reserve inadequate to meet demand.

EFFECTS RELATED DIRECTLY TO SYMPATHETIC NERVOUS SYSTEM ACTIVITY
REFLEX ARTERIOLAR CONSTRICTION: REDISTRIBUTION OF CARDIAC OUTPUT   Blood flow to skin and mesentery is decreased; heart, brain, and active muscles are supplied.

TACHYCARDIA   Reflects use of the cardiac reserve.

CARDIAC CONTRACTILITY   Increases less than normal because of myocardial deterioration.

INCREASED CENTRAL VENOUS PRESSURE   Due to increased venous tone; recruits length-tension property, but response is decreased by myocardial deterioration.

RELEASE OF RENIN   Controlled in part through sympathetic nerves to kidney.

EFFECTS RELATED INDIRECTLY TO SYMPATHETIC NERVOUS SYSTEM ACTIVITY
INCREASED BLOOD VOLUME   Fluid retention caused by impaired renal function.

RELEASE OF ALDOSTERONE   Caused by decreased renal perfusion, activation of renin-angiotensin system.

INCREASED HEART SIZE   Increased filling pressure (increased blood volume, increased venous tone) and decreased contractility: increased end-diastolic volume and decreased ejection fraction.

EDEMA   Increased venous pressure; capillary pressure exceeds plasma oncotic pressure.
More pronounced in lower limbs and soft tissues (viscera) due to effect of gravity.
Decreases in resting, recumbent subject.

SIGNS AND SYMPTOMS OF FAILURE
Reflect inadequate circulation and consequences of compensation.

UNILATERAL FAILURE

RIGHT VENTRICULAR FAILURE   Right ventricle adapted as volume pump and rarely fails because of volume load (preload).
Fails because of pressure load (afterload).

Back pressure from left ventricular failure most common cause.
Systemic venous congestion and peripheral edema.

LEFT VENTRICULAR FAILURE   Pulmonary congestion.

DYSPNEA   Shortness of breath; rapid, shallow breathing.
Reflexes initiated by distended pulmonary vessels.
Rigidity of lungs that contain excess fluid.
Impaired uptake of oxygen: hypoxemia, cyanosis.

ORTHOPNEA   In supine subject: pulmonary blood volume increases; air space reduced.
In erect subject: because of gravity, pulmonary blood volume decreased, air space increased.
Subject more comfortable propped up or sitting rather than lying.

BRONCHIAL CONGESTION   Increased airway resistance (cardiac asthma).
Edema of mucosal membranes decreases air passages.
Productive cough: mucus; may be tinged with blood from ruptured capillaries.

EVENTS LEADING TO FAILURE   Continuous high rate of metabolic activity by heart leads to compensatory hypertrophy, eventually to exhaustion.

TREATMENT OF CARDIAC FAILURE

DIGITALIS   Increases contractility of myocardium.
Decreases inappropriate use of cardiac reserve.
Improves renal function.

DIURETICS   Cause excretion of salt and water; with side effects of compensation controlled, subject may tolerate reduction of cardiac reserve.

VENESECTION (BLEEDING)   Emergency reduction of blood volume to control side effects of compensation.

TREATMENT AFTER MYOCARDIAL INFARCTION   Therapeutic agent that increases contractility, or vasodilator drug to decrease afterload.

BIBLIOGRAPHY

Arnold, S.B.; Byrd, R.C.; Meister, W.; et al. 1980. Long-term digitalis therapy improves left ventricular function in heart failure. *N. Engl. J. Med.* 303:1443.

Braunwald, E., editor. 1980. *Heart disease: a textbook of cardiovascular medicine*. Philadelphia: W. B. Saunders Co.

Bristow, M.R.; Ginsburg, R.; Minobe, W.; et al. 1982. Decreased catecholamine sensitivity and β-adrenergic receptor density in failing human hearts. *N. Engl. J. Med.* 307:205.

Cannon, P.J. 1977. The kidney in heart failure. *N. Engl. J. Med.* 296:26.

Cohn, J.N., and Franciosa, J.A. 1977. Vasodilator therapy of cardiac failure. *N. Engl. J. Med.* 297:27 and 254 (two parts).

Davis, J.O. 1965. The physiology of congestive heart failure. *Handbook of physiology*. Sect. 2: Vol III: 2071. Washington, D.C.: American Physiological Society.

Dawber, T.R. 1980. *The Framingham study: The epidemiology of arteriosclerotic heart disease*. Cambridge, Mass: Harvard University Press.

Dzau, V.J.; Colucci, W.S.; Williams, G.H.; et al. 1980. Sustained effectiveness of converting-enzyme inhibition in patients with severe congestive heart failure. *N. Engl. J. Med.* 302:1373.

Dzau, V.J.; Colucci, W.S.; Hollenberg, N.K.; et al. 1981. Relation of the renin-angiotensin-aldosterone system to clinical state in congestive heart failure. *Circulation* 63:645.

Finch, C.A., and Lenfant, C. 1972. Oxygen transport in man. *N. Engl. J. Med.* 286:407.

McKee, P.A.; Castilli, W.P.; McNamara, P.M.; et al. 1971. The natural history of congestive heart failure: The Framingham report. *N. Engl. J. Med.* 285:1441.

Meerson, F.Z. 1969. The myocardium in hyperfunction, hypertrophy, and heart failure. *Circ. Res.* 25 (Suppl. II).

Meerson, F.Z. (A.M. Katz, editor). 1983. *The failing heart: Adaptation and deadaptation*. New York: Raven Press.

Rushmer, R.F. 1976. *Cardiovascular dynamics*, 4th ed. Philadelphia: W. B. Saunders Co.

Weber, K.T.; Kinasewitz, G.T.; West, J.S.; et al. 1980. Long-term vasodilator therapy with trimazosin in chronic cardiac failure. *N. Engl. J. Med.* 303:242.

Zelias, R.; Flaim, S.F.; Liedtke, A.J.; et al. 1981. Circulatory dynamics in the normal and failing heart. *Ann. Rev. Physiol.* 43:455.

23

Hypotension: Circulatory Shock

CHAPTER CONTENTS

Circulatory shock is an acute state of circulatory insufficiency in which the cardiac output is too small to perfuse the major organs normally, and tissues are damaged because the rate of blood flow in the capillaries is inadequate. The principal sign of circulatory shock is the sudden development of abnormally low arterial blood pressure in a subject who is in the supine position.

The condition of the cardiovascular system is assessed most commonly by the measurement of arterial blood pressure, and "normal" arterial pressure might be taken to indicate adequate perfusion of the tissues. This indication may not be correct, however, as arterial pressure is the product of cardiac output and peripheral resistance and it can be maintained near normal for some time, even when neither cardiac output nor peripheral resistance is normal. Thus, the seriousness of the condition may be masked by the intrinsic compensation of the cardiovascular system.

DEFICIENCY OF BLOOD VOLUME

Hemorrhagic Shock

Hemorrhagic shock, a type of hypovolemic shock, has been studied extensively; it occurs in patients frequently, it is convenient to study in animals, and its pathophysiology is typical of shock in general.

EFFECTS OF SMALL LOSS OF BLOOD

A normal adult human contains about 5 liters of blood and can lose about 10% (500 ml) of it without adverse effects; the benign nature of such a small loss of blood is confirmed every time someone donates a pint of blood. Figure 23-1 outlines the acute responses that compensate for the loss of a small amount of blood. These responses represent only temporary homeostatic adjustments, however, and ultimately

346

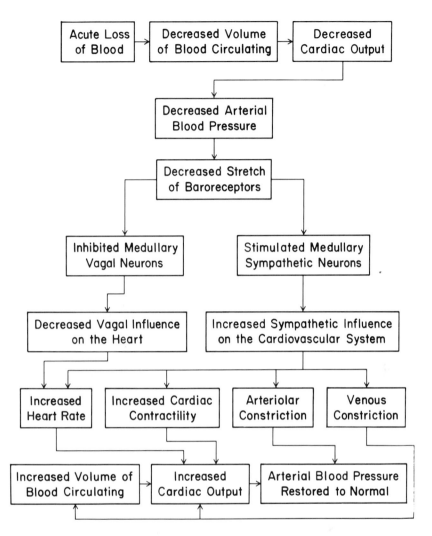

Figure 23-1. Immediate compensation for a small loss of blood. The arterial pressure is restored to normal. (Redrawn, by permission, from Jacobson, E.D. 1968. *N. Engl. J. Med.* 278:835.)

the blood volume must be restored. Water and electrolytes are replaced by the ingestion of fluid and salts and conserved by the augmented secretion of ADH and aldosterone. The liver replaces plasma albumin, and the hematopoietic tissues replace erythrocytes and other cellular elements of the blood.

EFFECTS OF
LARGE LOSS OF BLOOD

If as much as 30%–40% of the blood volume is removed, the compensatory mechanisms of the

body are inadequate and signs and symptoms of shock develop. The skin is cold and pale, perhaps cyanotic, due to vasoconstriction; however, the hands and feet may be moist because of sweating induced by the sympathetic nervous system. The mucous membranes may be dry, also due to vasoconstriction. The arterial blood pressure is low and may be difficult to measure by the cuff method, and the arterial pulse is weak and rapid. The rate of formation of urine is low or no urine is formed, and the subject may be thirsty; these symptoms reflect the loss of fluid volume. The subject may be mentally disturbed or somnolent and may breathe rapidly or irregularly.

IRREVERSIBLE SHOCK

If the patient is in shock too long, because of insufficient compensatory mechanisms or the lack of emergency care, a state of *progressive,* or *irreversible,* circulatory shock develops. Because of the inadequate perfusion, the cardiovascular system has been damaged so that it cannot maintain the circulation even if the blood volume is restored. If this condition occurs, the patient ultimately will die, regardless of treatment. If emergency medical treatment or the compensatory mechanisms of the patient are adequate to prevent the progression of shock, the patient will recover and may suffer no permanent damage. In this event, the patient is said to have been in *nonprogressive,* or *reversible,* shock.

Experimental work indicates that only a few additional minutes of inadequate capillary perfusion may cause a patient to move from nonprogressive to progressive shock. Figure 23-2 illustrates this situation by presenting the results of experiments in which four rabbits were bled, and their mean arterial pressures were kept at 40 mm Hg for different lengths of time. Note that rabbit III died, even though it was treated by the reinfusion of blood only a few minutes

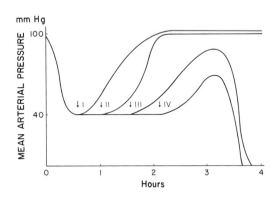

Figure 23-2. Effects of prolonged hypotension caused by loss of blood. Four rabbits were bled until the mean arterial pressure decreased to 40 mm Hg; the pressure was maintained at that level until the animals were re-infused, one at a time, after intervals of increasing duration. Arrows indicate the time at which the blood was returned to each animal. After a critical duration of hypotension, rabbits III and IV died, despite the restoration of blood.

later than was rabbit II, which survived. Thus, whether a case of shock is reversible or irreversible is a retrospective determination. If the patient lives, the shock was reversible; if the patient dies, the shock was irreversible.

CAUSES OF IRREVERSIBLE SHOCK

No organ can be subjected to prolonged, severe ischemia without damage, not only to itself, but to other organs also (Figure 23-3). Hypoxia of the intestines, which results from prolonged vasoconstriction, causes the release of toxic substances, including bacteria and their products, proteins, peptides, and vasoactive agents; decreased perfusion of the reticuloendothelial organs (liver, spleen, lungs, and lymphatic tissue) inhibits the normal ability of the body to inactivate the circulating toxins. Because of diminished renal blood flow, the kidneys secrete renin, which results ultimately in more vasoconstriction, if any more is possible. In addition, the kidneys cannot regulate acid-base and electrolyte balance, and acidosis develops. Thrombi may form in the inadequately perfused capillaries; H^+ and catecholamines enhance this process. Ischemia of tissues in general causes the release of proteolytic enzymes, catecholamines, histamine, serotonin, kinins, and other vasoactive polypeptides. The capillary endothelium is damaged, massive leakage of plasma occurs, and fluid volume is reduced further. The heart fails because of hypoxia and the effects of toxins. In recent years, a myocardial depressant factor has been isolated and studied extensively. As the circulation fails, the brainstem deteriorates and vasoconstriction wanes; however, adequate perfusion no longer is possible (Figure 23-4). The terminal event is ventricular asystole or respiratory failure.

REPLACEMENT THERAPY

The blood that was lost may be replaced by whole blood, packed red cells, plasma, or albumin; bicarbonate or tris (tromethamine) buffer may be used to treat the acidosis. Care must be taken to give the proper amount of fluid; adequate venous pressure is needed for cardiac filling, but venous pressure also can increase because the heart is failing (see Figure 23-5).

ADRENERGIC
α-RECEPTOR ANTAGONISM

Drugs that block α-receptors oppose compensatory vasoconstriction, but this opposition is

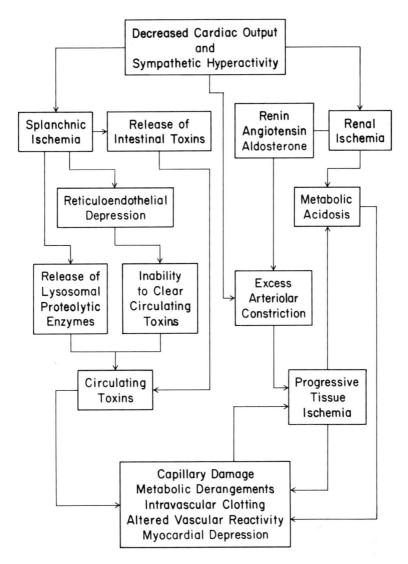

Figure 23-3. Middle stage of shock during which compensation is inadequate and the cardiovascular system is damaged because of inadequate perfusion of many tissues, in particular, the gastrointestinal tract and the kidneys. If these conditions persist too long, irreversible harm will have been done and the subject will die regardless of what measures are taken subsequently. (Redrawn, with permission, from Jacobson, E.D. 1968. *N. Engl. J. Med.* 278:835.)

justified because the system is paying a high price in its attempt to assure blood flow to the heart and the brain by maintaining the central arterial pressure. Much of the normal arterial pressure is used to oppose gravity when the person is upright and to accelerate the flow of blood when activity demands an increase of cardiac output. When the person is quiet and supine, the system requires much less arterial pressure. Preventing the deterioration of the kidneys, the intestines, and the liver by decreasing the extreme vasoconstriction actually may increase the probability of survival.

REPLACEMENT THERAPY AND α-RECEPTOR ANTAGONISM
The combination of fluid and α-receptor antagonism is more nearly ideal, as it provides volume to fill the vascular bed and to maintain

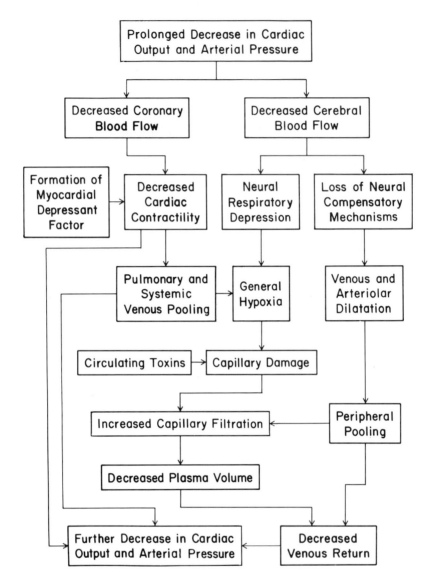

Figure 23-4. As a result of prolonged hypotension and inadequate cardiac output, the cardiovascular system has been damaged, as outlined in Figure 23-3, and the heart and the brain have begun to fail. Because of damage to the capillaries, the circulating blood volume is decreasing further, and any blood or other fluid given by transfusion would not remain in the circulation. When this condition is reached, the shock is progressive and irreversible. (Redrawn, with permission, from Jacobson, E.D. 1968. *N. Engl. J. Med.* 278:835.)

perfusion at a higher arterial pressure with less vasoconstriction.

ADRENERGIC
β-RECEPTOR STIMULATION

Drugs that stimulate β-receptors decrease the peripheral resistance while increasing the contractility of the heart. These actions may help to increase tissue perfusion.

ADRENAL CORTICOIDS

The use of adrenal steroids in treating shock probably is based on the role of the adrenal cortex in the resistance of the body to "stress." These hormones are believed to stabilize the membranes of cellular lysosomes, which contain hydrolytic enzymes, so that they rupture less readily in ischemic tissues. In addition, the corticoids oppose the production of kinins, and

CLINICAL CORRELATION
23.1   Traumatic Shock

CASE REPORT

The Patient: A 26-year-old woman.

Reason for Admission: Multiple trauma.

Clinical Course: The patient had been well before she was involved in an automobile accident. She was transported to the emergency room by helicopter, dazed but conscious. Her arterial pressure was 55/30 mm Hg (normal, 90–140/60–90 mm Hg), and her heart rate was 96/min (normal, 60–100/min). No head injury was indicated, and the heart and lungs were normal, although an x-ray film showed widening of the mediastinum (this suggests injury to the aorta) and three broken ribs. The abdomen was swollen and tender; this suggests intra-abdominal hemorrhage. The right tibia appeared to be broken, and the right patella was severely lacerated. The hematocrit was 34% (normal, 37–48%), and the platelet count was 20,000/mm³ (normal 150,000–350,000/mm³). An intravenous line was inserted and infusion of 10% glucose in saline was begun. Packed red cells, platelets, and fresh-frozen plasma were given. The urinary bladder was catheterized (for monitoring the production of urine).

Because of the evidence of internal bleeding, the patient was taken to the operating room, and an exploratory laparotomy was performed. One and one-half liters of blood and clots were removed from the peritoneal cavity, and several bleeding arteries were clamped and tied. A small tear in the ileal serosa was repaired. The patient was given additional packed red cells, albumin, fresh-frozen plasma, and lactated Ringer's solution during the operation, and her arterial pressure stabilized in the range of 90/50 mm Hg. To assess the cause of the widened mediastinum, thoracic arteriography was done (fluoroscopy of contrast medium injected at the root of the aorta). A traumatic rupture was found, just distal to the origin of the left subclavian artery. The vessel was repaired through a left thoracotomy, using a Dacron graft. Additional cells and fluids were given, and her arterial pressure increased to 115/70 mm Hg.

Comment: This patient was fortunate to receive prompt and expert care so that she did not remain hypotensive long enough for progressive shock to develop.

Outcome: After the bleeding was stopped and the arterial pressure had stabilized, her external wounds were treated and her broken bones were set. Recovery was uneventful.

---

most important, they decrease the permeability of the capillaries, either directly or by preventing the formation or release of other damaging factors.

Traumatic Shock

Injuries to soft tissues or bone, such as those sustained in automobile or industrial accidents and in casualties of war, may cause shock. The most likely problem is leakage of blood or plasma into the interstitial spaces of the damaged tissue; therefore, this is a type of hypovolemic shock. If the skin is not broken, localized swelling, or hematoma, occurs. However, an increase of one liter of blood may increase

the diameter of the thigh of a 75 kg adult male by only about 1 cm. Thus, the severity of the hemorrage may not be apparent.

Although traumatic shock is a form of hypovolemic shock, it has several distinctive features. Trauma causes pain, which can inhibit the vasomotor center and thereby contribute to the hypotension. If muscle is crushed, myoglobin and other products of muscle damage may be released into the circulation; these materials can obstruct glomerular capillaries and cause renal failure or further diminish renal function that already is impaired.

Shock lung, a syndrome of respiratory distress characterized by the development of pulmonary interstitial edema, has been associated with traumatic shock. The causes of shock lung still are being investigated. They may include pulmonary arterial hypertension accompanied by venous constriction, the formation of microemboli and the consequent infarction of lung parenchyma, the release of substances that increase the permeability of the capillaries of the lungs, the obstruction of pulmonary blood vessels by fat released from damaged bone, and an effect of trauma that causes fat dispersed in the circulation to coalesce into large particles.

Burn Shock

LOSS OF SKIN

Burn shock is another form of hypovolemic shock, but it also has certain distinctive characteristics. Normally, the skin prevents the passage of water from the tissues to the external environment; this important function is impaired severely when the skin is burned. If 15% or more of the body surface is burned, and if 50% of the burn extends through the full thickness of the skin, the loss of fluid will lead to shock. Destruction of large areas of the skin allows large quantities of plasma and interstitial fluid to leak out; the plasma proteins are lost, but most of the cellular elements of the blood are retained. The loss of plasma protein causes the plasma oncotic pressure to decrease, and water moves along a gradient of hydrostatic pressure from the vascular space to the interstitial space. The increased hematocrit increases the viscosity of the blood and makes the capillary blood-flow more sluggish. The viscosity of the blood also increases in the small vessels as the velocity of flow decreases (see Chapter 12).

DERANGED COAGULATION

In burned skin, the endothelial linings of blood vessels are damaged extensively, and subendothelial collagen is exposed to the blood. The exposed collagen causes aggregation of platelets and activation of factor XII (Hageman factor), the first component of the intrinsic coagulation cascade. Thus, localized intravascular coagulation may cause localized ischemia or even infarction of tissues; if the damage is extensive enough, clotting factors will be consumed, leading to consumption coagulopathy and generalized bleeding.

INFECTION AND
IMMUNE RESPONSE

Bacterial sepsis is a frequent and often fatal complication of burn shock. In fact, sepsis caused by gram-negative bacteria and the endotoxins they produce is the leading cause of death in patients who have been burned. Burned skin is an important portal of entry into the circulation for bacteria and bacterial toxins. In addition, evidence indicates that a toxin released from burned skin is absorbed into the circulation, damages the capillary endothelium of the intestines, and thereby allows endotoxin and bacteria from the lumen of the intestines to enter the circulation. The circulating toxins produced in burn shock are being investigated; there is evidence that other toxins also are produced, which cause hemolysis, renal damage, neurotoxicity, and cardiodepression. In addition, thermal injury has been shown to alter molecules in the skin so that they become antigenic, and the body mounts an immune response against them. Antibodies against these altered molecules also may attack normal tissue components, and a self-destructive autoimmune response can ensue.

The treatment of patients in burn shock is to replace lost fluids and prevent infection. The patient's requirements for fluid may more than double because of the burn. When replacing fluid, one must take into account that both plasma and interstitial fluid are lost through the burned area. Thus, various combinations of colloidal (albumin or dextran) and crystalloidal (lactated Ringer's or normal saline) solutions are given.

Dehydration

Dehydration may be caused by excessive sweating, severe diarrhea or vomiting, low intake of water and salts, adrenal cortical insufficiency, or diabetes insipidus. It can be severe enough to cause hypovolemic shock, and the results may be classified into several clinical types on the basis of the tonicity of the extracellular fluid in the dehydrated patient. The concentration of sodium in the plasma, $[Na^+]$, is used clinically as the index of the tonicity of the extracellular fluid. If a patient shows signs of dehydration, and plasma $[Na^+]$ is low, he is said to be in hypotonic dehydration; if plasma $[Na^+]$ is normal, the patient is in isotonic dehydration, and if plasma $[Na^+]$ is high, he is in hypertonic dehydration. In isotonic and hypertonic dehydration, the extracellular fluid volume usually is maintained fairly well because the extracellular solutes tend to retain water osmotically. By contrast, in hypotonic dehydration, the tonicity of the extracellular fluid is low and the osmotic gradient favors the movement of water from the extracellular space into the cells. Therefore, hypotonic dehydration is more likely to cause circulatory shock than hypertonic and isotonic dehydration are. Hypotonic dehydration can occur if, over a period of time, the patient loses more salt than water. This situation can develop readily, because of high renal losses of Na$^+$ in Addison's disease, for example, or when body fluid lost through diarrhea or sweating is replaced by water alone. Shock due to dehydration is treated by giving fluids intravenously, and the electrolyte composition of the replacement fluid is determined on the basis of the type of dehydration, whether isotonic, hypotonic, or hypertonic.

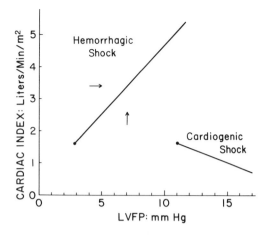

Figure 23-5. Effects of increasing the left-ventricular-filling pressure (LVFP) in nonprogressive hemorrhagic shock and in cardiogenic shock. In hemorrhagic shock, lack of blood limits the cardiac output; in cardiogenic shock, failure of the heart as a pump is the limiting factor. Arrows indicate typical normal values of LVFP and cardiac index in an adult human.

CARDIOGENIC SHOCK

Cardiogenic shock is caused by acutely decreased ability of the heart to function as a pump; the most common cause is myocardial infarction. Cardiogenic shock also can be caused by rupture of the intraventricular septum, trauma to the heart, pericardial tamponade, disturbance of heart rate or rhythm, or any other insult that compromises the ability of the heart to function as a pump. The most significant hemodynamic aberration is diminished cardiac output, and this is the physiological indicator of cardiogenic shock. In contrast to hypovolemic shock, the left ventricular filling-pressure (LVFP) is elevated in cardiogenic shock, as illustrated in Figure 23-5. Increasing LVFP by infusing fluid does not improve the cardiac index because the problem is not caused by reduced intravascular volume.

INCREASED VASCULAR CAPACITY

Neurogenic Shock

Neurogenic shock occurs when the vascular capacity increases so that the normal blood volume does not fill the circulatory system adequately; the ventricular filling-pressure is diminished, and consequently, the cardiac output is diminished. The increase of vascular capacity can be caused by several mechanisms, each of which decreases vasomotor tone. Brain damage, especially injury that involves the vasomotor center in the brainstem, may cause neurogenic shock. Deep general anesthesia also can depress the vasomotor center enough to cause vas-

cular collapse; spinal anesthesia, if it extends up the spinal cord far enough, can block sympathetic outflow and cause neurogenic shock. The treatment of neurogenic shock mainly is supportive; one attempts to maintain life until the cause of the vasomotor inhibition is treated.

FAINTING
Fainting, or "syncope," is caused by sudden cerebral ischemia. Severe emotional disturbances, such as fear or extreme dejection, may cause sudden peripheral vasodilatation, hypotension, and syncope. If bystanders with good intentions do not force the subject into a vertical stance, the body will assume a horizontal position naturally, the flow of blood to the brain will be maintained, and the patient probably will recover without intervention.

DRUG EFFECTS
Many drugs, such as barbiturates, certain tranquilizers, and opiates, depress respiration, and some of them also depress the vasomotor center. When taken in large doses, they may produce hypotension and coma, hence, a type of circulatory shock. Historically, efforts to treat patients in this condition by the use of vasopressor drugs largely were unsuccessful, and frequently patients who were given only supportive treatment fared better. Observation and

study of cases like these led eventually to the use of vasodilator drugs as part of the therapy for shock.

Anaphylactic Shock

In anaphylaxis, a portion of the individual's immune system responds in an excessive manner to an antigen that is less dangerous to the individual than the immune response itself. Anaphylaxis may be caused by a variety of antigens to which the individual has been sensitized previously. It may be incited by certain foods, insect venom, spider venom, and various drugs, especially antibiotics of the penicillin group. Sensitization is caused by the production of a specific type of antibody that covers mast cells or basophils. When antigen becomes attached to it, the mast cell or basophil releases chemical mediators that cause anaphylaxis. Histamine and slow-reacting-substance-of-anaphylaxis (SRS-A) are two such mediators. These substances cause bronchoconstriction, peripheral arteriolar dilatation, and increased capillary permeability. Arteriolar dilatation causes hypotension, and the increased capillary permeability permits loss of fluid from the vascular space. The state of anaphylactic shock can be complicated further by laryngeal edema and bronchial constriction that block the flow of air into and out of the lungs and may cause hypoxemia.

Early treatment of anaphylactic shock is mandatory, as death may occur in a few minutes. If the antigenic material entered the body through an injection into an extremity, absorption of the material may be reduced by applying a tourniquet to the area or by injecting a vasoconstrictor such as epinephrine into the area. Next, epinephrine should be injected intravenously. Epinephrine relieves bronchoconstriction and increases blood pressure, and it has been proposed that epinephrine prevents the release of anaphylactic mediators. The administration of oxygen may be beneficial when bronchoconstriction causes hypoxia.

Septic Shock

Sepsis is a disease state caused by microorganisms or their products in the bloodstream. Most cases of septic shock are due to gram-negative bacilli, but gram-positive organisms, fungi, and viruses also cause septic shock occasionally. Endotoxin is a high-molecular-weight lipopolysaccharide that exists in the cell walls of gram-negative bacteria; it is believed that this material is mainly responsible for the toxicity that occurs during gram-negative sepsis.

Gram-negative organisms, or the endotoxin that is elaborated by them, may enter the circulation in various ways. A perforated appendix, an intestinal diverticulum, pelvic surgery, septic abortion, urethral instrumentation, and abscesses have been shown to produce septicemia. Furthermore, ischemia of the large bowel may disrupt the mucosal barrier and allow absorption of bacteria or endotoxin into the circulation; thus, septic shock may occur in the late stages of other types of shock.

The vascular effects of septicemia appear to be indirect. Histamine and other vasoactive substances released from cells by endotoxin produce hypotension promptly. Catecholamines released through autonomic nervous system stimulation cause extreme splanchnic vasoconstriction and probably assure additional release of endotoxin. Initially, blood volume need not be affected; however, hypovolemia develops later as increased capillary permeability permits the extravasation of fluid. Before systemic antibiotics became available, septic shock, which also is called blood poisoning, was greatly feared.

STUDY OUTLINE

Definition of shock: acute circulatory insufficiency; principal sign, sudden hypotension.
Assessed most frequently by arterial pressure.
Cardiovascular compensation may mask seriousness.

DEFICIENCY OF BLOOD VOLUME

HEMORRHAGIC SHOCK Most studied; serves as prototype.

EFFECTS OF SMALL LOSS OF BLOOD
Immediate: vasoconstriction, cardiac stimulation.
   Long-term: replacement of water, electrolytes, and formed elements.

EFFECTS OF LARGE LOSS OF BLOOD
Extreme sympathetic nervous system activity; strong vasoconstriction; weak, rapid pulse; decreased renal function; lethargy.

IRREVERSIBLE SHOCK Compensation inadequate; cardiovascular system damaged, so no therapy effective. Time a critical factor; retrospective determination.

CAUSES OF IRREVERSIBLE SHOCK Hypoxia of intestines; releases toxic substances.

Failure of reticuloendothelial system to inactivate toxins.

Secretion of renin by kidneys; enhances vasoconstriction.

Inadequate renal acid-base control: acidosis.

Thrombi in underperfused capillaries.

Release of proteolytic enzymes and vasoactive materials from ischemic tissues.

Capillary endothelium damaged, permeability increases, fluid not held in vascular system.

Heart and nervous system damaged by hypoxia.

REPLACEMENT THERAPY Blood, packed cells, plasma, or albumin.

Must give appropriate amount; overtransfusion produces congestion; heart may be failing.

ADRENERGIC α-RECEPTOR ANTAGONISM Relieves excessive vasoconstriction; perfusion pressure may be adequate in quiet, supine subject.

REPLACEMENT THERAPY AND α-RECEPTOR ANTAGONISM Relieves vasoconstriction and provides circulating volume.

ADRENERGIC β-RECEPTOR STIMULATION Aids perfusion by decreasing peripheral resistance and increasing cardiac contractility.

ADRENAL CORTICOIDS Stabilize cellular lysosomes; protect capillaries.

TRAUMATIC SHOCK Internal hemorrhage; severity may not be apparent.

Pain may be a factor.

Products of muscle damage released into circulation can decrease renal function.

Shock lung: pulmonary interstitial edema associated with traumatic shock.

BURN SHOCK

LOSS OF SKIN Permits loss of plasma; viscosity of blood increases.

DERANGED COAGULATION Caused by exposed collagen of damaged blood vessels.

INFECTION AND IMMUNE RESPONSE Loss of skin, which is normal barrier to entry of bacteria.

Toxin released from burned skin damages capillary epithelium of intestines; allows bacteria and endotoxins to enter circulation.

Other toxins damage erythrocytes, kidneys, nervous system, and heart.

Altered molecules of burned skin become antigenic; self-destructive autoimmune response may occur.

DEHYDRATION Caused by excess loss or inadequate intake of water and electrolytes.

May be hypotonic, isotonic, or hypertonic dehydration, depending on [Na$^+$] of plasma.

Correct with appropriate fluid.

CARDIOGENIC SHOCK Acutely decreased ability of heart to function as pump.

Myocardial infarction, trauma, pericardial constriction, or dysrhythmia.

Decreased cardiac output despite high venous pressure.

INCREASED VASCULAR CAPACITY

NEUROGENIC SHOCK Decreased vascular tone; injury to or depression of vasomotor center; too-deep anesthesia.

FAINTING Sudden cerebral ischemia, often due to severe emotional disturbance: decreased vascular tone.

Self-correcting if subject allowed to assume horizontal position.

DRUG EFFECTS Barbiturates, tranquilizers, opiates, and others.

Subject quiet, supine, may need only supportive treatment.

Use of vasopressors may cause harm (tissue ischemia).

ANAPHYLACTIC SHOCK Excessive response of immune system to antigen.

Release of histamine and other unidentified substances; causes bronchoconstriction, arteriolar dilatation, and increased capillary permeability.

Early treatment essential: intravenous injection of epinephrine.

SEPTIC SHOCK Caused by microorganisms or products in bloodstream.

Mostly gram-negative bacilli, effect due to endotoxins from cell walls.

Organisms or endotoxin enter through wounds, ruptures, or disruption of mucosal barrier of intestines by ischemia (caused by other types of shock).

Effects indirect: hypotension from release of histamine and other vasodilators; catecholamines released reflexly cause vasoconstriction.

Subsequent increased capillary permeability.

BIBLIOGRAPHY

Clowes, G.H.A. 1974. Pulmonary abnormalities in sepsis. *Surg. Clin. North Am.* 54:993–1013.

Cohn, J.N., and Luria, M.H. 1966. Studies in clinical shock and hypotension. IV. Variations in reflex vasoconstriction and cardiac stimulation. *Circulation* 34:823–832.

Colman, R.W. 1974. Formation of human plasma kinin. *N. Engl. J. Med.* 291:509–515.

Egdahl, R.H.; Meguid, M.M.; and Aun, F. 1977. The importance of the endocrine and metabolic responses to shock and trauma. *Crit. Care Med.* 5:257–263.

Glenn, T.M., editor. 1974. *Steroids and shock.* Baltimore: University Park Press.

Haddy, F.J.; Emerson, T.E., Jr.; Scott, J.B.; and Daugherty, R.M., Jr. 1970. The effect of the kinins on the cardiovascular system. In *Handbook of experimental pharmacology,* Vol. 25, Bradykinin, kallidin and kallikrein, editor E.G. Erdos. Berlin: Springer-Verlag, pp. 362–384.

Hardaway, R.M., III. 1966. *Syndromes of disseminated intravascular coagulation with special reference to shock and hemorrhage.* Springfield, Ill.: Charles C Thomas, Publisher.

Jacobson, E.D. 1968. A physiologic approach to shock. *N. Engl. J. Med.* 278:834.

Kovack, A.G.B., and Sander, P. 1976. Cerebral blood flow and brain function during hypotension and shock. *Ann. Rev. Physiol.* 38:571.

Ledingham, I.McA. 1976. *Shock: clinical and experimental aspects.* Amsterdam: Excerpta Medica.

Lefer, A.M. 1976. The role of lysosomes in circulatory shock. *Life Sc.* 19:1803–1810.

Lefer, A.M., and Glenn, T.M. (symposium chairmen). 1978. Toxic factors in shock. *Fed. Proc.* 37:2717.

Lefer, A.M., and Schumer, W., editors. 1983. *Molecular and cellular aspects of shock and trauma.* Progress in Clinical and Histological Research, Vol. III. New York: Alan R. Liss.

Rudowski, W.; Nasilowski, E.; Zietkiewicz, W.; and Zienkiewicz, K. 1976. *Burn research and therapy.* Baltimore and London: Johns Hopkins University Press.

Schumer, W. 1975. Cellular metabolism in shock. *Circ. Shock* 2:109–127.

Schumer, W., and Nyhus, L.M. 1974. *Treatment of shock: principles and practice.* Philadelphia: Lea & Febiger.

Shires, G.T. 1977. Pathophysiology and fluid replacement in hypovolemic shock. *Ann. Clin. Res.* 9:144–150.

Shoemaker, W.C. 1976. Pathobiology of death; structural and functional interactions in shock syndromes. *Pathobiol. Ann.* 6:365–407.

PART V

BLOOD AND IMMUNITY

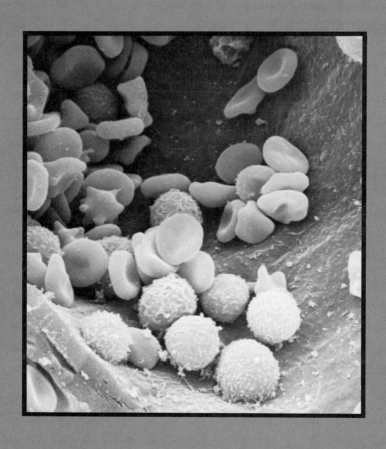

Photomicrograph from *Tissues and Organs: A Text-Atlas of Scanning Electron Microscopy* by
Richard G. Kessel and Randy H. Kardon. W.H. Freeman and Company. © 1979.

Erythrocytes

CHAPTER CONTENTS

Blood is a liquid tissue. It consists of a variety of cellular elements, including erythrocytes, leukocytes, and platelets, all suspended in a protein-rich plasma (Table 24-1). Blood makes up about 7% of the body weight of a normal adult human; thus, a 70 kg person has about 5 liters of blood. Normally, about 55% of the blood volume is plasma, and about 45% is erythrocytes; leukocytes and platelets, although extremely important, normally comprise less than 1% of the total volume of blood. The blood itself represents only a part of the hematologic system, which also includes active bone marrow, the spleen, the lymph nodes, and the macrophages of the reticuloendothelial system.

FORMED ELEMENTS

Hematopoiesis

CHANGES WITH AGE

During fetal development, blood cells are produced first in the yolk sac, then in the liver and spleen as the yolk sac regresses. By the fifth month of fetal life, bone marrow cavities have begun to develop; by the time of birth the bone marrow is the site of essentially all production of red cells, or hematopoiesis. After birth, virtually all hematopoiesis continues to be due directly or indirectly to bone marrow activity. In the infant, the marrow cavities barely are large

TABLE 24-1
Composition of human blood by weight

Plasma (55%)	Water (91%)
	Proteins (7%)
	Albumin (55%)
	Globulins (42%)
	Fibrinogen (3%)
	Electrolytes, urea, glucose, etc. (2%)
Cells (45%)	Erythrocytes ($\sim 5 \times 10^6/\mu l$)*
	Leukocytes ($\sim 7 \times 10^3/\mu l$)+
	Neutrophils (59%)
	Lymphocytes (34%)
	Monocytes (4%)
	Eosinophils (2.5%)
	Basophils (0.5%)
	Platelets ($\sim 3 \times 10^5/\mu l$)+

* Almost 100% of total blood cell mass.
+ Less than 1% of total blood cell mass.

enough to contain all of the hematopoietic tissue; in the adolescent, the marrow space becomes more than adequate, and fat infiltrates the marrow space not needed to produce blood cells. Fat appears first in the bones of the appendages, and by age 18, only the bones of the axial skeleton (cranium, sternum, ribs, ver-

tebrae, and pelvis) are engaged in hematopoiesis (Figure 24-1). The production of blood cells in the liver, spleen, and lymph nodes is a distinctly abnormal finding in adults; however, because of the limited marrow space in infants and children, it may be a normal response to stresses such as blood loss or infection in these age groups.

STRUCTURE OF BONE MARROW
The bone marrow is arranged in a spokelike manner (Figure 24-2), with cords of hematopoietic tissue separated by venous sinuses that empty into a central vein. Arterial blood flows through the cords, drains into the venous sinuses, and finally reaches the central veins. Reticular cells support the cords, and vascular endothelial cells line the cavities of the central vein and venous sinuses. A fenestrated basement membrane produced by the endothelial cells separates the hematopoietic cords from the vascular lumina, and mature erythrocytes, leukocytes, and platelets must squeeze through the membrane to enter the general circulation.

STEM CELLS
Each cell line of blood cells—granulocytic, lymphocytic, monocytic, and thrombocytic—goes through an orderly sequence of maturation in which it is transformed from precursor cells

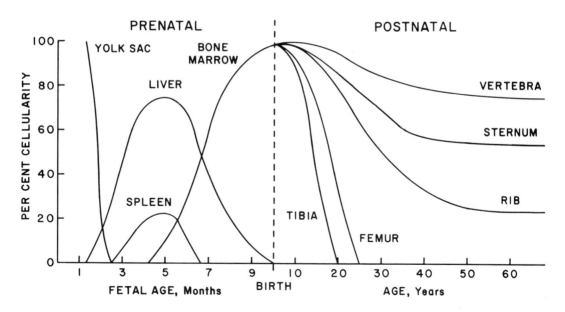

Figure 24-1. Changes in the cellularity of bone marrow with age. 100% equals magnitude of cellularity at birth. (Redrawn, with permission, from Erslev, A.J., and Gabuzda, T.G. 1979. *Pathophysiology of Blood.* Philadelphia: W.B. Saunders Co.)

A

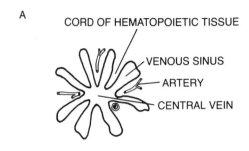

CORD OF HEMATOPOIETIC TISSUE

VENOUS SINUS

ARTERY

CENTRAL VEIN

B

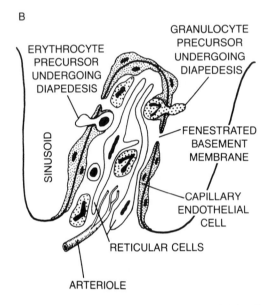

ERYTHROCYTE PRECURSOR UNDERGOING DIAPEDESIS

GRANULOCYTE PRECURSOR UNDERGOING DIAPEDESIS

SINUSOID

FENESTRATED BASEMENT MEMBRANE

CAPILLARY ENDOTHELIAL CELL

RETICULAR CELLS

ARTERIOLE

Figure 24-2.   Structure of bone marrow: **A.** Blood flows through hematopoietic cords and into central vein. **B.** Blood cells develop in hematopoietic cords and enter blood by squeezing through fenestrated basement membrane. (Redrawn, with permission, from Gordon, A.S. 1970. *Regulation of Hematopoiesis,* Vol. 1. New York: Plenum Publishing Corporation.)

to functional blood cells. The cells of the blood are derived from identically appearing stem cells that may be uncommitted (multipotential) and capable of differentiating into any cell line or committed (unipotential) and capable of differentiating only into a particular cell line. The mechanisms that govern the development of these cell lines will be discussed in sections that follow.

Erythrocytes

Red blood cells (RBCs) are nonnucleated biconcave discs about 7 μm in diameter and about 2 μm across at their maximum thickness. Normally, the volume of the average cell is 80–95 μm^3, and the concentration of hemoglobin is 33%–38%. The average life span of an erythrocyte is 120 days, and the normal concentration of RBCs ranges from 4–6 million per mm^3 (5.4 million in men, 4.8 million in women). Red cells are produced at a rate of 10^{10} cells per hour, which is the highest of any tissue in the body.

PRODUCTION

Erythrocytes normally are produced in the bone marrow by an orderly process (Figure 24-3). A multipotential stem cell is transformed into one committed to the erythroid line. The progeny of this stem cell are rapidly growing, actively dividing proerythroblasts that have just begun to activate the biochemical machinery needed for the synthesis of hemoglobin. The next cell in the erythroid series is the basophilic erythroblast, which is smaller, more mature, and contains basophilic cytoplasm. The increased maturity and the basophilic cytoplasm reflect the increased rate of synthesis of globin, the protein of hemoglobin, and the assembly of hemoglobin on the polyribosomes. The heme portion is synthesized in the mitochondria. The next cell to appear is the polychromatophilic erythroblast, in which the concentration of hemo-

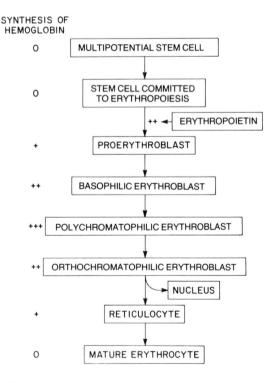

SYNTHESIS OF HEMOGLOBIN

0	MULTIPOTENTIAL STEM CELL
0	STEM CELL COMMITTED TO ERYTHROPOIESIS
++	◄ ERYTHROPOIETIN
+	PROERYTHROBLAST
++	BASOPHILIC ERYTHROBLAST
+++	POLYCHROMATOPHILIC ERYTHROBLAST
++	ORTHOCHROMATOPHILIC ERYTHROBLAST
	NUCLEUS
+	RETICULOCYTE
0	MATURE ERYTHROCYTE

Figure 24-3.   Erythropoiesis in bone marrow.

globin is high enough to produce a pinkish (eosinophilic) hue. The orthochromatophilic erythroblast (normoblast) appears next; due to decreased numbers of polyribosomes and increased concentration of hemoglobin, its cytoplasm is even more eosinophilic. The next event in development is the dramatic extrusion of the nucleus and transformation of the cell into a reticulocyte. The reticulocyte leaves the bone marrow by forming a pseudopod and interposing itself through one of the fenestrations in the basement membrane that lines the sinusoids. It is similar to a mature erythrocyte in appearance, but it still contains organelles such as the Golgi apparatus, mitochondria, and polyribosomes, which continue to function for several days to synthesize the last 20% of the hemoglobin of the mature erythrocyte.

DESTRUCTION

The mature erythrocyte functions with only the nonrenewable enzymes produced during its nucleated existence in the bone marrow. From this enzymatic machinery the RBC obtains enough energy to maintain transcellular ionic gradients, preserve the intracellular reducing environment needed to maintain heme-bound iron in the ferrous state, and maintain the integrity of a variety of proteins. These proteins include hemoglobin and enzymes such as 2-3 DPG and carbonic anhydrase, which are needed for the transport of O_2 and CO_2. As the red cells become senescent, they become less deformable, the membrane becomes more leaky, and the integrity of cellular proteins gradually is lost. The cell finally is destroyed during one of its passages through the small and tortuous sinusoids of the spleen. The remnants of the cell are engulfed by macrophages and recycled.

REGULATION OF ERYTHROPOIESIS

The production of erythrocytes is regulated carefully and is subject to feedback control. Any process that decreases the delivery of oxygen to the tissues (anemia, decreased arterial P_{O_2}, or shift of the hemoglobin-O_2 dissociation curve to the left) increases the concentration of erythropoietin in the plasma. Erythropoietin, a glycoprotein hormone that has a molecular weight of 35,000 daltons, increases the rate of production of erythrocytes by increasing the number of stem cells committed to eryth-

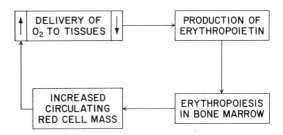

Figure 24-4. Regulation of erythropoiesis by erythropoietin.

ropoiesis. The increased mass of circulating erythrocytes increases the content of oxygen in the blood, which decreases the production of erythropoietin (Figure 24-4). The kidney appears to be the organ that senses the delivery of oxygen to the tissues; however, since no reliable chemical assay of erythropoietin is available, no one knows whether erythropoietin is produced in the kidney or the kidney elaborates a factor that causes erythropoietin to be made from a circulating precursor. In addition, hemolysis causes a greater stimulation of erythropoiesis than would be expected on the basis of tissue hypoxia alone; thus, some degradation product of red cells also may stimulate erythropoiesis.

Several other hormones also influence erythropoiesis. Thyroxine, testosterone, cortisol, and growth hormone stimulate erythropoiesis, and estrogens inhibit it. Presumably, these opposing actions by androgenic and estrogenic steroids are responsible for the differences of blood erythrocyte content between men and women.

METABOLISM OF IRON AND HEME

Iron

Adequate iron is essential for the normal production of hemoglobin, and iron is a necessary component in muscle myoglobin and various important intracellular enzymes, including cytochromes, peroxidase, and catalase. If iron is deficient, small erythrocytes low in hemoglobin are produced; the condition is called iron-deficiency anemia. A 70 kg human contains about 4 g of iron; 65% of it is in hemoglobin, 15%–30% is stored as ferritin, 4% is in myoglobin, and about 1% is associated with various cellular enzymes.

REQUIREMENTS AND ABSORPTION

The daily requirement of iron in the diet is about 10 mg for adult men and 20 mg for menstruating women. Of this amount, only 3%-6% is absorbed, so that the daily requirements for iron absorption are about 0.5 mg/day for men and 1 mg/day for menstruating women. Normally, about 20 mg of iron are needed to produce 70 ml of RBCs each day; nearly all of this iron comes from recycled RBCs, and only a small portion is provided by the diet. Most of the iron in the diet is in the ferric (Fe^{+++}) form and must be reduced to the ferrous (Fe^{++}) form before it can be absorbed in the upper small intestine (Figure 24-5). The environment of the stomach provides a favorable milieu for the reduction of Fe^{+++}; consequently, conditions such as gastrectomy or pernicious anemia, which decrease the gastric parietal cell mass, seriously impair the absorption of iron. In addition, phytic acid (found in cereals), oxylates, and phosphates can combine with iron to produce insoluble compounds that are not absorbed.

TRANSPORT AND DISPOSAL

Upon entry into the mucosal cells, Fe^{++} combines with apoferritin, a globular protein, to form ferritin (see Figure 24-5). Hemosiderin and ferritin, the storage forms of iron, are found in intestinal mucosal cells, macrophages of the liver, bone marrow, and spleen. Ferritin normally is not found in the circulation in appreciable quantities, but iron stored in ferritin, including that of the intestinal mucosa, is in equilibrium with transferrin, a β_1 globulin, the transport form of iron in the plasma. Thus, when body stores of iron are high and plasma transferrin is high, ferritin remains in the intestinal mucosal cells and is not absorbed into the blood. Since these mucosal cells normally are continuously and rapidly sloughed into the intestinal lumen, this mechanism functions as a "mucosal block" to prevent excessive absorption of iron. Conversely, when body stores of iron are low, the iron in ferritin is transferred to plasma transferrin and repletes the stores of iron. In idiopathic hemochromatosis, this mucosal block does not operate properly, and iron is absorbed as if the stores of it were low. Excess ferritin and hemosiderin are stored in various organs, including the liver, skin, heart, and pancreas, in which they may cause, respectively, cirrhosis, skin discoloration, heart failure, and diabetes.

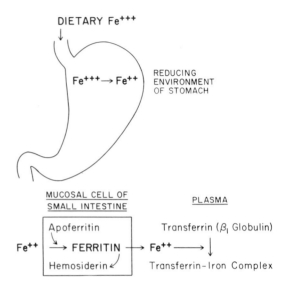

Figure 24-5. Absorption, storage, and transport of iron in plasma. Ferric iron is converted to ferrous form, which is absorbed in upper small intestine. After entry into intestinal mucosal cell, iron may be stored as ferritin or hemosiderin or released into plasma and transported bound to transferrin.

Recycling of Hemoglobin

NORMAL RECYCLING

Senescent erythrocytes are absorbed by macrophages of the reticuloendothelial system, particularly in the spleen, and the hemoglobin is recycled (Figure 24-6). The globin portion is broken down into its constituent amino acids, which are recycled into the body pool; the heme portion is metabolized to bilirubin, bound to albumin, and shuttled back to the liver for excretion in the bile. The iron portion of the heme is stored as ferritin and thereby is available for recycling into transferrin.

EXCESSIVE HEMOLYSIS

In disease states classified as hemolytic anemias, red cells can be destroyed in the vascular space rather than in macrophages. In these circumstances, hemoglobin is released directly into the blood; some of it is taken up by macrophages, and the rest is bound to several plasma proteins. One of the proteins is haptoglobin, an α_2 globulin. The complex that results is removed rapidly by the liver and recycled. Since this process consumes haptoglobin, depletion of serum haptoglobin is one of the consequences of hemolytic anemia. Albumin and hemopexin

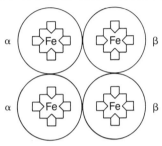

A. α-KETOGLUTARATE + GLYCINE → PYRROLE

B. 4 PYRROLE → PROTOPORPHYRIN III

C. PROTOPORPHYRIN III + Fe++ → HEME

D. 4 HEME + 4 POLYPEPTIDES → HEMOGLOBIN

HEMOGLOBIN

AMINO ACIDS FROM PROTEIN PORTION — RECYCLED INTO AMINO ACID POOL OF BODY

HEME

APOFERRITIN

CO   Fe++ → TRANSFERRIN — TO BONE MARROW FOR RECYCLING

BILIVERDIN

BILIRUBIN — TO LIVER FOR EXCRETION IN BILE

Figure 24-6. Recycling of hemoglobin obtained from senescent erythrocytes destroyed by macrophages of reticuloendothelial system. Globin portion yields amino acids. Heme is metabolized to bilirubin and shuttled back to liver and then excreted in bile. Iron may be released directly into plasma, where it combines with transferrin for transport, or it may remain in macrophage and be stored as ferritin and hemosiderin.

Figure 24-7. Hemoglobin A, composed of four subunits that consist of two β chains and two α chains, each combined with an iron-containing porphyrin moiety called heme.

urine because it is bound to albumin and therefore is not readily filtered by the glomeruli. Rupture of the porphyrin ring in heme to form biliverdin also produces carbon monoxide. This is essentially the body's only intrinsic source of carbon monoxide, and the rate of excretion of CO in exhaled air correlates well with the rate of hemolysis.

bind heme after it is oxidized and split apart from its globin bond; the heme-hemopexin and heme-albumin complexes then are removed by the liver and recycled. When excessive hemolysis saturates the hemoglobin-scavenging system, free hemoglobin, unattached to protein, appears in the plasma and is filtered into the urine, where it can be detected.

JAUNDICE CAUSED BY HEMOLYSIS

Jaundice, a common sign of hemolysis, is due to bilirubin released from free hemoglobin that has been captured and degraded by macrophages. In general, this indirectly reacting bilirubin (see also Chapter 51) does not reach dangerously high levels because the normal liver has a prodigious capacity to take up and metabolize it. Bilirubin does not appear in the

Hemoglobin

Hemoglobin, a globular protein that has a molecular weight of 64,500 daltons, serves as the oxygen-carrying protein in vertebrate blood. The molecule of hemoglobin is made up of four subunits, each consisting of a polypeptide chain combined with an iron-containing porphyrin moiety called *heme*. Collectively, the polypeptide chains are referred to as the *globin* portion of the molecule, and the porphyrin moieties are referred to as the heme portion. Both sections of the molecule are synthesized in developing erythrocytes. The heme portion is prepared by the porphyrin synthetic pathway, in which glycine and α-ketoglutarate are precursors; after a series of steps, iron is added to form heme. Four heme moieties then combine with four polypeptide chains, each containing about 140 amino acids, to form hemoglobin (Figure 24-7). The predominant type, in normal adult hemoglobin A, is characterized by its globin portion, which contains two β and two α polypeptide chains.

When hemoglobin is oxygenated, O_2 binds to the iron molecule in the heme moieties. O_2 attaches initially to a heme group in one of the α subunits, causing a change of conformation in the hemoglobin molecule that increases the affinity of the remaining three subunits for O_2. This effect is responsible for the upward inflection of the Hb-O_2 dissociation curve (see Figure 24-8 and Chapter 31).

The actual shape of the Hb-O_2 dissociation curve can be influenced further by the type of hemoglobin. Various types of hemoglobin have been described; Table 24-2 gives some of the more important ones and their characteristic protein compositions. As an example, in fetal hemoglobin (hemoglobin F, or HbF), the β chains are replaced by γ chains, which decreases the affinity of HbF for 2,3-DPG and shifts the Hb-O_2 dissociation curve (Figure 24-8) to the left. This situation is appropriate for the fetus, because it provides for efficient loading and unloading of O_2 in a relatively hypoxic environment, but persistence of appreciable quantities of HbF causes problems in adults (Figure 24-8). HbF becomes saturated at low P_{O_2} but also requires low P_{O_2} to unload oxygen in the tissues. Conversely, some of the other abnormal hemoglobins, such as Hb-Seattle and Hb-Kansas, require excessively high P_{O_2} to become saturated, and therefore do not take up O_2 in the lungs very well.

Abnormal Hemoglobins

Many abnormal hemoglobins have been described in humans. One group, called hemoglobinopathies, is characterized by plentiful but abnormal polypeptide chains; the other group, known as the thalassemias, is caused by deficient production of normal chains.

HEMOGLOBINOPATHIES

Several rare hemoglobinopathies have been named after the geographic areas in which they were discovered (for example, Seattle, Kansas, Harlem). The most common hemoglobinopathies are hemoglobin-S (HbS, or sickle-cell hemoglobin), and the similar but clinically milder hemoglobin-C (HbC) forms. Either of these variants can occur in the heterozygous (HbAS or HbAC) or homozygous (HbSS or HbCC) forms. The homozygous HbSS form causes sickle cell disease. In this circumstance,

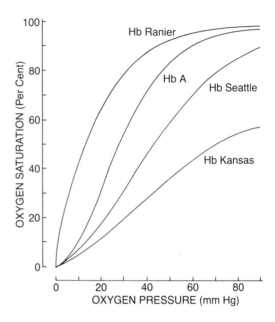

Figure 24-8. Hb-O_2 dissociation curves for normal hemoglobin (HbA) and in some of the hemoglobinopathies. Shift in curve for HbF is similar to that for Hb Rainier. (Redrawn, with permission, from Stamatoyannoupoulous, G. *Ann. Rev. Med.* 22:224. © by Annual Reviews, Inc. 1971.)

the glutamate at position 6 in the normal β chain is replaced by valine. Remarkably, this single substitution produces a hemoglobin that is insoluble at low P_{O_2}, forming a semisolid gel that causes sickle-shaped RBC. Sickle cells are fragile and relatively indeformable; thus, they are easily destroyed (hemolysis), and microinfarcts form because of their inability to get through capillaries.

The hemoglobin S gene is an example of a genetic mutation that originally had survival value and has persisted. HbS occurs in 40% of black Africans and 10% of black Americans; although the homozygous state causes serious disease, the heterozygotes essentially are asymptomatic because they have adequate normal hemoglobin. The survival value of the heterozygote (HbSA) state accrues from an increased resistance to falciparum malaria, which is indigenous to areas of Africa where the frequency of HbS is highest.

THALASSEMIAS

Thalassemias are caused by deficient production of normal hemoglobin chains. The genetic locus that directs synthesis of α chains is dupli-

CLINICAL CORRELATION
24.1   Sickle-Cell Trait

CASE REPORT

Patient: A 29-year-old black man.

Reason for Admission: Collapse while running.

History: The patient had been well until after he had run about 3 miles with a companion on a track in the city park. The site of the park, in a city in the western United States, is more than 4,000 feet above sea level. The patient was a visitor from a port city in the eastern United States and had arrived in this city the previous day to visit the person with whom he was running. Before he lost consciousness, the patient had complained of faintness and numbness of the legs. He was brought to the emergency room by helicopter, and had regained consciousness by the time he arrived.

Clinical Examination: At admission, the patient complained of pain and weakness in his legs, although he appeared to be in no other acute distress. His heart rate was regular, at 120/min (normal, < 100/min), and his arterial pressure was 96/65 mm Hg (normal, 90–140/60–90 mm Hg). The physical examination revealed nothing else medically significant. Laboratory findings were: hematocrit 34% (normal, 45%–52%), white cell count 14,800/mm^3 (normal, 4300–10,800/mm^3), Pa_{CO_2} 18 mm Hg (normal, 35–45 mm Hg), [Cl$^-$] 89 mEq/liter (normal 98–106 mEq/liter), [K$^+$] 7.1 mEq/liter (normal, 3.5–5.0 mEq/liter), [Na$^+$] 148 mEq/liter (normal, 136–145 mEq/liter), and arterial blood pH 6.9 (normal, 7.35–7.45). The prothrombin time was 26 seconds, compared with a control of 14.3 seconds, and the fibrinogen was 160 mg/dl (normal, 160–415 mg/dl). One hour after admission, he became apneic (stopped breathing) and lost consciousness. Pulmonary resuscitation was begun at once, and a regular heart beat and palpable pulse were obtained. His arterial pressure was 70/50 at that time, but suppor-

tive measures failed, and the patient died 6½ hours after admission.

Autopsy Findings: The gastrointestinal lumen was filled with bloody material, the lungs were heavy and filled with blood, the sinusoids of the liver were packed with sickled red cells, and blood was pooled around the splenic follicles. No areas of old visceral infarcts or deposits of hemosiderin (a glycoprotein that contains iron—a storage form of iron) were found. Electrophoresis revealed hemoglobin S (characteristic of sickle-cell trait).

Comment: Persons who have sickle-cell trait normally are asymptomatic. They are not anemic, and their blood does not hemolyze. However, hypoxemia, acidosis, dehydration, and the action of reducing agents (such as lactate) causes their abnormal hemoglobin, HbS, to form parallel bundles of fibers, or *tactoids,* which give the cell a rigid, elongated, sickle shape. The threshold for sickling in an individual cell is related inversely to the proportion of HbS in the cell. If all of the conditions listed above develop simultaneously, the patient is in danger of sudden death. Because of their rigidity and lack of deformability, sickled cells do not move easily through small arterioles and capillaries, and actually may cause infarcts (tissue death due to lack of blood flow). A moderately sickled cell may revert to normal when exposed to adequate oxygenation (sickling occurs in the reduced [deoxygenated] form of HbS). *In vitro* studies have shown that at pH 7.1, more than half of the cells sickle when the P_{O_2} is decreased to 15 mm Hg.

Exercise, such as running a moderate distance as the patient did, tends to cause localized hypoxemia, acidosis, and increased concentrations of lactate, especially at an elevated altitude to which the subject is not acclimated. Although dehydration also is a factor in sickling, the patient seems to have been taking adequate fluids and not to have perspired excessively during the run.

TABLE 24-2
Normal and some abnormal hemoglobins

	Composition	Percent of adult Hb	Abnormality
HbA (normal adult)	$\alpha_2\beta_2$	97	—
HbF (fetal)	$\alpha_2\gamma_2$	1	↓ O_2 unloading at tissues
HbA$_2$	$\alpha_2\delta_2$	2	—
HbS (a hemoglobinopathy)	$\alpha_2\beta_2$ with *defective* β-chains		RBC membrane resists deformation at low O_2 tensions
α-thalassemia	$\alpha_2\beta_2$ with *deficient* α-chain production		Ranges from mild anemia to intrauterine death, depending on degree of α-chain deficiency
β-thalassemia	$\alpha_2\beta_2$ with *deficient* β-chain production and varying amounts of $\alpha_2\gamma_2$ and $\alpha_2\delta_2$		Mild-to-severe anemia. Deficient β-chains can be partially replaced by γ- and δ-chains.

cated; therefore, each normal human cell has four genes for the production of the α hemoglobin chain (two from each parent). α-thalassemias occur when one or more of these four genes is missing. Absence of all four α genes is incompatible with life, because no other protein can substitute for the α protein; in this event, severe anemia causes death in utero in the condition known as hydrops fetalis. Absence of three, two, or one of the α genes causes a spectrum of α-thalassemia of decreasing severity.

The other type of thalassemia, called β-thalassemia, is caused by abnormal location of genes for synthesis of the β chain. The situation is different from that of α-thalassemia, because γ and δ peptides can substitute for the missing β peptide chains (Table 24-2). Thus, in β-thalassemia, the concentrations of fetal hemoglobin (HbF = $\alpha_2\gamma_2$) and hemoglobin A$_2$ (HbA$_2$ = $\alpha_2\delta_2$) are increased to replace the missing hemoglobin (HbA = $\alpha_2\beta_2$). It has been assumed that the clinically muted thalassemia conferred some survival advantage, but none has been identified. This possibility is suggested by the distinct geographical distributions of the diseases: β-thalassemia is found often in Mediterranean areas, and α-thalassemia occurs frequently in Southeast Asia.

BLOOD GROUPS AND TRANSFUSION

First Attempts to Transfuse

The first documented experiments in which blood was transfused into humans occurred in England and France in the late seventeenth century. Sheep blood was used, and in most instances severe reactions ensued. As a consequence, the practice was abandoned. In the early nineteenth century, an English obstetrician and physiologist named James Blundell found the death of hemorrhaged dogs could be prevented by transfusion of blood from other dogs. He later attempted human-to-human blood transfusions in some of his obstetric patients who had severe puerperal hemorrhage; considering the potential complications of clotting and blood group incompatibility, it is remarkable that he obtained successful therapeutic results in five of eight transfusions. Dog blood does not contain the isoagglutinins that are responsible for most transfusion reactions. Therefore, it was soon appreciated that human-to-human transfusion involved complications more frequently than dog-to-dog transfusion did.

TABLE 24-3
ABO genetics and blood types

Blood Type (Phenotype)	Genotype	Antigens on RBCs	Antibodies in Serum	Percent of Humans who have Blood Type	Compatible Donor Blood Types
A	AA	A	B ⎫		A,O
A	AO	A	B ⎭ 41		A,O
B	BB	B	A ⎫		B,O
B	BO	B	A ⎭ 9		B,O
AB	AB	AB	None	3	A, B, AB, O (universal recipient)
O	OO	None	A, B	47	O (universal donor)

ABO System

In the early twentieth century, Landsteiner mixed serum and RBCs from various individuals and demonstrated that serum from certain people would cause agglutination of erythrocytes from certain others. Agglutination indicated that the serum contained antibodies against the cells. Use of this methodology led to the recognition of four specific blood groups, each defined by varying patterns of expression or lack of expression of one or two RBC surface antigens, designated A or B. People who have type A blood express only type A antigen on their red cells, those who have type B blood express only type B antigen, those who have AB blood express both antigens, and those who have type O express neither antigen.

Normally, the immune system recognizes the organism's own red cell antigens as "self," and does not make antibodies against them; however, it does make antibodies against foreign antigens, which are recognized as "nonself." Thus, a reciprocal relationship exists between an individual's own RBC antigens and the antibodies in his serum. People who have type A blood have antibodies against B antigen but not against A antigen; those who have type B blood have antibodies against A antigen but not against B; those who have type AB blood have neither antibody; and those who have type O blood have antibodies against both A and B blood (Table 24-3).

GENETIC BASIS

The genetic basis of the ABO blood type system was established by extensive studies of families,

which showed that whether a person has type A, type B, or type O blood is determined by a pair of genetic components, each of which can be drawn from A, B, or O. Thus, as shown in Table 24-3, six possible genotypes can produce any of four possible phenotypes that manifest as a particular blood type.

TRANSFUSION REACTIONS

Transfusion reactions can occur when serum antibodies in the recipient are directed against antigens on donor red cells, which are agglutinated and hemolyzed rapidly. Extensive hemolysis and agglutination of RBCs can produce a complex of symptoms that includes fever, chills, back pain, nausea, vomiting, hypotension, and acute renal failure due to filling of the renal tubules with hemoglobin released from destroyed red cells. Table 24-3 lists ABO blood types compatible for transfusion.

It is not clear how a person who has a given set of ABO antigens on his or her RBCs can develop antibodies against nonself ABO antigens before he or she has been exposed to them. The most likely explanation is that the antigen composition of the cell walls of several common bacteria is similar to the ABO antigens and can cause individuals to develop antibodies against ABO antigens before exposure to donor blood.

Recent investigations have revealed the chemical nature of the surface antigens that make up ABO blood groups. The H antigen is a five-residue polysaccharide that serves as precursor for type A and type B antigens. As shown in Figure 24-9, A enzyme changes H

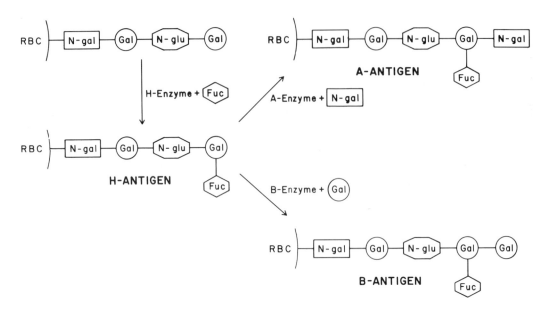

Figure 24-9.   Pathways for synthesis of ABO antigens. A precursor antigen is converted to H antigen, and H antigen may be converted to A or B antigen. The presence of H antigen alone results in expression of O blood type; A antigen results in A type, B antigen results in B type, and A antigen + B antigen result in AB-type. (Redrawn, with permission, from Thaler, M.S., et al. 1977. *Medical Immunology*. Philadelphia: Lippincott.)

antigen into A antigen, and type A blood is expressed. Likewise, B enzyme converts H antigen to B antigen, and type B blood results. A and B enzymes together produce AB type blood, and type O blood results if only H antigen is present.

A blood type that lacks H antigen—called "Bombay"—has been discovered. People who have this type of blood appear to be O type when their red cells are tested with standard anti-A and anti-B antisera, but they usually have serum antibodies directed against H antigen and may develop transfusion reactions if given type O blood.

Although about 30 different types of RBC surface antigens can cause transfusion reactions, ABO incompatibilities are by far the most likely to occur. When blood is transfused, the donor antibodies are diluted and removed from the recipient's blood; the hemolytic reaction is that of recipient serum antibodies against non-self antigens on donor RBCs. Since type O blood has only H antigen on RBCs, it usually is safe to give to people who have types O, A, B, or AB blood; hence, people who have type O blood often are designated as universal donors (see Table 24-3). Conversely, people who have type AB blood have neither A nor B antibodies in their serum; hence, they usually are able to receive transfusions from donors who have O,

A, B, or AB blood and sometimes are designated as universal recipients.

Rh Blood Groups

The Rh antigen on red cell surfaces is important in transfusion reactions and hemolytic anemia. The precise structure of this antigen has not been worked out, but unlike the antigens of ABO blood types, it has been shown to be a protein.

Rh-incompatible blood (Rh+ blood given to an Rh− recipient) occasionally causes transfusion reactions, but usually this does not occur unless repeated transfusions are given because, in contrast to anti-ABO antibodies, anti-Rh antibodies are not formed without prior exposure to Rh+ blood. Even after exposure, only about half of Rh− subjects develop Rh antibodies.

ERYTHROBLASTOSIS FETALIS

The most important condition that involves Rh blood types is hemolytic disease of the newborn, or *erythroblastosis fetalis,* which occurs to some degree about once in every 50 live births. This problem can occur when an Rh− mother carries an Rh+ fetus. The mother develops anti-Rh antibodies, which cross the placenta and cause hemolysis of the Rh+ erythrocytes of the fetus. Before birth, most of the indirect-reacting (unconjugated) bilirubin formed from hemolysis of fetal RBC passes across the placenta from fetus to mother, is conjugated by the maternal liver, and excreted. Immediately after birth, the infant can dispose of bilirubin only through his own liver, which is immature and therefore unable to clear the blood of the large quantity of bilirubin produced. When present in high concentration in the plasma, bilirubin crosses the immature blood-brain barrier of the infant, enters the basal ganglia, and causes *kernicterus*. The anemia and kernicterus can be fatal unless the fetal blood is replaced immediately by transfusion.

Erythroblastosis fetalis can be avoided by an ingenious therapeutic maneuver. An Rh⁻ woman who carries an Rh⁺ fetus usually becomes sensitized to the Rh⁺ fetal red cells and develops Rh⁺ antibodies before parturition, probably because small numbers of fetal red cells cross the placenta into the maternal circulation. Thus, the risk of erythroblastosis fetalis increases with each pregnancy. However, if the mother is given anti-Rh immunoglobulin around the time of parturition, any Rh⁺ fetal cells that she receives are destroyed, she does not develop anti-Rh antibodies, and the danger of erythroblastosis fetalis during the next pregnancy is diminished greatly.

Erythroblastosis fetalis usually is caused by Rh incompatibility and not ABO incompatibility. The latter does not develop because the expression of ABO antigens on the surface of fetal red cells is delayed, and in addition, the isoagglutinins that cause ABO agglutination are too large to pass from mother to fetus through the placenta. In contrast, Rh antigen is expressed on fetal red cells early in development, and the maternal anti-Rh antibody is small enough to pass through the placenta readily.

Blood Banking

Before a transfusion is done, the proposed donor and recipient must undergo a series of tests. First, ABO and Rh typing is done; then both donor and recipient bloods are screened for other antibodies that are not necessarily expected but that occasionally cause transfusion reactions. After these tests, a cross-match is performed by adding donor red cells to a sample of recipient serum and observing for agglutination or hemolysis. This serves as a final check and actually is an in vitro "preview" of the proposed transfusion. In addition, donor serum can be checked for its ability to agglu-

tinate recipient red cells, but this check usually is superfluous because donor antibodies are diluted sufficiently to prevent their reaction with recipient red cells. As most transfusions consist of packed red cells, from which the plasma has been removed, this "minor" cross-match is unnecessary.

ANEMIAS

The term anemia is derived from the Greek word *anaimia,* which means bloodlessness. Table 24-4 lists normal clinical laboratory values for red cell count, hemoglobin concentration, hematocrit, and red cell indices. A subject is considered to be anemic if the RBC count, hemoglobin concentration, or hematocrit is below the normal limits.

Anemia is caused by increased loss or decreased production of erythrocytes. Since the normal life span of an erythrocyte is 120 days, 1/120 of the red cells, or about 45,000/mm³ of blood, normally are destroyed and replaced each day.

TABLE 24-4

Normal erythrocyte data
in men and women

Test	Range of Normal Values
RBC count	
Men	5.4 ± 0.9 million/mm³ blood
Women	4.8 ± 0.6 million/mm³ blood
Hemoglobin concentration	
Men	16 ± 2 g/dl blood
Women	14 ± 2 g/dl blood
Hematocrit	
Men	47 ± 5 ml red cells/dl blood
Women	42 ± 5 ml red cells/dl blood
RBC indices	
Mean corpuscular volume (MCV)	83–97 μm³
Mean corpuscular hemoglobin (MCH)	27–31 pg
Mean corpuscular hemoglobin concentration (MCHC)	32–36 g/dl

Anemia decreases the oxygen-carrying capacity of the blood. Since arterial blood normally is about 95%–98% saturated with O_2, the only way to deliver more O_2 to the tissues is to increase the cardiac output. As the hematocrit decreases, the viscosity of the blood decreases, which decreases the resistance to flow and permits the cardiac output to increase (see Chapter 12). As cardiac output increases, the flow may become turbulent, and murmurs may be heard in the large vessels such as the aorta and pulmonary artery even at rest (see Chapter 13).

In clinical practice, measurement of the number of reticulocytes in the peripheral blood is useful in assessing the patient's erythropoietic capacity. When the erythropoietic mechanisms of the bone marrow are functioning properly, the response to anemia is a marked increase in the reticulocyte count; when the reticulocyte count does not increase adequately, some aberration in erythropoiesis is indicated.

Excessive Loss of Erythrocytes

Erythrocytes may be lost by hemorrhage or by destruction within the body. Blood may be lost acutely through vascular trauma, ruptured aneurysms, peptic ulcers, and hemorrhagic diathesis. Blood may be lost chronically by slow bleeding into the gastrointestinal or urinary tracts or, in women, by excessive menstruation. Sudden loss of one-third of the blood volume often is fatal, but with slower loss over 24 hours or more, the compensatory mechanisms outlined in Chapter 23 often are adequate to permit survival after even larger losses of blood.

Destruction of Erythrocytes

The average survival time of red cells may decrease so much that the bone marrow no longer can produce erythrocytes as rapidly as they are being destroyed. In general, RBCs are destroyed because of their own abnormalities or because of abnormalities outside the red cells.

ABNORMALITIES OF RBC ENZYMES

Energy for the erythrocyte is derived mainly from conversion of glucose to lactate by anaerobic glycolysis or the hexose monophosphate (HMP) shunt; deficiencies in any of the enzyme systems involved in these pathways can cause hemolytic anemia. The most common defect involves glucose-6-phosphate dehydrogenase (G6PD), an enzyme of the hexose monophosphate shunt. This is an X-linked defect that occurs in about 10% of black men and to a lesser degree in black women and Caucasians. Normally, G6PD catalyzes the production of NADPH, which maintains a proper reducing environment inside the erythrocytes. Without it, structural and enzymatic proteins do not function properly, and cells hemolyze. In patients who have G6PD deficiency, a severe hemolytic anemia can be initiated by a variety of drugs that promote oxidation. Like the sickle cell trait, G6PD deficiency decreases susceptibility to falciparum malaria, presumably because the malarial parasite utilizes the HMP shunt for optimal growth.

ABNORMALITIES OF RBC MEMBRANE

Several types of anemia are caused by abnormalities of the red cell membrane. In hereditary spherocytosis, the concentration of phospholipids in the cell membrane decreases, and the RBCs lose their normal shape, becoming small, round, more rigid, and less deformable. Anemia is caused by excessive trapping and destruction of the nondeformable erythrocytes in the spleen. Alcoholic liver disease can cause a similar situation, in which defective RBC phospholipid is produced and aberrant RBCs are formed. The abnormal cells are destroyed in the spleen.

IMMUNOLOGICAL ABNORMALITIES

In several varieties of hemolytic anemia, patients form antibodies against their own red cells, which cause anemia by agglutination and hemolysis. One of these diseases, autoimmune hemolytic anemia, is induced by certain drugs (especially α-methyldopa, L-dopa, penicillins, and cephalosporins) or may occur as a complication in various leukemias and autoimmune diseases. Autoimmune hemolytic anemias sometimes can be diagnosed by the direct Coomb's test, in which anti-IgG antibodies are added to a sample of the patient's blood. If the RBCs are coated with IgG, the anti-IgG antibodies cross-link these antibodies and cause agglutination (Figure 24-10). In some people, anti-RBC antibodies become active at low temperature (below 30 C); thus drinking cold water, washing the hands in cold water, or exposure to cold air may activate these antibodies and cause hemolysis.

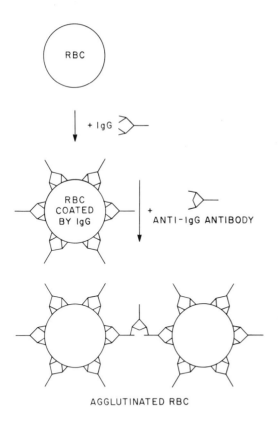

RBC

+ IgG

RBC
COATED
BY IgG

+

ANTI-IgG ANTIBODY

AGGLUTINATED RBC

Figure 24-10.   Direct Coomb's test to diagnose for autoimmune hemolytic anemias. If patient's RBCs are coated with IgG antibodies, addition of anti-IgG antibodies will cross-link IgG on adjacent cells and cause agglutination.

TRAUMA TO RED CELLS

Damage to any area of the cardiovascular system may subject RBCs to excessive stress and cause hemolysis. Long marches, fighting, or violent exercise may induce enough vascular trauma to cause hemolysis as red cells pass through the damaged areas. Defective natural or prosthetic cardiac valves, damaged microvasculature in circulatory shock, and disseminated intravascular coagulation (DIC, see Chapter 26) may cause hemolysis. Furthermore, various infectious agents, including hemolytic streptococci, clostridia, meningococcus, and malaria parasites, can cause hemolysis and anemia.

Depressed Production of RBCs

IRON DEFICIENCY

Iron deficiency anemia, which is the most common type of anemia, may be caused by chronic blood loss, diminished intake of iron, or inade-

quate absorption of iron. In the initial stages of iron depletion, plasma and RBC iron remain normal because the body's stores of iron are utilized and absorption of iron in the small intestine is enhanced. As iron deficiency progresses, the plasma concentration of iron decreases, and since adequate iron is not available to make RBCs, a hypochromic (erythrocytes have diminished hemoglobin concentration) microcytic (small red cells) anemia develops. Iron-deficiency anemia is diagnosed if the red cells are pale (hypochromic) and small (microcytic) and if special staining of bone marrow samples obtained by biopsy shows diminished concentrations of hemosiderin and ferritin.

DEFICIENCIES OF FOLATE AND VITAMIN B$_{12}$

Several other substances also are necessary for normal development of erythrocytes. Most notable are folic acid and vitamin B$_{12}$, which are necessary for protein synthesis and cell development. Deficiency of either of these vitamins causes early extrusion of the nucleus of the developing erythrocyte, which results in anemia characterized by large, immature erythrocytes and, hence, megaloblastic anemia.

APLASTIC AND MYELOPHTHISIC ANEMIAS

Other types of anemia are caused by decreased ability of the bone marrow to carry on erythropoiesis. Aplastic anemia can be idiopathic, may result from overdose of ionizing radiation, or may be caused by certain chemical agents and drugs, including benzene, arsenic, phenytoin, aspirin, and antineoplastic drugs. The myelophthisic anemias reflect depression of erythropoietic activity caused by invasion or replacement of bone marrow by other tissue, typically fibroblastic cells or cancer.

SIDEROBLASTIC ANEMIA

In one group of anemias, the bone marrow is hypercellular and contains many developing red cells laden with iron (sideroblasts). The biochemical cause of this anemia is unknown, but the condition has been associated with various cancers, rheumatoid arthritis, ethanol abuse, and lead poisoning. In sideroblastic anemia, the developing red cell is unable to incorporate iron into heme. As a result, iron is deposited in the mitochondria, where heme normally is synthesized, and special staining of the iron in these cells leads to the typical appearance of ringed sideroblasts. Pyridoxine (vitamin B_6) is required in heme synthesis, and large doses sometimes can improve sideroblastic anemia.

Destruction and Decreased Production of RBCs

HEMOGLOBINOPATHIES AND THALASSEMIAS

Hemoglobinopathies are characterized by RBCs of diminished life span caused by defective hemoglobin. Production of RBCs is subnormal in thalassemias because the production of normal hemoglobin is deficient. Anemia can develop in either of these diseases.

ANEMIA ASSOCIATED WITH CHRONIC DISEASES

Anemia may be associated with a variety of chronic diseases, including cancer, chronic infections, rheumatoid arthritis, renal insufficiency, and liver disease. Both impaired nutrition and decreased erythrocyte survival are involved, but the major problem appears to be diminished production of erythropoietin. Proper therapy of the anemia requires treatment of the underlying disease; supplementary iron and vitamins generally are of no benefit.

POLYCYTHEMIA

Polycythemia is a state in which the total mass of red cells is increased. The hematocrit, RBC count, and hemoglobin concentration all are increased; however, since dehydration can cause these changes without an actual increase in the total mass of red cells, a diagnosis of polycythemia may require intravenous injection of radiolabeled red cells, blood sampling, measurement of blood radioactivity, and application of the dilution principle to determine total red cell mass. The increased hematocrit (up to 70%–80%) increases the viscosity of the blood and increases the peripheral vascular resistance, which tends to decrease the cardiac output. However, the increase in total blood volume tends to aid cardiac filling, and the cardiac output generally is normal. The increased blood volume is responsible for minor events

such as nose bleeds and a high incidence of cerebral and gastrointestinal hemorrhages. The bleeding tendency also is explained by relatively less plasma to accommodate clotting factors. Conversely, sluggish blood flow caused by higher resistance in peripheral vessels predisposes to the formation of thrombi because activated clotting factors accumulate. In addition, sluggish blood flow increases the quantity of desaturated blood in the subpapillary venous plexus, which imparts a ruddy hue to the skin of patients who have polycythemia.

Primary Polycythemia

Primary polycythemia, or polycythemia vera (PCV), is characterized by malignant proliferation of all hematopoietic tissue, especially the precursors of erythrocytes. In patients who have PCV, a clone of erythroid cells develops in the bone marrow and proliferates rapidly despite a low level of erythropoietin. Treatment for PVC includes phlebotomy (bleeding), to reduce cell mass, or radioactive ^{37}P, which destroys the malignant cells.

Secondary Polycythemia

Secondary polycythemia is caused by either appropriate or inappropriate increases in the production of erythropoietin. Erythropoietin increases appropriately in tissue hypoxia caused by living at high altitude, pulmonary disease that causes $\dot{V}/\dot{Q}$ imbalance, the fetal environment, congenital cardiac abnormalities that cause hypoxemia (see Chapter 20), decreased O_2 transport in conditions such as methemoglobinemia (congenital absence of an enzyme that keeps heme iron in the Fe^{++} state), and carboxyhemoglobinemia (excessive amount of carbon monoxide binding to heme and displacing O_2; this is responsible for the polycythemia seen in heavy smokers), and increased affinity for O_2 by certain abnormal hemoglobins (Chesapeake, Rainier, HbF, and the thalassemias; see Figure 24-7). Erythropoietin is produced inappropriately in cases of certain neoplasms (hypernephromas, uterine myomas, pheochromocytoma, adrenal adenoma, and hepatoma), in certain renal lesions (polycystic disease and hydronephrosis), and in cases of familial erythrocytosis (autosomal recessive inheritance).

STUDY OUTLINE

Blood is 7% of body weight (5 liters in 70 kg person).

55% plasma, 45% erythrocytes, < 1% leukocytes and platelets.

FORMED ELEMENTS

HEMATOPOIESIS

CHANGES WITH AGE   In fetus, blood cells produced first in yolk sac, then liver and spleen; by time of birth, in bone marrow.

STRUCTURE OF BONE MARROW   Cords of hematopoietic tissue separated by venous sinuses.

Cells and platelets pass through fenestrated membrane to enter circulation.

STEM CELLS   Precursors of each type; orderly sequence of maturation.

ERYTHROCYTES   Nonnucleated biconcave discs, approximately 7 μm diameter, 2 μm maximum thickness.

Volume, approximately 80–95 $μm^3$, 33%–38% hemoglobin.

Approximately 5.4×10^6 cells/mm^3 in men, approximately 4.8×10^6 in women.

Mean life 120 days, 10^{10} cells/hr produced.

PRODUCTION   Normally in bone marrow.

Multipotential stem cell commits to erythroid line.

Hemoglobin synthesized.

Nucleus extruded, forming reticulocyte; leaves bone marrow.

Maturation.

DESTRUCTION   Nothing renewable in mature erythrocyte.

Deteriorates gradually with age, engulfed by macrophages and recycled.

REGULATION OF ERYTHROPOIESIS Feedback control.

Erythropoietin, a hormone activated by decreased oxygen delivery to tissues; increases production of erythrocytes.

Oxygen delivery sensed by kidneys.

Also influenced by products of red cell destruction.

Increased by thyroxine, testosterone, cortisol, and growth hormone.

Decreased by estrogens.

METABOLISM OF IRON AND HEME

IRON   70 kg person contains approximately 4 g.

Essential component of hemoglobin, muscle myoglobin, and intracellular respiratory enzymes.

REQUIREMENTS AND ABSORPTION Adult male needs approximately 10 mg/day in diet; menstruating female, about 20 mg/day.

Absorbed as Fe^{++}; formed from Fe^{+++} in stomach.

3%–6% absorbed, 0.5–1 mg/day added by diet; most obtained from recycled RBCs.

TRANSPORT AND DISPOSAL   In mucosal cell, Fe^{++} plus apoferritin (protein) form ferritin: storage.

Iron of ferritin in equilibrium with that of transferrin in blood; frequent sloughing of mucosal cells prevents excess absorption.

Ferritin and hemosiderin, a complex of ferritin, also are found in macrophages of liver, bone marrow, spleen.

Excess storage of iron damages liver, heart, pancreas, skin.

RECYCLING OF HEMOGLOBIN

NORMAL RECYCLING   Old and damaged RBCs absorbed by macrophages in spleen.

Globin yields amino acids that enter body pool.

Heme metabolized to bilirubin, which is excreted in bile.

Iron stored as ferritin.

EXCESSIVE HEMOLYSIS   Hemolytic anemias; RBCs destroyed in vascular space.

Some Hb taken up by macrophages; some bound to plasma proteins; recycled by liver.

If scavenger capacity exceeded, Hb appears in urine.

JAUNDICE CAUSED BY HEMOLYSIS Reflects high level of bilirubin in macrophages and blood.

HEMOGLOBIN   Globular, oxygen-binding protein.

Four subunits; each consists of polypeptide chain and iron-containing porphyrin compound.

Peptide chains form globin portion; porphyrin moieties form heme portion.

O_2 attaches to Fe of one heme group; increases affinity of others for O_2.

Hb that contains different polypeptide chains has different properties.

ABNORMAL HEMOGLOBINS

HEMOGLOBINOPATHIES   Abnormal polypeptide chains.

Some rare forms named for geographic areas.

HbS (sickle cell): insoluble at low Po_2, forms a semisolid gel that prevents deformation of RBC; impedes capillary perfusion.

THALASSEMIAS Deficient production of normal polypeptide chains.

BLOOD GROUPS AND TRANSFUSION

FIRST ATTEMPTS TO TRANSFUSE Animal to animal, animal to human, human to human.

ABO SYSTEM Serum contains antibodies against certain RBCs.

Type A blood: type A antigen on RBC; antibody against type B RBC in serum.

Type B blood: type B antigen on RBC; antibody against type A RBC in serum.

Type AB blood: both A and B antigens on RBC; neither A nor B antibodies in serum.

Type O blood: neither A nor B antigens on RBC; both A and B antibodies in serum.

GENETIC BASIS Six possible genotypes produce four possible phenotypes.

TRANSFUSION REACTIONS RBC agglutinated and hemolyzed; symptoms caused by release of Hb and other cell contents.

H antigen, precursor of A and B antigens, determined by A and B enzymes.

"Bombay" type: cells lack H antigen; serum contains H antibody and reacts with type O blood.

Recipient antibodies (serum) act on donor antigens (RBC); donor antibodies (serum), diluted into recipient serum, do not affect recipient antigen (RBC).

Type O: only H antigen on RBC; "universal donor."

Type AB: neither A nor B antibodies in serum; "universal recipient."

Rh BLOOD GROUPS Rh^+: Rh antigen on RBC.

Rh^-: no Rh antigen on RBC; Rh antibody develops in serum only after exposure to Rh^+ blood.

ERYTHROBLASTOSIS FETALIS Hemolysis in newborn.

Rh^- mother carrying Rh^+ fetus; anti-Rh antibodies develop in maternal blood, cross placental membrane, react with fetal RBC.

Effect greater in succeeding pregnancies.

BLOOD BANKING Compatibility between donor blood and recipient blood must be tested before transfusion.

ANEMIAS

EXCESSIVE LOSS OF ERYTHROCYTES

Hemorrhage or destruction within body.

DESTRUCTION   OF   ERYTHROCYTES
Own abnormalities or those outside cell.

ABNORMALITIES OF RBC ENZYMES Involve glucose-6-phosphate-dehydrogenase most often.

ABNORMALITIES OF RBC MEMBRANE Insufficient phospholipid; cell of abnormal shape: rigid, less deformable.

IMMUNOLOGICAL ABNORMALITIES Patient forms antibodies against own RBC.

TRAUMA TO RED CELLS Damage to cardiovascular system, violent activity, and so on.

DEPRESSED PRODUCTION OF RBC

IRON DEFICIENCY Most common type; RBCs have low hemoglobin content.

DEFICIENCIES OF FOLATE AND VITAMIN B_{12} Large, immature erythrocytes; factors necessary for protein synthesis and cell development lacking.

APLASTIC   AND   MYELOPHTHISIC ANEMIAS Decreased ability of bone marrow to make RBC.

SIDEROBLASTIC ANEMIAS Developing RBC unable to incorporate iron into heme.

DESTRUCTION AND DECREASED PRODUCTION OF RBCs

HEMOGLOBINOPATHIES AND THALASSEMIAS Short life span due to abnormal Hb.

Subnormal production of RBCs due to low rate of production of normal Hb.

ANEMIA ASSOCIATED WITH CHRONIC DISEASES Cancer, infections, others.

POLYCYTHEMIA Total mass of red cells increased.

Increased hematocrit increases viscosity of blood.

Increased blood volume predisposes to hemorrhage.

Sluggish flow favors formation of thrombi, increases quantity of desaturated blood, gives ruddy hue to skin.

PRIMARY   POLYCYTHEMIA Malignant production of all hematopoietic tissue; polycythemia vera.

SECONDARY POLYCYTHEMIA Appropriate increased production of erythropoietin due to tissue hypoxia.

Inappropriate production of erythropoietin in certain tumors, certain renal lesions, and inherited conditions.

BIBLIOGRAPHY

Adamson, J.W.; Fialkow, P.J.; Murphy, S.; et al. 1976. Polycythemia vera: a stem-cell and probably clonal origin of the disease. *N. Engl. J. Med.* 295:125.

Bank, A.; Mears, J.G.; and Ramirez, F. 1980. Disorders of human hemoglobin. *Science* 207:486.

Figueroa, W.G. 1981. *Hematology.* New York: John Wiley and Sons.

Junqueira, L.C.; Carneiro, J.; and Contopoulos, A.N. 1977. *Basic histology*, 2nd ed. Los Altos, Calif.: Lange Medical Publications.

Kapff, C.T., and Jandl, H.J. 1981. *Blood: atlas and sourcebook of hematology.* Boston: Little, Brown & Co.

Leavell, B.S., and Thorup, O.A. 1976. *Fundamentals of clinical hematology,* 4th ed. Philadelphia: W.B. Saunders Co.

Leon, M.B.; Borer, J.S.; Bacharach, S.L.; et al. 1979. Detection of early cardiac dysfunction in patients with severe beta-thalassemia and chronic iron overload. *N. Engl. J. Med.* 301:1143.

Mollison, P.L. 1983. *Blood transfusion in Clinical Medicine,* 7th ed. St. Louis: Blackwell/Mosby.

Munro, H., and Linder, M.C. 1978. Ferritin: structure, biosynthesis, and role in iron metabolism. *Physiol. Rev.* 58:317.

Nagel, R.L.; Lynfield, J.; Johnson, J. et al. 1976. Hemoglobin Beth Israel: a mutant causing clinically apparent cyanosis. *N. Engl. J. Med.* 295:125.

Quesenberry, P., and Levitt, L. 1979. Hematopoietic stem cells. *N. Engl. J. Med.* 301:755, 819, 868 (three parts).

Reich, P.R. 1978. *Hematology: physiopathologic basis for clinical practice.* Boston: Little, Brown & Co.

Schafer, A.I.; Cheron, R.G.; Dluhy, R.; et al. 1981. Clinical consequences of acquired transfusional iron overload in adults. *N. Engl. J. Med.* 304:319.

Williams, W.J.; Beutler, E.; Erslev, A.S.; et al. 1977. *Hematology,* 2nd ed. New York: McGraw-Hill Book Co.

Wintrobe, M.M.; Lee. G.R.; Boggs, D.R.; et al. 1981. *Clinical Hematology,* 8th ed. Philadelphia: Lea & Febiger.

Wintrobe, M.M. 1980. *Blood, pure and eloquent.* New York: McGraw-Hill Book Co.

White Blood Cells
and Immunity

CHAPTER CONTENTS

Normally, each cubic millimeter of blood contains between 4000 and 12,000 white blood cells, or leukocytes. These cells perform specific functions to protect the organism against invasion by microorganisms. Leukocytes can be grouped into *phagocytes* or *immunocytes* on the basis of function.

The first group, the phagocytes, consists of granulocytes and monocyte-macrophages. These cells destroy invading microorganisms or dispose of debris through phagocytosis, a process in which they detect the foreign material chemically (chemotaxis), move toward and become attached to it (adherence), and then engulf and destroy it. Granulocytes function as the first line of defense against invading mi-

croorganisms; the monocyte-macrophage system serves as a second line of defense and clears debris from aged and damaged cells. By contrast, lymphocytes and plasma cells are nonphagocytic immunocytes that kill invading microorganisms by elaborating cytotoxic chemicals (lymphokines) and antibodies.

PHAGOCYTES

Both types of phagocytes (granulocytes and cells of the monocyte-macrophage series) are produced in the bone marrow from a common stem-cell precursor. The mature granulocytes are about 9–12 μm in diameter, have multilobed, irregularly shaped nuclei, and contain distinct granules (lysosomes) in the cytoplasm. On the basis of the staining characteristics of the granules in their cytoplasm, granulocytes are classified as neutrophils (small, salmon-pink granules), eosinophils (larger, bright orange granules), or basophils (large, violet granules). Monocytes and macrophages are about 12–15 μm in diameter and, in contrast to granulocytes, have a single, nonsegmented nucleus and contain no cytoplasmic granules.

Granulocytes

GRANULOPOIESIS

As the immature stem cells for granulocytes develop by steps into the more mature cells of the granulocytic cell line, the size of the cell, the nucleus, and the ratio of nucleus to cytoplasm all decrease; the nucleus becomes denser, and the cytoplasm becomes darker, due to enhanced activity of organelles that synthesize protein. The stem cells develop into the still-immature myeloblasts, which in turn develop into the more mature promyelocytes. In addition to the signs of increased maturity mentioned earlier, nonspecific (azurophilic) cytoplasmic granules form in the promyelocytes. These early granules are nonspecific, since all types of granulocytes possess them; thus, they do not indicate the type of granulocyte that will develop. In later stages of development, these nonspecific granules are replaced by specific granules that are unique to each type of mature granulocyte.

KINETICS OF GRANULOPOIESIS.

Even though the mass of red blood cells far exceeds the total mass of leukocytes, the predominant cells in bone marrow are leukocyte precursors, mostly of the granulocytic cell line. The proportion of leukocyte precursors to erythrocyte precursors in the bone marrow, referred to as the myeloid-erythrocyte ratio, normally is about 3 to 1. The higher rate of production of granulocytes is consistent with the short average life of the granulocyte after it leaves the bone marrow (3 or 4 days) and the longer average life of the red blood cell (120 days). In addition, the bone marrow stores mature granulocytes, but not erythrocytes, and usually contains 10–20 times more granulocytes than the blood contains.

After they are released from the bone marrow, granulocytes remain in the vascular space for about 1 day. They are divided about equally between two areas—a circulating pool and a pool attached to vascular endothelium. The attached pool plus the storage pool in the bone marrow provide a reserve that can be transferred to the circulating pool when needed. At the end of its 1-day sojourn in the vascular space, the granulocyte migrates by diapedesis into the tissue space, where it is destroyed in defensive action or dies in senescence within 3 or 4 days.

REGULATION OF GRANULOPOIESIS.

Much less is known about the regulation of granulopoiesis than about the regulation of erythropoiesis. It is assumed that granulocyte levels in the blood somehow are sensed by the bone marrow, so that granulopoiesis can be adjusted; however, appreciable, rapid fluxes of granulocytes among the various pools can change the size of the circulating granulocyte pool quickly, which would make the operation of a control system difficult. Nevertheless, a plasma glycoprotein that stimulates granulopoiesis has been discovered. Its concentration in the plasma increases in granulocytopenic individuals (who have decreased numbers of granulocytes in their blood), and it may participate in the regulation of blood granulocyte levels.

NEUTROPHILS

The neutrophils are the most numerous of the granulocytes, as they normally comprise 60%–70% of all circulating leukocytes. The granules in the cytoplasm of neutrophils (lysosomes) contain enzymes that destroy foreign organisms after they have been engulfed. Neutrophils engulf and destroy bacteria effectively, and this function often can be used for clinical diagnosis. Leukocytosis (increased white blood cell count) is typical of infections, and if the population of leukocytes is found to consist mostly of neutrophils, one usually can assume that a bacterial infection exists somewhere in the body. This correlation is particularly useful in cases of meningitis (inflammation of the meninges that cover the brain); if many neutrophils are found in the cerebrospinal fluid, one may assume that the patient has bacterial meningitis and would benefit from antibiotic therapy.

EOSINOPHILS

Eosinophils are small (diameter about 9 μm) granulocytes that normally constitute only 1%–4% of the leukocytes in the blood. Like neutrophils, their granules are lysosomes that destroy phagocytosed material; however, eosinophils accomplish phagocytosis in a slower and more selective way than neutrophils do. Eosinophils are more likely to phagocytose antigen-antibody complexes, and the eosinophil count tends to increase during allergy, with some parasitic infestations, and in certain neoplasms and autoimmune diseases. In addition, eosinophils contain plasminogen (see Chapter 26), which helps to dissolve blood clots; thus, eosinophils probably are involved in fibrinolysis.

BASOPHILS

Basophils are granulocytes about 12 μm in diameter; they normally constitute 1% or less of the circulating leukocytes. The cytoplasm of basophils is filled with large basophilic granules that contain heparin (anticoagulant), histamine (systemic vasodilator; pulmonary vasoconstrictor and bronchoconstrictor), and slow-reacting substance of anaphylaxis (SRS-A). The exact function of basophils still is being investigated. They are active in phagocytosis, and by release of their granules can participate in or even cause anaphylactic reactions, typified by circulatory shock, increased vascular permeability, and bronchospasm. Basophils resemble the more numerous mast cells, which occur in connective tissue and the interstitial space near blood vessels, particularly in the lung. Mast cells have granules much like those in basophils, and it was thought once that basophils became mast cells when they left the vascular space. However, basophils now are known to be derived from hematopoietic precursors and mast cells from the undifferentiated mesenchymal cells, which also are precursors for connective tissue cells.

Monocytes-Macrophages

Monocytes and macrophages are two forms of the same cell. Monocytes develop in the bone marrow, enter the blood and remain for about 30–70 hours, then leave the vascular space by diapedesis and enter the tissue space to become the prodigiously phagocytic macrophages. Monocytes are large agranulocytes (diameter of 20–30 μm) that have nuclei of various shapes. Granules are not readily evident in the cytoplasm of the monocyte, but at higher magnifications, lyosomes have been found. The stepwise development of mature monocytes is difficult to recognize in the bone marrow, but it probably occurs by the same process of differentiation that other blood cells undergo.

Macrophages form a key element of the *reticuloendothelial system* (RES), which lines the vascular channels of the bone marrow, liver, lung, spleen, lymph nodes, and thymus. The RES consists of a meshwork of connective tissue inhabited by macrophages that carry out its primary function—phagocytosis of foreign organisms and cellular debris. Macrophages also interact with the immune system in various ways, such as processing antigens to augment the immune response. Later sections discuss how immunocytes produce antibody that coats macrophages, thus making their phagocytic attacks immunologically specific.

IMMUNOCYTES

General Characteristics

Immunocytes work in concert with phagocytes to protect the organism against foreign invaders. The immune system is responsible for first recognizing invaders and then removing or destroying them. The importance of this system is illustrated most dramatically in subjects who are completely deficient in immunity; typically, they die of overwhelming infection.

Lymphocytes

GENERAL ASPECTS

Lymphocytes and their derivatives, the cellular units of the immune system, are found throughout the body in lymphatic tissue, either primary or secondary. Thymus and bone marrow are classified as primary lymphoid organs because they are populated by lymphocytes early in their development. Secondary lymphatic tissues, which include tonsils, spleen, lymph nodes, and Peyer's patches, are populated later in development by lymphocytes from primary lymphoid organs. The lymphocyte is the only type of cell that can recognize a specific antigen as foreign and trigger a sequence of events that leads to destruction and removal of the antigen.

TYPES OF LYMPHOCYTES

Lymphocytes may differentiate morphologically along two pathways. Those that populate the thymus differentiate into T (thymic) lymphocytes, which are responsible for cell-mediated immunity. In the chicken, lymphocytes of a second group migrate to a hindgut organ called the bursa of Fabricius; these cells develop into B (bursal) lymphocytes, which produce antibodies. Humans have no bursa of Fabricius; apparently, in humans, B cells develop in the bone marrow. When confronted with an antigen, both B and T cells increase dramatically in size and number; the new cells are called *immunoblasts*. T and B cells and T and B immunoblasts are indistinguishable morphologically, but they can be distinguished by their functional differences, electrophoretic mobilities, different locations in lymph nodes, and different responses to mitogens (substances that stimulate mitosis).

Humoral Immunity

GENERAL ASPECTS

B cells activated by contact with antigen progress from immunoblasts to plasma cells (Figure 25-1). The plasma cell is larger and has proportionally more cytoplasm than the B cell, which enables it to accommodate the biochemical machinery for antibody synthesis. After this machinery has been activated, antibody is secreted into the surrounding fluid, where it can bind to antigens.

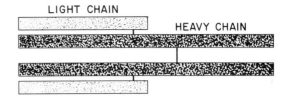

Figure 25-2. Basic structure of antibody molecule. Each light chain is joined to a heavy chain by a disulfide bridge; heavy chains also are linked by a variable number of disulfide bridges. (Redrawn, with permission, from Thaler, M.S., et al. 1977. *Medical Immunology*. Philadelphia: Lippincott.)

ANTIBODY PRODUCTION

Antibodies are composed of a basic structural unit that consists of four polypeptide chains—two light chains and two heavy chains—linked to each other by disulfide bridges (Figure 25-2). This antibody molecule actually is a bifunctional unit; enzymatic digestion with papain and pepsin (Figure 25-3) separates the components. The $F(ab)_2$ portion, obtained after digestion with pepsin, retains the specific antigen-binding properties of the molecule, and the Fc portion, obtained after digestion with papain, retains other biological functions, such as initiating inflammation and the ability to adhere to and coat macrophages and certain leukocytes.

CLONAL SELECTION THEORY

Over the years, a theory now called the *clonal selection theory* has developed; it states that each of the antibody-producing cells is committed to producing a single antibody against a single antigen, even before the body is presented with that antigen. This theory carries the astounding implication that the human body contains between 100,000 and 1,000,000 different types of B cells capable of responding to a like number of specific antigens.

TYPES OF ANTIBODIES

Antibodies (immunoglobulins) are divided into different classes on the basis of structural differences among the heavy chains. Thus, immunoglobulins that contain α, ϵ, δ, γ, or μ type heavy chains are called IgAn, IgE, IgD, IgG, and IgM, respectively. The structural differences, which include different positions of the intramolecular disulfide bridges and other variations in the molecule, lead to functional variations (Table 25-1). Abbreviated structures of

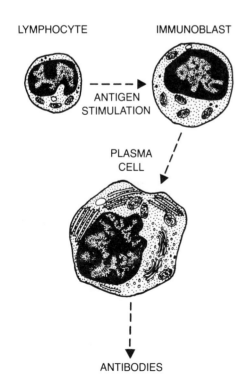

Figure 25-1. Differentiation of a lymphocyte (B cell) into plasma cell after antigenic stimulation.

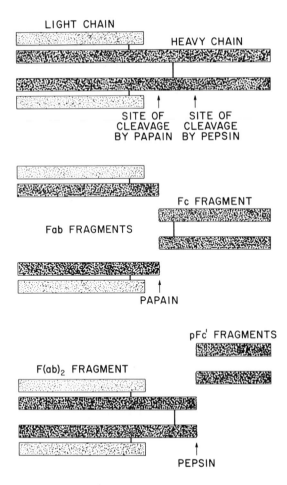

Figure 25-3. Papain breaks immunoglobulin molecule on aminoterminal side of heavy-chain junction, producing two identical Fab fragments and Fc fragment. Pepsin divides molecule on carboxyterminal side, leaving the Fab segments together, forming a single F(ab)$_2$ fragment and two pFc' fragments. (Redrawn, with permission, from Thaler, M.S., et al. 1977. *Medical Immunology.* Philadelphia: Lippincott.)

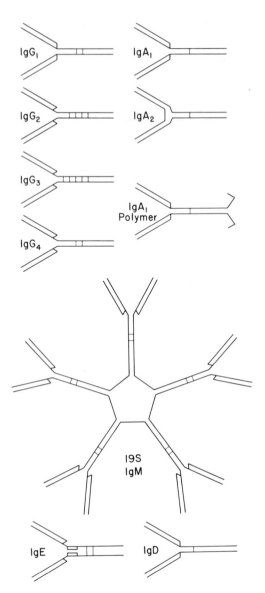

Figure 25-4. Structures of classes and subclasses of immunoglobulins. (Redrawn, with permission, from Thaler, M.S., et al. 1977. *Medical Immunology.* Philadelphia: Lippincott.)

the different classes of immunoglobulins are shown in Figure 25-4. All of the antibody types except IgM are composed of the basic single immunoglobulin structure; IgM is a pentamer, composed of five single immunoglobin molecules linked together.

COMPLEMENT SYSTEM

The complement system is a complex cascade of 11 proteins (C1 to C9; C1 has three components) that are activated during immune reactions. The complement system was discovered in the 1880s, when it was found that antibodies, which are heat-stable, depend on a heat-labile

component to destroy invading microorganisms. This heat-labile component was named complement, to indicate that it helps the antibody to perform its defensive function. Thus, the antibody identifies an invading organism as foreign, and the antigen-antibody complex activates the complement, which destroys the invader. In addition, components of the complement system mediate inflammatory responses by attracting phagocytes (through chemotaxis) and increasing capillary permea-

TABLE 25-1

Functional characteristics of different classes of antibodies as determined by their Fc regions

Antibody Type	Function	Characteristics						
		Complement Activation (Classical Pathway)	Crosses Placenta	Normal Serum Levels (g/dl)	Binds to Macrophages	Fixes to Mast Cells	Structure	Molecular Weight (daltons)
IgG	Part of systemic humoral reaction to antigen challenge	+	+	0.8–1.6	+	–	Monomer	150,000
IgM	Same as IgG	+	–	0.06–0.2	–	–	Pentamer	900,000
IgA	Present in saliva, bile, nasal, lacrimal, tracheo-bronchial, and intestinal secretions. Protects against foreign invasion via these routes.	–	...	0.15–0.4	–	–	Monomer with some polymeric forms	160,000
IgE	Responsible for imme-diate hypersensitivity reactions, including allergy and anaphylaxis. May function by increas-ing parasite shedding.	–	–	Trace	–	+	Monomer	180,000
IgD	?	?	...	Trace	–	–	Monomer	180,000

bility so that phagocytes can more readily gain access to the area. Complement proteins also attach to the foreign invader and cause phagocytes to devour it more rapidly; this is called *opsonization.* Thus, in addition to attacking invaders directly, the complement system "calls up" phagocytes and directs their action.

The sequence for complement-mediated destruction of invading cells is called the *classical pathway*—it is activated by interaction between antigen and antibody. However, for years it has been recognized that the body can launch a complement-mediated attack against foreign invaders even before specific antibody against the invader has been formed. This sequence, called the *alternate pathway*, can destroy some foreign invaders even in the absence of antibody.

Cell-Mediated Immunity

As mentioned previously, B lymphocytes oppose an antigenic challenge by producing antibody. On the other hand, animals respond to some antigenic challenges by activating T lymphocytes, which do not produce antibodies but, rather, attempt to annihilate the invader directly. This process, called cell-mediated immunity, appears to be more important than humoral immunity in defense against tuberculosis, leprosy, fungal infections, parasitic infections, and some viral infections. In addition, transplanted organs and tissues are rejected primarily through cell-mediated immunity. When sensitized to the antigen of a foreign invader, precursors differentiate into killer T cells, attach to the invader, and destroy it by mechanisms not completely understood. In addition to this direct destruction, activated T cells can elaborate a variety of immunologically active chemicals called lymphokines, which participate in immune reactions (Table 25-2).

Development of Immunity

GENERAL ASPECTS
A typical immune action involves elements of both humoral and cell-mediated immunity, and the two systems interact in complex ways. In addition, the macrophage processes foreign antigen so that T and B cell responses are augmented. Subpopulations of T cells also have been discovered: (1) helper T cells, which augment and often are required for B-cell-mediated antibody production, (2) suppressor T cells, which suppress inappropriate immune responses such as those that occur in autoimmune

TABLE 25-2

Some lymphokines elaborated by activated T lymphocytes

Lymphokines	Functions
Inhibitors of cell growth	Prevent multiplication of invading organisms or infected host cells.
Chemotactic factors	Attract phagocytes.
Activation factors	Convert lymphocytes to immunoblasts.
Interferon	Protein that blocks viral replication inside host cells.
Lymphocytotoxin	Directly kills invading cells.
Macrophage inhibition factors	Decrease mobility of macrophages so they tend to stay in area of immune response.
Macrophage activation factors	Increase phagocytic activity of macrophages.

diseases, and (3) memory T cells, which retain recognition of a previously encountered foreign antigen and mount a rapidly developing immune response when rechallenged.

RESPONSES TO ANTIGENS
When the organism initially contacts foreign antigen, it attempts to restrain the invader within local lymph nodes, where the immune response develops; this is the *primary* immune response. Circulating antibody to the foreign antigen usually can be found in the serum in 1 or 2 weeks. Coincident with the primary response, the immune system develops a "memory" of the invading antigen, which resides in B and T lymphocytes. If the organism is challenged again by the same antigen, it develops a *secondary* immune response, which is more rapid and of greater intensity than the primary response. The secondary responses are called *anamnestic*, because the immune system "recalls" having encountered the antigen before.

Allergy

GENERAL ASPECTS
About 10% of humans suffer to some degree from allergies, or immune reactions to antigens called *allergens,* which are innocuous to most

people. Allergens include material such as animal danders, pollens, dust, mites, and various foods or drugs. Typical moderate reactions include hay fever, asthma, hives (urticaria), and dermatitis; more severe reactions may include laryngeal edema, laryngospasm, and anaphylactic shock. Individuals are called *atopic* when they have an inherited tendency to be allergic without exposure to unusually large quantities of the allergens. Other subjects, who do not have an atopic familial background, may develop similar reactions when exposed to large quantities of the offending allergen.

IMMUNOLOGICAL BASIS OF ALLERGY

The immunological basis of allergy is not completely understood, but it seems to involve inappropriate production of high levels of IgE directed against the offending allergens. The IgE coats mast cells and basophils, allergen attaches to the IgE, and the coated cells release a variety of allergic mediators, including *histamine* and *slow-reacting substance of anaphylaxis* (Figure 25-5).

The basis of this abnormal tendency to produce high levels of IgE against seemingly innocuous antigens is being investigated. Recent work indicates that certain T lymphocytes (suppressor T cells) normally suppress IgE production by plasma cells, and lack of this suppression may be a factor in the development of allergy.

IMMUNOTHERAPY OF ALLERGY

Many patients benefit from periodic injection of the offending allergen. This treatment, known as *hyposensitization,* has been associated with reduction of IgE levels and IgE responsiveness to the allergen. The mechanism of hyposensitization is not completely clear, but it appears to involve activation of normal IgE inhibitory mechanisms that are dormant in allergic individuals and production of antiallergen IgG, which combines with allergen so that it cannot react with IgE-coated mast cells or basophils.

Chemical Mediators of Inflammation

GENERAL ASPECTS

Inflammation is the response of tissues to injury, especially when they are invaded by foreign organisms. Vasodilatation occurs first, then vascular permeability increases and the tissues are infiltrated by leukocytes. Although injured blood vessels may become leaky, most of the increased permeability is due to chemical mediators of inflammation.

TRIPLE RESPONSE

In the 1920s, Sir Thomas Lewis noted that when the skin is stroked firmly with a blunt instrument, a *red reaction* occurs almost immediately along the line of stroking; after 15–30 seconds, a reddish flare develops and spreads several centimeters from the line, and after 1 or 2 minutes, a wheal (local edema) appears (Figure 25-6). Lewis postulated that the red reaction was due to capillary dilatation in response to pressure, plus immediate release from the damaged tissues of a soluble mediator that he thought was identical with or similar to histamine. He thought the *flare* was due to an *axon reflex,* in which sensory impulses are propagated back through branches of the sensory nerve and cause the release of a substance (probably histamine) that dilates arterioles (see Figure 25-6). Lewis demonstrated that cutting the sensory nerve abolished the flare only if time were allowed for the nerve to degenerate. The third stage of this *triple response* was the *wheal,* which is local edema due to increased capillary permeability caused by tissue dam-

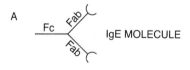

A

Fc Fab Fab IgE MOLECULE

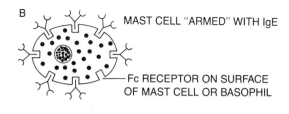

B

MAST CELL "ARMED" WITH IgE

Fc RECEPTOR ON SURFACE OF MAST CELL OR BASOPHIL

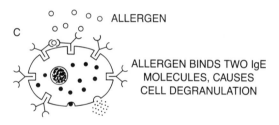

C

ALLERGEN

ALLERGEN BINDS TWO IgE MOLECULES, CAUSES CELL DEGRANULATION

Figure 25-5. Release of mediators in allergic reactions.

A

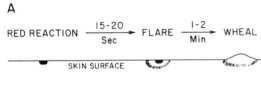

B

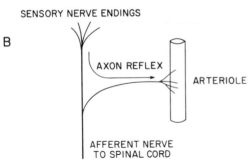

Figure 25-6. Stages of the triple response that occurs after the skin is stroked firmly with a blunt object. **A**, Red reaction, flare, and wheal. **B**, Axon reflex; thought to cause the flare.

A

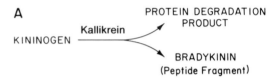

B

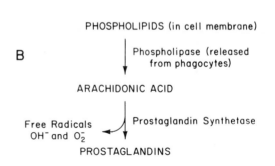

Figure 25-7. Production of kinins (**A**) and prostaglandins (**B**) during inflammation.

age and the release of mediator. Lewis was the first to postulate the presence and action of inflammatory mediators, and many additional mediators subsequently have been discovered.

COMPLEMENT
By-products of the complement cascade include increased capillary permeability, vasodilatation, release of histamine from mast cells, and chemotaxis for phagocytes. These by-products contribute significantly to the inflammatory response and are especially prominent when the complement cascade is activated to its fullest extent, which occurs in antigen-antibody reactions.

KININS
Urine, plasma, saliva, and a variety of tissues contain an enzyme, kallikrein (named after the Greek for "pancreas," a rich source of this material), which acts on a plasma globulin, kininogen, to produce a polypeptide, *bradykinin* (Figure 25-7). Bradykinin is one of a group of similar polypeptides, called *kinins,* which induce pain, increase capillary permeability, and dilate arterioles. The name bradykinin comes from an early observation that very small quantities of the peptide cause a slowly developing contraction of intestine (hence, from the Greek, "bradys" = slow, "kinin" = movement). The kinin system participates in the inflammatory response when it is activated by the

release of kallikreins from damaged tissues and because of the kallikrein activity of lysosomal enzymes released from damaged cells and phagocytes. Kinins contribute to inflammation by increasing capillary permeability and vasodilatation. In addition, kallikreins have chemotactic activity for leukocytes.

LYSOSOMAL ENZYMES
Lysosomal enzymes released from phagocytes and damaged cells during inflammation contribute to the inflammatory response. These substances cause tissue damage by acting as kallikreins, and some of them may initiate the production of prostaglandins.

PROSTAGLANDINS
Prostaglandins are fatty acid compounds that are involved in inflammatory reactions. Leukocytes in inflammatory exudates are a major source of prostaglandin production (see Figure 25-7), as they elaborate phospholipase, a lysosomal enzyme, during the process of phagocytosis. This enzyme acts on membrane lipids of any cells in the immediate area to produce arachidonic acid, which is further acted on by cyclo-oxygenase (prostaglandin synthetase) to produce endoperoxides that are converted into prostaglandins. The prostaglandin synthetase step also produces free radicals (OH^- and O_2^-), which by themselves can cause inflammation. Directly, prostaglandins sensitize blood vessels to the effects of other mediators such as histamine and bradykinin.

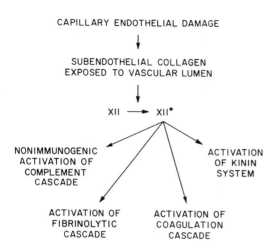

CAPILLARY ENDOTHELIAL DAMAGE

SUBENDOTHELIAL COLLAGEN
EXPOSED TO VASCULAR LUMEN

XII → XII*

NONIMMUNOGENIC
ACTIVATION OF
COMPLEMENT
CASCADE

ACTIVATION
OF KININ
SYSTEM

ACTIVATION OF
FIBRINOLYTIC
CASCADE

ACTIVATION OF
COAGULATION
CASCADE

Figure 25-8. Interactions of inflammatory mediators through activation of Hageman factor.

INTERACTIONS OF INFLAMMATORY MEDIATORS

Some major interactions among several systems that mediate inflammation are depicted in Figure 25-8. When the capillary endothelium is damaged, subendothelial collagen is exposed. Contact of circulating blood with the collagen activates factor XII (Hageman factor) of the intrinsic coagulation cascade (Chap. 26). This factor, besides activating coagulation, also activates the kinin, fibrinolytic, and complement cascades, which contribute to inflammation.

DISORDERS OF WHITE CELL FUNCTION

Leukemias

GENERAL ASPECTS

In leukemias, normal bone marrow is replaced by rapidly proliferating abnormal white blood cells. These cells can leave the bone marrow and infiltrate any tissue or organ in the body; liver, spleen, and lymph nodes most commonly are affected. Depending on the maturity of the abnormal cell type, leukemias are classified as acute (immature cell type) or chronic (more mature cell type). These cell types may come from either lymphocytic or myelogenous cell lines. Table 25-3 lists the four major types of leukemias.

SURVIVAL

The morbidity and mortality associated with leukemias reflect a variety of factors: (1) The rapidly proliferating leukemic cells place metabolic demands on the body that cause progressive debilitation. (2) Infiltration of the bone marrow by leukemic cells produces anemia, as the erythroid precursors are crowded out, and bleeding diathesis, as megakaryocytes are crowded out and the platelet count decreases. (3) Because leukemic white cells lack phagocytic and immunocytic function, fulminant infections develop. Thus, infections and hemorrhage are the most common causes of death in patients who have leukemia.

Immunodeficiencies

GENERAL ASPECTS

Immunodeficiencies are acquired or congenital abnormalities in the production or function of phagocytes, immunocytes, or complement. These diseases comprise a wide spectrum because, owing to the complexity of the immune system, these lesions may occur in many areas. In addition to specific abnormalities in immune function, immune deficiency may have nonspecific causes, such as renal loss of protein (including immunoglobulin) in nephrosis. Aging, debilitation, and, in newborns, immaturity of the immune system, can increase the susceptibility to infection.

TABLE 25-3
Leukemias

Type of Leukemia	Percent of Leukemias	Age Group	Average Survival with Treatment
Acute lymphocytic	20	Children	3–6 years
Chronic lymphocytic	30	Elderly	3–4 years or more
Acute myelogenous	25	All ages	6–12 months
Chronic myelogenous	25	Middle age	3–4 years

CLINICAL CORRELATION
25.1   Monomyeloblastic Leukemia

CASE REPORT

The Patient: A 63-year-old woman.

Principal Complaints: Weakness, fatigue, and dyspnea.

History: The patient appeared to be chronically ill. During the last year, she had gradually lost 25 pounds in weight. The weakness and fatigue had become noticeable several months before she was seen, and was progressing. She reported difficulty climbing even a single flight of stairs.

Clinical Examination: The jugular veins were visible (distended) almost to the angle of the mandibles when the patient was sitting at 45° to the horizontal. The heart was moderately enlarged, the heart rate was 198/min (normal, <100/min), and the rate of respiration was 20/min (normal, <17/min). The liver was enlarged—the lower edge was felt 4–5 cm (normal, 1–2 cm) below the right costal mar-

gin (edge of the rib cage)—and the upper edge, determined by percussion, was at the normal level of the 5th rib. Pitting edema* of the ankles and some cyanosis were detected. The oral temperature was 37.9°, and the arterial pressure was 115/60 mm Hg (normal, 90–140/60–90 mm Hg). The hematocrit was 32% (normal, 37–48%). The white cell count was 66,000/mm³ (normal, 4,300–10,800/mm³), with 1% neutrophils, 43% myeloblasts (immature granulocytes), 27% monocytes, 26% promonocytes (immature monocytes), and 10% lymphocytes (normal, neutrophils, 60–70%; immature forms, 0–25%; monocytes, 2.4–11.8%; and lymphocytes, 20–53%). The serum glutamic oxaloacetic transaminase (SGOT) was 20 u/ml (normal, 10–40 u/ml); the lactic dehydrogenase (LDH) was 295 u/ml (normal, 60–120 u/ml); and the creatine phosphokinase (CPK) was 5 u/ml (normal, 5–35 u/ml). High blood levels of these enzymes are consistent with myocardial damage.

LOSS OF GRANULOCYTE FUNCTION

Suppression of bone marrow function usually involves all cell lines (erythroid, myeloid, and megakaryocytes). When the myeloid series specifically is suppressed, agranulocytosis (lack of granulocytes) develops. The cause of agranulocytosis usually is unknown, but it may be tumors of the bone marrow, radiation, or toxins such as benzene and anticancer drugs. In addition, agranulocytosis is a rare side effect of some drugs, including phenothiazines, antithyroids, sulfonamides, and phenylbutazone. Complete lack of granulocytes permits overwhelming bacterial infection and certain death unless the patient can be put in total isolation or receive successful bone marrow transplants.

Some patients develop diseases similar to agranulocytosis but still have normal granulocyte counts. One of these disorders, known as

chronic granulomatous disease, is caused by the inability of lysosomes in phagocytes to generate peroxidase needed to destroy phagocytosed bacteria. Another disorder (Chédiak–Higashi syndrome) is caused by the inability of phagocytes to discharge their lysosomal enzymes into vacuoles that contain phagocytosed bacteria. In both of these syndromes, the phagocytes appear normal and can engulf bacteria but not destroy them.

IMMUNOCYTE DYSFUNCTION

The most important immunocyte dysfunctions are T cell deficiencies, B cell deficiences, and combined T and B cell deficiencies. The most common (1 in about 600 people) immunocyte dysfunction is IgA (secretory antibody) deficiency, which permits recurrent respiratory, gastrointestinal, and urinary tract infections due to lack of IgA in secretions.

The ECG revealed a normal sinus rhythm and first degree A-V block; the axis in the frontal plane was $+63°$ (normal, $-30°$ to $+110°$). Incomplete right-bundle-branch block (see Chapter 19, "Atrioventricular Block") was indicated; S-T segment and T-wave changes in the anterior chest leads (V_1-V_4) were consistent with acute myocardial infarction.**

Digoxin, which increases cardiac contractility (see Chapter 22, "Treatment of Cardiac Failure"), was begun. The S-T segment changes persisted, but the SGOT remained in the normal range. Five days after admission, bone marrow was aspirated from the left posterior iliac crest. Pathological examination revealed large numbers of immature mononuclear cells, consistent with the diagnosis of acute monocyte leukemia. Six days after admission, the hematocrit was 27%, the white-cell count was 167,000/mm³, with 27% monocytes and 36% immature forms (monoblasts). The patient became increasingly weak and dyspneic and died 9 days after admission.

Comment: Leukemia is characterized by an abnormally high concentration of one type of leukocyte without any demonstrable stimulus. The high proportion of immature forms is believed to represent some cellular defect in maturation. The concentrations of normal blood cells usually are decreased. The abnormal leukocytes infiltrate the organs and systems of the body, although the leukemic cells are not invasive in the way that the cells of malignant carcinomas are invasive. Enlarged spleen, liver, and lymph nodes are common. The CNS, the heart, the kidneys, and the GI system can be affected adversely.

In this patient, infiltration of the heart caused heart failure, incomplete bundle-branch block, and ECG changes consistent with myocardial infarction. However, changes of serum enzymes characteristic of infarction (SGOT, LDH, and CPK) were not seen. Post-mortem examination revealed leukemic infiltration of the heart, lungs, liver, and colon; the latter contained numerous leukemic ulcerations. Patients who have acute leukemia may die within a few days of diagnosis, or, with treatment, live for years. The anemia and organ degeneration of this patient precluded the usual chemotherapy and contributed to her early demise.

*The tissue is so swollen by the fluid contained in the interstitial space (edema) that it can be indented by pressure with the fingers. Edema forms first in the ankles because gravity increases the capillary pressure (see Chapter 12, "Effects of Transmural Pressure on Blood Vessels").

**Related to current that flows between the infarct and the normal tissue during diastole, causing an "injury potential."

SPLENIC DEFICIENCY SYNDROMES

The spleen is an important site for the production of antibody by B cells and an important part of the reticuloendothelial system. Splenic function can be impaired by congenital malformation, trauma, surgical splenectomy, or infarction. Loss of this important part of the immune system can permit serious infections, especially in infants or debilitated adults.

PLASMA CELL DYSCRASIAS

Plasma cell dyscrasias are a diverse group of disorders in which a clone of immunoglobulin-secreting cells proliferates and produces a single immunoglobulin that can be detected in large quantities in serum or urine. The following are the most important of these diseases:

1. *Multiple myeloma,* in which a clone of plasma cells produces immunoglobulin (IgA, IgD, IgE, or IgG), overruns the bone marrow, destroys bone, and infiltrates a variety of organs. The excess immunoglobulin produced may be deposited in organs as a proteinacceous material called *amyloid.* Typically, death is caused by destruction of bone marrow and organ failure, especially renal failure.

2. *Macroglobulinemia,* which involves cells that synthesize IgM. Excess of this high-molecular-weight protein increases the viscosity of the blood, which increases peripheral vascular resistance (see Chapter 12) and impairs tissue perfusion. Often, the heart fails because of overload.

3. *Heavy chain disease.* In these disorders, immunoglobulin heavy chains are produced in great excess. IgA, IgG, and IgM heavy chain diseases have been described. The symptoms that develop depend on the amount and type of heavy chain produced.

STUDY OUTLINE

4,000–12,000 white blood cells (leukocytes) per mm^3.

Protect body against microorganisms.

Phagocytes: engulf and destroy microorganisms or debris.

Immunocytes: destroy microorganisms by producing toxic chemicals and antibodies.

PHAGOCYTES   Granulocytes and monocytes-macrophages.

Produced in bone marrow.

Granulocytes contain granules (lysosomes); classified by staining as neutrophils, eosinophils, or basophils.

GRANULOCYTES

GRANULOPOIESIS   Granulocytes form from stem cells.

Kinetics of Granulopoiesis   Precursors of granulocytes predominate in bone marrow.

High rate of production because of short life span (3–4 days) of granulocytes.

Regulation of Granulopoiesis   Apparently, blood granulocyte levels monitored to adjust production in bone marrow; specific plasma glycoprotein may be involved.

NEUTROPHILS   Make up 60%–70% of all leukocytes.

Engulf and destroy bacteria; granules (lysosomes) contain enzymes.

Number in blood increases with infection; therefore, used in diagnosis.

EOSINOPHILS   1%–4% of leukocytes.

Phagocytose mainly antigen-antibody complexes; concentration increases during allergy.

Help to dissolve blood clots.

BASOPHILS   1% or less of leukocytes.

Granules contain heparin, histamine, and SRS-A.

Function uncertain; release of granules can cause anaphylactic reaction.

MONOCYTES-MACROPHAGES   Two forms of same cell.

Monocytes from blood enter tissue space to become macrophages.

Component of reticuloendothelial system; remove foreign organisms and debris.

Augment immune response.

IMMUNOCYTES

GENERAL   CHARACTERISTICS   Recognize foreign invaders first; work with macrophages to protect organism.

LYMPHOCYTES

GENERAL ASPECTS   Throughout body in lymphatic tissue.

Recognize specific antibody as foreign; begin efforts to destroy antigen.

TYPES OF LYMPHOCYTES   T cells from thymus; responsible for cell-mediated immunity.

B cells from bone marrow; produce antibodies.

Numbers increase greatly (immunoblasts) when antigen appears.

HUMORAL IMMUNITY

GENERAL ASPECTS   B cell immunoblasts become plasma cells; synthesize antibody.

ANTIBODY PRODUCTION   Two light (polypeptide) chains and two heavy chains linked by disulfide bridges.

F(ab)$_2$ portion binds antigen.

Fc portion initiates inflammation; adheres to and "coats" macrophages and certain leukocytes.

CLONAL SELECTION THEORY   Each antibody-producing cell produces single antibody against single antigen.

TYPES OF ANTIBODIES   Immunoglobulin classified by structure of heavy chains.

COMPLEMENT SYSTEM   Complex of proteins activated by immune reactions.

Proteins provide for chemotaxis; increase capillary permeability (aids dispersal of phagocytes); attach to foreign organism and aid phagocytosis.

"Classical pathway": defense activated by antigen-antibody interaction.

"Alternate pathway": defense activated by complement before antibody formed.

CELL-MEDIATED IMMUNITY   T lymphocytes attack invader directly.

Rejection of transplanted organs.

Sensitivity to antigen produces killer T cells.

Produce immunologically active chemicals (lymphokines).

DEVELOPMENT OF IMMUNITY

GENERAL ASPECTS   Both humoral and cell-mediated.

Helper T cells: augment B-cell-mediated antibody production.

Suppressor T cells: suppress inappropriate immune responses.

Memory T cells: recognize previously encountered foreign antigen and initiate immune response.

RESPONSES TO ANTIGENS Primary immune response: occurs in local lymph nodes; immune system develops memory.

Secondary immune response: response to repeated challenge by same antigen; more rapid, more intense.

ALLERGY

GENERAL ASPECTS Immune response to antigen (allergens).

Mild reactions: hay fever, asthma, dermatitis, others.

Severe reactions: laryngospasm, anaphylactic shock.

Inherited tendency without exposure—atopic.

IMMUNOLOGICAL BASIS OF ALLERGY Inappropriate production of IgE antibody against allergen.

IgE coats mast cells and basophils; allergen attaches, causes release of histamine and anaphylactic substance.

May be lack of suppressor T cells.

IMMUNOTHERAPY OF ALLERGY Hyposensitization: periodic injection of offending allergen.

Activates IgE inhibitory mechanisms.

Produces antiallergen IgG; prevents reaction with IgE-coated mast cells of basophils.

CHEMICAL MEDIATORS OF INFLAMMATION

GENERAL ASPECTS Response of tissues to injury, especially by foreign organisms. Vasodilatation, increased capillary permeability, infiltration by leukocytes.

TRIPLE RESPONSE Response of skin to firm stroke.

Red reaction: capillary dilatation or damage; effect of released histamine.

Flare: arteriolar dilatation; vasodilator substance released through axon reflex.

Wheal: local edema due to increased capillary permeability.

COMPLEMENT Contributes to inflammation by increased capillary permeability, vasodilatation, release of histamine, and chemotaxis for phagocytes.

KININS Activated by kallikreins released from damaged tissues and by kallikrein activity of lysosomal enzymes.

LYSOSOMAL ENZYMES Released from phagocytes and damaged cells during inflammation; act as kallikreins, may begin production of prostaglandins.

PROSTAGLANDINS Fatty acid compounds involved in inflammatory reactions.

Produced from membrane lipids by lysosomal and other enzymes; sensitize blood vessels to actions of other mediators.

Free radicals produced can cause inflammation.

INTERACTIONS OF INFLAMMATORY MEDIATORS Coagulation factor released from collagen, activates kinin, fibrinolytic, and complement cascades.

DISORDERS OF WHITE CELL FUNCTION

LEUKEMIAS

GENERAL ASPECTS Normal bone marrow replaced by rapidly proliferating abnormal white cells.

WBCs leave bone marrow, infiltrate other tissues, organs.

Acute or chronic, depending on maturity of abnormal cell type.

Lymphocytic or myelogenous cell lines.

SURVIVAL Metabolic demands of proliferating leukemic cells.

Anemia and bleeding, as red cell and platelet precursors crowded out of bone marrow.

Infections, because leukemic cells lack phagocytic and immunocytic function.

IMMUNODEFICIENCIES

GENERAL ASPECTS Abnormal production or function of phagocytes, immunocytes, or complement.

LOSS OF GRANULOCYTE FUNCTION Suppression of bone marrow function caused by tumors, radiation, toxins, drugs.

Disorders of phagocyte function.

IMMUNOCYTE DYSFUNCTION T cell and B cell deficiencies.

IgA deficiency.

SPLENIC DEFICIENCY SYNDROMES Congenital malformation, trauma, surgical removal, infarction.

PLASMA CELL DYSCRASIAS Overproduction of single immunoglobulin.

BIBLIOGRAPHY

Bach, J.-F., editor. 1982. *Immunology*. New York: John Wiley and Sons.

Bellanti, J., editor. 1978. *Immunology II*. Philadelphia: W.B. Saunders Co.

Butterworth, A.E., and David, J.R. 1981. Eosinophil function. *N. Engl. J. Med.* 304:154.

Colten, H.R.; Alper, C.A.; and Rosen, F.S. 1981. Current concepts in immunology; genetics and biosynthesis of complement protein. *N. Engl. J. Med.* 304:653.

Erslev, A.J., and Gabuzda, T.G. 1979. *Pathophysiology of blood*, 2nd ed. Philadelphia: W.B. Saunders Co.

Figueroa, W.G. 1981. *Hematology*. New York: John Wiley and Sons.

Golub, E.S. 1981. *The cellular basis of the immune response: an approach to immunology*, 2nd ed. Sunderland, Mass.: Sinauer.

Hood, L.E.; Weissman, I.L.; and Wood, W.B. 1978. *Immunology*. Menlo Park, Calif.: Benjamin/Cummings Pub. Co.

Junquiera, L.C.; Carneiro, J.; and Contopoulos, A.N. 1977. *Histology*, 2nd ed. Los Altos, Calif.: Lange Medical Publications.

Leavell, B.S., and Thorup, O.A. 1976. *Fundamentals of clinical hematology*, 9th ed. Philadelphia: W.B. Saunders Co.

McDevitt, H.O. 1980. Regulation of the immune response by the major histocompatibility system. *N. Eng. J. Med.* 303:1514.

Mayer, M.M. 1973. The complement system. *Sci. Am.* 229:54.

Reich, P.R. 1978. *Hematology: physiopathologic basis for clinical practice*. Boston: Little Brown & Co.

Reinherz, E.L., and Schlossman, S.F. 1980. Regulation of the immune response; inducer and suppressor T-lymphocyte subsets in human beings. *N. Engl. J. Med.* 303:379.

Rocklin, R.E.; Sheffer, A.L.; Greineder, D.K.; et al. 1980. Generation of antigen-specific suppressor cells during allergic desensitization. *N. Engl. J. Med.* 302:1213.

Sell, S. 1980. *Immunology, immunopathology, and immunity*, 3rd ed. Hagerstown, Md.: Harper & Row, Publishers.

Stites, D.P.; Stobo, J.D.; Fudenberg, H.H.; *et al.* 1982. *Basic and clinical immunology*, 4th ed. Los Altos, Calif.: Lange Medical Publications.

Thaler, M.S.; Kalusner, R.D.; and Cohen, H.J. 1977. *Medical immunology*. Philadelphia: J.B. Lippincott Co.

Wiggins, R.C., and Cochrane, C.S. 1981. Current concepts in immunology: immune-complex-mediated biologic effects. *N. Engl. J. Med.* 304:518.

Williams, W.J.; Beutler, E.; Erslev, A.J.; et al. 1977. *Hematology*, 2nd ed. New York: McGraw-Hill Book Co.

Wintrobe, M.M.; Lee, G.R.; Boggs, D.R.; et al. 1981. *Clinical hematology*, 8th ed. Philadelphia: Lea & Febiger.

Wintrobe, M.M. 1980. *Blood, pure and eloquent*. New York: McGraw-Hill Book Co.

Hemostasis

CHAPTER CONTENTS

Hemostasis is the prevention of blood loss. Capillaries and arterioles are ruptured continuously by the minor traumas of everyday life, and hemostatic mechanisms keep blood loss to a minimum. These mechanisms are crucial for survival when blood loss is appreciable. Their importance is especially obvious in patients who have defective hemostatic systems; anything more than minor vascular trauma may cause severe life-threatening hemorrhage in these patients.

EVENTS IN HEMOSTASIS

Vasoconstrictive Phase

Vasoconstriction is the immediate response to vascular injury. The factors involved are con-

traction of vascular smooth muscle in direct response to injury, vasoconstriction in response to pain, and some vascular compression by the pressure of the blood lost into the surrounding tissues. The value of these immediate responses is especially apparent in cases of severed appendages: the ability of vessels as large as the radial artery to constrict immediately can decrease blood loss significantly. In general, this mechanism is most effective in vessels damaged by blunt instruments (chains, bricks, or gunshot wounds) and is less effective when wounds are made by sharp objects (knives, broken bottles, or ice picks).

Platelet Phase

Platelets break off from large megakaryocyte prescursors in the bone marrow and enter the

TABLE 26-1
The coagulation system

Factor number	Name(s)	Function
I	Fibrinogen	Protein acted on by thrombin to produce fibrin polymer, which forms structure of clot.
II	Prothrombin	Precursor of thrombin.
III	Thromboplastin	Lipoprotein derived from tissue. In extrinsic coagulation cascade interacts with other factors to produce prothrombinase.
IV	Calcium ion	Necessary for function of extrinsic cascade, intrinsic cascade, and common pathway.
V	Proaccelerin	Precursor of factor VI.
VI	Accelerator globulin	Interacts with other factors to activate prothrombin in both extrinsic and intrinsic cascades.
VII	Serum prothrombin conversion accelerator (SPCA, stable factor, convertin)	Interacts with thromboplastin and Ca^{++} to activate factor X in extrinsic cascade.
VIII	Antihemolytic globulin (AHG, antihemolytic factor)	Interacts with other factors to activate factor X in *intrinsic* cascade.
IX	Plasma thromboplastin component (PTC, Christmas factor)	Interacts with other factors to activate factor X in *intrinsic* cascade.
X	Stuart–Prower factor	Accelerates and amplifies prothrombin activation. Point of *convergence* of *extrinsic* and *intrinsic* systems.
XI	Plasma thromboplastin antecedent	Activated by factor XII. Accelerates thrombin formation in intrinsic cascade.
XII	Hageman factor (glass factor)	Plasma factor activated by contact with negatively charged surfaces (collagen, glass, kaolin, fatty acids). Activates factor XI to initiate *intrinsic cascade*.
XIII	Fibrin stabilizing factor	Cross-links fibrin to make it stronger and less soluble.
	Fitzgerald factor (high molecular weight kininogen)	Interacts with factor XII in activation of XI (also serves as kinin precursor).
	Fletcher factor (prekallikrein)	Interacts with factor XII to activate XI (also serves as kallikrein precursor).

plasma, where their concentration normally is 200,000–400,000/mm^3. The platelet phase of coagulation begins within seconds after vascular injury. Normally, platelets do not adhere to each other or to vascular endothelium, but after injury they are attracted by the negative charge on subendothelial collagen exposed to the vascular lumen. The platelets that adhere to the collagen release granules that contain serotonin, which causes vasoconstriction, and adeno-sine diphosphate, ADP, which attracts more platelets to the area. Soon, enough platelets have accumulated to form a plug, which reduces further blood loss. Platelet plugs effectively stop blood leakage through small rents in blood vessels, which occur frequently in normal daily activity. Platelet deficiency compromises this important function and permits extensive bleeding into many areas, especially skin, the gastrointestinal tract, and the genitourinary tract. When blood vessels are damaged so extensively that a platelet plug does not provide hemostasis, the next stage, coagulation, is initiated by phospholipids (platelet factor 3) from the platelets.

Coagulation Phase

GENERAL ASPECTS

Many substances affect the coagulation of blood. Procoagulants tend to enhance it and anticoagulants oppose it. Normally, these substances are in balance, and inappropriate coagulation does not occur; however, coagulation must occur when needed for hemostasis. Table 26-1 lists the important procoagulants that currently are known. Thirteen of these (I–XIII) are the classical clotting factors; two additional factors, Fitzgerald factor and Fletcher factor, are designated as procoagulants because they interact with factor XII.

Either intrinsic or extrinsic mechanisms can initiate clotting. Factors within the vascular space activate the intrinsic system, and tissue thromboplastin from outside the vascular space activates the extrinsic system. These two systems converge in a final common pathway, the activation of factor X, which carries on the clotting sequence.

INTRINSIC CASCADE

The intrinsic coagulation cascade is initiated when vessels are damaged; blood comes into contact with subendothelial collagen, which causes activation of factor XII (Figure 26-1). The property of collagen that appears to be necessary for this activation is a negatively charged surface of a certain molecular configuration. In addition to collagen, other substances, including kaolin, glass, and fatty acids, can provide such a surface and thereby activate factor XII. Activated factor XII activates factor XI. Activated factor XI then activates factor IX, which triggers coagulation by combining with factor VIII, platelet phospholipid, and Ca^{++} (see Figure 26-1); this complex, referred to as factor VIII complex, specifically converts factor X to activated factor X.

EXTRINSIC CASCADE

The extrinsic cascade also activates factor X (see Figure 26-1), but it does it in fewer steps and therefore acts much more rapidly. When tissue is damaged, a substance called thromboplastin is released. Thromboplastin, composed of

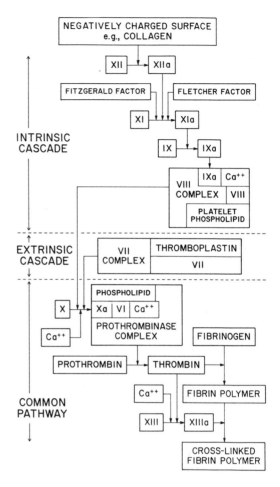

Figure 26-1. The intrinsic and extrinsic coagulation cascades and the common pathway on which they converge. The intrinsic cascade is initiated and carried out by factors wholly within the blood. The extrinsic cascade is initiated by thromboplastin, a product of tissue injury that is released into the blood.

phospholipid and protein, forms a complex with factor VII that can activate factor X.

COMMON PATHWAY

The activation of either the intrinsic or the extrinsic system leads finally to the activation of factor X. As shown in Figure 26-1, activated factor X (Xa) combines with factor VI, Ca^{++}, and phospholipid (either tissue or platelet phospholipid) to form prothrombinase complex. Prothrombinase complex acts on prothrombin to produce thrombin, which in turn causes fibrin to polymerize. In the presence of Ca^{++}, thrombin also activates factor XIII, which causes cross-linkage of polymerized

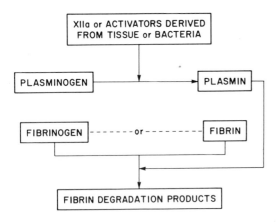

Figure 26-2. The fibrinolytic system for dissolving blood clots. When a clot occurs, the system acts quickly to remove it. Plasminogen is converted to plasmin, which degrades the fibrin in the clot.

fibrin and produces a stronger and less soluble clot. The end result is the formation of a blood clot composed of a meshwork of fibrin threads that traps blood and tissue cells, platelets, plasma, and debris. The fibrin threads adhere to damaged edges of blood vessels, and the clot seals off leakage.

Clot Retraction

Within about an hour of the initial formation, the clot is stabilized further by a process referred to as clot retraction, in which the clot shrinks and pulls the edges of the damaged vessel closer together. Apparently, thrombosthenin, a contractile protein found in the platelets trapped in the clot, causes the clot to retract. The energy for clot retraction may be derived from the relatively high concentration of ATP in the platelets. Thrombin also promotes a positive feedback by increasing the activities of factors V and VIII, enhancing platelet aggregation, and activating prothrombin. The general operation of systems such as the clotting cascade involves the production, early in the sequence, of small amounts of enzymes that act on certain substrates to produce other enzymes that act on other substrates. The final result can be a large, fulminant chemical reaction initiated by only a few molecules.

Fibrinolysis

The fibrinolytic system disposes of clots after they no longer are needed. Small clots form con-

tinually in all sizes of blood vessels throughout the body, and if they could not be removed, the microvasculature would gradually become plugged. Clots not needed for hemostasis after damaged vessels have healed also are removed by fibrinolysis.

A plasma protein called plasminogen, when activated, becomes a potent proteolytic enzyme, plasmin. Plasmin can digest fibrin threads and even fibrinogen. As shown in Figure 26-2, plasminogen can be activated by activated Hageman factor (factor XII), bacterial products (streptokinase), and tissue activators. Plasminogen activators have been found in a variety of tissues, but their most important physiological source is vascular endothelial cells, from which they are released readily. A clot in or around a blood vessel causes the adjacent vascular endothelium to release activator into the clot, and fibrinolysis begins. Thus, most of the plasmin activity is restricted to the clot, and any that strays into the plasma is inactivated quickly by circulating antiplasmins, which prevents destruction of circulating fibrinogens. Plasminogen activators also can be released from endothelial cells by acute stress or even exercise. Normally, this released activator has minor consequences, since it is cleared from the blood by the liver and has a half-life of only 10 or 15 minutes. However, in cases of stress such as shock, in which tissue blood flow is diminished, clearance of these materials diminishes and a generalized state of fibrinolysis and fibrinogenolysis can develop. Fibrinolysis can cause a tendency to bleed from damaged vessels, and fibrinogenolysis can decrease plasma fibrinogen to such low levels that adequate coagulation no longer is possible. Several of the fibrin degradation products (see Figure 26-2) have antithrombin activity; thus fibrinolysis, fibrinogenolysis, and fibrin degradation products may contribute to the tendency to bleed often seen in circulatory shock (see section on disseminated intravascular coagulation).

NATURAL INHIBITION OF COAGULATION

Once coagulation begins, the regenerative mechanisms favor progressive coagulation. The two mechanisms responsible for controlling coagulation are rapid removal and rapid inhibition of activated coagulation factors.

Removal of Coagulation Factors

For coagulation to occur, the concentration of activated clotting factors must reach a certain level. The cascading cycle of clot formation tends not to occur in moving blood because activated clotting factors are washed away. Therefore, extension of the clot usually stops when the clot contacts normally flowing blood. Additionally, as a clot develops, almost all of the thrombin formed is adsorbed to the fibrin threads, which prevents the spread of activated thrombin throughout the vascular system. Given adequate perfusion, the liver rapidly clears activated clotting factors from the circulation and degrades them.

Plasma Inhibitors of Coagulation

Normally, antithrombin III and a globular protein inhibit the activated clotting factors. The most important of these, antithrombin III, forms a stable complex and inhibits thrombin factors IXa, Xa, XIa, XIIa, and plasmin.

ANTICOAGULANT DRUGS

Anticoagulant drugs inhibit coagulation or dissolve thrombus material in blood vessels and thereby prevent occlusion or enhance recanalization of thrombosed blood vessels. Anticoagulation is important medical therapy in a variety of instances in which thrombosis or embolization is a serious problem.

Heparin

Heparin, a conjugated polysaccharide, is an effective anticoagulant that occurs naturally in mast cells and basophils. The major anticoagulant action of heparin is to enhance the action of antithrombin III; thus heparin acts indirectly at several points in the clotting cascade. This anticoagulant action essentially is instantaneous, which makes heparin the drug of choice for emergency anticoagulation in thromboembolic conditions. If the anticoagulant action of heparin must be reversed rapidly, a substance called protamine can be used; it carries a positive charge that combines with and thereby inactivates the negatively charged heparin.

Vitamin K Anticoagulants

Certain drugs act as anticoagulants by competitively inhibiting vitamin K. The plasma levels of the coagulation factors that depend on vitamin K, which include II (prothrombin), VII, IX, and X, are gradually reduced. In addition, lack of vitamin K is associated with the appearance of a protein anticoagulant in the plasma. Attainment of adequate anticoagulation by the use of vitamin K antagonists takes several days, because vitamin K levels must decrease, and after they do, the coagulation factors that depend on vitamin K must decrease. This class of drugs includes the coumarin (warfarin and dicumarol) and indandione derivatives. These drugs must be used carefully, as their effects are augmented in patients who have liver damage or are taking broad-spectrum antibiotics, which suppress the vitamin K–producing intestinal flora. The effectiveness of warfarin as a rat poison indicates its potential toxicity in humans.

In Vitro Anticoagulants

In vitro anticoagulants are valuable for preserving banked blood and blood used in laboratory tests. When blood is drawn, a small amount of heparin (one unit per ml) prevents coagulation, but vitamin K antagonists have no effect, because the clotting factors already are in the plasma. Agents such as citrate and oxalate salts chelate calcium and, as a result, prevent coagulation. Heparin, citrate, and oxalate compounds are used routinely for various laboratory tests that require unclotted blood. Oxalate compounds are too toxic for in vivo use, but citrate is used to prevent coagulation of bank blood.

BLOOD COAGULATION TESTS

Laboratory tests determine whether platelet, coagulation factor, or vascular disorders are involved in bleeding.

Tests of Vascular and Platelet Phases

The platelet count in the plasma must be greater than 150,000/mm^3 for normal coagulation to occur; if platelet function is abnormal, even a normal count may be inadequate and thrombus

CLINICAL CORRELATION
26.1   Hazards of Fibrinolytic Therapy

CASE REPORT

Patient: A 43-year-old woman.

Principal Complaint: Pain in the chest and right leg.

History: The patient had been well until pain began to develop in the calf of the right leg. On several occasions, moderate to severe pain was felt in the chest. These were short-lasting episodes, but on one occasion, some shortness of breath was felt, and the patient may have lost consciousness briefly.

Clinical Examination: On examination, the patient appeared well and in no acute distress. The right calf was tender, but no swelling was detected. The heart and thorax were normal by auscultation. A technetium–99 scan revealed no myocardial infarction, and an echocardiogram showed that the cardiac valves were normal. The prothrombin time (PT) and the activated partial prothrombin time (aPTT) were normal. A venous Doppler examination, which measures blood flow by reflected ultrasound, suggested the obstruction of a vein in the right calf. Venography (x-ray film taken after the injection of contrast medium) showed that the right popliteal vein was occluded, and the anterior and posterior tibial veins were partly occluded.

Treatment: Heparin was injected as a bolus and then infused continuously at a rate that kept the aPTT about two times the control value. After a week of heparin therapy, oral warfarin (another anticoagulant) was added to her regimen. One day later, Doppler examination indicated that additional veins were being obstructed, and a lung scan indicated a number of small, occluded areas in the pulmonary vasculature. Venography showed that the deep venous thrombus was growing, and streptokinase, an enzyme that causes the lysis of fibrin by converting plasminogen to plasmin, was administered. The heparin was discontinued, and vitamin K was injected intravenously. After this therapy, the PT and the aPTT were normal. After one hour, streptokinase was injected intravenously, then infused continuously. Four hours after streptokinase was first given, the thrombin clotting time (TCT) was almost twice normal, and no plasminogen could be detected in the patient's plasma. One hour later, however, the patient developed shortness of breath and chest pain, followed by cardiac arrest. Efforts to resuscitate her failed. Autopsy revealed massive bilateral pulmonary emboli and a large cylindrical embolus coiled in the right cardiac ventricle. Pulmonary infarcts, one to two weeks old, were found in both lungs.

Comment: Anticoagulant therapy with heparin did not prevent growth of the deep venous thrombus, despite the maintenance of adequate anticoagulation, as indicated by prolonged PT, aPTT, and TCT. Fibrinolytic therapy caused the lysis of the more recent clots, but the older thrombus, more resistant to plasmin, broke up and lodged in the lungs. This suggests that fibrinolysis should not be applied to a group of new and old thrombi in the deep veins.

---

formation may be deficient. The bleeding time is an in vivo test of platelet function performed by making a standardized (in length and depth) laceration on the skin of the forearm and measuring the time required for bleeding to stop. This test can be prolonged in vascular disorders and in disorders of platelet function or number. Tests for platelet function include (1) clot retraction time (platelets are responsible for clot retraction), in which blood is withdrawn and allowed to clot and the time for development of maximal clot retraction is recorded; (2) activity of platelet phospholipid (see Figure 26-1); (3) the ability of platelets to aggregate, determined by adding any of various substances (collagen, epinephrine, ADP, thrombin, or ristocetin) to platelet-rich plasma and monitoring the change in optical density of the solution.

Tests of Coagulation Phase

The important tests of the coagulation phase of clotting include prothrombin time (PT), partial thromboplastin time (PTT), whole blood clotting time, and specific assays for clotting factors. PT and PTT are performed on samples of oxalated blood; oxalate chelates Ca^{++} and thereby prevents coagulation until the tests are performed. PT is the time required for plasma to clot after adding Ca^{++} and a small amount of thromboplastin; thus defects in the extrinsic coagulation system and the common pathway (see Figure 26-1) prolong PT. PTT is the time needed for plasma to clot after addition of Ca^{++}, a standardized platelet substitute (cephalin or partial thromboplastin), and a material (celite or kaolin) that causes surface activation of XII. PTT is prolonged by defects in the intrinsic coagulation cascade. An additional test of the intrinsic cascade is the whole-blood clotting time, which is the time required for 1 ml of oxalated blood to clot after Ca^{++} is added and the sample is exposed to the surface of a specially standardized glass test tube.

Tests of Fibrinolysis

The term "fibrin split products" (FSP) refers to the degradation products (Figure 26-2) of fibrin or fibrinogen. The presence of FSP indicates disseminated intravascular coagulation (DIC). Increased fibrinolytic (plasmin) activity can be detected by the euglobulin lysis time. Euglobulin is a coagulum of plasma that separates out when plasma is acidified by acetic acid. The plasmin remains associated with euglobulin. The time required for the euglobulin to lyse is a function of the plasmin activity and is reported as the euglobulin lysis time.

DISORDERS OF HEMOSTASIS

Disorders of Blood Vessels

INCREASED VASCULAR FRAGILITY

The most common disorder of hemostasis caused by abnormality of blood vessels is increased vascular fragility. This inherited disorder is manifested most often as a tendency of postmenopausal women to bruise easily. Another inherited disorder, called hereditary hemorrhagic telangiectasis, also increases vascular fragility. Areas of dilated small blood vessels, or telangiectases, occur on the skin and mucous membranes and may bleed profusely when subjected to minor trauma.

ALLERGIC PURPURA

In the condition of allergic purpura, or Henoch-Schönlein purpura, the vascular endothelium is damaged by what is believed to be an immune reaction, often after streptococcal infections. Typically, bleeding into joints and abdominal viscera causes pain in these areas.

Disorders of Platelets

Disorders of platelets are divided into two types: insufficient platelets (thrombocytopenia) and disorders of platelet function.

THROMBOCYTOPENIA CAUSED BY DEFICIENT PRODUCTION

The production of platelets is deficient in bone marrow failure, which may be caused by radiation, tumor, infiltration of the marrow, deficiency of folate and/or vitamin B_{12}, or various drugs (chloramphenicol, benzene, and antineoplastic drugs).

THROMBOCYTOPENIA CAUSED BY INCREASED DESTRUCTION

Platelets are destroyed by several mechanisms, including specific antibodies produced, excessive removal by an enlarged spleen, exposure to toxins such as alcohol or snake venom, and trauma during heart-lung bypass surgery.

THROMBOCYTOPENIA CAUSED BY INCREASED USE

Platelet use may exceed platelet production in syndromes of disseminated intravascular coagulation (DIC) or conditions such as burn injuries, traumatic injuries, and neoplasms, and in hemangiomas (tumors composed of blood vessels), in which platelet thrombi form in the abnormal tissue. In addition, DIC can occur in all types of circulatory shock, especially septic shock due to gram-negative organisms. In idiopathic conditions such as hemolytic-uremic syndrome (HUS) and thrombotic thrombocytopenic purpura (TTP), platelet thrombi are formed in various vascular beds throughout the body.

DILUTIONAL THROMBOCYTOPENIA

Thrombocytopenia can occur simply by dilution if large transfusions of platelet-deficient blood or blood products are given.

ABNORMAL PLATELET FUNCTION

In a number of disorders, the platelet count is normal, but platelet function is aberrant. Various inherited disorders of this type have been described, including abnormal clot retraction, disordered platelet aggregation, and abnormal platelet morphology. In addition, drugs such as the nonsteroidal antiinflammatory agents (aspirin, indomethacin, and phenylbutazone) inhibit platelet function, and a circulatory substance that inhibits platelet function has been described in the condition of uremia. Recent evidence indicates that patients who have vaso-occlusive disease (coronary artery disease and cerebrovascular disease) caused by atherosclerosis may benefit from the use of drugs that inhibit platelet function.

Hereditary Disorders of Coagulation

HEMOPHILIAS

Hemophilias are bleeding disorders caused by inherited abnormalities of deficiencies of coagulation factors. The most common forms of abnormality are deficiencies of factors VIII or IX; they are called hemophilias A and B, respectively. Both of these disorders are inherited by X-linked recessive genes; therefore, they occur only in males and are carried by females. A woman who is a heterozygote for a hemophilia will not manifest the disease, but her plasma levels of the clotting factor may be reduced. She will transmit the gene to half of her male offspring, causing hemophilia, and to half of her female offspring, producing the carrier state. In patients who have untoward bleeding tendencies, a hemophilia is suspected if PTT is prolonged and PT is normal (remember, factors VIII and IX both are part of the intrinsic cascade, which PTT measures). The coagulation defect is not corrected by ad-

ding standard plasma known to be deficient in factors VIII or IX. Specific assays for VIII and IX also are useful, but plasma levels of these factors often are normal in hemophilia, which indicates that the hemophilias are caused by defective VIII or IX molecules rather than by reduced plasma levels of VIII or IX.

Symptoms of hemophilia begin early in life and typically are first noticed as abnormal bleeding after circumcision. Throughout life, bleeding from normally minor traumas can be life threatening. If the activities of the plasma factors are low enough, the subject may bleed spontaneously into joints (hemarthrosis), the urinary bladder (hematuria), the nasal mucosa (epistaxis), or the gastrointestinal tract.

VON WILLEBRAND'S DISEASE

Von Willebrand's disease produces symptoms akin to the hemophilias; however, it is transmitted as an autosomal dominant trait. The activity of factor VIII is abnormal, but in contrast to hemophilia A, plasma levels of VIII are decreased and another part of the VIII molecule, necessary for normal platelet adhesion to damaged vessel walls, is deficient. This is called Von Willebrand factor.

Acquired Disorders of Coagulation

DISSEMINATED INTRAVASCULAR COAGULATION

Disseminated intravascular coagulation (DIC) is a condition of widespread clotting caused by thromboplastic activity in the circulation. It may originate in several ways.

1. Damage to capillary endothelium, which permits exposure of subendothelial collagen to the vascular lumen and activation of the intrinsic coagulation cascade. This condition occurs in circulatory shock, especially septic shock.
2. Tissue factors produced during shock that function as thromboplastin. These may be derived from tissues associated with abruptio placenta, placenta previa, or metastatic carcinoma, and they may be released from red cells in hemolytic disorders.
3. Antigen-antibody complexes that activate factor XII and the intrinsic coagulation cascade.

The widespread formation of thrombi can damage a variety of organs, especially the kidneys. Paradoxically, in later stages of DIC, the consumption of coagulation factors and platelets permits massive bleeding. Thus, the optimum treatment for DIC is replacement of the depleted clotting factors with products such as whole blood, plasma, and platelets. In addition, heparin may help to prevent further coagulation in the later stages of DIC. This leads to the seemingly paradoxical circumstance of giving heparin to a bleeding patient.

VITAMIN K DEFICIENCY
Prothrombin and clotting factors VII, IX, and X are synthesized in the liver by processes that depend on vitamin K. Most of the vitamin K in the body is synthesized in the intestine by bacteria; thus, liver disease, depletion of the bacterial flora of the intestine (for example, by antibiotics or even in the sterile intestine of the newborn), and drugs that antagonize vitamin K (warfarin and dicumarol) may cause a tendency to bleed.

PRIMARY FIBRINOLYSIS
Neoplasms or major trauma may produce abnormal molecules that activate the fibrinolytic system and cause primary fibrinolysis. The activated plasmin attacks fibrin thrombi and circulating fibrinogen, which causes a marked tendency to bleed. The condition can be treated specifically with ε-aminocaproic acid, which prevents activation of the fibrinolytic system by these substances.

MISCELLANEOUS INHIBITORS OF COAGULATION
Antibodies against clotting factors, usually VIII or thrombin, or against thromboplastin may be produced. These substances cause bleeding that may be treated by plasmapheresis (removal of part of the patient's plasma and replacement with normal plasma or electrolyte solutions), which removes the abnormal molecules.

STUDY OUTLINE

Hemostasis is essential to prevent blood loss.

EVENTS IN HEMOSTASIS

VASOCONSTRICTIVE PHASE Immediate response to vascular injury.
Contraction of vascular smooth muscle.
Compression by blood lost into surrounding tissues.

PLATELET PHASE Within 30 seconds of vascular energy.
Platelets adhere to subendothelial collagen; form plug.
Serotonin released, causes vasoconstriction; ADP released, attracts more platelets.

COAGULATION PHASE
GENERAL ASPECTS Procoagulants and anticoagulants normally in balance.
Intrinsic anticoagulants in vascular space.
Extrinsic system initiated by tissue thromboplastin.
Two systems together in final common pathway.
INTRINSIC CASCADE Initiated by negative charge of exposed endothelial collagen.
Factor XII activated.
Factor XII activates XI; XI activates IX.
IX combines with VIII complex; activates X.
EXTRINSIC CASCADE Damaged tissue releases thromboplastin, which combines with factor VII to activate factor X.

COMMON PATHWAY Activation of factor X.
Xa, with VI, Ca++, and phospholipid, forms prothrombinase complex, which acts on prothrombin to produce thrombin.
Thrombin causes fibrin to polymerize; in presence of Ca++, activates factor XII, which strengthens clot.

CLOT RETRACTION Within hour of formation, clot shrinks and tightens; contractile protein in platelets.

FIBRINOLYSIS Removes clots not needed.
Plasminogen activated to plasmin, proteolytic enzyme.
Principal plasminogen activators in vascular epithelial cells.
Circulating plasmin activator inactivated or cleared by liver.
In circulatory shock, diminished blood flow decreases clearance; fibrinolysis causes bleeding, prevents coagulation.

NATURAL INHIBITION OF COAGULATION

REMOVAL OF COAGULATION FACTORS
Critical concentration of activated factors needed.
Flowing blood removes factors, prevents clot extension.

PLASMA INHIBITORS OF COAGULATION
Antithrombin III most important; inhibits activated factors.

ANTICOAGULANT DRUGS   Important medical therapy.

HEPARIN   Enhances action of antithrombin III.
Inhibited by protamine.

VITAMIN K ANTICOAGULANTS   Production of several coagulation factors depends on vitamin K.
Effect slow, as factors must be used up.

IN VITRO ANTICOAGULANTS   For lab tests and banked blood.
Heparin.
Citrate and oxalate chelate Ca^{++}.

BLOOD COAGULATION TESTS

TESTS OF VASCULAR AND PLATELET PHASES   Platelet count $> 150,000/mm^3$ and normal platelet function needed.
Bleeding time: prolonged in platelet or vascular disorders.
Platelet function tested by clot retraction time, activity of platelet phospholipid, and platelet aggregation.

TESTS OF COAGULATION PHASE   Prothrombin time: time required for plasma to clot after Ca^{++} and thromboplastin added.
Partial thromboplastin time: time needed for plasma to clot after addition of Ca^{++}, standardized platelet substitute, and material that activates XII.
Whole-blood clotting time: time required for 1 ml of oxalated blood to clot after Ca^{++} added and sample exposed to glass.
Specific assays for clotting factors.

TESTS OF FIBRINOLYSIS   Fibrin split products: degradation products of fibrin or fibrinogen.
Euglobulin lysis time.

DISORDERS OF HEMOSTASIS

DISORDERS OF BLOOD VESSELS
INCREASED VASCULAR FRAGILITY Tendency to bruise easily in postmenopausal women.
Telangiectasis: areas of dilated small vessels that bleed easily.
ALLERGIC PURPURA   Vessels damaged by immune reaction; bleeding into joints and viscera.

DISORDERS OF PLATELETS
THROMBOCYTOPENIA CAUSED BY DEFICIENT PRODUCTION   Effects of vitamin deficiency, radiation, tumor, or chemicals on bone marrow.
THROMBOCYTOPENIA CAUSED BY INCREASED DESTRUCTION   Toxins, antibodies, trauma, excess removal by spleen.
THROMBOCYTOPENIA CAUSED BY INCREASED USE   Disseminated intravascular coagulation caused by injury or tumor.
Circulatory shock.
Hemolytic, thrombotic syndromes.
DILUTIONAL THROMBOCYTOPENIA Large transfusion of platelet-deficient blood.
ABNORMAL PLATELET FUNCTION Normal number, abnormal function.
Inhibition by drugs or circulating factors.
Beneficial in coronary artery and cerebrovascular diseases.

HEREDITARY DISORDERS OF COAGULATION
HEMOPHILIAS   Bleeding disorders caused by hereditary abnormalities or deficiencies of coagulation factors.
Most common forms occur in males; carried by females.
Even minor trauma can cause life-threatening hemorrhage.
VON WILLEBRAND'S DISEASE   Symptoms like hemophilias, but dominant trait.

ACQUIRED DISORDERS OF COAGULATION
DISSEMINATED INTRAVASCULAR COAGULATION   Widespread clotting due to thromboplastic activity.
Damaged capillary epithelium exposes subendothelial cartilage; occurs during circulatory shock.
Tissue factors released during shock.
Antigen-antibody complexes that activate intrinsic cascade.
Clotting factors may be depleted, causing bleeding.
VITAMIN K DEFICIENCY   Caused by liver disease, depletion of intestinal flora, drugs.
PRIMARY FIBRINOLYSIS   A fibrinolytic system activated by neoplasm or trauma.
MISCELLANEOUS INHIBITORS OF COAGULATION   Antibodies against clotting factors or thromboplastin.

BIBLIOGRAPHY

Bloom, A.L., and Thomas, D.P., editors. 1981. *Haemostasis and thrombosis.* New York: Churchill Livingstone.

Colman, R.W.; Hirsch, J.; Marder, V.J., et al. 1982. *Hemostasis and thrombosis: basic principles and clinical practice.* Philadelphia: W.B. Saunders Co.

Doolittle, R.F. 1981. Fibrinogen and fibrin. *Sci. Am.* 245:126.

Engelberg, H. 1977. Probable physiologic functions of heparin. *Fed. Proc.* 36:70.

Erslev, A.J., and Gabuzda, T.G. 1979. Plasma coagulation factors. In *Pathophysiology of blood,* 3rd ed. Philadelphia: W.B. Saunders Co.

Feinman, R.D., and Li, E.H.H. 1977. Interaction of heparin with thrombin and antithrombin III. *Fed. Proc.* 36:51.

Figueroa, W.G. 1981. *Hematology.* New York: John Wiley and Sons.

Firschein, S.I.; Hoter, L.W.; and Lazarchick, J. 1979. Prenatal diagnosis of classic hemophilia. *N. Engl. J. Med.* 300: 937.

Fischbach, D.P., and Fogdall, R.P. 1981. *Coagulation: the essentials.* Baltimore: Williams and Wilkins.

Gralnick, H.R.; Sultan, Y.; and Collier, B.S. 1977. von Willebrand's disease: combined qualitative and quantitative abnormalities. *N. Engl. J. Med.* 296: 1024.

Green, L.H.; Seroppian, E.; and Handin, R.E. 1980. Platelet aggregation during exercise-induced myocardial ischemia. *N. Engl. J. Med.* 302: 193.

Jaques, L.B. 1979. Heparin: an old drug with a new paradigm. *Science* 206: 528.

Joist, J.H.; Cowan, J.F.; and Zimmerman, T.S. 1978. Acquired von Willebrand's disease: evidence for a quantitative and qualitative factor VIII disorder. *N. Engl. J. Med.* 298:987.

Klein, H.G.; Aledort, L.M.; Bouma, B.N., et al. 1977. A co-operative study for the detection of the carrier state of classic hemophilia. *N. Engl. J. Med.* 296:959.

Kwaan, H.C., and Bowie, E.J.W. 1982. *Thrombosis.* Philadelphia: W.B. Saunders Co.

Moncada, S., and Vane, J.R. 1979. Arachidonic acid metabolites and the interactions between platelets and blood vessel walls. *N. Engl. J. Med.* 300:1142.

Riesenfeld, J.; Hook, M.; Bjork, I.; et al. 1977. Structural requirements for the interaction of heparin with antithrombin III. *Fed. Proc.* 36:39.

Rosenberg, R.D. 1977. Chemistry of the hemostatic mechanism and its relationship to the action of heparin. *Fed. Proc.* 36:10.

Shattil, S.J., and Bennett, J.S. 1981. Platelets and their membranes in hemostasis: physiology and pathophysiology. *Ann. Intern. Med.* 94:108.

Suttie, J.W., and Jackson, C.M. 1977. Prothrombin structure, activation, and biosynthesis. *Physiol. Rev.* 57:1.

Turitto, V.T., and Weiss, H.J. 1980. Red blood cells: their dual role in thrombus formation. *Science* 207:541.

Wintrobe, M.M. 1980. *Blood, pure and eloquent.* New York: McGraw-Hill Book Co.

Wintrobe, M.M., Lee, G.R., Boggs, D.R., et al. 1981. *Clinical hematology.* 8th ed. Philadelphia: Lea & Febiger.

Zimmerman, T.S.; Abildgaard, C.F.; and Meyer, D. 1979. The factor VIII abnormality in severe von Willebrand's disease. *N. Engl. J. Med.* 301:1307.

Zucker, M.B. 1977. Heparin and platelet function. *Fed. Proc.* 36:47.

PART
VI

RESPIRATORY
PHYSIOLOGY

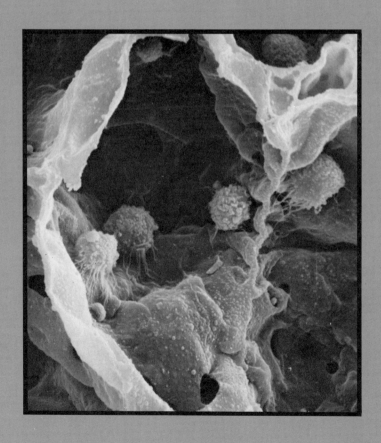

Photomicrograph from *Tissues and Organs: A Text-Atlas of Scanning Electron Microscopy* by
Richard G. Kessel and Randy H. Kardon. W.H. Freeman and Company. © 1979.

27

Introduction to Respiration: Pulmonary Ventilation

CHAPTER CONTENTS

OVERVIEW

The body has no significant stores of oxygen. The processes of respiration must function continuously to supply the oxygen that is needed and to eliminate the carbon dioxide that is produced by all of the tissues.

The respiratory system adds oxygen to the blood and removes carbon dioxide. The circulatory system transports the oxygen from the lungs to the tissues and the carbon dioxide from the tissues to the lungs. The lungs distribute air through a system of highly branching airways until the air reaches the alveoli, and the heart pumps blood through a system of vessels until the blood reaches the pulmonary capillaries, which surround the alveoli. At this point oxygen and carbon dioxide can diffuse across the alveolar-capillary membranes. For maximum efficiency, the quantity of air delivered to the alveoli should be appropriate for the quantity of blood delivered to the alveolar capillaries.

The two pumps differ inasmuch as the heart has valves while the lungs do not, and the heart forces blood to flow by increasing pressure, while the respiratory system causes air to flow partly by decreasing pressure. The chest enlarges actively during inspiration, which reduces the pressure in the alveoli, and air flows into the lungs because the pressure at the mouth is higher than that in the alveoli. During expiration, when the volume of the thorax decreases, air flows out because the pressure in the alveoli is higher than that at the mouth.

Ventilation is the first component of pulmonary gas exchange. A certain volume of air, which contains oxygen and a negligible amount of carbon dioxide, must be delivered each minute and distributed to all of the alveoli, while an equal volume of alveolar air, which contains carbon dioxide, must be eliminated. *Diffusion* is the second component. Oxygen diffuses from the alveolar air into the blood, and carbon dioxide diffuses from the blood into the alveolar air. Pulmonary gas exchange also involves *pulmonary capillary blood flow.* A certain volume of blood, which should be distributed to all of the alveoli that are ventilated, must flow during each minute. The pulmonary capillaries are very short vessels and are so extensive that they form virtually two continuous layers of endothelium between which blood flows, and this arrangement greatly facilitates the exchange of gases. A given red blood cell spends less than 1 sec in the pulmonary capillary, but during this short time, the oxygen and carbon dioxide of the alveolar air and the capillary blood come to equilibrium. Finally, pulmonary gas exchange requires *work.* The muscles of respiration must expand the lungs and the chest to stretch the elastic tissue and to overcome the resistance of the airway. The work that the heart must perform to pump the blood through the circulation is discussed elsewhere.

FUNCTIONAL ANATOMY

Pleurae

The lungs are paired organs, and one is located in each side of the thoracic cavity. In the human, the right lung has three lobes, and the left

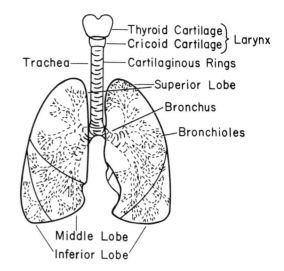

Figure 27-1.   Human lungs and tracheobronchial tree.

---

lung has two lobes (Figure 27-1). The thoracic cavity is lined by the *parietal pleura,* which, at the hilum of the lungs, continues into the *visceral pleura* and covers the lungs. The parietal and visceral pleurae are separated by a thin film of serous fluid, and the potential space between the pleural surfaces is referred to as the *pleural cavity,* or *intrapleural space.*

Air Passages

NASAL PASSAGES

The nasal passages function mainly as a filter. The entrance to the nasal passage is lined with hairs that filter large particles; smaller particles are trapped within the passages. The airway bends sharply; the gases of the air swirl on through the turn, but the nongaseous particles, which have greater mass, continue in a straight line and strike the nasal surfaces, where they are trapped in the moist nasal lining and, combined with the mucus, are removed periodically.

MOUTH AND LARYNX

The mouth and larynx perform special functions related to respiration. The mouth forms an auxiliary air passage that is used when the rate of air flow is great, as it is during strenuous exercise; relative to respiration, it serves primarily to produce speech. The larynx acts as a valve to protect the lungs and also contains the mechanism to form sounds.

Conducting Airways

There are approximately 23 generations of airways (Figure 27-2). The first 16 generations make up the *conducting zone,* which is a fairly rigid system of conduits that has a volume of approximately 150 ml. No gas exchange takes place in the conducting airways.

TRACHEA

The human trachea is approximately 10–12 cm long and 2.0–2.5 cm in diameter. It extends down through the lower part of the neck and through the superior mediastinum of the thorax. The trachea is kept open by a series of about 20 horseshoe-shaped cartilages that are connected at the open end by smooth muscle. Contraction or relaxation of the smooth muscle changes the size of the rings and thereby changes the cross-sectional area of the trachea. A reduction of the cross-sectional area permits the development of greater air velocity, which facilitates the expulsion of material from the trachea, as in coughing.

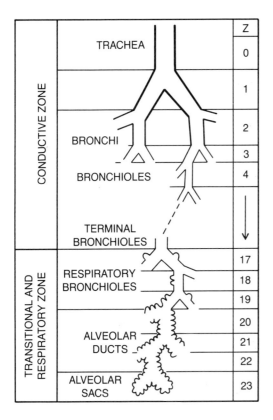

Figure 27-2. Schematic diagram of the airways. For detailed description see text. (Redrawn, with permission, from Weibel, E.R. 1963. *Morphometry of the human lung.* Heidelberg: Springer-Verlag.)

The mucous membrane that lines the trachea consists of pseudostratified, ciliated, columnar epithelium and contains mucus-secreting goblet cells. The ciliated respiratory epithelium forms the so-called *mucociliary escalator.* Small particles inspired with the air are trapped in the mucus and moved by the constant upward beating of the cilia toward the mouth, from which they are expelled or swallowed. In cigarette smokers the action of the cilia is greatly diminished and the mucus must be removed by coughing. The trachea also is important for warming and humidifying the inspired air. During this process, which begins in the nose, the air is warmed to body temperature and saturated with water vapor before it reaches the bronchi. The warm, moist air prevents fluctuations of temperature of the alveolar epithelium and protects it from drying.

BRONCHI

The trachea terminates by dividing into the left and right main bronchi (Figure 27-3). The right main *bronchus* gives off three *lobar bronchi,* and the left main bronchus gives off two lobar bronchi, which divide into *segmental bronchi.* The segmental bronchi branch and rebranch until their diameters are reduced to 2 mm or less. These structures contain less cartilage and fewer mucous glands as the bronchi become bronchioles and enter the lung tissue.

BRONCHIOLES

The bronchioles are the eleventh through the sixteenth generations of airways. At this level, the cartilage has disappeared, and the amount of smooth muscle has increased. These small airways are surrounded by respiratory tissue and held open by the traction of the surrounding structures. The respiratory epithelium becomes cuboidal, and goblet cells no longer are present. The *terminal bronchioles* are the last branches of the conductive airways. These tubes are less than 0.5 mm in diameter and have only patches of ciliated cells. Debris and other unwanted material below this level are removed by the alveolar macrophages.

Respiratory Airways

PRIMARY LOBULE

The next seven generations of airways usually are referred to as the *respiratory zone* (see Figure 27-2); it is the anatomical site for gas exchange, and its volume is approximately 2500 ml. These small airways are distended

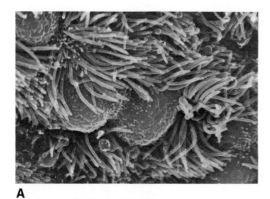

A

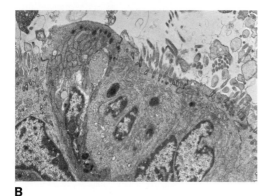

B

Figure 27-3. Scanning and transmission electron micrographs of bronchial mucosa. **A,** Scanning electron micrograph of bronchial mucosa. Note numerous, delicate cilia surrounding two nonciliated mucus goblet cells (x6,000). **B,** Transmission electron micrograph of bronchial mucosa. Note ciliated respiratory epithelial cells to right and elevated, nonciliated, mucus goblet cell to left (arrow) (x7500). (Courtesy Dr. M.L. Mace, Jr., Director, Electron Microscopy Laboratory, and Dr. S.D. Greenberg, Department of Pathology, Baylor College of Medicine.)

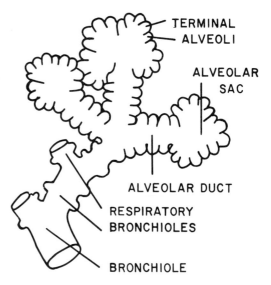

Figure 27-4. Basic respiratory unit of the lung. The primary lobule includes the respiratory bronchiole with its alveolar duct and the clusters of alveoli that constitute the alveolar sacs. (Redrawn, with permission, from Krahl, V.E. 1961. The lung. In *Encyclopedia of the biological sciences,* editor Peter Gray. London: Chapman and Hall, Ltd.

and compressed easily; the significance of this is discussed in Chapter 28. The *respiratory bronchioles,* the seventeenth to the nineteenth generations of airways, represent a transition between the conducting zone and the respiratory zone. The main function of these airways still is to serve as conduits, but now there are occasional outbuddings of alveoli along their walls, where gas can be exchanged. The respiratory bronchioles terminate in several *alveolar ducts,* which are the twentieth to twenty-second generations of airways; these, in turn, open into *alveolar sacs,* the last, or twenty-third generation. The basic respiratory unit of the lungs, which is called the *primary lobule,* consists of the respiratory bronchiole

with its alveolar duct and alveolar sacs (Figure 27-4). Alveolar sacs are clusters of alveoli that open into a chamber. They contain smooth muscle, which is particularly prominent at the openings of the sacs.

The total cross-sectional area of the airways increases greatly beyond the terminal bronchioles, as illustrated in Figure 27-5. The velocity of the air flow is related to the geometry of the airways: as the area increases, the velocity decreases. The mean velocity, v, is given by

$$v = \frac{\dot{V} \ (cm^3/sec)}{A \ (cm^2)} = cm/sec$$

where $\dot{V}$ is air flow in ml/sec and A is the cross-sectional area of the airways. The decreased mean velocity of air flow in the respiratory airways aids the exchange of gases between alveolar air and pulmonary capillary blood.

ALVEOLI

Gas exchange between alveolar air and mixed venous capillary blood takes place in the alveoli (Figure 27-6), of which there are 300 million in both lungs of an adult human. The alveoli are polygonal; they range in size from 70–300 μm in diameter and form a surface area of approximately 70–100 m^2 that is available

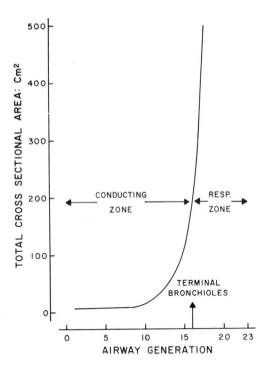

Figure 27-5. Total cross-sectional area of the various segments of the airways. Note the tremendous increase in area beyond the terminal bronchioles. The increase in total cross-sectional area is associated with a reduction in the velocity of the air flow, which facilitates the exchange of gases between the alveolar air and the blood in the respiratory zone. (Redrawn, with permission, from West, J.B. 1979. *Respiratory physiology.* Baltimore, Williams & Wilkins, p. 7.

for gas exchange. Adjacent alveoli communicate with each other through pores in the interalveolar septum. There are several distinct cell types in the interalveolar wall, such as the epithelial cells that line the alveolar spaces; endothelial cells that form the capillaries; several kinds of blood cells; alveolar cells, some of which produce pulmonary surfactant material; and alveolar phagocytes.

BLOOD-GAS INTERFACE

The thin-walled alveoli are surrounded by thin-walled capillaries. Gas is exchanged through structures interposed between the air in the alveoli and the mixed venous blood in the pulmonary capillaries. This blood-gas barrier consists of (1) a layer of surfactant that lines each alveolus; (2) the alveolar epithelium; (3) the interstitial space; (4) the capillary en-

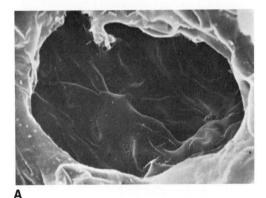

A

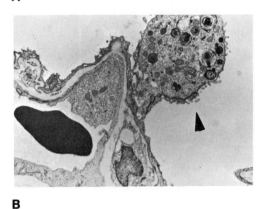

B

Figure 27-6. Scanning and transmission electron micrographs of alveolar wall. **A,** Scanning electron micrograph of an alveolus. Note its oval entrance ring and recessed, cavelike interior (x3000). **B,** Transmission electron micrograph of an alveolar wall. Alveolar lining consists of attenuated type I and cuboidal type II epithelial cells (arrow). Alveolar capillaries are lined by endothelial cells. Note electron-dense erythrocyte in capillary lumen. A single interstitial cell is seen within alveolar wall (x 14,000). (Courtesy Dr. M.L. Mace, Jr., Director, Electron Microscopy Laboratory, and Dr. S.D. Greenberg, Department of Pathology, Baylor College of Medicine.)

dothelium; (5) the blood plasma; (6) the red-cell membrane (Figure 27-7).

BLOOD SUPPLY

The respiratory tree has a dual blood supply derived from the pulmonary circulation and the bronchial circulation.

Pulmonary Circulation

The pulmonary system provides a relatively continuous flow of mixed venous blood to the alveolar-capillary membrane, where gas is ex-

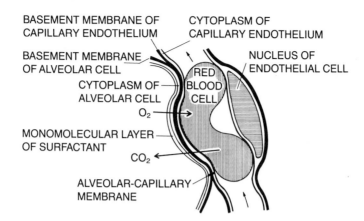

BASEMENT MEMBRANE OF
CAPILLARY ENDOTHELIUM

CYTOPLASM OF
CAPILLARY ENDOTHELIUM

BASEMENT MEMBRANE
OF ALVEOLAR CELL

NUCLEUS OF
ENDOTHELIAL CELL

CYTOPLASM OF
ALVEOLAR CELL

RED
BLOOD
CELL

O_2

MONOMOLECULAR LAYER
OF SURFACTANT

CO_2

ALVEOLAR-CAPILLARY
MEMBRANE

Figure 27-7.   The respiratory blood-gas interface. Short arrows indicate the direction of blood flow in the pulmonary capillary. Long arrows indicate the direction of diffusion of O_2 and CO_2 across the blood-gas barrier, a distance of approximately 0.5 μm.

changed. Partially deoxygenated blood from the right ventricle enters the lungs through the pulmonary arteries, which divide and run with the branches of the bronchial tree as far as the respiratory bronchioles. At this stage, terminal arterioles break up into a rich capillary network that surrounds the alveoli (Figure 27-8). The concentration of oxygen in the alveolar air is greater than that in the blood that enters the pulmonary capillaries; hence, oxygen diffuses from the alveoli into the capillaries. The concentration of carbon dioxide in the blood of the pulmonary capillaries is greater than that in the alveolar air; hence, carbon dioxide diffuses from the capillaries into the alveoli. The pulmonary circulation supplies the metabolic needs of the structures in the respiratory zone and, in addition, has other important nonrespiratory functions. It serves as a filter of blood for the systemic circulation and a reservoir for the left ventricle, and it is the site of chemical activation or deactivation of substances such as angiotensin, serotonin, bradykinin, and prostaglandins.

Bronchial Circulation

The bronchial arteries branch from the thoracic aorta and supply blood and substrates to the tissues of the conducting airways, which include the terminal bronchioles, the supporting tissues, the nerves, and the outer coats of the pulmonary arteries and pulmonary veins. When a pulmonary artery is blocked or constricted, the bronchial arteries can enlarge to make connections with vessels of the pulmonary circulation and nourish the tissues that had depended on blood from the pulmonary

artery. No oxygen is added to the blood under these conditions, however, because the blood of the bronchial arteries already is fully oxygenated.

NERVE SUPPLY

The smooth muscle of the tracheobronchial tree is innervated by the autonomic nervous system. The pulmonary plexus consists of two sets of fibers, both of which run with the pulmonary vessels. Branches of the vagus nerves carry the parasympathetic bronchoconstrictor fibers, whereas branches from the thoracic sympathetic ganglia carry the sympathetic bronchodilator fibers. In addition, there are parasympathetic ganglia in the bronchial walls. Acetylcholine, histamine, and some toxins act on bronchiolar smooth muscle and cause bronchoconstriction, whereas epinephrine and norepinephrine relax bronchiolar smooth muscle and cause bronchodilatation.

PHYSICAL BEHAVIOR OF GASES

Gas Laws

Gases, like liquids, conform to the shape of the container into which they are placed; however, unlike liquids, gases always fill the volume of a container completely. The general relationship among the volume (V), pressure (P), temperature (T), and mass (n) of a gas is expressed by the general gas law:

$$PV = nRT$$

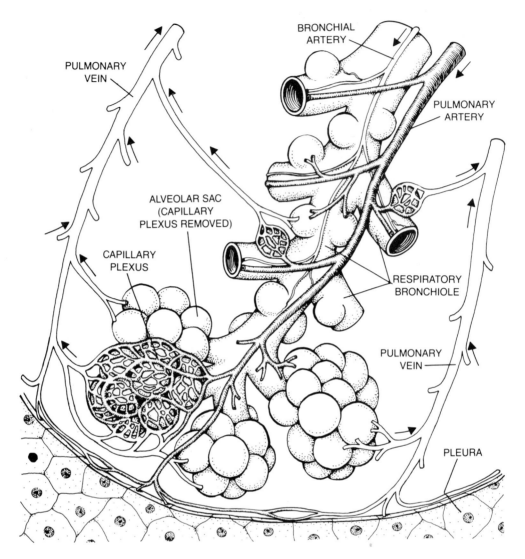

Figure 27-8.   The pulmonary microcirculation.

Since R is a constant (K), the equation may be rewritten as

$$PV/nT = K$$

The gas laws of Boyle and Charles are specific applications of the general law.

BOYLE'S LAW

Boyle's law relates the volume of a gas to its pressure and states that, at a constant mass and temperature, the volume of a gas varies inversely with the pressure. As the volume is compressed, pressure increases, and as the volume is decompressed, pressure decreases. Therefore, $P_1V_1 = P_2V_2$, where P is the pressure of the dry gas in millimeters of mercury,

V is the volume of dry gas in milliliters, and the subscripts 1 and 2 indicate two different conditions.

CHARLES' LAW

Charles' law relates the volume of a gas to the temperature and states that, at a constant pressure, the volume of a gas is related directly to the absolute temperature. As the temperature increases, the volume of gas increases. Therefore,

$$\frac{V_1}{V_2} = \frac{T_1}{T_2},$$

where T is the absolute temperature of the gas in degrees Kelvin (273° + °C). The volume of

1 mol of a gas at standard conditions (760 mm Hg and 0 C, or 273 K) is 22.4 liters. The same gas would occupy a volume of 25.4 liters at a body temperature of 37 C (310 K).

Correction of Gas Volumes

The laws of Boyle and Charles may be combined to write

$$\frac{P_1 V_1}{T_1} = \frac{P_2 V_2}{T_2}$$

from which:

$$V_2 = V_1 \frac{P_1}{P_2} \times \frac{T_2}{T_1}$$

Using this expression, one can solve for the conversion factor that is required to correct the volume of gas collected in the spirometer under ambient conditions (ATPS, or ambient temperature and pressure, saturated with water vapor) to the effective volume in the lungs at body conditions (BTPS, or body temperature and [ambient] pressure, saturated with water vapor), as follows:

$$V_2 = V_1 \frac{P_B - P_1 H_2 O}{P_B - P_2 H_2 O} \times \frac{273 + C_2}{273 + C_1}$$

where P_B is the barometric pressure, $P_1 H_2 O$ is the vapor pressure of water at ambient temperature, $P_2 H_2 O$ is the vapor pressure of water at body temperature, C_1 is the ambient temperature, and C_2 is the body temperature.

The volume of gas in the blood usually is expressed at standard conditions, which are 0 C (273 K), 1 atmosphere (760 mm Hg), and no water vapor. This is referred to as standard temperature and pressure, dry, and abbreviated as STPD. The volume of gas may be corrected from conditions at BTPS to conditions at STPD by the following factor:

$$V_2 = V_1 \frac{P_B - 47 \text{ mm Hg}}{760 \text{ mm Hg}} \times \frac{273}{273 + 37 \text{ C}}$$

where V_1 is the volume of the gas at BTPS, P_B is the barometric pressure, 47 mm Hg is the vapor pressure of the water at 37 C, and V_2 is the corrected volume at STPD.

Partial Pressure

Gas molecules in a container are in constant, random motion; when they strike the walls of the container, a force, which is called pressure, is exerted. Dry air is a mixture of gases that contains 20.93% oxygen, 79.03% nitrogen, and 0.04% carbon dioxide. The total pressure exerted by these gases at sea level is 760 mm Hg, or 1 atmosphere.

DALTON'S LAW

In a mixture of gases, the pressure exerted by each gas is the same as it would be if only that gas occupied the container; it is called the *partial pressure* of a particular gas, and it is related to the concentration of the gas in the mixture. The partial pressure of O_2 in dry air at sea level is 760 mm Hg × 0.2093, or 159 mm Hg (designated Po_2). The Po_2 of 100% O_2 at atmospheric pressure would be 760 mm Hg × 1.0, or 760 mm Hg. The P_{N_2} in dry air at sea level is 760 mm Hg × 0.7903, or 600.6 mm Hg. Finally, the partial pressure of CO_2 in air is so small— 760 mm Hg × 0.0004, or 0.3 mm Hg—that respiratory physiologists usually pretend that fresh air contains no carbon dioxide.

At altitudes higher than sea level, the total pressure is less; hence the pressure of each gas (partial pressure) also is less. However, the proportion of each of the gases in the air is the same.

Inspired air is warmed and saturated with water vapor by the time it reaches the alveoli. At any altitude, the pressure that water vapor exerts depends on the temperature, as shown in Figure 27-9. At sea level, the total pressure of the warm, moist, inspired air in the trachea still is 760 mm Hg, but because the partial pressure of the gaseous water is part of the total pressure, the partial pressure of each dry gas in the moist air is less. At a body temperature of 37 C, the vapor pressure of water is 47 mm Hg; thus, the total pressure of O_2, N_2, and CO_2 in the tracheal air decreases from 760 mm Hg to 713 mm Hg, and the partial pressure of O_2 in this moist tracheal air is (760 − 47 mm Hg) × 0.2093, or 149 mm Hg.

PARTIAL PRESSURE OF A GAS IN A LIQUID

O_2, CO_2, and N_2 are in physical solution in the blood and body fluids. When a liquid is exposed to a mixture of gases, the gases move from the air into the liquid and from the liquid into the air until equilibrium is established. Equilibrium is reached when the partial pressure of the gas on top of the liquid is equal to the partial pressure of that gas in solution. The more soluble a gas is, the easier it dissolves in

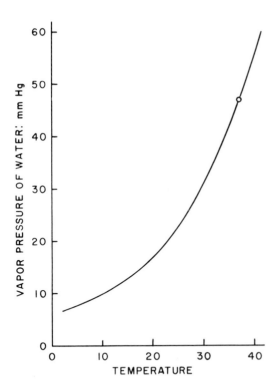

Figure 27-9. Relationship between temperature and vapor pressure of water. Circle indicates water vapor pressure (47 mm Hg) at normal body temperature (37 C). (Adapted from Slonim, N.B., and Hamilton, L.H. 1981. *Respiratory Physiology,* 4th edition. St. Louis: The C.V. Mosby Co.)

the liquid; however, more of a very soluble gas than of a poorly soluble one must dissolve to exert a given pressure. Therefore, at equilibrium, it is possible to have a greater number of molecules of a highly soluble gas in a liter of blood than in a liter of gas mixture on top of the blood. The amount of gas dissolved in a liquid depends on the pressure of the gas and how soluble the gas is in the liquid. Consequently, the partial pressure of a gas in blood is related directly to the volume of the gas dissolved and inversely to the solubility coefficient of the gas in blood. The same symbols are used to express the partial pressure of gases in blood and in air (P_{O_2}, P_{CO_2}, P_{N_2}). The student should always keep in mind, however, that in the blood only the dissolved gas contributes to the partial pressure; oxygen in chemical combination with hemoglobin does not contribute to the partial pressure of O_2 in the blood.

LUNG VOLUMES AND THEIR MEASUREMENT

There are four primary lung volumes in the resting subject; each is independent of the other, but all are influenced by the size, age, sex, and body position of the subject and by pulmonary disease.

Volumes (Figure 27-10)

The volume of air that is inspired and then expired during each breath moves back and forth, like the tides, over the air passages; hence, it is called the tidal volume (TV). An average tidal volume in a person at rest is approximately 600 ml, which is about 10% of the total capacity of the lungs. The maximum volume of air that can be taken in by the lungs at the end of a normal inspiration is the *inspiratory reserve volume* (IRV). As a reserve volume, the IRV can be used to increase total ventilation when it is needed; a typical normal value for the IRV is 3000 ml. The maximum volume of air that can be forced from the lungs at the end of a normal expiration is the *expiratory reserve volume* (ERV). The ERV is approximately 1200 ml, and it also can be used to increase total ventilation. The volume of air that remains in the lungs after a maximal expiration is called the *residual volume* (RV). The chest wall and diaphragm resist a decrease in resting lung volume; therefore, the amount of gas in the lungs at the end of a forceful expiration represents the balance between this resistance and the force generated by the muscles of expiration to overcome it. A typical normal value for the RV is approximately 1200 ml; this is about 20% of the total capacity of the lungs, and the proportion increases with age. The tidal volume multiplied by the rate of breathing gives the total ventilation each minute. This is known also as the *minute volume,* or *total pulmonary ventilation,* and is, at rest, approximately 6 liters/min.

Capacities

The four lung capacities, each of which includes two or more of the lung volumes, are shown in Figure 27-10.

Total lung capacity (TLC) is the sum of all four lung volumes, which is about 6 liters. TLC does not change with age, but, on the average, it is less for females than for males.

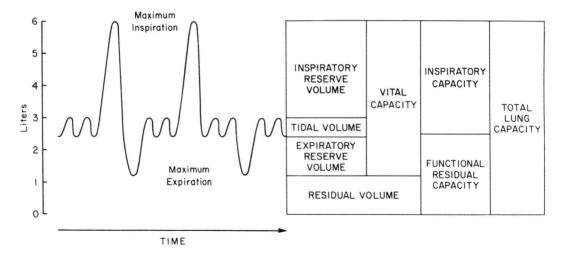

Figure 27-10. The lung volumes and their subdivisions. The diagram illustrates the relationship between lung volumes and capacities. Three of the four primary lung volumes can be measured by spirometry, as illustrated on the left-hand portion of the graph.

Vital capacity (VC) is defined as the maximum amount of air that can be exhaled forcefully after a maximal inspiration. VC includes three of the four lung volumes: IRV, ERV, and TV. It is used frequently as a reference value in pulmonary function tests; however, it may vary normally by as much as 20% in the same individual. Vital capacity may be reduced in individuals who have pulmonary diseases that cause obstruction to air flow or in whom the expansion of the lungs or the thorax is restricted.

The maximum amount of gas that one can inspire, beginning at the normal resting expiratory level, is called the *inspiratory capacity* (IC); it is the sum of IRV and TV. IC amounts to approximately 3600 ml, but it varies among subjects. The inspiratory capacity is decreased in patients who have pulmonary diseases that lead to stiffening of the pulmonary tissue (restrictive lung disease).

The volume of air that remains in the lungs at the end of a normal expiration is referred to as the *functional residual capacity* (FRC); it is the sum of ERV and RV, and normally it represents about 40% of the total lung capacity (2500 ml). The FRC, also known as the resting lung volume, acts as a reservoir that provides for the exchange of gases throughout the respiratory cycle (Figure 27-11). Under normal conditions, the Po_2 of the alveoli is kept at a mean value of approximately 100 mm Hg and the Pco_2 is kept at approximately 40 mm Hg.

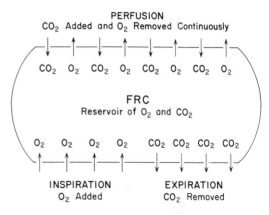

Figure 27-11. Reservoir function of the functional residual capacity (FRC). See text for further discussion.

However, if the FRC were very small, alveolar Po_2 and Pco_2 would tend to equilibrate with venous Po_2 and Pco_2 after expiration, and at the end of inspiration, alveolar Po_2 and Pco_2 would be close to that of the inspired air. Thus, by maintaining gradients of O_2 and CO_2 between the alveoli and the blood, the FRC facilitates the exchange of these gases.

Measurement

Because lung volumes are influenced by lung disease, they are used often to diagnose certain types of pulmonary disorders. Pulmonary function testing is discussed further in Chapter 35.

CLINICAL CORRELATION
27.1   Asthma

CASE REPORT

The Patient: A 53-year-old woman.

Principal Complaint: Wheezing precipitated by exposure to molds, feathers, and animals, and occurring after respiratory tract infections.

History: The patient has had bronchial asthma since childhood, and it has been severe for the previous 28 years. She had smoked one–two packs of cigarettes a day for 30 years, but had stopped about 10 years ago. During the past 12 years, she had been admitted to the hospital about once a year for 10–14 days at a time because of severe attacks. Her treatment had included theophylline (a bronchodilator) and adrenocorticosteroids for the asthma, and tetracycline, sulfonamides, and ampicillin (antibiotic and antibacterial drugs) for respiratory tract infections.

Clinical Examination: The patient's hematocrit was 39.6% (normal, 37%–48%), the white blood cell count was 5700/mm³ (normal, 4300–10,800/mm³), the neutrophil count was 3700/mm³ (normal, 100–2100/mm³). and the total eosinophil count was 1288/mm³ (normal, 0–700/mm³). The Pao_2 was 80 mm Hg (normal, 75–100 mm Hg), $Paco_2$ was 41 mm Hg (normal, 35–45 mm Hg), and the pH of the arterial blood was 7.42 (normal, 7.35–7.45). An x-ray film showed hyperinflation of the lungs. The results of pulmonary function tests, taken before and after the administration of a bronchodilator, are shown in Table 1.

Treatment: Aminophylline, a potent bronchial dilator, was injected intravenously to relieve the patient's acute attack of bronchospasm. Prednisone, an adrenal steroid, was given orally to prevent further attacks. The steroid therapy required a daily dose of 40 mg initially; this was reduced gradually and discontinued over a period of 2 weeks.

Comment: The significant improvement of timed spirometric values after administration of the bronchodilator indicates a reversible obstruction of the airways; this is especially prominent during expiration. The patient's asthmatic attacks are precipitated by exposure to allergenic agents, which cause bronchial constriction. Plugging of the bronchi with mucus and thickening of the bronchial walls further add to the airway resistance and produce wheezing, which is caused by turbulence in the narrowed airways. Increased airway resistance during expiration often builds up residual volume and total lung capacity (that is, overinflation); however, since RV usually increases proportionately more than TLC, the RV/TLC ratio increases significantly in patients who have longstanding asthma.

Outcome: The patient was urged to avoid, if possible, known allergens that may precipi-

SPIROMETRY

Most lung volumes, with the exception of the residual volume, may be measured by using a spirometer, which consists of an upright, water-filled cylinder that contains an inverted, counterweighted bell (Figure 27-12). Breathing into the bell changes the volume of the gases trapped inside, and the change of volume is recorded on the moving drum of a kymograph.

The subject is connected to the spirometer through a low-resistance valve assembly that insures unidirectional gas flow into and out of the spirometer; the CO_2 exhaled into the system is adsorbed by soda lime. More modern, automated versions of this instrument with digital display are available today, but the principle of the method remains unchanged. As the spirometer measures only the volume of air that can

(CLINICAL CORRELATION continued)

TABLE 1
Results of pulmonary function tests, showing effects of bronchodilator

Test	Measured	Predicted	After bronchodilator
Forced expiratory volume (FEV_1) (liters)	1.45	2.66	1.77
Forced vital capacity (FVC) (liters)	2.53	3.14	2.71
FEV_1/FVC	0.57	0.72	0.65
Peak expiratory flow rate (liters/min)	195	367	217
Forced expiratory flow ($FEF_{25\%-75\%}$) (liters/min)	65	116	98
Maximum voluntary ventilation (MVV) (liters/min)	58	99	71
Peak inspiratory flow rate (liters/min)	108		108
Total lung capacity (TLC) (liters)	5.21	4.73	
Residual volume (RV) (liters)	2.67	1.6	
RV/TLC	0.51	0.34	
Functional residual capacity (FRC) (liters)	3.41		
Airway resistance (cm H_2O/liter/sec)	1.66	0.8–2.4	

tate severe bronchoconstriction. She was continued on oral theophylline, and for mild, acute attacks, isoproterenol (which dilates bronchioles by stimulating adrenergic β_2-receptors) was prescribed, to be inhaled through a nebulizer. By taking these precautions, she was able to function normally.

---

be moved into or out of the lungs and collected in the container, it cannot be used to measure the residual volume or any capacities that include the residual volume.

PNEUMOTACHOMETRY
The pneumotachograph measures the rate of flow of air during breathing. It is a transducer, the function of which is based on the pneu-matic equivalent of Ohm's law, where

$$\text{Flow} = \frac{\text{Difference in pressure}}{\text{Fixed resistance of the pneumotachograph}}$$

Volumes can be calculated from the flow measurements because volume (ml) = flow (ml/sec) × time (sec). Only those volumes that are included in the vital capacity can be determined by this method.

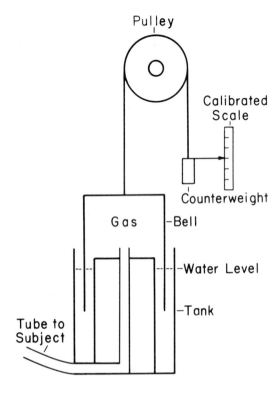

Figure 27-12. A spirometer. The spirometer measures only the volume of gas that can be moved into and out of the lungs; it cannot be used to determine residual volume or any of the capacities that include the residual volume. In a recording spirometer, the calibrated scale is replaced with a rotating kymograph.

GAS DILUTION

Residual volume, functional residual capacity, and total lung capacity may be determined by an application of the indicator-dilution principle. Since the gases used as indicators must not be metabolized, nitrogen is used most frequently. In this method, pulmonary nitrogen, N_2, is "washed out" of the lungs by breathing a gas that is free of N_2—usually 100% O_2. The N_2 in the lungs is diluted by O_2 with each breath, and the exhaled gas is collected in a second spirometer. Since the total volume of gas and the mean concentration of N_2 in the collected gas can be measured and the initial concentration of N_2 in the lungs is known (approximately 80%), the initial volume of the lungs may be calculated from the equation

$$\text{Conc}_L \times \text{vol}_L = \text{Con}_S \times \text{vol}_S$$

Where L = lungs and S = spirometer. Using this equality, one can solve for vol_L:

$$\text{vol}_L = \frac{[N_2]_S \times \text{vol}_S}{[N_2]_L}$$

FRC usually is measured by this method; however, RV and TLC also can be measured. To measure a specific volume, one must begin at the level of that volume (see Figure 27-10). Other information also may be gained from the nitrogen-dilution curve, which ideally is a simple exponential curve. For example, a faster-than-normal rate of washout may be associated with a small FRC, a large tidal volume, a small dead space, or a rapid rate of breathing. A

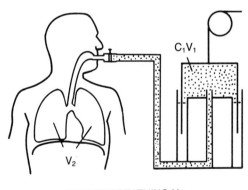

BEFORE BREATHING He

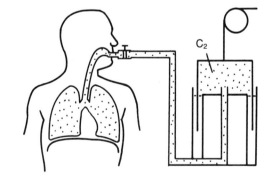

AFTER EQUILIBRATION

$$C_1 \times V_1 = C_2 \times (V_1 + V_2)$$

Figure 27-13. Application of the helium dilution method for measuring functional residual capacity. See text for detailed discussion of method.

slower-than-normal rate of washout of N_2 may indicate a large FRC, a small tidal volume, a large dead space (poorly ventilated areas), or a slow rate of breathing.

Another application of the dilution principle is the closed-circuit helium method (Figure 27-13). The principle is the same as that of the N_2 washout technique, except that the helium is washed into the lungs. The subject breathes from a spirometer that contains a known volume of gas, V_1, and a known concentration of helium, C_1. After a few breaths, the He is diluted in the lungs (FRC), and a new concentration of He (C_2) is established. The O_2 consumed by the subject is replaced continuously to keep the volume in the canister of the spirometer constant during the procedure. As the initial amount of He, C_1V_1, has not changed, it is equal to the amount in the spirometer plus the amount in the lungs, $C_2(V_1 + V_2)$. Therefore:

$$C_1V_1 = C_2 (V_1 + V_2)$$

and from this equation, the volume of the lungs, V_2 can be calculated:

$$V_2 = V_1 (C_1 - C_2)/C_2$$

PLETHYSMOGRAPHY

Plethysmography measures all of the gas contained in the thorax, whether it is in communication with the airways or not. The subject sits in an airtight body box, the plethysmograph (Figure 27-14), and breathes the surrounding air. At a certain time, the subject is asked to inhale (or exhale) against a closed airway. The thoracic gas volume, which is equivalent to the FRC, may be calculated from the change of pressure that accompanies the change of volume, according to Boyle's law, which states that, at constant temperature, $P_1V_1 = P_2V_2$.

ALVEOLAR VENTILATION

The amount of air that one breathes in or out during 1 min depends on the depth of respiration—that is, the tidal volume—and the rate of breathing. This combination is known as the *total pulmonary ventilation,* or the *minute volume.* However, gas is exchanged only in the alveoli; therefore, the important part of ventilation is the alveolar ventilation, which is the volume of fresh air that reaches the alveoli with each breath (VA) or during one minute ($\dot{V}A$),

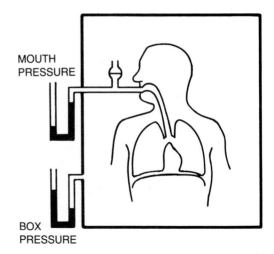

MOUTH PRESSURE

BOX PRESSURE

Figure 27-14. Body plethysmography. The plethysmograph, which can be used to measure functional residual capacity, is an airtight body box within which the subject sits or stands and breathes surrounding air. The volume of the box is constant; therefore, a change in the volume of gas in the thorax of the subject is accompanied by a corresponding change in the pressure within the box. The airway pressure (alveolar pressure) of the subject is measured at the mouth, while the subject is expanding or compressing the thorax (attempting to breathe) against a closed shutter that is triggered electrically. Assuming that the temperature is constant, the thoracic gas volume (FRC), can be calculated by applying Boyle's law, $P_1V_1 = P_2V_2$, where P_1 is the initial pulmonic pressure (atmospheric), V_1 is the initial lung volume (FRC) that is to be calculated, and P_2 is the intrapulmonic pressure that corresponds to the new lung volume, V_2. Neither V_1 nor V_2 is known, but the difference between them, ΔV, can be calculated from the change of pressure produced in the box by change of the volume of the thorax (which either compresses or expands the air in the box, depending on whether the subject inhales or exhales). The change of pressure per unit change of volume in the box is determined by introducing a known volume of air into the box and noting the change of pressure. Since the change of pressure in the lungs, ΔP, is known, one can use the expression

$$V_1\Delta P = P_2\Delta V,$$

which becomes

$$V_1 = P_2\Delta V/\Delta P = FRC$$

and which increases the arterial P_{O_2} and decreases the arterial P_{CO_2}. Alveolar ventilation always is less than total ventilation; the magnitude of the difference depends on tidal volume, dead space, and respiratory rate.

Dead Space

Dead space (V_D) may be defined as that portion of the inspired air that does not participate in gas exchange, either because it never reaches the alveoli or because the characteristics of the alveoli that contain it do not permit exchange.

ANATOMICAL DEAD SPACE
The volume of the conducting airways, which extend from the nose and mouth to the alveoli, represents the anatomical dead space. It is a morphological measurement that reflects the lack of a membrane across which gases can exchange, and it varies among individuals, depending on age, sex, activity, and lung volume. For a healthy, young, adult human, the volume of the anatomical dead space is estimated to be 1 ml for each pound of body weight. It increases with age and may be higher in subjects who have large tidal volumes, because of the expansion of the airways; this occurs during exercise. On the other hand, removal of any part of the conducting airways will reduce the volume of the anatomical dead space.

PHYSIOLOGICAL DEAD SPACE
The portion of the alveolar ventilation that cannot exchange with the blood because no blood reaches certain alveoli or because ventilation exceeds blood flow is known as the physiological dead space. This is a functional measurement that also includes the anatomical dead space. In a healthy person, the anatomical dead space and the physiological dead space are the same or nearly the same. In pulmonary disease, however, when air is trapped in the lungs, the physiological dead space may be significantly larger than the anatomical dead space.

CALCULATION
V_D can be calculated if the volume of expired gas (the tidal volume, or V_T), the partial pressure of CO_2 in the arterial blood (Pa_{CO_2}), and the partial pressure of CO_2 in the expired air (PE_{CO_2}) are known:

$$V_D = V_T \times \frac{Pa_{CO_2} - PE_{CO_2}}{Pa_{CO_2}} \text{ (Bohr equation)}$$

The measurement is based on the assumption that expired air is composed partly of the air that filled the dead space (which has the same composition as inspired air) and partly of al-

veolar air. Therefore, if the inspired air contains no CO_2, all of the CO_2 in the expired air must come from perfused alveoli. Essentially, the volume of the lung that does not eliminate CO_2 is measured. Arterial P_{CO_2} (Pa_{CO_2}) is used in the equation instead of alveolar P_{CO_2} (PA_{CO_2}) because PA_{CO_2} is more difficult to determine; the use is justified, because Pa_{CO_2} is in equilibrium with PA_{CO_2}.

Assessment of Alveolar Ventilation

A certain amount of alveolar ventilation ($\dot{V}_A$) is necessary to supply the O_2 that is consumed and to eliminate the CO_2 that is produced by the tissues. The average amount of O_2 consumed by a healthy young adult who weighs 70 kg and is at rest is 250 ml/min. The concentration of O_2 in ambient air is 20.93%; therefore, each 100 ml of inspired air contains approximately 21 ml of O_2. However, each 100 ml of expired air still contains 15 ml of O_2. To supply the 250 ml of O_2 used by a resting person during each minute, the alveolar ventilation must be at least

$$(250 \text{ ml } O_2/\text{min}) / (6 \text{ ml } O_2/100 \text{ ml air}) = 4200 \text{ ml air/min}$$

$\dot{V}_A$ is determined by the metabolic activity of the individual, and any increased demand for oxygen can be satisfied, to some extent, by increasing the alveolar ventilation. In addition, the blood supply of each individual organ is related to the rate of metabolism, and when the rate of metabolism increases, the tissues extract more oxygen from each unit of blood.

Determination of $\dot{V}_A$

SPIROMETRY
Alveolar ventilation can be measured by spirometry and compared to standard values that depend on the age, sex, and size of the individual. If the tidal volume, V_T, and the rate of breathing, RR, are known, and an average dead space, V_D, of 1 ml/lb of body weight is estimated, alveolar ventilation is approximately as follows:

$$\dot{V}_A = (V_T - V_D) \times RR$$

Calculations made using this formula may be compared to standard values determined from a large number of measurements for age, sex, and size of the subject. If the dead space is

TABLE 27-1

Effect of an increased depth of breathing and
a constant anatomical dead space on calculated alveolar ventilation

	V_T (ml)	RR (breath/min)	$\dot{V}$ (ml/min)	$\dot{V}_A$	$\dfrac{V_D}{V_T}$ %
A	500	15	7500	5250	30
B	750	10	7500	6000	20
C	1500	5	7500	6750	10

assumed to be constant, the alveolar ventilation that is calculated increases with increasing tidal volumes, even though the minute ventilation, $\dot{V}$, remains unchanged (Table 27-1).

Since the alveolar ventilation is influenced by factors other than the need for oxygen, the measurement of air flow alone may not always assess the alveolar ventilation adequately. The distribution of the inspired air within the lungs, the distribution of blood flow to the ventilated alveoli, and the rate of diffusion of gases across the blood-gas barrier also are important determinants of alveolar ventilation. Although we are concerned with the actual volume of the gases exchanged across the alveolar-capillary membrane, the pressure exerted by these gases may be used to evaluate the efficiency of alveolar ventilation. The partial pressures of O_2 and CO_2 are relatively constant in alveolar air and in arterial and venous blood and can be used as indicators of alveolar ventilation.

CALCULATION

An O_2 tension of approximately 100 mm Hg and a CO_2 tension of 40 mm Hg in the alveoli are adequate for adding O_2 to the venous blood and removing CO_2. The rate of ventilation is regulated to maintain the alveolar gas tensions around these levels. Because variation in alveolar ventilation affects the arterial blood gas tensions, the P_{O_2} and P_{CO_2} of the arterial blood are useful indices with which to evaluate the effectiveness of alveolar ventilation.

Alveolar ventilation, $\dot{V}_A$, can be calculated by using the dilution principle: the amount of CO_2 expired ($\dot{V}_{E_{CO_2}}$) is divided by the concentration of CO_2 in the alveoli. According to the formula

$$\dot{V}_A \text{ (BTPS)} = \frac{\dot{V}_{E_{CO_2}} \text{ (STPD)}}{P_{a_{CO_2}}}$$
$$\times \ 0.863 \text{ mm Hg} \cdot \frac{\text{liter}}{\text{ml}}$$

where $P_{a_{CO_2}}$ again is used as a convenient

reflection of $P_{A_{CO_2}}$. The factor 0.863 mm Hg · liter/ml corrects the volume of gas from STPD to BTPS and converts $P_{a_{CO_2}}$, a partial pressure in millimeters of mercury, to a fraction of CO_2.

Changes in Alveolar Ventilation

HYPOVENTILATION

When alveolar ventilation does not supply O_2 at the rate it is needed nor eliminate CO_2 at the rate it is produced, the subject is hypoventilating. Since O_2 is being added to the alveoli at a lower rate than it is being removed by the pulmonary capillary blood, hypoventilation usually causes $P_{A_{O_2}}$ and $P_{a_{O_2}}$ to be lower than normal. Because of the shape of the oxyhemoglobin dissociation curve (see Chapter 31), the extent of saturation of the arterial blood with oxygen does not decrease as much as the P_{O_2} decreases unless hypoventilation is severe. However, hypoventilation always causes CO_2 to accumulate, which increases both the $P_{A_{CO_2}}$ and the $P_{a_{CO_2}}$ and causes respiratory acidosis (Figure 27-15). An arterial P_{CO_2} greater than 44 mm Hg usually indicates hypoventilation. The accumulation of CO_2, which is called hypercapnia, causes headache, somnolence, mental confusion, weakness, and irritability.

HYPERVENTILATION

When alveolar ventilation exceeds that which is needed to satisfy the metabolic demands for O_2 and to eliminate CO_2, the subject is hyperventilating. Hyperventilation lowers both the $P_{A_{CO_2}}$ and the $P_{a_{CO_2}}$, because CO_2 is eliminated at a faster rate than it is produced, which causes hypocapnia and respiratory alkalosis. The side effects of hypocapnia are headache, fatigue, numbness and tingling in the hands, feet, and lips, and the inability to concentrate.

Hyperventilation increases $P_{A_{O_2}}$ and $P_{a_{O_2}}$; however, because the arterial blood is almost fully saturated (97.4%) with O_2 during normal,

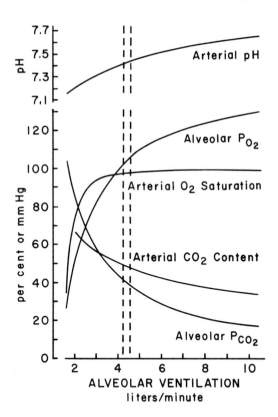

Figure 27-15. Relationships between alveolar ventilation and alveolar O_2 and CO_2 tensions; arterial blood O_2 saturation, CO_2 content, and pH. Broken vertical lines intercept curves in the physiological range of normal values. Oxygen consumption is assumed to be 250 ml/min. (Redrawn, with permission, from Comroe, J.H., Jr. et al. 1962. *The Lung: Clinical Physiology and Pulmonary Function Tests,* 2nd ed. Chicago: Year Book Medical Publishers, Inc.)

---

quiet breathing, the oxygenation of blood is not influenced significantly (see Figure 27-15). It is noteworthy that when hyperventilation follows an episode of hypoventilation, the Po_2 and the O_2 saturation of the arterial blood increase and Pa_{CO_2} decreases because of the improved ventilation.

Alveolar Gas Tensions

During respiration, normal ventilation replaces the O_2 that is used by the tissues (removed from the blood) and eliminates the CO_2 that is added to the blood; in this way it maintains the alveolar Po_2 and Pco_2 at optimal levels. The alveolar gas tensions fluctuate during the respiratory cycle, however. During expiration, be-

cause of the continuous removal of O_2 and addition of CO_2 by the blood that flows through the pulmonary capillaries, the Pa_{O_2} decreases and the Pa_{CO_2} increases. At the onset of inspiration the alveolar Po_2 continues to fall and the Pa_{CO_2} continues to rise because the air that reaches the alveoli first has the same composition as that of the alveolar air at the end of expiration; it is that portion of the tidal volume that is contained in the conducting airways (anatomical dead space). When "fresh" air, which has a high Po_2 and negligible Pco_2, reaches the alveoli, Po_2 increases and Pco_2 decreases sharply.

Alveolar Gas Equation

The Po_2 of alveolar gas is less than that of moist tracheal air, because O_2 is being removed continuously from the alveolar gas. The Pa_{O_2} is a balance between the supply of O_2 and the removal of O_2. Knowledge of the Pa_{O_2} is useful for assessing the alveolar ventilation; it may be obtained by using the alveolar gas equation:

$$Pa_{O_2} = Pi_{O_2} - Pa_{CO_2}\left[Fi_{O_2} + \frac{1 - Fi_{O_2}}{R}\right]$$

The expression contained within the brackets is a correction factor in which Fi_{O_2} is the fraction of O_2 in the inspired air and R is the respiratory exchange ratio (see the discussion that follows). The removal of O_2 from the alveoli is relatively difficult to measure; therefore, it is calculated by making use of the fact that the consumption of O_2 is nearly equal to the production of CO_2 and is relatively constant at rest. When the consumption of O_2 equals the production of CO_2, the respiratory quotient (RQ), which is the ratio $\dot{V}_{CO_2}/\dot{V}_{O_2}$, is 1.0. Because O_2 and CO_2 exchange for one another across the alveolar membrane, R, the respiratory exchange ratio, also is 1.0, and the amount of O_2 that is removed equals $Pa_{CO_2} \times 1 \simeq 40$ mm Hg. Therefore,

$$Pa_{O_2} = Pi_{O_2} - Pa_{CO_2}$$
$$= [149 \text{ mm Hg} - 40 \text{ mm Hg}]$$
$$= 109 \text{ mm Hg}$$

If R = 0.8, the correction fraction within the bracket in the alveolar gas equation becomes 1.2, and $Pa_{O_2} = Pi_{O_2} - (Pa_{CO_2} \times 1.2) = 149$ mm Hg $-$ (40 mm Hg $\times$ 1.2) = 149 mm Hg $-$ 48 mm Hg = 101 mm Hg. Therefore, if a person breathes air at sea level, the normal Pa_{O_2}

ranges from 101–109 mm Hg, depending on the value of R, and ultimately, on the value of RQ. The alveolar gas equation is based on the assumption that, under steady-state conditions, the sum of the fractions of oxygen, nitrogen, and carbon dioxide in dry alveolar gas must be 1.0.

Because the alveolar Po_2 is related to the Po_2 of the inspired air, the alveolar Po_2 decreases when the Po_2 of the inspired air decreases, and the rate at which O_2 is added to the blood decreases because the gradient for diffusion decreases. At the same time, however, the tissues continue to extract O_2 from the capillary blood at the same rate, which increases slightly the difference between the alveolar Po_2 and the venous Po_2; therefore, the gradient for diffusion increases slightly, and the rate of diffusion of oxygen across the alveolar-capillary membrane increases slightly.

Respiratory Quotient and Respiratory Exchange Ratio

The respiratory quotient (RQ) is obtained as follows:

$$RQ = \frac{CO_2 \text{ production, ml/min}}{O_2 \text{ consumption, ml/min}}$$

RQ and the respiratory exchange ratio (R) often are used interchangeably in respiratory calculations. Customarily, RQ is used in connection with oxidative metabolism and is related closely to the diet; it varies from a value of 1, when the diet consists only of carbohydrates, to 0.7, when the diet consists only of fats. The mean RQ of an individual who is taking an average mixed diet, which consists of carbohydrates, fats, and proteins, is 0.8. This individual produces 200 ml of CO_2 for every 250 ml of O_2 consumed each minute.

The respiratory exchange ratio (R) expresses the relative rates of transfer of respiratory gases across the alveolar-capillary membrane.

$$R = \frac{CO_2 \text{ transfer, ml/min}}{O_2 \text{ transfer, ml/min}}$$

Since the CO_2 produced and the O_2 consumed eventually diffuse across the blood-gas barrier, RQ eventually becomes identical to R.

STUDY OUTLINE

OVERVIEW Function of respiratory system is to supply oxygen and eliminate carbon dioxide.

Pulmonary gas exchange involves ventilation, diffusion, pulmonary capillary blood flow, and work.

FUNCTIONAL ANATOMY

PLEURAE Parietal pleura lines the thoracic cavity.

Visceral pleura covers lungs.

Pleural cavity is potential space between pleurae.

AIR PASSAGES 23 generations of airways.

NASAL PASSAGES Function: filter.

MOUTH AND LARYNX Mouth serves primarily for speech.

Larynx acts as a valve.

CONDUCTING AIRWAYS Consist of first 16 generations of airways.

Volume approximately 150 ml.

TRACHEA Kept open by rings of horseshoe-shaped cartilage connected by smooth muscle.

Lined with ciliated respiratory epithelium.

Mucociliary escalator removes small particles from airways.

Warms and humidifies inspired air.

BRONCHI Two main bronchi branch into lobar and then into segmented bronchi until diameter is less than 2 mm.

Smallest bronchi contain less cartilage and fewer mucous glands.

BRONCHIOLES Eleventh through sixteenth generations of airways.

Cartilage disappears; more smooth muscle.

Terminal bronchioles are last generation of conductive airways; less than 0.5 mm in diameter.

Alveolar macrophages take care of internal drainage.

RESPIRATORY AIRWAYS Generation 17 through 23.

Function: gas exchange.

Volume: approximately 2500 ml.

PRIMARY LOBULE Basic respiratory unit consists of respiratory bronchioles with alveolar ducts and alveolar sacs.

Respiratory bronchioles represent transition between conductive and respiratory function.

ALVEOLI   Smallest units for gas exchange.

BLOOD-GAS INTERFACE   Alveoli surrounded by capillaries.

Gas is exchanged across blood-gas barrier: layer of surfactant, alveolar epithelium, interstitial space, capillary endothelium, blood plasma, and red cell membrane.

BLOOD SUPPLY

PULMONARY CIRCULATION   Provides continuous flow of mixed venous blood for exchange of oxygen and carbon dioxide across alveolar-capillary membrane.

Supplies metabolic needs of respiratory zone.

Serves as filter for systemic circulation.

Serves as reservoir for left ventricle.

A site of chemical activation and deactivation of substances.

BRONCHIAL CIRCULATION   Supplies blood and substrates to tissues of conducting airways.

NERVE SUPPLY   Smooth muscle is innervated by autonomic nervous system.

Parasympathetic fibers cause bronchial constriction.

Sympathetic fibers cause bronchial dilatation.

PHYSICAL BEHAVIOR OF GASES

GAS LAWS
BOYLE'S LAW $P_1V_1 = P_2V_2$ at a constant temperature.
CHARLES' LAW $V_1/V_2 = T_1/T_2$ at a constant pressure.

CORRECTION OF GAS VOLUMES   Gas is collected in spirometer under ambient conditions (ATPS).

Lung gas volumes are expressed at body conditions (BTPS).

Blood gas volumes are expressed at standard conditions (STPD).

PARTIAL PRESSURE   Total pressure of gases in air at sea level is 1 atmosphere, or 760 mm Hg.

DALTON'S LAW   Pressure (P) exerted by each individual gas (G) in air is called partial pressure (P_G).

P_G is related to concentration of that gas in mixture. In air, at sea level:
   a. $P_{O_2} = 760$ mm Hg $\times 0.2093 = 159$ mm Hg.
   b. $P_{N_2} = 760$ mm Hg $\times 0.7903 = 600.6$ mm Hg.
   c. $P_{CO_2} = 760$ mm Hg $\times 0.0004 = 0.3$ mm Hg.

Inspired air is warmed and saturated with water vapor by time it reaches alveoli.

At 37 C (BTPS) vapor pressure of water is 47 mm Hg; part of total pressure (760 mm Hg at sea level).

Total pressure of dry gases in moist tracheal air is 760 mm Hg − 47 mm Hg, or 713 mm Hg (at sea level).

P_{O_2} of moist tracheal air is (760 mm Hg − 47 mm Hg) $\times 0.2093 \times 149$ mm Hg.

P_{O_2} of moist tracheal air when breathing 100% O_2 is (760 mm Hg − 47 mm Hg) $\times 1.00 = 713$ mm Hg.

PARTIAL PRESSURE OF A GAS IN A LIQUID O_2, CO_2, and N_2 are dissolved in body fluids.

Amount of gas dissolved is related to pressure and solubility.

P_{O_2}, P_{CO_2}, and P_{N_2} in blood are related directly to volume of each gas dissolved and inversely to solubility coefficient.

LUNG VOLUMES AND THEIR MEASUREMENT

VOLUMES   Four primary lung volumes: tidal volume (TV), inspiratory reserve volume (IRV), expiratory reserve volume (ERV), and residual volume (RV).

CAPACITIES   Total lung capacity (TLC): sum of TV, IRV, ERV, and RV.

Vital capacity (VC) = TLC − RV.

Inspiratory capacity (IC) = IRV + TV.

Functional residual capacity (FRC) = ERV + RV.

MEASUREMENT
SPIROMETRY   Measures only volume of air moved into or out of lungs.
   Cannot measure RV.
PNEUMOTACHOMETRY   Measures rate of flow of air.
   TV, ERV, IRV may be calculated.
GAS DILUTION   Application of indicator-dilution principle.
   Measures RV and capacities that include RV (TLC, FRC).
   Nitrogen "wash-out": open circuit.
   Helium: closed circuit.
PLETHYSMOGRAPHY   Body box; measures all air contained in thorax.
   Used to measure FRC.

ALVEOLAR VENTILATION   Minute volume or total pulmonary ventilation = TV $\times$ rate of breathing.

Alveolar ventilation: that part of inspired air that exchanges with pulmonary capillary blood.

Alveolar ventilation always is less than total ventilation; difference is volume of nonexchangeable air, or dead space.

DEAD SPACE   Volume of inspired air that does not participate in gas exchange.

ANATOMICAL DEAD SPACE   Volume of conducting airways.

Rule of thumb estimate: 1 ml/lb body weight.

PHYSIOLOGICAL DEAD SPACE   Functional measurement; includes anatomical dead space.

Volume of lung that does not eliminate CO_2.

CALCULATION   Bohr equation for calculating physiological dead space.

ASSESSMENT OF ALVEOLAR VENTILATION ($\dot{V}A$) $\dot{V}A$ determined by metabolic activity.

At rest, O_2 consumption 250 ml/min: $\dot{V}A$ at least 4200 ml air/min.

DETERMINATION OF $\dot{V}A$

SPIROMETRY $\dot{V}A = (TV - \text{dead space}) \times$ rate of breathing.

Assuming constant anatomical dead space, $\dot{V}A$ increases with increase in TV, even if total ventilation remains same.

CALCULATION $\dot{V}A$ calculated from $PaCO_2$ and $VeCO_2$: assumed all of expired CO_2 comes from alveolar air in equilibrium with arterial CO_2.

CHANGES IN ALVEOLAR VENTILATION

HYPOVENTILATION   Alveolar ventilation does not satisfy O_2 uptake and CO_2 elimination.

PaO_2 and $PaO_2 <$ normal.

$PaCO_2$ and $PaCO_2 >$ normal; i.e., hypercapnia and respiratory acidosis.

HYPERVENTILATION   Alveolar ventilation $>$ need for O_2 uptake and CO_2 elimination.

$PaCO_2$ and $PaCO_2 <$ normal; i.e. hypocapnia and respiratory alkalosis.

ALVEOLAR GAS TENSIONS   Normal alveolar O_2 tension about 100 mm Hg.

Normal alveolar CO_2 tension about 40 mm Hg.

Ventilation regulated to maintain alveolar gas tensions around normal levels.

ALVEOLAR GAS EQUATION PaO_2 useful for assessing alveolar ventilation.

PaO_2 related directly to PiO_2.

Po_2 of alveolar air less than that of moist tracheal air because O_2 continuously taken up by blood.

If rate of O_2 exchange same as rate of CO_2 exchange, i.e., $R = 1$, $PaO_2 = PiO_2 - PaCO_2$.

RESPIRATORY QUOTIENT AND RESPIRATORY EXCHANGE RATIO ($RQ = \dot{V}eCO_2/\dot{V}o_2$; related closely to diet.

R expresses relative rates of transfer of respiratory gases across blood-gas barrier:

$$R = (CO_2 \text{ transfer/min})/O_2 \text{ transfer/min})$$

RQ eventually equal to R.

BIBLIOGRAPHY

Comroe, J.H. 1974. *Physiology of respiration.* Chicago: Year Book Medical Publishers.

Comroe, J.H., Jr.; Forster, R.E., II; Dubois, A.B., et al. 1962. *The lung: clinical physiology and pulmonary function tests,* 2nd ed. Chicago: Year Book Medical Publishers.

Crapo, R.O.; Morris, A.H.; and Gardner, R.M. 1981. Reference spirometric values using techniques and equipment that meet ATS recommendations. *Am. Rev. Resp. Dis.* 123:659.

DuBois, A.B.; Botelho, S.Y.; Bedell, G.N., et al. 1956. A rapid plethysmographic method for measuring thoracic gas volume: a comparison with a nitrogen washout method for measuring functional residual capacity in normal subjects. *J. Clin. Invest.* 35:322.

Fowler, W.S. 1948. Lung function studies. II. The respiratory dead space. *Am. J. Physiol.* 154:405.

Krahl, V.E. 1961. The lung. In *Encyclopedia of the Biological Sciences,* editor P. Gray. London: Chapman & Hall, Ltd.

Norris, A.H.; Shock, N.W.; Landowne, M., et al. 1956. Pulmonary function studies: Age differences in lung volumes and bellows action. *J. Gerontol.* II: 379.

Proctor, D.F. 1964. Physiology of the upper airway. In *Handbook of physiology,* Section 3, Respiration, Vol. I, editors W.D. Fenn and H. Rahn. Washington, D.C.: American Physiological Society.

Radford, E.P., Jr. 1964. The physics of gases. In *Handbook of physiology,* Section 3, Respiration, Vol. I, editors W.D. Fenn and H. Rahn. Washington, D.C.: American Physiological Society.

Slonim, N.B., and Hamilton, L.H. 1981. *Respiratory physiology,* 4th ed. St. Louis: The C.V. Mosby Co.

Weibel, E.R. 1963. *Morphometry of the human lung.* Berlin: Springer-Verlag.

West, J.B. 1979. *Respiratory physiology: the essentials.* Baltimore: Williams & Wilkins Co.

West, J.B. 1982. *Pulmonary pathophysiology: the essentials,* 2nd ed. Baltimore: Williams & Wilkins Co.

28

The Mechanical
Aspects of Respiration

CHAPTER CONTENTS

MECHANICAL FACTORS

The principles that apply to the dynamics of blood flow also apply to the dynamics of air flow. Air flows into and out of the lung along a gradient of pressure and against resistance. The *forces* and *resistances* that determine the flow of gases into and out of the lungs constitute the mechanical factors of breathing.

Inspiration is an active process, as it requires the contraction of the inspiratory muscles. These muscles provide the forces necessary to overcome the elastic resistances of the lungs and the chest, the frictional resistance that develops during the movement of the lungs and the chest, and the frictional resistance to the flow of air through the respiratory apparatus.

Expiration normally is a passive process, as it uses potential energy that is stored in the elastic tissues of the lungs and the thorax during inspiration. The structures stretched by the contraction of the muscles of inspiration recoil when these muscles relax; the alveolar pressure increases, and air is exhaled. Active contraction of the expiratory muscles may be required in special circumstances and when ventilation is increased abnormally.

TABLE 28-1

Major muscles of respiration

Inspiratory	Expiratory
Diaphragm	Abdominal muscles
External intercostal muscles	External oblique
	Internal oblique
Accessory muscles of inspiration	Rectus abdominis
Sternocleidomastoid	Transversus abdominis
Anterior serrati	Internal intercostal muscles
Scalene	Diaphragm

FORCES

Although ventilation is a cyclic process, the muscles of respiration are skeletal muscles and must be stimulated to contract. The cyclic activity is generated by groups of neurons in the respiratory centers, and the impulses sent to the specific muscles come from the spinal cord via motor neurons of the anterior horn cells.

Table 28-1 lists the major muscles of respiration.

Muscles of Inspiration

The respiratory muscles that elevate and enlarge the chest cage when they contract are called the muscles of inspiration (Figure 28-1).

The *diaphragm,* which is the major muscle of inspiration, is a muscular partition that separates the thoracic cavity from the abdominal cavity. It is dome-shaped during expiration, when it is relaxed; during inspiration, when it contracts, it flattens out and is pulled downward. The movements of the diaphragm during the different phases of respiration have been compared to the movements of a piston in a cylinder; down in inspiration, to increase the volume of the thorax, and up in expiration, to decrease the volume of the thorax. Normal quiet breathing can be accomplished by the movement of the diaphragm alone; however, unless the other muscles of inspiration are paralyzed or the thorax becomes rigid and immobile, the diaphragm is not essential for ven-

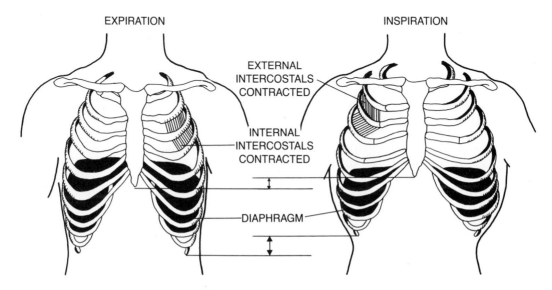

Figure 28-1.   The major muscles involved in expanding and contracting the thorax during inspiration and expiration. Contraction of the dia-phragm during inspiration increases both vertical and anteroposterior dimensions of the chest.

CLINICAL CORRELATION
28.1   Hypoventilation

CASE REPORT

The Patient: A 67-year-old woman.

Principal Complaint: Dyspnea.

History: The patient had difficulty breathing, especially when she was walking, even for only a short distance. She was slightly overweight and had been told earlier that she had emphysema.

Clinical Examination: The patient's heart rate was 86 beats/min (normal, 60-100 beats/min), her arterial pressure was 128/72 mm Hg (normal, 90-140/60-90 mm Hg), and her frequency of respiration was 24 breaths/min (normal, 13-17 breaths/min). A chest x-ray film showed that both hemidiaphragms (halves of the diaphragm) were greatly elevated (contracting poorly), and diaphragmatic movements during ventilation were minimal. Her serum [HCO_3^-] was 38 mEq/liter

(normal, 24-30 mEq/liter), arterial P_{O_2} (Pa_{O_2}) was 60 mm Hg (normal, 75-100 mm Hg), arterial P_{CO_2} (Pa_{CO_2}) was 69 mm Hg (normal, 35-45 mm Hg), and the pH of her arterial blood was 7.33 (normal, 7.35-7.45). She was asked to hyperventilate for several minutes to see whether her arterial P_{CO_2} could be decreased.* She tried hard to do this by using her accessory muscles of respiration to full extent; however, the Pa_{CO_2} was decreased by only 25% (to 51 mm Hg). Pulmonary function tests gave the following results:

FEV_1	= 1240 ml (48% of predicted)
FVC	= 1400 ml (40% of predicted)
FEV_1/FVC	
	= 89% (normal, >84%)
FRC	= 1850 ml (58% of predicted)
RV	= 1100 ml (65% of predicted)
TLC	= 2460 ml (50% of predicted)
MVV	= 52 liter/min (56% of predicted)

tilation. A paralyzed diaphragm moves up instead of down during inspiration; this is called the paradoxical movement of the diaphragm and may be detected by a deliberate, rapid inspiration, the so-called "sniff test." The reason for the paradoxical movement is that during inspiration, when the chest enlarges, the relaxed diaphragm is pushed upward by atmospheric pressure. The diaphragm is innervated by the phrenic nerves, which leave the anterior root at the third to the fifth cervical segments of the spinal cord.

The *external intercostal muscles* connect the ribs and, when they contract, pull the ribs upward and outward, increasing the lateral, or anteroposterior, dimension of the chest. At the same time, the ventral ends of the ribs move ventrocranially, also elevating the rib cage. Contraction of the external intercostal muscles also increases the stiffness of the tissues within the intercostal spaces and keeps them from

being pushed inward by atmospheric pressure during inspiration. The intercostal muscles are innervated by the intercostal nerves, which emerge from the spinal cord between the first and the eleventh thoracic segments.

Muscles of Expiration

The major muscles of expiration are the muscles of the abdominal wall, which are the *internal oblique, external oblique, transversus abdominis*, and *rectus abdominis* (see Table 28-1). When these muscles contract, the abdominal contents are depressed, intraabdominal pressure increases, the diaphragm is pushed up, and the volume of the chest is reduced. These muscles normally are not necessary for quiet expiration and usually are activated only when ventilation exceeds 40 liters/min; they contract vigorously when the rate of ventilation reaches 70-90 liters/min. The abdominal muscles are

(CLINICAL CORRELATION continued)

Comment: Low Pa_{O_2} and high Pa_{CO_2}, together with significant reductions of all lung volumes, indicate severe alveolar hypoventilation. Neither emphysema nor any other lung disease was apparent. The almost total absence of diaphragmatic movement during ventilation was associated with neuromuscular weakness. This conclusion was reinforced by greatly reduced maximum static inspiratory (25% of normal) and expiratory (35% of normal) pressures** (see Figure 28-4); these reductions indicate impairment of the respiratory pump. The chronically high Pa_{CO_2} was balanced by the high level of serum bicarbonate; hence, the arterial pH was almost within normal limits. Neurological examination and electromyograms revealed diffuse muscular fasciculation, general muscular weakness, and some atrophy, but no sensory or cerebellar changes. A clinical diagnosis of amyotrophic lateral sclerosis was made. Amyotrophic lateral sclerosis is a progressive degenerative disorder of motor neurons in the cerebral cortex, brainstem, and spinal cord. The disease usually appears in the sixth or seventh decade of the patient's life.

Treatment: No treatment is known for this or any other form of motor system disease.

Outcome: The patient's prognosis is poor. Muscular weakness usually progresses to failure of the respiratory muscles and death within about two to eight years from the onset of the disease.

*Voluntary hyperventilation is a test for patients who exhibit significant alveolar hypoventilation and retention of CO_2. It is used to determine whether the hypoventilation is caused by abnormal lung or chest mechanics or, in the absence of inherent abnormalities, by decreased sensitivity of the respiratory centers to CO_2. The latter condition is rare and usually is referred to as central, or primary, alveolar hypoventilation. Voluntary hyperventilation can lower the Pa_{CO_2} of these patients to normal values.

**The maximum reduction of intra-alveolar pressure that can be developed by maximum contraction of the muscles of inspiration (beginning from maximum expiration) is approximately 80 mm Hg below atmospheric pressure. The maximum increase of intra-alveolar pressure that can be developed by maximum contraction of the muscles of expiration (beginning from maximum inspiration) is approximately 100 mm Hg. These pressures, which are developed during static maneuvers, are expressions of the strength of the respiratory muscles (see Figure 28-4).

used during speech, singing, and straining; they are absolutely necessary for all expiratory efforts that require strong expulsive pressures or air flow of high velocity, such as sneezing or coughing. The abdominal muscles are inactivated early during anesthesia, making active expiration impossible; however, this is important only in patients who must exhale actively because of narrowing of the airway during expiration. These muscles are innervated by nerve fibers that arise from the six lower thoracic and five lumbar segments of the spinal cord.

The *internal intercostal* muscles contract during expiration, pulling the ribs downward and inward, thereby compressing the chest cage (Figure 28-1); they also stiffen the intercostal space and prevent bulging during coughing. In addition to the expiratory muscles listed previously, the *diaphragm* still is active during the early part of expiration and is

thought to smooth the beginning of expiration by preventing abrupt change in the size of the chest.

Pressures in Chest and Lungs

Figure 28-2 illustrates the normal pressures in and around the lungs, and Table 28-2 lists their definitions.

NEGATIVE-PRESSURE BREATHING

For air to enter the lungs, the pressure in the alveoli must be less than that at the mouth. During normal quiet inspiration, the pressure at the mouth is equal to atmospheric pressure, and the pressure in the alveoli is less than atmospheric. Normal breathing, which lowers all intrathoracic pressures during inspiration, usually is referred to as *negative-pressure breathing*. Subatmospheric intrathoracic pressure brings

FORCES AT REST

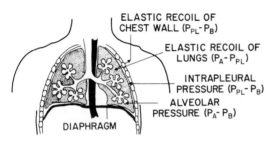

ELASTIC RECOIL OF
CHEST WALL ($P_{PL} - P_B$)

ELASTIC RECOIL OF
LUNGS ($P_A - P_{PL}$)

INTRAPLEURAL
PRESSURE ($P_{PL} - P_B$)

ALVEOLAR
PRESSURE ($P_A - P_B$)

DIAPHRAGM

Figure 28-2. Pressures in and around the lungs (for definitions see Table 28-2). At resting lung volume, or FRC, the elastic recoil force of the chest equals the elastic recoil force of the lungs but is opposite in direction, alveolar pressure (P_A) is equal to atmospheric pressure, and average intrapleural pressure (P_{PL}) is about 5 mm Hg less than atmospheric pressure.

air into the lungs and facilitates the flow of venous blood into the right side of the heart.

POSITIVE-PRESSURE BREATHING

Artificial respiration may be used when the muscles of inspiration are inactive or their efforts are inadequate. The air pressure in the mouth is made greater than that in the alveoli, and air flows in; this is referred to as *positive-pressure* breathing.

Positive-pressure breathing increases all intrathoracic pressures. In the circulation, this effect impedes the flow of venous blood into the right atrium; if the positive pressure in the chest is excessive, blood vessels may be compressed, and the resistance to pulmonary blood flow increases. The *Valsalva maneuver,* which consists of maximal expiratory effort against a closed glottis, increases the intrapleural and intra-alveolar pressures; however, because the *difference* between intrapleural pressure and intra-alveolar pressure does not change, the alveoli are not stressed. The main effect is on the circulation (see Chapter 17).

PRESSURE-VOLUME CHANGES DURING BREATHING

Figure 28-3 illustrates the pressures and the corresponding changes of volume that occur during a normal cycle of breathing. The changes in volume are measured by a spirometer to which the subject is connected. Intrapleural pressure is measured most frequently by an intraesophageal balloon. The subject swallows a thin tube that has a long balloon at the tip, which is situated in the middle third of the esophagus. The esophagus is located in the thorax, between the lungs and the chest wall; since it is a nonrigid structure, the pressure within it is nearly the same as the intrapleural

TABLE 28-2
Pressures in and around lungs when chest is in resting position

Pressure	Definition
Intra-alveolar Pressure (P_A)	Also known as intrapulmonary, or intrapulmonic, pressure, is the pressure within the alveoli. When the glottis is open and no air is flowing ($P_A - P_B = O$), P_A is the same as ambient pressure (P_B).
Intrapleural Pressure (P_{PL})	The pressure within the potential space between the two pleurae. Normally, because of the tendency of the lungs to pull away from the chest wall, it is about 5 cm H_2O less than ambient pressure and is expressed in negative units (-5 cm H_2O).
Elastic Recoil Pressure	The pressure caused by the elastic properties of the lungs. It is related to the wall tension that must be overcome to stretch the lungs during inspiration. Normally, at the resting lung volume, it is approximately 5 cm H_2O.
Transpulmonary Pressure	The difference of pressure between the inside and the outside of the alveoli ($P_A - P_{PL}$); it is a transmural pressure. With the lungs at FRC, P_A is atmospheric; therefore, the transpulmonary pressure equals the intrapleural pressure. The transpulmonary pressure conventionally is expressed in positive units.
Transthoracic Pressure	The difference of pressure across the chest wall, between the intrapleural space and the atmosphere.

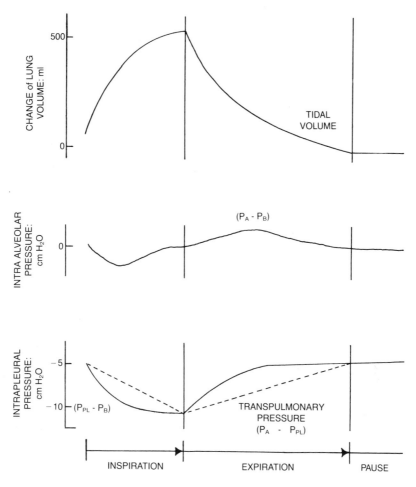

Figure 28-3. Change of volume and pressure in and around the lungs during one cycle of breath-ing. PA: intra-alveolar pressure; PB: atmospheric pressure; PPL: intrapleural pressure.

pressure. In humans, the intraesophageal pressure gives the most practical estimate of the intrapleural pressure.

Note in Figure 28-3 that the intra-alveolar pressure is zero (equal to atmospheric pressure), and the intrapleural pressure is 5 cm H_2O less than atmospheric pressure (-5 cm H_2O) at the beginning of inspiration, when the glottis is open, no air is flowing, and the volume of the lungs is at FRC. Then, as the muscles of inspiration contract, the chest expands, and the intrapleural pressure decreases further, from -5 to -10 cm H_2O. The lungs follow the chest, and in the process, the alveoli, alveolar ducts, and bronchioles also expand. As the volume of gas that occupies the alveoli increases, the intra-alveolar pressure falls below atmospheric, a gradient of pressure is set up, and ambient air

flows into the lungs through the nose and the mouth. At the end of inspiration, when flow is zero again, the volume of the lungs has increased by the amount of the tidal volume (500 ml). Intra-alveolar pressure is equal to atmospheric pressure again, and intrapleural pressure is decreased maximally (-10 cm H_2O).

The transpulmonary pressure, which follows the change of intrapleural pressure and is shown by the dashed line in Figure 28-3, represents the force needed to stretch the elastic lungs. The change of intrapleural pressure represents the total force that must be developed to overcome both the elastic resistance of the lungs and the frictional resistance to the flow of air during inspiration; the area between these two pressure lines represents the change of pressure that was required to overcome the airway resistance. The potential energy stored in the stretched lungs during inspiration is released during expiration, alveolar pressure exceeds atmospheric pressure, and air flows out of the lungs. At any time during the cycle, the difference between the intrapleural pressure and the transpulmonary pressure is the alveolar pressure.

MAXIMUM PRESSURES

Figure 28-4 shows the maximum pressures that can be generated by contracting the muscles of respiration during inspiration and expiration. The maximum decrease of intrapulmonary pressure that can be developed by inspiration against a closed airway, beginning from maximum expiration, is about 90 cm H_2O less than atmospheric pressure; the maximum increase of in-

trapulmonary pressure that can be developed by expiration against a closed airway, beginning from maximum inspiration, is about 120 cm H_2O. These extreme values are dangerous if maintained, since very low intrapulmonary pressure may cause the capillaries to hemorrhage, and very high intrapulmonary pressure may cause the lungs to rupture. The relaxation pressure curve in Figure 28-4 indicates the safe range of pressure, which is between –20 and +30 cm H_2O and which can be developed during normal passive inflation and deflation of the lungs. A certain volume of gas is inhaled from a spirometer, the valve is closed, the chest is relaxed (hence, relaxation curve), and the pressure in the airways is measured. At the normal resting position of the lung-chest unit (FRC), intra-alveolar pressure is the same as ambient pressure.

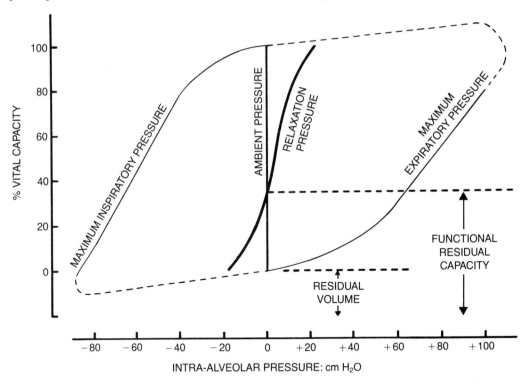

Figure 28-4. Relationship between intra-alveolar pressure and lung volume. Lung volume is expressed as percentage change of vital capacity beginning from 0%, or residual volume. The relaxation pressure curve reflects the elastic properties of the lung–chest wall unit. The curve is developed by inhaling a certain volume of air, holding the air while relaxing the chest muscles, and measuring the pressure at the mouth. The maximum pressures are those that can be developed by the muscles of respiration during (a) inspiration against a closed glottis beginning from the residual volume (point of maximal expiration) and (b) expiration against a closed glottis beginning from full inspiration. Air flows into or out of the lungs along the maximum pressure curves. The broken lines that connect the maximum pressure curves indicate danger zones. In the upper right corner there is danger of lung rupture, and in the lower left corner there is danger of capillary hemorrhage. (Redrawn, with permission, from Rahn, H., et al. *Am. J. Physiol.* 146:164. Copyright 1946, American Physiological Society.)

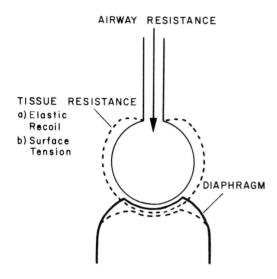

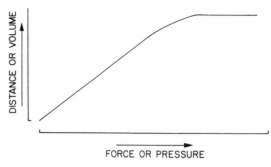

Figure 28-6. Force-distance (pressure-volume) relationship for an elastic system. The slope of the line reflects the compliance of the system.

Figure 28-5. Resistances in the respiratory system. Pulmonary resistance has a tissue resistance component and an airway resistance component. Because the lungs contain elastic fibers, and because tension develops at the liquid-gas interface, the lung tissues resist stretch (tissue resistance). Airway resistance develops during the flow of air into and out of the lungs.

RESISTANCES

The forces generated by the contraction of the muscles of respiration are opposed by the forces of resistance. There are two components of resistance to breathing: *tissue resistance* and *airway resistance* (Figure 28-5).

Tissue Resistance

Tissue resistance is influenced by three factors: (1) the *elastic* recoil properties of the respiratory tissue, or *true elastic resistance*; (2) the *recoil* of the lung due to *surface tension,* which is considered to be part of the elastic resistance; and (3) the *viscous resistance,* which is encountered during movement of the lung and the chest.

ELASTIC RESISTANCE OF LUNGS
Elasticity is that property that tends to return matter to its original or resting state after deformation by some external force. The elastic properties of the lungs and thorax are due mainly to the histologically identifiable elastic fibers of these structures, but all other tissues of the respiratory apparatus also contribute. Lung tissue, because of its elastic nature, behaves to some extent as a spring would; it stretches when

it is pulled by a force. Up to a certain point, the relationship between the force of the pull on the spring and the distance of the stretch is linear. In a lung, the pressure represents the force and the volume represents the stretch; hence, the pressure-volume relationship expresses the distensibility of the system (Figure 28-6). In a highly distensible lung, a small change of pressure causes a large change of volume (the slope approaches vertical), whereas a stiff lung requires a large change of pressure to produce the same or a small change of volume (the slope approaches horizontal).

ELASTIC RESISTANCE OF LUNG-THORAX
Because the lungs and the thorax are mechanically coupled elastic structures, the respiratory system may be compared to three sets of springs: the lungs, the chest, and the combination of the lungs and the chest as a unit. Each of these structures has a different resting state; however, as long as the pleurae are intact, the lungs and the chest wall are mechanically interdependent (Figure 28-7). At the end of a normal expiration, when the respiratory muscles are relaxed, the tendency of the lungs to recoil inward and that of the chest wall to recoil outward are balanced. The average intrapleural pressure is about 5 cm H_2O less than atmospheric pressure, and the volume of the lungs is at functional residual capacity (FRC). The volume at FRC is called the resting lung volume. although neither the lung nor the chest wall is at rest—the recoil forces are equal and opposite, and the pressure across these structures is algebraically zero. When this balance is upset—in pulmonary fibrosis, for example, where the recoil force of the lung increases—the volume of the lungs at FRC decreases. Conversely, in em-

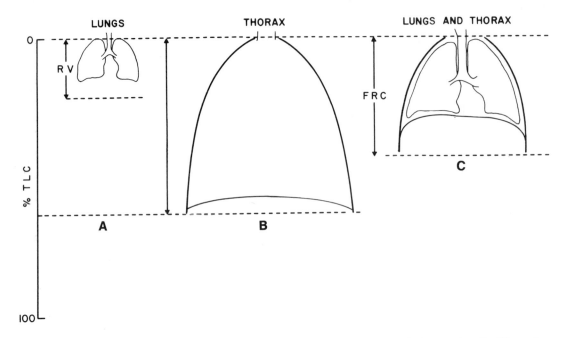

Figure 28-7.   Resting position of the lungs, thorax, and lungs and thorax combined. **A,** The lungs, removed from the chest, deflate to a minimal volume that is their resting position. **B,** The thorax alone, when not influenced by lungs, springs outward toward its resting position, which is approximately 70% of vital capacity. **C,** When the lung-thorax unit is at rest, the recoil force (inward) of the lung is balanced by the recoil force (outward) of the thorax. The volume of the lung is at *functional residual capacity,* also called *resting lung volume.*

physema, most of the elasticity of the lungs is lost, and FRC increases.

FRC also is influenced by the position of the body with respect to the earth's gravity. In a normal person in the upright position, the force of gravity pulls the abdominal contents and the diaphragm downward and also causes more of the blood volume to accumulate in the lower parts of the body, away from the thorax (see Chapter 12). Both of these effects increase the FRC. In the recumbent position, the effect of gravity is less; the abdominal contents and the diaphragm move toward the thorax, the pulmonary blood volume increases, and the FRC decreases. Under these conditions, lung recoil is decreased and the intrapleural pressure increases toward atmospheric (see the section that follows and Figure 28-8). Because of the influence of gravity on the FRC, pulmonary function tests usually are done in the sitting position, that is, on an upright lung.

PRESSURE-VOLUME RELATIONSHIPS

Figure 28-8 shows the pressure-volume (P-V) relationships of the lungs, the thorax, and the lung-thorax unit. The P-V curve for the lung and chest wall combined is the same as the curve of relaxation pressure shown in Figure 28-4; it is the sum of the separate curves for the lungs and the chest wall. The slopes of the lines represent distensibility, or compliance (see the discussion that follows). This curve is useful in determining the pressures required for breathing at any lung volume. When the volume of the lungs is at FRC, the curve intercepts the line of the ambient pressure (relative zero). At this point, the elastic force pulling on the lungs is equal to and directed opposite to the elastic force pulling on the chest wall. At lung volume less than FRC, the relaxation pressure is negative, mainly because of the tendency of the chest wall to spring out to an inspiratory position. At minimal lung volume, most of the pressure is due to the recoil of the thoracic cage. At any lung volume greater than FRC, the relaxation pressure is positive and due mainly to the tendency of the stretched lungs to retract toward the position they occupy in expiration. At more than about 60% of vital capacity, both elastic forces are directed inward (Figure 28-8E).

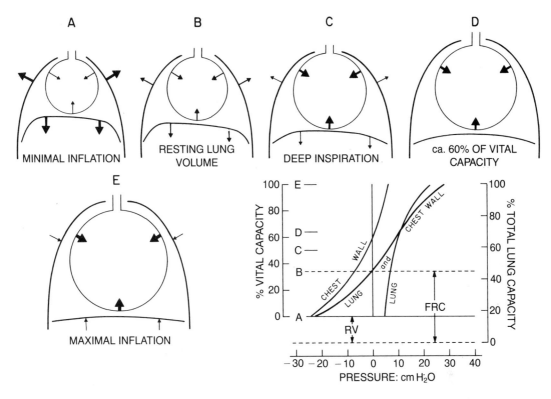

Figure 28-8. Pressure-volume curves (relaxation pressure curves) of the lungs, chest wall, and lung-chest wall combined. The letters on the pressure-volume plot indicate the lung-chest position at various lung volumes from A through E. The relaxation curve of the lungs and chest wall is the algebraic sum of the curves for the lungs and the chest wall individually. In **A** through **E**, the direction and thickness of each arrow represent the direction and relative magnitude of the recoil force of the lungs and the chest wall. In **A**, the lungs are inflated minimally (residual volume), and most of the recoil force is due to the tendency of the chest wall to spring outward; the relaxation pressure is negative. In **B**, the inward and outward forces are balanced; this is the resting lung volume, or FRC, and the difference of pressure is zero. During deep inspiration (**C**), the recoil force of the lungs is greater than that of the chest wall, and the relaxation pressure is positive. At about 60% of vital capacity (**D**), the chest is at its resting point (line of chest wall pressure intersects zero line), and all of the pressure developed is due to lung recoil, as indicated by the heavy arrows pointing inward. Finally, at maximal lung inflation (**E**), both the lung and chest wall forces are directed inward.

Compliance

The measure of the distensibility, or expandability, of the respiratory tissue is termed *compliance*. Compliance is the change of volume produced by a unit change of pressure:

$$C = \Delta V/\Delta P = liter/cm\ H_2O$$

Pulmonary compliance is expressed as a ratio of the volume of air inhaled to the change of intrapleural pressure; its units are liters of air per centimeter of H_2O. When distensibility is expressed as the change of pressure per unit change of volume, it is called *elastance*, or *elas-tic resistance*, which is the reciprocal of compliance; therefore, as the compliance of the lung increases, its elastic resistance decreases. Thus, a lung that offers little elastic resistance is highly compliant.

PRESSURE-VOLUME LOOPS

The pressure-volume loop of the lung (Figure 28-9) in a healthy subject is measured by inflating the lungs successively to several known pressures and measuring the lung volume at each pressure or by having the subject inhale successively several known volumes of gas from

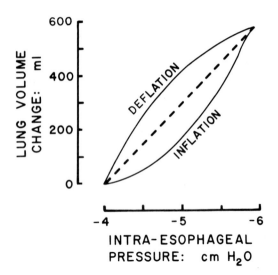

Figure 28-9. Static pressure-volume loop of the lung. The broken line represents the static compliance line (see text for further discussion).

a spirometer and measuring the pressure at each lung volume. Usually, intraesophageal pressure is measured and taken to be a satisfactory approximation of the change of intrapleural pressure. Note in Figure 28-9 that the subject begins to breathe from FRC, at which volume the intrapleural pressure is –4 cm H_2O. The lower curve is generated during inflation, or inspiration, and the upper curve is obtained during deflation, or expiration. The difference between these curves shows that at any given pressure the volume of the lung is greater during deflation than it is during inflation. This phenomenon, called *hysteresis,* is common to most elastic structures, including the lungs. It means that the rate of recoil of the lungs as the distending force is removed differs from the rate of expansion as the force was applied. Among the factors that produce hysteresis in the respiratory system are elastic fibers in the lungs and chest and surface tension in the lungs.

STATIC COMPLIANCE

The line that connects the lowest and highest points of the loop represents the slope of the pressure-volume curve, which is the *static compliance* of the lungs (see Figure 28-9). Under static conditions (that is, no flow), the pressure-volume relationship usually produces a thin loop. Static compliance depends on the volume of the lungs and is decreased when an individual breathes from a very high lung volume.

DYNAMIC COMPLIANCE

When compliance is measured during the flow of air into and out of the lungs, it is called *dynamic compliance.* This procedure produces a broader loop, the shape and size of which depend on the rate and depth of breathing. Dynamic pressure-volume loops are used to determine the work of breathing (see the section on work of breathing).

SPECIFIC COMPLIANCE

When static compliance is corrected for the volume of the lung at which it is obtained, usually FRC, it is known as *specific compliance:*

Specific compliance = Static compliance/FRC

The following example illustrates that static compliance may vary, depending on the volume of the lungs, while specific compliance remains the same: If two lungs require a pressure of 4 cm H_2O to be inflated by 0.8 liter of air, the static compliance for both lungs is 0.8 liter/4 cm H_2O, or 0.2 liter/cm H_2O. For one lung only, the inflation pressure remains the same, but the volume is reduced by one-half, and C = 0.4 liter/4 cm H_2O, or 0.1 liter/cm H_2O. For one of the lobes of one lung, C = 0.2 liter/4 cm H_2O, or 0.05 liter/cm H_2O. If the resting lung volume (FCR) of this individual is 3 liters, the specific compliance for both lungs under these different conditions is C/FRC = (0.2 liter/cm H_2O)/3 liters, or 0.067, and for only one lobe of one lung, C/FRC = (0.05 liter/cm H_2O)/0.75 = 0.067, also.

Specific compliance is useful to compare the elastic properties of adult lungs with those of newborn lungs. The compliance of a newborn lung is 0.006 liter/cm H_2O compared to 0.2 liter/cm H_2O for an adult lung; however, when expressed on the basis of lung volumes (FRC), we find that the specific compliance (C/FRC) is approximately 0.07 in both adult and newborn lungs.

A decrease in specific compliance indicates that the lungs are stiff, and more effort is required to move a normal tidal volume. To decrease this effort, an individual who has stiff lungs decreases his tidal volume but, to provide adequate alveolar ventilation, he must increase his rate of breathing. As the elastic resistance increases, the work of breathing may become so great that the subject does not ventilate adequately. When the compliance of the lungs increases, the alveoli are expanded more than usual by normal transpulmonary pressure; therefore, a person who has this condition has

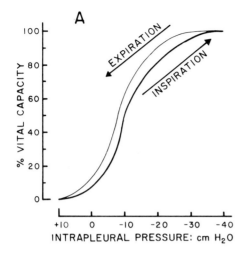

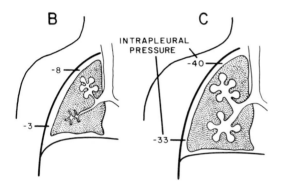

Figure 28-10. Relationship between intrapleural pressure and lung volume. Note the nonlinearity of the compliance curve (**A**). Because of a difference of intrapleural pressure between the apex and the base of the lungs, the apical alveoli are more distended but are not as well ventilated as the alveoli at the base (**B**). During deep inspiration, alveoli throughout the lungs are distended about equally (**C**).

an increased resting lung volume (FRC) and increased total lung capacity. A highly distensible lung loses its elastic recoil properties; therefore, air is trapped in the lungs after each expiration, and FRC increases.

REGIONAL LUNG COMPLIANCE

The compliance of the lungs is nonlinear; hence, the pressure-volume curves of the lungs are sigmoid. This indicates that the compliance is less at both high and low lung volumes than it is in the midrange (Figure 28-10). When a person is standing, ventilation is greater at the base of the lungs than at the apex, because the intrapleural pressure, which mainly is caused by

the pull of gravity on the mass of the lungs, is reduced more (more "negative") at the top than at the bottom of the lungs. As the intrapleural pressure decreases, the transpulmonary pressure increases, and the alveolar gas-volume increases; therefore, at FRC, the alveoli in the apex of the lungs contain more air than the alveoli in the base contain. However, as the basal alveoli are more compliant, they are ventilated better than the apical alveoli, which are on the upper part of the pressure-volume curve (see Figure 28-10). Uneven compliance leads to uneven gas tension within the lungs and an uneven ventilation-perfusion ratio, which influences the composition of the gas in the arterial blood (see Chapter 33 for further discussion).

TOTAL PULMONARY COMPLIANCE

More energy in the form of muscle contraction is required to move the lung-chest unit than to stretch either the lungs or the thorax separately, which indicates that the total system is less distensible or less compliant than either component is. Total pulmonary compliance is the sum of the compliances of the lungs and the chest wall. As the sum of parallel compliances is obtained by adding the reciprocals of the individual compliances, we get:

$$\frac{1}{C_{LT}} = \frac{1}{C_L} = \frac{1}{C_T}$$

where C_{LT} is total pulmonary compliance, C_L is lung compliance, and C_T is the compliance of the thoracic cage. If $C_L = 0.2$ liter/cm H_2O and $C_T = 0.2$ liter/cm H_2O, then $C_{LT} = 0.1$ liter/cm H_2O. Chest compliance is determined by the change in lung volume divided by the change in pressure across the chest wall (transthoracic pressure, or the difference between intrapleural pressure and atmospheric pressure).

Resistance Related to Surface Tension

CAUSE OF SURFACE TENSION

The surface of a liquid behaves like a stretched membrane that tends to retract to the smallest area possible. The force that develops on the surface of the liquid is exerted in the plane of the surface and is referred to as *surface tension*. It is expressed as force per unit length, in dynes per centimeter. Pressure, which is a force exerted on the area of the surface at right angles to the direction of the surface tension, is expressed

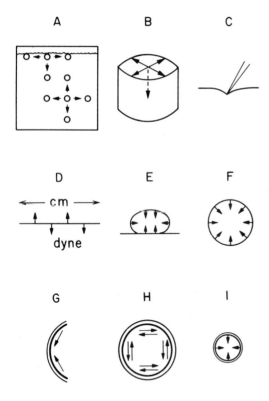

Figure 28-11. Development of surface tension at a gas-liquid interface. **A,** In a volume of water, the molecules away from the surface are attracted equally in all directions by other water molecules. However, at the surface, water molecules are attracted to the sides and downward, but not upward. The net force that develops, called *surface tension,* pulls the surface molecules toward the mass of the water. **B,** A diagram of the forces that act at the surface, seen from above. **C,** Nonwetting probe initially would depress the surface as if a film were stretched over it. **D,** Surface tension is expressed as the force required to hold together the edges of a slit in the hypothetical surface film. Hence, dyne/cm. **E,** Because the molecules at the surface all are pulled toward the center, a drop of water on a nonwettable surface tends to form a sphere, in which each molecule is the closest it can get to every other molecule. Because of the force of gravity, the drop tends to flatten a bit. **F,** A free-falling drop forms a perfect sphere. **G,** If water (heavier, inner line) covers a curved surface exposed to gas, molecules are attracted across the curvature, and the force tends to decrease the angle of the arc. **H,** If water lines the inside of a sphere filled with gas, attraction of molecules all around the sphere tends to decrease the angle of curvature. **I,** If water lines the walls surrounding a very small volume of gas, the forces act across the volume as well as around the arc. If the volume is small enough, the chamber tends to collapse, or resist expansion.

in units of dynes per square centimeter, and it should not be confused with tension.

The alveoli are lined with a thin layer of fluid; hence, the recoil properties of the lungs are influenced by the surface tension that develops in the alveoli at the gas-liquid interface (Figure 28-11). The combined surface tension of the more than 300 million alveoli contributes about one-half of the total recoil force of the lungs. This effect first was recognized in 1929 by Kurt von Neergaard, a Swiss physiologist, while he was constructing pressure-volume curves of the lungs of an anesthetized cat. von Neergaard noted that much less pressure was required to fill the lungs with saline than to fill them with gas. Saline-filled lungs have no surface tension; therefore, the pressure-volume curves reflect only the forces of retraction generated by stretching the elastic fibers. He concluded that when the lungs are filled with air and only a thin layer of fluid covers the surfaces of the alveoli, a high surface tension is added to

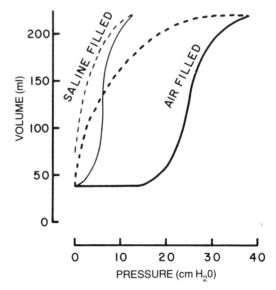

Figure 28-12. Pressure-volume curves of saline-filled and air-filled lungs. Solid lines represent inflation of the lungs; broken lines represent deflation. Resistance is higher in the air-filled lungs because of surface tension that develops at the air-fluid interface in the alveoli. The pressure that must be developed to inflate these lungs with a certain volume of air is much greater (decreased compliance) than that required to inflate them with the same volume of saline (Redrawn, with permission, from Radford, E.P., Jr. 1957. *Tissue elasticity,* editor J.W. Remington. Washington, D.C.: American Physiological Society.)

the recoil force of the lungs (Figure 28-12). The importance of this finding was not realized until about 30 years later, when it led to the discovery of surfactant (see following section).

The surface tension of water is 70 dynes/cm, and the surface tension of plasma is 50 dynes/cm; however, that of the lungs was found to be much less. Observation of these differences led to the conclusion that the fluid that lines the alveoli is not tissue fluid but some other material that decreases the surface tension, or is surface-active; hence, the name *surfactant*.

SURFACTANT

The surface-active material that lines the alveoli is composed mainly of a phospholipid, dipalmitoyl lecithin, which is the active compound, and a protein, which is thought to enhance secretion and transport. At about the thirteenth week of gestation, surfactant, which is secreted from type II alveolar cells, begins to coat the alveoli of the fetus. The balance between synthesis and loss of surfactant appears to be constant. Although the exact mechanism of inactivation and turnover is not known, the alveolar macrophages are involved in the removal of surfactant. Reduction of the blood supply, the precursors, or the availability of the substrates to the alveolar cells hinders synthesis. Very small as well as very large lung volumes seem to deplete surfactant about equally.

PHYSIOLOGICAL SIGNIFICANCE OF SURFACTANT.

The relationship between tension and pressure is expressed by the law of Laplace, which states that the tension (T) in the wall of a very thin-walled sphere equals one-half the product of the inside pressure (P) and the radius (r):

$$T = \frac{Pr}{2}$$

Thus, a bubble that has a low surface tension requires a low pressure inside to maintain a given radius, whereas a bubble that has a high surface tension requires a higher pressure inside to maintain the same radius. In the alveoli, which are almost spherical, the force of the surface tension tends to decrease the alveolar volume, but it is opposed by an internal force that is almost equal in magnitude. Alveoli in which the surface tension has been decreased require less pressure to inflate; as the compliance is greater when the surface tension is low, the work of breathing is reduced.

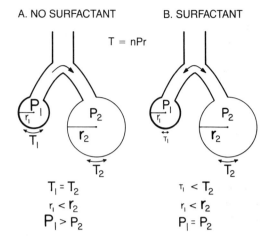

Figure 28-13. Relationship between wall tension and pressure inside a spherical structure, and its application to alveolar inflation. The relationship between T and P in a spherical structure is expressed by the Law of Laplace, which states that if the tension remains constant, the pressure varies inversely with the radius of the sphere. (T = nPr, where n is a numerical factor. In a sphere that has a very thin wall, n = 0.5.) Therefore in **A**, with different sizes of alveoli and equal surface tension, the pressure inside the smaller alveolus is higher, and the small alveolus empties into the large alveolus. In **B**, surfactant decreases the surface tension of the smaller alveolus more than that of the large alveolus, and the same pressure can maintain inflation in both despite the difference between their radii.

According to the law of Laplace, when the tension is constant and the radius decreases, more pressure is required to maintain the volume (Figure 28-13A). In the lungs, this means that if the surface tension were the same in all alveoli, more pressure would be required to inflate smaller alveoli than larger ones. Since the alveoli all communicate with each other, the difference of pressure would cause the smaller alveoli to empty into larger ones, creating only two types of alveoli: overinflated and collapsed. Surfactant prevents this (Figure 28-13B) and stabilizes the alveoli by changing the alveolar surface tension as the diameters of the alveoli change during the breathing cycle. Surface tension may change from 40–50 dynes/cm for large, inflated alveoli to 4–5 dynes/cm for small, deflated alveoli. Reduced surface tension also prevents transudation of fluid into the alveoli.

LACK OF SURFACTANT.

Inadequate production or release of surfactant causes the

alveoli to collapse during expiration, and maximal energy is required for each inspiration. This situation underlies the *respiratory distress syndrome* (RDS). In the newborn, especially those who have been born prematurely, the reduced rate of production of surfactant also is related directly to a thickening of the alveolar membrane (called hyaline membrane); hence, RDS in the infant (IRDS) also is known as *hyaline membrane disease.* The biochemical maturity of surfactant also has been linked to IRDS, as the amount of lecithin increases greatly in the last trimester of pregnancy. A test that determines the lecithin/sphingomyelin ratio in the amniotic fluid has been developed, and the results can be used to estimate the degree of maturation of the fetal lungs.

A person who has RDS, either infant or adult, requires much greater pressures to maintain inflation of the lungs than a healthy person does. The work needed to generate the increased pressures is debilitating, especially for the infant, and leads to dyspnea and hypoventilation. The treatment of RDS is directed toward maintaining a constant tidal-volume and keeping the alveoli open. These effects are accomplished by positive-pressure ventilation (forced ventilation).

Reduced production of surfactant is a problem in shock-lung syndrome. As a result of blood loss and hypotension in patients, the pulmonary arterial pressure may be too low to cause perfusion of the upper regions of the lungs, even though the individual is recumbent; therefore, the unperfused areas become ischemic, the substrates needed for the production of surfactant are depleted, the rate of production of surfactant decreases, and alveoli collapse. In such patients, forced ventilation (positive pressure) is used to inflate the lungs; however, the pulmonary arterial pressure also must be increased to assure perfusion of the apical regions of the lungs.

ALVEOLAR INTERDEPENDENCE
Alveoli also are kept from collapsing by traction from neighboring alveoli. This so-called alveolar interdependence has a stabilizing influence on the alveoli equal in importance to the presence of surfactant.

Airway Resistance

Resistance to the flow of air into and out of the respiratory system is governed by the general relationship

$$R = \Delta P/\dot{V}$$

where R is the resistance in cm H_2O/liter/min, ΔP is the difference of pressure in cm H_2O, and $\dot{V}$ is the air flow in liter/min. According to this relationship, when the flow of air either is kept constant against an increasing resistance or increased against a constant resistance, the driving pressure must increase.

TYPES OF AIRWAY RESISTANCE
The type of resistance to be measured determines the locations at which the pressures are measured. For instance, total airway resistance is

$$R_{aw} = [\text{mouth pressure} - \text{alveolar pressure}]/ \text{volume of air flow}$$

If only the resistance across the trachea is to be measured, then

$$R_{trach} = [\text{pressure in larynx} - \text{pressure at bifurcation of trachea}] /\text{volume of air flow}$$

Total pulmonary resistance includes tissue resistance; therefore,

$$R_{pulm} = [\text{mouth pressure} - \text{intrapleural pressure}]/\text{volume of air flow}$$

TYPES OF AIR FLOW
(FIGURE 28-14)
The laws that govern the relationships among pressure, air flow, and resistance were developed in physical models of rigid systems. When the flow in a rigid system is streamlined (that is, laminar flow), the driving pressure (P) required to produce a certain volume of flow ($\dot{V}$) is related directly to the viscosity of the gas; therefore,

$$\Delta P = K_1\dot{V}$$

where K_1 is a constant that includes the viscosity factor. When laminar flow exceeds a certain critical velocity, it becomes turbulent (see discussion in Chap. 12). Under these conditions, frictional resistance, or viscosity, becomes unimportant, the density of the gas becomes important, and

$$\Delta P = K_2\dot{V}^2$$

where K_2 is a constant that includes the influence of density. The pattern of air flow

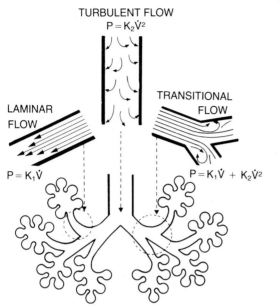

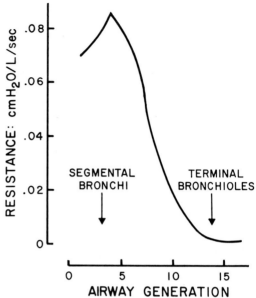

Figure 28-14. Types of airflow in the respiratory system. Broken lines with arrows point to the site at which each type of flow is most likely to be found within the tracheobronchial tree.

Figure 28-15. Airway resistance in the various segments of the respiratory system. Note that resistance to air flow is greatest in large- and medium-sized airways. (Redrawn, with permission, from Pedley, T.J.; Schroter, R.C.; and Sudlow, M.F. 1970. Prediction of pressure drop and variation of resistance within the human bronchial airways. *Resp. Physiol.* 9:87.)

through the respiratory passages is a combination of laminar flow and turbulent flow; therefore, the gradient of pressure needed to produce a given rate of flow is determined by the sum of the individual factors given previously (see Figure 28-14):

$$\Delta P = K_1 \dot{V} + K_2 \dot{V}^2$$

The tracheobronchial system is not rigid; the airways are supplied with smooth muscle that can change the diameter and the length of the air passages. When the flow is laminar in such a dynamic system, the relationship among pressure, flow, and resistance is described best by:

$$V = \frac{\Delta P}{R}, \text{ where } R = \frac{8\eta l}{\pi r^4}$$

which is based on Poiseuille's law. The resistance to flow is related directly to the viscosity of the gas (η) and the length of the airway (l) and inversely to the fourth power of the radius of the airway (r^4). In this system, r^4 is the dominating factor; for example, uniform constriction of the airways to one-half of their previous diameter causes a 16-fold increase in resistance to flow. Increasing the velocity of the flow of air also increases the resistance, which

explains why the resistance of the airways depends on the rate of breathing.

SITE OF RESISTANCE
In the bronchiorespiratory tree, the principal resistance occurs in medium-sized bronchi, approximately up to the seventh generation of airways (Figure 28-15). Small peripheral airways, less than 2 mm in diameter, contribute only 10% to the total airway resistance because, with each subdivision, the total cross-sectional area of airway increases greatly. In addition, as a large number of these small airways parallel each other, the total resistance, which is equal to the sum of the reciprocals of the individual resistances, is small.

Factors That Influence Airway Resistance

TRANSMURAL PRESSURE
The transmural pressure is the difference between the intraluminal and the extraluminal

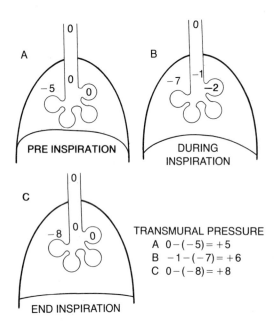

Figure 28-16. Changes in transmural pressure during breathing. When the pressure within the airways is greater than that surrounding them, the airways are kept open. Transmural pressure conventionally is expressed in positive units.

airway pressures. The patency of the airway is assured if the pressure in the airway exceeds that of the surrounding tissue. As most of the airways are located within the thorax, they are subjected to the intrathoracic pressure, which is approximately equal to the intrapleural pressure. If the pressure inside the airways is greater than the pressure around them, the transmural pressure is positive; positive transmural pressure is a distending force, which helps to keep the airways open. If the pressure in the tissues that surround the airways is greater than the pressure inside the airways, the transmural pressure is negative and the airways are compressed or collapsed unless they are supported by semirigid structures, as the trachea, bronchi, and bronchioles are. Smaller airways without structural support are kept open by traction from the surrounding lung tissue and are more easily compressed.

Figure 28-16 shows the changes in transmural pressure that occur during normal inspiration. During normal quiet inspiration, intrapleural pressure is reduced further and alveolar pressure decreases correspondingly; this decrease establishes a gradient from the mouth to the alveoli, which is necessary for air flow into the lungs. The transmural pressure increases

slightly during inspiration and is maximal at the end of inspiration, when intrapleural pressure is at its lowest value.

It was pointed out previously (see the section on regional lung compliance) that in the upright individual, intrapleural pressure is more negative (subatmospheric) at the top of the lungs than at the bottom. Consequently, transmural pressure is greater at the top and the airways are wider, while at the base of the lungs, where the intrapleural pressure is from 2–4 cm H_2O less negative, some airways actually may be closed.

DYNAMIC COMPRESSION

Airway resistance does not change much during normal quiet breathing. During inspiration, the airways are expanded, due partly to the increased transmural pressure (see previous section) and partly to the traction of the surrounding tissues; however, this increase of radius is offset by an increase in the length of the airways. During maximal breathing, however, transmural pressure and distensibility become the dominant factors even in normal healthy individuals.

Resistance decreases during maximal inspiration; therefore, airway obstruction can be overcome temporarily, although to do so increases the work of breathing. On the other hand, airways may be compressed during expiration (Figure 28-17), and airway resistance increases, especially during forced expiration. The contraction of muscles during forced expiration generates positive pressure within the thorax and alveoli, a gradient of pressure is established from the alveoli to the mouth, and air flows along it, out of the lungs. The pressure decreases along the airways, from the pressure in the alveoli, which exceeds atmospheric pressure, to that at the mouth, which equals atmospheric pressure; however, the intrathoracic pressure remains the same. Thus, at some point along the airways, the transmural pressure becomes zero; this is referred to commonly as the equal pressure point, or EPP. Theoretically, the airways can be divided into an upstream segment from the alveoli to the EPP and a downstream segment from the EPP to the mouth. Depending on the location of the EPP, airways in the downstream segment may be compressed or even collapsed by the high intrapleural pressure. In the upstream segment, the driving pressure now is the difference between the alveolar pressure and the intrapleural pressure, that is, the elastic recoil pressure. The net effect of increasing the intrapleural pressure further

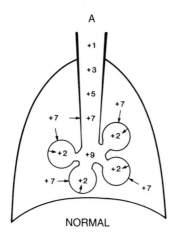

Figure 28-17. Effects of forced expiration on intrapleural and airway pressures. **A,** Normal lung. An intrapleural pressure of +7 cm H_2O develops in all of the thorax that surrounds the lungs. Intra-alveolar pressure is 2 cm H_2O (lung recoil force) higher (7 + 2 = 9), but because pressure decreases from the alveoli to the mouth (forming the gradient along which air flows out of the lungs) and intrapleural pressure remains the same, at some point along the airway, intrapleural pressure and airway pressure become the same (equal-pressure point, or EPP). Beyond that point, intrapleural pressure exceeds airway pressure, and some airways are compressed and partially collapsed. Thus, distal to the EPP, the determinant of air flow is not the difference between airway pressure and mouth pressure but the difference between airway pressure and intrapleural pressure. Airways that have least structural support will be affected most. **B,** Emphysematous lung. When the elasticity of the lung decreases, the force of elastic recoil decreases. In addition, the smaller airways normally held open by traction tend to narrow, and airway resistance increases. A larger gradient of pressure is required to maintain flow through this increased resistance, and there is a greater tendency for the airways to collapse beyond the point of narrowing. (Redrawn, with permission, from Campbell, E.J.M., et al. 1957. Mechanisms of airway obstruction. *Bull. J. Hopkins Hosp.* 101:337. Johns Hopkins University Press.)

by maximal contraction of the expiratory muscles is that the driving pressure is not changed, but the intrathoracic airways are compressed more. Therefore, during forced expiration, the maximum rate of flow of air ($\dot{V}max$) is related directly to the elastic recoil force of the lung (P_{el}) and inversely to the resistance of the segment of airway upstream (R_{us}) from the equal pressure point: $\dot{V}max = P_{el}/R_{us}$.

COMPRESSIBILITY OF AIRWAYS

Airway resistance is influenced by the compressibility of the airways. Large airways have cartilage in their walls, which helps to keep them open, and all of the airways receive some structural support from the traction of the surrounding tissue. When structural support is lost, as it is in emphysematous lungs that have lost their elastic recoil, the airways become narrower and are more likely to collapse during expiration (see Figure 28-17). This is true especially during forced expiration, because the transmural pressure downstream to the narrowed portion of the airway decreases. In this case, generating higher intrathoracic pressure by increased muscular effort actually can diminish the flow of air. The patient who has emphysema can increase the resistance at the mouth by exhaling through pursed lips, or sometimes through a straw, thereby increasing the pressure in the airways and keeping them open during forced expiration.

FLOW-VOLUME RELATIONSHIPS

When a subject does several vital capacity maneuvers, exhaling from TLC to RV slowly and then increasing the effort with each maneuver until expiration is as fast as possible and the effort is maximum, a family of flow-volume curves is obtained (Figure 28-18). During the rising phase of the curve, the rate of flow increases with the effort until it becomes maximal. Therefore, during that phase the flow is effort-dependent. Note, however, that the

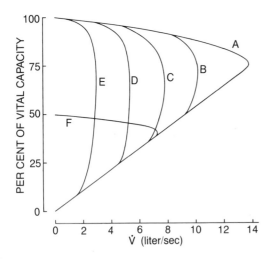

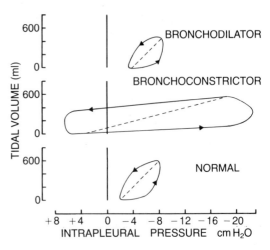

Figure 28-18. Flow-volume relationships. Curves A to E represent forced expirations from full lungs (100% VC) to residual volume (0% VC) exerting various degrees of effort, from maximal effort (A) to slow expiration (E). Curve F depicts expiratory flow using maximal effort but starting from a smaller lung volume (50% VC). Note that peak air flow (V̇EMAX) is reached early during forced expiration and is effort-dependent. Beyond the point of V̇EMAX, the rate of air flow decreases gradually as the volume of the lungs decreases; this part is effort-independent, and V̇E is determined by the elastic properties of the lungs as discussed in the text.

Figure 28-19. Pressure-volume loops in normal individuals after administration of a bronchoconstrictor and after a bronchodilator. Note the increased area of the loop after the bronchoconstrictor drug, which represents increased work. In addition, extra energy is added during expiration where intrapleural pressure becomes positive. The broken lines indicate static compliance.

volume of air exhaled is relatively small. With expiratory effort less than maximal, flow remains unchanged after a given effort is made. The most striking feature of these curves is that the descending limbs fall almost exactly on the same line. This part of the expiratory flow-volume curve is related to the dynamic compression of the small airways during forced expiration and is independent of the effort exerted.

PHYSIOLOGICAL FACTORS

The autonomic nervous system affects the tone of the bronchiolar smooth muscle. Stimulation of the vagus nerves in the parasympathetic division increases contraction of the smooth muscle, which constricts and shortens the bronchi, while activity of the sympathetic division causes bronchial dilatation by relaxing the tonically contracted smooth muscle. The airways may be narrowed reflexly in response to environmental stimuli such as cigarette smoke or dust. Receptors in the trachea and large bronchi are involved in this mechanism, and the

reflex is mediated through the vagus nerves. Adrenergic drugs, such as epinephrine or isoproterenol, relax the bronchial smooth muscle, which dilates the bronchi. The bronchodilators sometimes are used in laboratories during pulmonary function tests to determine whether increased resistance reflects the constriction of airways because of asthma (Figure 28-19) or some other obstructive lung disease.

RELATIONSHIP BETWEEN AIRWAY RESISTANCE AND LUNG VOLUME

Airway resistance varies inversely with lung volume. When the lungs expand, the size of the airways increases, and when the lungs recoil, some airways may be closed. Patients who have increased airway resistance (obstructive disease) compensate by keeping the lungs expanded abnormally, thus breathing from a large lung volume.

WORK OF BREATHING

The definition of physical work is force × distance, and the units are dynes × cm, or dyne · cm. Traditionally, physiologists substitute pressure for force and volume for distance, and define work as:

$$Work = pressure \times volume$$
$$= dyne\ cm^{-2} \times cm^3$$
$$= dyne \cdot cm$$

Work During Single Cycle of Breathing

The pressure developed and the corresponding changes of volume that occur during the normal cycle of breathing were discussed previously. It was shown that in a frictionless system, pressure and volume are related linearly (see Figure 28-6). However, when friction is added to the system, as it is during air flow, especially at higher rates of breathing, the relationship between pressure and volume is nonlinear, and a pressure-volume loop is generated. The area within the loop is a measure of the nonelastic work of breathing. In Figure 28-20, the work necessary to overcome the elastic resistance of the lung is designated by the area of the triangle ABC. The line that connects points A and B is the line of static compliance. The stippled area enclosed by the loop represents the work that had to be done to overcome the airway (frictional) resistance while air was flowing. Note that expiration is a passive process, because it uses the energy stored in the elastic tissue of the lung that is stretched during inspiration. The difference between the area within the triangle and that within the dynamic pressure-volume loop represents energy lost as heat. The total pressure that must be developed to overcome the resistances to breathing is:

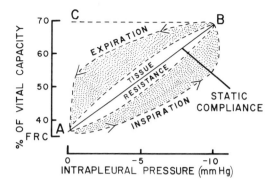

Figure 28-20.   The work of breathing. The area within the triangle ABC represents the work necessary to stretch the lungs, that is, elastic work. The enclosed area outside this triangle represents additional work done during inspiration, mostly to overcome airway resistance. A small portion of work is due to tissue viscous resistance, but normally this is negligible. Expiration uses energy stored in the stretched lung tissue; hence the work for expiration falls within the triangle; that is, normal expiration is passive.

***

$$\Delta P = K\dot{V} + K_1\dot{V} + K_2\dot{V}^2$$
$$+ \text{tissue viscous resistance}$$

where $K\dot{V}$ is the resistance of the elastic tissues, $K_1\dot{V}$ is the resistance of the airway due to friction during laminar flow, and $K_2\dot{V}^2$ is the resistance of the airway during turbulent flow.

Work in Pulmonary Diseases

In previous sections, it was implied that the work of breathing influences the pattern of breathing. Every person, whether healthy or

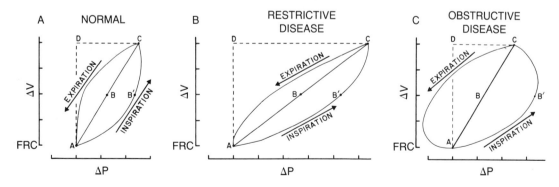

Figure 28-21.   The work of breathing in pulmonary disease. **A,** Total work, represented by the area AB′CD, consists of elastic work (ABCD) and frictional work (AB′CA). Note that restrictive disease increases the elastic component of work (**B**), whereas obstructive disease increases the frictional component (**C**). (See text for more discussion.)

not, finds a pattern of ventilation that uses the minimum energy to deliver the oxygen required and eliminate the carbon dioxide produced each minute. When the resistance to breathing increases, as it does in people who have pulmonary disease, the work of breathing increases. Figure 28-21 illustrates this relationship. When the lungs become stiff and noncompliant, as they are in the person who has a restrictive lung disease such as pulmonary fibrosis, the elastic resistance increases and the work necessary to distend the lungs (elastic work) increases (Figure 28-21B). To minimize the elastic work, this person develops a pattern of breathing in which the tidal volume is small and the rate is relatively fast. In contrast, the individual who has obstructive lung disease, in which the airways are narrowed, must work more to overcome the frictional resistance during air flow (Figure 28-21C). Therefore, this person, whose lung compliance is normal, develops a pattern of infrequent, deep breaths. In addition, because the resistance of the airways in obstructive lung disease is greatest during expiration, this individual expires actively, that is, energy is supplied in addition to that stored during inspiration and released during expiration. This condition is illustrated by the loop that overlaps the y axis in Figure 28-21C. Note the similarity between the respiratory loop of a normal person dur-

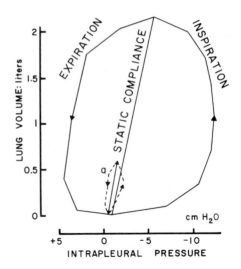

Figure 28-22. The work of breathing during exercise. Note the similarity of this pressure-volume loop to that described in a patient who has obstructive lung disease (Figure 2-21C). Normal work loop is shown by *a*. (Redrawn, with permission, from Rossier, P.H., et al. 1960. Physiologic principles and their clinical applications. In *Respiration,* editors P.C. Luchsinger and M.M. Moser. St. Louis: The C.V. Mosby Co.)

ing exercise (Figure 28-22) and that of a person who has obstructive lung disease (Figure 28-21C).

STUDY OUTLINE

MECHANICAL FACTORS   Forces and resistances that determine flow of gases into and out of lungs.

FORCES   Provided by respiratory muscles; necessary to overcome elastic and frictional resistances of breathing.

MUSCLES OF INSPIRATION   Contraction elevates and enlarges chest cage.

Diaphragm is major muscle of inspiration; moves downward in inspiration and increases volume of chest.

External intercostals pull ribs upward and outward, increasing lateral dimension of chest.

MUSCLES OF EXPIRATION   Contraction reduces volume of chest.

Major muscles of expiration: internal intercostals and muscles of abdominal wall.

Not necessary for normal quiet expiration.

Needed and used when high-velocity air flow or high expulsive pressures are required.

PRESSURES IN CHEST AND LUNGS   Around chest, atmospheric; around lungs, subatmospheric ("negative") and equal to intrapleural pressure.

With glottis open, alveolar pressure equals atmospheric pressure. (Definition of pressures: see Table 28-2.)

NEGATIVE-PRESSURE BREATHING   Normal breathing lowers all intrathoracic pressures during inspiration.

Air flows into lungs down gradient of pressure: atmospheric at mouth, subatmospheric in alveoli.

POSITIVE-PRESSURE BREATHING   Principle of artificial ventilation; increases all intrathoracic pressures.

Pressure at mouth is increased above that in alveoli; air is pushed into lungs.

PRESSURE-VOLUME CHANGES DURING BREATHING Volumes are measured by spirometer, intrapleural pressure is measured by esophageal balloon.

At beginning of inspiration, glottis is open and no air is flowing (lung volume is at FRC); intra-alveolar pressure equals atmospheric, and intrapleural pressure is 5 cm H_2O less (-5 cm H_2O).

During inspiration, intrapleural and intra-alveolar pressures are reduced; ambient air flows into lungs.

At end of inspiration, volume of lungs has increased by tidal volume; intrapleural pressure is reduced maximally (-10 cm H_2O), intra-alveolar pressure again equals atmospheric.

Change of intrapleural pressure (from -5 cm H_2O to -10 cm H_2O) represents total force developed by contracting muscles; part is required to overcome elastic resistance of lung, that is, to stretch lungs, and part is required to overcome frictional resistance to air flow.

With no air flowing, intrapleural pressure equals transpulmonary pressure.

MAXIMUM PRESSURES Maximum decrease of intra-alveolar pressure that can be developed by inspiration against closed airway, beginning from maximum expiration—about 90 cm H_2O less than atmospheric pressure.

Maximum increase of intrapulmonary pressure that can be developed by expiration against closed airway, beginning from maximum inspiration—about 120 cm H_2O.

Very low intrapulmonary pressure may cause capillary hemorrhage; very high pressure may cause lung rupture.

Safe range of pressure is between -20 and $+30$ cm H_2O.

RESISTANCES Two components: tissue resistance; airway resistance.

TISSUE RESISTANCE   Influenced by elastic recoil, surface tension, and viscous properties of respiratory tissues.

ELASTIC RESISTANCE OF LUNGS Due to elastic fibers.

Elastic lung tissue behaves as spring; stretches when pulled by force.

ELASTIC RESISTANCE OF LUNG-THORAX System analogous to three sets of springs: lung, chest, and lung-chest together, each with different resting state but mechanically interdependent.

At end of normal expiration (FRC), recoil forces of lungs and chest are equal and opposite.

FRC is decreased in pulmonary fibrosis, increased in emphysema.

FRC is increased in upright position, decreased in recumbent position; effects of gravity on abdominal contents and pulmonary blood volume.

PRESSURE-VOLUME RELATIONSHIPS Relaxation pressure (PV) curve of lung-chest unit is algebraic sum of lung and chest curves.

At FRC, elastic recoil of lungs (inward) equals elastic recoil of chest (outward); FRC is equilibrium point, or 0 relaxation pressure.

At less than FRC, relaxation pressure is negative ($<$ atmospheric), due to tendency of chest wall to recoil outward.

At greater than FRC, relaxation pressure is positive ($>$ atmospheric), due mainly to recoil of stretched lungs inward.

$> 60\%$ VC, both elastic forces are directed inward.

COMPLIANCE   Change of volume per unit change of pressure—measure of distensibility

PRESSURE-VOLUME LOOPS Lungs are inflated successively with known volumes, and intraesophageal pressure is measured.

STATIC COMPLIANCE Pressure-volume relationship under no-flow conditions (static); thin P-V loops—volume dependent.

DYNAMIC COMPLIANCE P-V relationship during air flow; wide loops—rate dependent.

SPECIFIC COMPLIANCE Static compliance corrected for lung volume (FRC).

Decreased compliance means stiff lungs that require increased effort to breathe.

Compliance greater than normal means loss of elastic recoil; greater volume at same pressure, that is, FRC and TLC are increased; does not necessarily mean better ventilation.

REGIONAL LUNG COMPLIANCE The PV curve of lung is S-shaped; compliance is less at high and low lung volumes.

In normal lungs, regional change in compliance is caused by regional change in intrapleural pressure.

TOTAL PULMONARY COMPLIANCE Sum of compliances of lungs and chest wall (add reciprocals).

RESISTANCE RELATED TO SURFACE TENSION

CAUSE OF SURFACE TENSION Intermolecular attraction at liquid-gas interface—force/unit length.

P-V curve of air-filled lung represents recoil force due to elasticity and surface tension.

SURFACTANT Surface active material lines alveoli; composed of phospholipid and protein.

Physiological Significance of Surfactant Reduces surface tension; work of breathing is reduced.

Stabilizes alveoli by changing alveolar surface tension when size changes.

Prevents transudation of fluid into alveoli.

Lack of Surfactant   RDS. Work of breathing must increase.

ALVEOLAR INTERDEPENDENCE   Collapse of alveoli also is opposed by traction from adjacent alveoli.

AIRWAY RESISTANCE $R = \Delta P/\dot{V}$.

TYPES OF AIRWAY RESISTANCE   Total airway resistance, tracheal resistance, and total pulmonary resistance.

TYPES OF AIR FLOW   Laminar flow: driving pressure required to produce flow is related to gas viscosity.

Turbulent flow: density of gas is important factor; viscosity is unimportant.

Pattern of air flow is result of sum of factors that determine laminar ($K_1\dot{V}$) and turbulent flow ($K_2\dot{V}^2$).

SITE OF RESISTANCE   Large- and medium-sized airways, 80%; small airway ($<$ 2 mm), 20%; inverse relationship between *total* cross-sectional area and resistance.

FACTORS THAT INFLUENCE AIRWAY RESISTANCE

TRANSMURAL PRESSURE   Difference between pressure inside and outside; patency is maintained when airway pressure exceeds extraluminal pressure.

DYNAMIC COMPRESSION   Changes of resistance during normal breathing are negligible; airway resistance increases during forced expiration because airways are compressed.

COMPRESSIBILITY OF AIRWAYS   Large airways have cartilage.

All airways have some structural support from traction of surrounding tissues; loss leads to collapse and increased resistance, especially during forced expiration.

FLOW-VOLUME RELATIONSHIPS
$>$ 75% VC, rate of flow is related to force of expiration: effort-dependent.

Descending limb of flow-volume curve is independent of effort because of compression of small airways.

PHYSIOLOGICAL FACTORS   Tone of bronchiolar smooth muscle is regulated by autonomic nervous system.

Parasympathetic: bronchial constriction; reflex in response to noxious agents.

Sympathetic: bronchial dilatation; bronchodilator drugs.

RELATIONSHIP BETWEEN AIRWAY RESISTANCE AND LUNG VOLUME   Airway resistance varies inversely with lung volume.

WORK OF BREATHING   Work = pressure $\times$ volume. Area within P-V loop is measure of nonelastic work.

WORK DURING SINGLE CYCLE OF BREATHING   Two components of work done during inspiration: (1) elastic work—pressure needed to stretch lungs; (2) frictional work—pressure needed to overcome frictional resistance during air flow.

Expiration normally is passive; uses energy stored during inspiration.

WORK IN PULMONARY DISEASES   Increased resistance means increased work.

Restrictive disease: increases elastic component of work; is compensated by small tidal volume and fast rate.

Obstructive disease: increases frictional work; is compensated by large tidal volume and slow rate.

BIBLIOGRAPHY

Agostoni, R. 1964. Action of respiratory muscles. In *Handbook of physiology,* Sec. 3. *Respiration,* editors W.O. Fenn and H. Rahn. Vol. 1, Washington, D.C.: American Physiological Society.

Comroe, J.H. 1974. *Physiology of respiration,* 2nd ed. Chicago: Yearbook Medical Publishers, Inc.

De Trayer, A.; Kelly, S.; and Zin, W.A. 1983. Mechanical action of the intercostal muscles on the ribs. *Science* 220:87.

DuBois, A.B.; Botelho, S.Y.; and Comroe, J.H., Jr. 1956. A new method for measuring airway resistance in man using a body plethysmograph: values in normal subjects and in patients with respiratory disease. *J. Clin. Invest.* 35:327.

Douglas, N.J.; Wraith, P.K.; Brash, J., et al. 1980. Computer measurement of dynamic compliance: technique and reproducibility in man. *J. Appl. Physiol.: Respirat. Environ. Exercise Physiol.* 48:903.

Farrell, P.M., editor. 1982. *Lung development: biological and chemical perspectives.* Vol. 1, *Biochemistry and physiology.* Vol. 2, *Neonatal respiratory distress.* New York: Academic Press.

Farrell, P.M., and Avery, M.E. 1975. Hyaline membrane disease. *Am. Rev. Resp. Dis.* 111:657.

Fry, D.L., and Hyatt, R.E. 1960. Pulmonary mechanics. *Am. J. Med.* 29:672.

King, Richard J. 1974. The surfactant system of the lung. *Fed. Proc.* 33:2238.

Mead, J. 1961. Mechanical properties of lungs. *Physiol. Rev.* 41:281.

Mead, J.; Turner, J.M.; Macklem, P.T.; et al. 1967. Significance of the relationship between lung recoil and maximum expiratory flow. *J. Appl. Physiol.* 22:95.

Neergaard, K., and Wirz, K. 1927. Über eine Methode zur Messung der Lungenelastizität am lebenden Menschen, insbesondere beim Ephysem. *Z. klin. Med.* 105:35.

Otis, A.B. 1954. The work of breathing. *Physiol. Rev.* 34:449.

Otis, A.B. 1964. The work of breathing. In *Handbook of physiology,* Sec. 3. *Respiration,* Vol. 1., editors W.O. Fenn and H. Rahn. Washington, D.C.: American Physiological Society.

Pattle, R.E. 1965. Surface lining of lung alveoli. *Physiol. Rev.* 45:48.

Radford, E.P., Jr. 1964. Static mechanical properties of mammalian lungs. In *Handbook of physiology,* Sec. 3. *Respiration,* Vol. I, editors W.O. Fenn and H. Rahn. Washington, D.C.: American Physiological Society.

Radford, E.P., Jr. 1957. Recent studies of mechanical properties of mammalian lungs. In *Tissue elasticity,* editor J.E. Remington. Washington, D.C.: American Physiological Society.

Rahn, H., et al. 1946. The pressure-volume diagram of the thorax and lung. *Am. J. Physiol.* 146:161.

Roussos, C., and Macklem, P.T. 1982. The respiratory muscles. *N. Engl. J. Med.* 307:786.

Shelley, S.A.; Koracevic, M.; Paciga, J.E., et al. 1979. Sequential changes of surfactant phosphatidalcholine in hyaline membrane disease of the newborn. *N. Engl. J. Med.* 300:112.

West, J.B. 1979. *Respiratory physiology—The essentials,* 2nd ed. Baltimore: Williams & Wilkins Co.

29

Control of Respiration

For the most part, breathing is an automatic activity generated by groups of neurons located in the brainstem of the central nervous system. This activity produces an alternating pattern of inspiration and expiration. The voluntary aspects of breathing are associated mainly with speech, singing, or such nonphysiological activities as voluntary hyperventilation and breath-holding.

The system is composed of three parts: (1) the sensors (receptors, afferent input), (2) the integrator (the decision-making center), and (3) the effector (efferent impulses to the muscles of respiration). Although a great deal is known about the sensors and the effectors, most of the information that is available on the integrators comes from data on anesthetized animals and is extrapolated to the awake human subject.

NEURAL CONTROL OF PATTERN OF BREATHING

The origin of the neural discharge that produces the rhythmic activity of inspiration and expiration has been studied by electrical stimulation of small areas of the brain and by serial transsection of the brain. On the basis of the respiratory patterns that emerge from such experiments, the concept of respiratory centers evolved. By definition, respiratory centers are groups of neurons and their synapses that receive and process information from the sensors and make decisions that emerge as a respiratory pattern appropriate for the occasion. The decision-making process still is unknown, but experiments with animals indicate that the reticular activating system, the part of the brain that is activated when attention and consciousness are necessary, is involved.

Respiratory Centers

Three centers are postulated to be responsible to varying degrees for the normal pattern of breathing in humans. These are (1) the respiratory centers located in the medulla oblongata, (2) the pneumotaxic center, and (3) the apneustic center.

MEDULLARY CENTERS

Two groups of neurons in the medulla initiate and perpetuate the alternating cycles of inspiration and expiration. Positioned bilaterally, they are known as the dorsal respiratory group (DRG) and the ventral respiratory group (VRG) (Figure 29-1). The DRG neurons, which are located in the ventrolateral nucleus of the tractus solitarius, exhibit activity related to inspiration only. The VRG neurons, which are associated with the nucleus ambiguus and nucleus retroambigualis, have both inspiratory and expiratory activity. It is postulated that the rhythmogenicity originates from the DRG neurons by some mechanism that still is not known, while the activity of the VRG neurons is tonic and interrupted periodically by impulses

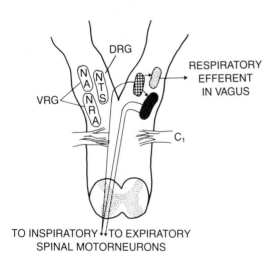

Figure 29-1. Medullary respiratory centers. Dorsal respiratory group (DRG; activity mainly inspiratory; probable site of rhythm). Ventral respiratory group (VRG; activity both inspiratory and expiratory). NTS, nucleus tractus solitarius. NA, nucleus ambiguus. NRA, nucleus retroambigualis. C$_1$, dorsal root of first cervical nerve. (Redrawn, with permission, from Berger, et al. 1977. *N. Engl. J. Med.* 297:140.)

from the DRG neurons. The model is based partly on the observation that axons of DRG neurons synapse on VRG neurons, but there is no innervation in the reverse direction. The DRG neurons may be the first center that receives and integrates input from the sensors (vagal afferents); in response, this center initiates inspiration by sending a signal through the phrenic nerves to make the diaphragm contract. The axons of VRG neurons project mainly to motoneurons that supply the muscles of expiration.

APNEUSTIC CENTER

When the brain is sectioned between the middle and lower portions of the pons, just above the cerebral peduncles, respiration becomes deep and slow, indicating that some inhibitory influence from above was removed. If the vagus nerves also are severed, a pattern of inspiratory breath-holding (*apneusis*) ensues; therefore, the respiratory center located in a diffuse area of the mid to lower part of the pons is known as the *apneustic center*. Normally, when not inhibited by higher centers of the brain or by impulses carried in the vagus nerves, the apneustic center prolongs the activity of the groups of neurons associated with inspiration and causes breath-holding in the inspiratory position.

PNEUMOTAXIC CENTER

The *pneumotaxic center* is located in the nucleus parabrachialis in the upper region of the pons. When the brainstem is sectioned above the pons, removing the influence of all other higher centers, the respiratory pattern does not change significantly even after the vagus nerves also are sectioned. The activity of the pneumotaxic center depends on impulses from the other respiratory centers; it is not needed to maintain rhythmic activity, which is generated by the center located in the lower brainstem (medulla). Rather, the pneumotaxic center is considered to "fine tune" the pattern of breathing. It is the highest level of control required if an optimal tidal volume and frequency of breathing are to be maintained.

CHEMICAL REGULATION OF VENTILATION

Ventilation is regulated by changes in concentrations of O$_2$, CO$_2$, and H$^+$ in the arterial blood.

At rest, pulmonary ventilation is adjusted to the level of metabolism. CO_2, the major metabolic end-product, normally is the principal chemical factor that regulates ventilation. Oxygen lack becomes an important factor for driving ventilation only when the Po_2 of the blood falls below 50 mm Hg; between 50 and 160 mm Hg, Po_2 has little effect on the normal regulation of breathing. The influence of CO_2 is important for several reasons: (1) CO_2 dissolves freely in the body fluids, (2) it can be eliminated by the lung as a gas, and (3) it can be hydrated to become H_2CO_3 and, as such, can influence the $[H^+]$ of the blood and other body fluids.

Sensors

The sensors, or receptors, that respond to changes of the concentrations of O_2, CO_2, and H^+ in their chemical environment are called *chemoreceptors*. There are two groups of chemoreceptors: central and peripheral. In general, the central chemoreceptors respond to changes in arterial Pco_2 and $[H^+]$, while the peripheral chemoreceptors are most sensitive to changes in arterial Po_2.

CENTRAL CHEMORECEPTORS
The central chemoreceptors are located bilaterally on the ventral surface of the upper medulla, approximately where the ninth and tenth cranial nerves leave the brainstem. These receptors are found close to the medullary respiratory centers but are not the same cells anatomically.

PERIPHERAL CHEMORECEPTORS
There are two groups of peripheral chemoreceptors: the carotid bodies and the aortic bodies. Recent work indicates that the carotid bodies are the main sensors for the reflex drive of ventilation in response to lack of O_2. The carotid bodies are located just above the bifurcation of the common carotid arteries, close to the carotid sinus baroreceptors (Figure 29-2). Afferent impulses from the carotid bodies are carried centrally by fibers that travel with the carotid sinus nerves and join the ninth (glosso-

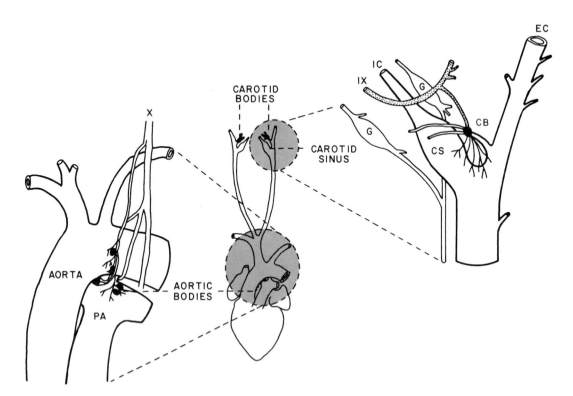

Figure 29-2. Location and innervation of the peripheral chemoreceptors. PA, pulmonary artery. X, tenth cranial nerve (vagus). IX, ninth cranial nerve (glossopharyngeal). IC, internal carotid artery. CS, carotid sinus. CB, carotid body. G, ganglion. EC, external carotid artery.

pharyngeal) cranial nerve. The receptors are stimulated when arterial P_{O_2} decreases or when arterial P_{CO_2} increases. The drive of ventilation by the peripheral chemoreceptors is related to changes in partial pressure of oxygen rather than to the content of O_2 or the degree of saturation of the arterial blood.

Response to CO_2

The level of alveolar ventilation is related directly to the level of arterial P_{CO_2}. The normal arterial P_{CO_2} is 40 mm Hg; it is regulated within approximately 3 mm Hg of that value by negative feedback. As P_{CO_2} increases, it stimulates respiration and increases alveolar ventilation; this eliminates more CO_2, and P_{CO_2} returns to normal.

A concentration of approximately 10% CO_2 in the inspired air stimulates ventilation maximally (Figure 29-3). When inspired air contains more than 15% CO_2, respiration may be depressed. Elderly people are less sensitive to increased P_{CO_2} than young people are.

A decrease in alveolar P_{O_2} to less than normal enhances the ventilatory response to increased CO_2. With P_{aO_2} in the range of 110–160 mm Hg, each 1 mm Hg rise in alveolar P_{CO_2} increases ventilation by about 3 liters/min. When alveolar P_{O_2} is less than 50 mm Hg, the increase in ventilation for each millimeter of mercury increase in P_{CO_2} is much greater, as indicated by the much steeper slope of the curve in Figure 29-4. The response to increased CO_2 decreases when CO_2 is increased chroni-

cally. Patients who have an obstructive lung disease and retain CO_2 do not increase their ventilation. The reason for this is not clear, but apparently a prolonged high level of P_{CO_2} reduces the sensitivity of the respiratory centers to CO_2. Drugs such as morphine and barbiturates, which depress the respiratory centers, also reduce the ventilatory response to CO_2.

Ventilation decreases when the alveolar P_{CO_2} decreases. This can be demonstrated by voluntary hyperventilation, which decreases the respiratory drive. The subject may stop breathing until the level of CO_2 in the blood builds up again.

MECHANISM OF RESPONSE TO CO_2

The medullary chemoreceptors involved in the CO_2 response are sensitive to the $[H^+]$ of their immediate environment. Ventilation is regulated by the influence of arterial P_{CO_2} on the

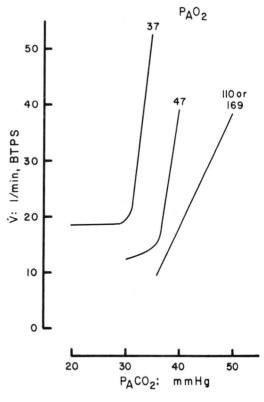

Figure 29-4. Modification of the ventilatory response to CO_2 by changing the alveolar P_{O_2} level. The increase in ventilation is much greater at any level of P_{CO_2} when the P_{AO_2} is lower than normal (37 or 47 mm Hg). (Redrawn, with permission, from Nielsen, M., and Smith, H. 1951. *Acta Physiol. Scand.* 24:298.)

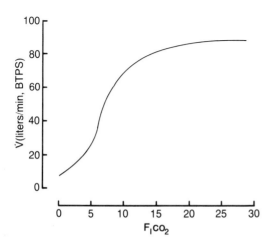

Figure 29-3. Relationship between minute ventilation and concentration of CO_2 in inspired air.

[H$^+$] of the cerebrospinal fluid (CSF), from which the interstitial fluid that surrounds these sensor cells is derived. The CSF is separated from cerebral capillary blood by the blood-CSF barrier, which is relatively impermeable to H$^+$ and HCO$_3^-$. However, CO$_2$ diffuses through these lipid membranes with ease, from the blood into the CSF, where it is hydrated and forms carbonic acid. The reaction yields H$^+$ that must be buffered immediately. CSF is like an ultrafiltrate, since it does not contain hemoglobin and is almost free of protein. Therefore, the H$^+$ that is released when H$_2$CO$_3$ dissociates is not buffered, the [H$^+$] of the CSF increases, the central chemoreceptors are stimulated, and the respiratory centers are excited. As alveolar ventilation increases, more CO$_2$ is excreted and normal alveolar P$_{CO_2}$ and arterial P$_{CO_2}$ are restored.

The pH of the CSF normally is regulated around 7.2, which is lower than the pH of the arterial plasma (7.4). It is not known at present how the pH ([H$^+$]) of the CSF is restored. A plausible explanation is that HCO$_3^-$ is transported actively into the CSF and the subsequent reaction (HCO$_3^-$ + H$^+$ $\rightleftharpoons$ H$_2$CO$_3$ $\rightleftharpoons$ CO$_2$ + H$_2$O) forms more CO$_2$, which diffuses out from the CSF and into the blood. The chemical changes in the CSF lag behind the chemical changes in the blood.

The central chemoreceptors are depressed easily by anesthesia or by drugs. If this occurs, and small increases of P$_{CO_2}$ do not stimulate respiration, P$_{CO_2}$ may increase temporarily to high levels. P$_{CO_2}$ of 70–80 mm Hg depresses ventilation.

Response to Oxygen

The only cells sensistive to changes in arterial P$_{O_2}$ are the peripheral chemoreceptors, mainly the carotid bodies. When the alveolar or arterial P$_{O_2}$ falls below 50 mm Hg, the frequency of afferent discharges from the peripheral chemoreceptors increases and the respiratory centers are stimulated reflexly. Decreased alveolar P$_{O_2}$ has no effect on the central chemoreceptors. The respiratory centers are depressed by arterial hypoxemia.

The sensitivity of the carotid bodies to low arterial P$_{O_2}$ and the reflex drive of ventilation increase when P$_{CO_2}$ increases simultaneously. The combined effects of low P$_{O_2}$ and high P$_{CO_2}$ on ventilation are greater than the sum of the individual effects. In the normocapnic individual, ventilation remains relatively constant in

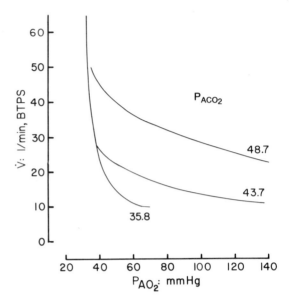

Figure 29-5. Relationship between minute ventilation and alveolar P$_{O_2}$. Note that below 50 mm Hg P$_{AO_2}$ the hypoxic drive dominates and ventilation is greatly increased even when P$_{CO_2}$ is below normal. (Redrawn, with permission, from Loeschke, H.H., and Gertz, K.H. 1958. *Arch. Ges. Physiol.* 267:465.

the face of decreasing alveolar P$_{O_2}$ until P$_{O_2}$ falls below 50 mm Hg. In the presence of hypercapnia, however, ventilation increases even when alveolar P$_{O_2}$ is normal, as shown in the so-called hypoxic response curve presented in Figure 29-5. When alveolar P$_{O_2}$ falls below 60 mm Hg, the reflex peripheral chemoreceptor drive of ventilation becomes dominant and ventilation increases, even if P$_{CO_2}$ is normal. The peripheral chemoreceptor drive can maintain ventilation in people whose alveolar P$_{O_2}$ chronically is low, even though the central nervous system and the respiratory centers are depressed directly by the hypoxia. In people who have chronic pulmonary disease, retained CO$_2$ enhances the reflex hypoxic drive of ventilation; however, if the hypoxemia is treated with increased [O$_2$] in the inspired air, the hypoxic drive is abolished by increasing arterial P$_{O_2}$, and ventilation is depressed severely. The P$_{CO_2}$ may increase to the point that it produces coma. Figure 29-6 shows the response of an anesthetized dog to breathing air of low [O$_2$] and subsequently to breathing 100% O$_2$. Note that breathing a mixture of air that contained low [O$_2$] increased both the rate and depth of breathing; when 100% O$_2$ was substituted for the low [O$_2$] mixture, respiration ceased because the stimulus for the reflex drive

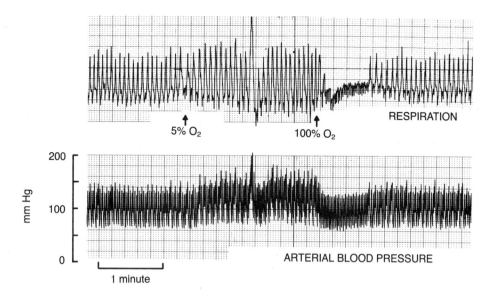

RESPIRATION

5% O$_2$ 100% O$_2$

200

mm Hg

100

0

ARTERIAL BLOOD PRESSURE

1 minute

Figure 29-6. Effects of inhaling low and high [O$_2$] on the ventilation of a dog anesthetized by a combination of morphine sulfate and sodium pentobarbital. At the beginning of the recording, the animal was breathing room air. A mixture of gas containing low [O$_2$] was introduced at the first arrow; minute ventilation increased significantly after only a few seconds. When the low [O$_2$] mix-ture was replaced with 100% O$_2$ (second arrow), respiration ceased for approximately 50 sec and then resumed, when (presumably) the alveolar O$_2$ and CO$_2$ levels returned to normal. Note the increase in blood pressure during the period of hypoxemia. Activity of the heart is reflected in the respiratory recording (impedance pneumograph), especially during the period of apnea.

(hypoxemia) was removed. Ventilation recovered, presumably when the alveolar Pco$_2$ was restored to normal.

Response to [H$^+$]

As the [H$^+$] of the arterial blood increases, ventilation increases. Changes of [H$^+$] in arterial blood are sensed primarily by the peripheral H$^+$ receptors. Although the changes in Pco$_2$ and [H$^+$] are interrelated, they are distinct stimuli. For example, an increase of [H$^+$] caused by accumulation of fixed acids (metabolic acidosis) stimulates respiration even when the Pco$_2$ is normal or below normal. In chronic metabolic acidosis, the ventilatory drive in response to increased [H$^+$] of the arterial blood is even greater, because when ventilation first increases, the arterial Pco$_2$ and the [H$^+$] of the CSF both decrease and, as a result, ventilation decreases. Eventually, the [H$^+$] of the CSF is restored and ventilation increases again, eliminating the central chemoreceptor drive and lowering the arterial Pco$_2$ (respiratory alkalosis). This is a compensatory effect that brings the arterial [H$^+$] closer to normal.

REFLEX CONTROL

Reflexes from Lungs

INFLATION-DEFLATION REFLEX

When the lungs are inflated by large tidal volumes, the frequency of respiration decreases; when the inflation is prolonged, breathing stops. The converse also is true: when the lungs are inflated less than normally, as occurs in pneumothorax, the frequency of ventilation increases. The inflation reflex was observed first in anesthetized dogs and was described by Hering and Breuer in 1868; hence, it also is called the *Hering-Breuer reflex*. The sensors are mechanoreceptors located in the smooth muscle of the bronchioles and the trachea; the stimulus is stretch. Afferent impulses initiated by the stretch receptors are carried centrally by fibers in the vagus nerves. In laboratory exercises, students frequently observe that when the vagus nerves of an anesthetized dog are stimulated, ventilation decreases in frequency or ceases entirely (Figure 29-7). This occurs because sensory fibers that form the afferent limb of the reflex are stimulated directly.

IMPEDANCE PNEUMOGRAM

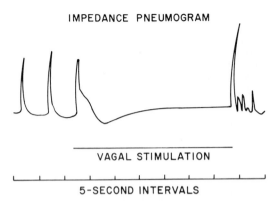

VAGAL STIMULATION

5-SECOND INTERVALS

Figure 29-7.   The inflation reflex in an anesthetized dog. The recording shows an impedance pneumogram before and after the afferent fibers in the left vagus nerve were stimulated. The control rate of breathing was 14 breaths/min. Respiration stopped for 28 seconds during vagal stimulation.

In humans, the inflation reflex is active only when the tidal volume is greater than 800 ml or when the sensitivity of the stretch receptors in the airways is increased by disease. Presumably, the reflex prevents overinflation of the lungs and reinforces the cyclic nature of respiration. The reflex may be part of the regulatory mechanisms that control the work of breathing. As pointed out earlier, patients who have restrictive or obstructive pulmonary diseases compensate by finding a combination of tidal volume and frequency of ventilation that is consistent with their condition and requires the least amount of work while still ventilating the alveoli adequately. Since the tidal volume determines the elastic work needed to stretch the lungs, a person whose lungs are stiff because of pulmonary fibrosis decreases the depth and increases the frequency of breathing. This pattern may be explained as follows: because of the increased elastic resistance offered by the stiff lungs, the large airways are relatively more compliant; hence, inspiration turns off sooner, decreasing tidal volume, and the rate of breathing increases. On the other hand, in an obstructive disease such as asthma, in which airway resistance increases, the airways become relatively less compliant and are relatively more difficult to stretch; therefore, inspiration lasts longer. A respiratory pattern of large tidal volume and slow rate develops. The slower rate of breathing decreases the velocity of air flow and consequently the resistance to flow; thus, less energy is required.

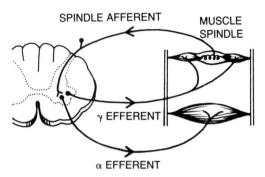

SPINDLE AFFERENT   MUSCLE SPINDLE

γ EFFERENT

α EFFERENT

Figure 29-8.   The stretch reflex. The sense organs, or muscle spindles, are specialized intrafusal muscle fibers that respond to the stimulus of stretch. The intrafusal fibers are arranged parallel to extrafusal fibers and are separated from them by a connective tissue capsule. The muscle spindle has its own motor system. The γ efferent neuron causes contraction of the two poles of the spindle and regulates the tension in the muscle spindle. The spindle is excited when the muscle is stretched. Afferent impulses enter the dorsal roots through the large spindle afferent nerve and synapse on α motor neurons, which form the efferent limb of the reflex and cause contraction of the main muscle.

IRRITATION REFLEXES

Receptors located in the upper airways, trachea, and large bronchi may cause cough, apnea, or reflex constriction of the airways when stimulated by dust, cigarette smoke, and other noxious agents. These mechanisms protect the lungs from injury.

PARADOXICAL REFLEX OF HEAD

When the inhibitory influence on inflation of the lungs is blocked by controlled cooling of the vagus nerves, inflation causes further inflation, up to a limit. This is an example of a positive feedback process; it is considered paradoxical because it differs from the dominant negative-feedback control of the lungs. The paradoxical reflex may be used in sighing or when a newborn infant takes the first breath. The receptors are located somewhere in the lungs.

Reflex from Chest Wall

Receptors in the muscles of respiration (muscle spindles) respond to stretch by causing the muscles to contract. The muscle spindles parallel the muscle fibers, and their length is adjusted through their own motor nerves, the γ-efferents.

CLINICAL CORRELATION
29.1   Ventilatory Response
to Oxygen Therapy—CO$_2$ Narcosis

CASE REPORT

The Patient: A 55-year-old man.

Principal Complaint: Cyanosis and dyspnea during even slight exertion.

History: The patient had a history of chronic pulmonary disease, and had several respiratory infections during the past year. He had smoked 1½–2 packs of cigarettes/day most of his adult life but had given up smoking two years ago.

Clinical Examination: The patient was alert but anxious. His arterial pressure was 130/80 mm Hg (normal, 90–140/60–90 mm Hg), and his heart rate was 125 beats/min (normal, 60–100 beats/min). His lips were blue, and his breathing was labored, at a rate of 25 breaths/min (normal, 13–17 breaths/min). The arterial P$_{O_2}$ (Pa$_{O_2}$) was 50 mm Hg (normal, 75–100 mm Hg), the Pa$_{CO_2}$ was 50 mm Hg (normal, 35–45 mm Hg), the hemoglobin saturation was 84% (normal, 96%–100%), and the pH of the arterial blood was 7.36 (normal, 7.35–7.45). Spirometry gave the following values (see Appendix for definitions):

$$\dot{V} = 11.4 \text{ liters/min}$$
$$\dot{V}_A = 3.0 \text{ liters/min}$$
$$V_T = 450 \text{ ml}$$

The diagnosis was alveolar hypoventilation caused by recurrent respiratory infection. To relieve his dyspnea and anxiety, the patient was given 100% O$_2$ to breathe by face mask. His color improved almost immediately, and he became quiet and rested comfortably. Later, however, the nurse had difficulty waking him. Analysis of blood gases revealed that the Pa$_{CO_2}$ was 90 mm Hg, and the pH of the arterial blood was 7.2: the patient had severe hypercapnia (excess CO$_2$) and respiratory acidosis.

Comment: In this patient, alveolar hypoventilation led to hypoxemia and hypercapnia. The high concentration of O$_2$ in the inspired air corrected the hypoxemia; however, the patient had been relying on his hypoxic drive to ventilate, and when the Pa$_{O_2}$ was increased, the hypoxic drive was eliminated, alveolar ventilation decreased further, and the Pa$_{CO_2}$ increased to dangerous levels. The response of the respiratory centers to chronically high P$_{CO_2}$ had decreased, and the high P$_{CO_2}$ simply depressed the central nervous system and the respiratory neurons, causing CO$_2$ narcosis. When the Pa$_{O_2}$ is increased so that adequate oxygenation occurs, the alveolar and arterial P$_{CO_2}$ should be decreased by mechanical ventilation and kept within normal limits, to prevent CO$_2$ narcosis.

Treatment: O$_2$ therapy was discontinued and the patient was roused and commanded to breathe deeply and frequently. Doxapram HCl, a drug that stimulates ventilation, primarily by increasing the depth of breathing, was administered intravenously in a single dose. Subsequently, the patient was placed on intermittent positive pressure breathing (IPPB), which increases alveolar pressure to above atmospheric during inspiration and lets it return to atmospheric at the end of expiration. Oxygen therapy was resumed, but at a much lower concentration than before. Pa$_{CO_2}$ was monitored carefully to assess adequate ventilation.

Outcome: This potentially dangerous situation was corrected, and the patient recovered. Subsequently, he was treated for his primary problem of pulmonary disease and hypoventilation.

When excited, the spindles excite their afferents, which leads to contraction of the main muscle (Figure 29-8). This reflex drives the respiratory muscles to develop more tension when the resistance to breathing increases; thus, the tidal volume can be restored or maintained.

Baroreceptor Reflexes

Blood pressure and respiration are related inversely. When the blood pressure increases, the rate of breathing decreases, and when the blood pressure decreases, the rate of breathing increases. Although this relationship may reflect some form of protective mechanism, its physiological significance is not clear.

Other Reflexes

Ventilation also is stimulated reflexly by pain and when joint receptors are stimulated by passive movement of a limb.

EFFECTS OF HIGHER CENTERS

The hypoxic drive and other pulmonary reflexes in humans are the same whether the person is awake or sleeping. However, in the alert human, hyperventilation is not followed by apnea as it is in the anesthetized human. Sleep, barbiturates, narcotics, and most anesthetic agents depress the response of the central chemoreceptors to increased P_{CO_2}. Observation of these and similar events led to the conclusion that the automatic phase of ventilation depends on the state of alertness, which implicates the part of the brain associated with consciousness and attention—the reticular activating system. Voluntary hypoventilation (breath-holding) is controlled by higher centers in the CNS, but the exact influence of these centers has not been determined. Strong emo-

tions, such as anger, fear, or anxiety, and sexual stimulation also influence ventilation. The response is evoked through the hypothalamus and mediated by the autonomic nervous system. A sympathetic response tends to decrease airway resistance by dilating the airways and decreasing bronchial secretion. A parasympathetic response causes bronchoconstriction and increased bronchial secretion.

PATTERNS OF BREATHING

Normal Patterns

The normal pattern of breathing consists of alternating cycles of inspiration and expiration at a rate of approximately 14 breaths per minute. This is referred to as *eupnea,* or *eupneic breathing.*

Cheyne-Stokes Breathing

An abnormal pattern of breathing seen frequently in clinical medicine is Cheyne-Stokes breathing, which consists of a burst of tidal volumes that first increase, then decrease gradually and alternate with periods of apnea (Figure 29-9). This pattern of periodic breathing frequently develops in patients who have neurological, cardiac, or combined neurological and cardiac disorders. Cheyne-Stokes respiration can be produced in the laboratory by increasing the circulation time from the heart to the brain; thus, one explanation for the pattern of oscillation is that changes of P_{CO_2} in the CSF are out of phase with changes of P_{CO_2} in the

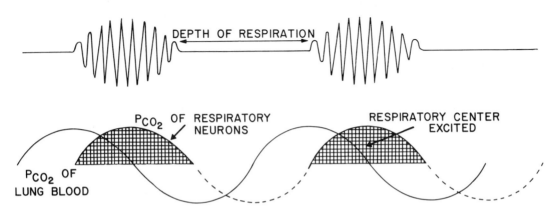

Figure 29-9. Cheyne-Stokes breathing. The pattern consists of bursts of tidal volumes of increasing and decreasing size, separated by a period of apnea (see text for more explanation). (Redrawn, with permission, from Guyton, A.C. 1981. *Textbook of medical physiology,* 6th ed., p. 570. Philadelphia: W.B. Saunders Co.)

arterial blood. The mechanism is explained as follows: The respiratory centers are perfused with blood high in CO_2, which increases ventilation and decreases arterial P_{CO_2}. When blood low in CO_2 perfuses the brain, ventilation is depressed, arterial P_{CO_2} increases again, and the cycle is repeated. The condition that initiates this sequence may be increased sensitivity of the respiratory centers to CO_2.

Other Breathing Patterns

Some other more common patterns of breathing follow:

Hyperpnea: Increased ventilation. Usually, tidal volume is increased; the rate of breathing may or may not be increased.

Polypnea, or *tachypnea:* Increased rate of breathing.

Hyperventilation: Alveolar ventilation exceeds metabolic requirements: more CO_2 is eliminated than produced. Usually, a self-limiting state.

Hypoventilation: Alveolar ventilation is inadequate to satisfy metabolic demands; less CO_2 is eliminated than produced; usually, a self-limiting state.

Apnea: Breathing stops, usually in expiration.

Apneusis: Breathing stops in inspiration, thus, inspiratory breath-holding.

Apneustic breathing: Inspiratory breath-holding interrupted periodically by expiration.

STUDY OUTLINE

Respiratory control system composed of sensors, integrator, and effectors.

NEURAL CONTROL OF PATTERN OF BREATHING Respiratory centers make decisions on basis of information from sensors to produce appropriate pattern of breathing.

RESPIRATORY CENTERS In brainstem: medullary, pneumotaxic, and apneustic.

MEDULLARY CENTERS Bilaterally located groups of neurons: dorsal respiratory group (DRG), ventral respiratory group (VRG).

DRG: inspiratory activity only; proposed site of rhythm generation; primary center for processing afferent information; drives VRG neurons.

VRG: inspiratory and expiratory activity; tonic activity interrupted by DRG input; axons project more peripherally.

APNEUSTIC CENTER Located in mid to lower pons.

If uninhibited, prolongs inspiration and causes breath-holding in inspiration (apneusis).

Normally inhibited by impulses from pneumotaxic center and vagus nerves.

PNEUMOTAXIC CENTER Located in upper pons.

No rhythmicity of its own.

Not necessary for maintaining rhythmicity.

Highest level of control required for optimal tidal volume and frequency.

CHEMICAL REGULATION OF VENTILATION Ventilation regulated by changes in concentration of O_2, CO_2, and H^+ in arterial blood.

CO_2 is major regulator at rest; depends on level of metabolism.

SENSORS Chemoreceptors.

CENTRAL CHEMORECEPTORS Bilaterally located on ventral surface of medulla; respond to changes of CO_2.

PERIPHERAL CHEMORECEPTORS Carotid and aortic bodies.

Carotid bodies are main sensors.

Respond to lack of O_2 ($P_{a O_2} < 50$ mm Hg).

Drive ventilation reflexly.

RESPONSE TO CO_2 $P_{a CO_2}$ is regulated around 40 mm Hg.

Level of alveolar ventilation is related directly to $P_{a CO_2}$.

Increased CO_2 in inspired air increases ventilatory drive.

Ventilatory drive caused by increased CO_2 is enhanced by low $P_{a O_2}$.

Altered by disease.

MECHANISM OF RESPONSE TO CO_2 Central chemoreceptors sensitive to $[H^+]$ of cerebrospinal fluid (CSF).

CO_2 diffuses easily from blood into CSF; forms H_2CO_3.

Liberated H^+ cannot be buffered by protein-poor CSF.

$[H^+]$ of CSF increases; respiratory centers are stimulated; pH of CSF is regulated around 7.2, probably by active transport of HCO_3^- into, or out of, CSF; chemical changes in CSF lag behind those in blood; central chemoreceptors are easily depressed by drugs, anesthesia, or high P_{CO_2}.

RESPONSE TO OXYGEN   Peripheral che-moreceptor activity increases when $Pa_{O_2} < 50$ mm Hg; respiration increases (hypoxic drive).

Response to low Pa_{O_2} (> 50 mm Hg) increases when Pc_{O_2} increases simultaneously.

In pulmonary disease, retention of CO_2 enhances hypoxic drive unless hypoxemia is treated with O_2 therapy.

RESPONSE TO [H+]   As [H+] of arterial blood increases, ventilation increases.

Peripheral H+ receptors are sensors.

Changes in Pc_{O_2} and [H+] are interrelated.

Changes of ventilation in response to metabolic acidosis or alkalosis are compensated for by greater elimination or retention of CO_2.

REFLEX CONTROL

REFLEXES FROM LUNGS

INFLATION-DEFLATION REFLEX   Hering–Breuer reflex.

When lungs are overinflated, frequency of respiration decreases.

When lungs are partially deflated, frequency of respiration increases.

Mechanoreceptors in bronchiolar and tracheal smooth muscles respond to stretch.

Afferent limb of reflex is carried by vagi.

In human, reflex prevents overinflation of lungs; operates when tidal volume > 800 ml; may be part of regulatory mechanisms that control work of breathing.

IRRITATION REFLEXES   Constriction of airways as result of noxious agents; receptors are located in upper airways (trachea and bronchi); protect lungs against injury.

PARADOXICAL REFLEX OF HEAD   Positive feedback; inflation on top of inflation; may play role in sighing and in infant's first breath.

REFLEX FROM CHEST WALL   Stretch reflex that increases tone of muscle spindles when resistance to breathing increases; respiratory muscles are driven to develop more tension and increase (maintain) tidal volume.

BARORECEPTOR REFLEXES   Blood pressure and respiration are related inversely.

OTHER REFLEXES   Pain and stimulation of joint receptors.

EFFECTS OF HIGHER CENTERS   Automatic phase of ventilation may depend on state of alertness; reticular activating system may be involved.

Voluntary hyperventilation or breath-holding is controlled by higher centers; exact centers are not known.

Ventilation is influenced by strong emotions (anger, fear); response is mediated by autonomic nervous system through hypothalamus.

PATTERNS OF BREATHING

NORMAL PATTERNS   Normal rate and tidal volume, known as eupnea.

CHEYNE-STOKES BREATHING   Abnormal pattern of waxing and waning of tidal volumes; pattern develops when changes of Pc_{O_2} in CSF and arterial blood are out of phase.

BIBLIOGRAPHY

Angell-James, J.E.; Elsner, R.; and Daly, M.D. 1981. Lung inflation: effects on heart rate, respiration, and vagal efferent activity in seals. *Am. J. Physiol.* 240 (Heart and Circ. Physiol. 9):H190.

Berger, A.J., Mitchell, R.A., and Severinghaus, J.W. 1977. Regulation of respiration. *N. Engl. J. Med.* 297:92, 138, 194 (3 parts).

Brown, H.W., and Plum, F. 1961. The neurologic basis of Cheyne-Stokes respiration. *Am. J. Med.* 30:849.

Cherniack, N.S. 1981. Respiratory dysrhythmias during sleep. *N. Engl. J. Med.* 305:325.

Cohen, M.I. 1979. Neurogenesis of respiratory rhythm in the mammal. *Physiol. Rev.* 59:1105.

Cohen, M.I. 1981. Central determinants of respiratory rhythm. *Ann. Rev. Physiol.* 43:91.

Comroe, J.H. 1974. *Physiology of respiration*, 2nd ed. Chicago: Yearbook Medical Publishers, Inc.

Guyton, A.C., Crowell, J.W., and Moore, J.W. 1956. Basic oscillating mechanism of Cheyne-Stokes breathing. *Am. J. Physiol.* 187:395.

Kalia, M. (Symp. Chairman). 1981. Central respiratory rhythmicity (Symposium). *Fed. Proc.* 40:2363.

Loeschcke, H.H., and Gertz, K.H. 1958. Einflusz des O_2-Druckes in der Einatmungsluft auf die Atemtätigkeit des Menschen, geprüft unter Fonstanthaltung des alveolaren CO_2-Druckes. *Pflüegers Arch.* 267: 460.

Nielsen, M., and Smith, H. 1951. Studies on the regulation of respiration in acute hypoxia. *Acta Physiol. Scand.* 24:293.

Pitts. R.F. 1946. Organization of the respiratory center. *Physiol. Rev.* 26:609.

Wang, S.C., and Ngai, S.H. 1964. General organization of central respiratory mechanisms. In *Handbook of Physiology*, Sec. 3. *Respiration*, Vol. I, editors W.O. Fenn and H. Rahn. Washington, D.C.: American Physiological Society.

Pulmonary Circulation

CHAPTER CONTENTS

The pulmonary circulation participates in the exchange of oxygen and carbon dioxide between the blood and the alveolar air. Mixed venous blood low in O_2 and high in CO_2 is pumped through the pulmonary capillaries that surround the alveoli, where O_2 is added to the blood and CO_2 is removed. The blood that enters the pulmonary capillaries is about 75% saturated with O_2, has a Po_2 of 40 mm Hg and a Pco_2 of 46 mm Hg. At sea level, blood leaving the pulmonary capillaries is about 97% saturated with oxygen, has a Po_2 of 100 mm Hg, and has a Pco_2 of 40 mm Hg. This arterial blood is delivered to the left ventricle and distributed to the rest of the body from there (Figure 30-1).

PULMONARY HEMODYNAMICS

The functional anatomy of the pulmonary vascular system and the relationships among the pressures, flows, and resistances in the pul-

monary circulation are discussed in some detail in Chapter 17. This discussion focuses on the features of the system that are relevant to the exchange of gases between blood and alveolar air; the topic of pulmonary hemodynamics is treated only briefly. Some of the nonrespiratory functions of the lungs also are discussed.

Pressures and Resistances

The pulmonary circulation is a low pressure system. Figure 30-1 shows normal values of intravascular pressures. The driving force of the pulmonary circulation, which must overcome the frictional resistance to the flow of blood, is the difference between the mean pressure in the pulmonary artery (13 mm Hg) and that in the left atrium (7 mm Hg). This relatively small gradient of 6 mm Hg is enough to drive through the pulmonary circulation the same volume of blood that is driven through the systemic circulation (5–6 liters/min) by a gradient of 90 mm Hg. This is possible because the pulmonary vascular resistance is only about

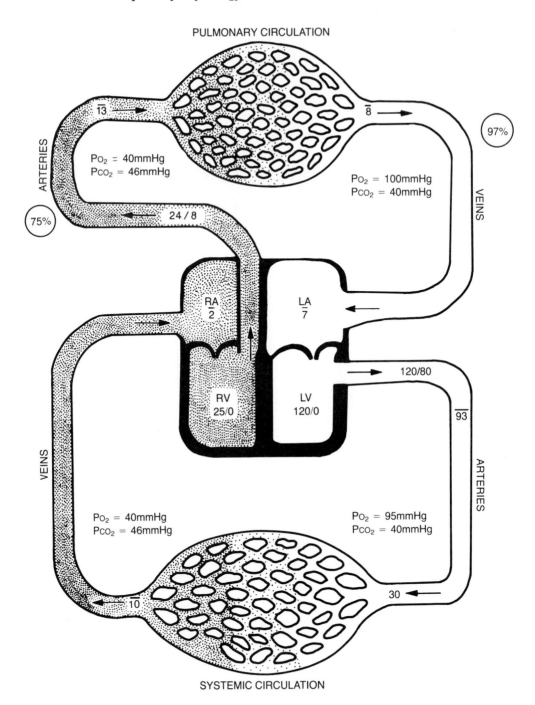

Figure 30-1.   Blood pressures and typical blood gas tensions at sea level in the pulmonary and systemic circulations.

Figure 30-2. Two likely mechanisms for decreasing pulmonary vascular resistance when blood flow increases. **A,** Normal. Not all available capillaries are perfused. **B,** Recruitment. All capillaries are perfused. **C,** Distention. Capillaries being perfused are distended.

one-fifteenth as great as the systemic vascular resistance.

$$\text{Rpulm} = \frac{6 \text{ mm Hg}}{83 \text{ ml/sec}} = 0.072 \text{ mm Hg/ml/sec}$$

Another characteristic of this system is that a relatively small change in driving pressure can increase the pulmonary blood flow to three to four times the resting value. This can occur because some vessels that normally are collapsed because of low perfusion pressure may be opened, that is, recruited (Figure 30-2), and other vessels are distended easily. Thus, pulmonary vascular resistance decreases when cardiac output increases. In addition, the increased surface area for diffusion aids the exchange of gases across the alveolar capillary membrane.

Factors That Influence Pressures and Resistances

BREATHING
The dimensions of the lungs change during breathing. Expansion of the chest during inspiration decreases the intrathoracic pressure and thereby increases the gradient of transmural pressure that distends most of the blood vessels contained within the thorax. Although the vessels lengthen, the effect on the radius is more important

$$R \simeq \frac{1}{r^4}$$

therefore, the overall effect is a decrease in resistance and a consequent increase in flow.

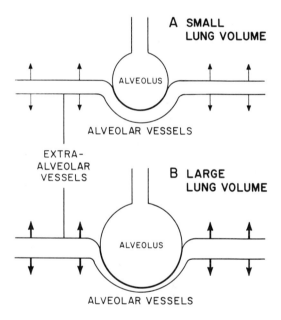

Figure 30-3. Effects of lung inflation on pulmonary capillaries. **A,** At small lung volumes (e.g., end of expiration), the capillaries are relatively unaffected. **B,** When the volume of the lungs increases (e.g., deep inspiration), the vessels adjacent to the alveoli are compressed, but the so-called extra-alveolar capillaries are distended by increased traction from the surrounding structures (indicated by arrows).

ALVEOLAR PRESSURE
The capillaries adjacent to the alveoli are subjected to the pressure of the air within the alveoli. Because pulmonary capillary pressure is low, alveolar capillaries are compressed to various degrees (Figure 30-3). However, during

normal breathing, the surface tension in the layer of fluid that lines the air-filled alveoli limits the inflation of the lungs and, hence, the compression of the vessels. This occurs because some of the air pressure is used to overcome the surface tension; therefore, when the alveolar pressure is the same as the capillary pressure, the vessels are not occluded. In contrast, if certain alveoli are filled with fluid, the flow of blood in the capillaries that surround them always stops when the alveolar pressure equals the vascular pressure. This occurs because in this case there is no surface tension, and all of the alveolar pressure opposes the capillary pressure. The increased vascular resistance in the compressed capillaries may redirect the flow of blood to alveoli that are ventilated better.

Total pulmonary vascular resistance increases during maximal inflation of the lungs and during forced expiration. During maximal inspiration, the alveoli enlarge excessively. The capillaries around and between the alveoli are stretched, their radii are reduced, and the resistance is increased (Figure 30-3). During forced expiration, the positive intrathoracic and intrapulmonary (intra-alveolar) pressures tend to compress all pulmonary blood vessels.

HYPOXEMIA

Although pulmonary arterioles are less muscular than their systemic counterparts, constriction of vascular smooth muscle can increase the pulmonary vascular resistance and thereby increase pulmonary arterial pressure. One of the most effective stimuli for pulmonary vasoconstriction is systemic hypoxemia, or decreased oxygen tension in the blood. This effect is mediated reflexly through the peripheral chemoreceptors. The resulting increase in pulmonary arterial pressure improves the perfusion of the apical capillaries.

Locally decreased alveolar Po_2 causes precapillary constriction, which decreases the perfusion of the hypoxic region and shifts the blood to alveoli that have higher Po_2. This mechanism improves the matching of ventilation and perfusion.

ACETYLCHOLINE

When the cholinergic neurotransmitter, acetylcholine, is injected into the pulmonary artery, it dilates constricted arterioles by relaxing arteriolar smooth muscles. Clinically, acetylcholine sometimes is used to distinguish between increased pulmonary resistance caused by vasoconstriction and that which may be caused by other vascular problems, such as obstruction of the capillary lumen by thrombi, emboli, or atherosclerosis.

Pulmonary Blood Flow

The pulmonary circulation is in series with the systemic circulation; hence, the pulmonary blood flow normally is equal to the cardiac output.

CAPILLARY FLOW

The pulmonary capillaries are part of the system of gas exchange. Because of their high density, these short vessels virtually form two sheets of endothelium held open by connective tissue supports. At any time, they contain approximately 75–100 ml of blood, or approximately the stroke volume of the right ventricle. The blood is spread out over an area of 70–100 m^2 and forms a layer about 10 μm thick. As a result of the low arteriolar resistance, the flow of blood in the pulmonary capillaries is pulsatile; this is advantageous, as the pause between pulses allows more time for the exchange of gases between the blood and the alveolar air. When the stroke volume of the heart increases, the time available for the oxygenation of the blood becomes less; however, there is a considerable reserve for equilibration of the partial pressures of O_2 and CO_2. A given red cell spends approximately 0.75 sec in a pulmonary capillary, but it is oxygenated during the first third of its journey through the vessel; therefore, the oxygenation of the blood normally is not hindered when the cardiac output increases.

The average capillary transit time can be calculated from:

$$\frac{\text{Volume of blood in the capillaries (ml)}}{\text{Cardiac output (ml/sec)}}$$

$$= \frac{75 \text{ ml}}{100 \text{ ml/sec}} = 0.75 \text{ sec}$$

MEASURING BLOOD FLOW

Pulmonary blood flow is measured by an application of the Fick method:

$$\dot{Q}\text{pulm} = \frac{\dot{V}o_2 \text{ (ml/min)}}{\text{a-}\bar{v} \text{ } O_2 \text{ difference (ml/liter)}}$$

CLINICAL CORRELATION
30.1   Respiratory Failure in Cardiogenic Shock

CASE REPORT

The Patient: A 43-year-old woman.

Principal Complaints: Dyspnea and severe chest pains over the left side.

History: The patient had been hospitalized because of myocardial infarction eight months before the current admission. Her medications included dopamine, an agent that improves cardiac contractility, and nitroprusside, a peripheral vasodilator, which decreases the afterload and, consequently, the O_2 demand of the myocardium. After initial stabilization on this treatment, her condition had begun to deteriorate, and she was admitted for evaluation.

Clinical Examination: The patient's arterial pressure was 105/62 mm Hg (normal, 90–140/60–90 mm Hg), and the heart rate was 155 beats/min (normal, 60–100 beats/min). Rales (rattling, scraping sounds) were heard over the lower lung fields, and an x-ray film showed that the right hemidiaphragm was elevated (not contracting well). An electrocardiogram indicated massive, healed myocardial infarction.* With the patient breathing a mixture of air that contained 30% oxygen, arterial blood Po_2 (Pao_2) was 74 mm Hg (normal, with the patient breathing room air, 75–100 mm Hg), the $Paco_2$ was 26 mm Hg (normal, 35–45 mm Hg), and the pH of the arterial blood was 7.54 (normal, 7.35–7.45). The pulmonary arterial pressure was 42/28 mm Hg (normal, 12–28/3–13 mm Hg), and pulmonary capillary wedge pressure (see Chapter 17) was 26 mm Hg (normal, 3–11 mm Hg). Her cardiac index was 1.95 liters/min/m² (normal, 2.5–3.6 liters/min/m²). She could not get her breath unless she was propped up to an almost-sitting position.**

Treatment: The patient was treated with furosemide, an effective diuretic agent, and morphine, to reduce her anxiety; in addition, the dopamine and nitroprusside were continued. Her condition improved somewhat. By the third day, when her pulse rate decreased to 120/min, her cardiac index increased to 3.2 liters/min/m², and her pulmonary wedge pressure decreased to 14 mm Hg. From the next day on, however, her condition deteriorated rapidly. The patient developed ventricular tachycardia, which initially was treated successfully with lidocaine (to depress myocardial excitability). Her shortness of breath became progressively worse. On the sixth day, she had to be intubated, and was ventilated at a rate of 12 liters/min with an F_1o_2 of 80%, but adequate oxygenation of the blood could not be maintained. The patient's pulmonary wedge pressure increased to 40 mm Hg, and she developed severe pulmonary edema, which further impeded the exchange of respiratory gases and oxygenation of blood.

Outcome: Eight days after she entered the hospital, the patient died of ventricular fibrillation. Resuscitation was attempted but was unsuccessful.

*The indications are diminished R waves and the appearance of Q waves in the affected area of the left ventricle. These changes occur because the diminished mass of active myocardium (damaged muscle is replaced by inactive scar tissue) produces less current.

**When a person sits or stands, the force of gravity causes some accumulation of blood in the lower parts of the body, which decreases the volume of blood in the thorax and increases the functional residual capacity (FRC). This aids respiration in a person whose FRC and lung compliance are decreased by pulmonary congestion.

where $\dot{V}_{O_2}$ is the volume of oxygen taken up by the blood each minute as it flows through the pulmonary capillaries, and a-v O_2 difference is the difference between the concentration of oxygen in the arterial blood and that in the venous blood. The equation also is used to determine the cardiac output, because under normal conditions, the pulmonary blood flow is equal to the output of the left ventricle (see Chapter 14).

DISTRIBUTION
OF BLOOD FLOW

The distribution of pulmonary blood flow depends on the position of the subject relative to the earth's gravity. When the subject is supine, the flow of blood is distributed relatively evenly throughout the lungs; in an upright person, however, the flow of blood is greater at the bottom of the lungs than at the top (Figure 30-4). This difference occurs because the hydrostatic pressure at the top of the lungs is not the same as that at the bottom (see Chapter 17). The weight of the column of blood in the vertical vessels of the lungs imposes a hydrostatic pressure that must be overcome to perfuse the apical portion of the lungs. In addition, the higher pressure at the base of the lungs in-

creases the diameter of the capillaries and increases the rate of blood flow in that portion according to the Poiseuille relationship (Chapter 12).

In Figure 30-5, the lungs are divided into four sections, from zone A at the apex through zone D at the base. In zone A, pulmonary capillary pressure is less than alveolar pressure, alveolar capillaries (PC) are collapsed, and flow is minimal. Near the base of the lungs (zone C), the addition of the hydrostatic pressure imposed by gravity increases arterial pressure and dilates the vessels. The rate of blood flow in this zone is the highest in the lungs; it depends on the difference between the arterial and venous pressures, both of which exceed alveolar pressure. In the middle of the lungs (zone B), alveolar pressure is less than arterial pressure but greater than venous pressure; the flow depends on the gradient between the arterial and alveolar pressures, which increases with the distance from the top to the bottom of the lungs. Since flow increases from top to bottom, vascular resistance decreases. Zone D represents the very bottom of the lungs. Because of the weight of the blood, the vessels in this area are compressed somewhat, and the vascular resistance is increased. The blood flow is slightly less in this part, and the capillaries are distended less than in zone C.

The effect of gravity causes relative underperfusion of capillaries in the apex of the upright lung (zone A in Figure 30-5). Therefore, under normal conditions, the apical alveoli in the upright lung are better ventilated than perfused, that is, ventilation and perfusion are mismatched. The excess ventilation represents dead space, as it does not participate in gas exchange. This concept is discussed in detail in Chapter 33. When the cardiac output increases (as in exercise), or the pulmonary arterial pressure increases (as at high altitude), more of the capillaries in zone A are perfused, which improves the matching of ventilation and perfusion and increases the surface area for diffusion of gases. On the other hand, when the cardiac output and the pulmonary arterial pressure decrease, as they do after hemorrhage, fewer of the apical capillaries are perfused, ventilation and perfusion are mismatched to a greater extent, and the alveolar dead space increases.

There also is a gradient of transpulmonary pressure (difference between alveolar pressure and intrapleural pressure) from apex to base. This is due to the more negative intrapleural

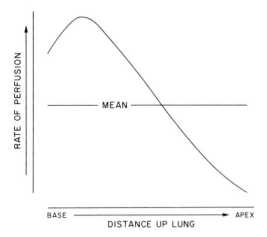

Figure 30-4. Topographic distribution of blood flow in the upright lung of a resting human. [133]Xe was injected intravenously and its distribution detected by external counters. Note the nearly linear decrease of blood flow from bottom to top. The mean value is determined by integrating the area under the curve; it gives the rate of flow if perfusion were even throughout the lungs. (Redrawn, with permission, from Hughes, J.M.B., et al. 1968. *Resp. Physiol.* 4:63.)

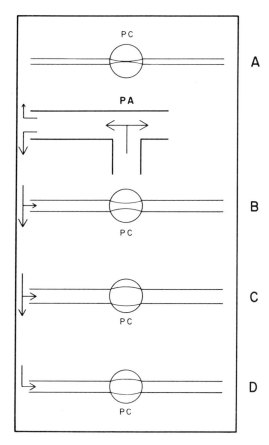

Figure 30-5. Pulmonary blood flow in various regions of the lungs from apex (**A**) to base (**D**). The scheme illustrates the effects of gravity on the pulmonary perfusion pressure and distribution of blood flow in the upright position. The circles represent the alveoli, through which the pulmonary capillaries are exposed to the pressure of the atmosphere, which is constant throughout the lungs. Arrows indicate direction of blood flow (PA, pulmonary artery; PC, alveolar capillary).

pressure at the apex, caused mainly by the effect of gravity on the mass of the lungs. Therefore, at the resting lung volume (FRC), the alveoli are inflated more at the top of the lungs than at the bottom, and at the top, intra-alveolar pressure may exceed the already low capillary pressure and further decrease the rate of blood flow. Perfusion increases almost linearly from the top of the lungs to the bottom (see Figure 30-4). The difference is attenuated to some extent by autoregulation, as vascular smooth muscle tends to resist passive dilatation by increasing tension when the transmural pressure increases.

The topographical distribution of pulmonary blood flow also is influenced by the volume of the lungs. Capillaries that are not exposed to the pressure in the alveoli, sometimes referred to as extra-alveolar capillaries, normally are held open by traction from the surrounding parenchyma. At low lung volumes, traction is less, and because of the regional differences of transpulmonary pressure (greater at the apex), the basal capillaries tend to collapse more than the apical ones. Consequently, when the lungs are deflated, pulmonary blood flow tends to be reduced more at the base than at the apex (see Figure 30-3).

During flights in space, the removal of the force of gravity (zero G force) equalizes the intravascular pressures within the lungs. Acceleration (positive G force) adds to the force of gravity, whereas deceleration (negative G force) decreases it. The effect on the distribution of blood in the lungs depends on the orientation of the body with respect to the direction of acceleration. A person standing in an elevator receives positive G force when the elevator begins its ascent; hydrostatic pressure increases at the base and decreases at the apex. As the elevator stops (decelerates), negative G force is applied to the lungs; hydrostatic pressure decreases at the base and increases at the apex. In a descending elevator, on the other hand, one experiences negative G force at the beginning of the descent and positive G force as the elevator stops.

MEASURING DISTRIBUTION OF BLOOD FLOW

The regional distribution of blood flow in the lungs can be measured by the use of radioactive markers. For example, radioactive xenon can be dissolved in saline and injected intravenously. It is not very soluble in the blood, however, and when the blood reaches the alveolar capillaries, xenon diffuses into the alveolar air. The distribution of the radioactivity in the lungs, assessed by externally placed counters, indicates the distribution of blood flow. Figure 30-4 shows a typical curve of distribution of xenon.

NONVENTILATED PULMONARY BLOOD FLOW

The partial pressure of oxygen in the systemic arterial blood is slightly less than that of the blood that leaves the pulmonary capillaries (see Figure 30-1), because some of the blood that flows through the lungs does not participate in the exchange of gases, and the arteries receive a small amount of systemic venous blood. For example, part of the coronary circulation drains directly into the left ventricle, and some of the bronchial venous blood drains into the pulmonary veins. Both of these anatomical arrangements are examples of absolute shunts; the blood that is shunted does not come into contact with the alveoli and therefore is not oxygenated. After this blood mixes with the rest of the arterial blood, the O_2 saturation is decreased slightly, and a small alveolar-arterial O_2 difference exists. Other nonventilated flow can result from the movement of blood past nonventilated alveoli or past no alveoli at all. When the difference between $P_{A_{O_2}}$ and Pa_{O_2} is greater than normal, shunting of blood is suspected. In the presence of large shunts, the outputs of the two ventricles may differ significantly. For further discussion and the estimation of shunts see Chapters 14 and 33.

Exchange of Fluid in Lungs

FACTORS THAT GOVERN EXCHANGE OF FLUID

The factors that govern the exchange of fluid across the systemic circulation also govern exchange across the pulmonary capillaries. The movement of fluid into or out of the capillaries depends on the net difference between the hydrostatic pressure (filtration) and the colloidal osmotic pressure (absorption). In the lungs, the interstitial space is between the capillary and the alveolus (Figure 30-6). Here, the forces that determine the outward movement of fluid from the capillary are the hydrostatic pressure within the capillary and the subatmospheric tissue pressure. The surface tension that develops in the alveolus, at the fluid-gas interface, tends to draw fluid from the interstitial space into the alveolus, thereby helping to maintain the tissue pressure below atmospheric pressure. The filtration pressure is the algebraic difference between hydrostatic pressure and tissue pressure. This force is opposed by the net oncotic pressure, which is produced by the plasma proteins inside and outside the capillary, and by the air pressure within the alveoli. The net oncotic pressure holds the fluid in the capillary, and the intra-alveolar pressure tends to compress the interstitial spaces so that the tissue pressure is increased. Normally, the mean pres-

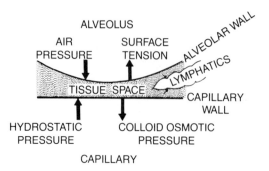

Figure 30-6.   Factors that affect the exchange of fluid in the lungs. Whether fluid leaves or enters a capillary depends on the difference between the net hydrostatic pressure (capillary pressure minus tissue fluid pressure) and the net colloidal osmotic pressure (plasma colloidal osmotic pressure minus tissue colloidal osmotic pressure). Two additional factors are involved in the lungs: (1) alveolar surface tension, which adds to the hydrostatic pressure, and (2) alveolar air pressure, which adds to the tissue fluid pressure. The relatively low pulmonary hydrostatic pressure (compared to the colloidal osmotic pressure) helps to protect against "wet" lungs. Excess interstitial fluid drains into the lymphatic system and is returned to the venous circulation. (Redrawn, with permission, from Greene, D.G. 1963. *Handbook of physiology,* Section 2, Circulation, Vol. II, p. 1534.)

sure in the pulmonary capillary is about 8 mm Hg, which is much lower than the plasma oncotic pressure (25–30 mm Hg); therefore, the alveoli and the interstitial spaces are kept relatively dry. This is an important concept from the standpoint of gas exchange. Excess fluid in the alveoli or in the interstitium increases the width of the pathway through which air must diffuse from the alveolus to the blood and thereby decreases the effectiveness of the gas-exchange apparatus. Fortunately, the anatomical arrangement between capillary and alveolus is such that one side of the capillary abuts directly on the alveolar epithelium with no interstitial space between. At this site, gas exchange is relatively undisturbed even in the presence of interstitial edema.

PULMONARY EDEMA

Fluid exudes into the tissue spaces and the alveoli when the net filtration pressure exceeds the net absorption pressure. This may happen when a reduction in plasma protein concentration decreases the colloidal osmotic pressure of the plasma or the hydrostatic pressure in the pulmonary capillary increases. The latter condition may occur when the pulmonary venous pressure is higher than normal because of left ventricular failure (see Chapter 22). Gravity also plays a role here, as it increases the hydrostatic pressure at the base of the lungs. In ambulatory patients who have a heart condition, the combined effects of the increased capillary pressure and gravity cause fluid to accumulate at the base of the lungs. This kind of mild pulmonary edema can be corrected by bedrest, which eliminates the effect of gravity and restores the conditions that favor the reabsorption of fluid from the tissue spaces. Increased vascular permeability due to endothelial damage by toxic agents also may cause pulmonary edema. Usually, this is referred to as "permeability" or "nonhydrostatic" pulmonary edema to distinguish it from that caused by hemodynamic changes. Pulmonary edema is a serious problem, because it hinders the exchange of gases between the blood in the capillary and the air in the alveolus, obstructs airways and thereby increases the airway resistance, and causes uneven distribution of air and blood in the lungs (uneven ventilation-perfusion ratio). Alveolar edema also leads to unstable alveoli, because of loss of surfactant, and causes alveoli to collapse at low lung volumes (see Chapter 28). All of these conditions eventually cause pulmonary shunts and systemic arterial hypoxemia. The treatment of pulmonary edema is directed first toward reducing the hydrostatic (filtration) pressure. Usually this can be done by decreasing the blood volume with a diuretic agent or aiding left ventricular function by the use of digitalis (increases contractility) or a systemic vasodilator (decreases afterload) (see Chapter 22).

DROWNING

The difference between hydrostatic pressure and colloidal osmotic pressure in the pulmonary capillaries provides a mechanism to absorb fluid from the alveoli; as a result, the alveoli are relatively dry, and the exchange of gas is facilitated. However, the low mean pulmonary blood pressure can be disadvantageous in circumstances such as drowning in fresh water, for example.

The normal response to immersion in water is breath-holding, swallowing, and laryngospasm. If the water is very cold, the response is reflex hyperventilation. These events are followed by aspiration of water into the lungs. When someone drowns in fresh water, which is a hypotonic solution, water is absorbed rapidly into the circulation through the alveoli, and the plasma is diluted. The red blood cells may swell and burst (hemolysis) in this hypotonic environment, and the changes in electrolyte concentration may alter the electrical activity of the heart. The final event often is ventricular fibrillation, which may be induced by the combined effects of hypoxia and low $[K^+]$ and $[Na^+]$ in the extracellular fluid. Salt water drowning, however, is associated more often with increased serum $[Na^+]$ and severe pulmonary edema. The terminal event in this condition is asphyxia.

Other Nonrespiratory Functions of the Pulmonary Circulation

BLOOD RESERVOIR

The volume of blood in the lungs at any one time is about 700–1000 ml, or about 12%–15% of total blood volume. Most of this blood is in the pulmonary veins and serves as a reservoir for the systemic circulation. It is available to support the output of the left ventricle when the output of the right ventricle is diminished temporarily (Figure 30-7), and it is the first

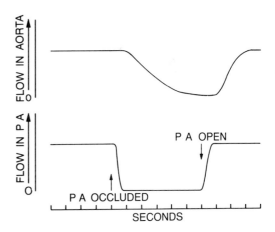

Figure 30-7. Blood flow recording that demonstrates the reservoir function of the pulmonary circulation. Note that the aortic blood flow continues for several seconds after the main pulmonary artery is occluded. When the occlusion is released, pulmonary arterial blood flow is restored immediately, while the output of the left side builds up gradually through several seconds.

source of accelerated filling of the left ventricle when the cardiac output is increased.

FILTRATION

The small vessels and capillaries of the pulmonary circulation trap emboli and thrombi and help to prevent obstruction of the more vital capillaries of the brain, the heart, or the kidneys. Small thrombi are dissolved by fibrinolytic substances released into the pulmonary circulation by endothelial cells. Although some of the pulmonary capillaries are sacrificed in this process, the number initially present exceeds that needed for gas exchange; therefore, unless the embolism is widespread, oxygenation of the blood is not affected significantly. In addition, the lungs have two blood supplies, and when a pulmonary vessel is occluded, part of the bronchial circulation perfuses the alveolar capillaries and helps to prevent the death of the cells.

NUTRITION

Pulmonary blood flow provides for the metabolic needs of structures in the primary lobule by supplying substrates to the respiratory bronchioles, the alveolar ducts, and the alveoli.

METABOLISM

Some of the metabolic functions of the pulmonary circulation are related to the 40 types of cells found in the lungs. Substances can be synthesized, stored, inactivated, or altered chemically while being transported through the lungs. Thus, the pulmonary circulation contributes significantly to the composition of arterial blood.

Pulmonary mast cells synthesize and store heparin and histamine for subsequent release into the pulmonary circulation. The local release of histamine may be responsible for the increased pulmonary vascular resistance that is caused by local hypoxemia.

SYNTHESIS OF PHOSPHOLIPID

Type II alveolar cells are known to incorporate lipid precursors from which they synthesize the surface-active material, dipalmitoylphosphatidylcholine. The surfactant is stored in the lamellar bodies of these cells and released locally to line the alveolar surfaces. The surfactant stabilizes the alveoli and reduces the alveolar surface tension, as discussed in Chapter 28. The lungs also synthesize certain proteins and carbohydrates.

METABOLISM OF HORMONES

Pulmonary endothelial cells are metabolically active, since they are responsible for the uptake, storage, and/or conversion of some of the substances that enter the lungs in the pulmonary arterial blood. Angiotensin I is converted to angiotensin II by these cells. Activation is rapid, as almost 80% of the angiotensin I is converted enzymatically to angiotensin II during one passage through the lungs.

Some of the substances inactivated by the endothelial cells are bradykinin, serotonin, prostaglandins E_1 and E_2, and acetylcholine. Other substances, prostaglandins A_1 and A_2, for example, pass through unaltered. The system is highly specific; for example, norepinephrine is inactivated, while epinephrine goes through unchanged.

IMMUNE RESPONSE

Alveolar macrophages are part of the system of defense that the lungs have against microorganisms and other small particles that are inhaled. These cells are specialized phagocytes that can bind immunoglobulins and complement and ingest particulate matter.

STUDY OUTLINE

Systemic venous blood is approximately 75% saturated with O_2; P_{O_2} is 40 mm Hg, P_{CO_2} is 46 mm Hg.

Systemic arterial blood is approximately 97% saturated with O_2; P_{O_2} is 100 mm Hg, P_{CO_2} is 40 mm Hg.

PULMONARY HEMODYNAMICS Relationships among pressure, flow, and resistance.

PRESSURES AND RESISTANCES A low pressure, hence, low resistance, system.

Small pressure gradient (mean pulmonary artery pressure minus mean left atrial pressure) drives same volume of blood as through systemic circulation.

Pulmonary blood flow increases threefold to fourfold with only small change in driving pressure; resistance decreases.

FACTORS THAT INFLUENCE PRESSURES AND RESISTANCES

BREATHING Decreasing intrathoracic pressure during inspiration distends blood vessels; resistance decreases ($R \simeq 1/r^4$) and flow increases.

ALVEOLAR PRESSURE Capillaries that surround alveoli are compressed by alveolar pressure.

In air-filled alveoli, surface tension limits inflation of lungs and prevents occlusion of vessels.

In fluid-filled lungs, alveolar pressure opposes capillary pressure.

Positive intrathoracic pressure compresses all pulmonary blood vessels.

HYPOXEMIA Systemic hypoxemia causes an increase in pulmonary arterial pressure; perfusion of apical capillaries is improved.

Local alveolar hypoxemia causes shift of blood to better-ventilated alveoli; ventilation-perfusion matching improved.

ACETYLCHOLINE Dilates constricted arterioles; used to determine cause of increased pulmonary vascular resistance.

PULMONARY BLOOD FLOW Equal to cardiac output.

CAPILLARY FLOW Part of gas exchange system; pulsatile.

Contains 75–100 ml of blood (one ventricular stroke volume) spread over area of 75–100 m^2.

Given red cell spends less than 1 sec in pulmonary capillary; oxygenation normally requires less than one-third of time; reserve for oxygenation when cardiac output increases.

MEASURING BLOOD FLOW Fick method.

DISTRIBUTION OF BLOOD FLOW Influenced by gravity and lung volume.

Lung upright: blood flow decreases almost linearly from base to apex; at base, added hydrostatic pressure distends capillaries; at apex, gradient of transpulmonary pressure from top to bottom distends alveoli, which tends to compress adjacent capillaries.

Removal of gravity equalizes pulmonary intravascular pressures; positive G force exaggerates effects of gravity.

At low lung volumes, basal capillaries collapse more than apical ones.

MEASURING DISTRIBUTION OF BLOOD FLOW Tracers: ^{133}xenon.

NONVENTILATED PULMONARY BLOOD FLOW Part of coronary and bronchial venous blood mixes directly with oxygenated blood (anatomical shunts); causes small P_{AO_2}–P_{aO_2} difference.

Blood flowing past nonventilated alveoli or no alveoli (physiological shunts); causes significant P_{AO_2}–P_{aO_2} difference.

EXCHANGE OF FLUID IN LUNGS

FACTORS THAT GOVERN EXCHANGE OF FLUID Same as in systemic circulation.

Outward fluid movement is determined by hydrostatic pressure and tissue pressure; filtration pressure is algebraic difference between hydrostatic pressure and tissue pressure.

Inward fluid movement is determined by colloidal osmotic pressure and alveolar pressure.

Net movement depends on difference between hydrostatic pressure and colloidal osmotic pressure; normally, hydrostatic pressure is much lower than colloidal osmotic pressure, and lungs are kept relatively dry.

PULMONARY EDEMA Net filtration pressure exceeds net reabsorption pressure.

Gas exchange between capillary blood and alveolar air is hindered; adds to ventilation-perfusion imbalance.

Causes obstruction and increases airway resistance.

DROWNING Fresh water: often causes ventricular fibrillation.

Salt water: causes asphyxia.

OTHER NONRESPIRATORY FUNCTIONS OF THE PULMONARY CIRCULATION AND LUNGS

BLOOD RESERVOIR Lungs contain 12%–15% of total blood volume; serve as reservoir for systemic circulation.

FILTRATION Emboli and thrombi are trapped in small vessels; protects systemic capillaries.

NUTRITION Pulmonary circulation perfuses primary lobule.

METABOLISM Function is related to many types of cells; mast cells: synthesize and store heparin and histamine.

SYNTHESIS OF PHOSPHOLIPID Type II cells: synthesize dipalmitoylphosphatidylcholine (surfactant).

METABOLISM OF HORMONES Function of endothelial cells.

Conversion of angiotensin I to angiotensin II.

Inactivation of bradykinin, serotonin, prostaglandins E_1 and E_2, acetylcholine, norepinephrine.

IMMUNE RESPONSE Alveolar macrophages are part of defense system of lungs.

BIBLIOGRAPHY

Bergofsky, E.H. 1980. Humoral control of the pulmonary circulation. *Ann. Rev. Physiol.* 42:221.

Comroe, J.H., Jr. 1974. *Physiology of respiration.* Chicago: Year Book Medical Publishers, Inc.

Culver, B.H., and Butler, J. 1980. Mechanical influences on the pulmonary microcirculation. *Ann. Rev. Physiol.* 42:187.

Downing, S.E., and Lee, J.C. 1980. Nervous control of the pulmonary circulation. *Ann. Rev. Physiol.* 42:199.

Fishman, A.P., and Renkin, E.D., editors. 1979. *Pulmonary edema.* Bethesda, Md.: American Physiological Society.

Fishman, A.P. 1980. Vasomotor regulation of the pulmonary circulation. *Ann. Rev. Physiol.* 42:211.

Gordon, S. 1977. Macrophage neutral proteinases and defense of the lung. *Fed. Proc.* 36:2707.

Greene, D.G. 1965. Drowning. In *Handbook of physiology,* Section 3, Respiration, Vol. II, Chap. 47. Editors W.O. Fenn and H. Rahn. Washington, D.C.: American Physiological Society.

Greene, D.G. 1965. Pulmonary edema. In *Handbook of physiology,* Section 3, Respiration, Vol. II, Chap. 70, editors W.O. Fenn and H. Rahn. Washington, D.C.: American Physiological Society.

Grossman, R.F.; Jones, J.G.; and Murray, J.F. 1980. Effects of oleic acid-induced pulmonary edema on lung mechanics. *J. App. Physiol.: Respir. Environ. Exercise Physiol.* 48:1045.

Hocking, W.G., and Golde, D.W. 1979. The pulmonary-alveolar macrophage. *N. Engl. J. Med.* 301:580.

Hughes, J.M.B.; Glazier, J.B.; Maloney, J.E., et al. 1968. Effect of lung volume on the distribution of pulmonary blood flow in man. *Resp. Physiol.* 4:58.

Kadowitz, P.J.; Gruetter, C.A.; Spannhake, E.W., et al. 1981. Pulmonary vascular responses to prostaglandins. *Fed. Proc.* 40:1991.

Lewis, R.A., and Austen, K.F. 1977. Nonrespiratory functions of pulmonary cells: the mast cell. *Fed. Proc.* 36:2676.

Mason, R.J.; Dobbs, L.G.; Greenleaf, R.D., et al. 1977. Alveolar type II cells. *Fed. Proc.* 36:2697.

Nunn, J.F. 1977. *Applied respiratory physiology.* London: Butterworth & Co.

Remolina, C.; Khan, A.U.; Santiago, T.V., et al. 1981. Positional hypoxemia in unilateral lung disease. *N. Engl. J. Med.* 304:523.

Ryan, J.W., and Ryan, U.S. 1977. Pulmonary endothelial cells. *Fed. Proc.* 36:2683.

Said, S.I. 1982. Metabolic functions of the pulmonary circulation. *Circ. Res.* 50:325.

Said, S.I. 1982. Pulmonary metabolism of prostaglandins and vasoconstrictor peptides. *Ann. Rev. Physiol.* 44:257.

West, J.B. 1979. *Respiratory physiology: the essentials,* 2nd ed. Baltimore: Williams & Wilkins.

31

Diffusion of Gases and Transport of Oxygen

CHAPTER CONTENTS

DIFFUSION OF GASES

The mechanics involved in the transfer of O_2 into the alveoli and CO_2 out of the alveoli were discussed in Chapters 27 and 28. The next phase of pulmonary gas-exchange is the transfer of O_2 and CO_2 across the alveolar-capillary membrane by the passive process of diffusion. The rate of diffusion of a gas ($\dot{V}$gas) through the blood-gas barrier depends on the overall rate of metabolism, the ventilation of the alveoli, the characteristics of the blood-gas barrier, and the characteristics of the gas itself.

Fick's Law

Fick's law of diffusion of a gas states that:

$$\dot{V}gas = P_1 - P_2 \times \frac{A}{T} \times D$$

where $P_1 - P_2$ is the difference between the partial pressures on the two sides of the membrane, A is the area available for diffusion, T is the thickness of the membrane, and D is the coefficient of diffusion.

Since

$$D = \frac{Solubility}{\sqrt{mol\ wt}}$$

and the molecular weight is related to the size of the molecule, Fick's law may be restated as

$$\dot{V}gas = \Delta P \times \frac{Area}{Thickness} \times \frac{Solubility}{Size}$$

The influence of these individual factors on the exchange of O_2 and CO_2 across the alveolar-capillary membrane are discussed in the sections that follow.

Difference of Partial Pressure

The partial pressure (ΔP) of a gas is related directly to the concentration of the gas. If the concentration of a gas is greater in one area, the partial pressure is greater in that area, and the gas will diffuse from the area of higher partial pressure to the area of lower partial pressure.

At sea level, the $P_{A_{O_2}}$ and $P_{A_{CO_2}}$ normally are 100 mm Hg and 40 mm Hg, respectively. When mixed venous blood enters the pulmonary capillaries, it has a P_{O_2} of 40 mm Hg and a P_{CO_2} of 46 mm Hg; therefore, O_2 diffuses from the alveolar air into the blood, and CO_2 diffuses from the blood into the alveolar air.

During a period of increased metabolism, the consumption of O_2 and the production of CO_2 increase; therefore, the P_{O_2} of the mixed venous blood decreases and the P_{CO_2} increases. Consequently, the difference of partial pressure of both gases across the alveolar-capillary membrane increases, and the rate of diffusion increases.

Diffusion Pathway

AREA OF DIFFUSION

An increase in the area of surface available for diffusion increases the rate of diffusion. In the lungs of an adult human, the total area available for diffusion varies from 70–100 m²; however, some of the total area may not be involved in gas exchange. The important area is that of the functional capillaries, which make contact with the functional alveoli and waste neither perfusion nor ventilation.

Figure 31-1 shows the factors that influence the surface area for diffusion. The functional surface area is reduced when the capillary blood flow is reduced or obstructed or when alveoli that have low P_{O_2} are perfused. Destruction of part of the exchange membrane decreases not only the functional area but also the total area available for diffusion. On the other hand, the surface area increases if the number of functional capillaries increases. This is part of the mechanism that assures adequate oxygenation of the blood during exercise, when the rate of blood flow through the pulmonary capillaries increases.

THICKNESS OF GAS-EXCHANGE MEMBRANE

The alveolar-capillary membrane is an anatomical barrier to diffusion. Normally, the gas-exchange membrane is less than 0.5 μm thick and consists of the following:

1. The alveolar epithelium and its basement membrane
2. The interstitial space
3. The capillary endothelium and its basement membrane
4. The blood plasma
5. The red cell membrane

The layer of surfactant that lines each alveolus is added to the thickness of the membrane (Figure 31-2). Although $\dot{V}$gas decreases as the thickness of the membrane (i.e., length of the perfusion pathway) increases, the advantage of surfactant to alveolar function more than offsets the increase of perfusion pathway. Figure 31-3 provides examples of increased length of the perfusion pathway that hinder alveolar functions.

Physical Properties of Gases

SOLUBILITY

The solubility of a gas is defined as the volume (in milliliters) of a gas that dissolves in 1 ml of water at body temperature (37 C) and 1 atmosphere of pressure (760 mm Hg). A gas diffuses faster through a substance in which it is more soluble. Both O_2 and CO_2 are soluble in the lipid membranes, but CO_2 is more soluble in blood plasma than O_2 is. For example:

$$\frac{\text{Solubility of } CO_2}{\text{Solubility of } O_2} = \frac{0.592}{0.0244} = \frac{24.3}{1.0} \simeq \frac{24}{1}$$

Therefore, since CO_2 is more soluble than O_2, CO_2 diffuses through the blood-gas barrier faster than O_2.

MOLECULAR SIZE

The smaller the gas molecule, the faster it moves through the exchange membrane. The size of the molecule is proportional to the square root of the molecular weight (mol wt). For O_2 and CO_2:

$$\frac{\text{Size of } O_2}{\text{Size of } CO_2} \propto \frac{\sqrt{\text{mol wt } O_2}}{\sqrt{\text{mol wt } CO_2}} = \frac{\sqrt{32}}{\sqrt{44}} = \frac{5.6}{6.6} = \frac{0.85}{1.00}$$

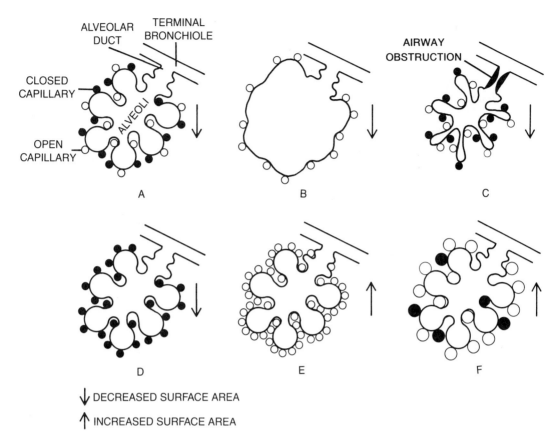

Figure 31-1. Factors that influence the area available for the exchange of gases. **A,** Normal condition. **B** through **D,** Conditions under which the area decreases. **B,** Some of the alveoli and capillaries have been destroyed. **C,** Ventilation is reduced by airway obstruction, which reduces effective alveolar surface area, although the total area for exchange is not altered. **D,** Capillaries closed due to obstruction of the pulmonary circulation (example of dead space ventilation). **E** and **F,** Examples of increased area for diffusion. **E,** All capillaries are open. **F,** Capillaries are enlarged. (Redrawn, with permission, from Comroe, J.H., Jr. *Physiology of respiration,* 2nd ed. Copyright, 1974, Year Book Medical Publishers, Inc. Chicago.)

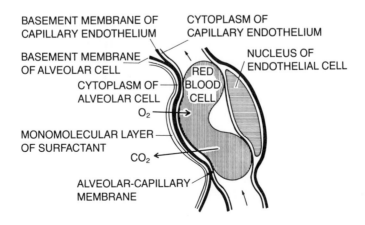

Figure 31-2. Structure of the alveolar-capillary exchange system.

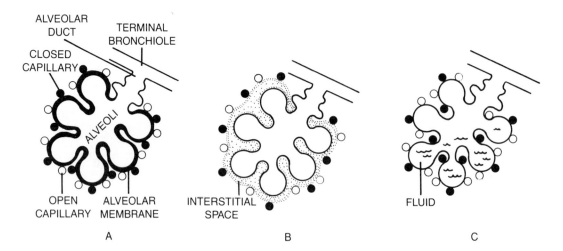

Figure 31-3.   Examples of increased length of diffusion pathway. **A,** Thickening of alveolar epithelium. **B,** Distance between alveolus and capillary increased. **C,** Alveoli filled with fluid.

COEFFICIENT OF DIFFUSION (D)

The area available for diffusion and the thickness of the membrane are the same for O_2 and CO_2; therefore, the difference between their rates of diffusion across the blood-gas barrier is related positively to the solubility of each in the blood plasma and negatively to the molecular size of each. For O_2:

$$D_{O_2} = \frac{0.024}{5.6} = 0.0043$$

For CO_2:

$$D_{CO_2} = \frac{0.592}{6.6} = 0.089$$

Oxygen is lighter than carbon dioxide; however, because the gases diffuse between a gas phase and a liquid phase, the greater solubility of CO_2 outweighs the smaller size of O_2, so that their relative rates of diffusion are:

$$\frac{D_{CO_2}}{D_{O_2}} = \frac{0.089}{0.0043} \simeq \frac{21}{1}$$

Thus, CO_2 diffuses through the alveolar-capillary membrane 21 times faster than O_2 does. Because of this, the rate of diffusion of O_2 is discussed more often in respiratory physiology, and it is assumed that the rate of diffusion of CO_2 under the same conditions always is greater.

Gas Transfer Across Alveolar-Capillary Membrane

Gas diffuses across the exchange membrane from alveolar air into the blood (Figure 31-4). The total amount of gas transferred may be limited by the characteristics of the membrane, the rate of blood flow, or both. Furthermore, the rate of diffusion of O_2 also is influenced by the number of red cells in the pulmonary capillary (which is related to the hematocrit), the rate of uptake of O_2 from the plasma, and the rate at which O_2 combines with the hemoglobin of the red blood cell.

A given red blood cell is within the confines of the pulmonary capillary for about 0.75 sec; therefore, the rate at which the partial pressure of a gas increases in the blood depends on diffusion, perfusion, or a combination of these processes. To illustrate, consider a pulmonary capillary associated with an alveolus that contains carbon monoxide (CO), nitrous oxide (N_2O), and oxygen (O_2). Each of these gases diffuses along its gradient of pressure from the alveolus to the blood. The limitations imposed on the diffusion of each of these gases are discussed in the sections that follow.

CARBON MONOXIDE

Mixed venous blood contains no carbon monoxide; therefore, even a small amount of CO in the alveolus sets up a pressure (P_{CO}) gradient

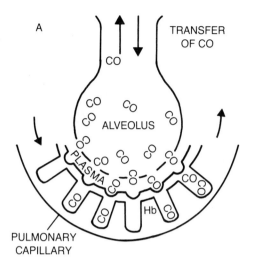

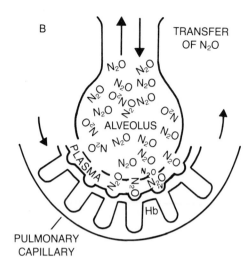

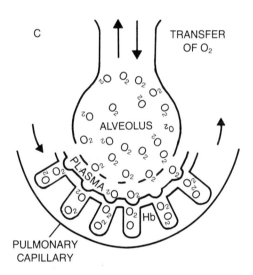

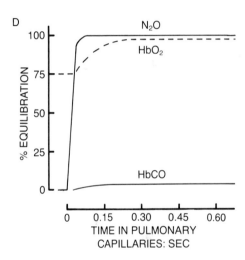

Figure 31-4.   Gas transfer across the alveolar-capillary membrane. Arrows indicate flow of blood through pulmonary capillaries. **A,** CO. A slight amount of CO in the inspired air establishes a gradient for diffusion from alveolar air to blood. The pockets represent hemoglobin in red blood cells. Because of the great affinity of hemoglobin for CO, the red cell takes up CO immediately, only a slight amount of the gas stays in the plasma in the dissolved form, and the gradient for diffusion is almost unaltered from the time the blood enters the capillary until it leaves the capillary (**D**). **B,** N_2O. Hemoglobin has no affinity for N_2O; therefore, all of the N_2O dissolves in the plasma and, as a result, P_{N_2O} equilibrates with alveolar P_{N_2O} almost in- stantly. The gradient of diffusion is eliminated and no more N_2O is transferred (**D**). **C,** O_2. When the blood enters the pulmonary capillary, the he- moglobin is already 75% saturated with O_2, and saturation is completed rapidly. At first, as the gradient for diffusion decreases, the rate of O_2 uptake along the capillary perfusing the alveolus decreases and some O_2 dissolves in the plasma, bringing the alveolar P_{O_2} and capillary blood P_{O_2} into equilibrium (see **D** and Figure 31-5). (Redrawn, with permission, from Comroe, J.H., Jr. *Physiology of respiration,* 2nd ed. Copy- right, 1974, Year Book Medical Publishers, Inc. Chicago.)

CLINICAL CORRELATION
31.1   Diffuse Pulmonary Interstitial Fibrosis

CASE REPORT

The Patient: A 48-year-old woman.

Principal Complaint: Breathlessness.

History: The patient had become short of breath after the slightest exertion for the last four to five months, and the condition was gradually worsening.

Clinical Examination: The patient was slightly overweight, her arterial pressure was 145/105 mm Hg (normal, 90–140/60–90 mm Hg), and she had a dry, unproductive cough. Radiographic (x-ray) examination of the chest showed mottled opacities throughout both lungs, and the left half of the diaphragm was elevated (not contracting well). The Pa_{O_2} was 80 mm Hg (normal, 75–100 mg Hg), and the Pa_{CO_2} was 36 mm Hg (normal, 35–45 mm Hg). Although these values are within normal limits, they are somewhat low. The results of pulmonary function testing are presented below.

  Lung volumes and capacities:
  TLC = 2.75 liters (58% of predicted)
  IRV = 1.94 liters (45% of predicted)
  FRC = 1.68 liters (60% of predicted)
  RV = 0.86 liter (54% of predicted)
  RV/TLC = 31% (92% of predicted)
  Timed spirometric tests:
  Forced vital capacity (FVC) = 2.18 liters
    (69% of predicted)
  Forced expiratory volume (FEV_1)
    = 1.78 liters (67% of predicted)
  FEV_1/FVC = 82% (normal, 84%–100%)

Lung compliance (C_L) = 0.06 liter/cm H_2O (30% of predicted)
Airway resistance (R_{aw}) = 0.78 cm H_2O/liter/sec (predicted 0.8–2.4 cm H_2O/liter/sec)
Diffusing capacity ($D_{L_{O_2}}$) = 19 ml/min/mm Hg (63% of predicted)

Comment: The combination of low lung volumes but normal ratios RV/TLC and FEV_1/FVC is characteristic of pulmonary restrictive diseases. A diagnosis of diffuse pulmonary interstitial fibrosis was confirmed by the x-ray films and the significantly decreased compliance and diffusing capacity of the lungs. $D_{L_{O_2}}$ was decreased because of the thickened alveolar-capillary membrane and the decreased surface area available for diffusion.

Treatment: Steroids were given and the symptoms improved. There is no specific therapy except to treat the primary disease that caused the fibrosis. Interstitial pulmonary fibrosis is caused by the process of healing after exposure to agents such as asbestos, silica, talc, drugs, and many other substances that damage the lung. The disease also may be caused by unknown factors. In some instances, corticosteroids provide effective treatment, as they seem to slow the progression of the disease during the acute inflammatory phase; however, they are not effective after the fibrosis is established.

Outcome: This patient's prognosis was poor. She developed a severe respiratory infection while hospitalized and died of pneumonia.

for diffusion from alveolar air to blood. CO diffuses through the membrane rapidly; however, because the affinity of the hemoglobin for CO is very great (210 times that for O_2), CO is taken up rapidly by the red cell and little accumulates in the plasma (Figure 31-4A). Since only the dissolved gas adds to the partial pressure of a gas in a liquid, the Pco of the plasma changes little while the blood is perfusing the alveolus; therefore, the gradient of pressure for diffusion remains the same, and equilibrium between alveolar Pco and capillary Pco is not reached (Figure 31-4D). Thus, the amount of CO transferred to the blood is determined by diffusion or, to put it another way, the accumulation of CO in the blood is *diffusion-limited.*

NITROUS OXIDE (FIGURE 31-4B)

N_2O diffuses rapidly through the lipid membranes, and since hemoglobin has no affinity for N_2O, all of the N_2O dissolves in the plasma. Equilibrium of P_{N_2O} between alveolar air and blood is achieved rapidly during the first 15–20 msec after the mixed venous blood enters the capillary. Once equilibrium of P_{N_2O} is reached, the gradient for diffusion is eliminated, and the amount of N_2O taken up from the alveolus depends only on the rate of blood flow (Figure 31-4D). Hence, the transfer of N_2O is *perfusion-limited.*

OXYGEN (FIGURE 31-4C)

The transfer of O_2 from alveolar air to capillary blood may depend on both diffusion and perfusion. O_2, like CO, is taken up by the red cells, but it is taken up less rapidly than CO; therefore, more O_2 dissolves in the plasma. Moreover, when the mixed venous blood enters the pulmonary capillary, the hemoglobin already is 75% saturated with O_2, and equilibrium between alveolar air and blood is established within 0.25 sec. This is only one-third of the total time that a particular red cell spends in the pulmonary capillary; therefore, the transfer of O_2 from alveolar air to blood is *perfusion-limited* (Figure 31-4D). When the alveolar-capillary membrane becomes thicker, however, because of pulmonary fibrosis, for example, the rate of uptake of O_2 may be both diffusion-limited and perfusion-limited.

PULMONARY DIFFUSING CAPACITY $(D_{L_{O_2}})$

Quantitatively, the pulmonary diffusing capacity is defined as:

$$D_{L_{O_2}} = \frac{O_2 \text{ transferred from alveolar air to blood (ml/min)}}{\overline{P}_{A_{O_2}} - \overline{P}_{a_{O_2}} \text{ (mm Hg)}}$$

where $D_{L_{O_2}}$ is the diffusing capacity of the lung for O_2, and $\overline{P}$ is mean pressure. If we substitute flow in the top portion and divide it by the difference of $\overline{P}_{O_2}$ (the driving pressure), we get the conductance of O_2 through the membrane:

$$\text{Conductance} = \frac{\text{Flow}}{\text{Driving pressure}}$$

The rate of diffusion of O_2 decreases along the length of the pulmonary capillary because, as

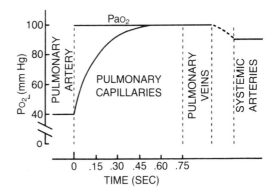

Figure 31-5. Equilibration between alveolar P_{O_2} and blood P_{O_2}. The blood enters the pulmonary capillaries at 0 time. Note that oxygenation of the blood is complete in less than 0.5 sec. The slight difference between alveolar P_{O_2} and arterial P_{O_2} is due to anatomical shunts. (Redrawn, with permission, from Comroe, J.H., Jr., et al. *The lung: clinical physiology and pulmonary function tests,* 2nd ed. Copyright, 1962, by Year Book Medical Publishers, Inc., Chicago.)

diffusion proceeds, the gradient decreases; therefore, diffusion becomes slower and slower until equilibrium is reached (Figures 31-4 and 31-5). Because of this, it is difficult to measure the mean P_{O_2} of the capillary blood and to calculate $D_{L_{O_2}}$. In contrast, $D_{L_{CO}}$ is almost constant, because the gradient in the pulmonary capillary is maintained throughout perfusion (see Figure 31-4D). CO is used clinically to measure the pulmonary diffusing capacity, and $D_{L_{O_2}}$ is calculated from $D_{L_{CO}}$. The amount of CO transferred is directly proportional to the diffusing capacity. $D_{L_{O_2}}$ may be changed by the factors discussed previously, which are changes in the area available for diffusion or in the length of the diffusion pathway (Figure 31-6).

TRANSPORT OF OXYGEN

The blood carries the oxygen as dissolved O_2 and as O_2 combined with hemoglobin (HbO_2).

Dissolved Oxygen

Henry's law states that the amount of a gas dissolved in a liquid is directly proportional to the partial pressure of that gas in contact with the liquid. The P_{O_2} of the blood equilibrates with the P_{O_2} of the alveolar air while the blood

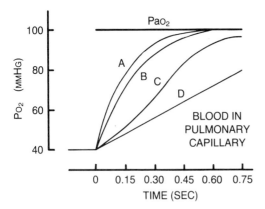

Figure 31-6. Equilibration between alveolar P_{O_2} and pulmonary capillary blood P_{O_2} in normal lungs (A) and under conditions of altered diffusing capacity (B-D). Note that the time was adequate to oxygenate the blood fully in condition B and almost was adequate in C; however; in D, alveolar P_{O_2} and pulmonary end-capillary P_{O_2} are significantly different; this situation leads to arterial hypoxemia. (Redrawn, with permission, from Comroe, J.H., Jr., et al. *The lung: clinical physiology and pulmonary function tests,* 2nd ed. Copyright, 1962, by Year Book Medical Publishers, Inc., Chicago.)

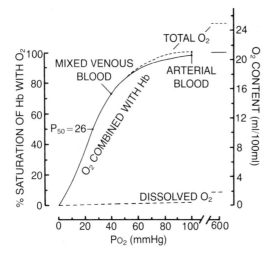

Figure 31-7. Oxygen-hemoglobin dissociation curve. The solid line indicates O_2 combined with hemoglobin and the degree of saturation at various partial pressures of O_2 (P_{O_2}). P_{50} is the P_{O_2} at which 50% of the hemoglobin is saturated with O_2. Note that at a P_{O_2} of 600 mm Hg, 2 ml of O_2 is dissolved in each 100 ml of blood, and the total O_2 content (dissolved plus combined with Hb) increases by only this amount. Normal Hb concentration of 15 g/100 ml is assumed.

is in the pulmonary capillary. The amount of O_2 that dissolves in the blood is related linearly to the Pa_{O_2} and, hence, to the P_{AO_2}. At a normal arterial blood P_{O_2} of 100 mm Hg, 0.3 ml of O_2 is dissolved in the plasma water of each 100 ml portion of blood. A person who breathes 100% O_2 at sea level has an arterial P_{O_2} of 673 mm Hg, and 2 ml of O_2 is dissolved in each 100 ml of blood (Figure 31-7). To deliver in the dissolved form all of the oxygen needed by the tissues would require a P_{AO_2} of 3 atmospheres, or at the normal P_{AO_2}, a cardiac output of 15 times normal (250 ml O_2/min)/(0.3 ml O_2/100 ml blood). However, oxygen under high pressure affects the body adversely and creates problems (for example, it interferes with the buffering capacity of hemoglobin; see Chapter 32), and such a high cardiac output would overtax the capacity of the heart as a pump (see Chapter 21). Therefore, some arrangement other than the delivery of O_2 in the dissolved form is essential. The mechanism that achieves this, of course, is the combination of O_2 with hemoglobin.

Combination of Oxygen with Hemoglobin

One must conclude from the foregoing discussion that only an insignificant portion of the total oxygen used normally is supplied in the form of dissolved O_2. The bulk of the O_2 that enters the blood in the lungs combines with the hemoglobin in the red blood cells and is transported as oxyhemoglobin (HbO_2). This system is so effective that if all of the O_2 were extracted from the blood each minute, a cardiac output of less than one-third normal would be adequate to supply O_2 to the body. It was pointed out previously, however, that not all of the O_2 carried by the blood is removed by the tissues. In the process of raising the P_{O_2} from 40 mm Hg ($P\bar{v}_{O_2}$) to 100 mm Hg (Pa_{O_2}) as the blood flows through the lungs, the concentration of O_2 increases from 15 ml/100 ml blood to 20 ml/100 ml blood; hence, 5 ml of O_2 is added to each 100 ml unit of blood during each minute, and 50 such units (a total of 5 liters) are needed to supply the 250 ml of O_2 required each minute. A blood flow of 5 liters/min is a normal cardiac output.

HEMOGLOBIN

The hemoglobin of a normal adult, HbA, consists of a heme group, which is a pigment and gives the blood its color, and globin, a protein. The protein of Hb consists of four polypeptide chains: two identical α chains, each of which contains 141 amino acids, and two β chains, each of which contains 146 amino acids. A heme group is associated with each polypeptide chain, and each heme group contains an atom of iron, which is the binding site for O_2 (see Chapter 24, Figure 24-7). Thus, a hemoglobin molecule has four sites for binding O_2; however, the iron must be in the ferrous (Fe^{++}) form. Each molecule of hemoglobin takes up four molecules of O_2 in the following steps:

$$Hb_4 + O_2 \rightarrow Hb_4O_2$$

$$Hb_4O_2 + O_2 \rightarrow Hb_4O_4$$

$$Hb_4O_4 + O_2 \rightarrow Hb_4O_6$$

$$Hb_4O_6 + O_2 \rightarrow Hb_4O_8$$

The process of binding is rapid and reversible. The combined form of Hb and O_2 is called *oxyhemoglobin,* and although the proper chemical formula is Hb_4O_8, customarily it is written as HbO_2. Hemoglobin from which the O_2 has been removed is deoxygenated hemoglobin or *deoxyhemoglobin.* Both the uptake (loading) and dissociation (unloading) of O_2 are facilitated by successive oxygenation or deoxygenation of hemoglobin; thus, the binding of one O_2 enhances the binding of the next one, and so on. Therefore, both the loading and the unloading of oxygen are very effective.

The affinity of hemoglobin for O_2, that is, the rate at which the reaction of O_2 with Hb proceeds, is regulated by the concentrations of H^+ (pH), CO_2 (P_{CO_2}), and an organic phosphate compound, 2,3-diphosphoglycerate (DPG), in the blood. The ways in which these factors influence the association and dissociation of O_2 and Hb are discussed in the section that follows.

Association and Dissociation of Oxygen and Hemoglobin

The amount of O_2 that is bound to hemoglobin depends on the P_{O_2} of the blood; however, the P_{aO_2} and the saturation of hemoglobin with oxygen are not related linearly. The so-called oxyhemoglobin dissociation curve of blood, which is a plot of the saturation of Hb against P_{O_2}, or the content of O_2 against P_{O_2}, is an S-shaped curve that has a steep slope between

10 and 50 mm Hg P_{O_2} and a plateau between 70 and 100 mm Hg P_{O_2} (see Figure 31-7). The physiological advantages of this slope will become obvious later in the discussion. For the moment, consider the HbO_2 dissociation curve. Under normal conditions—body temperature 37 C, blood pH 7.4, hematocrit 40%, and Pa_{O_2} 100 mm Hg—each 100 ml of arterial blood contains 19.7 ml of O_2 ($\simeq$ 20 vol %). A small amount of O_2, 0.3 ml, is in physical solution, and the rest is combined with Hb. Under these conditions, the hemoglobin is 97.4% saturated with O_2. The P_{O_2} of the mixed venous blood normally is 40 mm Hg, and the blood contains 15.06 vol % of O_2, of which 0.12 ml is dissolved and 14.94 ml is attached to Hb. At a P_{O_2} of 40 mm Hg, the mixed venous blood is 75% saturated with O_2 (see Figure 31-7).

SATURATION OF HEMOGLOBIN WITH OXYGEN
The percent saturation of hemoglobin (S_{O_2}) is calculated from the following relationship:

$$S_{O_2} = \frac{HbO_2}{O_2 \text{ capacity of Hb}} \times 100$$

where the O_2 capacity of Hb is the maximum amount of O_2 that can combine with the Hb in the blood. The calculation of O_2 capacity is based on the assumption that each 100 ml of blood normally contains 15 g of Hb, and each g of Hb can combine with 1.34 ml of O_2. When the Hb is fully saturated with O_2, it contains 20 vol %; that is, 15 g Hb/100 ml blood $\times$ 1.34 ml O_2/g Hb = 20 ml O_2/100 ml blood. Complete saturation occurs at a P_{O_2} of 250 mm Hg; however, since the Sa_{O_2} is 97.4% at a normal Pa_{O_2} of 100 mm Hg, little additional oxygen is added to the blood by increasing Pa_{O_2} above 100 mm Hg. When a subject breathes ambient air and hyperventilates maximally, both alveolar P_{O_2} and arterial P_{O_2} increase above 100 mm Hg (see Figure 27-11); however, because the saturation of Hb is almost complete during normal quiet breathing, only 0.3 ml of O_2 is added to each 100 ml of blood by hyperventilation, which in turn raises the O_2 content from 19.7 vol % to the maximum capacity of 20.

The sigmoidal shape of the HbO_2 curve also has other advantages. Figure 31-7 shows that Sa_{O_2} does not change dramatically when P_{O_2} changes over a range of 70–100 mm Hg; therefore, arterial blood still is almost saturated with O_2 at the lower tension. This becomes important when the O_2 tension of the inspired air

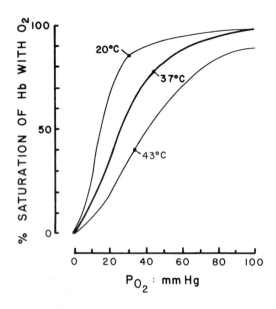

Figure 31-8. The effect of temperature on the HbO₂ dissociation curve.

(PIo₂), and consequently the Pao₂, is reduced (at higher altitudes, for example). Because of this relationship, a patient who has cardiopulmonary disease may not have hypoxemia (decreased saturation of arterial blood with O₂) even if his Pao₂ decreases from the normal 100 mm Hg to 80 mm Hg. On the other hand, on the steep portion of the HbO₂ dissociation curve, HbO₂ releases a large amount of O₂ when the Po₂ changes by only a small amount.

EFFECTS OF TEMPERATURE

Increased temperature decreases the affinity of Hb for O₂ and shifts the HbO₂ curve to the right (Figure 31-8). This means that at a given Po₂ and a higher temperature, the blood holds less O₂; therefore, fever hinders the uptake of O₂ to some extent. At the same time, a shift of the curve to the right also means that more O₂ is released at a particular Po₂; thus, active tissues, which are warmer than the average of the body, receive more O₂.

The dissociation curve is steep between 10 and 50 mm Hg Po₂; therefore, tissues can extract more O₂ from the blood without large changes in Po₂. One should keep in mind that the O₂ dissolved in the plasma is used first. As this O₂ diffuses out of the blood, the Pao₂ decreases, more O₂ is released from HbO₂, and more O₂ is available to the tissues.

The main effect of low temperature is to shift the dissociation part of the HbO₂ curve to the left (Figure 31-8). As a result, the hemoglobin holds on to the O₂; therefore, in cold weather, although the cheeks and ears are red, which indicates a relatively high rate of blood flow, little O₂ is released to these tissues.

EFFECTS OF Pco₂ and [H⁺] (BOHR EFFECT)

Increased Pco₂ and increased hydrogen ion concentration, [H⁺], decrease the affinity of Hb for O₂ and shift the curve to the right (Figure 31-9). Again, the uptake of O₂ is not influenced

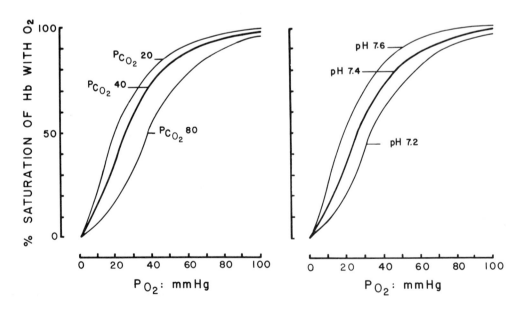

Figure 31-9. The effects of pH and Pco₂ on the HbO₂ dissociation curve.

significantly, but more O_2 is made available to the tissues by the shift to the right. For example, when the pH decreases from 7.4 to 7.2, the saturation of Hb at 30 mm Hg P_{O_2} decreases from 57% to 45%. The same effect occurs when the P_{CO_2} increases but the pH does not change. This is beneficial to the organism, because tissues that metabolize rapidly produce more CO_2 and more H^+, which increase the P_{CO_2} and the $[H^+]$ of the blood and promote the release of O_2 from HbO_2. All three of the factors just mentioned become significant during exercise: if temperature, P_{CO_2}, and $[H^+]$ increase, the affinity of Hb for O_2 at lower P_{O_2} decreases, and O_2 is released to the tissues more rapidly.

EFFECTS OF DIPHOSPHOGLYCERATE

2,3-diphosphoglycerate (DPG), which is formed in red blood cells during anaerobic glycolysis (Figure 31-10), regulates the release of O_2 from HbO_2. An increase in temperature, pH, or rate of glycolysis increases the rate of formation of DPG. Increase of DPG in the red cells shifts the HbO_2 curve to the right; however, before this can occur, DPG must bind to deoxygenated hemoglobin. The concentration of DPG is regulated by negative feedback of free DPG; thus, when the concentration of DPG increases, the enzyme that catalyzes the formation of DPG is inhibited and less DPG is produced. When the concentration of DPG decreases, the activity of the enzyme increases and more DPG is produced. When the level of deoxyhemoglobin increases, more DPG can be bound, and as the level of free DPG decreases, more DPG is produced. Certain hormones, such as testosterone, growth hormone, thyroid hormone, and the catecholamines, especially the β-receptor agonists, increase the formation of DPG, and some of the hormones act by stimulating the rate of metabolism of the red cell.

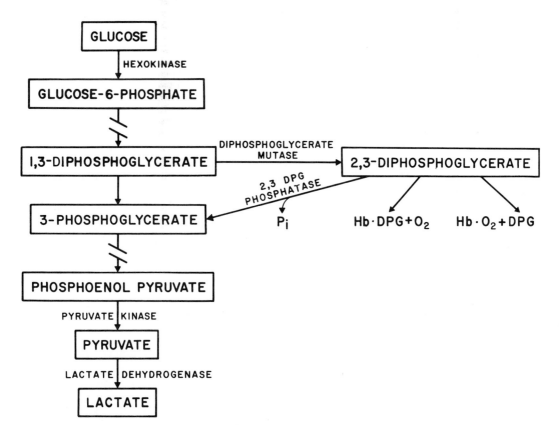

Figure 31-10. The glycolytic pathway and the formation of 2,3-diphosphoglycerate in red blood cells. (Redrawn, by permission of the American Heart Association, Inc., from Mulhausen, R.O. 1970. *Circulation* 42:195.)

P$_{50}$

The P$_{O_2}$ at which the hemoglobin is half-saturated with O_2, at a temperature of 37 C and a pH of 7.4, is designated as P$_{50}$; it is a measure of the affinity of hemoglobin for O_2. The P$_{50}$ of normal blood, which contains HbA, is 26 mm Hg (see Figure 31-7). A P$_{50}$ higher than this value indicates that the affinity of hemoglobin for O_2 is less; a lower value means that the affinity of Hb for O_2 is greater. Therefore, the P$_{50}$ increases under conditions in which the release of O_2 from HbO$_2$ is enhanced and O_2 is more readily available to the tissues. The change of P$_{50}$ reflects the influence of a mechanism that compensates for hypoxemia—whether caused by reduced P$_{IO_2}$, which occurs at high altitudes; by cardiopulmonary disease, in which alveolar ventilation is reduced; or by anemia, in which the volume of erythrocytes or the concentration of hemoglobin is diminished. The common link in all of these conditions is greater availability of deoxygenated hemoglobin, to which DPG binds. This association of Hb and DPG shifts the HbO$_2$ curve to the right (P$_{50}$ increases) (Figure 31-11) and reduces the concentration of free DPG, which permits the formation of more DPG. Other conditions that cause an increase in P$_{50}$ are exercise (increased production of DPG through glycolysis); sickle cell anemia; other abnormal, low-affinity variants of hemoglobin; and a deficiency in the enzyme pyruvate kinase (Figure 31-12), which

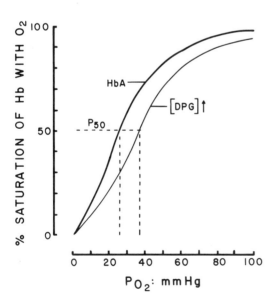

Figure 31-11. The effect of increasing concentration of 2,3-DPG in the blood on the dissociation of HbO$_2$.

drives the pathway of glycolysis toward increased formation of DPG.

Conditions that cause a lower P$_{50}$ increase the affinity of Hb for O_2 and therefore hinder the dissociation of O_2 from HbO$_2$. This is a problem with blood that has been stored to be used for transfusion; after about a week, the content of DPG is greatly depleted. Thus, blood that has been donated recently is preferred for patients who are very ill, or who undergo cardiac surgery and depend more on the normal delivery of oxygen. A deficiency of hexokinase in the red cells inhibits glycolysis; therefore, it decreases the formation of DPG and lowers P$_{50}$ (Figure 31-12). Hexokinase is the rate-limiting enzyme in glycolysis.

Carbon Monoxide and Hemoglobin

The affinity of Hb for CO is 210 times greater than that for O_2; hence, CO can compete with O_2 for Hb on an equal basis at a concentration 1/210 that of O_2. For example, blood exposed to a mixture of gases that contains 21% O_2 (air) and 0.1% CO (210:1) would contain, after a period of equilibration, 50% HbO$_2$ and 50% HbCO (carboxyhemoglobin).

Carbon monoxide readily displaces O_2 on the Hb molecule and thereby reduces the capacity of the blood to carry O_2. At the same time, HbCO causes a shift in the HbO$_2$ curve to the left, which means that the remaining O_2 dissociates less readily unless the blood perfuses tissues in which the O_2 tension is very low. Figure 31-13 shows the effects of various concentrations of HbCO in the blood on the HbO$_2$ dissociation curve. Note that the presence of 60% HbCO in the blood is more deleterious than severe anemia in which the Hb concentration is only 40% of normal. Although both of these conditions reduce equally the capacity of the blood to carry O_2, the HbO$_2$ dissociation curve shifts to the right in severe anemia (due to increased levels of DPG), which facilitates the release of O_2 to the tissues. By contrast, HbO$_2$ in the blood that contains HbCO holds on more tightly to the O_2.

Carbon monoxide is particularly perilous to any organism because it is a tasteless, colorless, odorless, nonirritating gas that does not stimulate respiration and does not cause respiratory distress. Cyanosis, the bluish discoloration of the skin and mucous membranes that characteristically is seen in most hypoxemic individ-

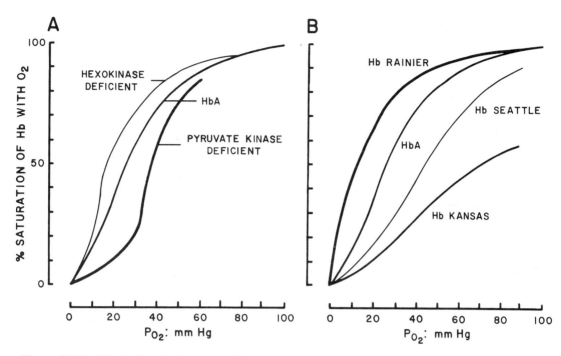

Figure 31-12. HbO_2 dissociation curves in abnormal conditions. **A,** Normal blood (HbA); hexokinase-deficient blood; pyruvate kinase–deficient blood. **B,** Examples of high and low affinity variants of Hb. (Redrawn, with permission, from Stamatoyannoupoulos, G., et al. *Ann. Rev. Med.* Vol. 22. Copyright, 1971, Annual Reviews, Inc.)

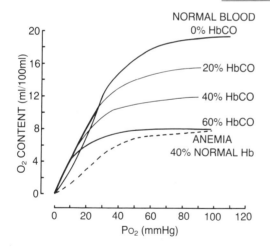

Figure 31-13. HbO_2 dissociation curves of human blood that contains various fractions of HbCO. Anemic blood is added for comparison. (Redrawn, with permission, from Roughton, F.J.W., and Darling, R.C. 1944. *Am. J. Physiol.* 141:17. Copyright, American Physiological Society.

uals, does not appear; instead, the color of the skin is bright (cherry) pink because of the useless HbCO in the arterial and venous blood.

Abnormal Forms of Hemoglobin

Adult hemoglobin has more than 120 variants. Sometimes, because of metabolic error, one or more of the amino acids in either one of the α or β polypeptide chains of HbA is replaced by another amino acid, and an abnormal hemoglobin is produced.

SICKLE CELL Hb

Perhaps the best-known abnormal hemoglobin is that of the sickle cell (HbS). It is responsible for the chronic hemolytic disease, sickle cell anemia, which affects a large segment of the population of black people. In HbS, glutamic acid is replaced by valine at the sixth position in the β chain. The affinity of HbS for O_2 is lower than that of HbA. In addition, HbS is relatively insoluble and crystallizes when the Po_2 is low. As a result, the shape of the red cells changes from a biconcave disk (donut shape) to a crescent or a sickle; hence the name sickle cell hemoglobin. These cells are sticky and tend to form long aggregates that block normal capillary blood flow. Consequently, as the Po_2 decreases, more deoxy HbS is formed, and sickle formation and cell aggregation are enhanced.

The episodes of crisis characteristic of this ailment are associated with the consequences of the blocked microcirculation and the severely decreased O_2 carrying capacity of HbS.

The other abnormal hemoglobins usually are named for the places or areas where they were discovered first. There are high and low affinity variants.

HIGH AFFINITY VARIANTS
The high affinity variants, such as Hb Rainier, shift the HbO_2 curve to the left and reduce the P_{50} (see Figure 31-12), which causes tissue hypoxia. The body tries to correct a deficiency by some form of compensation—in this case, by increasing the red cell volume and, hence, the amount of Hb (Figure 31-14). When the tissues have to function in an environment low in oxygen, production of the hormone erythropoietin increases (see Chapter 24), and the rate of formation of red cells increases. The end result is polycythemia, or increased red cell volume, which partially corrects the initial problem but unfortunately introduces others; for example, increased viscosity of the blood.

LOW AFFINITY VARIANTS
Certain variants of Hb, such as Hb Seattle and

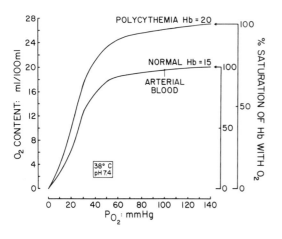

Figure 31-14. HbO_2 dissociation curves of normal blood and of blood with increased red cell concentration. (Modified/adapted from Slonim, N.B., and Hamilton, L.H. 1981. *Respiratory physiology,* 4th ed. St. Louis: The C.V. Mosby Co., and from Davenport, H.W. 1958. *The ABCs of acid-base chemistry,* 4th ed. Chicago: The University of Chicago Press.)

Hb Kansas, do not take on the usual load of O_2, even if alveolar ventilation is normal (see Figure 31-12).

METHEMOGLOBIN
The iron in hemoglobin must be in the ferrous (Fe^{++}) form before it can hold O_2. Nitrites, aniline, and sulfonamide, for example, oxidize Fe^{++} to Fe^{+++} and cause methemoglobin to form, which hinders the transport of O_2. A small fraction of HbO_2 is oxidized to methemoglobin even in normal healthy persons, but it is converted immediately to ferrous hemoglobin by the enzyme methemoglobin reductase, which reduces Fe^{+++} to Fe^{++}.

FETAL HEMOGLOBIN
Fetal blood contains a variant of normal hemoglobin in which the two β chains of HbA are replaced with γ chains. Since the γ chain of HbF binds 2,3-DPG less firmly than the β chain of HbA does, the affinity of HbF for O_2 is increased. This permits the uptake of a large amount of O_2 in the placenta, where the Po_2 is relatively low (Figure 31-15). HbF disappears slowly after birth, and only a small amount remains at a few months of age.

Myoglobin

Myoglobin, which is found in muscle, consists of a single polypeptide chain that contains 153 amino acids and only one atom of iron. Although myoglobin and hemoglobin are structurally and functionally similar, their O_2 dissociation curves are different (Figure 31-16). This difference is expressed by the low P_{50} of oxymyoglobin, which is 1 mm Hg, compared to that of oxyhemoglobin, which is 26 mm Hg. Myoglobin is almost fully saturated with O_2 at a Po_2 of 40 mm Hg, and it readily gives off O_2 at Po_2 less than 20 mm Hg.

The skeletal muscle of an adult human contains an average of about 700 mg of myoglobin per 100 g of tissue, although red muscle contains more than white muscle does. Myoglobin provides an O_2 reserve and facilitates the transport of O_2 within the cells.

Total Oxygen Transport

The total amount of O_2 delivered by the blood to the tissues each minute is determined by alveolar ventilation and the diffusion capacity of the respiratory membrane (which provide

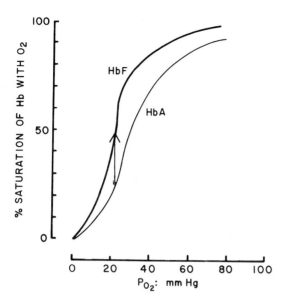

Figure 31-15. Saturation of fetal hemoglobin and maternal hemoglobin with O_2. Arrow indicates oxygenation of HbF at the expense of HbA. (Redrawn, with permission, from *Biochemistry*, 2nd ed., by Lubert Stryer, W.H. Freeman and Company. Copyright, 1981.)

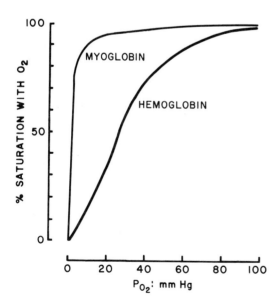

Figure 31-16. Oxygen dissociation curves of myoglobin and hemoglobin. (Redrawn, with permission, from *Biochemistry*, 2nd ed., by Lubert Stryer. W.H. Freeman and Company. Copyright, 1981.)

the proper P_{AO_2}, and therefore P_{aO_2}, respectively), the affinity of the Hb for O_2, the concentration of Hb in the blood, and the blood flow. When the hemoglobin is fully oxygenated, each 100 ml of arterial blood contains 20 ml of O_2; therefore, at a normal resting rate of blood flow (5 liters/min), 1 liter of O_2 is made available to the tissues each minute. As only 250 ml of O_2 is consumed per minute, approximately 15 vol % of O_2 is returned to the lungs in the mixed venous blood.

Increased demand for O_2 can be met in several ways: (1) more O_2 can be taken up by each unit of blood, (2) more O_2 can be released from each unit of blood, (3) the rate of perfusion of the tissues can increase, or (4) a combination of any of the conditions listed above may occur. Most of these mechanisms operate during exercise, for example. Alveolar ventilation increases, which increases the amount of O_2 supplied each minute, although the amount of O_2 contained in the blood does not increase significantly because of the shape of the oxygen-hemoglobin dissociation curve. Blood flow may increase as much as four to five times, however, and in addition, the exercising muscle extracts more O_2 from the blood. The effects of increased [H^+], temperature, and P_{CO_2}, which shift the HbO_2 dissociation curve to the right and make the O_2 more readily available to the tissues, also are added.

UPTAKE OF OXYGEN BY TISSUES

In general, the factors that determine the oxygenation of the blood in the lungs also determine the oxygenation of the tissues. These factors are the difference of partial pressure, the diffusion characteristics of the blood-tissue interface, and the temperature, pH, and P_{CO_2} of the blood and the tissue fluids. The cells use O_2 continuously, and O_2 diffuses from the blood to the tissues because the O_2 tension near the red cells is higher than that of the fluid that surrounds the tissue cells. The O_2 dissolved in the plasma is the most readily available, and when O_2 diffuses from the plasma into the interstitial fluid, the P_{O_2} of the plasma decreases. The HbO_2 of the red blood cells then releases more O_2, which diffuses into the plasma and consequently becomes available to the tissues.

The ultimate acceptors of O_2 are the respiratory enzymes of the mitochrondria; therefore, the P_{O_2} of the tissues must be high enough to allow the O_2 to diffuse to the mitochondria. The O_2 tension in the tissues varies according to the

TABLE 31-1
Blood flow, O_2 consumption, arteriovenous O_2 difference, and venous Po_2 of various tissues and organs*

Tissue or organ	Blood flow		O_2 used		a-v O_2	P_vo_2
	ml/min	% of total	ml/min	% of total	ml O_2/100 ml blood	mm Hg
Heart	250	4	26.4	11	11.4	23
Skeletal muscle	1200	21	72.0	30	8.4	34
Brain	750	13	48.0	20	6.3	33
Splanchnic (liver)	1400	24	60.0	25	4.1	43
Kidneys	1100	19	16.8	7	1.3	56
Skin	500	9	4.8	2	1.0	60

*Modified from Finch, C.A., and Lenfant, C. 1972. Oxygen transport in man. *N. Engl. J. Med.* 286:407.

rate of diffusion of O_2 and the length of the diffusion pathway between the blood and the cells and is affected by a variety of factors involved in the local regulation of blood flow to the individual organs or tissues.

ARTERIOVENOUS OXYGEN DIFFERENCE

The amount of O_2 contained in the blood (ml O_2/100 ml blood) also is important, as a certain quantity of O_2 is needed to satisfy the needs of all of the tissues. The O_2 content of whole blood is the sum of the O_2 dissolved and that carried by hemoglobin. The amount of O_2 taken up by the various tissues depends on the rate of metabolism of the tissues and the rate of blood flow to them. These factors also determine the difference between the O_2 content of the arterial blood that supplies the tissues and that of the venous blood that drains the tissues. Some organs that have a large blood flow use only a small fraction of the total O_2 available to them; others, which receive only a small share of the cardiac output, extract a large portion of the O_2 that comes to them. The largest arteriovenous O_2 difference occurs in the blood of the coronary circulation. Although the heart gets only 4% of the cardiac output, it consumes 11% of the O_2; this requires an a-v̄ O_2 difference of 11.4 vol % (Table 31-1). The normal a-v̄ O_2 difference for the entire circulation is approximately 5 ml O_2/100 ml blood, and it can be used to calculate the cardiac output by the Fick method (Chapter 14).

STUDY OUTLINE

DIFFUSION OF GASES   Rate of diffusion through blood-gas barrier is determined by:
   Metabolic rate.
   Alveolar ventilation.
   Characteristics of barrier and gas.

FICK'S LAW   Diffusion is related to partial pressure difference, area, membrane thickness, and diffusion coefficient.

DIFFERENCE OF PARTIAL PRESSURE   Gas diffuses from area of high pressure to one of low pressure.
   O_2 diffuses from alveoli to blood.
   CO_2 diffuses from blood to alveoli.

DIFFUSION PATHWAY
   AREA OF DIFFUSION   Rate of diffusion varies directly with functional area.
   THICKNESS OF GAS-EXCHANGE MEMBRANE   Normally, blood-gas barrier is less than 0.5 μm thick.

PHYSICAL PROPERTIES OF GASES
   SOLUBILITY   More soluble gas diffuses more rapidly; CO_2 is more soluble than O_2.
   MOLECULAR SIZE   Smaller gas molecules move faster.
      Size is proportional to $\sqrt{\text{mol wt}}$.
      O_2 is smaller than CO_2.
   COEFFICIENT OF DIFFUSION (D)   Rate of diffusion of O_2 and CO_2 is determined by solubility and size of molecule.
      Solubility factor is more important.
      Rate of CO_2 diffusion is 21 times greater than that of O_2.

GAS TRANSFER ACROSS ALVEOLAR-CAPILLARY MEMBRANE   Rate depends on membrane characteristics (diffusion), blood flow (perfusion), or both.
   CARBON MONOXIDE   Diffuses through membrane rapidly; is taken up rapidly by hemoglobin.
      Gradient for diffusion is unaltered; diffusion-limited transfer.
   NITROUS OXIDE   Hb has no affinity for N_2O; all that is transferred dissolves in plasma.
      Instantaneous $Pa_{N_2O} - Pa_{N_2O}$ equilibrium.
      Perfusion-limited transfer.
   OXYGEN   Perfusion-limited normally; increased thickness of barrier also limits diffusion.
   PULMONARY DIFFUSING CAPACITY DL_{O_2} = ml O_2 transferred/min for each mm Hg mean partial pressure difference of O_2 between alveolar and capillary blood; CO used to measure DL_{O_2}.

TRANSPORT OF OXYGEN   Carried in blood as dissolved O_2 and HbO_2.

DISSOLVED OXYGEN   Amount of gas dissolved is related to partial pressure (Henry's law).
   At PaO_2 100 mm Hg, 0.3 ml O_2 is dissolved in 100 ml blood.
   Very small portion of total.

COMBINATION OF OXYGEN WITH HEMOGLOBIN   Bulk of O_2 is carried in blood as HbO_2.
   HEMOGLOBIN   Binds four molecules of O_2; binding is cooperative and reversible.
      Affinity of Hb for O_2 is influenced by pH, Pco_2, temperature, and 2,3-DPG.

ASSOCIATION AND DISSOCIATION OF OXYGEN AND HEMOGLOBIN   Amount bound is determined by Po_2.
   HbO_2 dissociation curve is sigmoidal.
   At 100 mm Hg Po_2, Hb is 97.4% saturated with O_2; contains 19.7 ml O_2/100 ml blood.
   SATURATION OF HEMOGLOBIN WITH OXYGEN

$$\text{Percent saturation} = \frac{O_2 \text{ combined with Hb}}{O_2 \text{ capacity Hb}} \times 100$$

   Capacity: Each gram Hb combines with 1.34 ml O_2: 15 g Hb/100 ml blood; 20 ml O_2/100 ml blood, 100% SO_2.
   EFFECTS OF TEMPERATURE   Increased temperature: HbO_2 dissociation curve shifts to right; decreased temperature: shifts to left.
   EFFECTS OF Pco_2 AND $[H^+]$ Increased Pco_2 and $[H^+]$ shift curve to right (Bohr effect).
   EFFECTS OF DIPHOSPHOGLYCERATE   Regulates release of O_2 from HbO_2; increased DPG, shift to right.
   P_{50} Half-saturation pressure: 26 mm Hg Po_2.
      Increased P_{50}: more O_2 is released from HbO_2.
      Low P_{50}: hinders dissociation of HbO_2.

CARBON MONOXIDE AND HEMOGLOBIN   CO causes no respiratory distress.
   Hb affinity is 210 times greater for CO than for O_2.
   Reduces O_2 carrying capacity of blood.
   Shifts HbO_2 dissociation curve to left; O_2 release is hindered.

ABNORMAL FORMS OF HEMOGLOBIN
> 120 variants of adult Hb (HbA).

SICKLE CELL Hb   Glutamate is replaced by valine.

HbS affinity for O_2 is low.

At low Po_2, HbS crystallizes; red cell is sickle-shaped.

Aggregates of sickle cells block capillary blood flow.

HIGH AFFINITY VARIANTS   Shift HbO_2 dissociation curve to left; P_{50} is reduced.

LOW AFFINITY VARIANTS   Low O_2 content at normal Pao_2.

METHEMOGLOBIN   Iron-binding sites are in Fe^{+++} form; do not hold O_2; hinders O_2 transport.

FETAL HEMOGLOBIN   Increased O_2 affinity; uptake in placenta is facilitated.

MYOGLOBIN   In muscle: provides O_2 reserve and facilitates transfer within cells.

TOTAL OXYGEN TRANSPORT   Depends on Pao_2, concentration and affinity of Hb, and blood flow.

O_2 consumption is 250 ml/min.

O_2 uptake in lung is 250 ml/min.

100 ml blood provides 5 ml O_2; blood flow needed, 5 liter/min.

Increased demand is met by increased uptake, release, or blood flow.

UPTAKE OF OXYGEN BY TISSUES   Determined by same factors as uptake in lung.

Po_2 gradient between blood and tissue fluid. Dissolved O_2 used first.

ARTERIOVENOUS   OXYGEN   DIFFERENCE   Depends on blood flow and metabolic rate of tissue.

Normal average a-$\bar{v}$ O_2 difference $\simeq$ 5 ml/100 ml blood.

Used to calculate cardiac output (Fick).

BIBLIOGRAPHY

Comroe, J.H.; Forster, R.E., II; DuBois, A.B.; et al. 1962. *The lung: Clinical physiology and pulmonary function tests,* 2d ed. Chicago: Year Book Medical Publishers, Inc.

Comroe, J.H. 1974. *Physiology of respiration.* Chicago: Year Book Medical Publishers, Inc.

Finch, C.A., and Lenfant, C. 1972. Oxygen transport in man. *N. Engl. J. Med.* 286:407.

Forster, R.E. 1957. Exchange of gases between alveolar air and pulmonary capillary blood: pulmonary diffusing capacity. *Physiol. Rev.* 37:391.

Forster, R.E. 1964. Diffusion of gases. In *Handbook of physiology,* Section 3, Respiration, Vol I, editors W.O. Fenn and H. Rahn. Washington, D.C.: American Physiological Society.

Mulhausen, R.O. 1970. The affinity of hemoglobin for oxygen. *Circulation* 42:195.

Roughton, F.J.W. 1964. Transport of oxygen and carbon dioxide. In *Handbook of physiology,* Section 3, Respiration, Vol. I, editors W.O. Fenn and H. Rahn. Washington, D.C.: American Physiological Society.

Roughton, F.J.W., and Darling, R.C. 1944. The effect of carbon monoxide on the oxyhemoglobin dissociation curve. *Am. J. Physiol.* 141:17.

Slonim, N.B., and Hamilton, L.H. 1981. *Respiratory physiology.* St. Louis: The C.V. Mosby Co.

Stamatoyannopoulos, G.; Bellingham, A.J.; Lenfant, C., et al., 1971. Abnormal hemoglobin with high and low oxygen affinity. *Ann. Rev. Med.* 22:221.

Wagner, P.D. 1977. Diffusion and chemical reaction in pulmonary gas exchange. *Physiol. Rev.* 57:257.

West, J.B. 1979. *Respiratory physiology: The essentials,* 2d ed. Baltimore: Williams & Wilkins Co.

32

Transport of CO₂ and Regulation of Acid-Base Balance by the Lungs

CHAPTER CONTENTS

At rest, metabolically active tissues produce approximately 200 ml of CO_2 each minute; this also is the amount of CO_2 that normally is excreted by the lungs each minute. The excretion of CO_2 involves (1) the diffusion of CO_2 from the tissues into the surrounding tissue fluid and from there into the capillary blood, (2) the chemical reactions that CO_2 enters into within the blood plasma, (3) the chemical reactions that CO_2 enters into within the red blood cells, and (4) the reversal of these reactions and the diffusion of CO_2 from the blood into the air of the alveoli as the blood flows through the pulmonary capillaries.

TRANSPORT OF CO₂

CO_2 is carried in the blood in two forms: dissolved and chemically bound. Almost 90% of the CO_2 that the tissues add to the venous blood enters the red blood cells, where most of the chemical reactions of CO_2 occur. Although only 10% of the CO_2 stays in the plasma, 68% of the CO_2 transported in the blood is carried in the plasma, mostly as HCO_3^-.

Dissolved CO₂

About 10% of the CO_2 carried in the blood is in physical solution (Figure 32-1). The amount of CO_2 dissolved is related to the P_{CO_2} and the solubility of CO_2. Each millimeter of mercury partial pressure of CO_2 causes 0.06 ml of CO_2 to dissolve in 100 ml of blood. This means that when the P_{CO_2} of the blood increases from 40 mm Hg to 46 mm Hg, an additional 0.36 ml of CO_2 is dissolved in each 100 ml of blood.

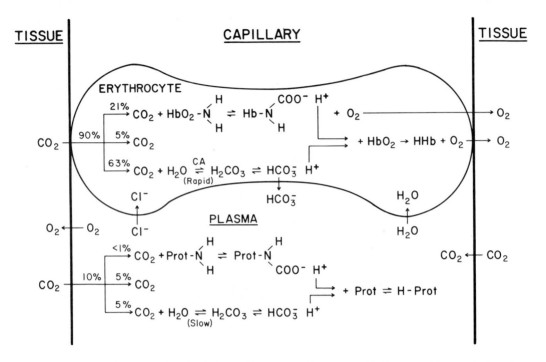

Figure 32-1. Reactions associated with uptake and transport of carbon dioxide by the blood. Note that only 10% of the total CO_2 added from the tissues stays in the plasma, while the bulk (90%) diffuses into the red cells, where the major reactions occur. (Redrawn, with permission, from Ruch, T.C., and Patton, H.D. 1965. *Physiology and biophysics.* Philadelphia: W.B. Saunders Co., p. 767.)

Chemically Bound CO_2

The bulk of the CO_2 that enters the blood participates in chemical reactions in the plasma and the red cells.

CARBAMINO COMPOUNDS
CO_2 reacts with the amino groups of proteins to form carbamino compounds (see Figure 32-1). The reaction is rapid and does not require a catalyst:

$$RNH_2 + CO_2 \rightleftharpoons RNHCOO^- + H^+$$

Only a very small amount (less than 1%) of the CO_2 combines with the plasma proteins; the majority of carbamates are formed in the red cells where CO_2 combines with hemoglobin:

$$HbNH_2 + CO_2 \rightleftharpoons HbNHCOO^- + H^+$$

The amount of CO_2 carried as carbamino hemoglobin depends on the degree of oxygenation of the hemoglobin. Deoxygenated hemoglobin combines with more CO_2 than oxygenated hemoglobin does (see section on Hal-

dane effect in this chapter). The H^+ formed from this reaction is buffered elsewhere on the Hb molecule. Recent studies indicate that 2,3-DPG (diphosphoglycerate) competes with CO_2 for sites on the hemoglobin; therefore, in the adult human, the amount of CO_2 transported as carbamino compounds may be less than half as great as it previously was thought to be.

BICARBONATE ION
The major portion of the CO_2 that enters the blood is hydrated rapidly in the red cells to form H_2CO_3, which dissociates into H^+ and HCO_3^- (see Figure 32-1).

$$CO_2 + H_2O \rightleftharpoons H_2CO_3 \rightleftharpoons H^+ + HCO_3^-$$

The enzyme *carbonic anhydrase* is necessary to catalyze the reaction. The plasma contains no carbonic anhydrase; therefore, the reaction goes slowly and little CO_2 is hydrated in the plasma. The H^+ released by the reaction is buffered by the plasma proteins.

In the red cells, the concentration of carbonic anhydrase is high, and H_2CO_3 forms rapidly. The H^+ produced by the reaction is buffered by the hemoglobin within the red cell. Most of the HCO_3^- formed in the red cells diffuses into the plasma, aided by both chemical and electrical gradients, and is carried to the lungs.

CHLORIDE SHIFT

The removal of HCO_3^- tends to develop a net positive charge inside the red cell; hence, Cl^- diffuses into the red cell down the electrical gradient. This exchange usually is referred to as the *chloride shift*. The Cl^- and HCO_3^- distribute according to a Donnan equilibrium, where the concentrations of the permeating anions on the two sides of the membrane are determined by the concentration of the nonpermeating anion within the cell. The chloride shift greatly increases the capacity of the plasma to carry CO_2. Because of the movement of Cl^-, the concentration of Cl^- in the red cells of venous blood is higher than that in the red cells of arterial blood. The total osmotic activity of red cells in venous blood also is greater because, although the proteins inside the red cell bind much of the H^+, the hydration of CO_2 also produces HCO_3^-, which is exchanged for osmotically active Cl^-. Therefore, to maintain osmotic equilibrium within the red cell in the venous blood, the shift of Cl^- is accompanied by a movement of water that slightly increases the size of the cells. Consequently, the venous hematocrit is slightly greater than the arterial hematocrit.

CO₂ Dissociation Curve

As the blood is pumped through the pulmonary capillaries, the content of CO_2 decreases from 52 ml/100 ml of venous blood to 48 ml/100 ml of arterial blood, and the P_{CO_2} decreases from 46 mm Hg to 40 mm Hg. Approximately 4 ml of CO_2 from each 100 ml of blood diffuses across the alveolar-capillary membranes into the alveolar air, where the concentration of CO_2 is lower; the driving force is the difference between the partial pressures on each side of the membrane. The relationship between the CO_2 content of the blood and the partial pressure of CO_2 is more nearly linear (Figure 32-2), especially in the physiological range, than that between the O_2 content of the blood and the partial pressure of O_2. The shape of the dissociation curve greatly influences the

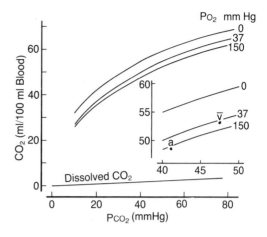

Figure 32-2. CO_2 dissociation curve. The CO_2 content of blood is plotted against the P_{CO_2} of blood (range, 0–80 mm Hg). The relationship between dissolved CO_2 and P_{CO_2} is approximately linear over the whole range. The total concentration of CO_2 in the blood (CO_2 content) depends on the P_{O_2}; blood fully saturated with O_2 carries less CO_2. The insert on the right illustrates the nearly linear relationship between CO_2 content and P_{CO_2} in the physiological range. The change in CO_2 content of the blood from point v̄ (mixed venous blood) to a (arterial) represents the release of CO_2 into alveolar air as the blood simultaneously takes up O_2 during the time it courses through the pulmonary capillaries. (Redrawn, with permission, from DeJours, P. 1963. *Respiration.* Paris: Editions Médicales Flammarion. Translation, Oxford University Press, Inc., copyright, 1966.)

rate of diffusion of CO_2 across the pulmonary membranes. A less steep curve means that CO_2 is not released rapidly with a very small drop of P_{CO_2}, compared with the rapid release of O_2 on the steep portion of the O_2 dissociation curve. On the other hand, there is no plateau region either, and therefore saturation does not occur.

HALDANE EFFECT

The amount of CO_2 the blood transports is influenced by the P_{O_2} of the blood. As the P_{O_2} decreases, the CO_2 dissociation curve shifts upward; at any P_{CO_2}, the greater the concentration of deoxygenated hemoglobin, the higher the CO_2 content of the blood. This phenomenon is called the *Haldane effect* (Figure 32-3). Because deoxyhemoglobin is a weaker acid than oxyhemoglobin, it can combine with, or buffer, more H^+; in turn, more CO_2 can combine with the amino groups of deoxyhemoglobin.

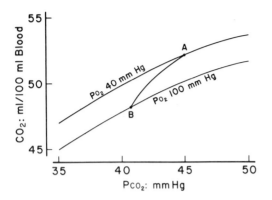

Figure 32-3.   Haldane effect. As the P_{O_2} of mixed venous blood (40 mm Hg) is raised to that of arterial blood (100 mm Hg), the concentration of CO_2 decreases from 50 to 48 ml CO_2/100 ml blood (line from point A to B). (Redrawn, with permission, from Guyton, A.C. 1981. *Textbook of medical physiology*, 6th ed. Philadelphia: W.B. Saunders Co.)

The loading and unloading of O_2 and CO_2 in the capillaries are mutually helpful. In the systemic circulation, the addition of CO_2 to the blood causes more O_2 to dissociate from the hemoglobin (Bohr effect), which allows more CO_2 to combine (Haldane effect). In the pulmonary circulation, the process is reversed; there the uptake of O_2 by the hemoglobin facilitates the release of CO_2. The Haldane effect is important because it doubles both the uptake of CO_2 from the tissues and the elimination of CO_2 in the lungs.

ELIMINATION OF CO_2

In the lungs, as the dissolved CO_2 diffuses from the pulmonary capillary blood into the alveoli, the following reaction shifts to the left and more CO_2 is released.

$$CO_2 + H_2O \rightleftharpoons H_2CO_3 \rightleftharpoons H^+ + HCO_3^-$$

At the same time, as O_2 is added to the blood, and HbO_2 forms, more CO_2 is released from the oxygenated hemoglobin. Simultaneously, HCO_3^- diffuses back into the red cells and combines with H^+ to form H_2CO_3, which the enzyme carbonic anhydrase breaks down to CO_2 and H_2O. Carbonic anhydrase in the lung parenchyma also may facilitate the movement of CO_2 across the blood-gas barrier into the alveoli, from which CO_2 is eliminated with each breath.

In spite of the 20-times-greater diffusing capacity of CO_2 than O_2 through the pulmonary membranes, alveolar P_{CO_2} and arterial P_{CO_2} equilibrate at about the same time that alveolar P_{O_2} and arterial P_{O_2} equilibrate. If the partial pressure gradient for the diffusion of O_2 and CO_2 were the same, CO_2 would equilibrate with alveolar air 20 times faster than O_2 does; however, other factors, such as the rate at which CO_2 enters into chemical reactions in the blood and the shape of the CO_2 dissociation curve, offset the effect of the greater diffusing capacity of CO_2.

Alterations in Transfer of CO_2

ALVEOLAR VENTILATION

The amount of CO_2 eliminated from alveolar air is related directly to alveolar ventilation. In hypoventilation, less CO_2 is excreted than produced, and alveolar P_{CO_2} increases. Therefore, arterial, venous, capillary, and tissue P_{CO_2} also increase. Because of the linear relationship between arterial P_{CO_2} and the CO_2 content of the blood, P_{CO_2} doubles if alveolar ventilation decreases by one-half. In hyperventilation, more CO_2 is eliminated than produced by the tissues, and alveolar P_{CO_2} decreases. Therefore, arterial, venous, and capillary P_{CO_2} decrease. P_{CO_2} decreases by one-half if alveolar ventilation doubles.

INHALATION OF OXYGEN

The transport of CO_2 is hindered by inhalation of 100% oxygen. As the Pa_{O_2} increases, more O_2 is carried to the tissues dissolved in the blood; therefore, less O_2 must be released from hemoglobin. Since HbO_2 binds CO_2 less readily than HHb does, the transport of CO_2 decreases, even though the P_{CO_2} of the venous blood increases slightly.

The diffusion of CO_2 may be impaired in patients who have hypoxemia caused by hypoventilation and are kept alive by the inhalation of a gas mixture in which P_{O_2} is high. Although the therapy corrects the hypoxemia, it does not correct the hypoventilation that is the primary problem; therefore, CO_2 accumulates in the alveolar air and in the blood.

ANEMIA

The blood of an individual who is severely anemic contains less hemoglobin and less carbonic anhydrase than the blood of a healthy individual. Less carbonic anhydrase is not a problem, as there usually is an excess of that enzyme. However, a reduction of the amount of hemoglobin in the blood causes the [H$^+$] and the P_{CO_2} to change because most of the H$^+$ produced by the chemical reactions of CO$_2$ normally is buffered by hemoglobin. If the amount of hemoglobin is not enough to accept all of the H$^+$, both the [H$^+$] and the P_{CO_2} of the venous blood and the tissues increase. However, anemia usually is compensated for by an increase of cardiac output, which increases the amount of Hb available each minute, even though the total amount in the blood remains the same.

EXOGENOUS INHIBITORS OF CARBONIC ANHYDRASE

Certain drugs, of which acetazolamide, a diuretic, is the best example, inhibit carbonic anhydrase. The hydration of CO$_2$ continues without the enzyme, but at such a slow rate that CO$_2$ accumulates in the plasma and the tissues, and P_{CO_2} of the blood in the systemic capillaries increases.

In the lungs, carbonic anhydrase also catalyzes the reaction that results in the release of CO$_2$ from the blood into the alveolar air (H$_2$CO$_3$ $\rightleftharpoons$ CO$_2$ + H$_2$O). If the enzyme is deficient, these reactions proceed so slowly that not enough CO$_2$ is released during the short time the blood is in the pulmonary capillaries. At the same time, the hydration of CO$_2$ continues. Therefore, under these conditions, alveolar P_{CO_2} is less than arterial P_{CO_2}.

REGULATION OF ACID-BASE BALANCE

Concentration of H$^+$

The body has three mechanisms for adjusting [H$^+$] and regulating its acid-base balance: (1) the buffering systems, which adjust the [H$^+$] within seconds; (2) the lungs, which excrete H$^+$ through the reaction

$$H^+ + HCO_3^- \rightleftharpoons H_2CO_3 \rightarrow H_2O + CO_2$$

and can adjust the [H$^+$] within minutes; and (3) the kidneys, which excrete H$^+$ as fixed acid and

are important for the long-term regulation of acid-base balance. The discussion in this section will be limited to the function of the lungs in acid-base regulation, but the reader is encouraged to study the contribution of the renal mechanism in the section on renal physiology.

NORMAL [H$^+$]

The normal mean [H$^+$] of the extracellular fluid is about 4×10^{-8} mol/liter, or 40 nanomoles (nmol) per liter; it must be maintained within relatively narrow limits, because most physiological processes have an optimal [H$^+$]. The [H$^+$] of body fluids influences the speed at which enzymatic reactions proceed, the degree of ionization of substances, the activity of some drugs, and the movement of ions across cell membranes. In addition, changes of [H$^+$] locally affect the cerebral and pulmonary circulations, the functions of smooth muscle and cardiac muscle, the propagation of nerve impulses, and renal function.

pH

[H$^+$] conventionally is expressed as the logarithm$_{10}$ of the reciprocal of the H$^+$ activity ([H$_\alpha^+$]), which is the pH:

$$pH = \log \frac{1}{[H_\alpha^+]}$$

or

$$pH = -\log [H_\alpha^+].$$

From this expression, it follows that as the [H$_\alpha^+$] increases, the pH decreases. Table 32-1 shows an approximate relationship between [H$_\alpha^+$] and pH.

CALCULATION OF pH

If the [H$_\alpha^+$] of the extracellular fluid is 4×10^{-8} mol/liter, then:

$$\begin{aligned} pH &= -\log [H_\alpha^+] \\ &= -\log 4 \times 10^{-8} \\ &= -\log 4 - \log 10^{-8} \\ &= -0.6 + 8.0 \\ &= 7.4 \end{aligned}$$

TABLE 32-1
Approximate relationship between [H$^+$] and pH

[H$^+$] (nmol/liter)	pH
20	7.7
30	7.5
40	7.4
50	7.3
60	7.2
70	7.15

The normal mean pH of arterial blood is approximately 7.4. The mean pH of venous blood is slightly lower (7.36) (that is, [H$_a^+$] is higher) because CO$_2$ is added continuously to the venous blood from the tissues. Figure 32-4 shows the range of pH within which life can be maintained. Note that because of the logarithmic scale, a change of one pH unit represents a tenfold change in [H$_a^+$].

Three systems regulate [H$^+$] in the extracel-lular fluid—the buffering systems, the lungs, and the kidneys. Their relative contributions to homeostasis are discussed briefly in the following sections.

Buffers and Buffering Systems

Buffers are chemical substances that prevent large changes of [H$^+$] when an acid or a base is added to the buffer solution. In this discussion, an acid or a base is defined according to the scheme of Brønsted, in which an acid (H$_2$CO$_3$) is a donor of protons (H$^+$)

$$H_2CO_3 \rightleftharpoons H^+ + HCO_3^-$$

and a base (HCO$_3^-$) is an acceptor of protons:

$$H^+ + HCO_3^- \rightleftharpoons H_2CO_3$$

A buffer pair consists of a weak acid and its conjugate base. In the previous example, H$_2$CO$_3$ and HCO$_3^-$ form a conjugate acid-base pair. Consider the addition of OH$^-$ to a solution of carbonic acid:

$$H_2CO_3 + OH^- \rightleftharpoons HCO_3^- + H_2O$$

In this reaction, H$_2$CO$_3$ is the weakly dissociated acid, and the anion HCO$_3^-$ is the base that can accept a proton.

Buffers are most effective at the pH at which the buffer pair is half dissociated ([HCO$_3^-$] = [H$_2$CO$_3$]); this is the pK of that buffer pair. The pK, usually derived from a titration curve, is the point at which the addition or removal of H$^+$ causes the smallest change of pH. An ideal physiological buffer has a pK within the normal range of pH of the body fluids.

The two most important buffer systems are bicarbonate-carbonic acid and protein. A third buffer system, the phosphate pair, HPO$_4^=$-H$_2$PO$_4^-$, has a pK of 6.8; therefore, it is very effective. However, as the blood contains only a small amount of phosphate, this system is relatively less important. The significance of the phosphate buffer system is discussed in detail in the section on the physiology of the kidney.

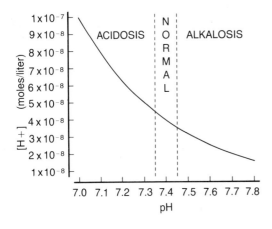

Figure 32-4. Relationship between [H$^+$] and pH within the extreme physiological range. Note the narrow range of normal pH from 7.35–7.45, which, however, corresponds to a change of about 25% in [H$^+$]. (Redrawn, with permission, from Gamble, J.L., Jr., 1954. *Chemical anatomy, physiology, and pathology of extracellular fluid.* Cambridge, Mass: Harvard University Press.)

BICARBONATE– CARBONIC ACID BUFFER SYSTEM

The pK of the HCO$_3^-$-H$_2$CO$_3$ buffer pair is 3.4; therefore, it is not a very effective buffering system in a chemical sense. The physiological importance of this system rests in the fact that H_2CO_3 is in equilibrium with CO_2; hence, the concentration of H_2CO_3 can be regulated through ventilation. This means of adjusting $[H_2CO_3]$ is a rapid process by which normal $[H^+]$ can be restored within minutes. The amounts of the products that result from the hydration of CO_2 at a pH of 7.4 are as follows (nmol/liter):

$$CO_2 + H_2O \xrightleftharpoons[\text{anhydrase}]{\text{Carbonic}} H_2CO_3$$
$$1,200,000 \qquad\qquad\qquad 2400$$

$$\rightleftharpoons H^+ + HCO_3^-$$
$$40 \quad 24,000,000$$

When the buffer ions combine with H^+, which is one of the end-products of the reaction, $[H^+]$ decreases and the reaction moves to the right.

PROTEIN BUFFERS
Proteins, which consist of amino acids, contain free basic (NH_2) and acidic (COOH) groups, which can buffer H^+. The most important pro-

tein buffer is hemoglobin, which is present in high concentration in the red cells and has a pK within the normal range of pH of the blood. Thus, hemoglobin is the most nearly ideal buffering system in the body.

Hb-HbO₂ BUFFER SYSTEM
As mentioned previously, deoxyhemoglobin (Hb) is a weaker acid than oxyhemoglobin (HbO_2) and therefore has a greater capacity to combine with CO_2 as carbamate. When HbO_2 is deoxygenated to the weaker acid Hb (in the systemic capillaries), the $[H^+]$ of the blood would decrease if CO_2 were not hydrated simultaneously and H^+ released by the dissociation of H_2CO_3 to $H^+ + HCO_3^-$. Approximately 50% of H_2CO_3 is neutralized by this means, which is known as the *isohydric shift of CO₂*, because it occurs without a change in the $[H^+]$ of the blood (Figure 32-5). The other 50% is absorbed by the nitrogen on the imidazole group of histidine (Figure 32-6). If more H_2CO_3 is formed than can be neutralized by this system, the blood becomes more acidic ($[H^+]$ increases, or pH decreases). The importance of the buffering capacity of hemoglobin is appreciated more fully when one calculates the difference of pH between arterial blood and venous blood that would occur in the absence of hemoglobin (arterial 7.4; venous 4.5). When an increase in the rate of production of CO_2 is accompanied by an increase in the rate of deoxygenation of HbO_2, as may be expected when moderate-to-heavy work is done, the amount of reduced Hb available to bind H^+ ions matches the need, and the change of pH is minimal.

Henderson-Hasselbalch Equation

The Henderson-Hasselbalch equation describes the relationship among CO_2, H_2CO_3,

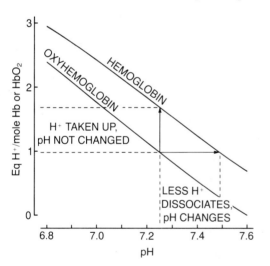

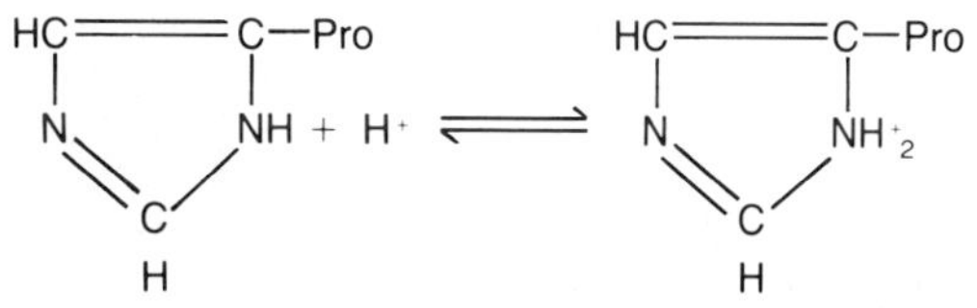

Figure 32-5. The isohydric shift in association with CO_2. When oxyhemoglobin is reduced to hemoglobin, a weaker acid is formed (that is, hemoglobin is less dissociated than oxyhemoglobin). If no H^+ were added to the system, the pH would increase as H^+ previously dissociated from oxyhemoglobin associates with hemoglobin. However, H^+ is formed by the reaction $CO_2 + H_2O \rightarrow H_2CO_3 \rightleftharpoons H^+ + HCO_3^-$ at the same rate that H^+ is taken up by hemoglobin, and the pH does not change.

Figure 32-6. The buffering action of the imidazole group of histidine in hemoglobin in the physiological range (pK of histidine = 7.1). "Pro" represents the protein of hemoglobin.

HCO_3^-, and pH. H_2CO_3 is a weak acid that dissociates into H^+ and HCO_3^-:

$$H_2CO_3 \rightleftharpoons H^+ + HCO_3^-$$

The reaction is reversible, and according to the law of mass action the velocity of the reaction in either direction is proportional to the concentrations of the reactants. Therefore,

$$\text{Velocity} \rightarrow \ = K_1 [H_2CO_3]$$

$$\text{Velocity} \leftarrow \ = K_2 [H^+] \times [HCO_3^-]$$

At equilibrium, the velocities of the reactions in each direction are the same; therefore,

$$K_1 [H_2CO_3] = K_2 [H^+] \times [HCO_3^-]$$

and transposing yields

$$\frac{K_1}{K_2} = \frac{[H^+] \times [HCO_3^-]}{[H_2CO_3]} = K$$

where K is the dissociation, or ionization, constant of the weak acid, H_2CO_3. To obtain the pH, take the log of each side:

$$\log K = \log \frac{[H^+][HCO_3^-]}{[H_2CO_3]}$$

Rearranging:

$$\log K = \log [H^+] + \log \frac{[HCO_3^-]}{[H_2CO_3]}$$

Transposing again:

$$-\log [H^+] = -\log K + \log \frac{[HCO_3^-]}{[H_2CO_3]}$$

Since $-\log [H^+] = $ pH, and $-\log K = $ pK, we can substitute these into the equation:

$$pH = pK + \log \frac{[HCO_3^-]}{[H_2CO_3]}$$

where the pK is 3.4.

   [H_2CO_3] in the blood is almost impossible to measure because H_2CO_3 dissociates continuously; however, since [H_2CO_3] is proportional to the amount of CO_2 dissolved in the blood, which can be measured, the equation may be written as:

$$pH = pK' + \log \frac{[HCO_3^-]}{[CO_2]}$$

The pK of this system is 6.1 (pK'). Furthermore, since the [CO_2] of the plasma, in millimoles per liter, is related to the Pco_2, we can substitute for CO_2 the product of the $Paco_2$ and the solubility factor of CO_2, which is 0.03 (mmol/liter)/mm Hg. Therefore, when the arterial Pco_2 is 40 mm Hg, the [CO_2] is (40 mm Hg × 0.03 mmol/liter)/mm Hg, or 1.2 mmol/liter. A useful form of the Henderson-Hasselbalch equation for calculating the pH of the arterial blood is:

$$pH = 6.1 + \log \frac{HCO_3^-, \text{mmol/liter}}{\begin{array}{c} Paco_2, \text{mm Hg} \\ \times (0.03 \text{ mmol/liter})/\text{mm Hg} \end{array}}$$

   Under normal conditions, [HCO_3^-] is about 24 mmol/liter, and

$$pH = 6.1 + \log \frac{24.0 \text{ mmol/liter}}{\begin{array}{c} 40 \text{ mm Hg} \\ \times (0.03 \text{ mmol/liter})/\text{mm Hg} \end{array}}$$

$$= 6.1 + \log \frac{24.0 \text{ mmol/liter}}{1.2 \text{ mmol/liter}}$$

$$= 6.1 + \log \frac{20}{1}$$

$$= 6.1 + 1.3$$

$$pH = 7.4$$

These last steps demonstrate that the pH of the arterial blood is determined not by the absolute amount of HCO_3^- or dissolved CO_2 but by the ratio of the two. At a normal ratio of HCO_3^--CO_2 of 20:1, the pH of the blood is 7.4; *as long as the ratio remains 20:1, the pH remains 7.4, even if the absolute amounts of HCO_3^- and CO_2 change.* Furthermore, this relationship demonstrates that mole for mole, CO_2 has a greater influence on the pH than bicarbonate has.

PHYSIOLOGICAL IMPORTANCE OF HCO_3^--H_2CO_3 BUFFER PAIR

The importance of the HCO_3^--H_2CO_3 buffer system does not depend on chemical capacity, since the pK of the system clearly is outside the normal range of pH. Furthermore, H^+ produced by the dissociation of H_2CO_3 must be buffered by other means, mainly hemoglobin in the red cells. *The bicarbonate buffer system is important because the CO_2 produced by all active tissues can be carried in the blood to the lungs in the form of HCO_3^- and conserved or eliminated as CO_2, as necessary, by pulmonary ventilation.*

   The central chemoreceptors are especially sensitive to changes in [CO_2] and respond by either stimulating or depressing the respiratory centers to maintain arterial P_{CO_2} close to 40 mm Hg. At the same time, the metabolic component of the bicarbonate buffer system, $[HCO_3^-]$, is regulated by the kidneys through glomerular filtration and tubular reabsorption. The contribution of the HCO_3^--H_2CO_3 system to the buffering of fixed acids is discussed in the section on renal regulation of acid-base balance.

To focus attention on the relationship between the metabolic component and the respiratory component of the bicarbonate buffer system, the Henderson-Hasselbalch equation often is expressed, quaintly, as:

$$pH = pK + \log \frac{\text{Metabolic (slow component)}}{\text{Respiratory (fast component)}}$$

or

$$pH = 6.1 + \log \frac{\text{Kidney}}{\text{Lung}}$$

pH-BICARBONATE DIAGRAM

Figure 32-7 shows the relationships among pH, $[HCO_3^-]$, and P_{CO_2} of the arterial blood. The curved lines that intercept the normal blood buffer line represent Pa_{CO_2} values of 20, 40, 60, and 80 mm Hg (P_{CO_2} isobars). The normal blood buffer line is obtained by equilibrating blood with various levels of P_{CO_2}, which yields a straight line in the physiological range of pH. For example, when CO_2 is added to the blood

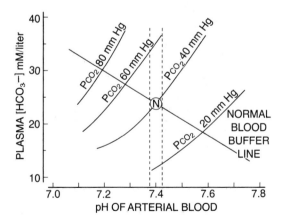

Figure 32-7. Relationship between plasma bicarbonate concentration and pH of arterial blood at various levels of P_{CO_2}. (Modified from Slonim, N.B., and Hamilton, L.H. 1981. *Respiratory physiology*, 4th ed. St. Louis: The C.V. Mosby Co., and from Davenport, H.W. 1958. *The ABC of acid-base chemistry*, 4th ed. Chicago: The University of Chicago Press.)

(that is, P_{CO_2} increases), the hydration reaction of CO_2 proceeds to the right, producing more H^+ and HCO_3^-. However, as blood proteins buffer H^+, $[HCO_3^-]$ increases. The reverse is true when P_{CO_2} decreases to less than normal; the reaction proceeds to the left. Therefore, more HCO_3^- combines with H^+ to form H_2CO_3, and $[HCO_3^-]$ decreases. Because $[HCO_3^-]$, P_{CO_2}, and pH are related by the Henderson-Hasselbalch equation, the intersection of any horizontal line with any vertical line provides a value for P_{CO_2}. The normal range at sea level is bracketed on the graph: at a normal pH of 7.4, $[HCO_3^-]$ is 24 mmol/liter, P_{CO_2} is 40 mm Hg, and $[CO_2]$ is 1.2 mmol/liter; therefore, the ratio HCO_3^-/CO_2 is 20:1. Similar diagrams have been developed to determine the acid-base status of patients when pH, $[HCO_3^-]$, and P_{CO_2} are known.

Acid-Base Shifts

Because pH is an expression of $[H^+]$, it is a useful index for evaluating the acidity or alkalinity of the blood. Physiologically, *acidosis* is a condition in which the $[H^+]$ of the system tends to increase; *acidemia* is a condition in which the pH of the arterial blood is less than 7.35. *Alkalosis* is a condition in which the $[H^+]$ of the system tends to decrease; *alkalemia* is a condition in which the pH of arterial blood is more than 7.45.

SIMPLE ACID-BASE DERANGEMENTS

The $[H^+]$ of the blood can be increased, or the pH decreased, in three ways: (1) by adding H^+, (2) by removing HCO_3^-, and (3) by adding CO_2. The condition that exists after H^+ has been added or HCO_3^- removed is called *metabolic acidosis* (point D on Figure 32-8). When the rate of elimination of CO_2 decreases relative to the rate of production, the CO_2 content of the blood, and hence the Pa_{CO_2}, increase. The condition produced is known as *respiratory acidosis* (point A on Figure 32-8).

The $[H^+]$ of the blood can be decreased, or the pH increased, in three ways: (1) by removing H^+, (2) by adding HCO_3^-, and (3) by removing CO_2 through the process of ventilation. The condition that exists after H^+ has been removed or HCO_3^- added is called *metabolic alkalosis* (point B on Figure 32-8). When the rate of elimination of CO_2 increases relative to the rate of production, the CO_2 content of the blood and the Pa_{CO_2} decrease. The condition

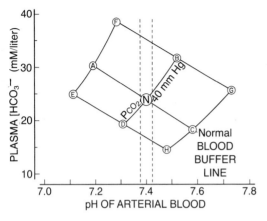

Figure 32-8. pH-bicarbonate diagram for predicting acid-base conditions. N represents normal values and their ranges at sea level. The line that connects A-N-C is the normal blood buffer line derived as indicated in the discussion of Figure 32-8 in the text. The line that connects points E-D-H is the blood buffer line of patients who have metabolic acidosis; the line that connects points F-B-G is the blood buffer line of patients who have metabolic alkalosis. The line that connects points E-A-F is the 80 mm Hg P_{CO_2} isobar; line H-C-G is the 20 mm Hg P_{CO_2} isobar. *Pure conditions of acid-base change* move either up or down on the 40 mm Hg P_{CO_2} isobar (that is, point B represents metabolic alkalosis; point D represents metabolic acidosis) or to the left or right on the normal blood buffer line (that is, point A represents respiratory acidosis; point C represents respiratory alkalosis). *In compensated acid-base conditions,* the pH is corrected toward the normal value by either retaining or eliminating more CO_2 (respiratory compensation for metabolic alkalosis [along line B-F] or acidosis [along line D-H]); or by absorbing or excreting more HCO_3^- (metabolic compensation for respiratory acidosis [along line A-F] or alkalosis [along line C-H]). Point E represents combined respiratory acidosis and metabolic acidosis; point G represents respiratory alkalosis plus metabolic alkalosis. (Modified from Slonim, N.B., and Hamilton, L.H. 1981. *Respiratory physiology,* 4th ed. St. Louis: The C.V. Mosby Co., and from Davenport, H.W. 1958. *The ABC of acid-base chemistry,* 4th ed. Chicago: The University of Chicago Press.)

---

produced is known as *respiratory alkalosis* (point C on Figure 32-8).

Simple acid-base disturbances occur only transiently and may be either corrected or compensated. The changes of pH and bicarbonate caused by ventilation (by either retaining or eliminating too much CO_2) follow the line N-A or N-C, respectively, on Figure 32-8. An acid-base disturbance is *corrected* if the process that caused it is reversed and the pH returns to normal. For example, in acidemia due to respiratory acidosis, an increase in ventilation would decrease the P_{CO_2} and restore the normal pH.

COMPENSATED ACID-BASE CONDITIONS

An acid-base abnormality is *compensated* if the pH is restored to normal by a process other than the one that caused the abnormality. For example, in acidemia due to respiratory acidosis, an increase in the reabsorption of HCO_3^- by the kidneys (metabolic alkalosis) would compensate for the abnormality and return the pH to normal.

On the pH-bicarbonate diagram (Figure 32-8), the buffer line of blood from patients who have metabolic alkalosis lies above the normal blood buffer line, and the buffer line of blood from patients who have metabolic acidosis lies below the normal blood buffer line. The changes of pH and bicarbonate caused by simple metabolic derangements (excess H^+ or HCO_3^-) follow the line B-N-D on Figure 32-8. It should be pointed out, however, that in practice the ventilatory responses to metabolic changes are immediate, and pure metabolic acid-base disturbances almost never are seen clinically.

When the pH of the arterial blood changes because of metabolic alkalosis or acidosis, ventilation changes to compensate for the derangement. For example, when metabolic acidosis causes acidemia, the increased [H^+] stimulates the respiration, CO_2 is eliminated by increased alveolar ventilation at a faster rate than it is released into the blood, and alveolar and arterial P_{CO_2} decrease. The blood is titrated along its buffer line toward a higher pH and a lower [HCO_3^-] (along line D to H, Figure 32-8). The end result of compensated metabolic acidosis is a lower-than-normal Pa_{CO_2}. The respiratory compensation for metabolic alkalosis is less predictable. Theoretically, ventilation should decrease and arterial P_{CO_2} should increase, which would decrease the pH along line B to F in Figure 32-8. However, the central chemoreceptors presumably would respond to the increased P_{CO_2} by stimulating the respiration. The respiratory response to metabolic al-

CLINICAL CORRELATION
32.1   Hyperventilation—Respiratory Alkalosis Related to Anxiety and Tension

CASE REPORT

The Patient: A 21-year-old female college student.

Principal Complaints: Recurrent bouts of dizziness, confusion, blurred vision, numbness or tingling sensation in fingers and toes or around the lips, and carpopedal spasm (characteristic spasms of the feet and hands).

History: The patient was a premedical student in her senior year. She came to the Family Practice Service of the university hospital with the complaints listed above. She seemed pale and anxious but otherwise normal. When she was questioned about the occurrence of her episodes, it became clear that they coincided with intensive studying for examinations or deadlines for term papers.

Clinical Examination: The patient's heart rate, blood pressure, blood gases, pH, and serum electrolyte concentrations all were within normal limits. Her electrocardiogram showed a normal sinus arrhythmia that was related to respiration. Chest x-ray films revealed normal lungs. It was suspected that the patient's symptoms were related to anxiety and tension associated with the stress of late hours of studying and the pressure of examinations. She was asked to hyperventilate voluntarily for a few minutes, and she was able to reproduce the symptoms of her illness.

Comment: Hyperventilation, in the absence of lung disease or certain kinds of brain injuries, frequently is a manifestation of anxiety and tension. The patient usually is unaware of hyperventilating, but suffers the consequences of acute respiratory alkalosis precipitated by the increased rate and depth of respiration. As CO$_2$ is eliminated by the lungs more rapidly than it is produced by metabolism, the P$_{CO_2}$ decreases. Because these attacks usually are short lasting, renal compensation by excretion of HCO$_3^-$ is not possible and the arterial pH is high. The symptoms of the hyperventilation (i.e., hyperventilation syndrome) are related to the effects of hypocapnia (low P$_{CO_2}$) and alkalemia. Low arterial P$_{CO_2}$ causes cerebral vasoconstriction and decreases the blood flow to the brain; this condition is associated with dizziness, blurred vision, and sometimes confusion. The tingling sensation and muscle spasms reflect enhanced irritability and spontaneous discharge of nerve fibers: the respiratory alkalosis causes these symptoms by decreasing ionized calcium.

Treatment: In this case, the patient's understanding of the problem was adequate treatment. She was told to reduce her ventilation voluntarily, to hold her breath for a short time, or to breathe in and out from a paper bag (rebreathing her own CO$_2$) if she should experience the sensations associated with respiratory alkalosis.

kalosis ultimately may depend on the difference in sensitivity of individuals to high P$_{CO_2}$. Nevertheless, some individuals do hypoventilate in response to metabolic alkalosis.

Compensation is maximal when the metabolic effect on pH is balanced by the respiratory effect through Pa$_{CO_2}$, and the pH is brought closer to the normal value. The P$_{CO_2}$ of arterial blood may be either high or low in acidemia or alkalemia; however, during hypoventilation, respiratory acidosis is caused by *hypercapnia* (excess CO$_2$), and during hyperventilation, respiratory alkalosis is caused by *hypocapnia*.

The kidneys compensate for respiratory alkalosis by excreting more HCO$_3^-$ to bring the ratio HCO$_3^-$/CO$_2$ closer to 20:1, but the Pa$_{CO_2}$ does not change. The kidneys compensate for respiratory acidosis by absorbing more HCO_3^- to increase the ratio HCO_3^-/CO_2 and consequently to increase the pH, but the $Paco_2$ does not change. Table 32-2 presents the changes of arterial pH, Pco_2, and $[HCO_3^-]$ in various conditions of acid-base disturbance. It should be remembered that the renal mechanisms of compensation require time, while the respiratory mechanisms respond immediately.

TABLE 32-2
Changes in arterial pH, Pco_2, and $[HCO_3^-]$ in various acid-base disturbances

	pH	Pco_2	$[HCO_3^-]$	$\dfrac{[HCO_3^-]}{[CO_2]}$
Normal	7.4	40	24.0	20/1
Acid-Base Disturbance				
Respiratory acidosis	↓	↑	↑	↓
Respiratory acidosis compensated	Closer to normal	↑	↑	Closer to normal
Respiratory alkalosis	↑	↓	↓	↑
Respiratory alkalosis compensated	Closer to normal	↓	↓	Closer to normal
Metabolic acidosis	↓	Normal	↓	↓
Metabolic acidosis compensated	Closer to normal	↓	↓	Closer to normal
Metabolic alkalosis	↑	Normal	↑	↑
Metabolic alkalosis compensated	Closer to normal	↑	↑	Closer to normal

STUDY OUTLINE

TRANSPORT OF CO_2

DISSOLVED CO_2 Amount related to Pco_2.

CHEMICALLY BOUND CO_2 Most of transport of CO_2.

CARBAMINO COMPOUNDS CO_2 reacts with amino groups of proteins; rapid reaction, no catalyst needed.

BICARBONATE ION 68% of total CO_2.
Hydration of CO_2 in red cells forms H_2CO_3; carbonic anhydrase catalyzes reaction.
H_2CO_3 dissociates into H^+ and HCO_3^-.

CHLORIDE SHIFT HCO_3^- diffuses from red cell to plasma.
Cl^- exchanges for HCO_3^- in red cell.
Water follows Cl^-; red cells in venous blood are slightly larger; venous hematocrit is slightly greater.

CO_2 DISSOCIATION CURVE CO_2 content and Pco_2 linear in physiological range.

About 4 ml CO_2 are transferred across membrane from each 100 ml blood.

HALDANE EFFECT Amount of CO_2 in blood is influenced by Po_2; deoxygenated Hb holds more CO_2.

ELIMINATION OF CO_2 Dissolved CO_2 diffuses from blood to alveolar air.
Loss of CO_2 shifts hydration reaction to release more CO_2.
Hb saturated with O_2 holds less CO_2.
HCO_3^- moves back into red cell, more H_2CO_3 forms, more CO_2 is released.

ALTERATIONS IN TRANSFER OF CO_2
Directly related to alveolar ventilation.

ALVEOLAR VENTILATION Hypoventilation: decrease of alveolar ventilation by half doubles Pco_2.
Hyperventilation: doubling alveolar ventilation decreases Pco_2 by half.

INHALATION OF OXYGEN CO_2 transport is hindered by inhalation of 100% O_2; more HbO_2 formed.

ANEMIA   Decreased Hb; buffering capacity of blood is decreased.

EXOGENOUS INHIBITORS OF CARBONIC ANHYDRASE   Enzyme catalyzes hydration reaction.

Hydration continues when enzyme is inhibited but very slowly.

Time in lungs is not adequate for CO_2 release; alveolar P_{CO_2} < arterial P_{CO_2}.

REGULATION OF ACID-BASE BALANCE

CONCENTRATION OF H^+ Regulated by buffering systems, lungs (excretion of CO_2), and kidneys (excretion of HCO_3^-).

NORMAL [H$^+$] 4×10^{-8} mol/liter; regulated within narrow limits for physiological reasons.

pH   Log of reciprocal of H^+ activity.

CALCULATION OF pH $pH = -\log [H_a^+]$; pH of normal arterial blood = 7.4.

BUFFERS AND BUFFERING SYSTEMS Prevent large changes of [H$^+$]; pK is pH at which buffer pair is half dissociated; in ideal buffer, pK is close to normal pH of blood.

BICARBONATE–CARBONIC ACID BUFFER SYSTEM CO_2 is in equilibrium with H_2CO_3, regulated by respiration; rapid (minutes) adjustment of [H$^+$].

PROTEIN BUFFERS   Free NH_2 and COOH groups.

Hb-HbO$_2$ BUFFER SYSTEM   Deoxyhemoglobin; weak acid, binds H^+.

Isohydric shift of CO_2 neutralizes 50% of H_2CO_3.

Hb buffering capacity is important.

HENDERSON-HASSELBALCH EQUATION   Relationship among pH, CO_2, H_2CO_3, and HCO_3^-:

$$pH = 6.1 + \log \frac{[HCO_3^-]}{[CO_2]}$$

Ratio $[HCO_3^-]/[CO_2]$ important; normal value is 20/1.

PHYSIOLOGICAL IMPORTANCE OF HCO_3^--H_2CO_3 BUFFER PAIR CO_2 is produced by all tissues; most is carried to lungs as HCO_3^- in plasma.

CO_2 is maintained by central chemoreceptors; regulated through ventilation.

pH-BICARBONATE DIAGRAM   Defines the acid-base status.

ACID-BASE SHIFTS   pH represents H^+ activity.

SIMPLE ACID-BASE DERANGEMENTS Increased [H$^+$], or decreased pH: caused by addition of H^+ or removal of HCO_3^- (metabolic acidosis); retention of CO_2 (respiratory acidosis).

Decreased [H$^+$], or increased pH: caused by removal of H^+ or addition of HCO_3^- (metabolic alkalosis); loss of CO_2 (respiratory alkalosis).

COMPENSATED ACID-BASE CONDITIONS   Respiratory alkalosis (low P_{CO_2}) compensates for metabolic acidosis.

Respiratory acidosis (high P_{CO_2}) compensates for metabolic alkalosis.

Metabolic alkalosis (increased renal absorption of HCO_3^-) compensates for respiratory acidosis.

Metabolic acidosis (increased renal excretion of HCO_3^-) compensates for respiratory alkalosis.

BIBLIOGRAPHY

Cohen, J.J.; Kassier, J.P; Gennert, F.J.; et al. 1982. *Acid-base.* Boston: Little, Brown, and Co.

Comroe, J.H. 1974. *Physiology of respiration.* Chicago: Year Book Medical Publishers, Inc.

Davenport, H.W. 1969. *The ABC of acid-base chemistry.* Chicago: The University of Chicago Press.

Gamble, J.L., Jr. 1954. *Chemical anatomy, physiology and pathology of extracellular fluid.* Cambridge: Harvard University Press.

Gamble, J.L., Jr. 1982. *Acid-base physiology: a direct approach.* Baltimore: Johns Hopkins University Press.

Michael, C.C. 1974. The transport of oxygen and carbon dioxide by the blood. In *Respiratory physiology* (MTP Internat. Rev. Sci.), Physiology, Series I, Vol. 2, editor J.G. Widdicombe, London: Butterworths & Co., Ltd., and Baltimore: University Park Press.

Porter, R., and Lawrenson, G., editors. 1982. *Metabolic acidosis* (CIBA Foundation symposium 87). Summit, N.J.: CIBA Pharmaceuticals.

Roughton, F.J.W. 1964. Transport of oxygen and carbon dioxide. In *Handbook of physiology,* Sect. 3, Respiration, Vol. 1, editors W.O. Fenn and H. Rahn. Washington, D.C.: American Physiological Society.

Slonim, N.B., and Hamilton, L.H. 1981. *Respiratory physiology.* 4th ed. St. Louis: The C.V. Mosby Co.

Wagner, P.D. 1977. Diffusion and chemical reaction in pulmonary gas exchange. *Physiol. Rev.* 57:257.

The Ventilation-Perfusion Relationship

Maximally efficient exchange of respiratory gases requires that alveolar ventilation and pulmonary blood flow be distributed evenly throughout the lungs and matched appropriately. Under these ideal conditions, the blood leaving each alveolar capillary would have exactly the same concentration of O_2 and CO_2 and would be in equilibrium with the alveolar Po_2 and Pco_2 (Figure 33-1). Such an ideal condition, although desirable, does not exist, even in the normal, healthy lung. In cardiopulmonary disease, one of the most frequent causes of arterial hypoxemia is a mismatch between pulmonary capillary blood flow and alveolar ventilation. The discussion that follows deals with some of the reasons for nonuniform ventilation and nonuniform perfusion in the lungs and the consequences that ensue.

VENTILATION

Causes of Nonuniform Ventilation

Ventilation may be uneven because of differences in frictional resistance to air flow within the airways of different regions or because of differences in compliance in different regions of the lungs. These conditions influence the ventilation-perfusion relationship. When both the airway resistance and the compliance change, the effects are additive.

REGIONAL CHANGE OF AIRWAY RESISTANCE
When airway resistance in a region of the lung increases, ventilation of that region decreases.

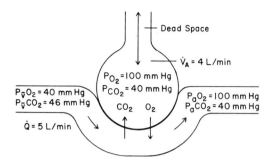

Figure 33-1. Gas exchange between alveolar air and pulmonary capillary blood. The sphere represents the lungs as a single compartment; the stem of the sphere represents the anatomical dead space. When mixed venous blood enters the capillaries that perfuse the lungs, O_2 and CO_2 diffuse across the alveolar-capillary membrane and equilibrium eventually is reached. As the blood leaves the pulmonary capillaries, arterial Po_2 and Pco_2 are the same as alveolar Po_2 and Pco_2, respectively.

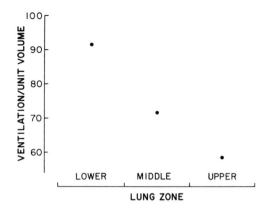

Figure 33-2. The distribution of inspired air in the lungs of a healthy, upright human. After ^{133}Xe was inhaled and held for 10 sec, the distribution of radioactive xenon in the various regions of the lungs was detected with externally placed scanners. (Redrawn, with permission, from Bryan, A.C., et al. 1964. *J. Appl. Physiol.* 19:397. Copyright, 1964, The American Physiological Society.)

In the lungs of the normal healthy individual in the vertical position, the effects of gravity cause a gradient of intrapleural pressure from apex to base. As intrapleural pressure becomes more subatmospheric, the airways dilate more, and resistance to air flow decreases. In asthmatic individuals, airways in some regions of the lungs may be partially obstructed and resistance increased. Airways also constrict reflexly when the inspired air contains irritants or when the secretion of mucus increases. Airways tend to collapse when they lose support from surrounding tissue, especially during expiration; this may be another reason for increased airway resistance.

REGIONAL CHANGE OF ELASTIC RESISTANCE

Lung volume is related inversely to elastic resistance; therefore, ventilation is decreased in areas of increased elastic resistance. Compliance is reduced in subjects who have restrictive lung disease, such as pulmonary or interstitial fibrosis, pulmonary alveolar or interstitial edema, or pulmonary congestion. On the other hand, loss of elasticity in some parts of the lungs causes increased compliance. The difference between the compliance of the alveoli at the top of the lungs and at the bottom of the lungs is caused by different intrapleural pressures and by the nonlinearity of lung compliance; this topic is discussed in the section that follows. As the compliance of a particular area of the lungs decreases, ventilation of that area decreases.

Measurement of Air Distribution

RADIOACTIVE TRACER METHOD

Radioactive xenon, an inert gas not very soluble in blood, is used commonly to reveal the distribution of inspired air. ^{133}Xe is inhaled during a single breath and held for 10 sec; the distribution of the gas in the lungs is monitored by externally placed radioactive counters. Figure 33-2 shows a typical distribution curve for xenon in the normal lungs of an upright individual. Note that ventilation decreases almost linearly from the base of the lungs to the apex. The reason for this was discussed in Chapter 28. Mainly because of the effect of gravity on the mass of the lungs, the pressure in the intrapleural space is further below atmospheric pressure at the top of the chest than at the bottom; this creates a gradient of negative pressure from top to bottom. Hence, because of increased transmural pressure, the alveoli at the apex are relatively distended, while the ones on the bottom are relatively compressed. However, the nonlinearity of the compliance curve offsets the influence of the gradient of alveolar size: the alveoli at the base of the lungs are more compliant than those at the top and therefore are ventilated better (see Figure 28-10).

SINGLE-BREATH
N_2 WASHOUT METHOD

The distribution of inspired gas also can be characterized by single-breath N_2 washout. The subject takes a single breath of 100% O_2, which dilutes the N_2 in his lungs; the concentration of N_2 is measured during exhalation. If the O_2 is distributed evenly after mixing, the concentration of N_2 in the expired air first increases sharply after the oxygen from the anatomical dead space is exhaled and then remains constant, as shown in the top portion of Figure 33-3. The result of uneven distribution of inspired air is depicted in the lower part of Figure 33-3. In one lung, the distribution of inspired O_2 is assumed to be uniform. In the other lung, which is assumed to be poorly ventilated, the O_2 may dilute the N_2 unevenly, and mixing may be incomplete; the concentration of N_2 would be higher in this lung. Consequently, the N_2 curve during exhalation shows a continuously increasing slope because the alveoli of the better ventilated lung, which have lower concentrations of N_2, empty first, and the alveoli of the poorly ventilated lung, which have higher concentrations of N_2, empty last.

PERFUSION

Causes of Nonuniform Blood Flow

INFLUENCE OF GRAVITY

Gravity also affects the distribution of pulmonary blood flow. The intravascular pressure at the base of the lungs is higher than at the top. This is caused by the force of gravity on the column of blood in the lungs, which is added to the pressure generated by the right ventricle. Since the blood vessels are distended by this force, blood flow increases in the basal region (recall that $R \propto 1/r^4$). Because of decreased perfusion, capillary hydrostatic pressure decreases from the bottom of the lungs to the top. In the top third of the lungs, the pressure within the capillaries may be less than that in the alveoli they perfuse; hence, in the upper region of the lungs, vascular resistance increases and

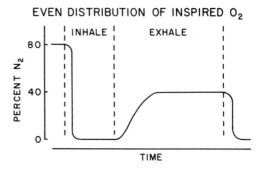

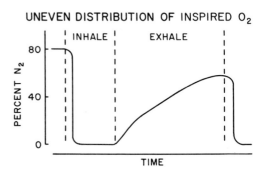

Figure 33-3. The distribution of inspired air in normal lungs and in lungs that are ventilated unevenly. The graph on the top shows the concentration of nitrogen measured at the mouth of a normal, healthy individual before and during inhalation and during exhalation of a single breath of pure O_2. At the beginning of inhalation, N_2 is 80%; during inhalation of 100% O_2, N_2 is 0. N_2 rises during the early part of exhalation and levels off as the oxygen contained in the anatomical dead space is washed out. The lower part of the figure shows what happens when the ventilation of one lung is reduced while the other lung is overventilated. A single breath of 100% O_2 dilutes the N_2 in the overventilated lung more than in the hypoventilated lung, in which the concentration of N_2 may be higher and mixing may be nonuniform. When this subject exhales, a continuously increasing fraction of N_2 is recorded, because the first air exhaled comes from the well-ventilated lung, which has a low concentration of N_2. The poorly ventilated lung, which has a higher but uneven concentration of N_2, empties last.

blood flow diminishes further. As a result, in the upright lung the flow of blood increases almost linearly from the apex to the base (see Figure 30-4 and discussion of blood flow distribution in Chapter 30).

INFLUENCE OF DISEASE

Certain pathological conditions also may cause uneven distribution of blood flow in the lungs. These include the partial occlusion or even complete obstruction of vessels by emboli or thrombi, the loss of capillaries in a certain region of the lung, or the collapse of blood vessels because of decreased perfusion pressure. Blood vessels also may collapse in shock or hypotension. Compression of intrathoracic vessels by a benign or malignant mass or by fluid in the chest also may increase the vascular resistance in some areas of the lungs, and if the perfusion pressure decreases concurrently, the nonuniform distribution of pulmonary blood flow is exaggerated.

Measurement of Blood Distribution

Several methods are used to measure the distribution of pulmonary blood flow.

ANGIOGRAPHY

When radio-opaque material is injected into a systemic vein or the pulmonary artery, external scanners can follow its distribution in the circulation of the lungs.

TAGGED ALBUMIN

Macroaggregates of albumin are labeled with iodine 131 or technetium 99 and injected intravenously. The distribution of radioactivity in the pulmonary circulation is detected by scanning the lung fields. Tagged albumin lodges in small arterioles in proportion to the blood flow. After a few hours, the aggregates break up, are metabolized in the liver, and excreted.

XENON 133

The use of radioactive xenon for measuring the regional distribution of blood flow in the lungs was discussed in Chapter 30.

VENTILATION-PERFUSION RATIO

The resting human consumes about 250 ml of O_2 and produces about 200 ml of CO_2 each minute. Under steady-state conditions, the O_2 consumed is replaced continuously by ventilation and taken up by the blood that flows through the pulmonary capillaries. The rate at which CO_2 is produced by the metabolizing tissues also is equal to the rate at which CO_2 is given up by the blood and excreted by ventilation.

A certain rate of ventilation is necessary to deliver the O_2 to the alveoli and to excrete the CO_2, and a certain rate of blood flow is required to transport these gases to and from the tissues. An alveolar ventilation ($\dot{V}A$) of approximately 4000 ml/min and a pulmonary blood flow ($\dot{Q}c$) of approximately 5000 ml/min meets the requirements. Therefore, the overall ventilation-perfusion ratio ($\dot{V}A/\dot{Q}c$) of a normal, healthy lung is:

$$\frac{\dot{V}A}{\dot{Q}c} = \frac{4000 \text{ ml/min}}{5000 \text{ ml/min}} = \frac{4}{5} = 0.8$$

Under these conditions, the mean alveolar P_{O_2} is maintained at 100 mm Hg and the mean alveolar P_{CO_2} is maintained at 40 mm Hg (see Figure 33-1). These values are optimal for the uptake of O_2 and the elimination of CO_2 by the pulmonary capillary blood.

Oxygen–Carbon Dioxide Diagram

The O_2-CO_2 diagram provides a practical and meaningful way to look at changes in the compositions of the alveolar and arterial blood gases (Figure 33-4). There are three special points on this diagram: (1) the normal point (N), at an alveolar P_{O_2} of 100 mm Hg and an alveolar P_{CO_2} of 40 mm Hg ($\dot{V}A/\dot{Q}c$ = 0.7–1.01), (2) the point (B) on the extreme left ($\dot{V}A/\dot{Q}c$ = 0), which represents venous blood ($\bar{v}$) with a P_{O_2} of 40 mm Hg and a P_{CO_2} of 46 mm Hg, (3) the point (C) on the extreme right ($\dot{V}A/\dot{Q}c$ = ∞), which is for inspired air (I), which has a P_{O_2} of 150 mm Hg and a P_{CO_2} of 0 mm Hg. The O_2-CO_2 diagram contains all possible simultaneous values of P_{O_2} and P_{CO_2} for all possible ventilation-perfusion ratios. If $\dot{V}A$ decreases relative to $\dot{Q}c$, or $\dot{Q}c$ increases relative to $\dot{V}A$ (that is, $\dot{V}A/\dot{Q}c$ is less than normal), then alveolar P_{O_2} decreases toward the venous P_{O_2}. Thus, the conditions in the lungs resemble those of a right-to-left shunt (blood flow bypasses lungs) (B). However, since this part of the curve (from N to $\bar{v}$) is almost horizontal, low $\dot{V}A/\dot{Q}c$ has little effect on the P_{CO_2}.

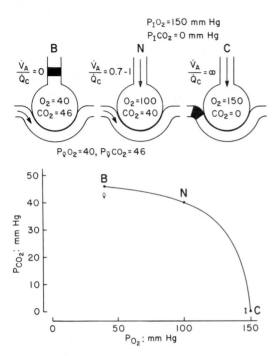

Figure 33-4. O_2-CO_2 diagram (top) and ventilation-perfusion line (bottom). Under normal condition (N), $\dot{V}_A/\dot{Q}c$ is between 0.7 and 1. B and C depict the extreme conditions. In B, blood flow is normal but there is no ventilation, that is, $\dot{V}_A/\dot{Q}c = 0$ (shunt). In C, ventilation is normal but there is no blood flow; that is, $\dot{V}_A/\dot{Q}c = \infty$ (dead space). The ventilation-perfusion line (bottom) shows the partial pressures of O_2 and CO_2 possible in alveolar air at different values of $\dot{V}_A/\dot{Q}c$ between the extreme cases of zero (B) and infinity (C). (Redrawn, with permission, from West, J.B. 1979. *Respiratory physiology—the essentials,* 2nd ed. Baltimore: The Williams & Wilkins Co.)

If $\dot{V}_A$ increases relative to $\dot{Q}c$, or $\dot{Q}c$ decreases relative to $\dot{V}_A$ (that is, $\dot{V}_A/\dot{Q}c$ is greater than normal), alveolar Po_2 and Pco_2 move toward the right, closer to the inspired gas point (I) (maximal Po_2 and no Pco_2). The conditions in the lungs now resemble those of alveolar dead space (ventilated but not perfused; point C).

Regional Differences in $\dot{V}_A/\dot{Q}c$

It was indicated previously that neither ventilation nor blood flow is uniform in the normal, upright lung. Both ventilation and perfusion increase from the top to the bottom of the lungs. At the bottom, however, perfusion is proportionately greater than ventilation, whereas, at the top, ventilation is proportionately greater than perfusion. Therefore, the ventilation-perfusion ratio is low at the base of the lung and high at the apex. The decrease in $\dot{V}_A/\dot{Q}c$ from apex to base is nonlinear and ranges from 3.0–0.6 (Figure 33-5). This means that at the top of the lung, alveolar ventilation is three times as great as capillary blood flow. The regional difference in ventilation-perfusion ratio is responsible for a slight difference of approximately 4 mm Hg between alveolar Po_2 and arterial Po_2. Small anatomic shunts slightly increase the difference and cause venous blood to mix directly with oxygenated arterial blood. The discussion that follows ignores the influence of this venous admixture.

$\dot{V}_A/\dot{Q}c$ Imbalance

Theoretically, adequate pulmonary function is possible despite nonuniform ventilation and nonuniform blood flow, provided the nonuniformities of air and blood are matched in each lung unit.

DEAD SPACE
If the inspired air is distributed uniformly but the flow of blood is not, some of the air does not contribute to the oxygenation of the blood (Figure 33-6). To illustrate the point with the

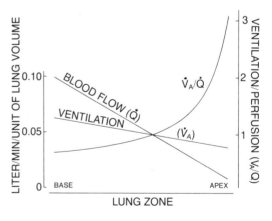

Figure 33-5. The distribution of ventilation and blood flow and the ventilation-perfusion ratio of the upright human lung. (Redrawn, with permission, from West, J.B. 1979. *Respiratory physiology—the essentials,* 2nd ed. Baltimore: The Williams & Wilkins Co.)

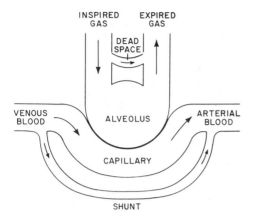

Figure 33-6. Uneven distribution of ventilation and blood flow in the lungs. The lung is depicted as a single compartment in which some of the alveoli are ventilated but not perfused. The part of the inspired air that does not participate in gas exchange represents dead space ventilation. Capillary blood flow is shown to consist of blood that comes in contact with alveoli (exchange of gases) and blood that bypasses the alveoli (no gas exchange), as indicated by the shunt. The arterial blood-gas composition depends on the relative magnitude of the shunt.

extreme case, it is possible to have normal ventilation and no blood flow, resulting in

$$\frac{\dot{V}_A}{\dot{Q}c} = \frac{4000 \text{ ml}}{0 \text{ ml}} = \infty$$

This condition exists in the trachea, which is ventilated but not perfused, and therefore by definition represents dead space (condition C in Figure 33-4). Another example would be the ventilation of alveoli that have no blood supply because of pulmonary embolism; this constitutes a physiological dead space. Ventilation of dead space is wasted, as it does not increase the arterial P_{O_2} or decrease the P_{CO_2}.

SHUNTS

When the blood flow is distributed uniformly but the inspired air is not, the blood is incompletely oxygenated in the poorly ventilated lung unit; since the poorly oxygenated blood mixes with the fully oxygenated blood from the other unit, it decreases the arterial P_{O_2} (see Figure 33-6). The extreme case here is normal blood flow and no ventilation. This gives

$$\frac{\dot{V}_A}{\dot{Q}c} = \frac{0 \text{ ml}}{5000 \text{ ml}} = 0$$

Under these conditions, no air is available to oxygenate the blood, and venous blood may flow unchanged into the systemic circulation. This condition by definition is an absolute shunt, also known as venous admixture (condition B in Figure 33-4). In a diseased lung, these extreme conditions may coexist with normally ventilated and perfused alveoli and cause overall ventilation-perfusion imbalance somewhere between zero and infinity. Figure 33-7 shows examples of conditions in which $\dot{V}_A/\dot{Q}c$ increases and others in which it decreases. Note that both ventilation and perfusion may decrease or increase without a change in the normal $\dot{V}_A/\dot{Q}c$ if the increases or de-

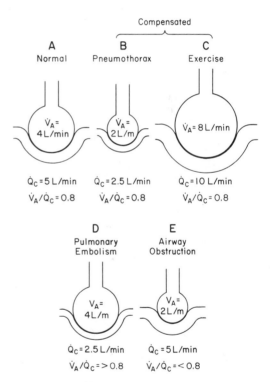

Figure 33-7. Some conditions in which the ventilation-perfusion ratio is normal, less than normal, and greater than normal. Examples B and C are compensated cases in which both ventilation and blood flow are changed proportionately so that $\dot{V}_A/\dot{Q}c$ remains normal. In D, a blood clot in a branch of the pulmonary artery has reduced blood flow significantly while ventilation is normal, producing a functional dead space. In E, obstruction of some of the airways has caused hypoventilation in the face of normal blood flow, creating a condition that resembles shunting of blood, or venous admixture.

CLINICAL CORRELATION
33.1   Ventilation-Perfusion Mismatching
After Pulmonary Thromboembolism

CASE REPORT

The Patient: A 45-year-old woman.

Principal Complaint: Sudden onset of severe dyspnea.

History: The patient had been healthy until four days before admission to the hospital for treatment of injuries she suffered in an automobile accident. Her left femur and ulna were fractured, and she had extensive intramuscular hemorrhage and other less serious cuts and bruises. In addition to medication for pain, she was given low prophylactic doses of an oral anticoagulant agent. Her leg and arm were in casts but otherwise she recovered uneventfully until she developed a slight fever during the third night. The next day she complained that she could not breathe.

Clinical Examination: The patient's blood pressure was 135/90 mm Hg (normal, 90–140/60–90 mm Hg), her heart rate was 110 beats/min (normal, 60–100 beats/min). Some rales* and localized wheezes were heard over the lower lung field. The arterial P_{O_2} was 53 mm Hg (normal, 75–100 mm Hg),

arterial P_{CO_2} was 35 mm Hg (normal, 35–45 mm Hg), and her arterial pH was 7.46 (normal, 7.35–7.45). Spirometric tests showed that her minute ventilation ($\dot{V}$) was 9.1 liters/min, alveolar ventilation ($\dot{V}_A$) was 4.1 liters/min or 46% of $\dot{V}$ (predicted, 60%–70%), and her physiological dead space** was 5 liters/min, or 54% of $\dot{V}$ (predicted, 30%–40%). Alveolar P_{O_2} was calculated to be 100 mm Hg (with the patient breathing room air), and the alveolar-arterial P_{O_2} difference (A-a O_2 gradient) was 47 mm Hg. Pulmonary thromboembolism was suspected, because it often is associated with fractures or other injuries of the lower extremities. Because of the severity and potentially lethal nature of the suspected disease, further tests were ordered. The patient was transferred to the cardiac catheterization laboratory, where a catheter was placed into the pulmonary artery. Cardiac output determined by the thermodilution method (see Chapter 14) was 3.8 liters/min (predicted, 4.8 liters/min), pulmonary arterial pressure was 65/45 mm Hg (normal, 12–28/3–13 mm Hg). The extent of vascular occlusion was determined by pulmonary angiography,*** which showed decreased filling of two lobes of the right lung.

creases are proportional, that is, compensated (Figure 33-7, B and C).

Assessment of $\dot{V}_A/\dot{Q}_c$ Disturbance

BLOOD GASES

The partial pressures of arterial blood gases are relatively easy to measure and may be used as indicators of $\dot{V}_A/\dot{Q}_c$ imbalance. However, arterial P_{O_2} also is influenced by other factors, mainly problems of diffusion, and arterial P_{CO_2} depends on the level of alveolar ventilation. Therefore, blood gas tensions by themselves are not useful in assessing ventilation-perfusion problems. The best estimates are the al-

veolar-arterial (A-a) differences of P_{O_2} and P_{CO_2}.

EFFECTS OF LOW $\dot{V}_A/\dot{Q}_c$ (SHUNTS)

Low ventilation-perfusion ratios may affect arterial P_{O_2} drastically and arterial P_{CO_2} very little because of the nonlinear shape of the oxyhemoglobin dissociation curve and the relatively straight line of the CO_2 curve. Figure 33-8 shows the effects of shunts on arterial P_{O_2} and P_{CO_2}. In a two-compartment model of the lungs in which the blood flow is distributed evenly to each compartment but the first compartment is overventilated and the second

(CLINICAL CORRELATION continued)

Comment: The respiratory consequence of pulmonary embolism is a significant increase in the physiological dead space. Since blood flow to sections of the lungs may be completely or partially obstructed by the clots, ventilation of these inadequately perfused alveoli is wasted. Because the patient frequently hyperventilates, arterial P_{CO_2} often is within normal limits, but alveolar P_{CO_2} is decreased, that is, is closer to the P_{CO_2} of inspired air. The airways constrict in response to the alveolar hypocapnia; this constriction diverts the air to better-perfused alveoli. Matching of ventilation and perfusion improves, and the dead space decreases. The decreased blood flow to an area also may decrease the availability of substrates for the synthesis of surfactant, which causes alveolar instability and collapse (see Chapter 29).

The hemodynamic consequences of pulmonary emboli depend largely on the degree of vascular obstruction. Moderate obstruction may cause only an increased heart rate, and more serious problems may not arise if the patient remains quiet and the demand for O_2 does not increase. In this patient, the loss of perfusion was great enough to produce arterial hypoxemia, presumably caused by decreased functional area available for gas exchange. When the ventilation and perfusion of the lung are significantly mismatched, the Pa_{O_2} is affected much more than the Pa_{CO_2} because the relationship between P_{CO_2} and CO_2 content is a straight line, whereas the O_2

dissociation curve is sigmoid (see Chapters 31 and 32). Blood gas values are important in diagnosing pulmonary embolism, which usually is associated with arterial hypoxemia, hypocapnia, respiratory alkalosis, and significant alveolar-arterial O_2 and CO_2 gradients.

Treatment: Therapy is directed toward dissolving the blood clots**** and restoring the pulmonary circulation. Vigorous anticoagulant treatment was begun. The patient initially received 10,000 units of heparin intravenously and then continuous infusion of heparin at the rate of 1000 units every hour for 7 days. She was switched to an oral anticoagulant several days before her discharge from the hospital, and this was continued for 3 months.

Outcome: The remainder of her recovery was uneventful.

*Abnormal sounds (rattling, scraping) heard by auscultation of the chest.

**The sum of the anatomical and alveolar dead spaces.

***A radio-opaque material is injected into the pulmonary artery and the distribution of the material in the circulation of the lung is detected by x-rays.

****Anticoagulants do not cause the clots to dissolve, but, by preventing expansion of the clots, they enable the fibrinolytic system of the body to dissolve them.

compartment is underventilated, the $\dot{V}_A/\dot{Q}_c$ of the first compartment is high and that of the second compartment is low. The blood that leaves the first lung is fully oxygenated (high P_{O_2}), but the blood that leaves the second lung is incompletely oxygenated and has a significantly lower P_{O_2}. When blood from lung 2 mixes with that from lung 1, the P_{O_2} decreases; the result is hypoxemia. One might assume that the blood from lung 1, which has excess ventilation, would correct the low P_{O_2} of the blood from lung 2. However, the P_{O_2} depends on the O_2 dissolved in the blood, which is a very small portion of the total oxygen. Most of the O_2 is combined with hemoglobin. Because of the saturation characteristics of Hb, most of the

binding sites are occupied by O_2 at a P_{O_2} of 100 mm Hg (flat portion of HbO_2 curve); therefore, an increase of P_{O_2} beyond about 100 mm Hg causes little additional O_2 to be carried in the blood. On the other hand, when the P_{O_2} decreases significantly, saturation and O_2 content both decrease significantly, since less O_2 is carried by the hemoglobin (steep portion of HbO_2 dissociation curve). Therefore, the hypoxemia caused by shunting of blood in some parts of the lungs cannot be corrected by extra uptake of O_2 in other parts. In contrast, because the system that carries CO_2 does not become saturated, the P_{CO_2} of the overventilated regions can be lowered more than usual, which compensates for the retention of CO_2 in the

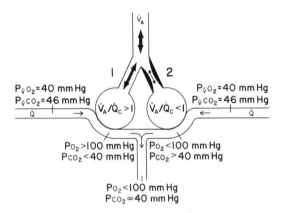

Figure 33-8. Effects of ventilation-perfusion mismatching on the composition of arterial blood gases. Lung 1 has excess ventilation relative to blood flow, whereas lung 2 is underventilated. Mixing equal volumes of blood, one part that has a high P_{O_2} and one that has a low P_{O_2}, produces a P_{O_2} that is not an average of the two values, because the O_2 content (ml O_2/100 ml blood) is not related linearly to the P_{O_2}. In this example, the maximum O_2 content of the blood that perfuses lung 1 is about 20 vol% (P_{O_2} = 150 mm Hg), and the minimum O_2 content of the blood that perfuses lung 2 is about 15 vol% (P_{O_2} = 40 mm Hg). Therefore, the mixed blood contains about 17.5 ml O_2/100 ml, which makes the P_{O_2} of the mixed blood about 55 mm Hg. Thus, hyperventilation of lung 1 cannot correct for the effects of hypoventilation of lung 2 on oxygenation of the blood. However, because the relationship between P_{CO_2} and CO_2 content in the physiological range is relatively linear, mixing blood that has low P_{CO_2} (40 mm Hg) with an equal volume that has high P_{CO_2} (46 mm Hg) produces a mixture that has a P_{CO_2} close to the average of the two values. Hence, the effects on blood CO_2 of hypoventilating one area of lung can be corrected by hyperventilating another area.

shunted blood. In addition, because of the rapid diffusion of CO_2, the normal arteriovenous difference of P_{CO_2} is small (40 versus 46 mm Hg) and not affected significantly by a low $\dot{V}_A/\dot{Q}c$. However, the larger arteriovenous difference of P_{O_2} (40 mm Hg versus 100 mm Hg) is affected significantly.

EFFECTS OF HIGH $\dot{V}_A/\dot{Q}c$ (DEAD SPACE)

Increased ventilation-perfusion ratio, or dead space, influences the difference between alveolar P_{CO_2} and arterial P_{CO_2} but changes P_{O_2} very little, for the reasons discussed previously.

Under these conditions, alveolar P_{CO_2} is less than arterial P_{CO_2}, the increased arterial P_{CO_2} drives the respiratory centers, and the work of the muscles of respiration increases. This work essentially is wasted, however, because it ventilates primarily dead space, and it may be exhausting to an ill patient.

DETECTION OF SHUNTS

To detect large shunts (>40% of total blood flow) and to distinguish between hypoxemia caused by a shunt and that caused by hypoventilation, the subject is given 100% O_2 to breathe. Eventually, even the poorly ventilated alveoli achieve the maximum P_{O_2} and, if there is no problem with diffusion, equilibrate with the arterial P_{O_2}; hence, the alveolar-arterial difference is small. However, if the arterial P_{O_2} does not reach the maximum and the alveolar-arterial difference of P_{O_2} is significant (alveolar P_{O_2} usually is calculated by the alveolar air equation (see Chapter 27), the diagnosis is a right-to-left shunt. In this case, administration of 100% O_2 does not correct the arterial hypoxemia but serves only as a diagnostic tool. If the hypoxemia is caused by hypoventilation or by problems with diffusion, O_2 therapy is beneficial as well as useful diagnostically.

CALCULATION OF SHUNTS

The equation for calculating the relative magnitude of a shunt is:

$$\frac{\dot{Q}s}{\dot{Q}T} = \frac{Cc\,O_2 - Ca o_2}{Cc\,O_2 - C\bar{v}o_2}$$

where $\dot{Q}s$ is the volume of blood flow in the shunt (that is, the blood that does not take up O_2 and does not eliminate CO_2), $\dot{Q}T$ is the total volume of blood flow (the cardiac output), $\dot{Q}s/\dot{Q}T$ is the shunt fraction, $Cc\,O_2$ is the O_2 content of pulmonary end-capillary blood in volumes percent (vol %), $Ca o_2$ is the O_2 content of systemic arterial blood (vol %), and $C\bar{v}o_2$ is the O_2 content of mixed systemic venous blood. Since the O_2 content is the amount of O_2 dissolved in the blood plus that combined with hemoglobin,

$$Cc\,O_2 = \frac{0.024 \times P_{O_2} \times 100}{760} + \frac{[Hb] \times 1.34}{100}$$

where 0.024 is the solubility coefficient of O_2 in milliliters of O_2 per milliliter of blood per atmosphere, [Hb] is the concentration of hemoglobin per 100 ml of blood, and 1.34 is the amount of O_2, in milliliters, bound per gram of Hb. Then,

$$Cc_{O_2} = (0.003 \times Pa_{O_2}) + [Hb] \times 1.34$$

Compensation for $\dot{V}_A/\dot{Q}c$ Imbalance

Mismatching of air and blood can be compensated in two ways. First, local alveolar hypoxia increases pulmonary arteriolar resistance; thus, blood flow is directed away from the alveoli that have low P_{O_2}. Second, when the blood flow to some of the alveoli is reduced and the alveolar P_{CO_2} decreases, the alveolar ducts constrict and alveolar ventilation is directed to alveoli that are perfused better; thus the overall matching of ventilation and perfusion improves.

STUDY OUTLINE

Ideal lung: uniform ventilation, uniform blood flow; normal lung: ventilation and blood flow increase from top to bottom.

VENTILATION

CAUSES OF NONUNIFORM VENTILATION

REGIONAL CHANGE OF AIRWAY RESISTANCE Effects of gravity, partial obstruction, increased mucus secretion, or loss of structural support.

REGIONAL CHANGE OF ELASTIC RESISTANCE Lung volume is related inversely to elastic resistance.

Increase of elastic resistance with restrictive disease, pulmonary edema, or congestion.

MEASUREMENT OF AIR DISTRIBUTION

RADIOACTIVE TRACER METHOD Distribution of inhaled xenon 133 in lung is detected by external counters.

SINGLE-BREATH N_2 WASHOUT METHOD N_2 in lung is diluted by single breath of 100% O_2.

Detects uneven distribution of inhaled air, not anatomical location.

PERFUSION

CAUSES OF NONUNIFORM BLOOD FLOW

INFLUENCE OF GRAVITY On bottom, hydrostatic pressure distends vessels; flow increases.

At top, capillary hydrostatic pressure is low, distended alveoli compress vessels; flow decreases.

INFLUENCE OF DISEASE Increased vascular resistance due to pathology of vessels or lungs.

MEASUREMENT OF BLOOD DISTRIBUTION

ANGIOGRAPHY The distribution of radioopaque material in lung circulation.

TAGGED ALBUMIN Detection of macroaggregates in small vessels is proportional to blood flow.

XENON 133 Evolves as gas from blood in pulmonary circulation; distribution mapped by measuring radioactivity.

VENTILATION-PERFUSION RATIO For optimal uptake of O_2 and elimination of CO_2, alveolar ventilation 4 l/min, pulmonary blood flow 5 l/min: ventilation-perfusion ratio, 0.8.

OXYGEN-CARBON DIOXIDE DIAGRAM Predicts composition of alveolar arterial gases at certain $\dot{V}_A/\dot{Q}c$.

Normal $\dot{V}_A$ and $\dot{Q}c$: $Pa_{O_2} = 100$ mm Hg, $Pa_{CO_2} = 40$ mm Hg, $\dot{V}_A/\dot{Q}c = 0.8$.

$\dot{V}_A\dot{Q}c < 0.8$: Pa_{O_2} decreased; shuntlike condition.

$\dot{V}_A/\dot{Q}c > 0.8$: Pa_{O_2} increased, Pa_{CO_2} decreased; dead-space-like condition.

REGIONAL DIFFERENCES IN $\dot{V}_A/\dot{Q}c$ Ventilation is proportionately greater at top of lungs; perfusion is proportionately greater at bottom.

$\dot{V}_A/\dot{Q}c$ low at base, high at apex; increase is nonlinear.

Causes slight alveolar-arterial P_{O_2} difference.

$\dot{V}_A/\dot{Q}c$ IMBALANCE Hypoxemia

DEAD SPACE Ventilation in excess of perfusion; no increase of Pa_{O_2} or decrease of Pa_{CO_2}.

SHUNTS Blood flow in excess of ventilation; venous admixture.

ASSESSMENT OF $\dot{V}_A/\dot{Q}c$ DISTURBANCE

BLOOD GASES Indicators of imbalance; also influenced by other factors.

Estimate alveolar-arterial differences of P_{O_2} and P_{CO_2} best.

EFFECTS OF LOW $\dot{V}_A/\dot{Q}c$ (SHUNTS)
Large alveolar-arterial Po_2 difference and low systemic arterial Po_2.

No significant effect on $Paco_2$, because perfused areas compensate for CO_2 retention in shunted blood.

EFFECTS OF HIGH $\dot{V}_A/\dot{Q}c$ (DEAD SPACE)
No significant effect on Pao_2.

Alveolar Pco_2 is less than arterial; attempted compensation by increased respiration is not effective.

DETECTION OF SHUNTS   Subject breathes 100% O_2: large alveolar-arterial O_2 difference indicates shunt; O_2 therapy is not useful.

CALCULATION OF SHUNTS   Fraction of total blood flow ($\dot{Q}s/\dot{Q}T$) not oxygenated.

$$\frac{\dot{Q}s}{\dot{Q}T} = \frac{Cc\,o_2 - Cao_2}{Cc\,o_2 - C\bar{v}o_2}$$

O_2 content (ml O_2/100 ml blood) = dissolved O_2 + HbO_2.

COMPENSATION FOR $\dot{V}_A/\dot{Q}c$ IMBALANCE   Local alveolar hypoxia causes shift of blood to better-ventilated alveoli.

Local ischemia causes shift of air to better-perfused alveoli.

BIBLIOGRAPHY

Comroe, J.H. 1974. *Physiology of respiration.* Chicago: Year Book Medical Publishers, Inc.

Comroe, J.H.; Forster, R.E.; Dubois, A.B.; et al. 1962. *The lung: clinical physiology and pulmonary function tests.* Chicago: Year Book Medical Publishers, Inc.

Comroe, J.H., and Fowler, W.S. 1951. Detection of uneven ventilation during a single breath of O_2. *Am. J. Med.* 10:408.

Dolfuss, R.E.; Milic-Emili, J.; and Bates, D.V. 1967. Regional ventilation of the lung studied with boluses of ^{133}xenon. *Resp. Physiol.* 2:234.

Rahn, H., and Farhi, L.E. 1964. Ventilation, perfusion, and gas exchange—the $\dot{V}_A/\dot{Q}$ concept. In *Handbook of Physiology,* Section 3, Respiration, Vol. I, editors W.O. Fenn and H. Rahn. Washington, D.C.: American Physiological Society.

Riley, R.L., and Cournand, A. 1951. Analysis of factors affecting partial pressures of oxygen and carbon dioxide in gas and blood of lungs: theory. *J. Appl. Physiol.* 4:77.

Slonim, N.B., and Hamilton, L.H. 1981. *Respiratory physiology,* 4th ed. St. Louis: The C.V. Mosby Co.

Wagner, P.D. 1977. Diffusion and chemical reaction in pulmonary gas exchange. *Physiol. Rev.* 57:257.

Wagner, P.D. 1980. Ventilation-perfusion relationships. *Ann. Rev. Physiol.* 42:235.

West, J.B. 1979. *Respiratory physiology—the essentials,* 2nd ed. Baltimore: Williams & Wilkins Co.

West, J.B. 1977. Ventilation-perfusion relationships. *Am. Rev. Resp. Dis.* 116:919.

West, J.B. 1970. *Ventilation/blood flow and gas exchange,* 2nd ed. Oxford: Blackwell Scientific Publications.

34

Physiological Adjustments in Respiration to Changes in the Environment

CHAPTER CONTENTS

BREATHING AT HIGH PRESSURE AND AT LOW PRESSURE

Boyle's law states that at constant temperature the volume of a gas is related inversely to the pressure to which it is subjected. The volume of a gas decreases by one-half when the pressure is doubled (for example, from 760–1520 mm Hg [Table 34-1]) and doubles when the pressure is decreased by one-half (for example, from 760–380 mm Hg). The practical application of Boyle's law becomes important when people change their environment by such activities as deep-sea diving or living at a high altitude.

High Pressure and Underwater Environment

Atmospheric pressure is standardized at sea level and 0 C; it is equivalent to a column of mercury 760 mm high or a column of sea water 10 m high. Therefore, when a diver descends into the sea, for every 10 m he goes under water, another atmosphere of pressure is added to the initial one at sea level. A person at a depth of 30 m is subjected to total pressure of 4 atmospheres or 4 × 760 (= 3040) mm Hg pressure.

The physiological consequences of the increased pressure are twofold: the direct effects of the change in total pressure and the changes in the partial pressures of the gases breathed.

DIRECT EFFECTS
OF INCREASED PRESSURE

When a person submerges in water while breathing through a hose, the muscles of inspiration must generate enough force to expand the chest against the pressure exerted by the water. Expansion of the thorax is limited by the ability of the respiratory muscles to reduce the intrapleural pressure by a maximum of about 100 mm Hg. This is equivalent to the hydrostatic pressure exerted on the chest in 4.5 ft of water; below this level, the chest cannot be expanded. In fact, inspiration becomes difficult or nearly impossible at a depth of only 2 ft of water when one tries to breathe through a tube that extends to the surface.

Because the human body consists mainly of fluids, its density is close to that of water and, as water, it is incompressible. Humans in water become part of the environment. The surrounding pressure is transmitted throughout body tissues without any harm to the individual. Therefore, the most important physiological aspect of the increased pressure is not its direct effect on the body but its effect on the air contained within the body. As the pressure increases under water, the air in structures such as the lungs, the nasal sinuses, the middle ear, and the gastrointestinal tract is compressed; as the pressure decreases during ascent from the deep, the volume of air contained in these spaces expands again. As long as the diver's airways communicate with the air supply, as they do when a scuba (self-contained underwater breathing apparatus) is used, the volume of air in the lungs is maintained despite the changing pressure. The problem arises when a diver uses no apparatus but simply holds his breath, or when the air in the tank is depleted and the diver keeps his glottis closed while returning to the surface.

EFFECTS OF BREATH-HOLDING DIVE.

Table 34-1 shows the relationship between increasing atmospheric pressure and the volume of gas in the lungs. If a diver takes a full breath (TLC), holds it, and dives to a depth of 10 m, his lung volume decreases to one-half its former volume. At a depth of 40 m, the volume of air in the lungs is one-fifth that of the volume at sea level, or approximately equal to residual volume. Compression of the lung air space to less than residual volume exceeds the limit of safety and produces the phenomenon that divers call the "squeeze." Although compression of air in the alveoli and airways decreases the lung volume, the more rigid thorax is not compressed, and its volume remains that of deep inspiration. Thus, as the alveoli and small airways become smaller, they exert a recoil force that decreases intrapleural pressure. This increases the difference of pressure across the capillary walls to unphysiological levels, which causes capillaries to rupture and bleed into the alveoli and airways.

EFFECTS OF ASCENT FROM A DIVE.

If the diver's lungs are full of air at a depth of 20 m, and he does not exhale on the way up, or his airway becomes obstructed, the lungs

TABLE 34-1
Relationship between pressure and gas volume
at various depths of sea water

Depth (Feet)	(Meters)	Pressure (Atmospheres)	Volume of air (Liters)
Sea level		1	6.0
33	10	2	3.0
66	20	3	2.0
99	30	4	1.5
132	40	5	1.2
165	50	6	1.0
330	90	10	0.6
495	140	15	0.4

may be overexpanded and some alveoli may rupture and cause pneumothorax. The situation becomes more dangerous as the ascent continues. Because the pressure decreases uniformly with decreasing depth, the volume of air that escapes from the alveoli into the thorax increases uniformly. The lungs may collapse; if they do, the structures in the chest will be pushed to the side, away from the pneumothorax. Air may be forced from the alveoli into the pulmonary venous circulation, causing air embolism (bubbles) in the systemic circulation. A diver is in the greatest danger from air embolism when surfacing from a relatively shallow depth, because lung volume changes most rapidly near the surface. This becomes clear when Table 34-1 is consulted. On the surface, the diver may experience severe pain and may die of ventilatory and circulatory failure. If the diver breathes from his air supply on the way up to the surface or exhales to eliminate the increasing volume of air in the lungs as the pressure decreases, there is no danger of overinflating the lungs.

INDIRECT EFFECTS OF INCREASED PRESSURE

DECOMPRESSION SICKNESS, OR THE BENDS. Air is 79% N_2, which is inert and has little effect on the body except at greatly increased pressure. At sea level, N_2 is dissolved in the blood and tissues and is in equilibrium with N_2 in the alveolar air. When a diver goes underwater, the total pressure of the gases he breathes must be equal to the pressure around him. When a scuba is used, the regulator on the apparatus automatically supplies the diver with air in equilibrium with the water pressure at any depth. However, in deep water, the increased pressure increases the amount of N_2 dissolved in the tissues, especially in the lipids of the body. This condition is of no consequence unless the diver returns to the surface too rapidly. If a diver remains underwater for a long time, his tissues are saturated with N_2. If the ascent is gradual, the change of pressure is gradual, and N_2 is removed slowly from the tissues and eliminated through the lungs. If the ascent is too fast, the pressure decreases so rapidly that the N_2 escapes as bubbles, or "boils" out of solution as CO_2 does when a bottle of carbonated drink is opened. The bubbles of N_2 cause pain, especially in the muscles and joints. The condition is referred to as "the bends." The

symptom of decompression sickness in the lungs is dyspnea, sometimes referred to as "the chokes." The rest of the syndrome consists of sensory disturbances, weakness or paralysis, dizziness, deafness, and in severe cases, pulmonary embolism from the bubbles that form in the venous blood. Bubbles occluding the microcirculation of a critical vascular bed may cause death.

Divers use tables that tell them how long they can remain at a certain depth before they encounter problems during decompression. To prevent the bends, they decompress gradually. Recompression followed by gradual decompression may be necessary if symptoms of the bends appear. Breathing a less soluble gas mixture, such as helium and O_2, will not prevent decompression sickness but will reduce the risk of its occurring. Since helium is about half as soluble as N_2, a diver could remain under compression twice as long before accumulating as much gas as when breathing N_2. In addition, because He-O_2 is a low-density gas mixture, the work of breathing is less.

Sometimes the diver breathes 100% O_2 before a dive, to replace the N_2 in the lungs and tissues. Once underwater, the diver breathes compressed air, and N_2 accumulates in the body again; however, it does so at a much slower rate, which allows the diver to be submerged longer. Working in deep water enhances the formation of bubbles during ascent because of the greater movement of tissue and body fluids. This process has been compared to shaking a bottle of carbonated drink before taking off the cap.

EFFECT OF INCREASED PRESSURE ON GAS DENSITY

Resistance to breathing, that is, resistance to air flow, increases when the density or viscosity of the inspired air increases. Since the density of a gas increases as the pressure increases, the work of breathing is greater under high pressure.

NITROGEN NARCOSIS

At high partial pressure, the effect of N_2 on the central nervous system is much like alcohol intoxication. At approximately 4.5 atmospheres, divers may experience euphoria, the so-called "rapture of the deep." At very high pressures, synaptic transmission may be impaired, with loss of coordination; finally, coma may develop.

The underwater depth humans can tolerate is limited by several factors. First, the total pressure of the gases a diver breathes must be equal to the ambient pressure. Second, the mixture of gases must contain O_2 and an inert gas (N_2) that dilutes the O_2 and maintains the total pressure. Last, the partial pressure of O_2 must be held within safe limits so that neither hypoxia nor oxygen poisoning occurs, and the inert gas must be held at a pressure that keeps decompression from becoming a major problem. The best gas mixture and the most commonly used one is air. It is used in the open-circuit scuba, in which exhaled gas is not rebreathed but eliminated. In the closed-circuit scuba, the diver rebreathes the exhaled gas after the CO_2 has been removed; in this system, O_2 must be used. However, O_2 toxicity becomes a problem when P_{O_2} approaches approximately 2 atmospheres. Thus, a diver who uses a closed-circuit scuba that contains O_2 cannot go deeper than 10 m (33 ft) without experiencing the toxic effects of O_2. On the other hand, diving while breathing air is limited to 300 ft by the development of N_2 narcosis.

HIGH ALTITUDE— LOW AMBIENT PRESSURE

Atmospheric pressure decreases with increased height above sea level. The proportion of O_2 in the air does not change; however, because of decreased total pressure, the partial pressure of O_2 in inspired air, and therefore in alveolar air, decreases (Table 34-2). At 40,000 ft (12.2 km), ambient pressure is 141 mm Hg. Above this al-

titude, hypoxemia occurs even when 100% O_2 is breathed, as shown below:

$$P_{A_{O_2}} = P_{I_{O_2}} - P_{A_{CO_2}},$$
$$P_{A_{O_2}} = (141 - 47)\,1.0 - 32$$
$$= 62 \text{ mm Hg}$$

$P_{A_{CO_2}}$ is estimated to be 32 mm Hg, because hyperventilation decreases it to less than the normal 40 mm Hg. (Note that when 100% O_2 is breathed, the correction factor for CO_2 becomes 1.00. See the alveolar air equation in Chapter 27.)

Ascent to High Altitude

Figure 34-1 shows the changes in ventilation and circulation experienced by a sea-level resident who transfers to an altitude of about 12,000 ft. Since alveolar P_{O_2} ($P_{A_{O_2}}$) is related directly to inspired P_{O_2}, and arterial P_{O_2} ($P_{a_{O_2}}$) is related directly to $P_{A_{O_2}}$, both $P_{A_{O_2}}$ and $P_{a_{O_2}}$ decrease significantly. Decreased $P_{a_{O_2}}$ stimulates the peripheral chemoreceptors, which reflexly drive the respiratory centers (hypoxic drive). Both tidal volume and respiratory rate increase; therefore, alveolar ventilation, the amount of O_2 delivered, and the amount of CO_2 eliminated increase. Because of the increased removal of CO_2, $P_{a_{CO_2}}$ and $[H^+]$ decrease, causing respiratory alkalosis. The decreased $[H^+]$ of the arterial blood acts through the carotid body chemoreceptors to decrease ventilation. At the same time, the $[H^+]$ of the cerebro-

TABLE 34-2
Relationship between pressure and inspired P_{O_2} at various altitudes

Altitude (Feet)	(Meters)	Barometric pressure (mm Hg)	Inspired P_{O_2} (mm Hg)
0	0	760.0	159.1
5,000	1,524	632.3	132.3
10,000	3,048	522.6	109.4
15,000	4,572	428.8	89.7
17,962	5,475	380.0	79.5
20,000	6,096	349.2	73.1
25,000	7,621	281.9	59.0
30,000	9,145	225.6	47.2
35,000	10,669	178.7	37.4
40,000	12,193	140.7	29.4

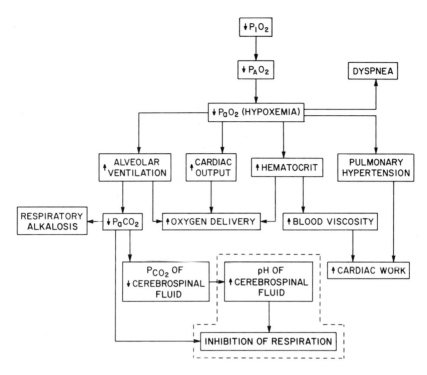

Figure 34-1. Acute and chronic adjustments of ventilation and circulation after ascent to high altitude (approximately 12,000 ft). Broken lines around certain boxes indicate the mechanism for immediate adjustment of ventilation to low P_{IO_2}.

spinal fluid (CSF) decreases (decreasing the P_{CO_2} shifts the reaction $CO_2 + H_2O \rightleftharpoons H_2CO_3 \rightleftharpoons H^+ + HCO_3^-$ to the left), and the ventilatory drive through the central chemoreceptors decreases also. However, the overall effect of hypoxia due to high altitude is to make ventilation greater than at sea level and to increase alveolar ventilation.

The combined effects of hypoxemia and respiratory alkalosis cause acute mountain sickness. The syndrome consists of dyspnea (shortness of breath, or air hunger), palpitations, fatigue, dizziness, mental sluggishness, dim vision, and, often, insomnia. After a few days, the symptoms diminish or disappear, but full acclimatization takes weeks.

After a few days at high altitude, the $[HCO_3^-]$ of the CSF decreases to match the low P_{CO_2}, and the $[H^+]$ of the CSF is restored to normal (pH 7.32). The kidney excretes the excess HCO_3^-, respiration no longer is inhibited, and ventilation increases further. Hence, when one lives at a high altitude, *chronic* hypoxemia stimulates ventilation more than *acute* hypoxemia does.

The short-term and long-term physiological adjustments to hypoxia tend to keep O_2 delivery and tissue P_{O_2} nearly normal. The heart rate and cardiac output increase almost immediately, which facilitates the delivery of O_2 to the tissues. Long-term compensation involves increased hematocrit and hemoglobin. Hypoxia stimulates the release of the hormone *erythropoietin* by the kidney, which stimulates the production of red cells by the bone marrow. Through these mechanisms, the blood can carry more O_2. In addition, the concentration of 2,3-diphosphoglycerate (2,3-DPG) in the red cells is increased by hypoxia, which shifts the oxyhemoglobin dissociation curve to the right and makes more O_2 available to the tissues. After some months at high altitude, O_2 delivery may be increased further by the growth of new capillaries, which decrease the distance that O_2 must diffuse from the blood to the tissues.

Not all of the compensatory responses are beneficial to the individual. People who reside permanently at high altitude (15,000 feet) have *polycythemia,* with hematocrits as high as 60%. The increased concentration of red cells increases the viscosity of the blood and, therefore, the work of the heart. In addition, these persons have pulmonary hypertension due to systemic

CLINICAL CORRELATION

34.1   Chronic Obstructive Pulmonary Disease (COPD)

CASE REPORT

The Patient: A 49-year-old man.

Principal Complaint: Breathlessness during even moderate activity.

History: The patient reported progressively severe shortness of breath. He has a history of several chest colds each year and has had a productive cough for more than half of his life. The shortness of breath had begun more than five years ago, but had become worse during the six months before admission. He had been hospitalized at that time for a severe respiratory infection and pneumonia, which had been treated with penicillin. When he had returned to his job (as an iron worker) after that episode, he found that he could not work, because the slightest exertion caused shortness of breath. He had recovered gradually but did not regain full strength, and had become dyspneic while walking even a single block. Before he had pneumonia, the patient had smoked two or three packs of cigarettes/day and had done so for most of his adult life.

Clinical Examination: The patient's arterial pressure was 130/80 mm Hg (normal, 90–140/60–90 mm Hg) and his heart rate was 80 beats/min (normal, 60–100 beats/min). His nail beds were blue, but no clubbing of fingers was apparent.* His breathing was labored, and he used his strap muscles for breathing (lifting the shoulders, which increases thoracic volume). The anterior-posterior diameter of his chest was increased, and the chest tended to remain in the inspiratory position during the respiratory cycle. Radiographic examination showed flattened diaphragms (intense contraction) and minimal excursions during ventilation. The heart sounds were loudest over the epigastrium but normal otherwise. The hemoglobin concentration was 14.0 g/dl (normal, 13–18 g/dl); the hematocrit was 40.5% (normal, 45%–52%); and the $[HCO_3^-]$ was 30 mEq/liter (normal, 24–30 mEq/liter). The Po_2 of

the arterial blood (Pa_{O_2}) was 74 mm Hg (normal, 96–100 mm Hg), the Pa_{CO_2} was 55 mm Hg (normal, 35–45 mm Hg), and the pH was 7.31 (normal, 7.35–7.45). When the fraction of O_2 in the inspired air (F_{IO_2}) was increased to 1.00 (100% O_2), the Pa_{O_2} was 290 mm Hg (normal, >500 mm Hg), Pa_{CO_2} was 70 mm Hg, and the pH of the arterial blood was 7.28. The results of pulmonary function tests are shown in Table 1.

Comment: The chronic cough with production of mucus, the increased airway resistance during expiration ($\downarrow\downarrow$ FEV_1), which did not improve after administration of a bronchodilator, and hyperinflation of the lungs and chest are associated most often with chronic bronchitis and emphysema. The syndrome is known as chronic, obstructive pulmonary disease (COPD); it is caused most often by heavy smoking. Alveolar ventilation and gas exchange are decreased significantly, as indicated by the low Pa_{O_2}, high Pa_{CO_2}, and low CO diffusing capacity ($D_{L_{CO}}$). The factors that influence $D_{L_{CO}}$ most are the area of diffusion, which is decreased by destruction of the alveolar-capillary membrane (emphysema), and the shuntlike condition that exists in the lungs. Failure of the Pa_{O_2} to increase maximally with an F_{IO_2} of 1.00 indicates that a significant portion of the pulmonary blood flow was either bypassing ventilated alveoli or perfusing collapsed (nonventilated) alveoli. A right-to-left shunt often is associated with COPD. Administration of 100% O_2 improved the HbO_2 (hemoglobin) saturation but diminished the respiratory drive**; the Pa_{CO_2} increased further, which enhanced the respiratory acidosis.

Treatment: The treatment was directed toward improving ventilation and oxygenation of the blood. The patient was put on an intermittent positive pressure ventilator (IPPV), which is a mechanical device used to assist ventilation. The IPPV applies positive pressure during inspiration and uses the natural lung recoil for expiration; at the end of expiration, alveolar pressure returns to at-

(CLINICAL CORRELATION continued)

TABLE 1
Results of pulmonary function tests

	Measured	Predicted
Lung volumes:		
Total lung capacity (TLC; liters)	7.2	5.5
Residual volume (RV; liters)	5.1	1.4
Functional residual capacity (FRC; liters)	5.7	
RV/TLC	0.72	0.25
Diffusing capacity (DL_{CO}; ml/min/mm Hg)	8	25
Timed spirometric tests:		
Forced vital capacity (FVC; liters)	1.5	4.2
Forced expiratory volume (FEV_1; liters)	1.1	3.2
FEV_1 after bronchodilator	1.2	
FEV_1/FVC	0.41	0.78
Maximum voluntary ventilation (MVV; liters/min)	27	128

mospheric and lung volume is at FRC. In addition, the O_2 concentration of the inspired air was increased. The combination of IPPV and an O_2-rich gas mixture increased the Pa_{O_2} and decreased the Pa_{CO_2}, and the pH returned to normal.

Aminophylline, a bronchodilator, was given intravenously, and tetracycline, an antibiotic, was prescribed (1 g three times a week) as a prophylactic measure to prevent respiratory infections. The patient was put on an exercise regimen to strengthen his respiratory muscles, and he was taught to inhale through his nose and exhale slowly through pursed lips while contracting his abdominal muscles. After two weeks of treatment his breathing improved, and he was discharged from the hospital.

Outcome: The patient was instructed to reduce his physical activity to a minimum and especially to watch for signs of infection, because both of these conditions increase the need for oxygen. He continued his IPPV

treatments for 10–15 minutes 3–4 times daily, or whenever he became breathless, using a portable unit for home use and a nebulizer to administer the bronchodilator. He continued his breathing exercises and, in addition, used a snug abdominal belt that provided firm support during coughing. Coughing is an important part of the therapy to remove excess bronchial secretions and prevent further airway obstruction. Prevention of respiratory infection is most important. It could lead to irreversible respiratory failure and death.

*Broadening ("clubbing") of the fingers is caused by chronic hypoxemia. The mechanism is not known, but the capillarity of the enlarged area is increased.

**During prolonged hypoxemia and hypercarbia, the respiratory center becomes refractory to CO_2, and the principal respiratory drive is the hypoxemia acting through the peripheral chemoreceptors. If the hypoxemia is relieved by the patient's breathing 100% O_2, respiration is suppressed, and Pa_{CO_2} increases further.

hypoxemia (Chapter 30), and the work of the right ventricle increases even more. The syndrome that results from the combined effects of hypoxemia, polycythemia, and pulmonary hypertension is called chronic mountain sickness.

Adaptation to Altitude. One of the adaptations to chronic high altitude hypoxemia is increased lung size. Most of the natives of high altitudes are not as tall as their counterparts at low altitudes, but they have larger chests. The increased lung size increases the area available for diffusion of respiratory gases and is associated with increased O_2 diffusing capacity.

Another characteristic of residents at high altitude is that their peripheral chemoreceptors (carotid bodies) are less sensitive to hypoxemia, even when they move to sea level, than those of people who live at sea level. When a person who was born at high altitude is given 100% O_2 to breathe, his respiration is not depressed. On the contrary, people born at low altitudes retain their sensitivity to hypoxia, that is, removal of the hypoxic stimulus depresses their ventilation.

Descent from High Altitude

When a person returns to sea level after spending several weeks at high altitude, respiration is stimulated again but for different reasons (Figure 34-2). At sea level, the Po_2 of inspired air increases; therefore alveolar Po_2 increases. As the hypoxic stimulus to respiration is removed, alveolar ventilation decreases, and the Pco_2 and $[H^+]$ of arterial blood and cerebrospinal fluid increase. Hence, respiration is stimulated through both peripheral and central chemoreceptor mechanisms, and ventilation increases. Hyperventilation continues for several days, until the pH of the CSF is restored to 7.32; then ventilation returns to normal. The pH is corrected by increased absorption of HCO_3^- by the kidney and probably by active transport of HCO_3^- into the CSF.

EXERCISE

Ventilation is adjusted in three stages during exercise. At the beginning of exercise, minute ventilation ($\dot{V}E$) increases suddenly (phase I), followed by a gradual, exponential increase as the exercise continues (phase II); finally, $\dot{V}E$ reaches a plateau, or steady-state (phase III; Figure 34-3). During moderate exercise, $\dot{V}E$ reaches phase III in approximately 3–4 min, but

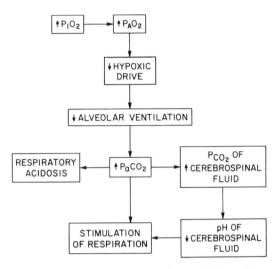

Figure 34-2. Adjustments of ventilation after descent to low altitude.

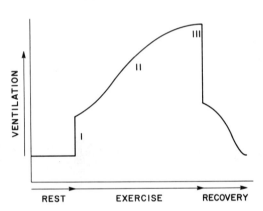

Figure 34-3. Exercise-related changes of ventilation. $\dot{V}E$ increases abruptly at the beginning of exercise, I; increases more slowly and linearly with the intensity of exercise, II; reaches steady-state during moderate exercise, III; decreases abruptly at the end of exercise and returns to baseline exponentially during the recovery phase. (Redrawn, with permission, from Wasserman, K. 1978. *N. Engl. J. Med.* 298: 782.)

if exercise is heavy enough to induce metabolic acidosis, phase II may last longer and ventilation may not level out at all. Throughout moderate exercise, $\dot{V}E$, O_2 consumption ($\dot{V}O_2$), and CO_2 production ($\dot{V}CO_2$) are related linearly to the intensity of the exercise, while arterial Po_2, Pco_2, and pH remain constant. Minute ventilation increases with increased tidal volume and frequency of breathing. At the end of exercise, ventilation decreases as abruptly as it increased at the beginning, and then decreases exponentially to the resting level (see Figure 34-3).

Mechanisms of Exercise Hyperpnea

The mechanisms that control the changes in ventilation during exercise are not clearly identified. The sudden increase in $\dot{V}E$ at the beginning and the sudden decrease at the end of exercise is thought to be mediated by neural mechanisms in response to inputs from various sources, perhaps from the cerebral cortex, the muscle spindles of the exercising muscles, and joint receptors. The slower component of exercise-related hyperpnea (phase II) probably is mediated humorally.

CARBON DIOXIDE

Although CO_2 would seem to be the most logical regulator of ventilation, arterial Po_2, Pco_2, and [H$^+$] remain unchanged during moderate exercise. One of the theories offered is based on the knowledge that alveolar Po_2 and Pco_2 fluctuate with each breath during normal ventilaion. It is suggested that the respiratory centers may be more sensitive to rapid fluctuations of CO_2 than to slower changes in the mean values. An alternate theory is that the respiratory system keeps the Pco_2 and pH close to the control values and increases ventilation in response to the increased load of CO_2 presented to the lung (product of blood flow and CO_2 content of mixed venous blood). Ventilation does increase when CO_2 is injected into the venous circulation, although the arterial Pco_2 remains unchanged. However, receptors sensitive to changes of Pco_2 in the venous blood have not been discovered.

In heavier exercise, metabolism shifts to anaerobic pathways, and the production of lactic acid increases. At first, lactic acid is buffered by $NaHCO_3$, and the pH is regulated. The reaction liberates CO_2, which is added to that produced by the increased metabolism. At this point, more CO_2 is excreted by the lungs than is produced by the tissues; although both $\dot{V}E$ and $\dot{V}co_2$ increase, $\dot{V}E$ increases proportionately more than $\dot{V}co_2$, and both increase more than $\dot{V}o_2$. If the work load increases further, [H$^+$] increases and ventilation increases to an even greater extent; arterial Pco_2 decreases, and respiratory alkalosis partially compensates for the metabolic acidosis. The increase of ventilation at this stage of exercise seems to be mediated through chemoreceptors of the carotid bodies. People who have no carotid bodies do not hyperventilate in response to metabolic acidosis during exercise; hence, they experience a greater degree of acidosis because it is not compensated by respiratory alkalosis.

OTHER FACTORS

Other factors that may contribute to the hyperventilation of exercise are:

1. Low Po_2. Although hyperpnea and oxygen consumption are related during moderate exercise, and breathing a gas mixture rich in O_2 decreases ventilation, low O_2 has not been proved conclusively to be a stimulus for increased ventilation during exercise.
2. Temperature. The temperature of the body core increases during exercise, but much more slowly than ventilation; therefore, although increased temperature may be an added factor, it probably is not the cause of the hyperpnea related to exercise.
3. Blood pressure. Undoubtedly, the cardiovascular and respiratory systems interact during exercise. Since the amount of O_2 that can attach to hemoglobin is limited, the velocity of blood flow must increase to deliver more O_2 to the tissues per unit of time. Arterial systolic pressure increases during exercise, due to increased heart rate and contractility and decreased arterial compliance. Diastolic pressure usually decreases because of decreased peripheral resistance, although this depends on the type of exercise performed. Mean arterial pressure may be relatively unchanged or increased. Arterial pressure and ventilation are related inversely; when the arterial pressure increases, ventilation decreases.

Exercise at High Altitude

When an individual exercises in a low O_2 environment, hypoxemia may be exaggerated because the driving pressure for O_2 diffusion from the blood to the tissues decreases. Since the blood spends less time in the pulmonary capillary, equilibration between alveolar and arterial O_2 may not occur (see Figure 31-5).

FETAL AND NEONATAL RESPIRATION

Gas Exchange in the Fetus

The lungs of the fetus contain fluid and do not participate in gas exchange. O_2 and CO_2 are transferred between fetal blood and maternal blood in the placenta; Figure 34-4 illustrates this arrangement. In this scheme, the circulation of the mother is equivalent to alveolar ventila-

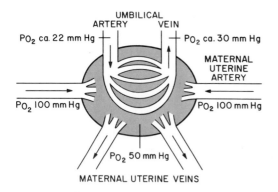

Figure 34-4. Diagram of a possible arrangement for gas exchange between fetal and maternal blood in the human placenta.

tion (high in O_2 and low in CO_2), and the umbilical circulation of the fetus is equivalent to the postpartum pulmonary circulation. Fetal blood, which is low in O_2 and high in CO_2, flows through the umbilical artery and into umbilical loops that project into the sinusoids of the placenta. Maternal blood enters these sinusoids through the uterine arteries and contacts the umbilical loops. The mean Po_2 of the placental blood is approximately 50 mm Hg and that of fetal blood is about 22 mm Hg; O_2 is taken up and CO_2 is given off by the fetal blood. Blood returning to the fetus in the umbilical vein has a Po_2 of about 30 mm Hg, and the hemoglobin is 65%–75% saturated with O_2. Before this blood returns to the heart of the fetus, it mixes with blood from the portal system and the inferior vena cava, which decreases the Po_2 somewhat; it then mixes with blood from the superior vena cava, which decreases Po_2 even further. However, because of intracardiac shunts, the heart muscle and brain are supplied with blood that has the highest possible O_2 content (see Chapter 20). Most of the blood from the right ventricle is pumped through the ductus arteriosus into the descending aorta and joins in the perfusion of all of the other tissues before it returns to the placenta for more oxygen.

OXYGEN DELIVERY
IN THE FETUS
Delivery of O_2 by the fetal circulation is aided in several ways. Fetal blood contains more red cells and hemoglobin than adult blood does and therefore can carry more O_2 in each unit. In addition, fetal hemoglobin (HF) has a greater affinity for O_2 than maternal hemoglobin (HA) does and, at a given Po_2, can combine with more O_2 than HA can. Thus, although the Po_2 of fetal blood is low, its oxygen content and capacity to supply the tissue are facilitated by these adjustments.

Changes at Birth

The parasitic relationship of the fetus with the mother ceases as soon as the umbilical circulation is tied off and cut at birth. The neonate is exposed to many new stimuli, not the least of which are the hypoxemia, hypercapnia, and acidemia that develop during the process of birth. Central and peripheral chemoreceptors probably are stimulated maximally, and as a result of all of these stimuli, the infant takes its first breath. During development in utero, the fetus makes breathing movements that help to strengthen the respiratory muscles. The neonate must reduce his intrathoracic pressure some 40–80 cm H_2O below atmospheric pressure to overcome all of the resistive forces encountered during the first inspiration. This probably is achieved mainly by maximal contraction of the diaphragm. The first expiration also is important, since the residual volume and functional residual capacity must be built up during the first few minutes of breathing. The work of breathing is maximal with the first breath, then diminishes after a few breaths, and the residual volume remains relatively stable after a few minutes of breathing following birth. Figure 34-5 shows the enormous effort that must be

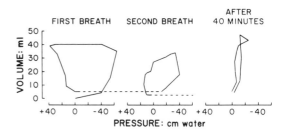

Figure 34-5. Pressure-volume loops for the lung of the neonate. The area inside each loop represents the work of the respiratory muscles on the lungs. Although work is maximal during the first breath, after 40 min of breathing following birth, the pressure-volume loop is close to that of the normal adult lung. (Redrawn, with permission, from *The First Breath*. Smith, C.A. Copyright, 1963, Scientific American, Inc. All rights reserved.)

developed during the first breath; in less than an hour after birth, however, the pressure-volume loop of the newborn is in the normal range.

Part of the fluid that fills the lungs of the fetus to about 40% capacity is squeezed out during birth and part is aspirated, but some remains in the lungs. The fluid that remains in the alveoli helps to inflate them after birth. This is explained by the Laplace relationship between wall tension, radius, and distending pressure in a spherical structure ($P = 2T/r$). The alveolus that is partly filled with fluid has a greater radius, therefore less pressure is required to inflate it. Later, the fluid is absorbed into the pulmonary circulation or the lymphatic system.

Inhalation of air comparatively rich in O_2 causes the alveolar and arterial Po_2 of the newborn to increase quickly to the normal adult level ($\simeq 100$ mm Hg). As arterial Po_2 increases, the pulmonary vasoconstriction that exists in the fetus because of hypoxemia decreases; hence, pulmonary vascular resistance decreases and the blood flow through the lungs increases.

Other circulatory changes that occur at birth are discussed in detail in Chapter 20.

Control of Ventilation. The full-term infant has a fairly well-developed respiratory control mechanism. His ventilation increases in response to hypoxia, and his respiration is depressed if he breathes a gas mixture rich in O_2. He has active inflation and deflation reflexes and a paradoxical reflex (Head). It has been suggested that all of these factors added to the initial stimuli cause the baby to continue breathing spontaneously.

An infant who has hyaline membrane disease (respiratory distress syndrome) has difficulty expanding the lungs and overcoming all of the resistance to breathing; for such an infant each breath requires maximal work. Premature infants are especially prone to respiratory problems at birth for several reasons, among which are the lack of surfactant, aspiration of fluid into the lungs, hypoventilation caused by drugs given to the mother during labor, and hypoxia because some alveoli fail to open.

STUDY OUTLINE

BREATHING AT HIGH PRESSURE AND AT LOW PRESSURE   Application of Boyle's law; PV = K.

HIGH PRESSURE AND UNDERWATER ENVIRONMENT   One atmosphere of pressure is added for every 10 m under water.

DIRECT EFFECTS OF INCREASED PRESSURE   Muscles of inspiration have to overcome water pressure on chest (4.5 ft of H_2O $\simeq 100$ mm Hg = maximum P_{PL}).

Changes in pressure affect volume of air within body.

Effects of Breath-Holding Dive   As pressure increases, volume of air in lungs decreases; at depth of 40 m, is reduced to residual volume (RV).

Decrease of lung air volume, but not volume of thorax, decreases intrapleural pressure and causes rupture of pulmonary capillaries.

Effects of Ascent from a Dive   As pressure decreases, lung volume increases.

Closed airways cause overexpansion of lungs on ascent; may cause pneumothorax and air embolism.

Greatest danger occurs while surfacing from relatively shallow depth—greatest change of lung volume.

INDIRECT EFFECTS OF INCREASED PRESSURE

Decompression Sickness: The Bends   Increased pressure increases N_2 dissolved in blood and tissues; rapidly decreasing pressure causes N_2 bubbles, joint pain ("bends"); prevented by gradual decompression.

EFFECT OF INCREASED PRESSURE ON GAS DENSITY   Increased density of gases increases work of breathing.

NITROGEN NARCOSIS   High P_{N_2} intoxication—"rapture of the deep"—at 4.5 atmospheres. Higher P_{N_2} causes nitrogen narcosis (coma).

Limit of diving while breathing air: 300 ft.

HIGH ALTITUDE–LOW AMBIENT PRESSURE   Atmospheric pressure and P_{IO_2} decrease with increasing height above sea level.

ASCENT TO HIGH ALTITUDE   Acutely—net effect is increased $\dot{V}_A$:

$\downarrow P_{IO_2} \rightarrow \downarrow P_{AO_2} \rightarrow \downarrow P_{aO_2} \rightarrow \uparrow \dot{V}_A \rightarrow \downarrow P_{CO_2} \rightarrow$ Respiratory alkalosis.

Acute mountain sickness: effects of hypoxemia and respiratory alkalosis.

Chronically—ventilatory and circulatory adjustments to hypoxia tend to maintain O_2 delivery and tissue P_{O_2}.

Arterial and CSF pH restored and $\dot{V}_A$ increased further.

O_2 delivery aided by increased blood flow, polycythemia, increased vascularization.

Chronic mountain sickness: combined effects of hypoxemia, polycythemia, pulmonary hypertension.

Adaptation to Altitude   Increased lung size → increased O_2-diffusing capacity.

DESCENT FROM HIGH ALTITUDE
Acutely—net effect is increased ventilation:

$\uparrow P_{IO_2} \rightarrow \uparrow P_{AO_2} \rightarrow \uparrow P_{aO_2} \rightarrow \downarrow$ Hypoxic drive; $\downarrow \dot{V}_A \rightarrow \uparrow P_{CO_2} \rightarrow \uparrow$ Ventilation.

After several days at low altitude, pH is restored and ventilation returns to normal.

EXERCISE   Moderate: $\dot{V}_E$, $\dot{V}_{O_2}$, and $\dot{V}_{CO_2}$ linearly related to intensity.

Ventilation ($\dot{V}_E$) adjusted by sudden increase at beginning; gradual, exponential increase; period of constancy; sudden decrease at end of exercise.

MECHANISMS OF EXERCISE HYPERPNEA   No single, clearly identifiable mechanism.

Sudden increase and decrease in $\dot{V}_E$ are mediated neurally.

Slower component is mediated humorally.

CARBON DIOXIDE   Attractive humoral mechanism, but arterial P_{CO_2} and pH remain constant in moderate exercise.

In heavy exercise, P_{aCO_2} decreases—compensation for lactic acidosis.

OTHER FACTORS   May include low P_{O_2}, temperature, arterial pressure.

EXERCISE AT HIGH ALTITUDE   Altitude-related hypoxemia is exaggerated.

FETAL AND NEONATAL RESPIRATION

GAS EXCHANGE IN FETUS O_2 and CO_2 are exchanged between fetal and maternal blood in placenta.

Umbilical venous blood P_{O_2} is about 30 mm Hg; HbO_2 saturation is 65%–75%.

Heart muscle and brain are perfused with blood of highest O_2 content available.

OXYGEN DELIVERY IN THE FETUS Compensation includes higher HbO_2 capacity and greater affinity for O_2.

CHANGES AT BIRTH   First breath: result of many stimuli (O_2, CO_2, pH, etc.); work of breathing is maximal.

Residual volume is built up during first few minutes of breathing.

Fluid remaining in lungs helps to inflate alveoli.

As arterial P_{O_2} increases, pulmonary vascular resistance decreases and pulmonary blood flow increases.

Control of Ventilation   Full-term: well-developed respiratory control mechanism.

Premature: prone to various respiratory problems at birth.

BIBLIOGRAPHY

Beaver, W.L., and Wasserman, K. 1970. Tidal volume and respiratory rate changes at start and end of exercise. *J. Appl. Physiol.* 29:872.

Bye, P.T.P.; Pugh, C.E.; and Jones, N.L. 1983. Respiratory factors limiting exercise. *Ann. Rev. Physiol.* 45:439.

Chiodi, H. 1957. Respiratory adaptations to chronic high altitude hypoxia. *J. Clin. Invest.* 10:81.

Comroe, J.H., Jr. 1944. The hyperpnea of muscular exercise. *Physiol. Rev.* 24:319.

Dejours, P. 1964. Control of respiration in muscular exercise. In *Handbook of physiology*, Section 3. Respiration, Vol. I, editors W.O. Fenn and H. Rahn. Washington, D.C.: American Physiological Society.

Dempsey, J.A.; Vidruk, E.H.; and Mastenbrook, S.M. 1980. Pulmonary control systems in exercise. *Fed. Proc.* 39:1498.

Deneke, S.M., and Fanburg, B.L. 1980. Normobaric oxygen toxicity of the lung. *N. Engl. J. Med.* 303:76.

Eldridge, F.L.; Millhorn, D.E.; and Waldrop, T.G. 1981. Exercise hyperpnea and locomotion: parallel activation from the hypothalamus. *Science* 211:844.

Flenly, D.C., and Warren, P.M. 1983. Ventilatory responses to O_2 and CO_2 during exercise. *Ann. Rev. Physiol.* 45:415.

Hackett, P.H.; Reeves, J.T.; Reeves, C.D.; et al. 1980. Control of breathing in Sherpas at low and high altitude. *J. Appl. Physiol: Respirat. Environ. Exercise Physiol.* 49:374.

Heath, D., and Williams, D.R. 1977. *Man at high altitude: the pathophysiology of acclimatization and adaptation.* Edinburgh, London, and New York: Churchill Livingstone.

Houston, C.S. 1980. *Going high: The story of man and altitude.* Burlington, Vt.: Charles S. Houston, and New York: American Alpine Club.

Hurtado, A. 1964. Animals in high altitudes: resident man. In *Handbook of physiology,* Section 4, Chapter 54, Adaptation to Environment, editors W.D. Fenn and H. Rahn. Washington, D.C.: American Physiological Society.

Lahiri, S.; Delaney, R.G.; Brody, J.S.; et al. 1976. Relative role of environmental and genetic factors in respiratory adaptation to high altitude. *Nature* (London) 261:133.

Lanphier, E.H. 1957. Diving medicine. *N. Engl. J. Med.* 256:120.

Miles, S., and Mackay, D.E. 1976. *Underwater medicine,* 4th ed. Philadelphia: J.B. Lippincott Co.

Polgar, G., and Weng, T.R. 1979. The functional development of the respiratory system. From the period of gestation to adulthood. *Am. Rev. Resp. Dis.* 120:625.

Smith, C.A. 1963. The first breath. *Sci. Am.* 209:27.

Snyder, L.R.G. 1981. Deermouse hemoglobins: is there genetic adaptation to high altitude. *Bioscience* 31:299.

Strauss, R.H. 1979. Diving reflexes. *Am. Rev. Resp. Dis.* 119:1001.

Sutton, J.R.; Jones, N.L.; and Houston, C.S. 1982. *Hypoxia: Man at altitude.* New York: Thieme-Stratton.

Sutton, J.R.; Griffith, L.; Pugh, C.E.; et al. 1983. Exercise at altitude. *Ann. Rev. Physiol.* 45:427.

Wasserman, K. 1978. Breathing during exercise. *N. Engl. J. Med.* 298:780.

Weil, J.V.; Bryne-Quinn, E.; Sodal, I.E.; et al. 1971. Acquired attenuation of chemoreceptor function in chronically hypoxic man at high altitude. *J. Clin. Invest.* 50:195.

West, J.B., editor. 1981. *High altitude physiology.* Stroudsburg, Pa.: Hutchinson Press.

Whipp, B.J. 1983. Ventilatory control during exercise in humans. *Ann. Rev. Physiol.* 45:393.

35

Respiratory Insufficiency: Lung Disorders and Pulmonary Functions

CHAPTER CONTENTS

RESPIRATORY INSUFFICIENCY

Respiratory insufficiency means that the lungs are unable to maintain normal arterial blood gas levels when the subject breathes air (21% O_2) at sea level. Respiratory insufficiency may be confirmed by analyzing the blood gases and by pulmonary function testing. The consequences of respiratory insufficiency are *hypoxemia* and *hypercapnia*. Hypoxemia ensues when the lungs are unable to oxygenate adequately the blood that flows through the pulmonary capillaries. Hypercapnia occurs when the lungs are unable to excrete adequately the

CO_2 produced by the metabolizing tissues. These conditions were discussed in Chapters 28, 31, and 32.

Hypoxias

The term *hypoxia* generally is defined as low partial pressure or insufficient concentration of oxygen anywhere in the system from the inspired gas to the tissues. Hypoxemia specifically refers to low partial pressure of O_2 or low saturation of oxyhemoglobin in the arterial blood. Hypoxia may be caused by a variety of conditions related to ventilation, circulation, and the diffusion of oxygen from the lungs to the blood or from the blood to the tissues. The various forms of hypoxia, based on these conditions, are discussed below.

HYPOXIA RELATED TO VENTILATION

At high altitudes, the partial pressure of O_2 of inspired air decreases; consequently, the alveolar Po_2, arterial Po_2, and arterial oxyhemoglobin saturation are low. This form of hypoxia is known as *hypoxic hypoxia*. The effects of high altitude hypoxia on ventilation and circulation were discussed in Chapter 34. *Hypoventilation* (decreased V_A) of any origin causes hypoxia and hypoxemia and, in addition, usually causes CO_2 to accumulate in the blood and alveolar air. A patient who has hypoxemia due to inadequate ventilation, but who is treated only by O_2 inhalation, may develop hypercapnia because the hypoventilation itself is not corrected. Hypoventilation may be caused by disease of the respiratory muscles; drugs, anesthetics, or other substances that depress the respiratory centers; any muscular, mechanical, or neural condition that limits the expansion of the thorax; any mechanical condition that limits the expansion of the lungs; diseases that decrease the functioning tissue of the lungs; diseases that increase the elastic resistance of the lungs (restrictive lung disease); and diseases that cause congestion and obstruction of airways. Hypoxia also may occur when ventilation and perfusion are mismatched (see Chapter 33).

HYPOXIA RELATED TO DIFFUSION

Hypoxia can develop when the O_2-diffusing capacity of the lungs decreases. This occurs when the functional area of the gas exchange system decreases or the thickness of the alveolar-capillary membrane increases. Examples of these conditions were given in Chapter 30. Hypoxia also can occur when the diffusion of oxygen from the capillaries to the tissues is hampered, for example, in conditions such as interstitial edema.

HYPOXIA RELATED TO CIRCULATION

Some types of hypoxia involve the transport and delivery of oxygen to the tissues. When venous blood mixes with arterial blood (right-to-left shunt), the oxygen content of the arterial blood decreases and less oxygen is delivered to

the tissues. Hypoxia may occur when anemia or abnormal hemoglobin production decreases the oxygen-carrying capacity of blood. Hypoxia due to carbon monoxide poisoning is in this category; even though the concentration of Hb is normal in this condition, many of the sites that normally carry oxygen are occupied by CO, for which Hb has a much greater affinity. These types of hypoxia sometimes are called *anemic hypoxias*. Decreased cardiac output, as in shock, hypotension, cardiac failure, or embolism, or decreased blood flow to specific vascular beds cause tissue hypoxia, even though both the partial pressure and the content of oxygen are normal. This condition sometimes is referred to as *ischemic,* or *stagnant, hypoxia.*

HYPOXIA RELATED TO UTILIZATION OF OXYGEN

In certain conditions, the tissues are unable to use oxygen, although there is no lack of it. *Histotoxic hypoxia* occurs when the respiratory enzymes are inactivated by a poisonous substance such as cyanide. Since little oxygen is removed from the arterial blood, the venous Po_2 is higher than normal (> 40 mm Hg). Finally, *utilization hypoxia* may develop when tissues utilize oxygen at rates greater than normal, as in thyrotoxicosis.

CYANOSIS

Hypoxemia sometimes is diagnosed by the bluish appearance of the skin, especially around the lips, nail beds, and mucous membranes. This condition is known as *cyanosis,* and the blue color is caused by deoxygenated hemoglobin in the blood. Cyanosis may develop when more than 5 g Hb/100 ml of arterial blood is in the deoxy state, but it is not a reliable index. For example, when anemia is severe, or in hypovolemic shock, the skin of the patient is pale rather than blue, although the tissue is hypoxic. In cyanide or CO poisoning, the tissues are deprived of oxygen even though the color of the skin is bright pink or red.

Oxygen Therapy

Hypoxia means a deficit of oxygen; therefore, the most logical therapy is to administer oxygen to a person who is hypoxic. However, additional oxygen is useful only in hypoxia related to problems of ventilation or diffusion. When the Pa_{O_2} is low because the partial pressure of oxy-

CLINICAL CORRELATION

35.1   Adult Respiratory Distress Syndrome (ARDS)

CASE REPORT

The Patient: A 32-year-old man.

Principal Complaints: Chills, fever, hemoptysis,* and severe shortness of breath.

History: The patient had become ill two days before entering the hospital. The diagnosis was diffuse pulmonary infection of unknown viral origin. He had no other history of illness.

Clinical Examination: The patient had labored breathing and in general appeared to be very ill. His respiratory frequency was 34 breaths/min (normal, 13–17 breaths/min), his arterial pressure was 90/60 mm Hg (normal, 90–140/60–90 mm Hg), his heart rate was 130 beats/min (normal, 60–100 beats/min), and his temperature was 39.4°C (normal, approximately 37°C). Diffuse rales** were audible over both lungs. Oxygen was administered by nasal cannula, at a rate of 1.5 liters/min. During this time, the Pa_{O_2} was 34 mm Hg (normal, 75–100 mm Hg), the Pa_{CO_2} was 27 mm Hg (normal, 35–45 mm Hg), and the pH of the arterial blood was 7.47 (normal, 7.35–7.45). A chest x-ray showed bilateral alveolar infiltrates.*** Pink, frothy fluid was aspirated from the lungs during the first 12 hours after admission.

Treatment: During the first two days in the hospital, the patient was artificially ventilated with 100% O_2. A positive end-expiratory pressure (PEEP)**** of 10–15 cm H_2O was required to maintain the Pa_{O_2} at approximately 75 mm Hg. In addition, he was given an antibiotic drug (erythromycin) to combat bacterial infection. His condition improved gradually, and he was extubated (the endotracheal tube was removed) one week later. Pulmonary function tests four weeks after admission revealed:

Forced vital capacity (FVC) = 2.9 liters (53% of predicted)
Total lung capacity (TLC) = 3.74 liters (67% of predicted)
Diffusing capacity (DLco) = 18.8 ml/min/mm Hg (50% of predicted)

Six weeks later, the chest x-ray was normal, and, relative to the predicted values, the FVC was 95%, the TLC was 92%, and DLco was 62%.

Comment: Injury to the pulmonary capillaries and alveoli permits plasma and blood to invade the interstitial and intra-alveolar spaces. Pulmonary compliance is decreased if congestion and early formation of collagen progress to acute interstitial fibrosis. The production of surfactant also may be decreased, which decreases the functional residual capacity (FRC). Since mortality of patients who are treated for adult respiratory distress syndrome with 100% oxygen and PEEP for longer than 48 hours usually is high, the use of an antibiotic probably was an important factor in the survival of this patient. Patients who require prolonged treatment often develop restrictive lung disease.

Outcome: Ten weeks after admission to the hospital, the chest x-ray and lung function were normal and the patient was asymptomatic.

*Spitting blood.

**Abnormal sounds (rattling, scraping) heard by auscultation of the chest.

***Fluid, cells, or other substances in a fluid or tissue space.

****Used to keep the airways expanded between expiration and inspiration.

gen in the ambient air is low, increasing the $P_{I_{O_2}}$ corrects the alveolar and arterial hypoxia. When hypoxia is caused by hypoventilation, inhalation of a gas mixture rich in oxygen corrects the hypoxemia but does not remove the CO_2 that has accumulated. When a patient who has pulmonary disease hypoventilates to the extent that his ventilatory drive depends solely on the hypoxic stimulus, he may be in greater danger when given oxygen than before. The administered oxygen eliminates the stimulus to the peripheral chemoreceptors, which in this condition drive the respiratory centers; therefore, the hypoventilation may become worse, and enough CO_2 may be retained to cause respiratory failure, coma, and even death. In the person who is both hypoxic and hypercapnic, it is important to increase V_A by either stimulating ventilation or providing artificial respiration to eliminate excess carbon dioxide.

Oxygen inhalation is useful to treat hypoxia caused by $\dot{V}_A/\dot{Q}_c$ disturbances (shuntlike condition in the lungs) or diffusion problems. An increased alveolar-arterial P_{O_2} gradient facilitates diffusion.

Hypoxemia caused by venous admixture (right-to-left shunt) cannot be corrected by breathing oxygen because the arterial blood is fully saturated before the mixing occurs. In this situation, oxygen is used as a diagnostic tool to detect the shunt. Oxygen therapy also is of no help when the fault is in the delivery of oxygen to the tissues. Therapy should be applied to correct the primary dysfunction, which may be decreased perfusion, anemia, abnormal hemoglobin, hypovolemia, or other conditions.

Oxygen Toxicity

Although humans cannot survive without oxygen, they cannot live in an environment of pure oxygen either. Although the administration of 100% O_2 may mean the difference between life and death in some emergencies, high concentrations of oxygen in inspired air also can be dangerous. A $P_{I_{O_2}}$ greater than 0.6 atmosphere injures the lungs; damage to alveolar and endothelial cells leads to pulmonary congestion and edema. The extent of the damage depends on the partial pressure of oxygen and how long the subject is exposed to it. The bases of these injuries are not fully understood; they appear to be related to peroxidation of membrane lipids.

Hyperbaric oxygen treatment for only a short time can damage the central nervous system. Convulsions may occur when the $P_{I_{O_2}}$ is 2.5 atmospheres. The adverse effect on the central nervous system seems to be related to deactivation of certain enzymes, mainly dehydrogenases that have sulfhydryl groups.

At about 3 atmospheres of arterial P_{O_2}, enough oxygen dissolves in the blood to supply all of the oxygen the tissues use. However, transport of oxygen in this manner interferes with the transport of CO_2. Since only dissolved oxygen is used, none is released from the hemoglobin, and fully oxygenated Hb carries less than the normal amount of CO_2; therefore, CO_2 accumulates in the tissues.

Hypercapnia

When alveolar ventilation does not keep up with increased metabolism or when ventilation and perfusion are unevenly matched and compensatory hyperventilation does not develop, the CO_2 concentration of arterial blood increases; this condition is *hypercapnia*. Acute retention of CO_2 causes respiratory acidosis, dyspnea, headache, drowsiness, confusion, and cerebral vasodilatation that causes a sensation of fullness in the head. In very high concentration, CO_2 causes unconsciousness, anesthesia, and convulsion. The buildup of CO_2 in blood and tissues due to chronic pulmonary insufficiency or failure is gradual and accompanied by compensatory metabolic alkalosis. Prolonged hypercapnia also decreases the sensitivity of the CO_2 receptors that participate in the control of respiration.

CIRCULATORY EFFECTS
OF CO_2 RETENTION
In conscious individuals, excess CO_2 increases the activity of the sympathetic nervous system, which increases peripheral resistance, heart rate, and myocardial contractility. The direct effect of excess CO_2 is systemic arteriolar dilatation, which decreases the blood pressure in unconscious or anesthetized individuals, in those whose α-adrenergic receptors are blocked, or those who have suffered spinal cord injuries. Cerebral vasodilatation increases the cerebral blood flow; this is a form of autoregulation that facilitates the removal of excess CO_2 (see Chapter 16).

CO$_2$ IN INSPIRED AIR

Ventilation increases as the rate and the tidal volume increase. The effects of CO$_2$ in the inspired air are discussed in Chapter 29.

Combined Effects of Low P$_{O_2}$ and High P$_{CO_2}$

When hypoxemia and hypercapnia occur together, the effect on ventilation is greater than the sum of the individual effects (see Chapter 29, pp. 451–452).

Hypocapnia

When alveolar ventilation is greater than needed to eliminate the CO$_2$ produced by the tissues, arterial P$_{CO_2}$ and [H$^+$] decrease, producing respiratory alkalosis. Involuntary hyperventilation may be caused by anxiety, certain types of brain injury, fever, hypoxia, metabolic acidosis, pulmonary disease, or the improper use of mechanical ventilators. Too little CO$_2$ causes fatigue, cerebral ischemia associated with a sensation of light-headedness, irritability, and increased neuromuscular activity. Respiratory alkalosis due to hyperventilation predisposes some people to seizures, presumably because the decreased [H$^+$] decreases the ionization of calcium, which is necessary for the proper function of nerve and muscle. In addition, it causes a loss of intracellular potassium. Fortunately, the symptoms associated with hypocapnia are reversible.

BASIC LIFE SUPPORT

The American Heart Association, the American Red Cross, and other agencies have launched a major drive to teach essentially all of the population to recognize and assist victims of respiratory and cardiac arrest. The aim of cardiopulmonary resuscitation is to assure the survival of the most vital organs—the heart and the brain—by delivering oxygen to the lungs of the victim and assisting the circulation in order to assure gas exchange.

Respiratory Arrest and Pulmonary Resuscitation

Some of the more common causes of respiratory arrest are cardiac arrest, stroke, drowning, electrocution, airway obstruction, drug overdose, head injury, and trauma.

UPPER AIRWAY OCCLUSION (UAO)

The most frequent cause of respiratory failure in a conscious individual is obstruction of the upper airway by a foreign object, most often by inadequately chewed meat. Upper airway obstruction may be partial or complete; if it is complete, neither speech, cough, nor ventilation is possible. UAO may be relieved by abruptly increasing airway pressure through sharp blows to the back of the victim followed by thrusts to the upper abdomen or lower chest. Alternating the back blows and manual thrusts forces air out of the lungs and can remove an obstruction. Once the airway is open, mouth-to-mouth ventilation may be administered if necessary. The same procedure is used if the victim is unconscious. In this circumstance, one also must distinguish between respiratory failure caused by UAO and that caused by a heart attack, stroke, or drug overdose. In the latter instances, mouth-to-mouth ventilation alone or complete cardiopulmonary resuscitation may be needed. Regardless of whether compression of the chest is required, proper ventilation must be maintained.

MOUTH-TO-MOUTH BREATHING

One of the most effective methods of pulmonary resuscitation is mouth-to-mouth breathing. The rescuer places his mouth firmly over the victim's mouth or nose and exhales at a rate of about 12 breaths/min; the procedure inflates the victim's lungs. The air the rescuer exhales contains approximately 16% oxygen, which is adequate to oxygenate the blood. In addition, it contains about 5% CO$_2$, which stimulates respiration. With the exception of a mechanical ventilator, the mouth-to-mouth technique moves more air than any other method, and the pressure used to inflate the victim's lungs is in the safe range. This technique also allows the rescuer to feel any resistance caused by airway obstruction, to see the chest move during inspiration and expiration, and to feel escaping air.

Cardiopulmonary Resuscitation (CPR)

Three major concepts are emphasized in CPR techniques. These are called the "ABCs" of CPR.

OPENING THE AIRWAY

The rescuer must clear the airway of blockage by anatomical structures, secretions, or foreign bodies. The single most common cause of airway obstruction in unconscious victims is the tongue, which falls back against the pharynx. The initial and most important procedure in opening the airway is tipping the victim's head backward. This is done by placing one hand on the forehead and the other under the neck—the *head-tilt-neck-lift* procedure—or by placing one hand on the forehead while the other lifts the victim's chin—the *head-tilt-chin-lift* procedure. During this procedure, the rescuer determines whether the victim is breathing or not.

RESCUE BREATHING

If the victim does not breathe spontaneously, mouth-to-mouth ventilation is performed.

CIRCULATION

The next essential step in CPR is to determine the presence or absence of a pulse. Cardiac arrest may occur in the form of ventricular fibrillation, ventricular standstill, or asystole, or in the form of dissociated electrical and mechanical events of the heart, also referred to as cardiovascular collapse. If the rescuer is satisfied that the victim has no pulse, he should compress the chest to assist circulation. The combination of mouth-to-mouth breathing and chest compression can prolong life or stabilize a victim's condition until a more sophisticated advanced life-support system is provided.

Mechanical Ventilation

Artificial ventilation may be indicated in a patient who has respiratory failure to the point that hypoxemia, hypercapnia, and respiratory acidosis occur or in a person who has taken an overdose of drugs such as narcotics or barbiturates. Overventilation may cause hypocapnia. Therefore, when artificial ventilators are used, arterial blood gases, especially P_{CO_2}, should be monitored frequently to determine the status of alveolar ventilation.

"NEGATIVE-PRESSURE" VENTILATION (IRON LUNG)

Negative-pressure ventilation mimics natural breathing most closely. The patient is placed in a cylindrical container; a flexible cuff around the neck makes the cylinder airtight. A pump alternately decreases the pressure in the container to less than atmospheric and returns it to atmospheric by moving a leather diaphragm on the other end of the cylinder. When the pressure around the patient in the cylinder decreases, the volume of the thorax increases, and the intrathoracic and intra-alveolar pressures decrease. Ambient air flows through the mouth and nose into the alveoli. The patient exhales when the tank pressure returns to atmospheric and the stretched, elastic tissues of the lungs recoil to their preinspiratory position (FRC).

"POSITIVE-PRESSURE" VENTILATION

The positive-pressure ventilator pushes air into the lungs. The patient usually is connected to the apparatus by a face mask or endotracheal tube. Some of the positive-pressure devices can be set to deliver a certain tidal volume, others can be triggered automatically by the inspiratory efforts of the patient, and the frequency of all of them can be adjusted. The devices referred to as intermittent positive-pressure ventilators generate positive pressure to inflate the alveoli but rely on lung recoil for expiration. Positive end-expiratory pressure (PEEP) is used to keep the alveoli open if the elastic recoil force of the lungs is lost, or in adults who have respiratory distress syndrome, known as the shock lung phenomenon.

Effects of Increased Intrathoracic Pressure

The alveoli can be ventilated adequately by either positive or negative pressure; however, increased pressure in the chest affects the circulation in the same way the Valsalva maneuver does (Chapter 28). The increased pressure in the thoracic cavity decreases the inflow of venous blood to the right ventricle and decreases cardiac output. This is especially dangerous in a person who is anesthetized or whose sympathetic nervous system is blocked by drugs that prevent a reflex increase of venous pressure that would restore venous inflow and, hence, cardiac output.

LUNG DISORDERS AND PULMONARY FUNCTIONS

The most frequently occurring pulmonary disorders can be classified into two groups: obstructive diseases and restrictive diseases. These conditions are identified and evaluated by pulmonary function tests.

Pulmonary Function Testing

Pulmonary diseases change the mechanical characteristics of lungs and, consequently, the lung volumes. Lung volumes and capacities can be determined easily by spirometry. Static lung volumes (TLC, VC, FRC, RV–Chapter 27) can be used to diagnose restrictive diseases.

Timed spirometric tests can be used to diagnose obstructive diseases. When these tests are made before and after bronchodilators are administered, increased airway resistance, increased pulmonary tissue resistance, or increased thoracic cage resistance can be distinguished. The following tests are used most frequently:

1. *Forced expiratory volume* (FEV). A one-breath test that indicates resistance to air flow during expiration. FEV is the maximum volume of air that can be exhaled forcefully in 1, 2, or 3 sec. The volume usually is expressed as a percentage of the total *forced vital capacity* (FEV/FVC). The average FEV for a healthy person is approximately 83% of FVC in 1 sec (FEV_1).
2. *Maximum midexpiratory flow* (MMEF). This also is a one-breath test, which indicates resistance by measuring the air flow during the middle half of the FEV spirogram, between 25% and 75% of vital capacity.
3. *Maximum voluntary ventilation* (MVV). Also known as maximum breathing capacity. This test is somewhat difficult to administer to a patient who has lung disease, because it requires the understanding, cooperation, coordination, and maximum work effort of the patient.

Obstructive Diseases

Lung disorders that involve the respiratory airways and generally are associated with increased resistance to air flow are defined as *obstructive pulmonary diseases*. Specific conditions in this category include emphysema, bronchitis, asthma, and the so-called chronic obstructive pulmonary disease, which consists of a combination of emphysema and chronic bronchitis.

Emphysema in its purest form is caused by the loss of functional lung tissue. In the later stages of the disease, the airways also are involved, and on that basis it is classified as an obstructive disease.

EMPHYSEMA

Emphysema means, literally, "to puff up"; in respiratory pathophysiology, it describes a condition in which the lungs are overinflated. Pure emphysema results when collagen fibers and elastin are destroyed by proteolytic enzymes released from leukocytes in the lungs. Patients in whom this occurs are deficient in α_1-antitrypsin, an antiproteolytic enzyme. The disease usually begins at birth and is seen in young people after its development. The loss of the elastic recoil force of the lung upsets the normal balance between the tendency of the chest to recoil outwardly and the lungs to recoil inwardly. Since this balance determines the functional residual capacity, the FRC increases in these individuals. Total lung capacity also increases; the lungs are overinflated due to the loss of recoil force. Residual volume (RV), which is determined mainly by the closure of small airways, also increases, but since the increase of RV is proportionately greater than the increase of TLC, the vital capacity decreases in emphysema. Expiratory flow rates decrease because the driving pressure derived from the elastic recoil of the lungs is lost and because the airways are narrower at all lung volumes. As the small airways are kept open primarily by the elasticity of the lungs, the resistance to air flow increases when this structural support is lost and the small airways tend to close. However, small airways normally contribute relatively little to airway resistance; therefore, by the time this closure becomes a problem, the disease usually is fairly advanced, and the large airways also are involved. The decrease of ventilation caused by regional changes in compliance often is accompanied by a decrease in blood flow; thus, $\dot{V}_A/\dot{Q}_C$ may not be changed significantly. The diffusing capacity of the lungs (DL_{CO}) decreases because some of the alveoli and capillaries are destroyed in the course of the disease.

BRONCHITIS

Airway resistance increases in a person who has chronic bronchitis, because the mucous glands in the wall of the airways secrete excess mucus or may be swollen with edema, which causes partial or even complete bronchial obstruction.

ASTHMA

When a person has an asthma attack, both large and small airways constrict spasmodically and airway resistance increases markedly. The lungs are overdistended distal to the obstruction, and total lung volume increases as air is trapped in some parts of the lungs. Compliance remains normal unless air trapping persists, in which case it increases, because the constant overdistention of the lung tissue decreases elastic recoil. Air flow is reduced, especially the forced expiratory volume (FEV_1) and maximum midexpiratory flow rate (MMEF). RV and FRC increase because of the transient loss of lung recoil and the increased resistance to air flow. Vital capacity decreases. The symptoms of asthma are prolonged expiration and wheezing. Because of increased airway resistance, ventilation is uneven and $\dot{V}/\dot{Q}$ decreases, which causes a shuntlike condition in the lungs; the alveolar-arterial Po_2 difference is large and the patient is hypoxic. These effects can be reversed by administering bronchodilator agents, which decrease airway resistance.

CHRONIC OBSTRUCTIVE PULMONARY DISEASE

Chronic obstructive pulmonary disease (COPD) usually is considered to include chronic bronchitis, emphysema, and mixed disorders. Early in the disease, most of the effects are associated with increased resistance in the small airways, which tend to collapse at lower pleural pressures. Airway resistance upstream from the obstruction also is increased, which decreases the driving pressure between the alveoli and the small airways. The maximum midexpiratory flow (MMEF) decreases markedly. In more severe COPD, both the large and small airways are involved; therefore, airway resistance increases significantly. MMEF and forced expiratory volume as a percentage of forced vital capacity (FEV_1/FVC) both decrease severely. The elastic recoil is decreased markedly (emphysema), and all effects are additive. TLC is increased because of loss of elastic resistance. Ventilation-perfusion is uneven, and the patient has hypoxemia and pulmonary hypertension, which often leads to right ventricular failure.

Restrictive Diseases

Any disorder that restricts the expansion of the lungs may be classified as a restrictive pulmonary disease. Most commonly, the pulmonary membranes become thick because the lung parenchyma is replaced by nonelastic, fibrous tissue. The result is a stiff lung, or reduced compliance, and decreased diffusing capacity. TLC and VC are smaller than predicted, but RV represents a greater precentage of the total lung capacity. FEV_1 is smaller than normal but about the same or larger than normal when expressed as a percentage of FVC.

STUDY OUTLINE

RESPIRATORY INSUFFICIENCY Lungs are unable to maintain normal blood gas levels.

HYPOXIAS Low Po_2 or low $[O_2]$ anywhere in the system. Hypoxemia—low Po_2 or $[O_2]$ in the blood.

HYPOXIA RELATED TO VENTILATION Low Po_2 in inspired air: hypoxic hypoxia.

Hypoventilation: hypoxemia and hypercapnia.

Hypoxia caused by mismatched $\dot{V}A/\dot{Q}c$.

HYPOXIA RELATED TO DIFFUSION Diffusion of O_2 is related directly to area of diffusion and inversely to length of pathway.

HYPOXIA RELATED TO CIRCULATION Involves O_2 transport and delivery.

Right-to-left shunt: O_2 content of blood decreases as venous blood dilutes arterial blood.

Anemic hypoxias: decreased [Hb] decreases O_2-carrying capacity (e.g., anemia, abnormal Hb, CO toxicity).

Ischemic or stagnant hypoxia: decreased blood flow; Po_2 and [Hb] normal.

HYPOXIA RELATED TO UTILIZATION OF OXYGEN Histotoxic hypoxia: respiratory enzymes inactivated.

Utilization hypoxia: O_2 used at a higher rate than normally supplied.

CYANOSIS   Subjective index of hypoxemia: bluish discoloration of skin due to increase of deoxygenated Hb in blood.

OXYGEN THERAPY O_2 inhalation is useful for treating hypoxemia related to low PI_{O_2}, low $\dot{V}_A/\dot{Q}c$, or diffusion problems.

When hypoxemia due to low $\dot{V}_A$ is treated with O_2 inhalation, alveolar ventilation must be increased to prevent CO_2 retention.

Hypoxia caused by venous admixture; diagnosed but not treated by O_2.

OXYGEN TOXICITY   Damage depends on P_{O_2} and length of exposure.

$PI_{O_2} > 0.6$ atmosphere injures lungs.

$PI_{O_2} > 2$ atmospheres injures central nervous system.

HYPERCAPNIA   Due to hypoventilation; prolonged hypercapnia decreases sensitivity of receptors to CO_2.

CIRCULATORY EFFECTS OF CO_2 RETENTION   In conscious person, increases sympathetic activity.

In unconscious person, may cause hypotension.

Cerebral blood flow increases.

CO_2 IN INSPIRED AIR   Stimulates respiration.

COMBINED EFFECTS OF LOW P_{O_2} AND HIGH P_{CO_2} Effects on ventilation additive.

HYPOCAPNIA   Reversible symptoms of cerebral ischemia; fatigue, irritability, increased neuromuscular activity.

BASIC LIFE SUPPORT   Provides assistance to victims of respiratory and cardiac arrest.

RESPIRATORY ARREST AND PULMONARY RESUSCITATION

UPPER AIRWAY OCCLUSION   Caused most often by foreign object.

May be relieved by abruptly increasing airway pressure.

MOUTH-TO-MOUTH BREATHING   Effective method of pulmonary resuscitation; rescuer inflates victim's lungs by exhaling into his mouth or nose.

CARDIOPULMONARY RESUSCITATION (CPR)   "ABCs" of CPR are:

OPENING THE AIRWAY   Airway must be cleared.

Head-tilt–neck-lift or head-tilt–chin-lift procedure is used.

RESCUE BREATHING   Mouth-to-mouth ventilation.

CIRCULATION   Determine pulse.

Compress chest to assist circulation.

Continue ventilation and compression.

MECHANICAL VENTILATION   Indicated when respiration fails.

"NEGATIVE-PRESSURE" VENTILATION (IRON LUNG)   Mimics natural breathing.

Pump lowers pressure in cylinder around patient; chest expands, lungs inflate.

Pressure returns to atmospheric; lungs recoil and deflate to expiratory position.

"POSITIVE-PRESSURE" VENTILATION   Inspiration: air is pushed into lungs by positive pressure.

Expiration is via lung recoil.

Positive end-expiratory pressure is added when lung recoil is lost.

EFFECTS OF INCREASED INTRATHORACIC PRESSURE   Decreases venous return and cardiac output.

LUNG DISORDERS AND PULMONARY FUNCTIONS

PULMONARY FUNCTION TESTING   Static lung volumes (TLC, VC, FRC, RV) are used to diagnose restrictive disease.

Timed spirometric tests (FEV/FVC, MVV, MMEF) are used to diagnose obstructive diseases.

OBSTRUCTIVE DISEASES   Airway resistance is increased.

EMPHYSEMA   Lungs are overinflated but underventilated.

Elastic recoil of lungs is lost.

Loss of structural support causes small airways to close.

Increased RV, FRC, and TLC.

Decreased MMEF, FEV_1/FVC, and MVV.

Decreased diffusing capacity due to destruction of alveolar-capillary membrane.

BRONCHITIS   Excess mucus secretion; increased airway resistance.

ASTHMA   Large and small airways constrict spasmodically; airway resistance increases.

TLC increases because of regional overdistention by trapped air.

Compliance is normal or increased.

FEV_1, MMEF, and VC are decreased.

Hypoxia with large $P_{A_{O_2}} - P_{a_{O_2}}$ difference.

CHRONIC OBSTRUCTIVE PULMONARY DISEASE   Emphysema and chronic bronchitis.

Early signs: resistance in small airways is increased; driving pressure is decreased.

MMEF is decreased markedly.

Severe COPD: both large and small airways are involved; airway resistance is significantly increased.

MMEF and FEV_1/FVC are severely decreased.

Decreased elasticity (emphysema) and increased TLC.

All effects are additive: hypoxemia, pulmonary hypertension, and, often, right ventricular failure.

RESTRICTIVE DISEASES Expansion of lungs is restricted (pulmonary fibrosis).

Stiff lungs (compliance decreased).

TLC and VC are smaller than normal.

FEV_1/FVC is normal or greater than normal.

O_2 diffusion is decreased.

BIBLIOGRAPHY

Barnes, P.; Fitzgerald, G.; Brown, M.; et al. 1980. Nocturnal asthma and change in circulating epinephrine, histamine, and cortisol. *N. Engl. J. Med.* 303:263.

Bates, D.V.; Macklem, P.T.; and Christie, R.V. 1971. *Respiratory function in disease.* Philadelphia: W.B. Saunders Co.

Comroe, J.H., Jr. 1974. *Physiology of respiration,* 2nd ed. Chicago: Year Book Medical Publishers, Inc.

Comroe, J.H., Jr.; Forster, R.E., II; Dubois, A.B.; et al. 1962. *The lung: clinical physiology and pulmonary function tests,* 2nd ed. Chicago: Year Book Medical Publishers, Inc.

DeJours, P. 1966. *Respiration,* translator L.E. Farhi. New York: Oxford Univerity Press.

Hutchison, D.C.S.; Cook, P.J.L.; Barter, C.E.; et al. 1971. Pulmonary emphysema and α_1-antitrypsin deficiency. *Br. Med. J.* 1:689.

Macklem, P.T. 1972. Obstruction in small airways. A challenge to medicine. *Am. J. Med.* 52:721.

Macklem, P.T., and Permutt, S. 1979. *The lung in the transition between health and disease.* New York: Marcel Dekker, Inc.

Standards and guidelines for cardiopulmonary resuscitation (CPR) and emergency cardiac care (ECC) 1980. *J.A.M.A.* 244:453.

West, J.B. 1982. *Pulmonary pathophysiology: the essentials,* 2nd ed. Baltimore: Williams & Wilkins Co.

PART VII

RENAL PHYSIOLOGY AND BODY FLUIDS

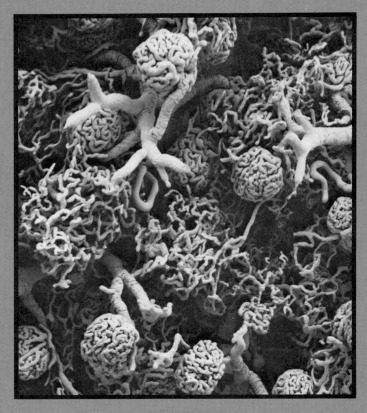

36

Body Composition

CHAPTER CONTENTS

STUDIES OF BODY COMPOSITION

The study of body composition is the study of the biochemical phases, both fluid and solid, that constitute the living body. The composition of the human body is of interest because body weight is not an adequate unit of reference for metabolic studies. Changes in body weight may reflect changes in the amount of one or more of the components of the body (for example, total body water, cellular mass, or fat tissue).

The composition of the human body may be studied in many ways. Because of technical and legal complications, only a few direct analyses, using human cadavers, have been performed. By contrast, much work has been done on spaces, components, and cell masses of the human body using indirect estimations. Indirect methods for estimating the gross composition of the human body in vivo are useful for eval-

uating the nutritional status of an individual and for performing metabolic studies. However, these methods must be validated by comparing the results with data obtained by direct analysis.

COMPARTMENTS OF THE BODY

The entire human body can be compartmentalized in many ways, depending on the purpose of the study. Most schemes include body fat as one of the compartments. In most of the in vivo methods the gross composition of the total body can be divided into two, three, or four components.

Two-Component Model

In the most elementary analysis body mass is divided, on the basis of metabolism, into a relatively active part and a relatively inactive part. The fat-free mass, or lean-body mass, is considered to be the metabolically active phase, and the mass of fat is the nonactive phase. This concept was conceived originally by Dubois and Benedict in 1915. The chemical composition of the lean body mass is assumed to be relatively constant, whereas body fat is more variable.

Three-Component Model

In the three-compartment model the body mass is divided into an active tissue, or body cell mass, a nonactive fat component, and a nonactive extracellular component. The last compartment consists of the extracellular fluid (ECF), the mineral portion of the skeleton, and a negligible part composed of nails, hair, and horny epidermis.

The body cell mass may vary from 35% to 65% of total body weight, but it accounts for virtually all of the energy consumption. The smallest values for cell mass would be found in obese, edematous (see Chapter 22) individuals, and a large value would be found in lean, muscular people.

Four-Component Model

From a biochemical viewpoint, the human body can be reduced to its four elemental constituents: fat, water, protein, and minerals. The latter can be divided further into an osseous (horny) component and a nonosseous component. The four-compartment model, derived from analyses of cadavers, provides the basis of indirect methods for estimating the gross com-

position of the body in vivo. The concept of the "reference body" has emerged from this approach.

BODY COMPOSITION DURING GROWTH

Both body size and body composition change during growth from birth to adulthood. Using information from a variety of sources, the body compositions of a male reference infant and a male reference adult have been estimated (Table 36-1). Certain trends in the composition of the body from infancy to adulthood are apparent. Total body water decreases from 94% of body weight early in utero to 76% at delivery and continues to decline thereafter. There is no gender-related difference during the years of growth. Protein, fat, and mineral all increase during this period of growth. The increase in protein largely reflects the increase of cell mass; this has been confirmed by the increase of total body potassium that occurs (the potassium content of cells is greater than that of extracellular fluids).

Data on body composition often are expressed in terms of the lean body mass. Adipose tissue is excluded from the calculation because fat is the greatest variable in the composition of the mammalian body. Because fat contains relatively little water and electrolytes, the accumulation of fat decreases the percentage of other components calculated on the basis of body weight. At a particular time during the process of growth, the proportions of water, proteins, and minerals in the fat-free

TABLE 36-1
Composition and density of the infant and adult male reference bodies

Component	Infant Body weight = 3.5 kg Density = 1.024 g/ml % body fat	Adult Body weight = 65.3 kg Density = 1.064 g/ml % body fat	% fat-free body
Water	75.1	62.4	73.8
Protein	11.4	16.4	19.4
Fat	11.0	15.3	—
Mineral	1.7	5.9	6.8
Residue	0.8	—	—
Fat-free body	89.0	84.7	—

component, or lean body mass, stabilize. When this condition is achieved, the body reaches "chemical maturity."

TOTAL BODY WATER

The total body water (TBW) is the largest component of the body. TBW is about 76% of body weight in the newborn infant; however, the body dries out during growth, and the TBW of an adult is between 45% and 70% of body weight. The variation depends on the amount of fat in the body because fatty tissue contains only about 10% water. The age at which the volume of TBW stabilizes is uncertain; by some estimates, it may be early adolescence. The adult female usually has a lower percentage of water than the adult male because females generally have proportionately more fat than males (this is a consequence of hormonal influences). This difference is eliminated if TBW is calculated on the basis of fat-free body weight, or lean body mass; the TBW averages 73.2% in both genders. As the body grows, the various tissues change in their relationship to body weight and in their contribution to TBW. An approximate distribution of TBW by tissue in the adult human is given in Table 36-2. Total body water is divided into an extracellular

compartment and an intracellular compartment.

Extracellular Water

Extracellular water (ECW), as a percentage of body weight, decreases with increasing age—from about 42% at birth to about 20% in the adult. Extracellular water is subdivided into blood plasma, interstitial fluid, lymphatic fluid, and transcellular fluid.

Interstitial fluid (ISF), which makes up 15% of the body weight, constitutes the immediate environment of the body cells. This fluid exchanges with the plasma through the capillaries and the lymphatic system. All nutrients, minerals, and hormones are delivered to the tissues by the blood, diffusing through the ISF to reach the cells. The metabolic waste products of the cells follow the same route in the opposite direction.

Lymph is a small fraction of the total ISF drained continuously out of the ISF by lymphatic channels and returned to the circulation via the subclavian veins (see Chapter 12).

The transcellular fluids are the digestive, cerebrospinal, intraocular, pleural, peritoneal, and synovial fluids. These specialized fluids in body cavities, which are produced by active transport processes that operate across epithe-

TABLE 36-2
Distribution of total body water in the adult human

Tissues	% body weight	% water	Water in tissues as % body weight	Liters of water
Muscle	41.7	75.6	31.53	22.10
Skin	18.0	72.0	12.96	9.07
Blood	8.0	83.0	6.64	4.65
Skeleton	15.9	22.0	3.50	2.45
Brain	2.0	74.8	1.50	1.05
Liver	2.3	68.3	1.57	1.10
Intestine	1.8	74.5	1.34	0.94
Adipose tissues	8.5	10.0	0.01	0.70
Lungs	0.7	79.0	0.55	0.39
Heart	0.5	79.2	0.40	0.28
Kidneys	0.4	82.7	0.33	0.23
Spleen	0.2	75.8	0.15	0.11
Total body	100.0	62.0	60.48	43.07

lial membranes, make up about 1%–3% of body weight. Because they are not simple transudates, their compositions differ from that of an ultrafiltrate of plasma. The composition of each of these fluids is adapted to the specific function it subserves. Of the various transcellular fluids, water in the lumen of the gastrointestinal tract makes up the largest fraction—about 7.5 ml/kg of body weight.

Intracellular Water

Intracellular water (ICW) makes up approximately 40% of body weight, and that value is relatively constant during growth. The principal metabolic reactions of the body occur within the cells and in the intracellular water.

MEASUREMENT OF BODY FLUID COMPARTMENTS

Indicator-Dilution Method

It is important theoretically, and sometimes practically, to measure the volume of one or more of these body fluid compartments. The indicator-dilution method is used. The principle behind this procedure is that a known quantity of a substance is dissolved in an unknown volume of fluid, a sample of the solution is taken, and the concentration of the substance is determined. The volume of fluid is calculated from the following formula:

$$\text{Volume of compartment} = \frac{\text{quantity of test substance dissolved}}{\text{concentration of substance in solution}}$$

For example, if the total amount of substance used is 20 mg and the final concentration of substance after equilibration has occurred is 0.004 mg/ml, the volume of fluid is as follows:

$$\text{Volume of compartment} = \frac{20 \text{ mg}}{0.004 \text{ mg/ml}}$$
$$= 5000 \text{ ml}$$

A substance used to measure the volume of a body fluid compartment must be distributed evenly within the compartment, must be confined to the compartment being measured, must not alter the volume to be measured, must not be toxic, and must not be metabolized or synthesized in the body. If the substance is excreted during the time needed for equilibration, the amount excreted must be measured and a correction made using the following formula:

$$\text{Volume of compartment} = \frac{\text{amount administered} - \text{amount excreted}}{\text{concentration of diluted substance in plasma}}$$

TOTAL BODY WATER

Deuterium oxide (D_2O) and tritiated water (T_2O) are used most often to measure the volume of total body water; D_2O has the advantage of not being radioactive. The hydrogens of D_2O and T_2O exchange not only with the hydrogen of body water, but also with the exchangeable hydrogen atoms of organic molecules. However, during the time required for equilibration with the hydrogen atoms of TBW, the error caused by exchange with the organic molecules is small—from 0.5% to 2.0% of body weight—and can safely be ignored.

Antipyrine has been used as an indicator to measure TBW, but its use has diminished. Antipyrine is metabolized by the body and excreted in the urine; hence, one must correct for its loss. Antipyrine also binds to proteins to some degree, which introduces an additional small error.

EXTRACELLULAR WATER

Unfortunately, no substance used to measure ECW remains exclusively in the extracellular compartment and instead distributes rapidly and uniformly through plasma, interstitial fluid, transcellular fluid, and the interstitial spaces of connective tissue, cartilage, and bone. All of the substances that are used enter the cells in differing amounts. Thus, although the extracellular space is easy to define anatomically, it is not as easy to characterize physiologically. Because of these conditions, the true volume of ECW never is measured; rather, the space or volume of distribution of the particular substance used is measured (e.g., "inulin space").

Two general types of substances are used to measure the volume of the extracellular compartment: (1) saccharides, such as inulin, sucrose, and mannitol, and (2) ions, such as thiosulfate, thiocyanate, radioactive sulfate, radioactive chloride, and radioactive sodium. The volumes of distribution of the various substances differ; for example, inulin space is about 16% of body weight, while the radioisotope spaces of Na^+ and Cl^- each comprise about 30% of the body weight. This difference is caused partly by the entry of the ions into the cells and partly by the slow diffusion of the relatively large inulin molecule into the interstitial fluid of connective tissues.

Intracellular Water and Interstitial Fluid Volume

The volumes of the intracellular water (ICW) and the interstitial fluid compartment (ISF) cannot be measured directly but must be calculated. The volume of ISF is the difference between the ECW and the plasma volume, and the volume of ICW is the difference between TBW and ECW. Because these two volumes are obtained from the difference between the volumes of distribution of two substances, the errors of measurement are large.

PLASMA VOLUME

Several indicators are used to measure the volume of plasma, which constitutes about 5% of body weight. The substance first used widely was a dye, T-1824, or Evan's blue, which binds firmly and rapidly to plasma proteins. Currently, the substance used most commonly is radioiodinated serum albumin (RISA); ^{125}I is bound in vitro to albumin to form RISA, which then is injected. Both of these indicators measure the volume of distribution of albumin.

RED CELL VOLUME

The circulating red cell volume can be measured by tagging the cells with either ^{55}Fe, ^{59}Fe, or ^{51}Cr. The latter is used most commonly at present. The red cells are exposed to the radioactive element in vitro, and the radioisotope is bound firmly to or incorporated into the red cell.

BLOOD VOLUME

Blood volume, which constitutes approximately 8% of body weight, is measured most accurately when both plasma and red cell volumes are determined simultaneously. This is true because the hematocrit, or concentration of red cells, is not the same in all blood vessels. Because of axial streaming in small vessels (see Chapter 12), the mean hematocrit of the total blood volume is only 91% of the venous hematocrit. However, under most circumstances,

blood volume can be calculated reasonably well from a measurement of either plasma volume or red cell volume obtained by using the hematocrit. Because the contribution of plasma to blood volume is given by [(100 − hemotocrit)/hematocrit], and plasma volume is equal to blood volume times the percentage of plasma,

$$\frac{\text{Total blood volume}}{\text{hematocrit}} = \frac{100}{100 - \text{hematocrit}} \times \text{plasma volume}$$

If the red cell volume is used, blood volume can be calculated by the following equation:

$$\text{Total blood volume} = \text{red cell volume} \times \frac{100}{\text{hematocrit}}$$

COMPOSITION OF BODY FLUID COMPARTMENTS

The total quantity of solutes in the body is the primary determinant of the TBW volume. Therefore, it is important not only to estimate the total quantity of ions in the body and their distribution in the different body compartments, but also to understand the factors that affect their distribution.

Method of Isotope Dilution

Although the total body content of ions has been measured directly only in cadavers, the data from those measurements provide the standard with which the results from indirect methods are compared. Indirect methods that have been developed recently use radioisotopes of the ions to be measured. This is another example of the use of the dilution principle (see the previous section on the indicator-dilution method). This method measures the quantity of exchangeable ions, which may not equal the total amount of ions in the body. However, the exchangeable pool of a particular ion is important because the exchangeable pool is readily available when excessive amounts of that particular ion have been lost. The isotopes that are used must meet two special criteria: (1) they must not influence the size and composition of the compartment to be measured, and (2) the body must not distinguish between the labeled and the unlabeled molecule.

SODIUM

The total amount of Na$^+$ in the body depends on the balance between intake and output. Usually, intake greatly exceeds need; thus, Na$^+$ must be eliminated from the body. The kidneys form the primary route of elimination, since 90%–95% of the Na$^+$ excreted appears in the urine. The remaining 5%–10% is lost in the feces and the perspiration.

An adult human contains approximately 58 mEq of Na$^+$ per kilogram of body weight, or approximately 4000 mEq in 70 kg. The extracellular space contains 98% of the Na$^+$, of which 43% is in the skeleton. The intracellular fluid contains only 2% of the total body Na$^+$.

The isotopes ^{22}Na or ^{24}Na are used to measure exchangeable Na$^+$. However, total body Na$^+$ is not measured, because the isotope exchanges with only about 71% of sodium ions. Most of the Na$^+$ that does not exchange is a fraction in the inner layer of bone. The outer layer of the bone contains recently deposited Na$^+$ that does exchange with the Na$^+$ isotope. All exchangeable Na$^+$ is in equilibrium with the plasma Na$^+$ and serves as a reservoir when loss of Na$^+$ is excessive.

POTASSIUM

The K$^+$ content of the body is regulated carefully, and under normal circumstances total K$^+$ varies only slightly from day to day. Total body K$^+$ is estimated either by counting the whole body content of the naturally occurring radioisotope ^{40}K or by injecting the isotope ^{42}K and using its concentration in the dilution method. Typically, the body contains 42 mEq/kg of K$^+$ per kilogram of body weight. It is not clear whether injected ^{42}K exchanges with the total K$^+$ pool. Some investigators believe that ^{42}K exchanges with 99%–100% of the total pool, but others place the figure at approximately 90%. The K$^+$ of the red blood cells, brain, and bone exchanges slowly with injected ^{42}K, and equilibration of the injected isotope with body K$^+$ requires at least 48 hours.

CHLORIDE

Chloride is the principal anion of the ECF. However, red blood cells and the cells of the gastric mucosa that secrete HCl also contain Cl$^-$. Connective tissue and skeletal muscle contain little Cl$^-$. The amount of intracellular Cl$^-$ is much smaller than that of intracellular Na$^+$.

Total body Cl$^-$ can be estimated by the injection of a number of isotopes such as ^{36}Cl, ^{38}Cl, and ^{82}Br. An average estimated value for total body Cl$^-$ is 33 mEq/kg of body weight. Movement of Cl$^-$ into and out of the body generally is coupled closely with that of Na$^+$ and is affected by the same factors that influence Na$^+$ balance.

DISTRIBUTIONS OF IONS

Effects of Proteins and Barriers to Diffusion

Disturbance of the normal electrolyte distribution always is accompanied by disturbance of the body fluids, because the distribution of water in the different fluid compartments depends on the ions. Consequently, a basic understanding of the normal distribution of electrolytes in the different compartments is essential for the proper correction of fluid and electrolyte imbalances. The main constituents of the body fluid compartments are shown in Figure 36-1. Electrical potential differences exist at the interface between the compartments. The separation of charges is restricted to the immediate region of the interface, and the ma-

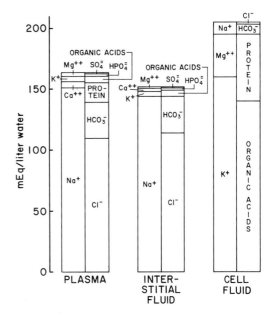

Figure 36-1. The principal solutes of the body fluids.

jor portion of the fluid within a compartment is electrically neutral. Figure 36-1 shows that the total number of equivalents differs among compartments because of the different concentrations of protein in the different compartments. At the pH of body fluids, the protein molecule has multiple negative charges. Therefore, because intracellular fluid contains appreciably more protein and other organic polyanions, it has more total charges than the extracellular fluid has. For the same reason, the total number of equivalents in the plasma is greater than that in the interstitial fluid.

EFFECTS OF CAPILLARY MEMBRANE

Figure 36-1 shows that Na^+ is the most abundant cation of the ECF compartment, and Cl^- and HCO_3^- are the most abundant anions. The concentrations of diffusible ions in the plasma and ISF are similar because the two compartments are separated only by the capillary endothelium, through which solutes of low molecular weight pass readily. However, the concentrations of protein are different because the capillary endothelium prevents the passage of larger molecules from the plasma into the intracellular fluid (ICF). The concentrations of diffusible ions in these two compartments differ by about 5%; in the plasma, the levels of cations are slightly higher, and those of the anions are slightly lower. The Gibbs-Donnan equilibrium (see Chapter 22) accounts for most of this difference, but binding to the proteins by certain cations, such as Ca^{++} and Mg^{++}, also contributes.

EFFECTS OF CELL MEMBRANE

The most abundant cation in the ICF is K^+, and the major anions are protein and organic acids, the latter mainly phosphates. The intracellular compartment is separated from the interstitial compartment by the cell membrane, which, like the capillary endothelium, is selectively permeable and limits the passage of organic polyanions. Further, Na^+ is transported out of the cell and K^+ is transported in. Because most of the intracellular organic anions are not present in the ISF, the Gibbs-Donnan force accounts for the low intracellular concentration of HCO_3^- and Cl^-. Finally, considerable amounts of certain ions are bound to intracellular protein and phosphates. Thus, the differences between the composition of the ECF and ICF are due to the selective permeability of the cell membrane, active transport, the Gibbs-Donnan equilibrium, and the binding of ions.

STUDY OUTLINE

STUDIES OF BODY COMPOSITION   Individual components of body form better reference base than body weight alone forms.

Studied by indirect methods in vivo, validated by direct studies in cadavers.

COMPARTMENTS OF THE BODY

TWO-COMPONENT MODEL   This divides body mass into metabolically active fat-free mass (lean body mass) and nonactive fat mass.

THREE-COMPONENT MODEL   Divides body mass into metabolically active lean body mass, nonactive fat mass, and nonactive extracellular tissue mass.

FOUR-COMPONENT MODEL   This divides body into four constituents: fat, water, protein, and minerals.

BODY COMPOSITION DURING GROWTH   Decrease in total body water and increase in total protein, fat, and minerals, as percentage of body weight, from birth to adulthood.

Data are expressed in terms of lean body mass because of variability of fat component.

When proportions of water, protein, and minerals in lean body mass become constant, body is said to be chemically mature.

TOTAL BODY WATER   Approximately 76% of body weight at birth, decreases to 45%–70% in adult.

Proportionately less in adult female because of higher fat content.

Same (approximately 73%) in male and female on basis of lean body mass.

EXTRACELLULAR WATER Approximately 42% of body weight at birth, 20% in adult.

Interstitial fluid provides immediate environment of cells.

Lymph returns ISF to blood.

Transcellular fluids secreted for special purposes.

INTRACELLULAR WATER Approximately 40% of body weight; principal metabolic reactions of body occur in ICW.

MEASUREMENT OF BODY FLUID COMPARTMENTS

INDICATOR-DILUTION METHOD Volume is calculated from concentration of solution produced by dissolving known amount of substance.

TOTAL BODY WATER Deuterium oxide or tritiated water is used most often as indicator.

EXTRACELLULAR WATER Usually saccharides or ions are used as indicators.

Different indicators distribute differently, each gives characteristic "space."

INTRACELLULAR WATER AND INTERSTITIAL FLUID VOLUME Interstitial volume is obtained by subtracting blood volume from total extracellular volume.

Intracellular volume is obtained by subtracting extracellular volume from total body water volume.

Values vary with indicators used.

PLASMA VOLUME Radioiodinated serum albumin is used—measures albumin "space."

RED CELL VOLUME Isotopes of iron, chromium, or phosphorus are used.

BLOOD VOLUME Can measure either plasma volume or red cell volume and calculate other from hematocrit.

Most accurate if both are measured and added.

COMPOSITION OF BODY FLUID COMPARTMENTS

METHOD OF ISOTOPE DILUTION Limited by distribution of isotope (i.e., exchangeability).

SODIUM Approximately 58 mEq/kg body weight.

Intake usually exceeds need; mostly excreted by kidneys, but also in feces and perspiration.

Ninety-eight percent in extracellular fluid, largely determines volume.

Measured with ^{22}Na or ^{24}Na; approximately 71% is exchangeable.

POTASSIUM Approximately 42 mEq/kg of body weight.

Measured by counting whole-body ^{40}K (naturally occurring) or injecting ^{42}K as indicator.

Most potassium is inside cells.

90% to 99% exchanges; investigators disagree.

CHLORIDE Approximately 33 mEq/kg of body weight.

Principal extracellular anion, but also in red cells and gastric secretory cells.

Movement generally is coupled with Na^+.

Measured with isotopes.

DISTRIBUTIONS OF IONS

EFFECTS OF PROTEINS AND BARRIERS TO DIFFUSION Separation at interfaces of compartments produces electrical potentials.

Polyanionic proteins alter distribution.

EFFECTS OF CAPILLARY MEMBRANE Small molecules pass readily.

Protein retained in plasma increases concentration of cations and decreases that of anions by approximately 5% (Gibbs-Donnan effect).

EFFECTS OF CELL MEMBRANE K^+ is principal intracellular cation; protein and organic acids are major anions.

Intracellular composition is altered by selective permeability, active transport, Gibbs-Donnan effect, and binding of ions.

BIBLIOGRAPHY

Andersson, B. 1977. Regulation of body fluids. *Annu. Rev. Physiol.* 39:185.

Andersson, B. 1978. Regulation of water intake. *Physiol. Rev.* 58:582.

Deetjen, P., Boylan, J.W., and Kramer, K. 1975. *Physiology of the Kidney and of Water Balance.* New York: Springer-Verlag.

Edelman, I.S., and Liebman, J. 1959. Anatomy of body water and electrolytes. *Am. J. Med.* 27:256.

Gauer, O.H., and Henry, J.P. 1976. Neurohumoral control of plasma volume. *Int. Rev. Physiol.* 9:145.

Goetz, K.L., Bond, G.C., and Bloxham, D.D. 1975. Atrial receptors and renal function. *Physiol. Rev.* 55:157.

Guyton, A.C., Taylor, A.E., and Granger, H.J. 1975. *Dynamics and Control of the Body Fluids.* Philadelphia: W.B. Saunders Co.

Nicoll, P.A., and Taylor, A.E. 1977. Lymph formation and flow. *Annu. Rev. Physiol.* 39:73.

Pitts, R.F. 1974. *Physiology of the Kidney and Body Fluids.* Chicago: Year Book Medical Publishers, Inc.

Relman, A.S., and Levinsky, N.G. 1971. Clinical examination of renal function. In *Diseases of the Kidney.* Edited by M.B. Strauss and L.B. Welt. Boston: Little, Brown and Co.

Rose, B.D. 1977. *Clinical Physiology of Acid-Base and Electrolyte Disorders.* New York: McGraw-Hill.

Smith, K. 1980. *Fluids and Electrolytes: A Conceptual Approach.* New York: Churchill Livingstone.

Stein, J.H., and Reineck, H.J. 1975. Effect of alteration in extracellular fluid volume on segmental sodium transport. *Physiol. Rev.* 55:127.

Valtin, H. 1983. *Renal Function: Mechanisms Preserving Fluid and Solute Balance in Health.* 2nd ed. Boston: Little, Brown and Co.

Whittembury, G., and Grantham, J.J. 1976. Cellular aspects of renal sodium transport and cell volume regulation. *Kidney Int.* 9:103.

37

Renal Function

CHAPTER CONTENTS

REGULATORY FUNCTIONS OF THE KIDNEY

The kidneys contribute significantly to homeostasis in the internal environment of the body, although often they are thought of only as the organs that eliminate from the body the end products of metabolism, such as urea, uric acid, creatinine, sulfates, and phosphates. In their homeostatic role, the kidneys stabilize the volume, chemical composition, and acid-base balance of the body fluids. The concentrations of ions, especially those of Na^+, K^+, Ca^{++}, H^+, Mg^{++}, Cl^-, HCO_3^-, $HPO_4^=$, and $SO_4^=$ in the extracellular fluid compartment and, thus, indirectly in the intracellular fluid compartment, are regulated within normal limits by the kidneys. In their regulatory function, the kidneys remove, or "clear," waste substances or other excess substances from the plasma as it passes through the kidneys.

PROCESSES IN RENAL FUNCTION

The kidneys adjust the concentrations of substances in the plasma by three processes: (1) glomerular filtration, (2) tubular reabsorption, and (3) tubular secretion (Figure 37-1).

Glomerular Filtration

A large volume of plasma, about one-fifth of the total that comes to the kidneys, is filtered through the glomerular membrane of the renal corpuscles into the renal tubules. The glomerular filtrate, which passes through the glomerular membrane at a rate of about 120 ml/min, is an ultrafiltrate that essentially is free of protein and contains practically all of the constituents of the plasma that have molecular weights of less than 5000 daltons.

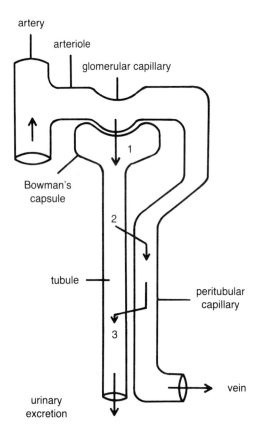

Figure 37-1. The kidney represented as a single large nephron rather than as a great many small ones operating in parallel. The three principal mechanisms by which the kidneys adjust the composition of the plasma are: (1) glomerular filtration, (2) tubular reabsorption of filtrate, and (3) tubular secretion of certain substances.

Tubular Reabsorption and Secretion

As the filtrate flows along the renal tubules, it is processed selectively by the tubular epithelial cells. The volume and composition of the filtrate are altered by reabsorption of about 99% of the water and by reabsorption and secretion of solutes. The remaining 1% of the filtrate, which is approximately 1.5 liters/day in humans, is excreted in the urine. The term *reabsorption* refers to the movement of substances from the tubular lumen into the interstitium or peritubular blood, regardless of whether the transport is active or passive. Conversely, the term *secretion* refers to the movement of substances from the peritubular blood, the interstitium, or the tubular epithelial cells into the tubular lumen; thus, secretion supplements

filtration. In the processing of the tubular fluid, the total amount of material reabsorbed greatly exceeds the amount secreted; however, secretion is especially important in removing waste products from the body.

REABSORPTION
Because of the large volume of plasma water and solutes they filter and the large volume they reabsorb, the kidneys are responsible almost entirely for the composition of the internal environment of the body. To accomplish their function, the kidneys save some substances from the glomerular filtrate and reject others. Those substances that are needed by the body (especially water), many of the electrolytes (Na^+, K^+, Ca^{++}, Mg^{++}, Cl^-, HCO_3^-, $HPO_4^=$, and $SO_4^=$), and substances of nutritional value (e.g., glucose, amino acids, and several vitamins) are reabsorbed into the plasma of the peritubular capillaries by the tubular cells. Thus, by adjusting the reabsorptive capacity of the tubules, the kidneys regulate the balance of water and electrolytes in the body. The value of reabsorption is illustrated by the fact that the volume of urine excreted each day is only a fraction of the volume of fluid filtered at the glomeruli. For example, 180 liters of plasma, or 170 liters of plasma water, are filtered daily, but only about 1.5 liters of urine are excreted. The volume filtered each day greatly exceeds the total volume of body water, since a normal man who weighs 70 kg contains approximately 42 liters of water and approximately 3.5 liters of plasma.

SECRETION
In addition to filtering substances at the glomeruli, the kidneys also transport certain substances from the peritubular capillaries to the tubular fluid. The most important substances secreted by the tubular epithelial cells are K^+, H^+, ammonia (NH_3), and weak acids and bases foreign to the body and either not metabolized or metabolized slowly and incompletely. Thus, tubular secretion supplements glomerular filtration by helping to eliminate excess electrolytes and other compounds that cannot be disposed of by metabolism alone.

CLEARANCE

The glomerular filtration rate, the renal plasma flow, and the functions of the renal tubules can be determined readily by the application of the principle of clearance, which is another form of the dilution principle (see Chapter 14). The clearance technique permits the study of renal functions without surgical intervention, but it provides only indirect information that reflects the overall behavior of the nephron population.

General Principle

The term *renal plasma clearance* is used to express the ability of the kidneys to remove from or to "clear" the plasma of various substances. The renal plasma clearance of any substance is defined as the volume of plasma necessary to supply the quantity of a substance that appears in the urine during a unit of time. The quantity of a substance y that is excreted in the urine ($\dot{Q}_{y\cdot u}$) is equal to the quantity of y that is cleared from the plasma ($\dot{Q}_{y\cdot p}$) per unit of time:

$$\dot{Q}_{y\cdot p} = \dot{Q}_{y\cdot u}$$

Therefore,

$$P_y \times \dot{V}_p = U_y \times \dot{V}_u$$

where P_y is the concentration of y in the plasma, $\dot{V}_p$ is the volume of plasma cleared of y per unit of time, U_y is the concentration of y in the urine, and $\dot{V}_u$ is the volume of urine formed per unit of time, and

$$\dot{V}_p = \frac{U_y \times \dot{V}_u}{P_y} = C_y$$

where C_y is the clearance of substance y.

The renal plasma clearance of a substance can be calculated by using the formula given above. If the concentration of substance y in the plasma is 0.1 mg/ml, and the rate of excretion of y in the urine is 20 mg/min, the quantity of the substance excreted in the urine in one minute was contained in 200 ml of plasma. Therefore, the plasma clearance of y is 200 ml/min.

Uses of Clearance

The ratio $U_y \dot{V}_u / P_y$ permits a quantitative assessment of the ability of the kidneys to excrete a given substance y in relation to the concentration of the substance in the plasma, but it does not reveal the actual mechanism of excretion of the substance. Depending on how the substance is handled by the renal tubular

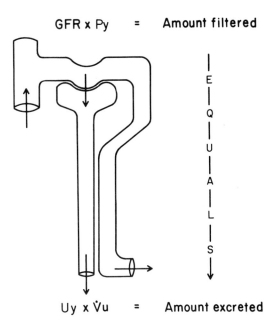

Figure 37-2. The principles that underlie the equation of the glomerular filtration rate with the clearance of a substance y that is filtered freely at the glomeruli and neither reabsorbed nor secreted by the tubules.

cells and whether tubular activity adds to or subtracts from the amount of substance that was present in the glomerular filtrate initially, the clearance technique can be used to determine the glomerular filtration rate (GFR), net secretion or net reabsorption by the renal tubular cells, and the renal plasma flow.

Estimation of Glomerular Filtration Rate (GFR)

A knowledge of the rate of filtration of plasma by the kidneys is necessary to evaluate renal function and to interpret the mechanism by which the kidneys excrete any substance. The principle of the clearance technique is illustrated in Figure 37-2. To estimate the rate of glomerular filtration, it is necessary to employ a substance that is filtered freely at the glomeruli and neither reabsorbed nor secreted by the tubules. The rate at which such a substance y is filtered is given by the product of the GFR and the concentration of the substance in the plasma (P_y), and the rate of excretion of the substance is given by the product of the concentration of the substance in the urine (U_y) and the rate of formation of urine ($\dot{V}_u$). If the substance is neither secreted nor reabsorbed by the tubules, the quantity that leaves the kidneys must equal the quantity that enters the kidneys during a particular period. Thus,

$$U_y \times \dot{V}_u = GFR \times P_y, \text{ and}$$

$$GFR = \frac{U_y \times \dot{V}_u}{P_y}$$

Hence, the clearance of any substance that fits the criteria given above is a measure of the volume of plasma filtered through the glomeruli in one minute.

The ideal indicator for estimating the GFR should: (1) be physiologically inert and cause no toxic or injurious effects, (2) not be bound to plasma proteins, so that it is filtered freely and completely at the glomeruli (Figure 37-3A), (3) be neither reabsorbed nor secreted by tubular cells, so that the quantity of the substance that appears in the urine is identical to the amount that is filtered at the glomeruli, (4) be neither destroyed, stored, nor synthesized within the kidneys, and (5) yield a uniform value of clearance over a wide range of concentrations in the plasma (Figure 37-3B). If the substance is filtered freely at the glomeruli and is neither reabsorbed nor secreted by the tubular cells, its clearance is constant and independent of its concentration in the plasma.

INULIN AND POLYFRUCTOSAN

A number of substances have been proposed for use in estimating the GFR, but the two used most commonly are inulin, a fructose polymer that has a molecular weight of 5000 daltons, and polyfructosan, a synthetic polymer of fructose that has a molecular weight of about 3000 daltons. Both of these substances meet all of the criteria for an ideal indicator.

The use of the clearance of inulin (C_{in}) to measure the GFR is illustrated in Figure 37-4. The substance is infused intravenously at a constant rate, so that the concentration in the plasma remains at a suitable level during the period of observation. Samples of urine are collected frequently, usually at intervals of 10–15 minutes. The rate of excretion of inulin divided by the concentration of inulin in the plasma gives the volume of plasma filtered per unit of time because each unit of inulin excreted represents a corresponding quantity of plasma filtered.

CREATININE

Although the clearance of inulin measures the GFR accurately, it is not practical for patients because it requires the continuous intravenous infusion of inulin and catheterization of the bladder to measure the volume of urine excreted. An ideal substance would be one that is produced in the body, has a stable plasma

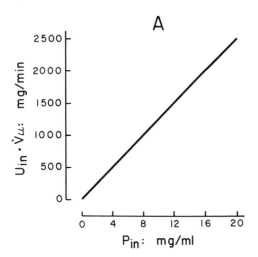
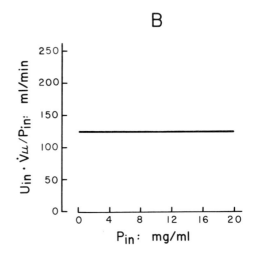

Figure 37-3. Relationships of the rate of excretion of inulin (**A**) and the clearance of inulin (**B**) to the plasma concentration of inulin. The clearance of inulin is independent of the plasma concentration and the rate of excretion of inulin. U_{in} is the concentration of inulin in the urine; $\dot{V}_u$ is the volume of urine formed in a unit of time; and P_{in} is the concentration of inulin in the plasma.

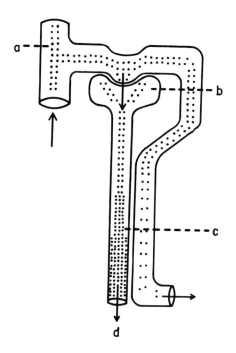

Figure 37-4.   Diagram of inulin clearance (C_{in}) as a measure of the glomerular filtration rate (GFR). **a.** The concentration of inulin in the plasma is 1 mg/ml. **b.** The glomerular filtration rate is 120 ml/min, and the concentration of inulin in the filtrate is 1 mg/ml; therefore, inulin is filtered at a rate of 120 mg/min. **c.** Water and certain solutes are reabsorbed; inulin is neither reabsorbed nor secreted. **d.** Urine is formed at the rate of 1 ml/min. The concentration of inulin in the urine is 120 mg/ml; therefore, inulin is excreted at the rate of 120 mg/min.

$$C_{in} = \frac{\text{Rate of excretion of inulin (mg/min)}}{\text{Plasma concentration of inulin (mg/ml)}}$$

$$= \frac{120 \text{ mg/min}}{1 \text{ mg/ml}} = 120 \text{ ml/min} = \text{GFR}$$

concentration, is filtered freely at the glomeruli, is neither reabsorbed nor secreted by the renal tubules, and can be measured easily in the plasma and urine. Although creatinine does not meet these criteria, it approaches them. It is a naturally occurring substance derived from the breakdown of creatine and phosphocreatine in muscle. The plasma concentration of creatinine in a given subject is relatively stable, and creatinine is filtered freely by the glomeruli, but it is secreted to some extent by the renal tubules in humans. Therefore, the true clearance of creatinine overestimates the GFR.

However, the method used in clinical laboratories to measure the concentration of creatinine in the plasma also measures the so-called noncreatinine chromogen. Because these substances are not present in the urine, the concentration of creatinine in the urine is measured accurately. The overestimation of the concentration of creatinine in the plasma causes the clearance of creatinine to be underestimated, which approximately offsets the increased clearance caused by tubular secretion. Thus, $C_{creatinine}$ provides a convenient estimate of GFR in a normal subject. In renal disease, such as glomerulonephritis, the GFR is decreased, but the tubular secretion of creatinine continues; as a consequence, creatinine is cleared proportionately more by secretion and less by filtration. Thus, as the GFR decreases, it is overestimated by $C_{creatinine}$.

Clearance of Substances Secreted or Reabsorbed

In contrast to C_{in}, the clearances of most substances either secreted or reabsorbed by the tubular cells change as the concentrations of these substances in the plasma change. The differences among the clearances of three different substances, inulin, para-aminohippurate (PAH), and glucose (Figure 37-5), are attributed to the way these substances are

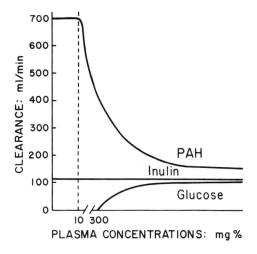

Figure 37-5.   Relationships of the clearance to the plasma concentration of para-aminohippurate (PAH), inulin, and glucose in humans. PAH is secreted by the tubules, glucose is reabsorbed by the tubules, and inulin is neither reabsorbed nor secreted by the tubules.

handled by the kidneys. The clearance of inulin, filtered freely but neither reabsorbed nor secreted by the tubular cells, is constant over a wide range of concentrations in the plasma. The clearance of PAH, filtered freely and also secreted by the tubular cells, is greater than that of inulin, but it decreases as the concentration in the plasma, P_{PAH}, increases. This decrease occurs because the secretory system is saturated at a relatively low P_{PAH}, approximately 10 mg/dl. As the P_{PAH} increases further, the amount secreted remains constant and the amount filtered increases; hence, secretion contributes relatively less and filtration contributes relatively more to the total amount of PAH excreted in the urine. As shown in Figure 37-5, when P_{PAH} is high, C_{PAH} approaches C_{in} asymptotically. On the other hand, the clearance of glucose, filtered freely but normally reabsorbed completely by the tubular cells, increases as the $P_{glucose}$ increases (Figure 37-5) because the mechanism for the reabsorption of glucose is saturated at a $P_{glucose}$ of about 300 mg/dl. As $P_{glucose}$ increases, the amount reabsorbed becomes a smaller proportion of the amount filtered, so that reabsorption has less of an effect and filtration has more of an effect on the amount of glucose excreted.

Estimation of Renal Plasma Flow

The clearance technique, which is a variation of the dilution principle used to measure the total systemic blood flow (see Chapter 14), also can be used to measure the rate of plasma flow through the kidneys. To measure the cardiac output (CO), the formula is as follows:

$$CO = \frac{\text{Rate of consumption of oxygen}}{\text{Arteriovenous difference of oxygen content}}$$

To calculate the renal plasma flow, the formula is as follows:

$$RPF = \frac{\text{Rate of excretion of substance } y}{\text{Arteriovenous difference of concentration of } y}$$

$$= \frac{U_y \times \dot{V}_u}{RA_y - RV_y}$$

where RPF is the renal plasma flow (ml/min), $U_y \times \dot{V}_u$ is the rate of excretion of y (mg/min),

RA_y is the concentration of y in the plasma of the renal artery (mg/ml), and RV_y is the concentration of y in the plasma of the renal vein (mg/ml). (Although this formula is not strictly correct, because the renal venous outflow is less than the renal arterial inflow by the amount of the urinary flow, the renal plasma flow is so much greater than the urinary flow that the error is insignificant.) The arteriovenous difference in the concentration of y is the quantity removed from a unit of plasma as it perfuses the kidneys. Dividing the rate of excretion of y by the arteriovenous difference of y yields the volume of plasma that must perfuse the kidneys each minute to supply the quantity of y excreted in the urine (clearance of y).

Theoretically, any substance that is extracted from the blood but is neither stored nor synthesized by the kidneys can be used to measure renal plasma flow if the small error mentioned above is ignored. The actual mechanism of excretion of the substance, whether it is filtered, secreted, or partly reabsorbed, is of no consequence as long as the rate of excretion by the kidneys and the quantity removed from each unit of plasma can be measured. The quantity of the substance excreted in the urine can be obtained easily, and the concentration of the substance in the plasma can be measured in a sample of blood taken from any peripheral artery. The difficulty in this procedure is to obtain a sample of plasma from the renal vein. The need for a sample of renal venous blood can be avoided by choosing a substance that is extracted from the blood completely during its passage through the kidneys, so that its concentration in the renal vein is zero. If this is done, the equation reduces to:

$$RPF = \frac{U_y \times \dot{V}_u}{RA_y}$$

No substance is extracted from the plasma completely during its passage through the kidneys, although the extraction of a number of substances, such as PAH or iodopyracet (Diodrast) is, on the average, about 90% complete. These substances are filtered freely by the glomeruli and transported from the peritubular blood into the tubular fluid by the proximal tubular cells; about 90% of the substance is transferred from the blood into the urine during its passage through the kidneys. Physiologists generally believe that all of the plasma that flows through the renal cortex is completely cleared of PAH and Diodrast (Figure

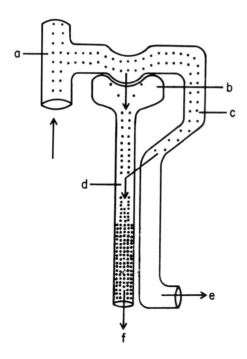

The extraction ratio of PAH can be estimated by using the following equation:

$$\text{Extraction ratio} = \frac{RA_{PAH} - RV_{PAH}}{RA_{PAH}}$$

In practice, the error introduced by incomplete extraction is disregarded, and C_{PAH} and $C_{Diodrast}$ are taken as estimates of effective renal plasma flow.

Extraction is maximal only over a restricted range of plasma concentrations for each of the reference materials. C_{PAH} in humans is constant (at about 700 ml/min) up to a plasma level of 10 mg/dl. $C_{Diodrast}$ is constant up to a plasma level of 5–6 mg/dl. Higher concentrations of these substances in the plasma saturate the transport capacity of the tubules, and the clearance decreases progressively. In disease states, extraction may be reduced by damage to the mechanisms of tubular transport. To obtain a true measure of renal plasma flow in this case, the extraction ratio must be determined and C_{PAH} or $C_{Diodrast}$ corrected as appropriate.

Estimation of Renal Tubular Function

The tubular transport of various substances that are filtered freely at the glomeruli can be estimated indirectly by using the following principles (Figure 37-7). The amount of any

Figure 37-6. Ideal clearance of iodopyracet (Diodrast) as a measure of the renal plasma flow. **a.** The concentration of Diodrast in the plasma in 0.01 mg/ml, and the renal plasma flow is 700 ml/min. **b.** The glomerular filtration rate is 120 ml/min, and the concentration of Diodrast in the filtrate is 0.01 mg/ml; therefore, Diodrast is filtered at a rate of 1.2 mg/min. **c.** The peritubular capillary plasma flow is 580 ml/min; therefore, the total flow of Diodrast through these vessels is 5.8 mg/min. **d.** Diodrast is secreted at a rate of 5.8 mg/min; therefore, in the ideal situation, all of the plasma is cleared of Diodrast during one passage through the kidneys. **e.** The renal venous blood contains no Diodrast. **f.** Diodrast is excreted at a rate of 7 mg/min (1.2 mg/min filtered + 5.8 mg/min secreted). These conditions are believed to exist for the perfusion of active renal tissue.

37-6). Whatever is not cleared is believed to flow through the nonsecreting part of the kidneys, such as the connective and supportive tissue, and accounts for about 10% of the total renal plasma flow. Therefore, C_{PAH} measures the so-called effective renal plasma flow (ERPF) and is approximately 90% of the total renal plasma flow (TRPF). TRPF can be estimated by dividing C_{PAH} or $C_{Diodrast}$ by its extraction ratio, as follows:

$$TRPF = \frac{C_{PAH}}{\text{Extraction ratio}}$$

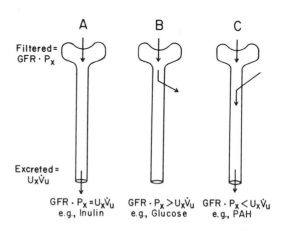

Figure 37-7. Tubular functions. P_x is the concentration of the substance in the plasma; U_x is the concentration of the substance in the urine; and $\dot{V}_u$ is the volume of urine that is formed in a unit of time.

substance filtered in a unit of time is the product of the GFR and the concentration of the substance in the plasma. As the filtrate flows along the tubule, tubular secretion may add more of the substance to the filtrate, tubular reabsorption may remove some or all of the substance from the filtrate, or the substance may be both secreted and reabsorbed in different areas of the tubule. When the amount excreted equals the amount filtered, none of the substance is transported by the tubules (Figure 37-7A), and the clearance of the substance measures the GFR (e.g., C_{in}). When the amount excreted is less than the amount filtered, net tubular reabsorption has occurred, and the clearance of the substance is less than C_{in} (e.g., $C_{glucose}$) (Figure 37-7B). When the amount excreted is greater than the amount filtered, net tubular secretion has occurred, and the clearance of the substance is greater than C_{in} (e.g., C_{PAH}) (Figure 37-7C). Therefore, the quantitative aspects of renal tubular transport can be deduced from the amounts of the substances filtered and excreted in the urine.

Advantages and Limitations of the Clearance Method

The clearance method has several advantages: it is technically and analytically easy, it does not require altering the physiological state of the individual (e.g., by anesthesia, surgery, or manipulation of the kidneys), it is safe because it can be continued for prolonged periods and repeated in the same individual, it is relatively noninvasive, it can be used in humans, and it provides information about the function of the kidney as a whole.

The clearance method has limitations: it gives only indirect information that reflects the overall behavior of the entire population of nephrons, and it does not detect variation among nephrons; it cannot separate the reabsorption or secretion of substances that undergo both processes, although it indicates the direction of net transport; it does not localize the functions of specific segments of the nephron; and it cannot define the transport mechanisms that are involved.

STUDY OUTLINE

REGULATORY FUNCTIONS OF THE KIDNEY Important organ in homeostatic control of internal environment of body; stabilizes volume and chemical composition of body fluids.

PROCESSES IN RENAL FUNCTION

GLOMERULAR FILTRATION Ultrafiltrate of plasma is formed; about one-fifth of total renal plasma flow is involved.

TUBULAR REABSORPTION AND SECRETION Composition of ultrafiltrate is altered.

REABSORPTION Solutes and water from tubular lumen move into interstitium of peritubular blood.
    Substances needed by body are reabsorbed—about 99% of ultrafiltrate.

SECRETION Substances from peritubular blood, interstitium, or tubular epithelial cells move into tubular lumen.
    Secretion supplements process of filtration.
    Eliminates excess K^+, H^+, and other substances not needed by body.

CLEARANCE

GENERAL PRINCIPLE   Dilution principle; calculated by formula

$$C_y = \frac{U_y \times \dot{V}_u}{P_y}$$

Volume of plasma necessary to supply quantity of substance that appears in urine during a unit of time (ml/min).

USES OF CLEARANCE   Determine glomerular filtration rate, net secretion or absorption by renal tubular cells, and renal plasma flow.

ESTIMATION OF GLOMERULAR FILTRATION RATE (GFR)   Indicator substance filtered freely at glomeruli and neither reabsorbed nor secreted.
    Amount filtered increases with plasma concentration; clearance is constant.
    INULIN AND POLYFRUCTOSAN   Used to measure GFR.

CREATININE Endogenous substance; convenient, clearance about the same as inulin.

Can be used to measure GFR in normal subject.

Overestimates GFR in renal failure.

CLEARANCE OF SUBSTANCES SECRETED OR REABSORBED
PAH—secreted; clearance exceeds that of inulin, decreases as P_{PAH} increases; secretory system becomes saturated.

Glucose—reabsorbed; clearance less than that of inulin, increases as $P_{glucose}$ increases; reabsorptive process becomes saturated.

ESTIMATION OF RENAL PLASMA FLOW
Indicator substance is completely extracted from renal blood—clearance equals renal plasma flow.

No substance is cleared completely, but PAH and iodopyarcet (Diodrast) measure effective renal plasma flow (perfusion of active tissue).

ESTIMATION OF RENAL TUBULAR FUNCTION
Clearance equals GFR when amount of substance excreted equals amount of substance filtered (e.g., C_{in}).

Clearance $> C_{in}$ indicates net tubular secretion.

Clearance $< C_{in}$ indicates net tubular reabsorption.

ADVANTAGES AND LIMITATIONS OF THE CLEARANCE METHOD
Advantages—technically easy, no alteration of physiological state, safe, relatively noninvasive.

Limitations—provides information about total nephron population but not about individual nephrons; transport mechanisms and functions of specific segments of nephron are not defined.

BIBLIOGRAPHY

Levinsky, N.G., and Levy, M. 1973. Clearance techniques. In *Handbook of Physiology*. Section 8. Renal Physiology. Chapter 4. Edited by J. Orloff and R.W. Berliner. Washington, D.C.: American Physiological Society.

Pitts, R.F. 1974. *Physiology of the Kidney and Body Fluids* (3rd ed.). Chapters 3, 5, and 9. Chicago: Year Book.

Smith, H.W. 1951. *The Kidney: Structure and Function in Health and Disease*. New York: Oxford University Press.

Smith, H.W. 1956. *Principles of Renal Physiology*. New York: Oxford University Press.

38

Functional Anatomy of the Kidney

CHAPTER CONTENTS

GROSS ANATOMY

The major gross anatomical features of the human kidneys are illustrated in Figure 38-1; note in particular the distinction between the outer, or cortical, substance, which contains the renal corpuscles, and the inner, or medullary, substance, which consists of 8 to 10 renal papillae. The renal papillae are pyramidal in shape and contain the tubular portions of the nephrons. The spaces between the medullary pyramids are filled with parenchymal tissue.

GROSS VASCULAR SUPPLY

Each human kidney is supplied with blood by a single renal artery that branches from the abdominal aorta (Figure 38-2). The renal artery enters the kidney alongside the ureter and branches progressively into the interlobar arteries, the arcuate arteries, and the interlobular arteries. The interlobar arteries course between the papillae, or medullary pyramids, and the arcuate arteries arch over the bases of the

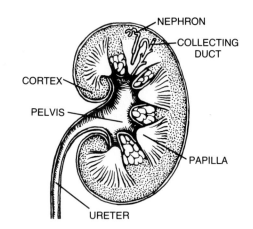

Figure 38-1. Longitudinal section of the kidney. An enlarged nephron and collecting duct are superimposed to show the spatial arrangement. The nephrons lie in the outer, or cortical, region and the inner, or medullary, region. The medulla also contains 8 to 10 renal papillae and parenchymal cells between the papillae. The collecting ducts drain into the papillary ducts, which, in turn, drain into the minor calix, the major calix, the renal pelvis, and, finally, via the ureter to the urinary bladder.

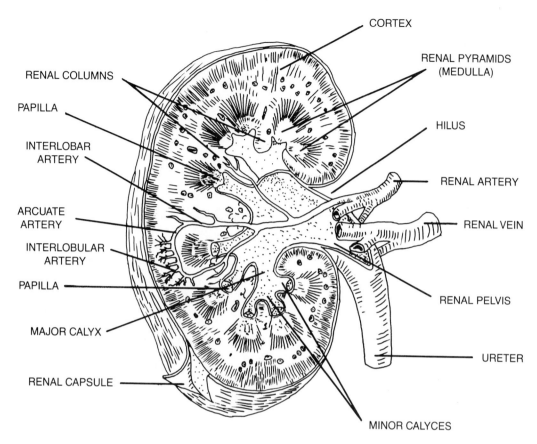

Figure 38-2.   Longitudinal section of a kidney illustrating its internal structure.

medullary pyramids. The interlobular arteries perfuse the cortical region and supply the afferent arterioles that lead to the glomerular capillaries. The pattern of the major venous drainage of the kidneys parallels that of the arterial supply. The interlobular veins, which empty into the arcuate veins, drain the capillaries and venules from the cortical region and the ascending vasa recta from the medullary region. The arcuate veins empty into the interlobar veins, which course between the medullary pyramids and then assemble to form the renal vein, which drains into the vena cava.

NEPHRON

General Arrangement

The nephron is the functional unit of the kidneys, and each human kidney contains approximately 1 million nephrons. All of the nephrons are similar in structure and probably

are grossly similar in function because each is able to carry out the processes of filtration, absorption, and secretion. Each nephron consists of a renal (or malpighian) corpuscle, a proximal convoluted tubule, a proximal straight tubule, a thin descending limb of the loop of Henle, a thin ascending limb of the loop of Henle, a thick ascending limb of the loop of Henle, a distal convoluted tubule, and a collecting duct (Figure 38-3).

Types of Nephrons

Nephrons can be categorized roughly into two general populations, the cortical and the juxtamedullary, depending on where they are located in the kidneys. In humans, 85% of the nephron population are cortical nephrons, while the remaining 15% are juxtamedullary nephrons. The principal anatomical difference between the cortical nephron and the juxtamedullary nephron is the length of the loop of Henle.

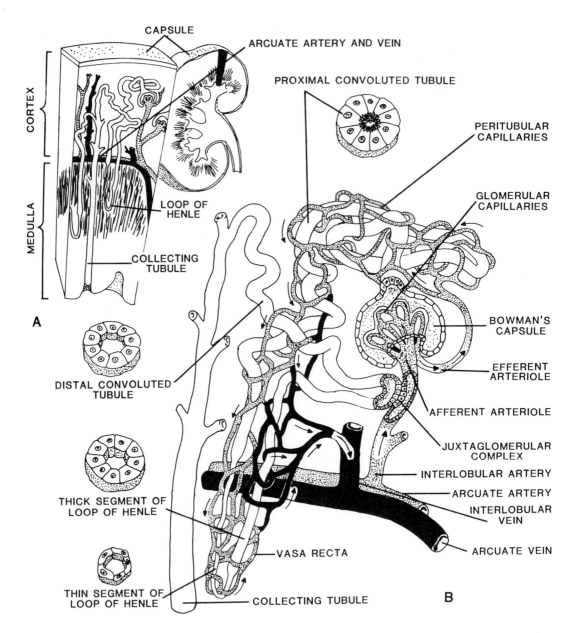

Figure 38-3.   The nephron. **A.** Longitudinal section of a kidney showing the location of the nephrons. **B.** Enlargement of a nephron and its blood supply. The cross-sections illustrate the types of cells that are characteristic of each region of the nephron. The arrows indicate the general direction of the blood flow.

CORTICAL NEPHRONS

The renal corpuscles of the cortical nephrons are situated in the cortex and are connected to relatively short loops of Henle. Some of these nephrons lie entirely within the cortex, and the loops have no thin segments, while the loops of other nephrons penetrate the outer zone of the medulla to varying depths and generally have short thin-segments.

JUXTAMEDULLARY NEPHRONS

The renal corpuscles of the juxtamedullary nephrons lie in the deeper region of the cortex and have longer loops of Henle than the cortical nephrons do; the extra length is contributed by the thin-walled segments of the descending and ascending limbs of the loop of Henle. The thin segments of the juxtamedullary nephrons extend into the inner medullary region to varying depths, and some of the thin segments extend to the tips of the papillae. Loops of all lengths between the extremes also are found in human kidneys. In most mammals, the width of the renal medulla relative to that of the cortex, hence the length of the long-looped nephron, correlates well with the maximum concentration of the urine that can be produced.

Renal Corpuscle

To consider the nephron unit, it is logical to begin with the renal corpuscle. The renal corpuscle consists of a tuft of capillaries called the *glomerulus*, which receives its blood supply from the afferent arteriole, and Bowman's capsule, which is an expanded blind end of the uriniferous tubule. The production of urine begins in this portion of the nephron as an ultrafiltrate of plasma is formed—about 20% of the plasma that enters the kidneys passes through the glomerular membrane into Bowman's capsule. In mammals, the filtering membrane consists of three major layers (Figure 38-4): (1) a layer of capillary endothelium, (2) a basement membrane, and (3) a layer of specialized epithelial cells, which is a contin-

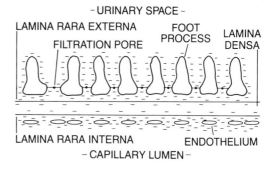

Figure 38-5. The glomerular capillary wall, showing the distribution of polyanionic substances (−) in the glomerular extracellular matrix.

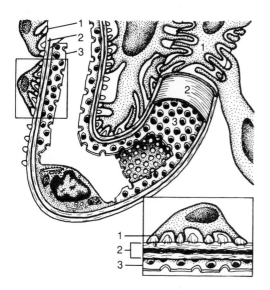

Figure 38-4. Diagram of the structure of a glomerular capillary as revealed by the electron microscope. **1.** Epithelial cells of the capsule. **2.** Basement membrane. **3.** Capillary endothelium. (Redrawn, with permission, from Pease, D.E. 1955. Fine structures of the kidney seen by electron microscopy and cytochemistry. *J. Histochem. Cytochem.* 3:297. © 1955. The Williams & Wilkins Co., Baltimore.)

uation of the parietal cells that line Bowman's capsule.

The capillary endothelium is interrupted by numerous fenestrations, or pores, 50–100 nm in diameter, and the cell surface is covered by a polyanionic coating that is up to 12 nm thick (Figure 38-5). The epithelial cells of Bowman's capsule do not form a continuous sheath in the region of the glomerular capillaries, but are characterized by a large number of *foot processes* that project from the body of the cell and contact the basement membrane. These cells, called *podocytes*, branch freely and their foot processes interdigitate with each other. Adjacent foot processes are separated by filtration slits, or *slit pores,* which are 20–30 nm wide. The spaces between the foot processes are filled by the polyanionic epithelial cell coating. The basement membrane is composed of fibrillar material packed into a dense network—the lamina densa—and two peripheral, less dense laminae rarae—the lamina rara interna, in which the endothelial cells are embedded, and the lamina rara externa, in which the epithelial cells are embedded. Both laminae rarae stain with polycationic reagents, which indicates that they contain polyanionic radicals. Calculations based on the behavior of substances of different size at the basement membrane indicate that most of the channels within this membrane have radii between 0.4 and 4.8 nm.

Experiments have shown that macromolecules cross the glomerular filtering membrane through extracellular pathways that include the endothelial fenestrae, the basement membrane, and the slit pores. Because most of the channels within the basement membrane have radii less than 4.8 nm, particles larger than about 4.5 nm, which corresponds to a molecu-

CLINICAL CORRELATION

38.1   Nephrotic Syndrome Caused by Lipoid Nephrosis

CASE REPORT

The Patient: A 46-year-old man.

Principal Complaint: Decreased urine production (renal failure).

History: The patient had been well until 10 days before admission, when he had had a brief episode of fever and sore throat followed by swelling of the feet and ankles. The output of urine decreased to less than 400 ml/day. He reported no previous significant illness, and no one else in his family had had renal disease.

Clinical Examination: The patient had a pasty appearance, with pale, puffy skin. The body temperature was normal, the heart rate was 88/min (normal, 60–100/min), and the arterial pressure was 145/80 mm Hg (normal, 90–140/60–90 mm Hg). The heart was not enlarged, the chest was clear by percussion, and the abdomen was normal. Peripheral edema was severe, but soft and pitting (the skin can be indented temporarily by compression with the fingertips). The specific gravity of the urine was 1.02, and the concentration of protein was > 1 g/dl. The urinary sediment* contained 2 white cells, 13 red cells, 1 hyaline cast, and 2 cellular casts per high-power field (normal, no more than 1–2 white cells, 1–2 red cells, and 1–2 epithelial cells per high-power field, and only an occasional hyaline cast per low-power field). The hematocrit was 39% (normal, 45%–52%), the leukocyte count was 13,000 cells/mm³ (normal, 4300–10,800 cells/mm³) with normal differential (distribution of cell types), the sedimentation rate** was 115 mm/hr (normal, 0–9 mm/hr), and coagulation was normal. The serum cholesterol was 293 mg/dl (normal, 120–220 mg/dl), and the serum triglyceride was 248 mg/dl (normal, 40–150 mg/dl). An open-renal-biopsy*** specimen (cortical) was taken and examined. Light microscopy revealed slight increases in the mesangial matrix (the suspensory system that

supports the capillary loops of the glomeruli), but no other significant changes. Diffuse interstitial edema was indicated by separation of tubules, but no evidence of tubular damage was seen. Immunofluorescence microscopy disclosed no evidence of immunological injury, and no immunoglobulins or complement (see Chapter 25, "Humoral Immunity") were found in peripheral capillary loops. Studies with the electron microscope revealed no tubular abnormalities, but in the glomeruli, the epithelial foot processes were largely destroyed, and the cytoplasm of the epithelial cells contained vacuoles and surface villi. These findings support the diagnosis of lipoid nephrosis, or minimal change disease.

Comment: The only identifiable lesion of minimal change disease is the loss of the polyanionic material that makes up the glomerular foot-processes. In the absence of the normal negative charge on the basement membrane, the rate of filtration of the anionic plasma proteins, mainly albumin, increases greatly. The cause of the destruction of the foot-process is not known.

The functional deficiency in minimal change disease is the filtration and excretion of plasma proteins, mainly albumin. The decreased concentration of plasma protein decreases the plasma oncotic pressure, which normally balances the capillary hydrostatic pressure, and intravascular fluid moves into the interstitial fluid compartment (edema forms), particularly in the feet, legs, and abdomen. The plasma volume is decreased, and the body reacts to conserve the extracellular fluid volume. Because of the decreased blood volume, systemic arterial pressure tends to decrease, and reflexly mediated sympathetic nervous system activity decreases renal blood flow by constricting the afferent arterioles. The decreased blood volume is sensed by volume receptors, primarily in the atria, which cause the release of antidiuretic hormone (ADH) by the neurohypophysis, and the kidney reabsorbs water more avidly (see Chapter

41). The decreased renal blood flow is sensed by baroreceptors in the kidney, in the juxtaglomerular apparatus (see Chapter 38), and renin is released, activating the renin-angiotensin-aldosterone system. Renin also is released by direct sympathetic nervous system input to the kidney. Aldosterone increases the reabsorption of Na^+ by the distal renal tubules (see Chapter 40). The result of all of these responses to decreased plasma volume is decreased formation of urine. If the rate of formation is too low, metabolic products accumulate (for example, urea (BUN) and creatinine). The decreased excretion of urine also may be caused in part by intrarenal edema, which compresses the renal tubules, increases the pressure in Bowman's capsule, and decreases the glomerular filtration rate (GFR).

Treatment: The patient was placed on a diet low in sodium, to avoid increasing the edema further, and high in protein, to assure maximum production of plasma proteins by the liver. Care was taken to provide adequate total calories, so that the protein would not be used for energy (see Chapter 69, "Caloric Intake and Protein Use"). Furosemide, a diuretic agent, was given orally, 80 mg a day initially, and the dose was increased until a satisfactory diuretic response was obtained with 300 mg/day, given in 2 equal doses 12 hours apart. Care was taken not to decrease

the blood volume and thus to produce acute renal failure. Prednisone, a synthetic corticosteroid, was given in a dose of 1 mg/kg (body weight)/day, in a single dose. Although the treatment is empirical, corticosteroids have been shown to aid remission in this disease.

Outcome: Drug and dietary therapy was continued for four weeks, at which time the proteinemia diminished, and the diuretic was discontinued. The special diet was continued for two additional weeks. The dose of prednisone was decreased exponentially, to permit resumption of normal ACTH control, which had been suppressed by the administered corticosteroid (see Chapter 60, "Secretion of ACTH").

*A 15 ml sample of urine is centrifuged and the supernatant is discarded. The sediment is resuspended in the small amount of urine remaining and examined under a light microscope.

**A sample of blood is anticoagulated with sodium citrate (chelates Ca^{++} essential to coagulation—see Chapter 26, "Coagulation Phase"), drawn up into a special calibrated tube, and allowed to stand for one hour. The rate at which the red cells settle toward the bottom depends mostly on the concentration of fibrin in the serum, and to a smaller extent on the concentration of globulins.

***The kidney is visualized through a small incision.

lar weight of about 90,000 daltons, are not filtered. The transglomerular passage of macromolecules also is affected by electrical charges on the particles. Because the endothelial cell coat, the epithelial cell coat, and the laminae rarae of the basement membrane all are polyanionic in nature, positively charged macromolecules filter more readily than negatively charged macromolecules. Since plasma albumin, the smallest plasma protein, has a molecular weight of 69,000 daltons and is anionic at the pH of blood (7.4), it is filtered to a limited extent; however, the plasma globulins are not filtered, because their molecular weights are more than 90,000 daltons. Therefore, the glomerular membrane prevents the filtration of all substances that have molecular weights equal to or greater than those of the plasma

globulins; however, because of the great number of fenestrae and slit pores, fluid and substances of small molecular weight move rapidly from the plasma into Bowman's capsule.

The renal corpuscle also contains mesangial cells, which, with the surrounding matrix material, form the mesangium of the glomerulus. The mesangial cells are believed to phagocytize the immune complexes that enter the mesangium in various forms of glomerulonephritis (see Chapter 44).

Proximal Tubule

The next portion of the nephron is the proximal tubule, which is composed of a single layer of epithelial cells. On the basis of gross and macroscopic anatomical features, the proximal tubule is divided into two regions: the convoluted part and the straight part. The convoluted part coils extensively in the neighborhood of the parent renal corpuscle before the straight part descends in the medullary ray toward the medulla. Morphologically, the proximal tubules of mammals consist of at least three anatomically distinct segments (S_1, S_2, and S_3) that do not conform to the division of the proximal tubule into the convoluted part and the straight part. In the superficial nephrons of the rat, the S_1 segment is in the early convoluted part, the S_2 segment includes the more distal portions of the convoluted part and about half of the straight part, and the S_3 segment encompasses the remainder of the straight part to its transition into the thin descending limb of the loop of Henle.

Figure 38-6 shows schematically the general morphological features of the tubular cells. These cells have a high rate of metabolism and can absorb large quantities of solutes from the glomerular filtrate. The tubular cells contain a dense population of mitochondria to support the active transport that occurs in this region.

The luminal surface of the cells is covered with numerous cytoplasmic filaments, forming the *brush border* that greatly increases the absorptive area. In addition, the membranes of these cells enfold extensively at the basal aspect to form a labyrinth of basal channels, and these, together with the apical and basal lateral processes that interdigitate with adjacent cells, form a complex extracellular compartment known as the *basolateral intercellular space*.

Marked structural differences can be observed among the three different cell types. Cells of S_1 are taller and contain more mitochondria; the lateral interdigitations with adjacent cells and the invaginations of the basal membrane are more extensive than in either S_1 or S_2 cells. Cells of S_3 are cuboidal and have the fewest mitochondria and lateral interdigitations. The brush border is developed more extensively in S_3 cells than in either S_1 or S_2 cells.

The fluid in the intercellular space is separated from that in the tubular lumen by the *tight junction*, which acts as a seal between adjacent cells. The tightness of this seal between

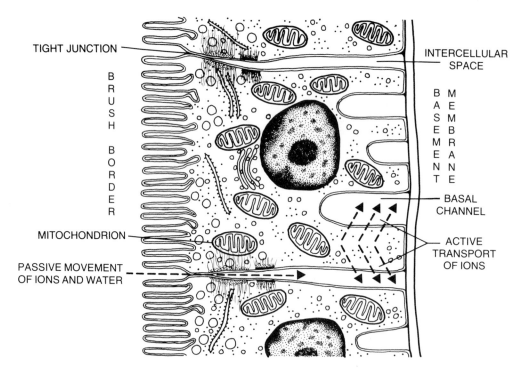

Figure 38-6. A proximal tubular cell, showing the structural features of a transporting epithelial cell. Note the numerous microvilli that form the brush border along the luminal edge, the dense population of mitochondria, and the basolateral intercellular space. The intercellular tight junction appears to be "leaky" in the proximal tubule; this property allows the rapid transfer of ions and water from the lumen of the tubule into the peritubular capillary.

cells varies considerably along the length of the renal tubule; the junction is relatively permeable to ions (or "leaky") in the proximal tubules and is virtually impermeable in the distal tubules, especially in the collecting ducts. The importance of the permeability of these junctions is discussed in Chapter 40.

Structure and function are correlated in the proximal tubule. The brush border, high density of mitochondria, Na^+, K^+-ATPase activity in the basal membrane, leaky junctions, and extensive basolateral intercellular spaces are consistent with the absorption of isosmotic fluid and the maximal transport of glucose, amino acids, and inorganic phosphates in the straight part, which corresponds to segment S_1. In addition, the apical region of the cells in the convoluted part contains a highly developed endocytic apparatus, which is consistent with the reabsorption of filtered proteins by pinocytosis. The basement membrane in the proximal tubule appears to be similar to that in the glomerulus, which may explain why substances that are filtered at the glomerulus can pass freely through the basement membrane.

Thin Limb of the Loop of Henle

The transition from the straight part of the tubule to the thin limb of the loop of Henle marks the boundary between the outer and inner stripes of the outer zone of the medulla. The descending thin limb penetrates the medulla to varying depth, makes a hairpin turn, and continues as the ascending thin limb before making its transition into the thick limb. The cells of both the descending and ascending thin limbs form a low-lying squamous epithelium, flattened and thin except in the nuclear region, which bulges out into the tubular lumen. These cells contain only a few small mitochondria and do not possess a brush border. Morphologically, the thin limbs are adapted for simple diffusion of solutes through their walls, and it seems unlikely that they participate in the active transport of solutes. The permeabilities of the descending and ascending thin limbs to solutes and water are different. The descending thin limb is highly permeable to water but is relatively impermeable to solutes, while the ascending thin limb is relatively impermeable to water but is permeable to solutes. These different physiological characteristics cannot be explained on the basis of any obvious morphological features.

Distal Tubule

The distal tubule is made up of the ascending thick limb of the loop of Henle (or straight part of the distal tubule) and the distal convoluted tubule. The transition of the thin limb to the thick limb occurs at the tip of the loop just before the hairpin turn in nephrons that have short loops of Henle, and at the region between the inner zone and the outer zone of the medulla in nephrons that have long loops of Henle. In the cortical region of the kidney, the ascending thick limb of the nephron passes close to the glomerulus from which the proximal tubule originates. In this region, the epithelial cells of the distal tubule are columnar, are packed more densely than the other distal tubular cells, and are collectively called the *macula densa*. The cells of the straight part and the convoluted part of the distal tubule are cuboidal and differ from the epithelial cells of the proximal tubules in morphological characteristics. In the distal epithelial cells, the mitochondria generally are packed less densely than those in the proximal tubule, the luminal surface of the cells has only a rudimentary brush border, and the basal labyrinth branches less copiously.

The straight part and the convoluted part of the distal tubule contain distinct cell types. Smooth-surfaced S cells that are largely devoid of microvilli predominate in the medullary segment, and R cells predominate in the cortical segment of the straight part. Indirect evidence suggests that the two different cell types have different functional properties; for example, the R cells are sensitive to the action of the thiazide diuretics but the S cells are not.

A major function of the ascending thick limb of the loop of Henle is to create a dilute tubular fluid by transporting Na^+ and Cl^- out of the lumen. Morphological data relating to water permeability in this segment are incomplete; however, experimental data suggest that the tight junction between cells is extremely impermeable to water. The distal convoluted tubule is morphologically similar to the ascending thick limb of the loop of Henle, but the tight junctions permit the movement of both solutes and water.

Collecting Duct

The collecting duct is not merely a conduit because it also modifies the composition and volume of the tubular fluid. The collecting duct includes the cortical collecting segment, the outer medullary segment, and the inner medullary segment—the latter segment terminates at the papillary duct. The cells of this part of the nephron are cuboidal to columnar, with luminal and basal surfaces and a paucity of mitochondria. The tight junction between the cells virtually is impermeable to ions.

The permeabilities of the different segments of the collecting duct to urea differ; the cortical segment is impermeable, but the medullary segment is very permeable. Because of these differences, the collecting duct functions in the countercurrent system for concentrating urine in mammalian kidneys by its effect on the cycling of urea (see Chapter 41).

The permeability of the cells in this region to water is controlled by antidiuretic hormone (ADH). In the presence of ADH, the permeability to water is increased, more water is absorbed from the tubular fluid, and a concentrated urine is excreted. In the absence of ADH, less water is absorbed, and a relatively dilute urine is excreted (see Chapter 41).

VASCULAR SUPPLIES OF NEPHRONS

The *afferent arteriole* breaks up into a capillary network within the renal corpuscle (the glomerulus), where plasma is filtered. The glomerular capillaries reunite to form the *efferent arteriole*. The blood supplies to the two types of nephrons, cortical and juxtamedullary, differ in several respects.

Cortical Nephrons

In the cortical nephrons, the efferent arteriole divides immediately into a rich, freely anastomosing network of capillaries that envelops the convolutions of the proximal and distal tubules, the cortical reaches of the straight part of both the proximal and distal tubules, and the collecting ducts. The capillary net that is derived from one glomerulus communicates freely with the capillary net of the adjacent nephrons; therefore, the blood that flows through one glomerulus is associated with the tubules of several nephrons. These peritubular networks of capillaries recombine into venules that enter the interlobular veins.

Juxtamedullary Nephrons

The vascular supply of the juxtamedullary nephrons is more complex than that of the cortical nephrons. Shortly after it leaves the renal corpuscle, the efferent arteriole gives off one or more side branches to supply a capillary net that envelops the cortical convolutions of the proximal and distal tubules; this capillary net is analogous to that of the cortical nephrons. Further along, the descending efferent arteriole branches repeatedly to form straight-bore tubes (vasa recta) that follow the descending limbs of the loop of Henle through the medullary region, turn at the bend of the loop, and ultimately reassemble into a venule that enters an interlobular vein close to its junction with an arcuate vein. This arrangement of the descending and ascending limbs of the vasa recta in a hairpin loop is a unique feature of the medullary blood supply, and it permits the vessels to function as countercurrent exchangers in the system that concentrates the urine (see Chapter 41).

JUXTAGLOMERULAR APPARATUS

The juxtaglomerular apparatus of the kidney consists of a vascular component and a tubular component (Figures 38-7 and 38-8). The vascular component includes the terminal portion of the afferent arteriole just before it enters the

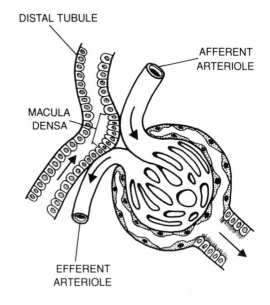

Figure 38-7. The juxtaglomerular apparatus. (Redrawn, with permission, from Deetjen, P., et al. 1975. *Physiology of the Kidney and of Water Balance.* New York: Springer-Verlag.)

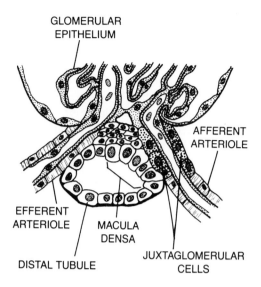

GLOMERULAR
EPITHELIUM

AFFERENT
ARTERIOLE

EFFERENT
ARTERIOLE   MACULA
DENSA

DISTAL TUBULE   JUXTAGLOMERULAR
CELLS

Figure 38-8. The juxtaglomerular apparatus. (Redrawn, with permission, from Guyton, A.C. 1981. *Textbook of Medical Physiology.* 6th ed. Philadelphia: W.B. Saunders Co.)

glomerulus, and the tubular component consists of the macula densa region of the distal tubule (see page 563). The extraglomerular mesangial region adjacent to the macula densa, also known as the *polkissen* (polar cushion), consists mostly of agranular cells. The smooth muscle cells of the afferent arterioles that lie close to the macula densa, known as juxtaglomerular cells, differ from the other smooth muscle cells of the arterioles in that they are swollen and contain heavy granules composed mainly of renin or its precursor, prorenin. Although the nature of the relationship between the vascular components and the tubular components of the juxtaglomerular apparatus is unclear, physiologists agree that the juxtaglomerular apparatus is a major anatomical component of the renin-angiotensin-aldosterone hormonal system (see Chapter 42).

RENAL INTERSTITIAL CELLS

In general, the magnitude of the interstitial space and the number of interstitial cells increase from the cortical to the papillary region of the kidneys. Because the functional characteristics of most of the interstitial cells are not known, only one type of medullary interstitial cell will be mentioned here. These cells, which are most abundant in the inner medullary region, often are stellate in shape and contain lipid droplets composed largely of both saturated and unsaturated fatty acids. These lipid droplets contain precursors of prostaglandins, mainly arachidonic acid and the endoperoxide PGG_2, and may be involved in the renal synthesis of prostaglandins.

STUDY OUTLINE

GROSS ANATOMY Kidney composed of outer cortical substance (contains mostly glomeruli) and inner medullary substance (contains tubular portions of nephrons).

GROSS VASCULAR SUPPLY Blood flows through renal, interlobar, arcuate, and interlobular arteries; afferent arterioles; glomerular capillaries; vasa recta; and interlobular, arcuate, interlobar, and renal veins.

NEPHRON

GENERAL ARRANGEMENT Functional unit of kidney.

Performs filtration, reabsorption, and excretion.

Consists of renal corpuscle, proximal tubule, loop of Henle, distal tubule, and collecting duct.

TYPES OF NEPHRONS Eighty-five percent are cortical, 15% are juxtamedullary; main difference is length of loop of Henle.

CORTICAL NEPHRONS Renal corpuscles are located in cortex; short loop of Henle, thin limb short or absent.

JUXTAMEDULLARY NEPHRONS Renal corpuscles lie in deeper region of cortex.

Long loop of Henle; descends into medulla, lengths vary.

Length correlates with ability to concentrate urine.

RENAL CORPUSCLE Consists of glomerulus and Bowman's capsule.

Filtering membrane consists of capillary endothelium, basement membrane, and podocytes.

Functional pores pass ions and small molecules but retain most of plasma proteins.

Polyanionic material coats cells and comprises basement membrane—aids retention of (anionic) plasma proteins.

PROXIMAL TUBULE   Grossly divided into convoluted part and straight part.

Based on morphology of cells, divided into segments S_1, S_2, and S_3.

Highly metabolic epithelial cells are adapted for active absorption of most solutes.

Accounts for 65%–80% of total reabsorption; 65%–80% of total secretion.

Brush border increases surface area for reabsorption.

Tight junction between adjacent cells; "leaky" to ions and water.

THIN LIMB OF LOOP OF HENLE   Descending and ascending limbs are arranged in form of hairpin loops.

Adapted for simple diffusion of solutes.

Descending thin limb is permeable to water.

Ascending thin limb is relatively impermeable to water but is permeable to solutes.

No obvious morphological basis for these differences of permeability.

DISTAL TUBULE   Epithelial cells are less metabolic than proximal tubular cells on morphological basis.

Ascending thick limb passes close to glomerulus of origin; packed, columnar cells form macula densa.

Urine is diluted in ascending thick limb by transport of Na^+ and Cl^- out of lumen; tight junctions are impermeable to water.

Movement of water and solutes is permitted in distal convoluted part.

COLLECTING DUCT   Tight junctions between adjacent cells are impermeable to ions.

Cortical segment is impermeable to urea; medullary segment is permeable.

Permeability to water is controlled by antidiuretic hormone (ADH)—concentrated urine is secreted in presence of ADH; dilute urine is secreted in absence of ADH.

VASCULAR SUPPLIES OF NEPHRONS Afferent arteriole breaks up into glomerular capillaries that reunite to form efferent arteriole.

CORTICAL NEPHRONS   Efferent arteriole divides into peritubular capillary network, recombines into venule that drains into interlobular vein.

Capillaries of one nephron communicate with those of other nephrons.

JUXTAMEDULLARY NEPHRONS   Efferent arteriole branches into peritubular capillary network, as in cortical nephrons; also branches into *vasa recta* that penetrate medullary region as hairpin loops and function as countercurrent exchangers; reunite into venules that drain into interlobular veins.

JUXTAGLOMERULAR APPARATUS Interposition of afferent arteriole and distal tubule at macula densa—part of renin-angiotensin-aldosterone system.

Juxtaglomerular cells—modified smooth muscle cells of afferent arteriole that contain renin precursor.

Macula densa cells—modified epithelial cells of distal tubule.

RENAL INTERSTITIAL CELLS Contain precursors of prostaglandins, may be involved in synthesis of prostaglandins.

BIBLIOGRAPHY

Andrews, P.M., and Porter, K.R. 1974. A scanning electron microscopic study of the nephron. *Am. J. Anat.* 140:81.

Beeuwkes, R., III. 1980. The vascular organization of the kidney. *Annu. Rev. Physiol.* 42:531.

Brenner, B.M. (Chairman). 1977. Functional and structural determinants of glomerular filtration (symposium). *Fed. Proc.* 36:2599.

Deetjen, P.; Boylan, J.W.; and Kramer, K. 1975. *Physiology of the Kidney and of Water Balance*. New York: Springer-Verlag.

Pease, D.C. 1955. Fine structures of the kidney seen by electron microscopy and cytochemistry. *J. Histochem. Cytochem.* 3:295.

Pitts, R.F. 1974. *Physiology of the Kidney and Body Fluids* (3rd ed.). Chapter 1. Chicago: Year Book.

Tisher, C.C. 1976. Anatomy of the kidney. In *The Kidney.* Volume I. Edited by B.M. Brenner and F.C. Rector, Jr. Philadelphia: Saunders.

39

Renal Blood Flow
and
Glomerular Filtration

CHAPTER CONTENTS

GENERAL
CONSIDERATIONS

Renal Fraction

Under resting conditions, the two kidneys in the human receive about 20%–25% of the cardiac output, or about 1000–1200 ml/min, although these organs constitute only about 0.4% of the body weight. As blood flows through the kidneys, its composition is altered by the processes of filtration, tubular reabsorption, and secretion. The portion of the total cardiac output that flows through the kidneys of the resting person—the *renal fraction*—is kept relatively constant, under normal conditions, by intrarenal mechanisms.

Measurement of
Renal Blood Flow

The normal blood flow to the entire kidney and the variations of blood flow that are caused by drugs or other interventions have been studied by both direct and indirect methods. Measuring renal arterial or renal venous blood flow directly would require opening the abdominal cavity, inserting a cannula into the appropriate blood vessel, and collecting a series of blood samples. One of the indirect methods, the use of an arterial flowmeter, also requires opening the abdominal cavity. Because these two methods require anesthesia and surgical procedures, they are not used in humans. Furthermore, these procedures may alter the physiological state of the subject. The indirect method of measuring renal blood flow that is employed most frequently is the clearance technique using substances such as para-aminohippurate (PAH) or iodopyracet (Diodrast).

Distribution of Renal Blood Flow

Blood flows nonuniformly within the kidneys because of different local functional requirements. Under normal circumstances, approximately 95% of the renal blood flows through the cortical region, where filtration and most of the reabsorption and secretion occur, and about 5% of the blood flows through the medulla.

Vascular Properties

The vascular supply to the kidneys is composed of several microcirculations, each of which has specialized properties that are suited for the normal functions of the nephron (see Chapter 38). The glomerular circulation is specialized for the filtration of plasma, the cortical peritubular capillaries are suited for the absorption of solutes and fluid, and the medullary circulation is adapted to perfuse that region without dissipating the osmotic gradient that enables the kidneys to concentrate the urine. Damage to

the vascular supply of any region impairs the normal function of the nephron.

PRESSURES IN THE RENAL CIRCULATION

As the blood flows from the renal artery to the renal vein, it traverses three areas of resistance, which cause the pressure to decrease from an initial value of approximately 95 mm Hg in the arcuate arteries to about 8 mm Hg in the renal vein. Typical pressures in the different parts of the renal circulation are shown in Figure 39-1. The two major areas of resistance to blood flow are the afferent arterioles and the efferent arterioles; normally, the resistances of the two arterioles are adjusted so that the filtration pressure remains approximately constant. The resistance in the afferent arterioles ensures that the glomerular capillaries are protected from fluctuations in the systemic arterial pressure, whereas the resistance in the efferent arterioles supports the pressure in the glomerular capillaries and reduces the pressure in the peritubular capillaries. Because of the resistance in the afferent arterioles, the mean pressure falls from 95 mm Hg in the artery to approximately 60 mm Hg in the glomerular capillaries. The latter pressure has been calculated to be as high

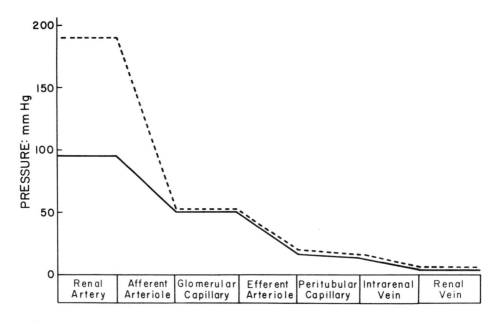

Figure 39-1. Pressure gradients in the renal circulation of the rat. At arterial pressures between about 95 mm Hg (solid line) and 190 mm Hg (dashed line), variation of the resistance of the afferent arterioles keeps the glomerular capillary pressure constant.

as 70 mm Hg in the dog and has been measured as low as 45 mm Hg in the rat. As the blood flows from the glomerular capillaries to the peritubular capillaries through the efferent arterioles, the pressure decreases to a mean of 10 mm Hg. The difference between the hydrostatic pressures of the two capillary beds accounts for the different directions of net fluid movement; that is, filtration from the high-pressure glomerular capillaries and reabsorption into the low-pressure peritubular capillaries. Resistance to blood flow also occurs in the veins distal to the peritubular capillaries—probably the arcuate and interlobar veins. However, the decrease of pressure in these vessels is small as compared to the decreases in the afferent arterioles and the efferent arterioles.

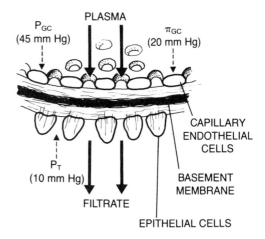

Figure 39-2. Ultrafiltration of plasma from the glomerular capillary into Bowman's space. The filtering membrane is composed of capillary endothelial cells, basement membrane, and epithelial cells of Bowman's capsule. The driving force for ultrafiltration is the hydrostatic pressure in the glomerular capillary (P_{GC}); the opposing forces are the hydrostatic pressure in Bowman's space (P_T) and the oncotic pressure in the glomerular capillary (π_{GC}).

GLOMERULAR CIRCULATION AND GLOMERULAR FILTRATION

Filtration Fraction

As the blood flows through the glomerular capillaries, plasma is filtered through the glomerular membrane and into Bowman's space. If both the renal blood flow and the glomerular filtration rate are measured simultaneously, the fraction of plasma that becomes glomerular filtrate, called the *filtration fraction*, can be calculated. In the normal adult the glomerular filtration rate is about 120 ml/min, and the renal plasma flow is about 700 ml/min; thus, the filtration fraction is 120/700 = 0.17, or 17%. In the normal human the filtration fraction varies between 16% and 20%.

Process of Filtration

NET FILTRATION PRESSURE

Glomerular filtration is a passive process because it does not require the local expenditure of metabolic energy. The net driving force for filtration is the difference between the hydrostatic pressure gradient and the osmotic pressure gradient across the capillary membrane (Figure 39-2). The hydrostatic pressure in the glomerular capillaries is higher than the hydrostatic pressure in other capillary beds because the afferent arterioles, which are located upstream from the glomeruli, are short, straight branches of the interlobular arteries that can transmit a relatively high pressure, and the

efferent arterioles, which are located downstream from the glomeruli, have a relatively high resistance to flow. The capillary hydrostatic pressure of 45–70 mm Hg (actual pressure depends on the species and the methods of measurement) causes fluid to pass through the filtering membrane, whereas the hydrostatic pressure of about 10 mm Hg in Bowman's capsule opposes filtration. The colloidal oncotic pressure gradient across the glomerular membrane also opposes filtration; this pressure gradient is caused by the plasma proteins in the capillaries, which virtually do not cross the glomerular membrane. The net filtration pressure calculated for the rat is shown in Figure 39-3; this figure also shows the calculated change in the net filtration pressure along the course of an idealized glomerular capillary. Studies in the rat reveal that the hydrostatic pressure decreases slightly through the course of the glomerular capillaries, but the plasma colloidal oncotic pressure increases significantly as fluid is filtered and the concentration of the plasma proteins increases. At some point along the glomerular capillary, the gradient of osmotic pressure, which opposes filtration, exactly balances the gradient of hydrostatic pressure, which favors filtration. This equilibrium

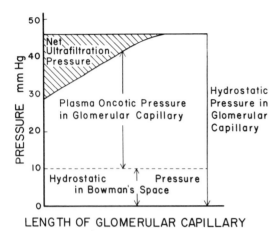

LENGTH OF GLOMERULAR CAPILLARY

Figure 39-3. Net ultrafiltration pressure calculated for the rat along the course of an idealized glomerular capillary. The hydrostatic pressure in the capillary, which favors filtration, remains relatively constant along the length of the capillary. The plasma oncotic pressure, which opposes filtration, increases because of increased protein concentration as ultrafiltration proceeds. The point at which the sum of the hydrostatic pressure in Bowman's space and the plasma oncotic pressure exactly balances the hydrostatic pressure in the glomerular capillary is unknown. If it occurs before the end of the capillary is reached, as shown here, ultrafiltration would not occur over the entire length of the glomerular capillary. (Redrawn, with permission, from Valtin, H. 1983. *Renal Function: Mechanisms Preserving Fluid and Solute Balance in Health.* 2nd ed. Boston: Little, Brown and Co.)

usually occurs before the end of the capillary is reached (Figure 39-3). Thus, the distal portions of the glomerular capillaries normally do not form glomerular filtrate, and a decrease in the rate of rise of oncotic pressure in the plasma alone would increase the rate of filtration because the length of the capillary in which filtration occurs would be increased.

ULTRAFILTRATION
In 1924, Wearn and Richards, using a micropuncture technique, proved that the fluid that enters Bowman's capsule through the glomerular membrane is an ultrafiltrate of plasma. Thus, the glomerular filtrate virtually is free of protein, and the concentrations of dissolved substances of low molecular weight in the glomerular filtrate differ only slightly from the concentrations of these same substances in the plasma water (Table 39-1). Two factors are responsible for this small, but definite, difference of concentration: (1) the binding of weak electrolytes to plasma proteins, and (2) the existence of a Gibbs-Donnan equilibrium (see Chapter 2) across the filtering membrane. As a consequence of the Gibbs-Donnan equilibrium, the concentration of univalent anions is about 5% higher and the concentration of univalent cations is about 5% lower in the glomerular filtrate than in the plasma water. The high permeability of the glomerular filter to water

TABLE 39-1
Ionic composition of plasma and glomerular filtrate
based on the Gibbs-Donnan distribution

Substance	Plasma water (mEq/liter)	Glomerular filtrate (mEq/liter)
Na$^+$	151	144
K$^+$	4.3	4
Ca^{++}	5.4	2.5
Mg^{++}	3.2	1.5
Cation	163.9	152.0
Cl$^-$	109.7	114
HCO$_3^-$	28.7	30
Phosphates	2.1	2.0
SO$_4^=$	1.1	1.0
Organic acid	5.3	5.0
Protein	17	0.0
Anion	163.9	152.0

and small solutes and the almost complete exclusion of albumin and other large plasma proteins from the urinary space can be explained by the structural characteristics of the glomerular filter (see Chapter 38).

EFFECT OF MOLECULAR SIZE

The size of the filtering "channels" in the basement membrane of the glomerulus is an important determinant of the size of the molecules that can be filtered. Table 39-2 shows various substances arranged in the order of their molecular weights and their molecular radii. The rates of filtration of the individual substances relative to that of creatinine, which is as filterable as water, also are shown in Table 39-2. The data reveal that as the radius of the molecule increases, the rate of filtration decreases. Inulin, which has a molecular weight of 5000 daltons, filters as rapidly as creatinine. The rate of filtration of serum albumin, which has a molecular weight of 69,000 daltons and a radius of approximately 3.9 nm, is less than 1% that of creatinine; therefore, the limiting molecular weight for filtration across the membrane is calculated to be between 80,000 and 90,000 daltons, which corresponds to a pore radius of 4–5 nm (see Chapter 38). For practical purposes, the glomerular membrane is almost completely impermeable to all plasma proteins but is highly permeable to essentially all other substances that normally are dissolved in the plasma.

EFFECT OF MOLECULAR CHARGE

The presence of polyanionic glycoproteins in the surface coats of both endothelial and epithelial cells and on the laminae rarae of the basement membrane is important in the transglomerular passage of macromolecules (see Chapter 38). Dextran, which is electrically neutral and has a molecular radius similar to that of albumin, is filtered approximately 100 times as rapidly as albumin. Thus, factors other than molecular size also are responsible for the restricted passage of albumin. Studies using polarized polymers show that cationic molecules penetrate the basement membrane faster than neutral molecules of the same size, and anionic molecules penetrate more slowly. In certain experimental disorders of the glomeruli characterized by proteinuria, the increased glomerular permeability to plasma proteins is caused by a decrease of negative charge in the area of filtration.

Factors That Affect the Glomerular Filtration Rate

The factors that govern filtration through the wall of the glomerular capillaries are the same as those that govern filtration from other capillaries; that is, capillary permeability, the total surface area available for filtration, and the mean net filtration pressure. These factors can be described by the following equation:

TABLE 39-2
Physical properties of molecules and the ability of the molecules to pass through the capillary wall

Substance	Molecular weight (daltons)	Radius of equivalent sphere (nm)	Glomerular filtration relative to creatinine
Water	18	0.06	1.0
Urea	60	0.12	1.0
Glucose	180	0.2	1.0
Inulin	5,000	1.1	1.0
Myoglobin	17,000	1.9	0.75
Egg albumin	43,500	3.1	0.22
Hemoglobin	68,000	3.9	0.03
Serum albumin	69,000	3.9	< 0.01

$$GFR = [k \times S] \times [(P_{GC} - P_T) - (\pi_{GC} - \pi_T)]$$
$$= [k \times S] \times [P_{UF}]$$
$$= [K_f] \times [P_{UF}]$$

where k is the capillary permeability, S is the total capillary surface area, P_{GC} is the hydrostatic pressure in the glomerular capillary, P_T is the hydrostatic pressure in Bowman's capsule, π_{GC} is the oncotic pressure in the glomerular capillary, π_T is the oncotic pressure in Bowman's capsule, P_{UF} is the net filtration pressure, and K_f is the coefficient of filtration. The coefficient of filtration (K_f) is the product of the capillary permeability and the total capillary surface area available for filtration. Both determinants of K_f appear to be significantly higher in the glomerular capillaries than in the systemic capillaries. The equation above shows that the net filtration pressure and the coefficient of filtration determine the GFR.

CHANGES IN COEFFICIENT OF FILTRATION

The coefficient of filtration probably does not change greatly under normal circumstances, but it may be different in diseased kidneys. In many renal disorders, the capillary permeability to proteins is increased, and the plasma proteins are excreted in the urine (*proteinuria*). When larger amounts of albumin escape, the term *albuminuria* is used. In both proteinuria and albuminuria, the rate of formation of urine can be increased by increasing the GFR.

Various renal diseases that destroy the glomeruli, but which may or may not destroy the renal tubules (for example, glomerulonephritis), decrease the total area of the glomerular capillary bed and, hence, the GFR. Certain surgical interventions, such as partial nephrectomy, decrease the same functions.

CHANGES IN NET FILTRATION PRESSURE

The four factors that determine the net filtration pressure—the glomerular capillary pressure, the plasma oncotic pressure, the hydrostatic pressure, and the oncotic pressure in Bowman's capsule—influence the GFR in a predictable manner.

In general, the GFR increases when the P_{GC} (pressure in the glomerular capillary) increases, and decreases when the P_{GC} decreases. Under normal conditions, a slight change in the systemic arterial blood pressure does not affect P_{GC} because of the changes in renal vascular resistance due to autoregulation (see Chapter 16). When the mean systemic arterial pressure decreases slightly, the efferent arterioles constrict more than the afferent arterioles do; thus, the GFR is maintained, even though renal blood flow decreases. When the mean systemic arterial pressure drops to less than about 80 mm Hg, however, autoregulation cannot offset the effects of decreased perfusion pressure, and P_{GC} decreases.

Any change of the pressure in Bowman's capsule affects the GFR. Ureteral obstruction, for example, which increases the pressure in Bowman's capsule, opposes filtration and decreases the GFR. In normal circumstances the concentration of protein in the filtrate is very low, so that the oncotic pressure in Bowman's capsule is negligible. However, when the glomerular permeability is increased in certain disease states, a large amount of plasma protein is filtered, and the concentration of protein in the filtrate increases. The increased oncotic pressure in Bowman's capsule, which decreases net plasma oncotic pressure, increases the GFR.

A change in the concentration of plasma proteins, which changes the plasma oncotic pressure, also affects the GFR. In hypoproteinemia, the plasma oncotic pressure is decreased and the GFR is increased; however, the effects on the GFR of changes of plasma oncotic pressure that occur physiologically are small relative to the effects of changes of hydrostatic pressure.

CHANGES IN BLOOD FLOW

The rate of blood flow through the nephrons affects the GFR because it affects the net colloidal oncotic pressure in the glomerular capillaries. An increase in the rate of flow of plasma decreases the rate of rise of plasma oncotic pressure as filtration proceeds; thus, the point at which filtration stops is moved toward the end of the glomerular capillary, and the area of filtration is increased (see Figure 39-3). Consequently, the GFR increases or decreases with an increase or decrease in the rate of flow of plasma into the glomerulus.

RESISTANCE IN AFFERENT ARTERIOLES AND EFFERENT ARTERIOLES

The GFR is affected by the resistances of the afferent arterioles and the efferent arterioles. Constriction of the afferent arterioles decreases the GFR by decreasing both the rate of flow of plasma into the glomerulus and the pressure in the glomerular capillary. Conversely, dilatation of the afferent arterioles increases both the rate of flow of plasma and the glomerular pressure. Constriction of the efferent arteriole increases the resistance to outflow from the glomeruli, which increases the glomerular capillary pressure and the filtration fraction. The rate of flow of plasma through the glomeruli decreases at the same time, however, and if the efferent arteriole is constricted severely, the GFR decreases despite the higher glomerular capillary pressure.

EFFECTS OF STRESS

Both the renal blood flow and the GFR are affected by stress because the input of the sympathetic nervous system to both the afferent arterioles and the efferent arterioles increases. In general, the renal blood flow is regulated to keep the GFR relatively stable. This regulation involves alterations of the caliber of both the afferent arterioles and the efferent arterioles so as to keep the effective filtration pressure constant. In mild stress the sympathetic nervous system input to the kidneys is slight; however, the afferent arterioles are constricted preferentially, and the renal blood flow is decreased. Because the mean systemic arterial pressure also increases in stress, the decrease in renal blood flow is minimal, with little or no change in the GFR. If the stress is more marked, renal blood flow decreases significantly, but the GFR may remain constant. Accordingly, the filtration fraction increases. In this case both the afferent arterioles and the efferent arterioles are involved, and effective filtration pressure is maintained. In severe stress, however, the sympathetic nervous system input to the kidneys is strong, and renal blood flow and glomerular capillary pressure are reduced to the extent that the GFR falls drastically. In grave emergencies, both renal blood flow and the GFR are sacrificed to assure the perfusion of the heart and the brain (see Chapter 23).

CORTICAL PERITUBULAR CIRCULATION

Tubular reabsorption is a two-stage process that involves the transfer of fluid and solutes from the tubular lumen into the interstitium and the passive uptake of fluid and solutes by the capillaries. Because the proximal tubule reabsorbs isosmotically about 65%–80% of the filtrate and virtually all of the glucose and amino acids, the rate of flow into the interstitium of the cortex is large. This fluid and the smaller volume that is reabsorbed by the distal tubule and the cortical portion of the collecting duct enter the peritubular capillaries of the cortex. The blood pressure in the peritubular capillaries is only 6–10 mm Hg; the interstitial pressure has not been determined directly but probably is small. The colloidal oncotic pressure at the beginning of the peritubular capillary network is about 35 mm Hg; therefore, the net driving force favors reabsorption into the capillaries. The net froce ranges from about 25–30 mm Hg at the beginning of the capillary network to about 10–15 mm Hg at the end because of the decrease in plasma colloidal oncotic pressure as fluid is reabsorbed. Unlike the condition in the glomerular capillaries, hydrostatic pressure and colloidal oncotic pressure do not reach equilibrium in the peritubular capillaries.

Any factors that affect uptake by the peritubular capillaries also affect reabsorption by the tubules. If uptake by the capillaries is impaired, either by an increase in hydrostatic pressure or by a decrease in colloidal oncotic pressure in the capillaries, some of the solutes and water that are reabsorbed by the tubules leak from the interstitium back into the tubular lumen.

MEDULLARY CIRCULATION

The vascular supply to the medulla is structured to meet diverse functional roles, which are to perfuse the medulla and to enhance the renal concentrating mechanism. The outer medullary capillary network, which is derived from the efferent arterioles, surrounds and perfuses the thin descending and thick ascending limbs of the loop of Henle. The blood vessels of the inner medulla form hairpin loops in close apposition to the loops of Henle. The arrangement of these vessels (the vasa recta) (see Figure 38-3) in this fashion, with the blood flowing first in one direction and then in the other, provides the basis for a *countercurrent exchanger system* (see Chapter 41). Such a system can provide metabolic substrates, transport waste products, and remove solutes and water that are reabsorbed from the collecting duct, but still does not interfere with the osmotic gradient set up by the activity of the loop of Henle.

RENAL BLOOD FLOW AND OXYGEN CONSUMPTION

As in other tissues, an important function of the blood flow to the kidneys is to perfuse the cells of the kidneys; however, the rate of blood flow relative to the needs of the tissues is higher in the kidneys than in most other tissues. This high rate of flow is required more to provide the large volume of fluid that is processed than to supply the metabolic demands of the kidneys, because the oxygen and other substrates that are available are not utilized fully. Nevertheless, the metabolic rate of the kidneys is relatively high. A large volume of water and solutes is reabsorbed by the tubular cells, and most of the reabsorptive processes require energy.

Because of the high rate of blood flow in the kidneys relative to the amount of oxygen consumed, the arteriovenous difference is low: 1.7 ml of oxygen/dl of blood compared to the average of 4–6 ml of oxygen/dl of blood in the entire systemic circulation (see Chapter 22).

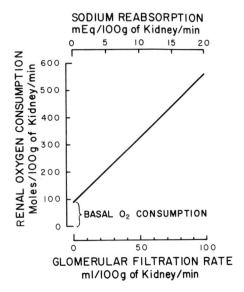

Figure 39-5. Proportionality between the GFR and oxygen consumption: the relationship is linear over the entire range of GFR studied. In the experiment that is illustrated, plasma [Na$^+$] did not change; hence, the rate of filtration of Na$^+$ (GFR $\times$ P$_{Na}$) is directly proportional to the GFR. Because most of the filtered Na$^+$ is reabsorbed, the oxidative energy required to reabsorb Na$^+$ is the factor that determines the renal oxygen consumption. Therefore, renal oxygen consumption is also a linear function of the rate of reabsorption of Na$^+$. When glomerular filtration ceases at very low rates of blood flow, the basal level of oxygen consumption reflects that required to preserve structural integrity. (Redrawn, with permission, from Valtin, H. *Renal Function: Mechanisms Preserving Fluid and Solute Balance in Health.* © 1983. 2nd ed. Boston: Little, Brown and Co.)

The relationship between oxygen consumption and blood flow in the kidneys differs from that in most other organs of the body, and in the whole body, in which the arteriovenous oxygen difference increases as the work load and the rate of perfusion increase (see Chapter 22). When the rate of renal blood flow is between about 200 and 700 ml/100 g/min, the rate of oxygen consumption is proportional to the rate of blood flow, and the arteriovenous oxygen difference is constant (Figure 39-4). This is because the rate at which the kidneys must work is related to the rate of blood flow. The kidneys extract more oxygen from each unit of blood flowing through them only at very low rates of renal blood flow (less than 200 ml/100 g/min).

The factor that determines renal oxygen consumption physiologically is the GFR (Figure 39-5), which establishes the work load of

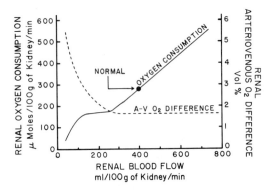

Figure 39-4. Changes in renal oxygen consumption and renal arteriovenous oxygen difference with changes in renal blood flow. The arteriovenous oxygen difference does not change with renal blood flow between 200 and 700 ml/100 g/min, but the oxygen consumption changes with blood flow. At very low rates of blood flow, the rate of oxygen consumption becomes independent of blood flow, and the arteriovenous oxygen difference increases. (Redrawn, with permission, from Valtin, H. *Renal Function: Mechanisms Preserving Fluid and Solute Balance in Health.* © 1983. 2nd ed. Boston: Little, Brown and Co.)

the tubules. If the concentration of Na⁺ in the plasma (P_{Na}) is constant, the rate of filtration of Na⁺ into the tubular system (GFR × P_{Na}) varies directly with the GFR. Under normal circumstances, more than 99% of the filtered Na⁺ is reabsorbed by an active process that depends on energy derived from oxidative metabolism. When the renal blood flow is very low, glomerular filtration ceases; therefore, filtration and reabsorption of Na⁺ also cease. Under these conditions, the renal oxygen consumption reflects only the basal requirements of the renal tissue, which amounts to about one-third of the total oxygen consumption of the normally functioning kidneys.

REGULATION OF RENAL BLOOD FLOW AND GLOMERULAR FILTRATION RATE

In the range of mean renal arterial pressures from 80 to 180 mm Hg, the renal blood flow (RBF) and the GFR in the human remain nearly constant at 1200 ml/min and 120 ml/min, respectively. The relationships between these two variables and renal arterial pressure are illustrated in Figure 39-6.

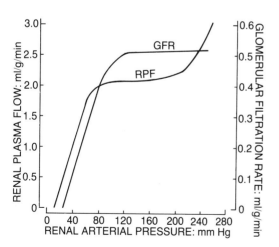

Figure 39-6. Changes in the renal plasma flow (RPF) and the glomerular filtration rate (GFR) with renal arterial pressure. Over a range of 80–200 mm Hg, autoregulatory mechanisms keep the RPF and the GFR relatively constant. (Redrawn, with permission, from Shipley, R.E., et al. 1951. Changes in renal blood flow. *Am. J. Physiol.* 167:682.)

The factors that influence total renal blood flow are given in the following equation:

$$RBF = \frac{\Delta P}{R}$$

where ΔP is the difference of pressure between the renal artery and the renal vein, and R is the renal vascular resistance. The renal vascular resistance can be affected by intrinsic control mechanisms, such as those responsible for the phenomenon of autoregulation (see the following section entitled "Intrinsic Control"), and extrinsic factors, such as the activity of renal nerves and hormones that affect the contraction of vascular smooth muscle (see the section entitled "Extrinsic Control"). The renal vascular resistance is localized at three sites along the vascular network: the afferent arterioles, the efferent arterioles, and the arcuate and interlobar veins.

Intrinsic Control

ARTERIOLAR RESISTANCE

When the arterial pressure fluctuates, the major variable that regulates renal blood flow is the renal vascular resistance. The afferent arteriolar resistance is adjusted so that the renal blood flow remains relatively constant over a wide range of arterial pressures, from about 80 to 180 mm Hg. When the blood pressure is decreased to less than the range of autoregulation, the resistance becomes relatively constant, and the blood flow decreases in proportion to the blood pressure. The venous resistance usually is small and is not altered greatly when the arterial pressure changes.

The autoregulation of vascular resistance also regulates the glomerular capillary pressure. Because the glomerular capillary pressure is one of the factors that determines the GFR, renal autoregulation also controls the GFR. Therefore, the relationship between the renal arterial pressure and the GFR is similar to that between the renal arterial pressure and the renal blood flow (Figure 39-6).

MECHANISMS OF INTRINSIC CONTROL

At least three mechanisms contribute to the autoregulation of the renal blood flow and the GFR: the myogenic component, alterations in the glomerular vascular resistance mediated by angiotensin II, and tubuloglomerular feedback.

The myogenic mechanism involves an in-

CLINICAL CORRELATION
39.1   Polycystic Kidneys and Arterial Hypertension

CASE REPORT

The Patient: A 40-year-old woman.

Principal Complaint: Low back pain.

History: The patient reported pain in the lumbar region, made worse by exertion and eased by lying down. She admitted to having passed reddish-to-brown-tinged urine on occasion.

Clinical Examination: The arterial pressure was 210/140 mm Hg (normal, 90–140/60–90 mm Hg), and the heart rate was 88 beats/min (normal, 60–100 beats/min). Ophthalmological examination revealed contraction of the fundal arteries and sclerosis consistent with the hypertension. The heart was enlarged radiographically, and the electrocardiogram indicated left ventricular hypertrophy (see Chapter 19). The kidneys and the spleen were palpable. Intravenous pyelography (injection of a radio-opaque material and observation of the kidneys by serial x-ray films) revealed greatly enlarged kidneys. The renal pelves were elongated on both sides, and indentions, interpreted to be caused by cysts, were seen. The patient was placed on a low-sodium diet for 3 days and given a diuretic agent (furosemide) 3 times daily.* Plasma renin activity in the inferior vena cava below the kidney, measured in the upright position** after 3 hours of moderate ambulation, was 41 ng/ml/hr*** (normal, 10 ng/ml/hr). Plasma renin activity in the left renal vein was 80 ng/ml/hr, and in the right renal vein was 77 ng/ml/hr. Thus, the diagnosis of hypertension due to a renopressor mechanism, obstruction of renal blood flow by enlarging cysts, was reached.

Treatment: The hypertension was treated with a combination of propranolol (an adrenergic β-receptor blocker), hydrochloro-thiazide (a diuretic agent), and hydralazine (a vascular smooth muscle relaxant). Good control was established, with a typical arterial pressure of 135/80 mm Hg during an office visit. No specific treatment for the cysts is known.

Comment: Polycystic kidney disease is a condition in which normal renal tissue is replaced by multiple cysts of the renal parenchyma. The cysts encroach on the normal tissue and may produce renal ischemia that leads to hypertension through activation of the renin-angiotensin-aldosterone mechanism. The condition is familial, usually appearing during the fourth to sixth decade of life. The principal symptom is lumbar and/or abdominal pain, caused by the weight of the kidneys pulling on the pedicles. Bleeding into the urine also may occur. Hypertension appears in association with renal insufficiency. Survival depends on the rate of progression (growth of the cysts). The average patient's life span is 50–60 years, but individuals may live to a normal age (70 years or more).

Outcome: One year after treatment was begun, the patient's arterial pressure was controlled adequately, but the underlying disease (renal cysts) will progress.

---

*The low-sodium diet combined with the diuretic increases the production of renin, which makes the test more accurate. The increased production is recognized in a higher value for normal plasma renin activity.

**Reflex baroreceptor activity increases sympathetic nervous system input to the kidneys, increasing the release of renin, as part of the adaptation to posture.

***Plasma renin (enzyme) activity is measured by the quantity of angiotensin generated/unit of plasma/unit of time.

herent property of the vascular smooth muscle to contract in response to stretch (see Chapter 16), which causes the afferent arteriole to constrict at high pressure and to dilate at low pressure.

The second mechanism proposes the existence of a stretch receptor in the afferent arteriole. When the blood pressure in the afferent arterioles decreases to less than about 80 mm Hg, in which condition the stretch receptor is not activated, the juxtaglomerular cells secrete renin. Renin acts on angiotensinogen, a plasma globulin, to produce angiotensin I, which is converted to angiotensin II, a vasoconstrictor (see Chapter 21). Angiotensin II increases vascular resistance, particularly in the efferent arterioles. Angiotensin III, an analogue of angiotensin II that contains one less amino acid, also produces effects similar to those of angiotensin II in the kidney but its possible role has not been clarified.

According to the tubuloglomerular feedback theory, a receptor in the macula densa (in the ascending limb of the loop of Henle) senses some correlate of tubular flow in the distal portion of the nephron (possibly the Na^+ load, the Cl^- load, or the total osmolality of the fluid) and sends an appropriate message to the adjacent afferent arterioles and efferent arterioles. The vascular resistance of the arterioles changes as needed to keep the GFR more or less constant. The precise signal to which the macula densa responds is uncertain. The fact that a change in the rate of flow of fluid in the tubular system causes a change in the GFR, and possibly in the renal blood flow, indicates that a feedback mechanism adjusts the GFR to the functional capacity of the tubules. This could be caused either by a predominant increase of resistance in the afferent arteriole (preglomerular site) or by a predominant decrease of resistance in the efferent arteriole (postglomerular site). The former mechanism seems more likely.

It is possible that all of the proposed mechanisms work under the appropriate conditions. The myogenic component probably operates over the entire range of arterial pressures, whereas at arterial pressures less than 80 mm Hg, the GFR is controlled by afferent vasodilatation mediated myogenically and efferent vasoconstriction regulated by angiotensin II. At arterial pressures greater than 80 mm Hg, the GFR is controlled by myogenically mediated afferent vasoconstriction and the tubuloglomerular feedback mechanism.

Extrinsic Control

NEURAL FACTOR

In addition to regulation by an intrinsic, or autoregulatory, mechanism, the renal blood flow also is influenced by the sympathetic nervous system. The kidneys are richly supplied with sympathetic nerve fibers, which course through the splanchnic nerves, the aortic plexus, and the renal plexus and follow the renal vessels to terminate in the smooth muscle of the afferent arterioles and the efferent arterioles. The vasomotor supply is largely, if not entirely, vasoconstrictor in function; there is little evidence to suggest innervation by parasympathetic or sympathetic dilator fibers. Changes of posture (the effect of gravity—see Chapter 12), physical activity, and stress increase the activity of the sympathetic nerves to the kidneys, which increases the resistance in both the afferent arterioles and the efferent arterioles and causes the release of renin from juxtaglomerular cells. If the stress or activity is mild, the renal blood flow is decreased only slightly, and the rate of filtration remains relatively constant. In severe stress, strenuous activity, or volume depletion, such as hemorrhage, the resistances of both the afferent arterioles and the efferent arterioles increase. Generally, the afferent arteriole constricts more than the efferent arteriole; thus, renal blood flow and glomerular pressure decrease. The concomitant decrease in the GFR accounts for the decrease in urinary flow.

HORMONAL FACTORS

Certain hormones also affect renal hemodynamics by their actions on the renal vascular resistance. The catecholamines regulate the renal blood flow via predominantly α-receptor–mediated vasoconstriction. Although vasoconstriction occurs in most portions of the renal vascular beds, the sensitivities of various sites differ. Stimulation of the adrenergic α-receptors decreases renal blood flow or alters renal perfusion in pathophysiological conditions such as hemorrhage. Although the renal vasculature contains adrenergic β-receptors, α-receptor–mediated vasoconstriction predominates over β-receptor–mediated vasodilatation in renal vessels.

Other hormones important in the regulation of the renal blood flow and its distribution are the prostaglandins, the renin-angiotensin system, and the kallikrein-kinin system. Renin and kallikrein are enzymes that are formed and stored in the kidneys. When released, these enzymes act on plasma globulins to liberate the decapeptides angiotensin I and lysyl-bradykinin. A converting enzyme transforms angiotensin I to angiotensin II but degrades lysyl-bradykinin. Therefore, inhibiting the activity of the converting enzyme depresses the renin-angiotensin system but augments the kallikrein-kinin system.

The concentrations of renin and kallikrein both are highest in the outer cortex and decrease toward the corticomedullary junction. However, renin is contained primarily in the vascular system, whereas kallikrein occurs primarily in the tubules. The renin-angiotensin system is a major factor in determining renal perfusion pressure when the renal blood flow is decreased. Angiotensin II causes systemic arteriolar constriction, which increases systemic arterial pressure, and efferent arteriolar constriction, which maintains the GFR despite the decreased renal blood flow. This mechanism is important in the autoregulation of the GFR. The kallikrein-kinin system, on the other hand, increases the blood flow to the kidneys by dilating the renal arterioles.

Although renin-angiotensin and kallikrein-kinin have opposing effects on renal hemodynamics, both systems promote the synthesis and alter the metabolism of prostaglandin. The renal prostaglandins are 20-carbon, unsaturated fatty acids that are the end products of lipid metabolism. Although the various prostaglandin (PG) compounds are similar in chemical structure, they affect the renal circulation differently—some are vasodilators and others are vasoconstrictors. They also differ quantitatively. PGE_2 occurs in the greatest amount in the medulla, whereas PGI_2 is produced in the cortical tissues. Both PGE_2 and PGI_2 are vasodilators. It has been proposed that when vasoconstrictors, such as catecholamines and angiotensin II, are released, or sympathetic activity is enhanced, the renal circulation is maintained by increased production of PGE_2 in the kidneys. Thus, all of the hormonal systems discussed above interact to modify the renal circulation and the excretion of salt and water by the kidneys.

STUDY OUTLINE

GENERAL CONSIDERATIONS

RENAL FRACTION Portion of total cardiac output that flows through kidneys; one-fifth to one-fourth of cardiac output at rest.

MEASUREMENT OF RENAL BLOOD FLOW Direct method—cannulate renal artery or renal vein.

Indirect methods—arterial flowmeter, clearance of para-aminohippurate (PAH) or iodopyracet (Diodrast).

DISTRIBUTION OF RENAL BLOOD FLOW Nonuniform because of different local functional requirements.

Cortical flow—95% of renal blood flow.

Medullary flow—5% of renal blood flow.

VASCULAR PROPERTIES Microcirculations specialized for normal function of nephron.

Glomerular circulation—filtration of plasma.

Cortical peritubular capillaries—reabsorption of solutes and fluid.

Medullary circulation—perfusion of medulla without dissipation of osmotic gradient.

PRESSURES IN THE RENAL CIRCULATION Two major areas of resistance to blood flow—afferent arterioles and efferent arterioles.

High-pressure glomerular capillaries favor filtration.

Low-pressure peritubular capillaries favor reabsorption.

GLOMERULAR CIRCULATION AND GLOMERULAR FILTRATION

FILTRATION FRACTION Fraction of plasma that becomes glomerular filtrate; 16%–20% of renal plasma flow.

PROCESS OF FILTRATION

NET FILTRATION PRESSURE Glomerular filtration is passive process.

Net driving force for filtration $(P_{UF}) = (P_{GC} - P_T) - (\pi_{GC} - \pi_T)$, where

P_{GC} = hydrostatic pressure in glomerular capillary (45–70 mm Hg),

P_T = hydrostatic pressure in Bowman's capsule (10 mm Hg),

π_{GC} = plasma oncotic pressure in glomerular capillary (20 mm Hg), and

π_T = oncotic pressure of fluid in Bowman's capsule (0 mm Hg).

Net filtration pressure decreases along glomerular capillary as fluid is filtered.

ULTRAFILTRATION   Glomerular filtrate is ultrafiltrate of plasma—virtually free of protein.

Concentrations of low molecular weight substances in plasma and ultrafiltrate differ slightly because of binding to plasma proteins and the Gibbs-Donnan effect.

EFFECT OF MOLECULAR SIZE   Low molecular weight solutes (less than 5000 daltons) are filtered freely.

Molecules of molecular weight 80,000–90,000 daltons—radius 4–5 nm—are virtually unfiltered.

EFFECT OF MOLECULAR CHARGE
Electrical charge on solutes also an important determinant of transglomerular passage.

Polyanionic glycoprotein in basement membrane and cell coats opposes passage of negatively charged particles and favors passage of positively charged particles.

Plasma proteins carry net negative charge at pH of blood (7.4).

FACTORS THAT AFFECT THE GLOMERULAR FILTRATION RATE   GFR = net filtration pressure × coefficient of filtration.

Coefficient of filtration = capillary permeability × area of capillary surface.

CHANGES IN COEFFICIENT OF FILTRATION   In renal disease (e.g., nephrosclerosis, glomerulonephritis).

Changes in capillary permeability.

Changes in total capillary surface area.

CHANGES IN NET FILTRATION PRESSURE   Changes in glomerular capillary pressure, plasma oncotic pressure, hydrostatic pressure in Bowman's capsule, and oncotic pressure in Bowman's capsule.

Autoregulation prevents change of filtration pressure with small changes of arterial pressure.

CHANGES IN BLOOD FLOW   Increase in blood flow increases the GFR and the area of filtration.

RESISTANCE IN AFFERENT ARTERIOLES AND EFFERENT ARTERIOLES   Constriction of afferent arterioles decreases

the GFR and dilatation increases the GFR.

Moderate constriction of efferent arterioles increases the GFR and the filtration fraction; severe constriction increases the filtration fraction but decreases the GFR.

EFFECTS OF STRESS   Increased sympathetic nervous system input to kidneys.

Mild—minimal change in the renal blood flow and the GFR.

Moderate—renal blood flow decreases but the GFR may remain constant; filtration fraction increases.

Severe—renal blood flow and the GFR decrease.

CORTICAL PERITUBULAR CIRCULATION   Balance of hydrostatic and oncotic pressures favors capillary absorption of solutes and fluids put into interstitium by absorption of filtrate in proximal tubule, distal tubule, and cortical collecting duct.

MEDULLARY CIRCULATION   Perfuses medulla and enhances renal concentrating mechanism by forming countercurrent exchanger system.

RENAL BLOOD FLOW AND OXYGEN CONSUMPTION   Oxygen consumption rises and falls with renal blood flow—increases and decreases work load (reabsorption and secretion)—different from other organs.

Reabsorption of Na^+ main determinant of oxygen consumption.

Small arteriovenous oxygen difference.

REGULATION OF RENAL BLOOD FLOW AND GLOMERULAR FILTRATION RATE   Renal blood flow and the GFR relatively constant at arterial pressures of 80–180 mm Hg.

INTRINSIC CONTROL

ARTERIOLAR RESISTANCE   Adjusts with change in systemic arterial pressure to keep renal blood flow and glomerular capillary pressure constant within limits.

MECHANISMS OF INTRINSIC CONTROL
Three mechanisms contribute to autoregulation.

Myogenic effect—smooth muscle increases tone in response to stretch.

Feedback from stretch receptors in afferent arteriole at juxtaglomerular apparatus—renin released from juxtaglomerular cells when pressure decreases and receptor not stretched—renin ultimately causes formation of angiotensin.

Receptor in macula densa senses some aspect of flow (e.g., $[Cl^-]$, osmolality, etc.), communicates with afferent arterioles and efferent arterioles and adjusts the GFR to functional capacity of tubules.

EXTRINSIC CONTROL

NEURAL FACTOR Sympathetic vasoconstrictor fibers increase renal arteriolar resistance and cause release of renin with changes in posture, physical activity, and stress.

HORMONAL FACTORS Catecholamines produce mainly α-receptor–mediated vasoconstriction.

Angiotensin II constricts efferent arterioles and helps to maintain the GFR.

Vasodilator agents (e.g., bradykinin, prostaglandins) oppose vasoconstriction locally and help to maintain renal blood flow.

BIBLIOGRAPHY

Aukland, K. 1980. Methods for measuring renal blood flow: Total flow and regional distribution. *Annu. Rev. Physiol.* 42:543.

Barger, A.C., and Herd, J.A. 1973. Renal vascular anatomy and distribution of blood flow. In *Handbook of Physiology*. Section 8. Renal Physiology. Chapter 10. Edited by J. Orloff and R.W. Berliner. Washington, D.C.: American Physiological Society.

Beeuwkes, R., III, and Bonventre, J.V. 1975. Tubular organization and vascular-tubular relations in the dog kidney. *Am. J. Physiol.* 229:695.

Brenner, B.M.; Deen, W.M.; and Robertson, C.R. 1976. Determinants of glomerular filtration rate. *Annu. Rev. Physiol.* 38:9.

Brenner, B.M. (Chairman). 1977. Functional and structural determinants of glomerular filtration (symposium). *Fed. Proc.* 36:2599.

Brenner, B.M., and Humes, H.D. 1977. Mechanics of glomerular ultrafiltration. *N. Engl. J. Med.* 297:148.

Erdös, E.G. (Chairman). 1979. Enzyme inhibitors of the kallikrein and renin systems (symposium). *Fed. Proc.* 38:2751.

Feigin, L.P., and Hyman, A.L. (Chairmen). 1981. Vascular influences of prostaglandins (symposium). *Fed. Proc.* 40:1985.

Levens, N.R.; Peach, M.J.; and Carey, R.M. 1981. Role of the renin-angiotensin system in the control of renal function. *Circ. Res.* 48:157.

McGiff, J.C. (Chairman). 1976. Kinin, renal function, and blood pressure regulation (symposium). *Fed. Proc.* 35:172.

McGiff, J.C., and Wong, P. Y-K. 1979. Compartmentalization of prostaglandins and prostacyclin within the kidney: Implications for renal function. *Fed. Proc.* 38:89.

Navar, L.G.; Ploth, D.W.; and Bell, P.D. 1980. Distal tubular feedback control of renal hemodynamics and autoregulation. *Annu. Rev. Physiol.* 42:557.

Oates, J.A.; Whorton, A.R.; Gerkins, J.F., et al. 1979. The participation of prostaglandins in the control of renin release. *Fed. Proc.* 38:72.

Renkin, E.M., and Gilmore, J.P. 1973. Glomerular filtration. In *Handbook of Physiology*. Section 8. Renal Physiology. Chapter 9, Edited by J. Orloff and R.W. Berliner. Washington, D.C.: American Physiological Society.

Wright, F.S., and Briggs, J.P. 1979. Feedback control of glomerular blood flow, pressure, and filtration rate. *Physiol. Rev.* 59:958.

Wright, F.S. (Chairman). 1981. Feedback control of glomerular filtration rate (symposium). *Fed. Proc.* 35:172.

40

Renal Tubular Transport

CHAPTER CONTENTS

GENERAL CONSIDERATIONS

As the glomerular filtrate flows along the proximal tubule, the loop of Henle, the distal tubule, and the collecting duct, its volume and composition change as substances are reabsorbed or secreted by the tubular epithelial cells. By filtering a large volume of plasma and reabsorbing approximately 99% of the water and different amounts of the dissolved substances, the kidneys control the composition of the internal environment of the body.

To maintain homeostasis, the urinary excretion of salts of Na^+, K^+, and Ca^{++}, and of H^+ in the form of titratable acids or ammonium salts, must be controlled carefully. The proper regulation of these substances depends on the balance between filtration in the glomeruli and transport in the renal tubules.

The final concentration of the various substances in the urine depends on the extent to which the substances are reabsorbed relative to the reabsorption of water and on whether they are secreted by the tubular cells. If the proportions of a substance and water reabsorbed are the same as in the filtrate, the ratio of the concentration of the substance in the tubular fluid to that in the plasma (TF/P) is 1.0, and the concentration of the substance in the urine is the same as that in the plasma. If the rate of reabsorption of the substance is proportionately greater than that of water, TF/P is less than 1.0, and the concentration of the substance in the urine is less than that in the plasma. Substances that are particularly important to the body (certain electrolytes, glucose, amino acids, proteins, and vitamins) are reabsorbed completely, or almost completely, from the filtrate, mainly by the proximal tubular cells, and their concentrations decrease almost to zero before the tubular fluid becomes urine. If some dissolved constituent of the filtrate is not reabsorbed by the tubules, or is reabsorbed proportionately less than water is reabsorbed, the concentration of the substance in the tubular fluid increases, and the ratio TF/P is greater than 1.0. Tubular cells also transport certain substances from plasma into tubular fluid, which supplements filtration and contributes to excretion of those substances.

METHODS USED IN THE STUDY OF TRANSPORT

The development of new techniques has increased the understanding of transport mechanisms in the kidneys. Transport can be studied by the clearance method, micropuncture and microperfusion, or by the use of membrane vesicles.

Clearance

The net transport of a substance can be determined by comparing the clearance of the substance to that of inulin (see Chapter 37). The clearance method permits the study of renal function without surgical procedures, but it provides information only about the overall behavior of the nephron population.

Micropuncture and Microperfusion

The methods of micropuncture and microperfusion permit the study of tubular transport in particular segments of a single nephron.

MICROPUNCTURE

With the aid of micromanipulators, glass capillary tubes with pointed tips only a few microns in diameter can be introduced into any of the accessible tubular structures. The micropuncture method can be applied to tubular structures near the surface of the kidney in certain species of small rodents, such as the proximal and distal convoluted tubules of superficial nephrons in the golden hamster, the rat, and the guinea pig. In addition, the renal pelvis can be exposed to reveal the structures in the inner medullary region, such as the descending and ascending thin limbs of the loop of Henle and the medullary collecting tubule.

The simplest method of micropuncture is to collect samples of fluid from the various segments of nephrons, using the glass capillary tubes, and determine the concentrations of the various substances in the fluid. This permits one to compare the compositions of the fluid in the different segments of the tubule.

The reabsorptive activity of isolated segments of the nephron can be investigated by employing a "split" oil droplet. In this method, a drop of oil is introduced into a tubule, and a small quantity of Ringer's solution is injected, which divides the oil droplet into two portions. The rate at which the two portions come together depends on the rate at which the tubular cells absorb the Ringer's solution.

MICROPERFUSION

Portions of nephrons that are not accessible to micropuncture can be dissected out and perfused and their transport characteristics studied in vitro.

Membrane Vesicles

Transport mechanisms also can be studied in isolated vesicles derived from either the luminal or basolateral portions of the tubular cell membrane. These closed vesicles behave like intact "cells" composed entirely of membranes from their area of origin. They permit the study of transport across cell membranes (e.g., cotransport of D-glucose and Na^+ in the proximal tubule).

TRANSEPITHELIAL TRANSPORT OF SOLUTES AND WATER

The epithelial cells of the tubules have enormous absorptive capacities that depend on their ability to transport specific substances from the lumen of the tubule into the interstitial fluid, from which they diffuse into the capillaries. The substances that are secreted move in the opposite direction, from the peritubular capillaries to the lumen of the tubule. Generally, solutes and water cross the epithelium through two parallel pathways, transcellular and paracellular, which will be discussed later in this chapter with regard to the reabsorption of Na^+ and water (see the section entitled "Transport of Sodium, Chloride, and Water"). The structures of the epithelial cells and their transport functions differ in the different segments of the nephron. The transport of substances in the various parts of the nephron is represented schematically in Figure 40-1.

Tubular Reabsorption

PROXIMAL TUBULE

The glomerular filtrate that leaves Bowman's space has essentially the same composition as the plasma except for proteins and substances bound to proteins. As the glomerular filtrate traverses the convoluted part of the proximal tubule, a number of substrates, such as Na^+, Ca^{++}, Mg^{++}, HCO_3^-, Cl^-, $HPO_4^=$, $SO_4^=$, glucose, and amino acids are reabsorbed preferentially, and by the time the filtrate reaches the straight part of the proximal tubule, about 80% of the electrolytes and almost all of the glucose and amino acids have been reabsorbed.

In the proximal tubule the transport of one substance may affect the transport of one or more of the others; for example, the transport of both glucose and amino acids depends on the concurrent transport of Na^+. Because sodium salts constitute more than 80% of the total substance dissolved in the glomerular filtrate,

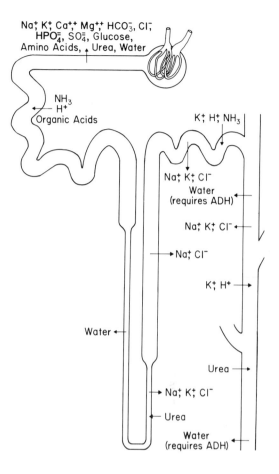

Figure 40-1.   The transport of substances at various sites in the nephron. As the glomerular filtrate flows along the tubule, its composition and volume are modified by reabsorption and secretion. Most of the filtered solutes, accompanied by water, are reabsorbed preferentially in the early proximal convoluted tubule. Further uptake of Na^+, Cl^-, and water in the straight part of the proximal tubule results in the reabsorption of about 80% of the filtrate. The fluid that flows into the loop of Henle is isosmotic. Reabsorption of Na^+ and Cl^- in the ascending thin limb of the loop of Henle and the straight part of the distal tubule, and the impermeability of these segments to water, cause the formation of fluid that is hypo-osmotic to plasma. The reabsorption of Na^+, Cl^-, and water in the distal segment of the nephron (distal convoluted and collecting tubules) is variable, depending on the needs of the individual, and is sensitive to hormones. The reabsorption of Na^+ and Cl^- and the secretion of K^+ are sensitive to aldosterone. The final reabsorption of water from the cortical and medullary collecting tubules to form a concentrated urine depends on the action of antidiuretic hormone (ADH).

the reabsorption of Na^+ and its accompanying anions exceeds that of all other solutes. Under normal circumstances, approximately 80% of the filtered Na^+ is reabsorbed in the proximal tubule, accompanied by either HCO_3^- or Cl^-. Water is reabsorbed in the same proportion as Na^+, so the concentration of Na^+ in the tubular fluid, $[Na^+]$, remains unaltered. Thus, approximately 80% of the filtrate is reabsorbed isosmotically in the proximal tubules, and when the tubular fluid reaches the thin limb of the loop of Henle, it still is isosmotic with plasma.

DISTAL SEGMENTS

The segments of the nephron distal to the proximal tubule—the thin descending limb of the loop of Henle and the thin and the thick ascending limbs of the loop of Henle, the distal convoluted tubule, and the collecting tubule—continue to reduce the volume and alter the chemical composition of the tubular fluid. The fluid produced by the distal structures differs significantly from the glomerular filtrate and varies in composition, depending on what the organism needs to excrete. Despite these differences, however, the proximal and distal portions of the nephron operate in basically similar modes: the reabsorption of sodium salts leads to the movement of water along an osmotic gradient, and the diverse waste materials that remain in the tubule are concentrated by the reduction of volume. The transport of Na^+ in the distal convoluted tubule and the collecting tubule is affected by the hormone aldosterone, and the transport of water in the collecting tubule is affected by antidiuretic hormone (ADH). Aldosterone increases the rate of reabsorption of Na^+, and ADH increases the reabsorption of water. In the absence of ADH, the collecting tubule is impermeable to water, and very little water is reabsorbed; however, when ADH is present, the permeability of the duct to water is increased, and the reabsorption of water is increased.

Tubular Secretion

The tubular epithelial cells contain pathways for the secretion of wastes and certain excess substances. In particular, foreign substances are secreted by the proximal tubular cells; for example, penicillin and organic acids such as para-aminohippuric acid. In the regulation of the acid-base balance of the body fluids, excess H^+ is secreted into the tubular fluid by

the proximal, distal, and collecting tubules. The ability of the tubular cells to secrete H^+ is limited by the extent to which the concentration of H^+ in the urine, $[H^+]$, can be increased; the maximum corresponds to a urinary pH of 4.5. The tubular structures secrete ammonia into the tubular fluid to combine with the H^+; thus, additional H^+ can be excreted as ammonium salts. In addition, the distal convoluted and collecting tubules secrete K^+ into the tubular fluid; this is an important mechanism for the excretion of excess K^+.

Types of Transport

By convention, the transport mechanisms in the kidneys can be categorized grossly as either *active* or *passive*. A mechanism is *active* if it transports a substance against an electrochemical gradient; that is, against a gradient of electrical potential, chemical activity, or both. A mechanism is *passive* if the substance moves down gradients of electrical potential or chemical activity.

ACTIVE TRANSPORT

The transport process may be linked either directly to a source of metabolic energy ("primary" active transport) or to the active transport of another solute ("secondary" active transport). Examples of substances in the glomerular filtrate that are reabsorbed actively by the tubular cells are Na^+, K^+, Ca^{++}, $HPO_4^=$, urate, glucose, and amino acids. When their concentrations in the plasma are low, these substances are reabsorbed almost completely from the tubular fluid. The tubular cells also can actively secrete H^+, K^+, urate, and certain organic acids (see the earlier section on tubular secretion). Systems of active transport are specific for certain solutes and can be saturated; in addition, similar molecules compete for the carrier sites. The immediate source of energy for active transport in mammalian cells is adenosine triphosphate (ATP). The presence of the enzyme Na^+, K^+-ATPase in the basolateral plasma membrane of the renal tubular cells is taken as evidence that Na^+ is transported actively in this region.

PASSIVE TRANSPORT

In passive transport, no energy is expended directly in moving the substance in question; instead, energy is used to establish a concentration gradient of some other substance or a gradient of electrical potential along which the substance diffuses. In the renal tubule, the active reabsorption of Na^+ establishes a gradient of electrical potential down which either HCO_3^- or Cl^- moves. Water is absorbed passively down an osmotic gradient established and maintained largely by the absorption of Na^+.

COUPLED TRANSPORT

Coupling processes also are important in the transport of substances by the tubular epithelial cells; the movement of one solute across the cell membrane depends on the movement of another solute. In cotransport, the dependent solute moves in the same direction as the solute that is transported. The transport of both D-glucose and L-amino acids across the luminal membrane, for example, has been shown by microperfusion studies and isolated membrane vesicles to depend on the concentration gradient of Na^+ that is established. The $[Na^+]$ in the lumen of the proximal tubule (approximately 140 mEq/liter) is higher than that in the cell (approximately 15 mEq/liter); thus, Na^+ moves passively from the lumen into the cell. The gradient is maintained by the active transport of Na^+ across the basolateral membrane from the tubular cell into the interstitial space. The influx of both D-glucose and L-amino acids is accelerated by the Na^+ gradient because the substances cross the luminal membrane of the tubular epithelial cell together with Na^+ in a positively charged carrier-complex. This system of entry is passive, but the transport and intracellular accumulation of glucose and amino acids depend on the maintenance of the concentration gradient of Na^+, which is active.

In another system of coupled transport in the renal tubule, the movement of Na^+ from the lumen into the tubular cell provides the driving force for the secretion of H^+ from the tubular cell into the lumen. The secretion of K^+ into the lumen of the distal tubule also involves an exchange for Na^+. This process, called countertransport, is particularly important for the excretion of H^+ and K^+.

SOLVENT DRAG

Another form of transport involves the passive transport of a solute by the movement of water, or solvent drag. In the proximal tubule, for example, the transport of Na^+ across the basolateral membrane into the intercellular space causes water to move along an osmotic gradient from the lumen through the "leaky" tight junction into the intercellular space. A slight gradient of hydrostatic pressure then moves the water on into the interstitium. The water carries the substances dissolved in it (e.g., urea) into the interstitium.

FACILITATED DIFFUSION

Some solutes are transported passively in the renal tubules by a process known as *facilitated diffusion,* in which the solutes move at a greater rate than would be predicted on the basis of their concentration gradients and the area and permeability of the membrane. One explanation for facilitated diffusion is that *transport proteins,* which penetrate the lipid matrix of the plasma membrane, provide specific "channels" for the entry of solutes and ions. These proteins have "recognition sites" that are supposed to bind certain specific solutes or analogues of solutes and transport them at a faster rate. Because of these binding sites, compounds that are similar in structure may compete for transport, and the sites may become saturated. Even though this mechanism is highly specific and transports the particular solute at a faster rate than would be predicted, it is passive because it cannot transport the solute against an electrochemical gradient. The transport of urea across the tubular cells and the efflux of glucose from the cells to the pertitubular fluid probably proceed by facilitated diffusion.

FUNCTIONAL CHARACTERISTICS OF TUBULAR CELLS

The tubular epithelial cells have many features that affect their role in transport.

Cell Surfaces of the Proximal Tubule

The extensive brush border at the luminal side of the proximal tubule increases the area of absorptive surface, as shown in Figure 38-6. Many of the cotransport processes occur here. On the basal aspect of the cell, the plasma membrane enfolds extensively to form basal channels, which, together with the intercellular space, form the basolateral intercellular space. The basolateral membrane has a high content of Na^+, K^+-ATPase, which indicates that Na^+ is transported actively there.

Mitochondria

The proximal tubular cells have a dense population of mitochondria to support the high rate of metabolism required by the active transport processes. Distal tubular cells contain fewer mitochondria.

Tight Junction

The intercellular space is separated from the lumen of the tubule by the tight junction (see Figure 40-2), which prevents the luminal fluid from invading the interstitium of the renal tubules; however, the permeability of the tight junction varies considerably along the length of the nephron. This difference is important in the transport of ions and water across the epithelium.

The junctions in the proximal tubule are relatively permeable to ions; thus, they form a low-resistance pathway between the cells for the reabsorption of ions and water. Because of the ease with which anions (mostly Cl^-) follow Na^+, the transepithelial potential in this area is low.

The tight junctions in the distal tubule and the collecting duct provide high resistance to

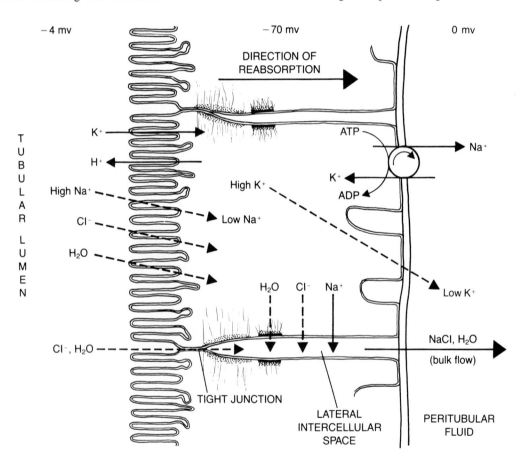

Figure 40-2. The transport of ions and water in a proximal tubular cell characterized by numerous microvilli along the border, basolateral channels (the lateral intercellular spaces, but not the basal channels, are shown in the figure), and a transepithelial potential difference of 4 mv. The solid lines represent active transport and the dashed lines represent passive transport. The transepithelial transport of Na^+ involves (1) an active process at the basolateral membrane that depends on ATP as an energy source. This reaction extrudes Na^+ and accumulates K^+ in the cell. (2) Passive movement across the luminal membrane. The active transport of Na^+ causes passive transport of Cl^- along an electrical gradient and passive transport of water along an osmotic gradient. In addition, Cl^- and water flow across the "leaky" tight junction; this flow of fluid carries solutes along with it by solvent drag. The passive transport of Na^+ across the luminal membrane causes either reabsorption of Cl^- or exchange of Na^+ and H^+ at the luminal border. K^+ is transported actively across the luminal membrane into the cell.

the movement of anions and establish a large transepithelial potential difference in this portion of the nephron. This condition is suitable for the exchange of cations (e.g., the exchange of K$^+$ and H$^+$ for Na$^+$ (see the section entitled "Relation of Potassium Ion to Hydrogen Ion" in this chapter).

Capillary Oncotic Pressure

The plasma oncotic pressure in the peritubular capillaries is an important factor in the transport of water and solutes from the intercellular space, across the basal membrane into the interstitium, and into the capillaries. Because the plasma water is filtered by the glomeruli but the plasma proteins are not, the concentration of the plasma proteins in the peritubular capillaries is greater than that in the general circulation. The decreased chemical activity of the plasma water establishes a gradient of water activity from the intercellular space to the capillary. Thus, the water flows along an osmotic gradient, and the solutes are carried by solvent drag.

Transepithelial Potential Difference

The transepithelial potential difference can be measured with microelectrodes. When both reference and recording electrodes are placed in the interstitium around the renal tubule, no potential difference is recorded. If the recording electrode is advanced into the tubular epithelial cell, a potential difference of about 90 mv is recorded; the interior of the cell is negative with respect to the interstitium. If the recording electrode is advanced farther into the tubular epithelial cell, so that the tip emerges into the lumen, a potential difference of 3–4 mv is recorded in the proximal convoluted tubule, and a mean potential of 50 mv is recorded in the distal convoluted tubule; in both areas, the lumen is negative with respect to the interstitium.

TRANSPORT OF SODIUM, CHLORIDE, AND WATER

Because Na$^+$ is the major extracellular cation, large amounts of it are filtered. Normally, approximately 99% of the filtered load is reabsorbed—about 80% in the proximal tubule and most of the rest in the distal tubule. When the body is in sodium balance, the amount of Na$^+$ excreted equals the amount ingested over a wide range of dietary intakes. The reabsorption of Na$^+$ is accompanied by the reabsorption of Cl$^-$ or HCO$_3^-$, the secretion of H$^+$, or, in the distal tubule, the secretion of K$^+$.

Transport in the Proximal Tubule

The proximal tubule functions as a high-capacity transport system that reabsorbs approximately 80% of the filtered Na$^+$. The Na$^+$ is reabsorbed isosmotically, as water follows in the same proportion, so that the [Na$^+$] of the fluid at the end of the proximal tubule is the same as that in the glomerular filtrate.

TRANSEPITHELIAL MOVEMENT

The transepithelial transport of Na$^+$ involves two steps: (1) passive movement across the luminal membrane of the tubular cells, and (2) active transport across the basolateral membrane. The latter step depends on ATP and the enzymatic action of Na$^+$, K$^+$-ATPase for energy. This process extrudes Na$^+$ from the cell into the peritubular fluid and accumulates K$^+$ in the cell; the result is low intracellular [Na$^+$] and high intracellular [K$^+$]. Another type of active transport, which does not depend on Na$^+$, K$^+$-ATPase in the renal tubule, is suggested by the observation that the transepithelial movement of Na$^+$ in the proximal tubule is inhibited only partially (maximum 50%) by ouabain. (Inhibition by ouabain is considered to be a specific indication of Na$^+$, K$^+$-ATPase activity—see Chapter 2). The exact nature of this second transport system has not been established.

Because of the active transport of Na$^+$ across the basolateral membrane, the [Na$^+$] in the cell is lower than that in the luminal fluid, and Na$^+$ moves passively across the luminal membrane into the cell. This movement of Na$^+$ establishes a potential driving force for either the reabsorption of filtered Cl$^-$ or a counter-transport mechanism that involves the exchange of Na$^+$ and H$^+$ at the luminal border. The H$^+$ that is secreted comes from the rapid dissociation of intracellular carbonic acid (H$_2$CO$_3$) into H$^+$ and HCO$_3^-$. The HCO$_3^-$ enters the peritubular capillary in association with Na$^+$ transported actively across the basolateral membrane. The secreted H$^+$ reacts with filtered HCO_3^- in the tubular lumen to form H_2CO_3 which then dissociates into H_2O and CO_2 (see Figure 43-2). Thus, HCO_3^- is reabsorbed from the tubular fluid indirectly by a process that involves the exchange of Na^+ and H^+ at the luminal border. This exchange is important in the acidification of the urine (see Chapter 43).

"LEAKY" TIGHT JUNCTION

The permeability of the proximal tubule to ions and water is greatest in the spaces between the cells. The tight junction is "leaky" in the proximal tubule; therefore, the pathway through the tight junction and the lateral intercellular space is important in the transport of ions and water by the proximal tubule. The active transport of Na^+ out of the epithelial cell into the lateral intercellular space slightly increases the $[Na^+]$ in this space relative to that in the luminal fluid. The leaky junction provides a low-resistance pathway for Cl^-, which moves into the intercellular space along the gradient of electrical potential set up by the movement of Na^+. Therefore, the concentration of ions in the intercellular space increases relative to the luminal fluid, and this difference of concentration creates an osmotic gradient that causes water to flow from the lumen through the tight junction into the intercellular space. The flux of water increases the hydrostatic pressure in the intercellular space, which drives fluid into the interstitium and the capillaries. Because of the bulk flow of fluid along the lateral intercellular pathway, anions, other solutes (e.g., urea), and some Na^+ may be reabsorbed passively by solvent drag. The transport of Na^+, anions, and water by the proximal epithelial cell is represented schematically in Figure 40-2.

Apparently, all of the processes described above contribute to the bulk reabsorption of Na^+ and fluid by the proximal tubule, especially in the convoluted part, which reabsorbs approximately two-thirds of the glomerular filtrate. When the tubular fluid leaves the straight portion of the proximal tubule, as much as 80% of the volume that was filtered has been reabsorbed.

SODIUM GRADIENT

Unlike the reabsorption of some solutes (e.g., glucose), the reabsorption of Na^+ is not limited to some quantity that can be transported per minute; rather it is limited by the concentration gradient that can be established between the tubular fluid and the plasma. Under normal circumstances, there is no $[Na^+]$ gradient across the proximal epithelial cells because Na^+ and water are reabsorbed at the same rate. However, if a substance that is not readily reabsorbed enters the tubular lumen, water is retained in the lumen by the osmotic effect of the solute. Because the rate of reabsorption of Na^+ exceeds that of water in this circumstance, the $[Na^+]$ in the tubular fluid declines and a $[Na^+]$ gradient develops between the tubular fluid and the plasma. As long as the $[Na^+]$ gradient is less than about 35 mEq/liter, the epithelial cell continues to reabsorb Na^+. However, when the $[Na^+]$ gradient equals or exceeds 35 mEq/liter (e.g., when $[Na^+]$ in the plasma is 145 mEq/liter and $[Na^+]$ in the tubular fluid is 110 mEq/liter or less), net reabsorption of Na^+ ceases. When this limiting gradient is reached, Na^+ remains in the tubular fluid with the water, and less fluid is reabsorbed in this region of the tubule.

Transport in the Thin Limb of the Loop of Henle

The transport of Na^+, its associated anions, and water in the thin limb of the loop of Henle differs from that in the proximal tubule. The epithelial cells in the thin limb of the loop appear to be adapted for simple diffusion of solutes and water along their concentration gradients. However, the permeabilities of the descending and ascending limbs of the loop of Henle are different. The descending limb is relatively impermeable to Na^+ and other solutes but is very permeable to water, whereas the ascending limb is highly permeable to Na^+ but is relatively impermeable to water. This difference of permeability between the two aspects of the thin limb of the loop of Henle is important in the renal mechanism for concentrating the urine, which will be discussed in Chapter 41.

Transport in the Distal Tubule

When the fluid reaches the thick ascending limb of the loop of Henle, additional Na^+ and its associated anions are reabsorbed. The permeability of the thick ascending limb of the loop of Henle to water is very low. Because Na^+ and anions, but not water, are reabsorbed in this region, the concentration of solutes in the tubular fluid decreases. When the fluid reaches the beginning of the distal convoluted tubule, $[Na^+]$ is only 60 mEq/liter as compared to approximately 145 mEq/liter at the end of the proximal tubule; thus, the tubular fluid is considerably more dilute. Reabsorption of the remainder of the filtrate (10%-20% of the total that was filtered) in the distal convoluted tubule and collecting duct varies depending on the needs of the body.

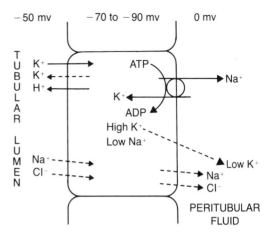

Figure 40-3. The transport of ions in a distal tubular cell. The solid lines represent active transport and the dashed lines represent passive transport. The transepithelial reabsorption of Na^+ is similar to that of the proximal tubular cell because it involves energy-dependent extrusion across the basal membrane and passive diffusion across the luminal membrane. The major difference is that the tight junctions are impermeable and do not provide a "shunt pathway" for the transport of solutes and water. Therefore, the resistance to the movement of Cl^- is high, and a large electrical potential develops. The high transepithelial difference of potential favors the exchange of ions (e.g., the exchange of Na^+ for H^+ and Na^+ for K^+). K^+ is transported actively across the luminal membrane into the cell.

TRANSEPITHELIAL MOVEMENT

The reabsorption of Na^+ in the distal tubule is similar to that in the proximal tubule because it involves passive diffusion across the luminal membrane and energy-dependent extrusion across the basal membrane. Two modes of active transport also are indicated: one that is inhibited by ouabain and another that is not inhibited by ouabain.

TIGHT JUNCTION

The transport of other ions in the distal tubule differs from that in the proximal tubule because the tight junctions virtually are impermeable and do not provide a "shunt pathway" for the transport of solutes and water. The resistance to the movement of Cl^- is considerable, and Cl^- must traverse the cell membrane to follow the Na^+ that is reabsorbed actively. Therefore, the transepithelial potential difference in the distal tubule is much higher than the transepithelial potential difference in the proximal tubule. This condition favors the exchange of cations (e.g., H^+ for Na^+ and K^+ for Na^+). The characteristics of transport in the distal tubule are shown in Figure 40-3.

ALDOSTERONE

Micropuncture experiments in the rat have shown that $[Na^+]$ declines steadily from 60 mEq/liter in the first part of the distal tubule to about 30 mEq/liter in the last portion. Thus, the distal tubule differs from the proximal tubule because it can reabsorb Na^+ against a high concentration gradient. The hormone al-

dosterone is necessary for adequate reabsorption of Na^+ in the distal convoluted tubule and the collecting tubule; aldosterone is assumed to cause the synthesis of a protein that is important for the transport of Na^+.

Transport in the Collecting Tubule

When the hypotonic tubular fluid reaches the collecting tubule, most of the Na^+ that remains in it is reabsorbed, since only about 1% of the Na^+ that is filtered is excreted. The transport processes of Na^+ and its associated anions in the collecting tubule are similar to those in the distal convoluted tubule, that is, active reabsorption of Na^+ followed either by passive reabsorption of an anion, such as Cl^- or HCO_3^-, or by countertransport with another cation such as K^+ or H^+.

Antidiuretic Hormone

Whether the fluid remains hypotonic in the collecting tubule or is concentrated depends on the action of antidiuretic hormone (ADH). In the absence of ADH, the collecting tubule is impermeable to water, and the reabsorption of Na$^+$ and anions dilutes the urine further. However, in the presence of ADH, the permeability to water increases, and water is reabsorbed osmotically as the tubular fluid flows from the cortical collecting tubule to the papillary duct. This effect of ADH is very important in the process of concentrating the urine. When the intake of water is inadequate (hydropenia) and water must be conserved, less than 1% of the fluid that is filtered is excreted as urine.

Glomerulotubular Balance

The reabsorption of fluid by the proximal tubules varies with the glomerular filtration rate (GFR). An increase in the GFR increases the rate of reabsorption of Na$^+$, water, and the other substances that are filtered, and a decrease in the GFR decreases the rate of reabsorption of these substances. Over a wide range of spontaneous and experimental variations in GFR, the proximal tubules reabsorb about 80% of the filtrate. The proportionality between filtration and tubular reabsorption is referred to as *glomerulotubular balance*. The more distal segments of the nephrons reabsorb a variable fraction of the load delivered to them from the proximal tubules, depending on the specific needs of the body.

MECHANISMS

The exact mechanism that governs the relationship between the filtered load and proximal tubular reabsorption is not known, although the effect appears to be mediated by a balance between the volume of fluid filtered and the hemodynamic forces that determine the uptake of fluid by the peritubular capillaries. For example, the plasma oncotic pressure in the peritubular capillaries, which aids the passive transport of water and solutes (see the section entitled "Capillary Oncotic Pressure"), is related to the filtration fraction. If the filtration fraction is large, the plasma oncotic pressure in the peritubular capillaries is greater, and the reabsorption of filtrate is enhanced.

TRANSPORT OF POTASSIUM

The kidneys handle K$^+$ and Na$^+$ differently. The amount of Na$^+$ that is excreted involves a balance between filtration and reabsorption, and the Na$^+$ that appears in the urine was filtered by the glomeruli but not reabsorbed by the tubular cells (i.e., Na$^+$ is not secreted). The excretion of K$^+$ in the urine depends very little on the amount of K$^+$ filtered. Most of the K$^+$ that is filtered is reabsorbed in the proximal tubule and only about 20% of it remains in the tubule at the end of that segment. The same fraction of filtered K$^+$ is reabsorbed in the proximal tubule, regardless of the K$^+$ balance and the dietary intake of K$^+$; thus, all variation in the excretion of K$^+$ occurs in the distal part of the nephron. When an individual needs to conserve K$^+$, most of the K$^+$ that is not reabsorbed in the proximal tubule can be reabsorbed in the distal convoluted and collecting tubules; thus, as little as 1% of the K$^+$ that is filtered may be excreted. However, when K$^+$ is in excess in the body, the distal tubular cells secrete K$^+$. Thus, the distal convoluted and collecting tubules determine the excretion of K$^+$.

Transport in the Proximal Tubules

K$^+$ is reabsorbed actively in the proximal tubule, the ascending thick limb of the loop of Henle, the distal convoluted tubule, and the collecting tubule. In the proximal tubule, K$^+$ is reabsorbed in a solution that is isosmotic with the plasma; thus, the [K$^+$] in the tubular fluid remains the same throughout the length of the tubule. K$^+$ is transported actively across the luminal membrane into the cell and passively across the basolateral membrane into the interstitium (see Figure 40-2). The intracellular [K$^+$] is about 150 mEq/liter, and the [K$^+$] of the tubular fluid is about 4 mEq/liter. According to the Nernst equation (see Chapter 2), this gradient of chemical activity (150/4) is equivalent to an electrical potential difference of 97 mv acting to move K$^+$ from the cell into the lumen. Since the cellular potential relative to the lumen, which acts to keep K$^+$ in the cell, is only 86 mv (see the earlier section entitled "Transepithelial Potential Difference"), an electrochemical gradient of 11 mv (97 mv − 86 mv) acts to move K$^+$ from the cell into the lumen. Thus, when K^+ moves from the lumen into the cell, it must be transported actively. The electrical potential difference between the cell and the interstitium, which acts to hold K^+ in the cell, is 90 mv (see the earlier section entitled "Transepithelial Potential Difference"). Since the intracellular $[K^+]$ is 150 mEq/liter and the interstitial $[K^+]$ is 4 mEq/liter, the electrical equivalent of the chemical gradient that acts to move K^+ from the cell to the interstitium is 97 mv. Thus, an electrochemical gradient of 7 mv (97 mv − 90 mv) acts to transport K^+ passively from the cell into the interstitium and from there into the peritubular capillary.

Transport in the Loop of Henle

The transport of K^+ in the thin limb of the loop of Henle is similar to that of Na^+ in the same region. Because of the permeability of the epithelial cells of the ascending thin limbs, K^+ simply diffuses down its electrochemical gradient from the lumen to the interstitial space.

Transport in the Distal and Collecting Tubules

K^+ is actively reabsorbed in the ascending thick limb of the loop of Henle. Because water is not reabsorbed in this region, the $[K^+]$ of the tubular fluid has decreased to less than the $[K^+]$ of the plasma by the time the tubular fluid reaches the distal convoluted tubule.

The rate of excretion of K^+ is modulated to the greatest extent in the distal convoluted and collecting tubules. In this region, K^+ is both absorbed and secreted, and the balance of these processes determines the direction and the magnitude of the net movement of K^+ (see Figure 40-3). The mechanisms by which ions are concentrated in the epithelial cells of the distal and collecting tubules are similar to those that function in the proximal cells. Na^+ enters the cell passively and is extruded across the basal membrane actively. K^+ is accumulated actively in the cell and crosses the basal membrane passively. The active transport of K^+ requires ATP for energy.

ACTIVE REABSORPTION

K^+ is transported actively across the luminal membrane from the tubular lumen into the cells against its electrochemical gradient (see the section entitled "Transepithelial Potential Difference" in this chapter). K^+ then diffuses passively across the basal membrane down its electrochemical gradient.

PASSIVE SECRETION

K^+ diffuses passively from the cell into the tubular lumen because of the high $[K^+]$ in the cell, the low $[K^+]$ in the tubular fluid, and the electrical potential difference between the lumen and the peritubular fluid (electrochemical gradient). This potential develops because Na^+ is transported out of the lumen actively, and the relative impermeability of the tight junction of the epithelial cells impedes the flux of Cl^- that would follow passively. In the distal tubule the transepithelial potential difference increases from 19 mv (lumen-negative) at the beginning of the distal convoluted tubule to 60 mv (lumen-negative) at the end of the distal convoluted tubule. This potential difference provides a driving force that favors the accumulation in the lumen of cations in general and K^+ in particular. Therefore, the secretion of K^+ in the distal tubule depends on the delivery and rate of reabsorption of Na^+ in the distal nephron because the transepithelial potential difference depends on the transport of Na^+.

RELATION OF POTASSIUM ION TO HYDROGEN ION

Because both K^+ and H^+ are countertransported across the luminal membrane of the distal convoluted and collecting tubules, the intracellular concentration of one ion may affect the secretion of the other. Although the relationships between the secretion of K^+ and H^+ are complex, when the intracellular $[H^+]$ is high (acidosis), the secretion of H^+ generally increases and the secretion of K^+ generally decreases (see Chapter 43).

TRANSPORT OF GLUCOSE

Transport Capacity

Glucose is filtered freely at the glomerulus and, if the concentration in the plasma is in the normal range, is reabsorbed completely by the renal tubular cells. Although the reabsorption of glucose is said to be complete, trace amounts of glucose can be detected in normal urine

CLINICAL CORRELATION

40.1   Impaired Renal Tubular Secretion of Potassium

CASE REPORT

The Patient: A 23-year-old woman.

Reason for Admission: Hyperkalemia associated with previously diagnosed systemic lupus erythematosus.

History: The patient had a 6-year history of systemic lupus erythematosus (SLE). On a previous admission, her serum creatinine concentration had been 1.8 mg/dl (normal, 0.6–1.5 mg/dl), and urinalysis had revealed 12 erythrocytes/high-power field, with occasional granular casts and a protein concentration of 0.5 g/dl (normal, < 0.1 g/dl). At that time, she was taking prednisone, a synthetic corticosteroid, and azathioprine, an immunosuppressive agent.

Clinical Examination: At admission, plasma $[K^+]$ was 6.8 mEq/liter (normal, 3.5–5 mEq/liter), $[Na^+]$ was 136 mEq/liter (normal, 135–145 mEq/liter), $[Cl^-]$ was 103 mEq/liter (normal, 100–106 mEq/liter), $[HCO_3{}^-]$ was 23 mEq/liter (normal, 21–28 mEq/liter), the serum creatinine was 1.6 mg/dl, the blood urea nitrogen (BUN) was 28 mg/dl (normal, 8–25 mg/dl), and the other results of urinalysis were similar to those on the previous admission (above). The creatinine clearance was 61 ml/1.73 m² body surface (normal, 104–125 ml/1.73 m²), and the urine-protein excretion was 900 mg/24 hr (normal, < 150 mg/24 hr). The arterial pressure was 125/80 mm Hg, the hematocrit was 23%, the ECG was normal, and the chest was shown to be clear by x-ray films. The patient had alopecia (loss of hair), skin rash, and polyarthritis. To elucidate further the cause of the arterial hyperkalemia, the patient was placed on a constant diet until she achieved K^+ and Na^+ balance (4 days). On the fourth day, the rate of secretion of aldosterone in the urine was measured for 24 hours (2.8 μg/day; normal, 5–19 μg/day), and the plasma renin activity and aldosterone concentration were measured in a sample of blood taken while the patient was supine.* Plasma renin activity was 0.4 measured as ng of angiotensin II generated/ml/hour (normal, 0.3–1.9 ng/ml/hour), and the plasma aldosterone concentration was 113 pg/ml (normal, 19–77 pg/ml). After 3 days of a low-sodium diet (maximum 20 mg/day) and the administration of an effective sodium-mobilizing diuretic (furosemide, 60 mg/day for 2 days), the patient's ability to increase renin and aldosterone was measured. The patient walked for 2 hours before the plasma samples were taken. Plasma renin activity stimulated in this fashion was 1.9 ng of angiotensin generated/ml/hour (normal, 6.3–13.7 ng/ml/hour), and the plasma aldosterone concentration was 270 pg/ml (normal, 304–760 pg/ml). The patient was returned to the control diet and allowed to reach Na^+ balance (Na^+ excretion was 13.5 mEq/day). Then she was given fludrocortisone acetate, a synthetic mineralocorticoid (has actions like aldosterone), for 5 days. Na^+ excretion decreased to 23 mEq/day, but the rate of excretion of K^+ (35 mEq/day) did not change. Finally, the patient was allowed to stabilize again on the control diet, and then was given a combination of $NaHCO_3$ and acetazolamide, a diuretic agent that acts by inhibiting carbonic anhydrase (thus preventing exchange of H^+ for Na^+ in the distal tubule—see Chapter 43, Figure 43-2). The excretion of Na^+ increased from 130 mEq/day to 176 mEq/day, but the excretion of K^+ increased by only 5 mEq/day (expected, increase of about 30 mEq/day).

Comment: The principal abnormality of renal function in this patient was inadequate secretion of potassium. Potassium balance is maintained by variable secretion of K^+ in the distal tubule, in association with the reabsorption of Na^+ and under the control of aldosterone. Decreased secretion of K^+ might be caused by an insufficient tubular load of Na^+ to maintain the coupled exchange, by deficient secretion of aldosterone because of some defect in the renin-angiotensin-aldosterone system, or by a specific tubular defect.

However, measurement of 24-hr Na^+ excretion showed that the tubular Na^+ load was not deficient. Furthermore, the Na^+ load was increased by the actions of diuretic agents and the administration of $NaHCO_3$, without increasing the excretion of K^+. A defect in the renin-angiotensin-aldosterone system was ruled out by the demonstration that both plasma and urinary aldosterone increased in response to depletion of Na^+ and extracellular fluid volume. Finally, unresponsiveness of the tubular mechanism was demonstrated by the administration of a large dose of an effective synthetic mineralocorticoid (which produces effects like those of aldosterone), which did not increase the secretion of K^+, although it increased the uptake of Na^+. These combined results indicate a specific tubular defect in the secretion of K^+.

Systemic lupus erythematosus is considered to be an autoimmune disease. The serum of patients who have SLE contains substances called antinuclear antibodies, which are antibodies to DNA, nucteoproteins, and other constituents of the cellular nucleus. These antibodies do not harm cells, because they do not penetrate the cellular membrane. However, small amounts of DNA and the other nuclear materials do appear in the bloodstream, and then these antibodies complex with them. Small amounts of DNA bind to collagen and collagen-like structures in the glomeruli, where antinuclear antibodies react with them to form immune complexes on the glomerular basement membrane. These deposits have been associated with the nephrotic syndrome** and may account for the moderate loss of protein and decreased glomerular function in this patient. Immune formations also have been found on the basement membrane of tubules and might account for the specific defect in K^+ secretion seen in this patient. It should be emphasized, however, that this proposed mechanism is highly speculative.

Therapy: Before the current admission, the patient had been taking prednisone, a synthetic glucocorticoid that often is effective in the treatment of autoimmune disease, and azathioprine, an immunosuppressive agent. That regimen was continued.

Outcome: There is no cure for SLE; however, antiinflammatory and immunosuppressive therapy controls flare-ups and may prolong life. Eventually, no therapy is effective.

*When a subject stands, sympathetic nervous system activity initiated reflexly by the arterial baroreceptors increases the release of renin from the kidneys.

**Increased permeability of the glomeruli to the plasma proteins, particularly albumin, which leads to widespread systemic edema and acute renal failure (see Clinical Correlation 38.1).

---

by enzymatic methods. The ratio of glucose in the urine to glucose in the plasma (U/P ratio) is approximately 0.06. The transport of glucose by the renal tubular cells has been studied by the methods of microperfusion and micropuncture. In the rat, microperfusion studies indicate that the absorptive capacity essentially is the same along the length of the proximal convoluted tubule. The concentration of glucose in the filtrate decreases rapidly and then levels off at a low value; when the fluid leaves the proximal tubule, more than 98% of the glucose that was filtered has been reabsorbed. The remainder may be reabsorbed in the collecting duct.

At normal plasma concentrations, most of the glucose is reabsorbed in the first third of the proximal convoluted tubule. As the concentration of glucose in the plasma (P_G) increases, the amount that is filtered ($P_G \times GFR$) increases, and successive segments of the tubule also reabsorb glucose. If the P_G increases to the extent that the filtered load of glucose exceeds the total capacity of the tubule to reabsorb it, glucose appears in the urine (glucosuria). In this case, the maximum quantity of glucose that can be reabsorbed in a given time, or the transport maximum for glucose (T_mG), is reached. The value for T_mG varies among species and individuals but is relatively constant for a given individual during an extended period.

Transport Mechanism

ACTIVE TRANSPORT

Glucose is reabsorbed actively. The mechanism is carrier-mediated, Na^+-dependent, and stereospecific; D-glucose is reabsorbed preferentially. The first step in reabsorption involves the transport of glucose across the luminal membrane in association with Na^+ in a positively charged carrier-complex. The entry of Na^+ into the cells provides the energy for cotransport and the intracellular accumulation of glucose against a gradient of chemical activity; hence, the process is termed "secondary" active transport. The second step in reabsorption involves the efflux of glucose from the cells to the peritubular fluid by facilitated diffusion, which does not depend on Na^+. Experiments that involve labeling glucose with isotopes have demonstrated that glucose is transported from the tubular lumen into the peritubular capillaries within a few seconds, and its structure remains intact.

SPECIFICITY

A number of sugars (e.g., xylose, fructose, and galactose) compete with glucose for the carrier mechanism. The reabsorption of these sugars also is stereospecific because the D forms are reabsorbed preferentially. The transport parameters for these sugars differ from one another and from those of glucose with regard to the renal plasma threshold, maximal transport capacity (T_m), and affinity for the carrier system. The reabsorption of glucose and all of the monosaccharides listed above is inhibited specifically by phlorizin, a glucuronide obtained from the roots of certain fruit trees. Apparently, phlorizin combines with the carrier complex. The glycosuria induced by phlorizin is reversible, which indicates that the hypothetical phlorizin-carrier complex dissociates.

Glucose Titration Curve

The response of the kidneys to an increasing concentration of glucose in the tubular fluid can be described by a glucose titration curve (Figure 40-4). The rate at which glucose is filtered is given by the product of P_G and GFR. When the GFR is constant, the quantity of glucose filtered per minute is a linear function of the P_G. Under normal conditions, at a P_G of 80 mg/dl, essentially all of the glucose that is filtered is reabsorbed, and no glucose is excreted in the urine. Thus, the rate of reabsorption normally is equal to the rate of filtration. If the load of glucose in the tubules is increased progressively by raising the P_G, and the GFR remains constant, the rate of reabsorption of

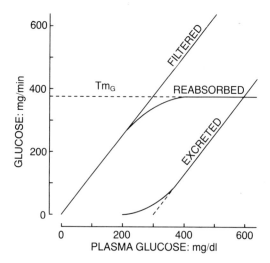

Figure 40-4.   Titration of the renal tubules of a human with glucose. The sharply breaking curves represent an idealized situation, and the rounded curves describe the true relationship. (Redrawn, with permission, from Smith, H.W. 1957. *Principles of Renal Physiology*. New York: Oxford University Press.)

glucose increases proportionately. However, a P_G is reached at which the transport mechanism becomes fully saturated; this critical level is known as the *renal plasma threshold for glucose*. Once the plasma threshold concentration is exceeded, glucose is excreted at a rate that is a linear function of the P_G because glucose then is reabsorbed at a constant rate. This constant rate of reabsorption of glucose is the tubular maximal reabsorptive capacity for glucose, or T_mG. The average value of T_mG in the human is about 375 mg/min.

The rate at which glucose is reabsorbed is the difference between the rate at which it is filtered ($P_G \times$ GFR) and the rate at which it is excreted ($U_G \times \dot{V}_u$):

Rate of glucose reabsorption
$$= (P_G \times GFR) - (U_G \times \dot{V}_u)$$

where U_G is the concentration (mg/dl) of glucose in the urine, and $\dot{V}_u$ is the rate of flow of urine (ml/min). At the renal plasma threshold, the reabsorptive mechanism is saturated, essentially no glucose is excreted, and $U_G \times \dot{V}_u$ = 0. Therefore, the maximum rate of reabsorption of glucose, T_mG, = ($P_G \times$ GFR) − 0. Thus,

$$P_G = \frac{T_mG}{GFR} = \frac{375 \text{ mg/min}}{125 \text{ ml/min}}$$

$$= \frac{300 \text{ mg}}{100 \text{ ml}}, \text{ or } 300 \text{ mg/dl}$$

The theoretical renal plasma threshold for glucose is calculated to be 300 mg/dl. However, the true renal plasma threshold is less than that because glucose begins to appear in the urine at a P_G as low as 180–200 mg/dl. These values seem to indicate that glucose is excreted before the reabsorptive mechanisms become saturated.

SPLAY IN THE TITRATION CURVE

The glucose titration curves are drawn in two ways in Figure 40-4: as sharply breaking curves that represent an idealized situation and as rounded curves that describe the true relationships more accurately. The rounding of the titration curve, termed *splay,* can be explained by the degree of heterogeneity of the population of nephrons.

In the idealized situation, it is assumed that the filtration and transport capacities of all of the nephrons in both kidneys are the same. However, it has been shown that nephrons are not identical in all respects (Figure 40-5). The surface area available for filtration in the glomerulus and the surface area available for reabsorption in the proximal tubule vary in different nephrons. The transport system of nephrons that produce "normal" volumes of filtrate but have subnormal tubular reabsorptive capacities for glucose are saturated at a low P_G, and these nephrons pass glucose into the urine before the T_mG for most nephrons is reached. The transport system of nephrons that produce less than the "normal" volume of filtrate, but have "normal" tubular reabsorptive capacity, are not saturated until higher P_G have been reached. These nephrons continue to reabsorb glucose after the T_mG for most nephrons has been exceeded. Thus, part of the splay in the titration curve reflects the variation of the functional characteristics of the glomeruli and the tubules.

Renal Glucosuria

One of the many congenital disorders that are associated with renal tubular dysfunction is renal glucosuria, in which glucose appears in the urine despite a normal P_G. This condition

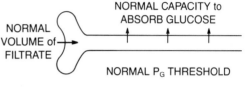

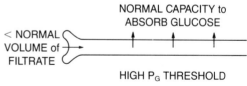

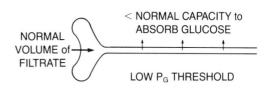

Figure 40-5. Glomerulotubular imbalance as a cause of splay in the glucose titration curve.

indicates a decrease in the renal plasma threshold for glucose and involves a tubular defect that interferes with the reabsorption of glucose. The most common pattern is defective tubular transport of glucose, with no other sign of impaired renal function; however, other tubular defects, such as aminoaciduria, may be associated with renal glucosuria. Glucose titration curves indicate that individuals who have renal glucosuria can be placed in two groups. One group has a reduced T_mG; thus, the renal plasma threshold for glucose is decreased proportionately. The splay in the titration curves is within normal limits. The other group has a normal T_mG, but the splay is marked, which indicates that the basic abnormality may be an abnormal degree of glomerulotubular imbalance.

TRANSPORT OF AMINO ACIDS

Amino acids are filtered freely at the glomerulus and are reabsorbed almost completely by the renal tubules at normal plasma levels, although a trace amount usually is present in normal urine. About 98% of the filtered amino acids are reabsorbed, predominantly in the proximal convoluted tubules. The reabsorption of amino acids is Na^+-dependent and stereospecific; the L-amino acids are reabsorbed preferentially. The processes of amino acid transport are similar to the processes involved in the transport of glucose. The first step is the entry of L-amino acids into the cells, across the luminal membrane, associated with Na^+ in a positively charged carrier-complex. This process is termed "secondary" active transport because, as a consequence of the movement of Na^+ into the cell, the amino acid enters and accumulates in the cell against a concentration gradient. The second step involves efflux by facilitated diffusion from the cells into the peritubular fluid.

The characteristics of transport differ for different amino acids. Some amino acids may have a maximum transport capacity (T_m), but not all amino acids do. Information on the transport of amino acids in the tubules has come from studying individuals who have inherited specific defects of the transport system. According to these studies, neutral amino acids, dibasic amino acids, dicarboxylic amino acids, and the iminoglycine system all are reabsorbed through separate pathways. However, these major classes of amino acids are not transported entirely independent of one another because the different classes compete for reabsorption to some extent.

Aminoaciduria

Aminoaciduria is a condition in which amino acids are excreted excessively in the urine. It may be caused by an inherited disorder that selectively affects the reabsorptive mechanism for either a particular amino acid or a group of chemically related amino acids. For example, Hartnup disease, a clinical disorder associated with mental deficiency and a pellagra-like skin rash, is characterized by excessive excretion of all neutral amino acids. In cystinuria, which is characterized by excretion of the dibasic amino acids, stones composed of cystine form in the urinary tract.

Other factors also may cause aminoaciduria. It can be caused by a metabolic defect that increases the concentration in the plasma of one of the amino acids that usually is reabsorbed completely. Because of the high plasma level, the filtered load exceeds the T_m, and the amino acid appears in the urine. The reabsorption of all of the amino acids may be affected when tubular function is suppressed

by a nephrotoxic substance such as carbon tetrachloride.

TRANSPORT OF PROTEINS

The glomerular membrane largely prevents the filtration of the plasma proteins, but a small amount, mostly albumin, is filtered. The concentration of albumin in the glomerular filtrate is less than 10 mg/dl, and more than 99% of the albumin filtered is reabsorbed in the proximal tubule. Protein is accumulated intracellularly by pinocytosis. The first step in protein transport is the adherence of the protein to the luminal cell membrane, which invaginates to form a membrane vesicle. The pinocytotic vesicle then migrates toward the basal pole of the cell. During this process, the vesicle fuses with lysosomes that contain proteolytic enzymes, and the proteins are degraded by enzymatic action into molecules small enough to be released into the cytoplasm.

TRANSPORT OF CALCIUM

Calcium and phosphate are kept in proper concentrations in the extracellular fluid by the control of absorption from the intestine, release from bone, and excretion in the urine (see Chapter 62).

About 50% of the calcium in the plasma is in the form of Ca^{++}, which is the physiologically important form. Only the Ca^{++} is filtered in the glomeruli. The reabsorption of Ca^{++} by the renal tubules is similar to the reabsorption of Na^+. Approximately 80% of the filtered Ca^{++} is absorbed isosmotically in the proximal tubule; hence, the ratio of $[Ca^{++}]$ in the tubular fluid to $[Ca^{++}]$ in the plasma remains at unity. The reabsorption of Ca^{++} requires energy and is linked to the reabsorption of Na^+. An increase in the reabsorption of Na^+ leads to an increase in the reabsorption of Ca^{++}, and, conversely, a decrease in the reabsorption of Na^+ results in a decrease in the reabsorption of Ca^{++}.

Parathormone

The reabsorption of Ca^{++} by tubular cells is affected by parathyroid hormone (parathormone), which is secreted when the plasma $[Ca^{++}]$ is low (see Chapter 62). Parathormone affects the reabsorption of Ca^{++} in two ways: reabsorption in the proximal tubule is decreased, whereas reabsorption in the distal tubule is increased. The net effect is an increase in the reabsorption of Ca^{++}. However, this direct effect on tubular reabsorption may be offset because parathormone increases plasma $[Ca^{++}]$ by enhancing the resorption of bone; the filtered load of Ca^{++} is increased, and the excess Ca^{++} appears in the urine.

TRANSPORT
OF PHOSPHATE

Phosphate has several functions in the body (see Chapter 62). Calcium phosphate is a prominent constituent of skeletal structures, organic phosphate complexes are key substances in the transformation of energy within cells, and inorganic phosphates contribute to acid-base balance in the body.

Normally, 80%–95% of the phosphate that is filtered is reabsorbed, mostly in the first part of the proximal convoluted tubule. Phosphate is reabsorbed by a "secondary" active transport process that is carrier-mediated, Na^+-dependent, and similar to the transport processes of glucose and amino acids.

Phosphate Titration Curve

The response of the kidneys to an increasing load of phosphate in the tubular fluid can be described by a phosphate titration curve (Figure 40-6). When the plasma concentration of phosphate is low, the filtered load is low, and the phosphate is reabsorbed almost completely. When the concentration of phosphate in the plasma increases, the filtered load increases, and when it exceeds the maximum tubular reabsorptive capacity (T_mPO_4), the excess phosphate is excreted. Any further increase above the renal plasma threshold for phosphate causes a proportionate increase in the rate of excretion of phosphate in the urine. The value for T_mPO_4 ranges between 0.1 and 0.15 mM/min, and, like the glucose titration curve, the titration curve for phosphate is splayed because of the heterogeneity of the population of nephrons.

Unlike the renal plasma threshold for glucose, the renal plasma threshold for phosphate lies very close to the normal plasma level (about 1 mM/liter); thus, only a slight increase or decrease of phosphate concentration in the plasma changes the rate of excretion. Therefore, the kidneys are important in the regulation of the plasma phosphate concentration.

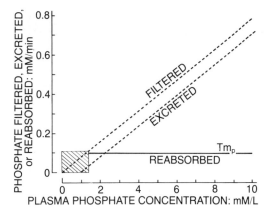

Figure 40-6. Renal titration curve for phosphate. The box shows the normal range. (Redrawn, with permission, from Pitts, R.F., and Alexander, R.S. 1944. The renal absorptive mechanism for inorganic phosphate in normal and acidotic dogs. *Am. J. Physiol.* 142:651.)

Parathormone

The absorptive capacity for phosphate is variable; it is influenced by the body stores of phosphate and by the level of circulating parathormone. Parathormone inhibits the proximal tubular reabsorption of phosphate, or T_mPO_4, and thereby augments the excretion of phosphate (see Chapter 62). Parathormone has also been proposed to increase the secretion of phosphate in the distal tubule.

TRANSPORT OF URATE

Urate is a major end product of protein metabolism in some vertebrates, although it accounts for only about 5% of the total urinary nitrogen in mammals. However, the mechanism of excretion of urate by the kidneys is of interest because of its relationship to gout, which is a condition caused by a defect of purine metabolism. In gout, the concentration of urate in the blood is abnormally high, and chalky deposits that consist mostly of urates form in the cartilage of the joints. Patients who have gout may be divided into two categories: the "overproducers," in whom the rate of synthesis of urate is abnormally high and who may or may not also have a defect in the renal secretion of uric acid, and the "normoproducers," in whom the renal secretion of uric acid is abnormal.

Urate is transported in both directions in the proximal tubular cells; the relative magnitudes of reabsorption and secretion vary from one species to another. In humans, tubular reabsorption predominates, and only about 10% of the filtered load is excreted. Both reabsorption and secretion are carrier-mediated, but the exact nature of the transport mechanism is not known.

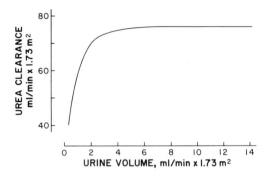

Figure 40-7. Changes of urea clearance with increasing rates of urine flow.

Uricosuric Drugs

The transport of urate is affected by the actions of many drugs, most of which also are transported by the tubular cells. The drugs may either increase or decrease the excretion of urate. An increase in the rate of excretion of urate is attributed either to decreased reabsorption or to increased secretion, and increased retention of urate is attributed either to increased reabsorption or to decreased secretion. Drugs that increase the excretion of urate are called *uricosuric drugs.* Most of these drugs are organic acids (e.g., salicylate and probenecid). Uricosuric drugs are unusual in that they exhibit "paradoxical action." In small doses, the drugs decrease the excretion of urate, which may be accomplished by the inhibition of secretion, but in large doses they increase the rate of excretion, which may be achieved by the inhibition of reabsorption.

TRANSPORT
OF UREA

Urea is the principal end product of protein catabolism in mammals and probably is one of the least toxic endogenous substances. The blood level of urea can vary from 8 to 20 mg/dl, depending on the protein content of the diet. The concentration of urea in the blood increases in various conditions, such as hypercatabolism of protein and advanced renal insufficiency; the latter term is a general one for decreased function of the kidneys. Urea crosses most biological membranes, except the blood-brain barrier (see Chapter 16), with relative ease. Urea is filtered freely at the glomerular membrane and is transported in both directions by the tubular cells. Urea is transported by facilitated diffusion down a concentration gradient, but it also may be accelerated in the direction of net water flow by solvent drag.

Urea Clearance

The concept of urea clearance (C_{urea}), the volume of plasma required to supply the urea excreted in a unit of time, can be used to test renal function; however, C_{urea} is influenced by the rate of flow of urine. C_{urea} increases with an increase of urine flow to a rate of approximately 2 ml/min; thereafter, it increases only slightly, if at all (Figure 40-7). When the rate of flow of urine is more than 2 ml/min, the average C_{urea} is about 75 ml/min, which is approximately 60% of the clearance of inulin (C_{in}). These figures indicate that only about 60% of the filtered urea is excreted in the urine and that 40% of this filtered urea is reabsorbed during the passage along the renal tubules. Because C_{urea} decreases with decreasing urine flow when the rate of flow is less than 2 ml/min, the concepts of *maximum clearance* and *standard clearance* were introduced. When the rate of flow of urine is more than 2 ml/min, the usual, or maximum clearance, formula is used. In this case, the average C_{urea} is about 75 ml/min:

$$C_{urea} = \frac{U_{urea} \times \dot{V}_u}{P_{urea}} = 75 \text{ ml/min}$$

If the rate of flow of urine is less than 2 ml/min, the standard clearance formula is used. The average C_{urea} obtained by using this formula is 57 ml/min:

$$C_{urea} = \frac{U_{urea} \times \sqrt{\dot{V}_u}}{P_{urea}} = 57 \text{ ml/min}$$

The rate of flow of urine changes C_{urea} because it changes the rate of excretion of urea. The relationship between the rate of formation

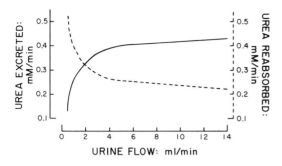

Figure 40-8. Influence of the rate of urine flow on urea reabsorption and urea excretion in the human. The rate of formation of urine first was decreased by decreasing the consumption of water and then increased by increasing the consumption of water. The solid line represents excretion and the dashed line represents absorption. (Redrawn, with permission, from Valtin, H. *Renal Function: Mechanisms Preserving Fluid and Solute Balance in Health.* © 1983. 2nd ed. Boston: Little, Brown, and Co.)

of urine and the rate of excretion of urea is illustrated in Figure 40-8. In the example depicted in this figure, the volume of urine was varied by varying the amount of water consumed. Since the amount of urea that was filtered (P_u × GFR) did not change appreciably, the increased rate of excretion of urea with increased rate of formation of urine must reflect decreased tubular reabsorption of urea. Since the increased volume of urine was caused by decreased reabsorption of water from the collecting duct, the urea in the duct was diluted, and the difference between the concentration of urea in the tubular fluid and the concentration of urea in the interstitial fluid decreased. Because the passive transport of urea depends on this concentration gradient, decreasing the gradient decreases the rate of reabsorption in the collecting duct. The rate of excretion of urea changes more rapidly at low rates of flow of urine than at high rates because the concentration gradient changes proportionately more at low rates of flow. The permeability of the medullary collecting ducts to urea also is decreased in the well-hydrated subject (less ADH is secreted) (see Chapter 41), but the contribution of that variable has not been assessed.

The way the kidneys handle urea at normal rates of flow of urine is shown in Figure 40-9, which is based on micropuncture studies in rats. The numbers within the lumen indicate the percentage of the filtered load of urea that flows at the various sites. Approximately 50%

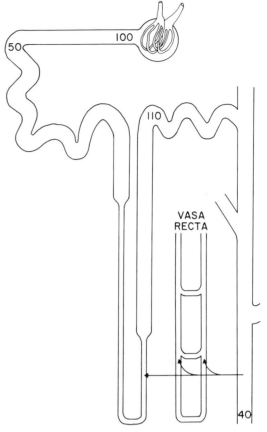

Figure 40-9. Representation of a nephron showing the handling of urea at normal rates of urine flow. The numbers within the lumen represent the percentages of the filtered load of urea that flows at the various sites. The urea that is reabsorbed from the collecting duct is partly removed from the medullary region by the vasa recta and is partly transported back into the loop of Henle to be recirculated through the distal segments of the nephron.

of the filtered load is reabsorbed in the proximal convoluted tubules. However, approximately 110% of the filtered load of urea appears at the beginning of the distal convoluted tubule, which indicates that urea must diffuse into the intermediate segments (the loops of Henle) and possibly into the straight part of the proximal tubule. Urea is reabsorbed again in the medullary collecting ducts, so that about 40% of the filtered load of urea is excreted. Thus, urea moves both ways. The possible advantage of this seemingly complicated handling of urea for the process of concentrating the urine is discussed in Chapter 41.

STUDY OUTLINE

GENERAL CONSIDERATIONS Composition of internal environment of the body is controlled by kidneys.

Regulation depends on balance between glomerular filtration and tubular transport.

Reabsorption and secretion change volume and composition of tubular fluid.

Substances to be retained in the body are reabsorbed completely or almost completely.

Substances to be eliminated are reabsorbed to lesser extent; also may be secreted.

METHODS USED IN THE STUDY OF TRANSPORT

CLEARANCE Minimum volume of plasma required to provide amount of substance excreted.

Provides information on net direction of transport and net action in population of nephrons.

MICROPUNCTURE AND MICROPERFUSION Used to study cellular processes involved in tubular transport.

MICROPUNCTURE Study transport characteristics of tubular structures near kidney surface and in inner medullary region.

Fluid is collected for analysis of concentration of substances.

Split oil droplet allows measurement of the rate of reabsorption of tubular fluid.

MICROPERFUSION Study of transport characteristics in vitro.

MEMBRANE VESICLES Closed vesicles derived from membranes of tubular cells used as models of cells in study of transport.

TRANSEPITHELIAL TRANSPORT OF SOLUTES AND WATER

TUBULAR REABSORPTION

PROXIMAL TUBULE Approximately 80% of filtered electrolytes and water reabsorbed.

Essentially all of filtered glucose and amino acids reabsorbed.

Reabsorption isosmotic—water follows solutes down osmotic gradient.

DISTAL SEGMENTS Composition of fluid varies depending on needs of body.

Transport of Na^+ is affected by aldosterone.

Transport of water is affected by ADH.

TUBULAR SECRETION Foreign substances secreted by proximal tubular cells.

In acid-base regulation, excess H^+ secreted into tubular fluid by proximal, distal, and collecting tubules.

Excess K^+ secreted into tubular fluid by distal convoluted and collecting tubules.

TYPES OF TRANSPORT

ACTIVE TRANSPORT Substance transported against gradient of electrical potential, chemical potential, or both (electrochemical gradient).

Linked either directly to source of metabolic energy ("primary" active transport) or to active transport of another solute ("secondary" active transport).

PASSIVE TRANSPORT Substance moves in reponse to chemical or electrical gradient.

COUPLED TRANSPORT Movement of one solute across cell membrane depends on another solute also moving.

In cotransport, solutes move in same direction across cell membrane. In countertransport, solutes move in opposite direction across cell membrane.

SOLVENT DRAG Transport of solute by movement of water in which solute is dissolved.

FACILITATED DIFFUSION Specific proteins increase rate of transport but cannot move substance against electrochemical gradient.

FUNCTIONAL CHARACTERISTICS OF TUBULAR CELLS

CELL SURFACES OF THE PROXIMAL TUBULE Brush border increases surface area for reabsorption.

Extensive basolateral intercellular space.

High content of Na^+, K^+-ATPase in basolateral membrane indicates active transport.

MITOCHONDRIA Dense population in cells of proximal tubule; support active transport.

Fewer mitochondria in cells of distal tubule.

TIGHT JUNCTION "Leaky" junction in proximal tubule—low-resistance pathway for Cl^- and large volumes of ions and water.

Impermeable to ions and water in distal tubule; higher transepithelial potential develops—favors countertransport of cations.

CAPILLARY ONCOTIC PRESSURE Increased plasma oncotic pressure in peritubular capillaries due to glomerular filtration; aids reabsorption.

TRANSEPITHELIAL POTENTIAL DIF-
FERENCE Three to four millivolts (lumen-
negative to interstitium) in proximal convoluted tubule; mean of 50 mv (lumen-negative) in distal convoluted tubule.

TRANSPORT OF SODIUM, CHLORIDE, AND WATER

TRANSPORT IN THE PROXIMAL TUBULE
Approximately 80% of filtered Na^+ and
water is reabsorbed isosmotically.

TRANSEPITHELIAL MOVEMENT Pas-
sive movement of Na^+ across luminal membrane into cells.

Active transport of Na^+ across basolateral
membrane; accumulates K^+ in cell—depends on
ATP as energy source.

Na^+ also transported by a system not
dependent on Na^+, K^+-ATPase—inhibited by
ethacrynic acid (diuretic).

"LEAKY" TIGHT JUNCTION Pathway for
bulk flow of solutes and water.

SODIUM GRADIENT Approximately 35
mEq/liter maximum.

Normally none across proximal epithelial
cells.

Can be established in presence of nonabsorbable solute.

TRANSPORT IN THE THIN LIMB OF
THE LOOP OF HENLE Descending limb
is relatively impermeable to Na^+ and other
solutes but is permeable to water.

Ascending limb is permeable to solutes and
Na^+ but is relatively impermeable to water.

TRANSPORT IN THE DISTAL TUBULE
Cl^- and Na^+ are reabsorbed in thick ascending
limb but water is not.

Hypotonic fluid reaches distal convoluted
tubule.

TRANSEPITHELIAL MOVEMENT Na^+
diffuses across luminal membrane, actively
transported across basal membrane.

TIGHT JUNCTION Impermeable to solutes
and water.

Cl^- must cross cell membrane to follow reabsorbed Na^+.

High transepithelial potential develops, provides mechanisms for countertransport of H^+
or K^+.

ALDOSTERONE Increases reabsorption of
Na^+ in distal tubule and collecting tubule.

TRANSPORT IN THE COLLECTING TU-
BULE Mechanism similar to that of distal
convoluted tubule.

ANTIDIURETIC HORMONE ADH in-
creases permeability to water; water is reabsorbed down osmotic gradient, urine becomes
concentrated.

GLOMERULOTUBULAR BALANCE Tu-
bular reabsorption related to glomerular filtration.

MECHANISMS Volume filtered and hemodynamic forces govern uptake of fluid by peritubular capillaries.

TRANSPORT OF POTASSIUM Depends
on K^+ balance of body and dietary intake of
K^+—net reabsorption in K^+ deficit and net secretion in K^+ excess.

TRANSPORT IN THE PROXIMAL TU-
BULES Active reabsorption across luminal
membrane.

Passive efflux across basolateral membrane
(down electrochemical gradient).

Reabsorption is isosmotic.

TRANSPORT IN THE LOOP OF HENLE
Passive diffusion along concentration gradient—similar to transport of Na^+.

TRANSPORT IN THE DISTAL AND COL-
LECTING TUBULES Active reabsorption
in thick ascending limb of loop of Henle.

Controlled secretion in distal convoluted and
collecting tubules.

Transported in both directions—balance depends on needs of body.

ACTIVE REABSORPTION K^+ transported
actively across luminal membrane, diffuses
across basal membrane down electrochemical
gradient.

PASSIVE SECRETION K^+ diffuses across
luminal membrane—down electrochemical
gradient.

Large electrical gradient favors accumulation
of K^+ in lumen of distal convoluted and collecting tubules.

*RELATION OF POTASSIUM ION TO HY-
DROGEN ION* Secretion of K^+ affected
by intracellular $[H^+]$—both ions are countertransported across luminal membrane.

TRANSPORT OF GLUCOSE

TRANSPORT CAPACITY Filtered freely at
glomerulus, reabsorbed completely by proximal tubular cells at normal plasma concentration.

TRANSPORT MECHANISM

ACTIVE TRANSPORT Carrier-mediated,

Na$^+$-dependent, stereospecific across luminal membrane.

Efflux across basal membrane by facilitated diffusion.

SPECIFICITY   D-xylose, D-fructose, and D-galactose compete with D-glucose for carrier mechanism.

GLUCOSE TITRATION CURVE   At low plasma concentration, rate of reabsorption equals rate of filtration; rate of reabsorption is directly proportional to P_G; no glucose is excreted.

When tubular reabsorptive capacity (T_mG) is reached, glucose is excreted in urine; rate of excretion equals rate of filtration minus T_mG; directly proportional to P_G.

Renal plasma threshold—plasma level at which T_mG reached.

SPLAY IN THE TITRATION CURVE   Explained by heterogeneity of nephron population.

RENAL GLUCOSURIA   Glucose in urine at normal P_G; defective tubular transport.

TRANSPORT OF AMINO ACIDS   Amino acids filtered freely at glomerulus, reabsorbed completely by proximal tubular cells at normal plasma levels.

Carrier-mediated, Na$^+$-dependent, stereospecific (L-amino acid form reabsorbed) across luminal membrane.

Efflux by facilitated diffusion across basal membrane.

Transport characteristics differ for different amino acids.

Separate pathways for groups of chemically related amino acids.

AMINOACIDURIA   Excessive excretion of amino acids in urine.

Defective tubular transport, metabolic defect, or nephrotoxic substances.

TRANSPORT OF PROTEINS   Some albumin is filtered, reabsorbed by pinocytosis in proximal tubule.

TRANSPORT OF CALCIUM   Only Ca^{++} is filtered.

Reabsorbed actively.

Eighty percent is reabsorbed isosmotically in proximal tubules.

PARATHORMONE   Secreted when plasma [Ca^{++}] is low.

Reabsorption of Ca^{++} is decreased in proximal tubule, increased in distal tubule; net effect is increased reabsorption.

Direct effect on reabsorption of Ca^{++} may be offset by increased plasma [Ca^{++}] caused by resorption of bone; filtered Ca^{++} is increased and excess Ca^{++} is excreted.

TRANSPORT OF PHOSPHATE   Eighty percent to ninety-five percent is reabsorbed, mainly in proximal tubule; carrier-mediated, Na$^+$-dependent.

PHOSPHATE TITRATION CURVE   Kidneys regulate plasma phosphate.

Renal plasma threshold close to normal plasma level (approximately 1 mM/liter).

PARATHORMONE   Inhibits proximal tubular reabsorption.

TRANSPORT OF URATE   Transported in both directions in proximal tubule.

About 10% of amount filtered is excreted.

URICOSURIC DRUGS   Excretion of urate is decreased by small doses, increased by large doses.

TRANSPORT OF UREA   Urea principal end product of protein catabolism in mammals; filtered freely at glomerulus.

Blood level varies with protein content in diet, increased by hypercatabolic states and renal insufficiency.

Transported in both directions by tubular cells—facilitated diffusion and solvent drag.

UREA CLEARANCE   Influenced by rate of urine formation; increased volume in tubule decreases gradient for passive reabsorption, and decreased secretion of ADH decreases permeability of medullary collecting ducts to urea.

BIBLIOGRAPHY

Burg, M., and Good, D. 1983. Sodium chloride-coupled transport in mammalian nephrons. *Annu. Rev. Physiol.* 45:533.

Burg, M., and Orloff, J. 1973. Perfusion of isolated renal tubules. In *Handbook of Physiology.* Section 8. Renal Physiology. Chapter 7. Edited by J. Orloff and R.W. Berliner. Washington, D.C.: American Physiological Society.

Erlij, D. 1976. Solute transport across isolated epithelia. *Kidney Int.* 9:76.

Gertz, K.H., and Boylan, J.W. 1973. Glomerular-tubular balance. In *Handbook of Physiology.* Section 8. Renal Physiology. Chapter 23. Edited by J. Orloff and R.W. Berliner. Washington, D.C.: American Physiological Society.

Giebisch, G., and Windhager, E. 1973. Electrolyte transport across renal tubular membranes. In *Handbook of Physiology.* Section 8. Renal Physiology. Chapter 11. Edited by J. Orloff and R.W. Berliner. Washington, D.C.: American Physiological Society.

Gottschalk, C.W., and Lassiter, W.E. 1973. Micropuncture methodology. In *Handbook of Physiology.* Section 8. Renal Physiology. Chapter 6. Edited by J. Orloff and R.W. Berliner. Washington, D.C.: American Physiological Society.

Hays, R.M. 1978. The kidney in health and disease—IV. Principles of ion and water transport in the kidney. *Hosp. Pract.* 13 (part 2): 79.

Jørgensen, P.L. 1980. Sodium and potassium ion pump in kidney tubules. *Physiol. Rev.* 60:864.

Koeppen, B.M.; Biagi, B.A.; and Giebisch, G. 1983. Electrophysiology of mammalian renal tubules: Inferences from intracellular microelectrode studies. *Annu. Rev. Physiol.* 45:497.

Lemann, J., Jr.; Adams, N.D.; and Gray, R.W. 1979. Urinary calcium excretion in human beings. *N. Engl. J. Med.* 301:535.

Mercer, P.F.; Maddox, D.A.; and Brenner, B.M. 1974. Current concepts of sodium chloride and water transport by the mammalian nephron. *West. J. Med.* 120:33.

Mudge, G.H.; Berndt, G.H.; and Valtin, H. 1973. Tubular transport of urea, glucose, phosphate, uric acid, sulfate, and thiosulfate. In *Handbook of Physiology.* Section 8. Renal Physiology. Chapter 19. Edited by J. Orloff and R.W. Berliner. Washington, D.C.: American Physiological Society.

Walser, M. 1973. Divalent cations: Physiochemical state in glomerular filtrate and urine and renal excretion. In *Handbook of Physiology.* Section 8. Renal Physiology. Chapter 18. Edited by J. Orloff and R.W. Berliner. Washington, D.C.: American Physiological Society.

Weiner, I.M. 1973. Transport of weak acids and bases. In *Handbook of Physiology.* Section 8. Renal Physiology. Chapter 17. Edited by J. Orloff and R.W. Berliner. Washington, D.C.: American Physiological Society.

Wright, F.S. 1974. Potassium transport by the renal tubule. In *MTP International Review of Science.* Volume 6. Physiology Series I. Kidney and Urinary Tract Physiology. Chapter 3. Edited by A.C. Guyton (Consultant Editor) and K.C. Thuran (Volume Editor). Baltimore: University Park Press.

41

Renal Concentrating and Diluting Mechanisms

CHAPTER CONTENTS

GENERAL CONSIDERATIONS

The human kidneys have the ability to excrete either a concentrated urine or a dilute urine, depending on the degree of hydration of the individual. The ratio of the osmotic activity of substances in the urine to that of substances in the plasma is given by the expression U_{osm}/P_{osm}. In conditions that require conservation of water, the osmolality of the urine can be increased to four times that of the plasma ($U_{osm}/P_{osm} = 4$), and when the body has excess water, urine that is one-sixth the osmolality of plasma ($U_{osm}/P_{osm} = 1/6$) can be excreted. This ability to excrete urine that is either more concentrated or more dilute than the plasma enables the kidneys to regulate the concentration of solutes and, hence, the osmolality of the body fluids, within narrow physiological limits, despite wide fluctuations in the intake of water and solutes.

The ability of the kidneys to concentrate urine varies among different species depending on the availability of water in the environment (Figure 41-1). Animals that live in or near plentiful supplies of fresh water tend to excrete rather dilute urine (e.g., $U_{osm}/P_{osm} < 2$ in the beaver), whereas animals that live in arid environments must conserve water (e.g., $U_{osm}/P_{osm} = 20$ in the desert rat). The thickness of the medulla relative to the cortex, and the maximum concentrating ability of the kidneys, are correlated closely (Figure 41-1); as the relative thickness of the medulla increases, the ability to concentrate the urine increases. The thickness of the medulla is determined by the lengths of the loops of Henle, especially the thin limbs, which are important parts of the urinary concentrating mechanism.

COUNTERCURRENT SYSTEM

The final concentration of the urine is determined by the passive transport of water out of the collecting ducts into the hypertonic milieu of the medulla. The osmolality of the interstitial fluid in the medulla of the mammalian kidneys increases steadily from the corticomedullary junction to the tip of the papilla. This

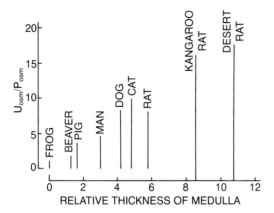

Figure 41-1. Relationship between the ability of the kidneys to concentrate urine and the thickness of the renal medulla relative to that of the renal cortex. Animals such as the frog cannot produce concentrated urine because their nephrons possess no loop of Henle. Animals such as the desert rat can produce concentrated urine because their nephrons possess long loops of Henle, especially the long thin limbs. (Redrawn, with permission, from Deetjen, P., et al. 1975. *Physiology of the Kidney and of Water Balance.* New York: Springer-Verlag.)

gradual increase of osmolality is the result of the combined functions of the loops of Henle of the juxtamedullary nephrons, which form a countercurrent multiplier system, and the vasa recta, which are arranged parallel to and in close proximity to the loops of Henle and act as a countercurrent exchange system.

In a *countercurrent* system, the inflow channel of the fluid runs closely parallel and counter to the outflow channel. This arrangement permits the fluid that is entering the system to reach equilibrium with the fluid that is leaving the system. In a countercurrent *multiplier* system, a small, active, single effect is enhanced, or multiplied, so that a concentration gradient develops along the system. In a countercurrent *exchange* system, equilibration between the entering and exiting fluids minimizes the washout of solutes, and thereby conserves the concentration gradient that is generated by the multiplier. The structures involved in the medullary countercurrent system are the descending and ascending limbs of the loops of Henle, the descending and ascending limbs of the vasa recta, the collecting ducts, and the interstitium around these structures.

Countercurrent Multiplication of Concentration

MODEL SYSTEM

A simple model may be used to describe how a concentration gradient can be built up by a countercurrent multiplier system (Figure 41-2). This model consists of a long narrow tube that doubles back on itself, so that the fluid flows into the limb S_1 parallel to and in the opposite direction from the fluid that is flowing out of the limb S_2, as depicted in the figure. Initially, all of the fluid in the system has an osmolality of 300 mOsm/liter (a). If the membrane that separates the two limbs (S_1 and S_2) is impermeable to water but can transport solute from the outflow limb (S_2) to the inflow limb (S_1), a difference of concentration can be created at each level of the loop. The creation of this concentration gradient at each level is called the *single effect*. In Figure 41-2, a concentration gradient of 200 mOsm/liter can be established at all levels of the limbs; the establishment of the single effect and the movement of fluid, which normally occur simultaneously, are depicted as occurring alternately. Because of the single effect, a difference of 200 mOsm/liter is established between the two limbs, and the concentration of solute in S_1 increases to 400 mOsm/liter, while that in S_2 decreases to 200 mOsm/liter (b). If enough fluid of the original osmolality of 300 mOsm/liter flows to displace half of the contents of S_1 forward into S_2, half of S_2 will be filled with a fluid that has an osmolality of 400 mOsm/liter (c). Once more, the single effect generates a concentration gradient of 200 mOsm/liter at each level of the loop, and a concentration of 500 mOsm/liter is created at the apex of S_1 (d); this is a greater concentration than could be achieved by the single effect alone; yet the maximum gradient is only 200 mOsm/liter. The effluent now has an osmolality of 150 mOsm/liter. Continuation of the flow of fluid and the repetition of the single effect generates a concentration of 700 mOsm/liter in the fluid at the apex of the loop and a concentration of 112 mOsm/liter in the fluid that leaves the loop (Figure 41-2, e-h). Because of the loop and the direction of flow from S_1 to S_2, a more concentrated fluid is brought to the transport sites in the apical region of S_2, and a more dilute fluid is presented to the base of the loop. Thus, the single effect at each level of the loop is multiplied; the osmolality of the fluid at the apex of the loop is high,

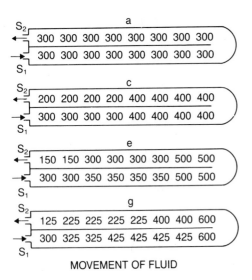

MOVEMENT OF FLUID

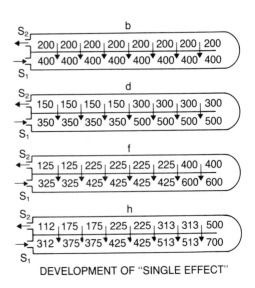

DEVELOPMENT OF "SINGLE EFFECT"

Figure 41-2. The principle of countercurrent multiplication of concentration. It is assumed that a gradient of 200 mOsm/liter can be established between the outflowing limb (S_2) and the inflowing limb (S_1) by the transport of solutes. In reality, the movement of fluid and the development of the single effect take place continuously, but for the sake of clarity, the two processes are treated as if they occurred in alternating steps. As a result of multiplication of the single effect by the countercurrent flow of fluid, a concentration gradient is developed between the beginning and the bend in a countercurrent system. See the text for further discussion. (Redrawn, with permission, from Pitts, R.F. 1974. *Physiology of the Kidney and Body Fluids* (3rd ed.). Chicago: Year Book Medical Publishers, Inc.)

but the osmolality of the fluid at the base of the outflow limb is low. If the individual steps in the process are infinitely small, the multiplier process is continuous, and the osmolality rises steadily from the base to the apex of the loop.

COUNTERCURRENT SYSTEM IN THE KIDNEYS

In the kidneys, the arrangement of the renal tubules approximates the arrangement that is described in the model above. As illustrated in Figure 41-3, the loop of Henle in the renal medulla has a hairpin configuration, so that the flow of tubular fluid in one limb of the loop is closely parallel and opposite to the flow in the other limb. Because of the characteristic permeabilities of the descending and ascending limbs of the loop of Henle to ions and water, the epithelial cells that line the loop build up and maintain a small osmotic gradient between the descending and ascending limbs at all levels of the loop. Because the tubular fluid moves in opposite directions in the two limbs, the small single effect at each level is multiplied, and the

concentration gradient between the base and the apex of the loop is established. The collecting duct runs parallel to the loop of Henle, and the fluid contained in it flows in a direction opposite to that in the ascending limb. Under the influence of antidiuretic hormone (ADH), the epithelial cells of the collecting duct become permeable to water, and water moves down an osmotic gradient into the hypertonic interstitium. As the tubular fluid flows through the collecting duct, it tends to equilibrate with fluid of increasing osmolality in the neighboring interstitium, and the osmolality of the urine that leaves the kidneys approaches the osmolality of the fluid at the apex of the loop.

MECHANISM

All of the metabolic work in the countercurrent multiplier system of the kidneys is channeled into the active transport of Na^+ and Cl^- out of the thick ascending limb of the loop of Henle. Since this region is impermeable to water, the active transport of Na^+ and Cl^- produces hypotonic fluid in the thick ascending limb. In the

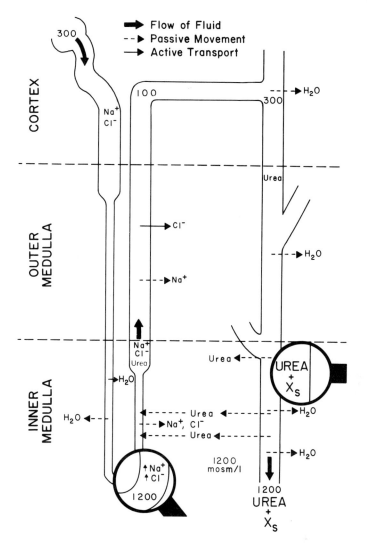

Figure 41-3. Countercurrent multiplication mechanism for concentrating the urine. The numbers refer to mOsm/liter. See the text for further discussion. ⟶ indicates flow of fluid; --⟶ indicates passive movement; ⟶ indicates active transport.

absence of ADH, the cortical and outer-medullary collecting tubules are impermeable to both urea and water. In the presence of ADH, these tubules become permeable to water but not to urea. Consequently, water is absorbed osmotically from the tubular fluid of these segments, and the concentration of urea increases. The inner medullary portion of the collecting ducts is permeable to urea. Urea diffuses out of the inner medullary and papillary collecting tubules, down its concentration gradient, and accumulates in the interstitium. The high concentration of urea in the inner medullary interstitium establishes an osmotic gradient that transports water from the descending

limb of the loop of Henle and, in the presence of ADH, from the collecting tubules. In this way, the metabolic energy used in the transport of solutes in the thick ascending limb of the loop of Henle is transferred to the medulla.

PERMEABILITIES
The permeabilities of the thin descending limb and the thin ascending limb of the loop of Henle are entirely different. The descending limb is highly permeable to water and is relatively impermeable to Na^+, Cl^-, and urea. The thin ascending limb, on the other hand, is very permeable to Na^+ and Cl^-, moderately per-

meable to urea, and impermeable to water. Consequently, when isotonic fluid from the proximal tubule enters the thin descending limb, it equilibrates with the hypertonic medullary interstitium, primarily by the movement of water from the tubular fluid into the interstitium down an osmotic gradient. The fluid that enters the descending limb contains NaCl, while the medullary interstitial fluid contains a mixture of NaCl and urea. Therefore, removal of water increases the concentration of NaCl in the tubular fluid to a level greater than that in the surrounding interstitial fluid, even though the osmolalities of the two fluids are equal.

Because the fluid that leaves the thin descending limb of the loop of Henle and enters the thin ascending limb of the loop has a higher concentration of NaCl and a lower concentration of urea than that of the adjacent interstitial fluid, a relatively hypo-osmotic tubular fluid is generated in the thin ascending limb strictly by passive means. NaCl diffuses from the tubular lumen into the interstitium, and urea diffuses from the interstitium into the tubular lumen, each down its concentration gradient. Because the tubular epithelium is more permeable to Na^+ and Cl^- than it is to urea and is impermeable to water, Na^+ and Cl^- diffuse out of the tubule faster than urea diffuses in, the luminal fluid becomes hypo-osmotic relative to the interstitium, and NaCl is added to the interstitial fluid. The high concentration of NaCl in the interstitium produces an osmotic gradient that concentrates the non-urea solutes in the final urine. The urea that enters the tubular fluid in the thin ascending limb is concentrated by the active transport of Na^+ and Cl^- out of the fluid in the thick ascending limb and the subsequent loss of water in the collecting tubules. Eventually, the urea is recycled into the inner medullary region, where it produces an osmotic gradient that removes water from the thin descending limb of the loop of Henle.

LOCATION OF NEPHRONS

All of the nephrons in the mammalian kidneys, both cortical and juxtamedullary, have thick ascending limbs that pass through the outer medullary region, but only the juxtamedullary nephrons possess loops of Henle that penetrate the inner medullary and papillary regions. According to the model of the countercurrent multiplier system described above, the meta-

bolic work is done in the thick ascending limbs of all of the nephrons, whereas the osmotic gradient is established by the nephrons that have long loops.

ROLE OF UREA

Micropuncture studies have shown that urea is both absorbed and secreted by the renal tubular cells. In fact, approximately half of the urea that is filtered remains in the fluid at the end of the proximal tubule and is recirculated between the tubular fluid and the interstitial fluid of the medulla. The ascending thin limb of the loop of Henle and the medullary collecting duct are permeable to urea but the distal convoluted tubules and the cortical collecting tubules are not. Because of the active transport of Na^+ and Cl^- out of the tubular fluid in the thick ascending limb of the loop of Henle and the distal convoluted tubules and the passive removal of water from the cortical and medullary collecting tubules in the presence of ADH, urea is concentrated in the tubular fluid and diffuses from the inner medullary collecting tubules into the medullary interstitium down its concentration gradient. From the interstitium, urea moves down its concentration gradient into the ascending thin limb of the loop of Henle and is carried by the tubular fluid up the ascending limb, through the distal tubule, and back again into the collecting tubule. Urea makes this circuit several times before it finally moves on through the collecting duct into the ureter. In the process, urea accumulates in high concentration in the medullary interstitium.

The accumulation of urea, Na^+, and Cl^- in the inner medulla increases the osmolality of the fluid in that region. In Figure 41-3 the value of 1200 mOsm/liter in the inner medullary region represents the combined osmolalities of Na^+, Cl^-, urea, and other solutes. This value is characteristic of an individual who is slightly dehydrated and in whom water is being conserved by the excretion of urine concentrated to four times the osmolality of the plasma.

The recirculation of urea constitutes a countercurrent multiplier system that enables the body to excrete urea, a metabolic end product, in the urine in a higher concentration than would be possible otherwise. The high concentration is caused by the continual, simultaneous buildup of urea in the collecting tubules and the medullary interstitium. In the presence of ADH, both the cortical and medullary collecting ducts are permeable to water, and the inner medullary collecting ducts also are significantly more permeable to urea. Therefore, water is reabsorbed from the tubular fluid, and the concentration of urea increases in the fluid that is delivered to the medullary collecting ducts. The increase in the concentration of urea in the tubular fluid, coupled with the increase of the permeability of the inner medullary collecting ducts to urea under the influence of ADH, enhances the passive diffusion of urea into the interstitium of the inner medulla. As a result, the concentration of urea in the inner medulla, and, hence, the osmolality of that area, is increased. Because the fluid in the collecting tubules of the medulla equilibrates with the fluid in the interstitium, the concentration of urea in the urine that leaves the papillary duct can become quite high. Thus, only relatively small amounts of water must be excreted, even though a large quantity of urea, the end product of protein catabolism, is excreted.

Countercurrent Exchange Mechanism

MAINTAINING GRADIENTS

The concentration gradient that is built up by the countercurrent multiplier system must be maintained and not washed away by the bloodstream. This requirement is met by the specialized anatomical arrangement of the medullary blood vessels, the vasa recta, which form another countercurrrent system parallel and in close proximity to that of the loop of Henle, and the collecting duct (Figure 41-4). Unlike the loop of Henle, the vascular countercurrent system does not contribute to the establishment of an osmotic gradient in the medullary region, but it does help to maintain one. Because the capillary endothelium is permeable to both solutes and water, the plasma of the vasa recta equilibrates with the medullary interstitial fluid. As the plasma flows through the descending vessels, it becomes more and more hyperosmotic through the passive loss of water and the passive uptake of solutes, each down its concentration gradient. By the time the plasma reaches the deep medullary region, it is concentrated to 1200 mOsm/liter, which is the concentration of the surrounding interstitium. The opposite occurs in the ascending vessels. As the plasma flows from a region of higher osmolality to one of lower osmolality, it becomes less and less hyperosmotic

through passive loss of solutes and uptake of water. By this means, the osmolality of the plasma that leaves the medulla is only slightly higher than that of the plasma that enters the medulla. Thus, through passive equilibration of the plasma with the fluid of the interstitium, the vasa recta remove the solutes and water that have been reabsorbed from the loops of Henle and the collecting tubules but do not disturb the longitudinal concentration gradients in the medulla.

RATE OF BLOOD FLOW

Although the exchange system of the vascular bed does not establish an osmotic gradient in the medullary region, the effective functioning of the tubules depends on the performance of the vasa recta. The rate of blood flow in the medulla is considerably less than that in the cortex and accounts for only about 5% of the total renal perfusion. However, changes in the rate of blood flow to the medullary region affect the capacity of the kidneys to concentrate urine because the maximum osmolality of the deep medullary region is affected. When the blood flow to the medulla increases, the effectiveness of the countercurrent exchange system decreases because some osmotically active solutes are washed away, and the concentration gradient in the medullary region is impaired. Under this condition, the maximum osmolality of the urine decreases, even though the rate of glomerular filtration virtually is constant.

Significance of Concentrating and Diluting Mechanism

An adult human who takes an adequate diet excretes approximately 900–1200 mOsm of "obligatory" solutes in the urine each day. This amount includes metabolic end products, such as urea and creatinine, and certain ions that often are ingested in excess. If the load of 900–1200 mOsm of substances were to be excreted in a solution isosmotic with plasma (300 mOsm/liter), approximately 3–4 liters of urine would be excreted each day. Ordinarily, the osmolality of human urine is about 2–3 times that of plasma, so that the volume of urine is only 1–2 liters/day. When excess water is taken in, it is excreted in the urine, and during water diuresis, the osmolality of the urine may be as low as one-sixth that of plasma. However, under conditions of water deprivation, when it is important to conserve water, the urine may

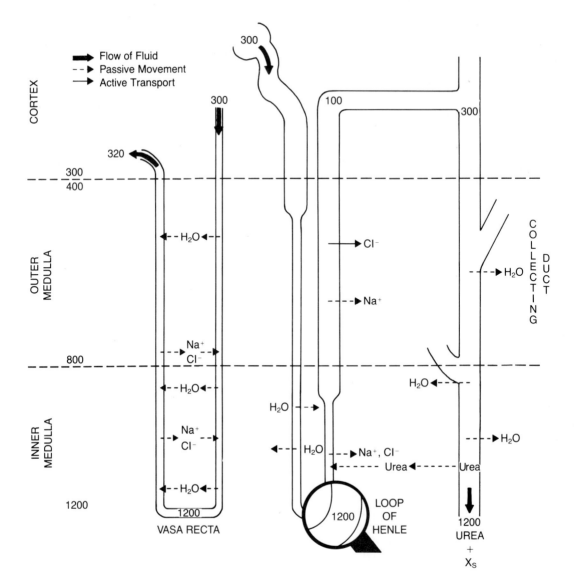

Figure 41-4. Countercurrent mechanism for concentrating the urine. The loop of Henle functions as the countercurrent multiplier, and the vasa recta function as the countercurrent exchanger. The arrangement of the vasa recta permits the perfusion of the medullary region and the final reabsorption of water from the collecting duct but prevents dissipation of the medullary osmotic gradient set up by the countercurrent multiplier. The numbers refer to mOsm/liter. ➡ indicates flow of fluid; - ➤ indicates passive movement; ➝ indicates active transport.

reach an osmolality four times that of the plasma, and the volume of urine can be reduced to about 1 liter/day.

EXCRETION OF CONCENTRATED URINE

In dehydration, because of the difference between the effect of ADH on the permeability of the distal convoluted tubules and the cortical and medullary collecting tubules to water and urea, urea accumulates in the inner medullary region. This effect contributes further to the high osmolality caused by the accumulation of NaCl, and the concentration of solutes in this region reaches 1200 mOsm/liter. The final reabsorption of water occurs in the collecting tubules, under the influence of ADH. As the fluid flows along the collecting tubules, it equilibrates with interstitial fluid of increasing osmolality; when the fluid flows into the ureter, its osmolality approaches 1200 mOsm/liter.

CLINICAL CORRELATION

41.1 Inappropriate Secretion of ADH

CASE REPORT

The Patient: A 43-year-old man.

Reason for Admission: Headache, nausea, weakness, thirst, and abrupt loss of vision in one eye.

History: At the age of 33, the patient had been diagnosed as having multiple sclerosis (MS). He had developed numbness and weakness on the right side of the body that progressed to quadriplegia. He had been treated successfully with adrenocorticotropic hormone (ACTH) (see Chapter 60, "ACTH, or Corticotropin") and dismissed in improved condition. During the intervening years, he had experienced episodes of hemiplegia or paraplegia that were ameliorated by ACTH.

Clinical Examination: Loss of vision was complete in the right eye and the pupil was fixed; deep tendon reflexes (see Chapter 6, "Clinical Applications of Spinal Reflexes") in the right leg were absent; and deep sensation was decreased in both legs. The arterial pressure was 95/70 mm Hg with the patient in the supine position, and 85/65 mm Hg in the standing position (normal, 90–140/60–90 mm Hg); this difference indicates a slight degree of postural hypotension—see Chapter 12, "Effects of Gravity on Vascular Pressure". Sodium concentration [Na$^+$] in the serum was 110 mEq/liter (normal, 135–145 mEq/l), [K$^+$] was 4.0 mEq/liter (normal, 3.5–5 mEq/liter), [Cl$^-$] was 75 mEq/liter (normal, 100–106 mEq/liter), blood urea nitrogen (BUN) was 7 mg/dl (normal, 8–25 mg/dl), creatinine was 0.3 mg/dl (normal, 0.6–1.5 mg/dl), hematocrit was 33% (normal, 45–52%), and serum osmolality was 235 mOsm/kg water (normal, 285–295 mOsm/kg water). The patient weighed 60.4 kg (usual weight, 57.4 kg). [Na$^+$] of the urine was 125 mEq/liter (normal, 50–130 mEq/liter), [K$^+$] was 45 mEq/liter (normal, 20–70 mEq/liter), specific gravity was 1.020 (normal, 1.015–1.022), and osmolality was 615 mOsm/kg water (normal, 500–800 mOsm/kg water).

Comment: The findings of normal osmolality and [Na$^+$] of the urine despite hypotonic plasma indicate inappropriate secretion of antidiuretic hormone (ADH) (see Chapter 42). The concentrations of several constituents of the plasma—Na$^+$, Cl$^-$, BUN, creatinine, and red cells (hematocrit)—were low, and the osmolality of the blood was low. Under these conditions, a dilute urine should have been excreted, to increase the osmolality of the blood. For this to occur, the secretion of ADH would have been inhibited by input from the osmoreceptors of the hypothalamus (see Chapter 56, "Control of Secretion of Vasopressin"). Inappropriate secretion of ADH in this patient probably is related to demyelinating lesions of the hypothalamus as one of the manifestations of MS. Other effects of hypothalamic damage also have been seen in patients who have MS. These include galactorrhea (excessive or spontaneous flow of milk), presumed to be associated with the absence of normal inhibition of the release of prolactin from the pituitary, and amenorrhea (absence of menstruation), presumed to reflect alteration of normal hypothalamic cycles (see Chapter 63, "Menstrual Cycle"). Consistent with this concept, the development of hypotonic plasma in this patient occurred during an exacerbation (worsening) of the MS, characterized by focal disorders of the central nervous system. The symptoms of headache, nausea, and weakness probably were related to hyponatremia.

Treatment: The patient was given hypertonic (5%) NaCl solution, intravenously, and his fluid intake was restricted, to establish normal osmolality of the plasma; he was given democlocycline, which antagonizes the action of ADH; and he was given ACTH. He also was given cyclophosphamide, which suppresses the immune system of the body. Evidence indicates that MS is an autoimmune disease associated in some way with viral infection.

Outcome: The patient improved rapidly, and the vision in his affected eye began to return after two days. He produced large amounts of urine, and his weight returned to normal in three days. He was discharged after five days with his blood chemistry normal and the MS in remission. However, MS is a progressive illness, and he will suffer relapse again.

EXCRETION OF DILUTE URINE

To eliminate excess water in the body, dilute urine is excreted. The tubular fluid that reaches the early distal convoluted tubules is hypotonic because more NaCl than water is transported out of the tubular lumens in the ascending limbs of the loops of Henle. Further reabsorption of Na^+ and anions in the distal convoluted tubules, which are impermeable to water, decreases the concentration of the tubular fluid from approximately 100 mOsm/liter to 50 mOsm/liter. In the absence of ADH, the collecting tubules are impermeable to water, and the fluid that is delivered into the collecting tubules remains hypotonic throughout its passage. Therefore, a very dilute urine of approximately 50 mOsm/liter is excreted.

FREE-WATER CLEARANCE

When urine more dilute than plasma is excreted, a higher proportion of the water than of the osmotically active solutes of the glomerular filtrate appears in the urine. The excretion of water essentially free of electrolytes is called *excretion of free water*, and the clearance of this solute-free water, or the volume of plasma that is required to supply this excess water each minute, is called *free-water clearance* (C_{H2O}). C_{H2O} reflects a different aspect of the ability of the kidneys to maintain the osmolality of the body fluids. ADH modulates the tubular reabsorption of free water by altering the permeability of the cortical and medullary collecting tubules to water, so that either a concentrated or a dilute urine is excreted. The C_{H2O} can be calculated by finding the difference between the rate of formation of urine ($\dot{V}_u$) and the volume of water necessary for the excretion of urine that is isotonic with plasma. The volume of water is termed *osmolar clearance* (C_{osm}).

$$C_{H2O} = \dot{V}_u - C_{osm}$$

$$= \dot{V}_u - \frac{(U_{osm} \times \dot{V}_u)}{P_{osm}}$$

where U_{osm} is the osmolality of the urine and P_{osm} is the osmolality of the plasma. When C_{osm} is less than $\dot{V}_u$ (i.e., C_{H2O} is positive), relatively more water than solute is excreted and the urine is hypotonic. Thus, excess water is excreted. Conversely, when C_{osm} is greater than $\dot{V}_u$ (i.e., C_{H2O} is negative), relatively more solute than water is excreted and the urine is hypertonic. Thus, water is conserved.

WATER DIURESIS AND OSMOTIC DIURESIS

An increased rate of flow of urine is termed *diuresis*. When the increase is caused by drinking a large volume of hypotonic fluid, *water diuresis* occurs and dilute urine is excreted. In contrast, *osmotic diuresis* is the excretion of a large volume of urine caused by the presence of large quantities of unreabsorbed solutes.

Water Diuresis

Normally, about 99% of the glomerular filtrate is reabsorbed by the renal tubules and approximately 1% is excreted as urine. The various segments of the nephron have different functions in the reabsorptive process. About 80% of the filtered fluid is reabsorbed in the proximal tubule, regardless of whether the individual is hydrated or dehydrated, and this portion of the absorbed fluid sometimes is referred to as *"obligatory" reabsorption*. The final reabsorption of water from the tubular fluid occurs in the collecting tubules under the influence of ADH. Absorption of water in this segment sometimes is referred to as *facultative*; it is determined by the level of circulating ADH, is variable, and depends on the water balance of the individual. In water diuresis, the maximal flow of urine is about 15% of the volume filtered (approximately 17 ml/min) because only water reabsorbed in the collecting tubules is affected. Because free water is excreted, the urine is hypo-osmotic with respect to plasma. The magnitudes of reabsorption of fluid in the various segments of the nephron during both antidiuresis (action of ADH) and water diuresis are illustrated in Figure 41-5.

Osmotic Diuresis

MECHANISM

Osmotic diuresis is caused by the presence in the renal tubules of large amounts of solutes that are not reabsorbed by the tubular cells. These solutes remain in the tubular lumen, where they exert an appreciable osmotic effect, and water remains in the tubular lumen. Under normal circumstances, the reabsorption of approximately 80% of the filtered Na^+ and anions in the proximal tubule is accompanied by the reabsorption of 80% of the water, and the concentration of Na^+ at the end of the proximal

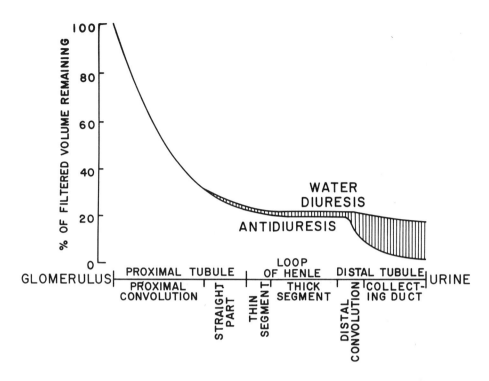

Figure 41-5.   Reabsorption of fluid in a superficial nephron of the rat during water diuresis and during antidiuresis. The fraction of the filtered water that remained in the tubular lumen was calculated from the increase in the concentration of inulin. (Redrawn, with permission, from Deetjen, P., et al. 1975. *Physiology of the Kidney and of Water balance.* New York: Springer-Verlag.)

tubule is similar to that in the plasma. Therefore, Na$^+$ is not reabsorbed against a concentration gradient. In the presence of a nonabsorbable and osmotically active substance (e.g., mannitol), Na$^+$ and water still are reabsorbed, but a portion of the water is retained by the osmotic effect of the nonabsorbable substance. The osmolality of the tubular fluid under this condition still is similar to that of plasma, but the osmolality is contributed by both the sodium salt and the unabsorbed solute. The [Na$^+$] in the tubular fluid decreases; hence, Na$^+$ must be reabsorbed against a concentration gradient. The proximal tubular cells can transport Na$^+$ against a gradient of about 35 mEq/liter between the tubular fluid and plasma. Therefore, if the plasma [Na$^+$] is a normal value of 145 mEq/liter, the luminal [Na$^+$] can fall to 110 mEq/liter before the reabsorption of Na$^+$ stops. Because of the larger volume of tubular fluid, more than the normal amount of Na$^+$ remains in the proximal tubule when this limiting gradient is reached. The result is an increase in the rate of flow of isosmotic fluid into the loop of Henle.

The nonabsorbable substance also inhibits the reabsorption of water and electrolytes in the thin limbs of the loop of Henle. Since less water leaves the tubule in the descending thin limb, the concentration gradient of NaCl between the lumen of the tubule and the interstitium is smaller and less NaCl leaves the tubule in the ascending thin limb. Thus, an increased volume of urine that contains a large amount of the unreabsorbable solute and larger than normal quantities of electrolytes (the most important of which is Na$^+$) flows through the loop of Henle into the distal collecting tubules. Therefore, during osmotic diuresis, electrolytes that normally are filtered and reabsorbed are excreted in the urine. Since the reabsorption of fluid from the proximal tubule is affected by osmotic diuresis, a very large flow of urine can be produced. As the load of unreabsorbable solute is increased, the osmolality of the urine approaches that of plasma, despite maximal secretion of ADH, because an increasingly large fraction of urine comes from isotonic fluid in the proximal tubules.

OSMOTIC DIURETIC AGENTS

Osmotic diuresis is produced by substances that are administered and filtered but not reabsorbed, such as urea, mannitol, polysaccharides related to mannitol, and large amounts of NaCl. Concentrations of normal constituents of the plasma that exceed the reabsorptive capacity of the renal tubules also cause osmotic diuresis. For example, in diabetes mellitus, the concentration of glucose in the plasma may exceed the renal plasma threshold; thus, glucose remains in the tubules and acts as an osmotic diuretic.

STUDY OUTLINE

GENERAL CONSIDERATIONS Human kidneys can concentrate urine to four times the osmolality of plasma and dilute it to one-sixth.

Concentrating ability related to length of the loop of Henle.

COUNTERCURRENT SYSTEM Inflow channel runs closely parallel to and in opposite direction (counter) to outflow channel.

Forms hyperosmotic interstitial fluid in renal medulla.

Countercurrent multiplier increases concentration.

Countercurrent exchanger minimizes washout of solutes from area of concentration.

COUNTERCURRENT MULTIPLICATION OF CONCENTRATION

MODEL SYSTEM Tube forms loop, solute transported actively from second segment to first segment; gradient develops.

Same gradient at successive stages builds up total concentration, not difference of concentration.

COUNTERCURRENT SYSTEM IN THE KIDNEYS Epithelial cells of loop of Henle build up and maintain small gradient between descending and ascending limbs.

Movement of tubular fluid in opposite directions multiplies effect and establishes gradient between base and apex of loop.

Collecting duct runs back through area of high concentration.

Tubular fluid tends to equilibrate with extracellular fluid; ADH controls permeability to water.

MECHANISM Na^+ and Cl^- are transported actively out of tubular fluid in thick ascending limb.

Thick ascending limb is impermeable to water; solute concentration decreases in tubular fluid and increases in interstitial fluid.

In presence of ADH, cortical and outer medullary collecting ducts are permeable to water but not to urea.

Water is absorbed from tubular fluid, concentration of urea increases.

Inner medullary collecting ducts are permeable to urea, which diffuses out and accumulates in medullary interstitium.

Water is transported osmotically from descending limb of loop of Henle; in presence of ADH, water is transported from collecting tubules.

PERMEABILITIES Thin descending limb is permeable to water but not to Na^+, Cl^-, and urea.

Medullary interstitial fluid contains mixture of Na^+ Cl^- and urea.

Isotonic fluid from proximal tubule loses water to interstitium; tubular $[Na^+ Cl^-]$ greater than medullary $[Na^+ Cl^-]$, tubular [urea] less than medullary [urea]; osmolalities of two fluids equal.

Thin ascending limb is permeable to Na^+ and Cl^-, moderately permeable to urea, and impermeable to water.

In thin ascending limb, Na^+ Cl^- diffuses from lumen, some urea diffuses into lumen; luminal fluid is hypotonic to interstitium, Na^+ Cl^- added to interstitium.

Urea in tubule is concentrated by active transport of Na^+ and Cl^- in thick ascending limb, loss of water in collecting duct.

High concentration of Na^+ Cl^- in medullary interstitium concentrates nonurea solutes in final urine.

LOCATION OF NEPHRONS Only loops of Henle of juxtamedullary nephrons penetrate inner medullary and papillary regions.

Metabolic work is done in thick ascending limbs of all nephrons, maximum concentration develops in nephrons that have long loops.

ROLE OF UREA About half of urea filtered recirculates between tubular fluid and interstitial fluid of medulla.

In presence of ADH, medullary collecting ducts are permeable to urea, which is concentrated in medullary interstitium by countercurrent system.

Contributes to high osmolality of medullary region.

Concentrates urea in urine, requires less water to excrete urea.

COUNTERCURRENT EXCHANGE MECHANISM

MAINTAINING GRADIENTS Medullary blood vessels (vasa recta), form loops, through countercurrent exchange do not wash out concentrated solutes.

RATE OF BLOOD FLOW Low in medulla, about 5% of total renal perfusion.

Increased medullary blood flow decreases effectiveness of countercurrent system, washes out more of concentrated solutions.

SIGNIFICANCE OF CONCENTRATING AND DILUTING MECHANISM Permits elimination or conservation of water as necessary, despite obligatory load of solute.

EXCRETION OF CONCENTRATED URINE In presence of ADH, tubular fluid equilibrates with concentrated fluid of medulla, osmolality of urine can reach 1200 mOsm/liter.

EXCRETION OF DILUTE URINE Reabsorption of Na^+ Cl^- in ascending limb and distal tubules makes fluid hypotonic (50–100 mOsm/liter).

In absence of ADH, collecting tubules are impermeable to water, dilute urine is excreted.

FREE-WATER CLEARANCE If urine is more dilute than plasma, some plasma is "cleared" of water.

WATER DIURESIS AND OSMOTIC DIURESIS

WATER DIURESIS Eighty percent of water is absorbed isosmotically in proximal tubule—"obligatory"—unaffected by state of hydration.

Variable absorption—"facultative"—depends on state of hydration and is under influence of ADH.

Maximum volume about 15% of GFR because only water in collecting tubules is affected.

OSMOTIC DIURESIS

MECHANISM Solutes that are not reabsorbed by tubular cells remain in lumen, retain water in lumen osmotically.

Limit of Na^+ absorption is 35 mEq/liter gradient—if plasma $[Na^+]$ is 145 mEq/liter, luminal $[Na^+]$ cannot be less than 110 mEq/liter; thus Na^+ also is retained in lumen.

Reabsorption of water and electrolytes is inhibited along all of nephron by osmotic effect of nonabsorbable solutes.

Increased urine volume is related to load of unabsorbable solute.

OSMOTIC DIURETIC AGENTS Administered substances are filtered but not absorbed—urea, mannitol, certain polysaccharides, excess NaCl.

Normal constituents of plasma that exceed reabsorptive capacity of tubules (e.g., glucose in diabetes mellitus).

BIBLIOGRAPHY

Andersson, B. 1977. Regulation of body fluids. *Annu. Rev. Physiol.* 39:185.

Andreoli, T.E., and Schaefer, J.A. 1976. Mass transport across cell membranes: The effect of antidiuretic hormone on water and solute flows in epithelia. *Annu. Rev. Physiol.* 38:451.

Deetjen, P.; Boylan, J.W.; and Kramer, K. 1975. *Physiology of the Kidney and of Water Balance.* New York: Springer-Verlag.

Jamison, R.L. 1976. Urinary concentration and dilution. The role of antidiuretic hormone and the role of urea. In *The Kidney.* Chapter 11. Volume I. Edited by B.M. Brenner and F.C. Rector, Jr. Philadelphia: Saunders.

Jamison, R.L., and Krig, W. 1982. *Urinary Concentrating Mechanism: Structure and Function.* New York: Oxford University Press.

Kokko, J.P., and Rector, F.C., Jr. 1972. Countercurrent multiplication system without active transport in inner medulla. *Kidney Int.* 2:214–223.

Pitts, R.F. 1974. *Physiology of the Kidney and Body Fluids* (3rd ed.). Chicago: Year Book.

Rector, F.C., Jr. 1977. In *Renal Concentrating Mechanisms In Disturbances in Body Fluid Osmolality.* Edited by T.E. Andreoli, J.J. Grantham, and F.C. Rector, Jr. Bethesda, Maryland: American Physiology Society.

Stephenson, J.L. 1978. Countercurrent transport in the kidney. *Annu. Rev. Biophys. Bioeng.* 7:315.

Stephenson, J.L. 1983. Renal concentrating mechanism. (Symposium). *Fed. Proc.* 42:2375.

Wirz, H., and Dirix, R. 1973. Urinary concentration and dilution. In *Handbook of Physiology.* Section 8. Renal Physiology. Chapter 13. Edited by J. Orloff and R.W. Berliner. Washington, D.C.: American Physiological Society.

42

Regulation of Sodium, Potassium, and Water Balance

CHAPTER CONTENTS

GENERAL CONSIDERATIONS

The maintenance of a relatively constant volume and electrolyte composition of both the extracellular and intracellular fluids is necessary to sustain animal life. The distribution of total body Na^+ and K^+ depends on an energy-consuming process that partially excludes Na^+ and increases the concentration of K^+, $[K^+]$, within the cell. This process ensures that $[K^+]$ normally is within the narrow limits of 4–5 mEq/liter in the extracellular fluid (ECF) and 150–160 mEq/liter within the cell, while $[Na^+]$ is kept at about 145 mEq/liter in the ECF and 12 mEq/liter within the cell.

Since sodium salts comprise 90%–95% of the total solute in the ECF, Na^+ and its major accompanying anions, Cl^- and HCO_3^-, contribute approximately 280 mOsm/kg of water to a total ECF osmolality of 300 mOsm/kg of water. This situation is true for both of the components of the ECF compartment, the plasma and the interstitial fluid, because the capillary endothelium, which separates the two components, allows solutes of low molecular weight to distribute in accordance with the Donnan equilibrium (see Chapter 2) and water to move freely down the osmotic gradient.

In the steady state, the volume of the ECF remains stable. Isotonic fluid moves across the capillary endothelium, between the vascular and the interstitial spaces, according to the balance between the intracapillary hydrostatic pressure and the plasma oncotic pressure (see Chapter 12). Normally, the net movement of fluid from the interstitial space to the vascular space nearly equals that from the vascular space to the interstitial space, while the lymphatic system returns a relatively small amount of the fluid to the intravascular space. On this basis, when the vascular volume is too large, the plasma proteins are diluted, and decreased plasma oncotic pressure permits increased movement of isotonic fluid into the interstitial space. Conversely, when volume is depleted, the accompanying increase of plasma oncotic pressure causes fluid to remain in the vascular space. Thus, the interstitial fluid space acts as a volume reserve that can accept some excess fluid.

Because Na^+ is the major osmotic component of the ECF, it determines the state of extracellular hydration. The osmolality of the intracellular fluid (ICF) compartment is the same as that of the ECF compartment, but the compositions of the fluids are different. Sodium salts contribute only about 30 mOsm/kg of water to the intracellular osmolality; the major osmotic solutes are K^+, Mg^{++}, organic and inorganic phosphates, and proteins. Since water moves freely between the ECF and ICF compartments, osmotic forces across the cell membranes are equal, and the body water is distributed according to the total amount of osmotically active solute in each compartment. Increasing the osmolality of the ECF causes water to shift out of the cells, and decreasing the osmolality of the ECF causes water to move into the cells. Thus, the volume of the ICF is a function of the osmolality of the ECF. A change of the $[Na^+]$ in the plasma affects the volumes of the ECF and the ICF and influences both blood volume and blood pressure. Therefore, the maintenance of a stable body composition of Na^+ is important.

The balance of Na^+, K^+, and water is maintained in the face of continuous variation of intake and excretion. The stability of total body K^+, Na^+, and water, and, hence, the volume and osmolality of the body fluids, depends largely on the regulation of excretion. The kidneys are important in this function because under normal conditions they provide virtually the only means for eliminating excess dietary K^+, Na^+, and water by adjusting the rates of excretion to match the rates of ingestion. Small changes in the composition, volume, or pressure of the body fluids are communicated to the kidneys and modify renal behavior. The afferent mechanisms that detect the changes and the efferent mechanisms that modulate renal excretion of K^+, Na^+, and water are understood incompletely but are being studied actively (Figure 42-1).

REGULATION OF VOLUME AND OSMOLALITY

Because the mass of extracellular Na^+, which reflects the total amount of Na^+ in the body, determines primarily the volume of the ECF, physiological mechanisms that maintain a con-

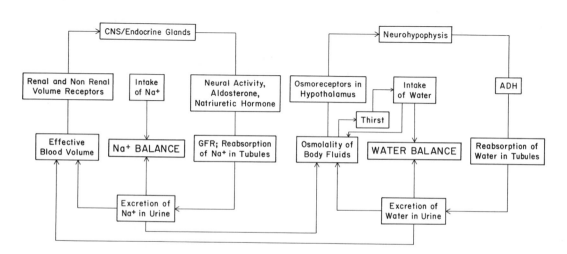

Figure 42-1.   Control of Na^+ and water balance.

stant total body Na^+ regulate the ECF volume directly and the ICF volume indirectly. Normally, the plasma osmolality is maintained within narrow limits and the proportion of Na^+ to water in the ECF remains unchanged. In response to an increase of plasma $[Na^+]$, the kidneys retain water and, thereby, increase the ECF volume. Conversely, in response to a decrease of plasma $[Na^+]$, the kidneys excrete water and, thereby, decrease the ECF volume. Thus, the volume of the ECF is regulated primarily by the excretion of Na^+ and secondarily by the excretion of water. Disturbances of ECF volume really are disturbances of Na^+ balance, whereas disturbances of osmolality or plasma $[Na^+]$ are disturbances of water balance.

Control of Sodium Balance

The control of Na^+ balance includes (1) the "Na^+ receptors" and the afferent pathways that lead to the central nervous system and/or the endocrine glands, (2) the hormonal and/or neural pathways to the kidneys, and (3) the renal effector mechanisms.

SODIUM RECEPTORS

It is difficult to define the so-called "Na^+ receptors" because it is practically impossible for the total body mass of Na^+ to be detected by any receptor. Because the total body mass of Na^+ is reflected in the amount of extracellular Na^+, which largely determines the volume of the ECF, a change in the body content of Na^+ is reflected in the ECF volume. Therefore, receptors that detect change or rate of change in either blood volume or interstitial volume have been proposed. It is believed that the volume receptors can sense the "fullness" of the circulation; hence, the blood volume is regulated to maintain the cardiac filling pressure, the cardiac output, and the arterial blood pressure within normal limits. The concept of an effective blood volume has been proposed; it is the portion of the blood volume that stimulates volume receptors and determines the renal excretion of Na^+. In normal circumstances, effective blood volume and ECF volume are correlated closely. A loss of salt and water, because of diarrhea or vomiting, for example, depletes interstitial volume and blood volume proportionately. The kidneys then retain both salt and water until the ECF volume and effective blood volume are restored. When excess salt is taken, the opposite occurs. The kid-

neys respond to the increase of blood volume by excreting more salt and water until the ECF and effective blood volume return to normal.

Many locations for the receptors have been suggested. Volume receptors that are sensitive to distention and influence the secretion of ADH are located in the walls of the cardiac atria (see Chapter 56). The central venous portion of the circulation may contain low-pressure receptors, and the arterial side of the circulation may contain high-pressure receptors, that influence the renal excretion of Na^+. It is likely that these receptors sense changes in blood pressure and thereby initiate reflex changes in the excretion of Na^+ that affect the body content of Na^+ and the volume of the ECF.

JUXTAGLOMERULAR APPARATUS

Volume receptors that regulate the $[Na^+]$ and the volume of the ECF are located in the kidneys, in the juxtaglomerular apparatus. These receptors influence the synthesis of renin by the juxtaglomerular cells in response to changes in the volume of the ECF and in renal perfusion. Two sites have been proposed for the receptors that mediate the secretion of renin from the juxtaglomerular cells: (1) baroreceptors in the afferent arterioles that sense distention, and (2) sensors in the macula densa area of the loop of Henle that are sensitive to changes in the load of solutes in the tubular fluid. A change in any of these parameters changes the rate of release of renin.

HORMONAL AND NEURAL PATHWAYS

The renin-angiotensin-aldosterone hormonal system modifies the renal excretion of Na^+. When the effective blood volume or blood pressure, the renal blood flow, or the tubular load of Na^+ decreases, the juxtaglomerular cells release renin. The release of renin is controlled by sympathetic nervous system activity and by intrarenal mechanisms (juxtaglomerular apparatus). Renin acts on a substrate (angiotensinogen) contained in the globulin fraction of the plasma proteins. It splits off four amino acids from the polypeptide chain of angiotensinogen, which contains 14 amino acids, to form angiotensin I (a decapeptide). Angiotensin I is converted to angiotensin II (an octapeptide) by a converting enzyme in the pulmonary circulation, the liver, and the kidneys.

Angiotensin II causes constriction of arterioles or precapillary sphincters and, in unrelated action, increases the secretion of aldosterone from the adrenal cortex. In normal individuals the rate of secretion of aldosterone is related closely to the electrolyte balance. A decrease of plasma [Na$^+$] or an increase of plasma [K$^+$] causes the adrenal cortex to release aldosterone. During stress, the secretion of aldosterone is affected also by adrenocorticotrophic hormone (ACTH), but the effect is transient.

NATRIURETIC HORMONE

Another element important in volume control is the "third factor," which presumably is a natriuretic hormone. This hormone may originate in the brain, perhaps in the hypothalamus or the posterior pituitary gland. The natriuretic hormone is released in response to hypervolemia caused by an increase in the Na$^+$ load; it decreases the tubular reabsorption of Na$^+$, and thus increases the rate of excretion of Na$^+$. However, the exact site of action of the natriuretic hormone on the renal tubule is not known.

The natriuretic hormone is important in patients who have renal failure but still are ingesting a normal amount of salt. In renal failure, the rate of glomerular filtration (GFR) is reduced, and if the tubular reabsorption of Na$^+$ is not changed, Na$^+$ is retained and the volume of the ECF increases. In this condition, the natriuretic hormone is released, tubular reabsorption of Na$^+$ decreases, and Na$^+$ balance may be maintained.

RENAL EFFECTOR SYSTEM

The rate of excretion of Na$^+$ in the urine is determined by two processes: filtration and tubular reabsorption. The equation for this is as follows:

Rate of Na$^+$ excretion
$$= \text{rate of Na}^+ \text{ filtration}$$
$$- \text{rate of Na}^+ \text{ reabsorption}$$
$$= P_{Na} \times GFR$$
$$- \text{rate of Na}^+ \text{ reabsorption}$$

Usually, the osmolality of the ECF is controlled within narrow limits by physiological mechanisms, such as the osmoreceptor-ADH system, so that the [Na$^+$] changes very little. In this case the volume of the ECF is regulated by reflex control of either the GFR or the tubular reabsorption of Na$^+$.

CONSERVATION OF SODIUM

Acute depletion of either extracellular [Na$^+$] or the ECF volume stimulates the secretion of aldosterone. The distal convoluted tubules of the kidneys respond to the increased circulating level of aldosterone by increasing the reabsorption of Na$^+$, thereby conserving Na$^+$ when the plasma [Na$^+$], and, consequently, the body content of Na$^+$, is low. The rate of discharge of the sympathetic nervous system also increases when the fluid volume is decreased; this activity decreases the rate of excretion of Na$^+$ because it increases the rate of release of renin and also changes the intrarenal hemodynamics to favor the reabsorption of Na$^+$ by the tubules.

ELIMINATION OF SODIUM

Excess Na$^+$ in the diet causes expansion of the ECF volume and increases the rate of excretion of Na$^+$ by the kidneys. The secretion of aldosterone by the adrenal cortex is suppressed, secretion of the natriuretic hormone is increased, and the rate of sympathetic nervous system discharge to the kidneys is decreased. All of these factors tend to eliminate excess Na$^+$ from the body and maintain a normal volume of ECF.

Control of Water Balance

FLUID COMPARTMENTS

The interrelationships among the intake of water, the distribution of water within the fluid compartments, and the routes for the loss of water from the body are summarized in Figure 42-2. Body fluid is divided into three major compartments: plasma, interstitial fluid, and intracellular fluid.

The volume of the blood plasma is approximately 3.2 liters, which comprises 5% of the body weight of a healthy 70-kg man. Plasma circulates throughout the body; it is the medium for transporting water and solutes from the influx channels to the efflux channels and for exchange with the largely uncirculated interstitial compartment.

The volume of the interstitial fluid is 8–10 liters, or about 15% of the body weight in a 70-kg man. This compartment exchanges with the plasma through the capillaries. Nearly protein-free plasma is filtered into the interstitium, and the small amount of protein that does pass through is absorbed by the lymph capillaries and returned to the circulation (see Chapter 12). In the steady state, the rates of

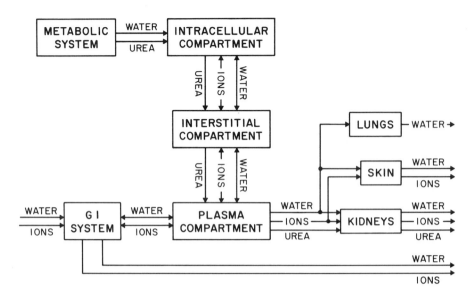

Figure 42-2.   Flow diagram of the systems that regulate body fluid.

filtration and reabsorption are equal, but under certain circumstances they are not equal, and fluid shifts from one compartment into the other.

The large intracellular fluid compartment is about 23–28 liters in volume, or 40% of the body weight in a 70-kg man. The intracellular fluid compartment exchanges with the interstitial fluid compartment. In the steady state, the two-way fluxes of water are large, but the fluxes of ions are much less because of the selective permeability of the cell (see Chapter 2). Water is exchanged by osmosis, and the ions move by diffusion, active transport, or both. In a transient state, the two-way fluxes of water may be unequal, which causes a net shift of water from one compartment to the other. The cells also produce metabolic water and waste products such as urea, which adds extra one-way fluxes of those compounds. The three major fluid compartments constitute dynamic pools of water and ions. Only the circulating plasma communicates directly with the external environment, but the other two compartments respond quickly to changes in the volume and composition of the plasma.

WATER BALANCE
Normally, intake of water into the body is matched by loss. Inequality between the total influxes (ingested water plus metabolic water) and the total effluxes alters the volume and

composition of the body fluid compartments. Disturbances of any of the other channels of influx or efflux (lungs, skin, or gastrointestinal system) elicits compensatory adjustment of the controlled efflux through the kidneys. The daily water balance of a 70-kg man whose diet provides adequate calories is represented in Table 42-1.

The term *insensible loss* describes the loss of water by diffusion through the skin (except as sweat) and evaporation from the surface, together with the loss of water from the respiratory passages, which occurs because expired air is saturated with water vapor. The loss of water through the skin and the respiratory system can be determined accurately from changes in body weight. On the average, this loss amounts to 0.5 ml/hr/kg of body weight, or 840 ml/24 hr in a 70-kg man (see Table 42-1).

The minimum volume of water required to contain the solutes that must be excreted in the urine is called the *obligatory volume*. A typical value is 760 ml/24 hr (Table 42-1). A typical individual ingests 156 mEq of Na^+ per day, and, unless the person is salt-deficient, all of this Na^+ will be excreted. The 156 mEq of Na^+, with its equivalent anions (mostly Cl^-), contributes 312 mOsm to the osmotic load that reaches the kidneys. The normal diet usually contains about 50 mEq of K^+, which, with its accompanying anions, adds 100 mOsm more to the load. The metabolism of 100 g of dietary protein requires the excretion of about 30 g/day of urea, which contributes another 500 mOsm. Therefore, a typical load of osmotically active substances that must be excreted each day is 912 mOsm. The human kidneys can excrete urine of different concentrations—as dilute as 50 mOsm/liter when the body contains excess water or as concentrated as 1200 mOsm/liter when water must be conserved (see Chapter 41). To excrete an osmotic load of 912 mOsm per day (the minimum volume of urine at the maximum osmolality of 1200 mOsm/liter) would require 760 ml of water. Since 840 ml were lost through the respiration, and the feces contain approximately 100 ml of water, the total unavoidable loss of water is 1700 ml/day. If water balance is to be retained, this loss must be matched by water ingested and water produced metabolically.

The water that is contained in food is called *preformed water,* and the water that is produced by the oxidation of food is called *water of oxidation,* or *metabolic water.* If the weight and constituents of the diet are known, the amounts of both preformed water and metabolic water can be determined. The content of preformed water can be calculated by assuming that about 60% of the food is water by weight; for example, if the dry weight of the food (40% of the total weight) is 500 g (Table 42-1), the amount of preformed water is approximately 750 ml.

The yield of metabolic water also can be calculated from a knowledge of the dietary constituents. Oxidation of 1 g of carbohydrate yields 0.6 g of water; one gram of protein degraded to urea produces 0.4 g of water. Fat, because of its high content of hydrogen, yields 1 g of water for each gram oxidized. Therefore, the calculated value for metabolic water is 320 ml, and a total of 1070 ml of water is either produced or obtained from food.

The chief source of water—drinking—is affected more by the habits of the individual, and, hence, is more difficult to estimate; however, a certain minimum amount must be taken if water balance is to be maintained. This minimum can be estimated by taking the difference between the obligatory water loss—1700 ml in the example above—and the water derived from food (1700 ml – 1070 ml = 630 ml), which gives the minimum intake needed to maintain water balance.

The driving force for the intake of water—the urge to drink—probably is stimulated in part by the shrinkage of osmoreceptors in the hypothalamus (see Chapter 67). This mechanism is very sensitive under normal circumstances, and the quantity of water ingested is almost exactly the amount needed to restore the balance of body water.

When the osmolality of the ECF changes because of gain or loss of water, the kidneys compensate by excreting more water (excretion of free water) or by reabsorbing water more completely from the collecting tubules. Normally, the fluid intake each day is about one liter more than the minimum needed; thus, the output of urine is larger than the minimum of 760 ml. Since the excess water is not accompanied by solutes, the osmolality of the urine is decreased to about 600–900 mOsm/liter.

TABLE 42-1

Components of water balance in a 70-kg man on a daily diet that contains 300 g of carbohydrate, 100 g of fat, 100 g of protein, and 156 mEq of Na^+

	Intake (ml/24 hr)			Output (ml/24 hr)	
Source	Obligatory	Facultative	Route	Obligatory	Facultative
Preformed water in food	750	—	Skin and lungs	840	—
Water of oxidation	320	—	Urine	760	1000
Drinking	630	1000	Feces	100	—
Minimum	1700	—	Minimum	1700	—
Total	2700		Total	2700	

ACTIONS OF
ANTIDIURETIC HORMONE

Water balance is controlled through antidiuretic hormone (ADH) and its actions on the collecting tubules of the kidneys. ADH is a nonapeptide synthesized by a group of neurons that have cell bodies located in the supraoptic and paraventricular nuclei of the hypothalamus (see Chapter 56). After synthesis, ADH is contained in secretory granules that migrate down the axons of the supraopticohypophyseal tract to the neurohypophysis, where it is stored. Subsequently, ADH is released through appropriate stimuli, circulates in the plasma, and binds to specific receptor sites on the epithelial cells of the renal collecting tubules. This hormone-receptor complex activates adenylate cyclase, which promotes the formation of cyclic adenosine monophosphate (AMP) from ATP (see Chapter 55). A protein kinase, also activated by cyclic AMP, phosphorylates proteins in the luminal membrane of the cell and increases the permeability of the luminal membrane to water. Thus, more water is reabsorbed into the hyperosmotic medullary interstitium, and the solutes left behind are concentrated.

CONTROL OF THE RELEASE
OF ANTIDIURETIC HORMONE

The release of ADH from the neurohypophysis is controlled through two kinds of afferent pathways: osmoreceptors and stretch receptors. Osmoreceptors located in the hypothalamus are sensitive to changes in the plasma osmolality, and stretch receptors located in the left atrium are sensitive to changes in the atrial pressure, which reflects the blood volume.

Under normal circumstances, the release of ADH is regulated primarily by the osmoreceptors in or near the hypothalamic nuclei, in which ADH is synthesized. These osmoreceptors are sensitive to changes in the osmolality of the fluid that bathes them. They are thought to act like osmometers; when the ECF is hypertonic, water moves out of the cells, decreasing the volume of the receptor cell and increasing the osmolality of the ICF. When the ECF is hypotonic, water moves into the cells, increasing the volume of the receptor cell. Only a small increase in the osmolality of the plasma (1%–2%) is required to stimulate the release of ADH from the neurohypophysis. The permeability of the collecting tubules to water is increased, water is reabsorbed at a greater rate,

and more concentrated urine is produced. Conversely, only a small reduction in the osmolality of the plasma is needed to inhibit the release of ADH from the neurohypophysis, and the permeability of the collecting tubules to water is decreased. The reabsorption of Na^+ proceeds normally, but less water follows, and less concentrated urine is excreted (see Chapter 41). Thus, a feedback system based on the osmoreceptors restores and maintains the osmolality of the extracellular fluid.

Conservation of water by the kidneys can compensate only partly for a lack of water. Eventually, water must be ingested to replace any deficit. When the osmolality of the plasma increases, the centers in the hypothalamus that mediate thirst are stimulated; the sensation of thirst drives an individual to ingest water, and the deficit is corrected.

Physiologically, the most important nonosmolar factor that influences the release of ADH from the neurohypophysis is a change in the volume of the ECF. When the volume of the ECF increases, the atria become distended and atrial pressure increases. Stretch receptors in the left atrium are stimulated, and impulses that are transmitted to the hypothalamus via afferent nerves inhibit the production and release of ADH. Conversely, a decrease of atrial pressure causes less firing by the stretch receptors, and the production and release of ADH increases. Therefore, when the volume of the ECF decreases, ADH is released and water is reabsorbed from the tubular fluid. The decrease of ECF also increases the secretion of aldosterone, which increases the reabsorption of Na^+ in the renal tubules. Subsequently, these two effects lead to an expansion of ECF volume and effective blood volume, and the signals that caused decreased renal excretion of Na^+ and water are stopped.

REGULATION OF
POTASSIUM BALANCE

K^+ is necessary for the maintenance of the cellular potential, and K^+ is important in the metabolism of the cell because it helps to regulate the synthesis of glycogen and protein; thus, the normal functions of cells depend on a proper K^+ balance. The stability of body K^+ depends primarily on the controlled excretion of K^+ by the kidneys. Unlike the renal excretion of Na^+, the renal excretion of K^+ is largely independent of the GFR (see Chapter 40). Virtually all of the filtered K^+ is reabsorbed by the renal tubules. Excretion is regulated by the secretion of K^+ into the lumen of the distal convoluted tubule and the collecting tubule. When K^+ is in excess, the $[K^+]$ of the distal and collecting tubule cells is high, secretion is facilitated, and the excess K^+ is eliminated from the body. When the $[K^+]$ of these cells is low, secretion is reduced.

Intracellular/Extracellular Concentration of Potassium Ions

K^+ is distributed unevenly across the cell membrane; $[K^+]$ is maintained at 150–160 mEq/liter in the ICF and 4–5 mEq/liter in the ECF by energy-consuming processes. This ratio of $[K^+]$ in the ICF to $[K^+]$ in the ECF is extremely important because it is the major determinant of the cellular resting potential (see Chapter 2). Thus, both hypokalemia and hyperkalemia alter the resting potential and the normal functions of the nerves and muscles. The rhythm of the heart is particularly sensitive to the plasma $[K^+]$. Under normal circumstances, the exchange of K^+ between the ICF and the ECF is important in the regulation of plasma $[K^+]$. If the K^+ of the diet is increased, K^+ is transferred rapidly into the cells and the plasma $[K^+]$ does not change. Usually, K^+ balance is restored within 6–8 hours by the renal excretion of K^+. Conversely, if extracellular $[K^+]$ decreases, K^+ moves from the cells into the ECF to restore the normal value.

Insulin

The hormone insulin also participates in the regulation of plasma $[K^+]$. If extracellular $[K^+]$ increases, the rate of secretion of insulin increases, and if extracellular $[K^+]$ decreases, the rate of secretion of insulin decreases. Insulin facilitates the uptake of K^+ by the cell, but the mechanism of its action is not known.

Aldosterone

Hyperkalemia increases the rate of secretion of aldosterone by the adrenal cortex. Aldosterone promotes the transfer of K^+ into the cells and increases the rate of secretion of K^+ in the distal and collecting tubules. Therefore, excess K^+ is excreted in the urine. Aldosterone enhances the secretion of K^+ by increasing the rate of active transport of K^+ from the interstitium into the tubular cells and by increasing the permeability of the luminal membrane to K^+, which facilitates the diffusion of K^+ into the lumen.

DISTURBANCES OF SODIUM AND WATER BALANCE

Primary imbalance of Na^+ and water causes maldistribution of fluid between the extracellular and intracellular compartments. Disturbances of Na^+ and water balance may consist of either depletion or excess of Na^+ or water. Under normal circumstances, if the disturbances are not of renal origin, the kidneys compensate for the excess or deficit of Na^+ or water and thereby ensure that the volume and osmolality of the body fluids are stabilized within narrow limits.

Homeostasis

In general, water never is lost without electrolytes, nor are electrolytes lost without water, although the relative proportions of ions and water may vary in different circumstances. When the Na^+ balance is upset, the ECF volume also is altered; for example, the occurrence of generalized edema is related to excess Na^+. When the water balance is disturbed, the osmolality of the plasma, which is related mainly to $[Na^+]$, is abnormal. Hypernatremia usually is associated with water deficit, while hyponatremia usually is associated with water excess. Any disturbance of Na^+ and water balance has serious consequences because it can affect a variety of bodily functions. Therefore, appropriate treatment to restore homeostasis, based on an understanding of the mechanisms that produce either a deficit or a surfeit of Na^+ or water, is desirable.

Extracellular/Intracellular Concentration of Sodium Ions and Water

To understand the factors that underlie disturbances in the volume, osmolality, and distribution of body fluids that are seen clinically, certain fundamental physiological facts must be kept in mind. The fluid compartments are in osmotic equilibrium because water permeates the cell membrane and moves freely between the ECF and ICF compartments down osmotic gradients. By contrast, most solutes are distributed unevenly between the fluid compartments because of molecular size, electrical charge, or active transport. The major osmotically active solutes in the extracellular fluid are Na^+, Cl^-, and HCO_3^-, and the major osmotically active solutes within the cell are K^+, Mg^{++}, phosphates, and proteins. Normally, about two-thirds of the total body water is in the ICF compartment and one-third is in the ECF compartment. If the osmolality of the ECF is increased (e.g., if hypertonic saline solution is injected intravenously), water leaves the cells down the osmotic gradient that is created, concentrating the ICF and diluting the ECF until the osmolalities of the two compartments are equal. Conversely, when the osmolality of the ECF is reduced, water moves into the cells to equalize the osmolalities of the two compartments. Thus, the volume of either compartment is affected by the relative osmolality of the other.

The shift in the fluid compartments caused by changes in solutes or water can be calculated by using the dilution principle (see Chapter 37), $C = Q/V$, where C is the concentration of solute in a compartment, Q is the total quantity of solute in the compartment, and V is the volume of the compartment. When water is added to or subtracted from a compartment or the entire body, the product of the concentration of solute in the compartment and the volume of the compartment remains constant. Therefore,

$$C_{initial} \times V_{initial} = C_{final} \times V_{final}$$

When an osmotically active solute is added and the change in the total quantity of the solute can be determined, the relation between the concentration and the volume can be calculated. Figure 42-3 shows examples of various states in which either the volumes or osmolalities of the body fluid compartments are changed by alterations in either the Na^+ or water content of the ECF.

Excessive Intake of Water

If a person drinks a large amount of water rapidly and the capacity of the kidneys to excrete solute-free water is exceeded, the body fluids are diluted and *hyponatremia,* or *hypotonic hydration,* occurs. This condition also develops when water is retained because of impairment of the renal diluting process or because of oversecretion or administration of ADH.

OSMOTIC EFFECTS

The effects of oral ingestion of water on the volume and osmolality of the body fluid compartments are shown in Panel A of Figure 42-3. Water taken orally, especially when the stomach is empty, is absorbed rapidly and the plasma volume increases. The increase of intravascular volume and the decrease of plasma osmotic pressure cause water to shift from the intravascular to the interstitial fluid compartment. The solute concentration of all of the ECF is decreased, and water moves into the cells down the osmotic gradient. The final effect of the ingested water is to increase the volume and decrease the solute osmolality of all of the body water.

EXCRETION

Normal kidneys begin to eliminate excess water about 30 minutes after it is ingested. Water diuresis reaches its peak in approximately 1 hour, declines, and virtually is over in about 3 hours.

HYPOTONIC HYDRATION

Hypotonic hydration may occur when an individual who has lost salt and water through excessive perspiration drinks a large amount of water. The ingested water dilutes the ECF, hydrates the cells excessively, and decreases the concentration of electrolytes in the cells. The disturbed cellular metabolism may cause nausea, vomiting, muscular cramps, and cerebral edema, which leads to disorientation, convulsions, and coma.

Excessive Loss of Water

DEFECTS OF CONCENTRATING MECHANISM

When water is lost, the osmolality of the body fluids increases. The two most important disorders that cause primary loss of water are pituitary diabetes insipidus, produced by a defect in the synthesis or secretion of ADH (see Chapter 41), and nephrogenic diabetes insipidus, in which the kidneys do not respond to ADH. These disorders are characterized by polyuria and the loss of solute-free water because the kidneys are unable to concentrate the urine maximally.

INSENSIBLE LOSS

Water may be lost through excessive insensible perspiration (evaporation from the skin or upper respiratory tract) during fever; the effects of this condition on the volume and osmolality of the body fluids (Panel B of Figure 42-3) are opposite to the effects that are produced by hypotonic hydration. The insensible loss of water causes hyperosmolality if the individual cannot replace the water by drinking. The increased osmolality of the ECF causes water to move out of the cells, down the osmotic gradient into the interstitial space, and into the circulation. The volumes of the ECF and ICF compartments are decreased in proportion to their original volumes, and the osmolalities of the compartments are increased. ADH is released in response to the hypertonic plasma, the excretion of water is decreased, and the urine becomes more concentrated.

PRIMARY LOSS OF WATER

Loss of water alone when the body store of Na^+ is normal produces no severe effects unless a large quantity is lost. The signs of pure loss of water, which reflect mainly cellular dehydration and increased concentrations of cellular electrolytes, include thirst, weakness, and neurological symptoms. In many cases, both Na^+ and water are lost, although the loss of water is proportionately greater than the loss of Na^+. Water is lost from both the ECF and ICF compartments, while Na^+ is lost only from the ECF compartment. Hypotonic fluid of variable electrolyte content may be lost through the gastrointestinal tract (vomiting or diarrhea) or through the skin (excessive perspiration). In these instances, the kidneys conserve water and salt, so that a concentrated urine of low $[Na^+]$ is excreted. Intravenous infusion or oral ingestion of a balanced salt solution aids the kidneys in these efforts.

Excessive Gain of Solute

PRIMARY ALDOSTERONISM

When excess Na^+ is ingested or retained, the body fluids become hypertonic. Primary aldosteronism (see Chapter 60) causes mild hypernatremia and expansion of the ECF volume.

HYPERNATREMIA

The abrupt addition of large amounts of sodium salts to the ECF (e.g., accidental intravenous infusion of hypertonic saline solution or administration of sodium bicarbonate during cardiac resuscitation) causes hypernatremia. Because of the increase in plasma osmolality, water moves from the cells, increasing the volume of the interstitial and vascular compartments (Panel C in Figure 42-3) and decreasing the volume of the intracellular compartment. The renal response is an increased rate of ex-

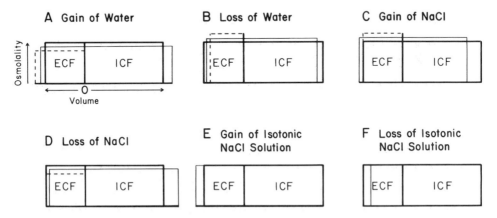

Figure 42-3. Changes in the distribution of fluids between extracellular and intracellular compartments during states of water and salt imbalance. The osmolality of the body fluids, about 300 mOsm/kg of water, is shown as the ordinate in the figure. The volumes of the compartments are shown as the abscissa. Normally, about one-third of the total body water is extracellular and two-thirds is intracellular. The total quantity of solutes in a compartment is represented by the area. In this figure, the heavy solid lines represent the initial, normal state, the dashed lines represent the immediate change caused by an imbalance of water or salt, and the light solid lines represent the final state after redistribution of body fluid. See the text for further discussion.

cretion of Na$^+$ for several hours. This condition can be exemplified by a survivor of a shipwreck at sea in a raft, who drinks sea water. The intake of the hypertonic sea water leads eventually to cellular dehydration and its attendant effects.

Excessive Loss of Solute

Na$^+$ is depleted by conditions that cause rapid and substantial loss of Na$^+$ from the body. A low total body Na$^+$ also involves a small ECF volume. This hypotonic hypovolemia is characterized by the loss of both salt and water, with the loss of salt exceeding that of water. The decrease in osmolality of the ECF causes water to move into the cells; the ICF volume increases (cellular hydration), and the ECF volume decreases (extracellular dehydration), as shown in Panel D of Figure 42-3. A disturbance of this kind may be of either renal or nonrenal origin. When the kidney is the source of salt wasting, the consequences are serious. Nonrenal causes include inadequate intake of salt and insufficiency of aldosterone. The state of low Na$^+$ can be recognized by poor skin turgor and dryness of the skin and mucous membranes, all of which reflect interstitial dehydration. The most important homeostatic response is the conservation of salt and water by the kidneys; however, salt and water also must be ingested for the compensation to be adequate.

Isotonic Expansion of Volume

Rapid oral intake or intravenous infusion of isotonic saline solution increases the plasma volume (Panel E of Figure 42-3). The consequent increase of capillary hydrostatic pressure and decrease of plasma oncotic pressure increase the effective filtration pressure and shift fluid from the plasma to the interstitial fluid compartment. However, because the fluid administered was isotonic, the osmolality of the ECF does not change, and water does not move across the cell membranes. Thus, although the volume of the ECF increases, the volume of the ICF does not change. The kidneys respond to the expansion of the ECF volume by excreting more salt and water. The consequence of the infusion of isotonic saline solution at a rate that exceeds urinary excretion is fluid retention, or *edema*. Edema also may be caused by either renal failure or cardiac failure (see Chapter 22), in which the excretion of salt and water is inadequate.

Isotonic Contraction of Volume

Isotonic dehydration is caused by the loss of both Na$^+$ and water from the body in proportion, so that the plasma [Na$^+$] is not altered. The volume of ECF is reduced, but the ICF compartment is not affected (Panel F in Figure 42-3). This condition may be caused by hemorrhage, loss of gastrointestinal fluid, or loss of plasma through burned skin. In these situations the renal excretion of salt and water is reduced markedly, and Na$^+$ and water are conserved. However, because of the limited ability of the kidneys to concentrate the solutes in the urine (hence the necessity to excrete at least a minimal volume of urine), electrolytes and water eventually must be ingested to replace that which is lost.

STUDY OUTLINE

GENERAL CONSIDERATIONS Principally Na$^+$ salts in extracellular fluid, K$^+$ salts within cell.

Extracellular [K$^+$] is regulated closely.

Water moves freely down osmotic gradients.

Isotonic fluid is distributed between vascular and interstitial spaces—balance between capillary hydrostatic pressure and plasma oncotic pressure.

Na$^+$, principal osmotic component, determines extracellular volume.

Volume of cellular fluid is determined by osmolality of extracellular fluid.

Body fluid volume and composition are regulated by kidneys.

REGULATION OF VOLUME AND OSMOLALITY Extracellular volume is regulated primarily by excretion of Na$^+$, secondarily by excretion of water.

Extracellular osmolality is regulated by excretion of water.

CONTROL OF SODIUM BALANCE

SODIUM RECEPTORS Volume receptors in heart and great vessels.

Renal excretion of salt and water adjusts volume as needed.

JUXTAGLOMERULAR APPARATUS Volume receptors in kidneys.

Influence secretion of renin.

HORMONAL AND NEURAL PATHWAYS Decreased renal blood flow or tubular load of Na^+ causes release of renin.

Renin, an enzyme, acts on angiotensinogen, a plasma globulin, to form angiotensin I.

Angiotensin I converted to angiotensin II by converting enzyme in lungs, liver, and kidneys.

Angiotensin II increases secretion of aldosterone by adrenal cortex.

Aldosterone causes renal retention of Na^+, increase of extracellular volume.

NATRIURETIC HORMONE Of uncertain origin, released during hypervolemia, decreases tubular reabsorption of Na^+.

Probably released only by high $[Na^+]$.

RENAL EFFECTOR SYSTEM Excretion of Na^+ is determined by the GFR and reabsorption.

CONSERVATION OF SODIUM Acute depletion of extracellular $[Na^+]$ or volume causes secretion of aldosterone.

Aldosterone increases reabsorption of Na^+ by distal tubules.

Sympathetic nerves to kidney cause secretion of renin, and arteriolar constriction that decreases GFR.

ELIMINATION OF SODIUM Excess Na^+ expands extracellular volume, suppresses secretion of aldosterone, decreases sympathetic nervous system discharge, and causes secretion of natriuretic hormone.

Excess Na^+ is excreted by kidneys.

CONTROL OF WATER BALANCE

FLUID COMPARTMENTS Plasma approximately 5% of body weight; medium for transport in body.

Interstitial fluid, approximately 15% of body weight, exchanges with plasma through capillaries; nearly protein-free filtrate of plasma.

Intracellular fluid, approximately 40% of body weight, exchanges with interstitial fluid; water moves passively, ions move passively and by active transport.

Only plasma communicates directly with external environment, but other two compartments exchange rapidly with plasma.

WATER BALANCE Intake equals loss.

Insensible loss through air passages and nonperspiratory loss through skin; obligatory loss through volume of water required to excrete solutes at maximum concentration.

Water is taken in by drinking and as preformed water in food; metabolic water is produced by oxidation of food.

Drinking is major source of water; partially discretionary.

Drinking is determined by thirst, habits, and social and psychological factors.

Intake usually exceeds minimum, urine of less than maximum osmolality is excreted.

ACTIONS OF ANTIDIURETIC HORMONE Controls water balance.

Released from posterior pituitary, increases permeability of collecting tubules to water, increases reabsorption of water into hyperosmotic interstitium.

CONTROL OF THE RELEASE OF ANTIDIURETIC HORMONE Osmoreceptors in hypothalamus, stretch receptors in left atrium, and stretch receptors in carotid sinuses and aortic arch.

Osmoreceptors located in supraoptic nuclei of hypothalamus.

Hypertonic extracellular fluid, water moves out, receptors shrink; hypotonic extracellular fluid, water moves in, receptors swell.

Sensitive to 1%–2% change of osmolality.

Regulate reabsorption of water in collecting ducts through release of ADH.

STRETCH RECEPTORS Most important stretch receptors are located in left atrium.

Extracellular volume increases, atrial pressure increases, receptors are stretched, release of ADH is inhibited by reflex action.

Extracellular volume decreases, atrial pressure decreases, ADH is released.

Release of aldosterone also is affected, more or less Na^+ is reabsorbed to match retention or excretion of water.

REGULATION OF POTASSIUM BALANCE Virtually all filtered K^+ is reabsorbed by proximal and distal tubules—excretion is regulated by secretion of K^+ in distal tubules and collecting ducts.

Determined by $[K^+]$ of distal and collecting tubular cells.

INTRACELLULAR/EXTRACELLULAR CONCENTRATION OF POTASSIUM IONS Determines resting cellular potential.

Exchange regulates plasma $[K^+]$.

INSULIN Released by increased extracellular $[K^+]$, increases uptake of K^+ by cells.

ALDOSTERONE Increased plasma $[K^+]$ increases rate of secretion.

Promotes transfer of K^+ into cells and increases secretion of K^+ by distal and collecting tubules.

DISTURBANCES OF SODIUM AND WATER BALANCE Depletion or excess of Na^+ or water.

Compensated by kidneys if not of renal origin.

HOMEOSTASIS If Na^+ balance is disturbed, ECF volume is altered.

If water balance is disturbed, osmolality of ECF is altered.

Hypernatremia is associated with water deficit, hyponatremia is associated with water excess.

EXTRACELLULAR/INTRACELLULAR CONCENTRATIONS OF SODIUM IONS AND WATER Fluid compartments in osmotic equilibrium—water moves freely.

Most solutes are distributed unevenly between compartments.

Na^+, Cl^-, and HCO_3^- are major osmotically active solutes in ECF; K^+, Mg^{++}, phosphates, and proteins are major osmotically active solutes in ICF.

Product of concentration of solutes and volume of water in compartment remains constant.

EXCESSIVE INTAKE OF WATER Body fluids are diluted—hyponatremia, or hypotonic hydration.

OSMOTIC EFFECTS Water taken orally distributes through all of body water.

EXCRETION Water is eliminated rapidly by normal kidneys.

HYPOTONIC HYDRATION Occurs if only water is ingested after both salt and water are lost (e.g., in perspiration).

Water decreases electrolyte concentrations in both ECF and ICF; cellular metabolism is disturbed.

EXCESSIVE LOSS OF WATER Osmolality of body fluids increases.

DEFECTS OF CONCENTRATING MECHANISM Pituitary diabetes insipidus—lack of synthesis or secretion of ADH.

Nephrogenic diabetes insipidus—kidneys not sensitive to ADH.

INSENSIBLE LOSS Evaporation through lungs and skin.

PRIMARY LOSS OF WATER Cellular dehydration, increased cellular electrolyte concentration.

Thirst, weakness, and neurological symptoms.

EXCESSIVE GAIN OF SOLUTE

PRIMARY ALDOSTERONISM Excess Na^+ is retained—hypernatremia and expansion of ECF volume.

HYPERNATREMIA Excess intake of Na^+ (e.g., drinking sea water).

Osmolality of ECF increases, water leaves cells.

Increased renal excretion of Na^+.

EXCESSIVE LOSS OF SOLUTE Hypotonic hypovolemia.

Decreased ECF osmolality, increased ICF volume.

Caused by inadequate intake of salt or by renal salt-wasting.

ISOTONIC EXPANSION OF VOLUME Intake of isotonic Na^+ solution.

Volume of ECF is increased, ICF is not changed.

May cause edema.

Kidneys excrete more salt and water.

ISOTONIC CONTRACTION OF VOLUME Loss of both Na^+ and water in proportion (e.g., hemorrhage).

ECF volume is decreased, ICF is not changed.

Kidneys conserve Na^+ and water.

Water and salt must be replaced.

BIBLIOGRAPHY

Andersson, B. 1978. Regulation of water intake. *Physiol. Rev.* 58:582.

Arruda, J.A.L., and Kurtzman, N.A. 1978. Relationship of renal sodium and water transport to hydrogen ion secretion. *Annu. Rev. Physiol.* 40:43.

Bauman, M.J. 1975. *Renal Function. Physiological and Medical Aspects.* St. Louis: Mosby.

Bie, P. 1980. Osmoreceptors, vasopressin, and control of renal water excretion. *Physiol. Rev.* 60:961.

Davis, J.O., and Freeman, R.H. 1976. Mechanisms regulating renin release. *Physiol. Rev.* 56:1.

Deetjen, P.; Boylan, J.W.; and Kramer, K. 1975. *Physiology of the Kidney and of Water Balance.* New York: Springer-Verlag.

deWardener, H.E. 1973. The control of sodium excretion. In *Handbook of Physiology.* Section 8. Renal Physiology. Edited by J. Orloff and R.W. Berliner. Washington, D.C.: American Physiological Society.

Feig, P.U., and McCurdy, D.K. 1977. The hypertonic state. *N. Engl. J. Med.* 297:1444.

Giebisch, G., and Stanton, B. 1979. Potassium transport in the nephron. *Annu. Rev. Physiol.* 41:241.

Gottschalk, C.W. 1979. Renal nerves and sodium excretion. *Annu. Rev. Physiol.* 41:229.

Handler, J.S., and Orloff, J. 1973. The mechanism of action of antidiuretic hormone. In *Handbook of Physiology*, Section 8. Renal Physiology. Chapter 24. Edited by J. Orloff and R.W. Berliner, Washington, D.C.: American Physiological Society.

Handler, J.S., and Orloff, J. 1981. Antidiuretic hormone. *Annu. Rev. Physiol.* 43:611.

Koushanpour, E. 1976. *Renal Physiology: Principles and Functions.* Philadelphia: Saunders.

Levens, N.R.; Peach, M.J.; and Carey, R.M. 1981. Role of the intrarenal renin-angiotensin system in the control of renal function. *Circ. Res.* 48:157.

Lohmeier, T.E.; Cowley, A.W.; Trippodo, N.C., Jr., et al. 1977. Effects of endogenous angiotensin II on renal sodium excretion and renal hemodynamics. *Am. J. Physiol.* 233:F388.

Peach, M.J. 1977. Renin-angiotensin system: Biochemistry and mechanisms of action. *Physiol. Rev.* 57:313.

Reid, I.A.; Morris, B.J.; and Ganong, W.F. 1978. The renin-angiotensin system. *Annu. Rev. Physiol.* 40:377.

Schafer, J.A., and Andreoli, T.A. 1979. Rheogenic and passive Na^+ absorption by the proximal nephron. *Annu. Rev. Physiol.* 41:211.

Schrier, R.W., and Berl, T.B. 1975. Nonosmolar factors affecting renal water excretion. *N. Engl. J. Med.* 292:81.

Sharp, G.W.G., and Leaf, A. 1973. Effects of aldosterone and its mechanism of action on sodium transport. In *Handbook of Physiology.* Section 8. Renal Physiology. Chapter 21. Edited by J. Orloff and R.W. Berliner. Washington, D.C.: American Physiological Society.

Stein, J.H., and Reineck, H.J. 1975. Effect of alterations in extracellular fluid volume on segmental sodium transport. *Physiol. Rev.* 55:127.

Whittembury, G., and Grantham, J.J. 1976. Cellular aspects of renal sodium transport and cell volume regulation. *Kidney Int.* 9:103.

43

Renal Regulation of Acid-Base Balance

CHAPTER CONTENTS

GENERAL CONSIDERATIONS

Importance of Plasma Concentration of Hydrogen Ions

The regulation of acid-base balance in mammals involves all of the chemical and physiological processes that maintain the concentration of hydrogen ion, $[H^+]$, in the body fluids at levels compatible with life and proper function. In a normal person, $[H^+]$ is maintained within narrow limits of approximately 40 nmoles/liter of plasma, which corresponds to a pH of about 7.4. The regulation of $[H^+]$ is essential for the proper functioning of the cells because H^+ reacts strongly with the negative charges on other molecules. For example, a change in $[H^+]$ of the body fluids changes the interactions of H^+ with the negatively charged functional groups of proteins. This alters the distribution of charges, and thereby affects the molecular conformation, which is important for the function of proteins (e.g., the actions of enzymes).

Control of Plasma Concentration of Hydrogen Ions

The [H^+] of the body fluids normally does not vary significantly from the normal value of 40 nmoles/liter of plasma, even though H^+ is being produced and consumed continuously by chemical reactions in the cells. Three fundamental processes underlie the regulation of [H^+]: (1) the chemical buffer systems of the body fluids, (2) the CO_2 level in the blood, which is controlled by adjusting the rate of alveolar ventilation (see Chapter 32), and (3) the excretion of excess acids or alkalis by the kidneys, which readjusts the buffer systems of the body fluids. When the [H^+] changes, both the chemical buffer systems and the respiratory system act rapidly; thus, marked changes of [H^+] in the body fluids are prevented. The renal regulatory system acts more slowly, but it is the only means of renewing the chemical buffers that are used up in the regulation of [H^+].

BUFFERS

The buffers in the body are located in the extracellular and intracellular fluids. The ability of a buffer system to oppose change of the pH of the fluids depends on the concentration of the buffer and the pK (equivalent to the pH at which the buffer consists of equal acid and base components) of the buffer relative to the pH of the body fluids. Two general classes of buffers are important physiologically: (1) the bicarbonate buffer system, which involves carbonic acid and bicarbonate as its buffer pair, and (2) the nonbicarbonate buffer system.

Bicarbonate Buffer System

The bicarbonate system is the most important buffer in the plasma of mammals. In the body fluids, H_2CO_3 formed from the hydration of CO_2 dissociates readily into H^+ and HCO_3^-. This buffer system can be described by the following equation:

$$CO_2 \leftrightarrows CO_2 + H_2O \leftrightarrows H_2CO_3 \leftrightarrows H^+ + HCO_3^-$$
(gaseous phase)   (aqueous phase)

The CO_2 in the aqueous phase is in equilibrium with CO_2 in the gaseous phase in the alveoli. Gaseous CO_2 dissolves in proportion to its partial pressure (P_{CO_2}), and the solution is affected by the chemical nature and tempera-

ture of the solvent and any other substances that are in solution. In a normal person, the P_{CO_2} of the arterial blood equilibrates with that of the alveolar air at about 40 mm Hg. This physiological value can be measured experimentally. For blood plasma at 37 C,

$$\begin{aligned} CO_2 \text{ dissolved} &= 0.03 \text{ (mmoles/liter)/mm Hg} \\ &\quad \times P_{CO_2} \\ &= 0.03 \text{ (mmoles/liter)/mm Hg} \\ &\quad \times 40 \text{ mm Hg} \\ &= 1.2 \text{ mmoles/liter} \end{aligned}$$

where 0.03 (mmoles/liter)/mm Hg is the proportionality constant for CO_2 in the plasma at 37 C. In the body fluids, the equilibrium of the hydration reaction of CO_2 ($CO_2 + H_2O \leftrightarrows H_2CO_3$) lies far to the left; thus, the solution contains 500 moles of CO_2 for every mole of H_2CO_3. This equilibrium is important to mammalian organisms because CO_2 diffuses readily across cell membranes. Therefore, changes in one fluid compartment influence [H^+] in all of the fluid compartments.

HENDERSON-HASSELBALCH EQUATION

The Henderson-Hasselbalch equation can be used to express the relationship among the components of the carbonic acid/bicarbonate buffer system (for a derivation of this equation see Chapter 32):

$$pH = pK' + \log \frac{[HCO_3^-]}{[CO_2 + H_2CO_3]}$$

The value of pK' for the bicarbonate buffer system is 6.1 for plasma at pH 7.4 and a temperature of 37 C. In this buffer system, HCO_3^- is the conjugate base, and the acid component is formed by the so-called "total carbonic acid pool," which consists of the dissolved CO_2 and H_2CO_3 in equilibrium. Since [H_2CO_3] is very low compared to the dissolved CO_2, it can be omitted from the equation. If 0.03 P_{CO_2} is substituted for the dissolved CO_2, the equation can be rewritten as follows:

$$pH = 6.1 + \log \frac{[HCO_3^-]}{0.03 \, P_{CO_2}}$$

where P_{CO_2} is the partial pressure of CO_2 (see Chapter 32).

A buffer system is most effective within one pH unit of its pK. Although the pK' of the carbonic acid/bicarbonate buffer system is 6.1, which is 1.3 pH units less than the pH of the plasma, this system still is important because the concentrations of the two components, CO_2 and HCO_3^-, are regulated and stabilized by two physiological mechanisms: (1) the respiratory system, which regulates $[CO_2]$, and (2) the kidneys, which regulate $[HCO_3^-]$. CO_2 is produced continuously by the cells and eliminated continuously by the respiratory system. Therefore, the body can regulate the concentration of CO_2 in the body fluids to meet changing needs by controlling the rate at which CO_2 is eliminated through the lungs. The $[HCO_3^-]$ of the plasma is regulated independently through the renal excretion of H^+. Thus, if an individual develops acidosis (low pH, or high $[H^+]$, in the plasma), the condition can be adjusted toward normal by decreasing the P_{CO_2} (through increased alveolar ventilation) or increasing plasma $[HCO_3^-]$ (through increased renal excretion of H^+).

Nonbicarbonate Buffer Systems

In addition to the bicarbonate buffer system, the mammalian body contains many compounds and functional groups in macromolecules that can act as buffers. However, most of these compounds and groups do not have significant buffer capacity in mammalian body fluids because their pK values differ too much from the physiological pH of 7.4. In mammals, the two general kinds of compounds other than the bicarbonate system that function as buffers in the physiological range of pH are phosphates and proteins.

PHOSPHATE BUFFERS

The phosphate system includes both inorganic and organic phosphates. The inorganic phosphate buffer system has an acid form, $H_2PO_4^-$, and a conjugate base form, $HPO_4^=$, and the equation for the system is as follows:

$$H_2PO_4^- \leftrightharpoons HPO_4^= + H^+$$

Since the pK of this system is 6.8, it functions well at the pH of the body fluids. However, it is quantitatively less important than the bicarbonate buffer in the plasma because of its relatively low concentration (1 mmole/liter of plasma phosphate as compared to 23 mmoles/liter of bicarbonate).

The organic phosphate compounds are important in the intracellular fluid. Many of these compounds function well as buffers under physiological conditions because their pK values are near 7.4. Examples of such compounds are glucose-1-phosphate, nucleoside monophosphates, nucleoside diphosphates, and nucleoside triphosphates.

PROTEINS

The proteins are macromolecules that function effectively as buffers in the body fluids, especially within the cells, where they occur in relatively large amounts. Hemoglobin, the most important buffer in the red cells, is effective in the pH range of 7–8. The equation for the buffer action of hemoglobin is as follows:

$$H^+ + HB^- \leftrightharpoons HHb$$

Proteins also function as extracellular buffers, although they are quantitatively less important than the bicarbonate buffer. The plasma proteins have pK values that range from 5.5 to 8.5, depending on the protein structure in the immediate environment. The equation for the buffer action of plasma protein is as follows:

$$H^+ + Pr^- \leftrightharpoons HPr$$

PROCESSING OF ACIDS AND ALKALIS

Response to Acid or Alkali

Although endogenous metabolic processes yield acids continuously (and to a lesser degree, bases), the $[H^+]$ of the body fluids of normal individuals does not vary greatly. The metabolism of foodstuffs may either acidify or alkalinize the body fluids, depending on the composition of the diet. The responses of the body to either an acid or alkali load are as given earlier in the chapter (see the section entitled "control of Plasma Concentration of Hydrogen Ion"), chemical buffering, adjustment of plasma $[CO_2]$ by the respiration, and adjustment of the secretion of H^+ by the kidneys. Under normal conditions, a steady state exists when the rates of excretion of CO_2 and H^+ equal their rates of production and the rate of excretion of excess alkali (mostly Na^+) equals its rate of intake.

Carbonic Acids

CO_2 is generated by the metabolism of glucose and triglycerides, and the majority of CO_2 is

CLINICAL CORRELATION
43.1   Metabolic Acidosis

CASE REPORT

The Patient: A 63-year-old man.

Reason for Admission: Lethargy and confusion.

History: The patient had a long history of hypertension and congestive heart failure, for which he took digitalis and a diuretic agent (see Chapter 22). He also had moderate renal disease: 10 months before the present admission, the creatinine clearance had been 45 ml/min/m² of body surface area (normal, 60–72 ml/min/m²), total urine protein had been 2.5 g/24 hours (normal, < 150 mg/24 hours), serum creatinine had been 1.6 mg/dl (normal, 0.6–1.5 mg/dl), and the blood urea nitrogen (BUN) had been 26 mg/dl (normal, 8–25 mg/dl). The serum sodium concentration, [Na⁺], had been 143 mEq/liter (normal, 135–145 mEq/liter), [K⁺] had been 4.1 mEq/liter (normal, 3.5–5 mEq/liter), [Cl⁻] was 103 mEq/liter (normal, 100–105 mEq/liter), and the CO_2 content was 26 mM/liter (normal, 24–30 mM/liter). The patient occasionally followed folk medicine, and on the advice of a friend, had begun to consume sulfur (Sublimed Sulfur, U.S.P., a fine powder of pure sulfur) for his malaise (general body weakness) and dyspnea (difficult breathing). He had been taking sulfur for a week before current admission, and it was estimated that he may have consumed as much as 75 g/day during each of the last 2 days before admission. He reported no bowel movements for at least 3 days before admission. Because of his apparently deteriorated condition, his family brought him to the hospital.

Clinical Examination: At admission, the patient's body temperature was normal, the heart rate was 95/min (normal, 60–100/min),

the arterial pressure was 165/95 mm Hg (normal, 90–140/60–90 mm Hg), and the respiratory rate was 22/min (normal, 13–17/min). The pH of the arterial blood was 7.18 (normal, 7.35–7.45), the serum [Na⁺] was 125 mEq/liter, [K⁺] was 8.7 mEq/liter, [Cl⁻] was 103 mEq/liter, the partial pressure of CO_2 (Pa_{CO_2}) was 28 mm Hg (normal, 35–45 mm Hg), the [HCO₃⁻] was 10 mEq/liter (normal, 21–28 mEq/liter), and the Pa_{O_2} was 90 mm Hg (normal, 75–100 mm Hg). The BUN was 44 mg/dl, and the serum creatinine was 2.1 mg/dl. The pH of the urine was 4.9, the concentration of protein in the urine was 0.3 g/dl (normal, undetectable), and the numbers of red and white blood cells were excessive.

Treatment: NaHCO₃ solution was infused, and enemas were given to remove sulfur from the colon. After four days, the blood gases, plasma electrolytes, and pH of the arterial blood were normal, and the patient was discharged.

Comment: Elemental sulfur is a relatively nontoxic substance, but it is converted to sulfide and then to sulfate by bacteria in the colon. Sulfur often produces diarrhea, because of irritation produced by its metabolites, but such did not occur in this patient. Thus, acidic products of sulfur were absorbed, producing severe metabolic acidosis. The patient's renal disease also contributed to the condition, because the excretion of H⁺ was slow. The decrease of Pa_{CO_2} reflects respiratory compensation for the metabolic acidosis (see Chapter 32, "Acid-Base Shifts"), and the decrease of [HCO₃⁻] reflects the movement to the left of the reaction that involves the hydration of CO_2 to H_2CO_3 and the dissociation of H_2CO_3 to form H⁺ and HCO₃⁻ (see Chapter 32). Complete correction of the condition requires the excretion of H⁺ by the kidneys.

hydrated to H_2CO_3. Approximately 15,000 mM of CO_2 are formed each day in a person who takes a typical diet. If the endogenously produced CO_2 were not excreted, acid would accumulate in the body fluids. This is prevented by the respiratory system, which eliminates CO_2 from the body and keeps the concentration of CO_2 in the body fluids constant.

Noncarbonic Acids

Noncarbonic acids also are produced by the metabolism of foodstuffs; for example, lactic acid is formed from glucose, acetoacetic acid and β-hydroxybutyric acid are formed from triglycerides, phosphoric acid is produced from phospholipids, and sulfuric acid is formed from sulfur-containing amino acids. Although these acids dissociate to form significant amounts of H^+, most of them cause no acid-base problems because the H^+ they yield is neutralized by chemical buffers in the body fluids. In addition, substances such as lactic acid, acetoacetic acid, and β-hydroxybutyric acid are metabolized further to CO_2 and water. If, in the process of metabolism, the plasma $[H^+]$ increases significantly, the respiration is stimulated; the increased alveolar ventilation decreases Pco_2, and the $[H^+]$ of the plasma is restored to its normal level. The kidneys eventually excrete the excess H^+ and, in so doing, readjust the buffer systems of the body. Compounds such as phosphoric acid and sulfuric acid cannot be metabolized further. The H^+ they yield is excreted by the kidneys, which simultaneously restore the conjugate bases—mainly bicarbonate—of the buffer systems.

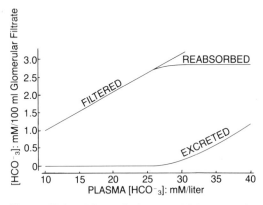

Figure 43-1. Effect of plasma $[HCO_3^-]$ on the renal handling of HCO_3^-. (Redrawn, with permission, from Pitts, R.F., et al. 1949. The renal regulation of acid-base balance in man. III. The reabsorption and excretion of bicarbonate. *J. Clin. Invest.* 28:37.)

Organic Salts

Salts of organic acids are the major source of alkali; for example, sodium lactate or sodium citrate, which are found in some fruits. These organic anions are metabolized to CO_2 and water, and the process consumes one mole of H^+ for every mole of organic anion that is metabolized. Thus, the concentrations of the conjugate-base forms of the chemical buffer systems increase, which increases $[HCO_3^-]$. The buffer systems and the respiratory compensation prevent a marked decrease of $[H^+]$, and the kidneys ultimately excrete the excess HCO_3^-.

ROLE OF THE KIDNEYS IN ACID-BASE BALANCE

The bicarbonate buffer system is the most important buffer in mammalian plasma; it is unique because it provides physiological mechanisms that regulate the concentrations of the acid component (CO_2) and the conjugate-base (HCO_3^-) component independently. The respiratory system contributes to acid-base balance by regulating the plasma $[CO_2]$, and the renal system contributes by regulating the plasma $[HCO_3^-]$. The kidneys regulate the plasma $[HCO_3^-]$ by (1) reabsorbing the HCO_3^- that is filtered at the glomeruli, (2) excreting the excess HCO_3^- that is ingested or produced in the body, and (3) replenishing depleted stores of HCO_3^- by hydrating CO_2 to H_2CO_3 and excreting H^+.

Reabsorption of Bicarbonate

RENAL PLASMA THRESHOLD
The $[HCO_3^-]$ of the plasma is approximately 24 mEq/liter in an individual who takes a high-protein diet, the metabolism of which produces acid. The HCO_3^- that is filtered is reabsorbed by the proximal, distal, and collecting tubules, although 90% of the reabsorption occurs in the proximal tubules (see Chapter 40). This process is one of conservation, which prevents the loss of HCO_3^- in the urine when the plasma $[HCO_3^-]$ is below a certain threshold level. The handling of filtered bicarbonate by the kidneys can be described by a bicarbonate titration curve (Figure 43-1). In normal humans, the renal plasma threshold for HCO_3^- is about 26–28 mEq/liter, which is only slightly higher than the normal plasma $[HCO_3^-]$. When the plasma $[HCO_3^-]$ is less than the renal plasma

threshold, reabsorption of bicarbonate by the tubules is a linear function of the filtered load and essentially is complete. When the plasma [HCO_3^-] exceeds the renal plasma threshold, the rate of reabsorption by the tubules does not increase in proportion to the filtered load. Consequently, the excess [HCO_3^-] is excreted in the urine, and the plasma [HCO_3^-] is returned to the threshold level.

SECRETION OF HYDROGEN IONS

The reabsorption of HCO_3^- into the proximal peritubular capillary involves the active secretion of H^+ into the tubular lumen by the tubular cells. The relationship between the secretion of H^+ and the reabsorption of HCO_3^- is shown schematically in Figure 43-2A. The first reaction is the hydration of CO_2 to H_2CO_3 in the tubular cells, which is catalyzed by carbonic anhydrase. The H_2CO_3 that is formed dissociates rapidly into H^+ and HCO_3^-, and the H^+ is secreted into the tubular lumen, coupled to the passive movement of Na^+ from the tubular fluid into the tubular cell. In the tubular fluid, H^+ combines with HCO_3^- to generate H_2CO_3, which then dissociates into H_2O and CO_2. The H_2O and CO_2 are reabsorbed. This reaction also is catalyzed by carbonic anhydrase, which is located along the brush border of the proximal tubular cells.

The HCO_3^- formed by the intracellular hydration of CO_2 enters the peritubular capillary in association with the active movement of Na^+ across the basolateral membrane. Thus, reabsorption of HCO_3^- from the tubular fluid is indirect. In this process, the Na^+ delivered to the peritubular blood comes from the luminal fluid (i.e., it is filtered Na^+). However, the HCO_3^- added to the peritubular blood is derived from the intracellular dissociation of H_2CO_3, and the HCO_3^- that was filtered is removed from the tubular fluid as CO_2 and H_2O. Nevertheless, for every H^+ that is secreted and captured by a filtered HCO_3^- in the tubular fluid, one HCO_3^- has been added to the peritubular blood. Therefore, Na^+ and HCO_3^- are reabsorbed by this circuitous pathway just as effectively as if they had been transported directly from the fluid of the lumen to the peritubular blood.

The importance of this system can be demonstrated by the response to acetazolamide, which is an inhibitor of carbonic anhydrase. The rate of the dissociation of H_2CO_3 to CO_2 and H_2O in the tubular fluid decreases, and as a

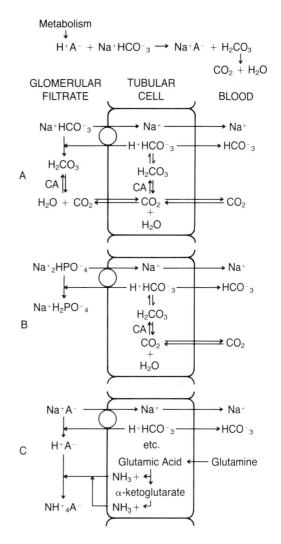

Figure 43-2. Participation of secreted H^+ in the reabsorption of HCO_3^- (**A**) and the excretion of H^+ (**B** and **C**) (CA = carbonic anhydrase).

consequence, [HCO_3^-] and [H^+] in the tubular fluid increase. Under these conditions, H^+ must be secreted against a steeper concentration gradient; thus, the rate of secretion of H^+ decreases, the reabsorption of HCO_3^- in the proximal tubule decreases, and HCO_3^- is lost in the urine.

DISTAL REABSORPTION

The distal and collecting tubules reabsorb the remaining 10% of the HCO_3^- that is filtered. The mechanism of reabsorption is similar to that in the proximal tubules, except that the distal tubules contain no carbonic anhydrase in the lumen. Because of this and the facilitation of the formation of H^+ by carbonic anhydrase in the cell, the breakdown of H_2CO_3 to CO_2 and H_2O is slow in the tubular fluid, and H_2CO_3 and H^+ tend to accumulate. However, the distal and collecting tubules can secrete H^+ against a much steeper concentration gradient, independent of Na^+ reabsorption, probably through H^+-ATPase in the luminal membrane. Thus, essentially all of the relatively small amount of HCO_3^- that is delivered from the proximal tubules is reabsorbed, and a pH of 4.5 in the urine is reached.

Regeneration of Bicarbonate

The secretion of H^+ by the tubular cells results in the delivery of HCO_3^- into the peritubular blood. If the H^+ that is secreted combines with HCO_3^- in the tubular fluid, CO_2 and H_2O are formed and absorbed, and HCO_3^- is regenerated. This mechanism conserves the HCO_3^- of the blood by preventing its loss in the urine. However, if the H^+ that is secreted combines with other buffers in the tubular fluid, and HCO_3^- is excreted, HCO_3^- is synthesized in the tubular cell and added to the peritubular blood. This ability of the kidneys to add HCO_3^- to the plasma is important because it replaces the HCO_3^- that is used to buffer the excess acid produced by the ingestion or metabolism of foodstuffs. The H^+ from these excess acids react with $Na^+HCO_3^-$ in the extracellular fluid and form H_2CO_3, which is excreted through the lungs as CO_2, and the sodium salt of the acid enters the glomerular filtrate. The equation for this buffer reaction is as follows:

$$H^+A^- + Na^+HCO_3^- \leftrightarrows Na^+A^- + H_2CO_3$$
$$\downarrow$$
$$CO_2 + H_2O$$

where A is an unspecified anion.

Excretion of Hydrogen Ions

To a limited extent, the kidneys can excrete acid anions in association with an equivalent amount of H^+ and simultaneously reabsorb Na^+, which is returned to the plasma in association with an equivalent amount of newly formed HCO_3^-. In humans, the minimum urinary pH that can be achieved is 4.5–5.0, which represents a $[H^+]$ less than 0.04 mEq/liter. Therefore, only insignificant amounts of free H^+ can exist in the urine. To excrete the 50–100 mEq of H^+ that is produced daily, H^+ must be excreted in combination with buffers that are filtered, for example, phosphates (referred to as titratable acids), and with NH_3 to form NH_4^+. The amount of H^+ excreted in these ways is equivalent to the amount of HCO_3^- generated by the renal tubules and returned to the plasma. In steady state, the net amount of H^+ excreted by the kidneys (titratable acid + NH_4^+ − HCO_3^-) must equal the quantity of acids that enter the extracellular fluid from dietary intake and from metabolism.

EXCRETION OF TITRATABLE ACIDS

Several anions of weak acids are filtered at the glomeruli and may act as buffers in the tubular fluid. The ability of a weak acid to act as a buffer is determined by its quantity and its pK. The most important of these weak acids is the phosphate buffer $HPO_4^=$ because of its relatively high concentration and its pK of 6.8. The H^+ that is bound to these buffers and excreted is known as titratable acid because it can be measured by the amount of alkali (NaOH) that must be added to titrate the pH of the urine back to that of the blood (7.4).

As the fluid passes through the renal tubules, the H^+ secretory system converts much of the $HPO_4^=$ to $H_2PO_4^-$ by the addition of H^+, mainly in the proximal segment (Figure 43-2B). In this way, the kidneys can excrete much of the H^+ that is formed in the production of noncarbonic acid during metabolism. For each H^+ captured by $HPO_4^=$ to yield $H_2PO_4^-$, one HCO_3^- is formed by the renal tubular cell and delivered to the peritubular blood, where it helps to restore the plasma HCO_3^- used to buffer the H^+.

EXCRETION OF AMMONIUM

The rate of excretion of titratable acid is determined by the pH of the tubular fluid and the quantity of buffer that is filtered. Usually, not enough buffer is filtered to permit all of the excess H^+ to be excreted as titratable acid. Therefore, excess H^+ also is eliminated in combination with ammonia (NH_3), which is produced by the renal tubular cells and added to the tubular fluid (Figure 43-2C). NH_3 is a base that reacts with H^+ to form ammonium (NH_4^+); the pK of this buffer system is 9.3. Since the pH of the proximal tubular fluid is approximately 7.0, most of the NH_3 that is secreted captures H^+ to yield NH_4^+. As the tubular fluid becomes more acid, more NH_3 is used to form NH_4^+.

Both the proximal and distal tubular cells can generate NH_3, which crosses cell membranes by passive nonionic diffusion and reacts with H^+ in the tubular fluid. Thus, H^+ is excreted with a minimal increase in the $[H^+]$ of the tubular fluid. This process depends on the solubility characteristics of NH_3 and NH_4^+; NH_3 is lipid-soluble and crosses cell membranes rapidly when a concentration gradient is established, but NH_4^+, which is a polar (water-soluble) compound, crosses lipid membranes poorly. Once NH_4^+ is formed in the lumen, it cannot diffuse out; thus, H^+ is neutralized and retained in the lumen as NH_4^+.

The tubular epithelial cells can generate NH_3 from a number of amino acids, the most important of which is glutamine. Glutamine is converted to glutamic acid and NH_3; this reaction is catalyzed by the enzyme glutaminase, which is abundant in tubular cells. Further deamination of glutamic acid by glutamic dehydrogenase yields α-ketoglutaric acid and NH_3. The reaction can be depicted as follows:

$$glutamine \rightarrow glutamic\ acid + NH_3$$

$$\rightarrow \alpha\text{-ketoglutarate} + NH_3$$

Therefore, for every molecule of glutamine that is metabolized, two molecules of NH_3 are formed. As the concentration of NH_3 within the cell increases, NH_3 diffuses out of the cell and down its concentration gradient into the tubular lumen. Because NH_3 combines with H^+ to form NH_4^+, tubular $[NH_3]$ remains low and more NH_3 diffuses into the lumen. The amount of NH_4^+ formed depends on the $[H^+]$ of the tubular fluid and the rate of production of NH_3.

Because the minimum pH that the urine can reach is 4.5–5.0, most of the H^+ that is secreted into the luminal fluid must be buffered by either $HPO_4^=$ or NH_3. The metabolism of glutamine, the source of NH_3, is pH-dependent; glutamine metabolism increases with acidosis and decreases with alkalosis. In acidosis, the tubular cells can secrete large amounts of NH_3 into the tubular fluid. The production of NH_3 and the excretion of NH_4^+ is the adaptive response of the kidneys to an acid load. By these means, the kidneys can excrete large amounts of noncarbonic acids in the urine and restore the acid-base balance of the body to normal.

FACTORS THAT AFFECT RENAL EXCRETION OF HYDROGEN IONS

Concentration Gradient of Hydrogen Ions

The secretion of H^+ into the tubular lumen is limited by a concentration gradient that corresponds to a pH of 4.5–5.0 in the tubular fluid. Under normal circumstances, most of the H^+ that is secreted is used to reabsorb HCO_3^-. However, when as much as 50–100 mEq of H^+ is produced daily and must be excreted, or when acidosis develops, H^+ cannot be excreted as such because the pH of the tubular fluid may well reach the limit of 4.5. The excretion of H^+ can be increased if more buffer is filtered or if the production of NH_3 by the tubular cells is increased.

Presence of Other Ions

The ability of the tubular cells to secrete H^+ also is affected by other ions such as Na^+, K^+, and Cl^-. Since the secretion of H^+ is coupled loosely to the entry of Na^+ into the cell, the availability of Na^+ may be an important factor in the secretion of H^+. The change in the rate of excretion of H^+ with a change in the rate of reabsorption of Na^+ can be seen in the condition of hypovolemia, in which the reabsorption of Na^+ is increased. To maintain electroneutrality, Cl^- and HCO_3^- are reabsorbed and H^+ or K^+ is secreted. Quantitatively, the reabsorption of Cl^- is the most important and the secretion of H^+ is the least important. Since $[Na^+]$ in the glomerular filtrate is 145 mEq/liter and $[Cl^-]$ is 114 mEq/liter, only 114 mEq/liter of Na^+ can be reabsorbed with Cl^-, and the rest of the $[Na^+]$ must be accompanied by the secretion of H^+, the reabsorption of HCO_3^-, or the secretion of K^+. Therefore, when the need to conserve body Na^+ is maximal, as it may be in hypovolemia, the secretion of H^+ or the reabsorption of HCO_3^- is increased. Conversely, after volume expansion, which decreases the reabsorption of Na^+, the secretion of H^+ or the reabsorption of HCO_3^- decreases.

In the distal and collecting tubules, where the tight junctions are relatively impermeable to ions and water (see Chapter 40), the reabsorption of Na^+ generates an electrical potential gradient of about 60 mv between the lumen and the interstitium; the lumen is negative. This increased electrochemical gradient (see Chapter 2) favors the secretion of K^+ and H^+ in exchange for the Na^+ that is absorbed. K^+ and H^+ are secreted reciprocally; however, since intracellular $[K^+]$ is greater than intracellular $[H^+]$, more K^+ than H^+ exchanges for Na^+. Loss of body K^+ (hypokalemia), which occurs in starvation (see Chapter 69) and in severe diarrhea (see Chapter 52), decreases intracellular $[K^+]$. This decreases the secretion of K^+ and increases the secretion of H^+.

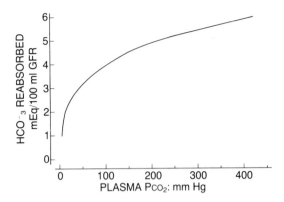

Figure 43-3. Relationship between arterial P_{CO_2} and the renal reabsorption of HCO_3^-. (Redrawn, with permission, from Rector, F.C., et al. 1960. The role of plasma CO_2 tension and carbonic anhydrase activity in the renal reabsorption of bicarbonate. *J. Clin. Invest.* 39:1709.)

Arterial Concentration of Hydrogen Ions

The secretion of H^+ is affected by the $[H^+]$ of the blood. The rate of secretion of H^+ increases when the arterial $[H^+]$ increases during acidosis and decreases when the arterial $[H^+]$ decreases during alkalosis. This response of the kidneys to arterial $[H^+]$ is important in the maintenance of acid-base homeostasis. For example, acidosis can be produced either by a decrease in the plasma $[HCO_3^-]$ or by an increase in the arterial P_{CO_2}. In either case, the increased rate of excretion of H^+ by the kidneys increases the plasma $[HCO^+]$, which tends to return the $[H^+]$ of the blood toward normal. The effect of arterial $[H^+]$ on the net excretion of H^+ by the kidneys is mediated by changes in the intracellular $[H^+]$ of the renal tubular cell. Thus, acidosis increases the intracellular $[H^+]$ and thereby increases the secretion of H^+ into the tubular fluid.

Respiratory Acidosis

Respiratory acidosis is a disturbance caused primarily by the inability of the respiratory system to excrete CO_2 as rapidly as is required to satisfy the existing needs of the body (see Chapter 32). The retention of CO_2 causes an excess of carbonic acid relative to the acid-base needs of the body. The increased P_{CO_2} of the arterial blood causes equivalent increases of P_{CO_2} and $[H^+]$ in the renal tubular cells, which determine the secretion of H^+ and the reabsorption of HCO_3^-. Although correction of this acid-base disorder requires the restoration of normal alveolar ventilation, the kidneys oppose the increase in the $[H^+]$ of the arterial blood by increasing the excretion of H^+ and the reabsorption of HCO_3^- (Figure 43-3). Since the arterial $[H^+]$ is a function of the ratio HCO_3^-/P_{CO_2} (see the section on the Henderson-Hasselbalch equation earlier in this chapter), the increase of plasma $[HCO_3^-]$ is an appropriate response to hypoventilation.

The renal response to respiratory acidosis occurs relatively slowly; although the response begins within 24 hours, it takes 4–5 days to develop fully. Although the renal compensation of respiratory acidosis is incomplete, it returns the arterial $[H^+]$ toward normal and is the predominant factor that regulates the plasma $[H^+]$.

Respiratory Alkalosis

Hyperventilation causes excess elimination of CO_2, which results in a fall in the P_{CO_2}, and alkalosis. The renal response to alkalosis is to decrease the secretion of H^+ and the reabsorption of HCO_3^-; thus, HCO_3^- is lost in the urine. Consequently, the plasma $[HCO_3^-]$ is decreased; the ratio HCO_3^-/P_{CO_2} and the arterial $[H^+]$ return toward normal.

Metabolic Acidosis

Metabolic acidosis can be caused either by the loss of HCO_3^- from the extracellular fluid (e.g., from severe diarrhea (see Chapter 52)) or by increased production of noncarbonic acids (e.g., from diabetic ketoacidosis) (see Chapter 61). The kidneys eliminate the excess acid as titratable acid and NH_4^+. The excretion of phosphate in the urine usually remains relatively constant in the presence of an acid load, and the capacity of the kidneys to increase the net excretion of H^+ by increasing the formation of titratable acid is limited. However, in diabetic ketoacidosis, large amounts of β-hydroxybutyrate are excreted. This compound can act as a buffer in the urine and augment the excretion of titratable acids. In this situation, as much as 500 mEq of H^+ can be excreted per day because of the large amounts of ketoacids in the tubular fluid and the acid pK of those compounds (about 4.8).

Metabolic Alkalosis

The normal renal response to increased $[HCO_3^-]$ is to reduce the secretion of H^+ and to excrete the excess HCO_3^- in the urine. In an uncomplicated acute metabolic alkalosis (e.g., during the metabolism of salts of organic acids, such as sodium lactate and sodium citrate, which are found in certain fruits), the excess HCO_3^- is excreted rapidly. However, when metabolic alkalosis is associated with the depletion of extracellular fluid volume caused by severe or prolonged vomiting (which causes the loss of gastric juice), the adaptive response of the kidneys is relatively ineffective. In this condition the depletion of volume is accompanied by the depletion of Na^+, H^+, and Cl^-. Hypovolemia and loss of Na^+ stimulate the kidneys to reabsorb Na^+ from the tubular fluid and to increase their reabsorption of HCO_3^- or secretion of H^+. When extracellular $[Cl^-]$ is decreased, the tubular fluid contains less Cl^-, and HCO_3^- is reabsorbed as the anion to accompany Na^+. When extracellular $[K^+]$ is decreased, intracellular $[K^+]$ decreases and the secretion of H^+ increases (see the previous section entitled "Presence of Other Ions"). The result is acidic urine free of HCO_3^-. Thus, the kidneys not only fail to excrete the excess HCO_3^-, they actually excrete H^+ and generate HCO_3^-, which prevents the correction of the alkalosis. In this situation, the attempt of the kidneys to restore the extracellular volume offsets any attempts to correct the systemic $[H^+]$. The excess HCO_3^- can be eliminated and the chronic metabolic alkalosis corrected by expanding the extracellular fluid volume with a solution of NaCl, which removes the stimulus to retain Na^+. The decreased reabsorption of Na^+ leads ultimately to decreased reabsorption and loss of HCO_3^- in the urine. Thus, correction of the volume deficit when K^+ and Cl^- are depleted permits the kidneys to respond more appropriately to chronic metabolic alkalosis.

STUDY OUTLINE

GENERAL CONSIDERATIONS

IMPORTANCE OF PLASMA CONCENTRATION OF HYDROGEN IONS H^+ reacts strongly with negative regions of proteins and other molecules, affects protein functions (e.g., enzymes).

CONTROL OF PLASMA CONCENTRATION OF HYDROGEN IONS   Normal is 40 nmoles/liter, or pH 7.4.
  Chemical buffer systems—act rapidly to prevent large changes of $[H^+]$.
  Blood CO_2 level—controlled by respiration.
  Renal excretion of excess acid or alkali—acts slowly, provides final adjustment.

BUFFERS   In body fluids; bicarbonate and nonbicarbonate.

BICARBONATE BUFFER SYSTEM   Most important in plasma.
  CO_2 hydrates to form H_2CO_3, which dissociates to form H^+ and HCO_3^-.
  Dissolved CO_2 is in equilibrium with gaseous CO_2 of lungs.
  Because CO_2 crosses membranes readily, change of $[H^+]$ in one compartment affects all others.

HENDERSON-HASSELBALCH EQUATION   Expresses relationship among components of bicarbonate buffer system.
  Buffer most effective at pK (equal acid and base components); in blood, if pK equals pH (7.4).
  Bicarbonate system maintained by respiratory system (regulates CO_2) and kidneys (regulate HCO_3^-).

NONBICARBONATE BUFFER SYSTEMS
Phosphates and proteins.
  PHOSPHATE BUFFERS   Good pK, but low concentration in plasma.
  More important in cellular fluid.
  PROTEINS   Effective, but low concentrations in plasma.
  More important in cells; hemoglobin in red cells very important.

PROCESSING OF ACIDS AND ALKALIS

RESPONSE TO ACID OR ALKALI
  Action of buffers.
  Change of alveolar ventilation to control plasma CO_2.
  Change of renal excretion of H^+ to regulate plasma $[HCO_3^-]$.

CARBONIC ACIDS   Hydration of CO_2.

Large amounts of CO_2 are produced, most is excreted through respiratory system, keeping CO_2 in body fluids constant.

NONCARBONIC ACIDS   From metabolism of foodstuffs.

H^+ is neutralized by chemical buffers.

Some acids are metabolized further to CO_2 and water.

Ultimate control through renal excretion.

ORGANIC SALTS   Major source of alkali.

ROLE OF THE KIDNEYS IN ACID-BASE BALANCE

Reabsorb filtered HCO_3^-. Excrete excess HCO_3^-.

Replenish HCO_3^- by forming H_2CO_3 and excreting H^+.

REABSORPTION OF BICARBONATE

RENAL PLASMA THRESHOLD   About 26–28 mEq/liter.

Normal plasma $[HCO_3^-]$ is 24 mEq/liter; HCO_3^- reabsorbed almost completely by renal tubules.

When plasma $[HCO_3^-]$ exceeds threshold, excess is excreted in urine.

SECRETION OF HYDROGEN IONS   To effect reabsorption of HCO_3^-.

CO_2 is hydrated in proximal tubular cells, H^+ is exchanged for Na^+ in lumen.

$Na^+HCO_3^-$ enters body fluids.

H^+ combines with HCO_3^- in lumen, forms H_2CO_3, which dissociates to H_2O and CO_2 and is reabsorbed.

DISTAL REABSORPTION   About 10% of reabsorption.

Through secretion of H^+, but process is slow, not catalyzed by carbonic anhydrase in lumen.

Distal and collecting tubules can secrete H^+ against larger concentration gradient; facilitates reabsorption of HCO_3^-.

REGENERATION OF BICARBONATE

HCO_3^- added to blood by tubular cells replaces HCO_3^- used to buffer H^+ produced by metabolism.

EXCRETION OF HYDROGEN IONS   Less than 0.04 mEq/liter of H^+ can appear in urine (pH 4.5–5).

H^+ is excreted mostly in combination with filtered buffers or NH_3.

EXCRETION OF TITRATABLE ACIDS
H^+ is combined with buffers.

Phosphate most important.

More H^+ is excreted by converting $HPO_4^=$ to $H_2PO_4^-$.

EXCRETION OF AMMONIUM   Excretion of buffers usually is not adequate.

NH_3 is produced by tubular cells, reacts to form NH_4^+ salts, which are excreted.

Production of NH_3 increases with acidosis; means of excreting large amounts of H^+.

FACTORS THAT AFFECT RENAL EXCRETION OF HYDROGEN IONS

CONCENTRATION GRADIENT OF HYDROGEN IONS   Limits secretion of H^+ by tubular cells.

Most H^+ secreted is used to reabsorb HCO_3^-.

Excess H^+ excreted must be buffered or combined with NH_3.

PRESENCE OF OTHER IONS   Secretion of H^+ is coupled loosely with absorption of Na^+, affected by $[Na^+]$ of tubular fluid and need of body to reabsorb Na^+.

In distal and collecting tubules, reabsorption of Na^+ is coupled to secretion of either H^+ or K^+; H^+ and K^+ are excreted reciprocally, determined by $[K^+]$ and $[H^+]$ of tubular cells.

ARTERIAL CONCENTRATION OF HYDROGEN IONS   Secretion of H^+ varies with arterial $[H^+]$; mediated through intracellular $[H^+]$ of renal tubular cells.

RESPIRATORY ACIDOSIS   Inability of respiratory system to excrete CO_2 fast enough.

Excess of H_2CO_3.

Kidneys excrete H^+, reabsorb HCO_3^-.

RESPIRATORY ALKALOSIS   Excessive elimination of CO_2 by respiratory system.

Low P_{CO_2}.

Kidneys secrete less H^+, reabsorb less HCO_3^-.

METABOLIC ACIDOSIS   Loss of HCO_3^- (e.g., from diarrhea) or excess production of noncarbonic acid (e.g., from diabetic ketoacidosis).

Kidney excretes H^+ with buffer and NH_3.

METABOLIC ALKALOSIS   Alkaline diet—kidneys secrete less H^+, reabsorb less HCO_3^-.

Loss of gastric acid by vomiting—Na^+, K^+, and Cl^- also are lost; kidneys reabsorb Na^+, accompanied by HCO_3^-, or secrete H^+—prevents compensation.

Correction requires therapeutic intervention—expand extracellular fluid volume with NaCl solution to stop retention of Na^+, corresponding retention of HCO_3^-, and excretion of H^+.

BIBLIOGRAPHY

Adler, S., and Fraley, D.S. 1977. Potassium and intra-cellular pH in renal secretion of potassium. *Kidney Int.* 11:433.

Arruda, J.A.L., and Kurtzman, N.A. 1978. Relationship of renal sodium and water transport to hydrogen ion secretion. *Annu. Rev. Physiol.* 40:43.

Cohen, J.J.; Kassier, J.P.; and Gennari, F.J. 1982. *Acid-Base.* Boston: Little, Brown.

Deetjen, P.; Boylan, J.W.; and Kramer, K. 1975. *Physiology of the Kidney and of Water Balance.* New York: Springer-Verlag.

Davenport, H.W. 1974. *The ABC of Acid-Base Chemistry.* Chicago: University of Chicago Press.

Gamble, J.L., Jr. 1982. *Acid-Base Physiology; a Direct Approach.* Baltimore: Johns Hopkins University Press.

Giebisch, G., and Stanton, B. 1979. Potassium transport in the nephron. *Annu. Rev. Physiol.* 41:241.

Karlmark, B., and Danielson, B.G. 1974. Titratable acid, P_{CO_2}, bicarbonate, and ammonium ions along the rat proximal tubule. *Acta Physiol. Scand.* 91:243.

Malnic, G., and Giebisch, G. 1972. Mechanism of renal hydrogen ion secretion. *Kidney Int.* 1:280.

Malnic, G., and Steinmetz, P. 1976. Transport processes in urinary acidification. *Kidney Int.* 9:172.

Malen, T.H. 1974. Chemistry of the renal reabsorption of bicarbonate. *Can. J. Physiol. Pharmacol.* 52:1041.

Pitts, R.F. 1973. Production and excretion of ammonia in relation to acid-base regulation. In *Handbook of Physiology.* Section 8. Renal Physiology. Chapter 15. Edited by J. Orloff and R.W. Berliner. Washington, D.C.: American Physiological Society.

Pitts, R.F.; Ayer, J.L.; and Schiess, W.A. 1949. The renal regulation of acid-base balance in man. III. The reabsorption and excretion of bicarbonate. *J. Clin. Invest.* 28:35.

Porter, R., and Lawrenson, G. (eds.). 1982. *Metabolic Acidosis* (Ciba Foundation Symposium 87). Summit, N.J.: CIBA Pharmaceutical.

Rector, F.C., Jr. 1973. Acidification of the urine. In *Handbook of Physiology.* Section 8. Renal Physiology. Chapter 14. Edited by J. Orloff and R.W. Berliner. Washington, D.C.: American Physiological Society.

Rector, F.C., Jr.; Seldin, D.W.; Roberts, A.D., Jr., et al. 1960. The role of plasma CO_2 tension and carbonic anhydrase activity in the renal reabsorption of bicarbonate. *J. Clin. Invest.* 39:1706.

Rose, B.D. 1977. *Clinical Physiology of Acid-Base and Electrolyte Disorders.* New York: McGraw-Hill.

Schwartz, W.B., and Cohen, J.J. 1978. The nature of the renal response to chronic disorders of acid-base equilibrium. *Am. J. Med.* 64:417.

Steinmetz, P.R. 1974. Cellular mechanisms of urinary acidification. *Physiol. Rev.* 54:890.

Tannen, R.L. 1980. Control of acid secretion by the kidney. *Annu. Rev. Med.* 31:35.

Warnock, W., and Rector, F.C., Jr. 1979. Proton secretion by the kidney. *Annu. Rev. Physiol.* 41:197.

44

Renal Dysfunction

CHAPTER CONTENTS

TESTS OF RENAL FUNCTION

Various tests can be used to determine whether the function of the kidneys is impaired. For example, a careful analysis of freshly voided urine can yield valuable information. Other tests that should be done to confirm and quantify diagnoses include measurements of substances in the blood that normally are excreted by the kidneys and determination of the renal clearance of various substances.

Urinalysis

The major evaluations include physical and chemical measurements of the urine and microscopic examination of the urinary sediment.

VOLUME

The volume of urine formed per day is important and is easily measured. The normal amount of urine for an adult ranges from 750–2000 ml/day, depending on the degree of hydration, and averages about 1500 ml/day. In chronic renal failure, the urinary output may be diminished; urinary flow of 50–400 ml/day is considered *oliguria*. *Anuria,* less than 50 ml/day, occurs mainly in acute renal failure. However, in moderate renal failure, urinary flow may be unchanged or even increased (*polyuria*) because the remaining nephrons overfunction.

SPECIFIC GRAVITY

Measuring the maximal and minimal specific gravity of the urine permits one to assess the concentrating and diluting powers of the kidneys. To measure the ability of the kidneys to concentrate urine, all fluids are withheld for 12–24 hours and the maximal specific gravity of the urine is measured. A value of 1.026 or higher is considered normal. To test the ability of the kidneys to dilute urine, the patient takes a suitable water load, usually 1 liter during a 30-minute period. A normal person excretes at least one urine specimen with a specific gravity of less than 1.005 in the first hour or so. The dilution test is less useful than the concentration test and is not advisable in conditions such as Addison's disease (see Chapter 60).

The specific gravity of urine can vary greatly because it depends on the concentration of substances dissolved in the urine and the types of substances excreted. When the concentrations of some of the urinary constituents, especially glucose and protein, are abnormally large, the specific gravity of the urine may increase to as much as 1.050 or more. This condition may occur in patients who have diabetes mellitus or nephrosis. In certain kidney diseases in which the renal tubules are damaged, such as pyelonephritis, the specific gravity of the urine may be low because the kidneys have lost their ability to concentrate urine. A fixed, low specific gravity (approximately 1.010) indicates severe renal damage (*isosthenuria*—inability of the kidneys to produce either concentrated or dilute urine).

MICROSCOPIC EXAMINATION OF SEDIMENT
A qualitative or semiquantitative evaluation of urinary sediment can yield valuable information. The occurrence of protein, erythrocytes, leukocytes, and large numbers of renal epithelial cells or casts not only indicates renal disease but also identifies the cause of the disease.

Blood Analyses
The plasma concentrations of various substances that normally are excreted by the kidneys reflect the functional ability of the kidneys. Two simple measures, the concentration of blood urea nitrogen (BUN) and the serum concentration of creatinine, help to establish the presence of renal disease.

BLOOD UREA NITROGEN (BUN)
Azotemia, the accumulation of nitrogenous waste products (mainly urea), indicates renal failure. The normal value for the BUN concentration ranges from 8-25 mg/ml, depending on the protein intake of the individual. In renal disease, if the glomerular filtration rate (GFR) is reduced, the filtered load of urea nitrogen is decreased. If the daily production of urea remains normal, the concentration of BUN increases. However, a high BUN level may be associated with a normal GFR in a person who is taking a high protein diet. Despite this potential problem, the concentration of BUN still is used as a measure of glomerular function because it is easy to determine.

SERUM CREATININE
The concentration of creatinine in the serum reflects the GFR more accurately. The principal source of serum creatinine, derived from creatine phosphate, is the metabolism of the muscles. Since muscle metabolism is relatively constant in a given individual, the rate of production of creatinine is relatively constant. If the rate of elimination of creatinine equals the rate of production, the serum creatinine concentration remains at about 1 mg/dl. In humans, creatinine is excreted mainly by glomerular filtration, although a small amount is secreted by the renal tubular cells (see Chapter 37). The decreased GFR in renal disease decreases the amount of creatinine that is filtered. Therefore, as with urea, if the rate of production of creatinine remains normal, the concentration of creatinine in the serum must increase.

Renal Clearance Tests
Although glomerular function can be estimated by the levels of BUN and serum creatinine, an accurate determination of the GFR requires the inulin clearance test. The renal clearances of other substances, for example, iodohippurate sodium (Hippuran) or iodopyracet (Diodrast), also can be used as tests of renal function. If the clearances of these substances are determined simultaneously, the GFR, effective renal plasma flow, and filtration fraction all can be estimated. However, most of these clearance tests are unsatisfactory for routine clinical use because they involve continuous intravenous infusion of the substances and catheterization to measure the volume of urine that is formed. Instead, the clearance of endogenous creatinine and observation of the handling of iodinated compounds (pyelography) normally are used.

CREATININE CLEARANCE

The clearance of endogenous creatinine is widely used to estimate GFR because the concentration of creatinine in the plasma of a normal individual is relatively stable and can be measured readily in the plasma and the urine. Although creatinine is partly secreted by the renal tubules in humans, and its determination in the plasma measures also the noncreatinine chromogen, the value obtained from the clearance of endogenous creatinine approximates that of inulin. In renal damage, the clearance of endogenous creatinine is decreased because the GFR is decreased. In this condition, the amount of creatinine that is secreted by the renal tubules becomes more important because secretion contributes proportionally more to the clearance of creatinine. Thus, as the GFR decreases, the clearance of creatinine deviates further from the true GFR, as measured by inulin.

RADIOGRAPHY AND RADIOACTIVE PYELOGRAPHY

Radiography and radioactive pyelography are useful because they measure the function of each kidney separately, rather than together as other tests do.

Several substances that contain iodine in their molecules, for example, iodopyracet (Diodrast) and iodohippurate sodium (Hippuran), are cleared rapidly by the kidneys, by both glomerular filtration and tubular secretion. Because of the iodine, these substances are relatively opaque to x-rays, and shadows of the renal pelvis, the ureters, and the urinary bladder can be formed on x-ray film. After intravenous administration, enough of the substance is excreted within a few minutes to show a good image of the renal pelvis. The lack of a distinct image within this period indicates that renal function is depressed.

If these substances are prepared with *radioactive* iodine, the radioactivity in the urinary tract can be monitored by placing an appropriate counter over the region. Using this method, the functional status of each kidney can be determined.

CAUSES OF RENAL DYSFUNCTION

Disturbances of Nonrenal Origin

CIRCULATORY DISORDERS

The function of the kidneys depends on an adequate blood supply. When perfusion of the kidneys is decreased, the GFR decreases and urinary flow decreases (oliguria). If the cause of the ischemia is corrected before the renal cells are damaged, the oliguria can be reversed. In severe circulatory shock, acute renal damage occurs (see Chapter 23).

HORMONAL IMBALANCE

The renal transport of water and electrolytes (i.e., Na^+, K^+, Ca^{++}, and $HPO_4^=$) is regulated hormonally. Therefore, when certain endocrine functions are abnormal, the renal transport systems are affected (see Chapter 41).

Antidiuretic hormone (ADH), which is secreted from the neurohypophysis, increases the permeability of the renal collecting tubules to water (see Chapters 41 and 56). In pituitary diabetes insipidus, the deficiency of ADH permits the excretion of dilute urine because less water is reabsorbed from the renal collecting tubules.

Aldosterone increases the reabsorption of Na^+ and the secretion of K^+ in the distal tubules. In hyperaldosteronism, the increased level of circulating aldosterone causes abnormal retention of Na^+ and depletion of K^+. In adrenal insufficiency, Na^+ is lost in the urine because of the low level or absence of circulating aldosterone (see Chapter 60).

Parathormone regulates the reabsorption of phosphate from the renal tubules; hence, the abnormal secretion of parathormone causes an imbalance of phosphate in the body fluids (see Chapter 62). *Hypoparathyroidism* is associated with increased plasma levels of phosphate, and *hyperparathyroidism* is associated with the loss of phosphate in the urine.

Disturbances of Renal Origin

Diseases of the kidney that affect normal renal function can be divided roughly into two groups. The first group includes inflammatory and degenerative diseases that involve the kidneys diffusely. Segments of nephrons and, eventually, entire nephrons and their functions are affected. The second group of disorders involves specifically one or more of the transport mechanisms of the renal tubules. The first of these two classes of disorders is more important, although the second group is interesting because of the clinicophysiological correlations. A few of the renal diseases will be discussed briefly to provide background for the correlation of renal disease and disturbances of renal function.

ACUTE RENAL FAILURE

In acute renal failure, the kidneys are unable to regulate solute and water balance. The onset is abrupt and is manifested either by oliguria (decreased formation of urine) or anuria (50 ml or less of urine formed per day). Almost any condition that seriously interferes with kidney functions can cause acute renal failure.

In acute renal failure due to renal causes, the initial damage may involve the tubular epithelium or the glomerular capillaries and other small renal vessels. However, since the renal vascular system is closely connected with the renal tubular system, both anatomically and functionally, damage to one of the structures quickly involves the other.

The small renal vessels may be injured by disorders of the immunocomplex (e.g., *acute glomerulonephritis,* or inflammation of the glomeruli). Infection by a certain type of Group A β-hemolytic streptococcus causes antibodies to develop against the streptococcal antigen. The antigen-antibody reaction forms a precipitate that is trapped in the glomeruli and causes inflammation. Both the endothelial cells on the vascular side of the glomerular membrane and the epithelial cells of Bowman's capsule proliferate. These inflammatory reactions can cause partial, and even total, blockage of large numbers of glomeruli. Many of the glomeruli that are not blocked become more permeable, which allows the plasma proteins to be excreted in the urine—a condition called *proteinuria*. In cases of severe inflammation, the glomerular membrane ruptures and red blood cells appear in the urine, or total renal shutdown may occur. The acute inflammation of the glomeruli often subsides in about 2 weeks, and the function of the nephrons may return to normal. However, if the inflammatory reactions are severe, many of the glomeruli may be destroyed and their functions lost permanently.

In *acute tubular necrosis*, mainly the epithelial cells of the tubules are damaged, usually by renal ischemia or nephrotoxic substances. Examples of nephrotoxins are carbon tetrachloride and heavy metals such as Hg^{++}. When epithelial cells are destroyed, they slough away from the basement membrane; the renal tubule may be occluded. If the basement membrane is not destroyed, epithelial cells usually grow again and the renal tubule is repaired.

CHRONIC RENAL FAILURE

As nephrons are destroyed progressively, the ability of the kidneys to function decreases; destruction of more than 60% of the nephrons causes chronic renal failure. Chronic renal failure begins gradually and progresses. However, adaptive mechanisms develop, and the kidneys can maintain solute and water balance well enough to enable an individual to survive on a normal diet. Examples of the common causes of chronic renal failure are chronic glomerulonephritis and pyelonephritis.

Chronic glomerulonephritis is caused by diseases that damage primarily the glomeruli. The basic lesion is similar to the one that develops in acute glomerulonephritis, in which precipitated antigen-antibody complex accumulates in the glomerulus and causes inflammation. In chronic glomerulonephritis, the glomerular membrane thickens progressively and is invaded by fibrous tissues. The glomerular filtration coefficient is reduced greatly because of the reduced number of filtering capillaries in the glomerular tufts and because of the fibrous tissues. In the later stages of the disease, many of the glomeruli are replaced by fibrous tissues, and the functions of the nephrons are lost completely.

Pyelonephritis is caused by infectious and inflammatory processes that begin in the renal pelvis and extend progessively into the renal parenchyma. Many different types of bacteria can cause the infection. The bacteria invade the kidneys and destroy the structures they encounter. The infection usually involves the tissues in the medullary region before it affects the cortical area. Therefore, an individual who has pyelonephritis still may have reasonably normal renal function, except for the inability to concentrate urine (see Chapter 41).

NEPHROTIC SYNDROME

An important feature of the normal kidney is the selective permeability of the glomerular membrane—the plasma water and solutes of low molecular weight are filtered freely, but the blood cells and plasma proteins are retained in the circulation. The failure of circulating polyanions (of which plasma proteins are an example) to cross the glomerular membrane is due in part to negative fixed charges on the glomerular membrane (see Chapter 38). In many disorders of the kidney, the negative fixed charge is decreased, which increases the permeability of the glomerulus to protein macromolecules. Abnormal amounts of plasma proteins are filtered and excreted in the urine (*proteinuria*). Therefore, any disease that increases the permeability of the glomerular membrane to proteins can cause the nephrotic syndrome.

In severe nephrosis, as much as 30–40 g of plasma proteins can be lost into the urine each day. In this event, the plasma oncotic pressure decreases from a normal of about 28 mm Hg to as low as 6–8 mm Hg. Because of the low oncotic pressure, plasma water moves into the interstitial spaces and the potential spaces of the body (edema and ascites) (see Chapter 12).

SPECIFIC TUBULAR DISORDERS

Renal function also may be decreased by deficiencies of certain transport mechanisms. Many of these defects are congenital and benign, but some may be caused by nephrotoxic substances. However, such disorders are uncommon compared to the diffuse inflammatory kidney diseases.

In the condition of *renal glycosuria,* the transport mechanism for glucose is defective, and glucose is excreted in the urine, even though the concentration of glucose in the plasma is normal (see Chapter 40).

Nephrogenic diabetes insipidus is a rare congenital disorder in which the distal renal tubules are not sensitive to ADH. Thus, water is not reabsorbed from the collecting tubules, and a large volume of dilute urine is excreted (polyuria) (see Chapter 41). Nephrogenic diabetes insipidus and pituitary diabetes insipidus are characterized by the same signs and symptoms; however, in pituitary diabetes insipidus, the distal renal tubules respond normally to ADH. The disorder in pituitary diabetes insipidus is a lack of ADH secretion because of injury to the neurohypophysis and/or the hypothalamus (see Chapter 56). Pituitary diabetes insipidus occurs more frequently than the nephrogenic type.

Renal tubular acidosis is characterized by the inability to secrete adequate quantities of H^+ and by the excretion of abnormally large amounts of HCO_3^- in the urine (see Chapter 43). Because of the inability to secrete enough H^+ and the loss of HCO_3^-, the subject remains in a state of metabolic acidosis. Normal body function can be restored by increased intake of alkaline substances.

Renal hypophosphatemia is characterized by the excretion of phosphate in the urine, even when the plasma concentration of phosphate is low. This congenital disorder is caused by insufficient reabsorption of phosphate by the renal tubules.

Aminoaciduria is characterized by the excretion of amino acids in the urine. Generalized aminoaciduria, a condition caused by deficient reabsorption of all amino acids, rarely occurs. More often, the specific carrier system for a particular group of amino acids is deficient, and a condition such as cystinuria or simple glycinuria, for example, is produced.

FUNCTIONAL CHANGES IN RENAL FAILURE

Acute Renal Failure

Acute renal failure almost always causes oliguria or anuria. Different theories have been proposed to explain the occurrence of oliguria. One theory proposes that filtration across the glomerular membrane is normal, but because of the damaged tubular epithelial cells, most of the filtrate is reabsorbed into the peritubular interstitium. Another theory proposes that the damaged tubular epithelium sloughs away from the basement membrane and occludes the tubular lumen; hydrostatic pressure in the tubules increases and opposes glomerular filtration. Still another theory proposes that the GFR is decreased by constriction of the arterioles. Evidence to support each of these theories has been obtained, and none of them can be ruled out.

Chronic Renal Failure

FUNCTIONAL ANATOMY

In chronic renal disease, as in normal kidneys, structure and function are correlated. The kidneys are small, the glomeruli may vary from normal to hypertrophied, and the number of tubules is less than normal. The tubules may be atrophied, normal, or hypertrophied. Normal glomeruli may be attached to abnormal tubules, and the reverse also may occur. Therefore, the population of nephrons is structurally more heterogeneous in the diseased kidney than in the normal kidney. Despite this condition, the external balance (intake plus production equals output) of various substances can be maintained either completely or almost completely because the tubular transport of the substances changes. For example, Na^+ and water balance can be maintained by altering the rate of tubular reabsorption, and K^+ balance can be maintained by altering the rate of tubular secretion.

CLINICAL CORRELATION
44.1   Renal Failure After Viral Infection

CASE REPORT

The Patient: A 35-year-old woman.

Principal Complaints: Sore throat, headache, fever, urinary frequency, dark urine, and peripheral edema.

History: The patient had been healthy until a week before admission, when she experienced a sore throat, headache, and fever. At the same time, she had begun to experience urinary frequency and urgency, and to have peripheral edema. Dark urine was noted.

Clinical Examination: Laboratory examination revealed elevated blood urea nitrogen (BUN) and creatinine levels. The BUN level was 108 mg/dl (normal, 8–25 mg/dl) and the creatinine was 12 mg/dl (normal, 0.06–1.5 mg/dl). Such accumulation of these normal products of metabolism indicates severe renal failure.

The urine gave a strong positive test for protein. The urinary sediment contained numerous white cells, numerous red cells, and occasional red cell casts (a coagulated mass that contains red cells). This extent of bleeding into the urine indicates a glomerular lesion. The results of blood tests showed the features of the nephrotic syndrome: hypoproteinemia (total plasma protein 5.8 g/dl—normal, 6–8.4 g/dl), and hypoalbuminemia (plasma albumin 2.5 g/dl—normal, 35.5–5 g/dl). The plasma electrolyte profiles also confirmed the occurrence of renal failure: sodium, 128 mEq/liter (normal, 135–145 mEq/liter); chloride, 96 mEq/liter (normal,

100–106 mEq/liter); potassium, 6.5 mEq/liter (normal, 3.5–5 mEq/liter), carbon dioxide, 16 mM/liter (normal, 24–30 mM/liter). The elevated potassium level caused slightly peaked T waves in the electrocardiogram. The low concentration of carbon dioxide indicates acidemia (see Chapter 32), but studies of blood gases are needed to confirm this indication.

Treatment: The patient was placed on a high-protein, low-potassium diet, and peritoneal dialysis was begun. After 6 days, the BUN was 48 mg/dl, and the serum creatinine was 7 mg/dl. A renal biopsy was performed, and electron microscopic studies of the tissues taken revealed extensive tubular damage. In many tubules the basement membrane was disrupted, epithelium had degenerated, and cells were necrotic. In several glomeruli, the foot-cell processes (see Chapter 38) were destroyed. Despite the low rate of output of urine ($<$ 200 ml/day), loss of protein remained high (5–10 g/day). Prednisone (a synthetic corticosteroid) was administered, in an effort to aid tubular regeneration. After 8 days, the output of urine began to increase, and after 31 days, dialysis was discontinued. As renal function improved, the BUN and the creatinine levels declined toward normal, and loss of protein decreased. The dose of prednisone was decreased logarithmically and discontinued after 3 months.

Outcome: Six months after the beginning of therapy, the patient's renal function was normal, and no protein appeared in her urine.

FUNCTIONAL MASS

Because the number of functioning nephrons is decreased in chronic renal disease, the kidney cannot excrete large loads of electrolytes or other substances. If as many as one-third of the normal number of nephrons are functioning (two healthy kidneys contain about 2 million nephrons), the kidneys can eliminate essen-

tially all of the usual waste products. However, if the number of functioning nephrons is reduced any further, these substances accumulate in the body fluids.

ISOSTHENURIA

In chronic renal disease, the overall function of the two kidneys is less than normal, but the work load of the nephrons that continue to function is increased. The blood flow through each glomerulus, and, hence, the GFR, may increase as much as two- to threefold. Therefore, two to three times more water and solute than normal traverse each nephron. In chronic renal disease, the excretion of Na^+ and other solutes in each of the remaining nephrons may be two to three times greater than in the nephron of a normal kidney. Therefore, if the intake of water is normal in chronic renal disease, the individual nephron experiences osmotic diuresis because of the increased flow of water and solutes. The greater the reduction in the number of nephrons, the greater the degree of osmotic diuresis. Because of this, the ability of the kidneys to concentrate or dilute the urine is decreased. Patients who have advanced chronic renal failure usually excrete urine at a fixed specific gravity of about 1.010, which corresponds to an osmolality of about 300 mOsm/kg of water. The excretion of urine of a fixed specific gravity is known as *isosthenuria*, which means urine that has the "same strength" as plasma. In isosthenuria, an individual cannot handle either an excess or a deficit of water. If he cannot dilute his urine further, he cannot excrete additional water as rapidly as a normal person can. If he cannot increase the concentration of his urine, he needs more time to adjust to a deficiency of water than a healthy person does. Therefore, the volume of body water in an individual who has chronic renal failure may change considerably during the period of adjustment to either an excess or a deficit of water. Even though chronically diseased kidneys can maintain complete or nearly complete balance if intake is controlled carefully, they are not as flexible as normal kidneys in dealing with changes of intake.

EFFECTS OF RENAL FAILURE ON BODY FLUIDS

The effects of acute renal failure on body fluids depend on the individual's dietary intake. If the person continues to ingest a normal amount of food and water, various substances are retained in the extracellular fluid. The results are: (1) high concentrations of nonprotein nitrogen because of the deficient excretion of the end products of protein catabolism, especially urea; (2) generalized edema as a result of the retention of Na^+ and water; (3) hyperkalemia caused by the inability of the kidneys to excrete excess K^+; and (4) metabolic acidosis because of the failure of the kidneys to excrete the acidic products of normal metabolism.

Uremia

The term *uremia* is applied to the condition of the body fluids during renal failure. Although the term implies an increased concentration of urea in the blood, retention of urea is not primarily responsible for the signs and symptoms that accompany advanced renal insufficiency. The symptoms of nausea, vomiting, weakness, twitching, convulsions, and coma are caused by abnormal electrolyte, water, and acid-base balances and by the accumulation of the toxic products of metabolism. However, because the BUN is easily measured, it is used to indicate the severity of the disturbance.

Edema

Unless the intake of water is decreased to match the decreased rate of excretion by the acutely failing kidneys and the normal loss through the respiratory tract and skin, the body fluid volume expands rapidly. The blood volume increases, the plasma proteins are diluted, and edema forms in the dependent areas and the potential spaces. If a normal amount of Na^+ also is ingested, the increased volume may be confined to the extracellular compartment. The accumulation of Na^+ and water usually can be prevented by restricting the intake of Na^+ and water.

Hyperkalemia

The degree of hyperkalemia depends principally on the amount of K^+ ingested and the endogenous K^+ released by the catabolism of protein as a result of starvation, infections, or tissue damage. When the plasma concentration of K^+ reaches 8 mEq/liter, toxic effects on the heart are seen. Therefore, it is essential to control the intake of K^+ so as to maintain the balance of K^+ despite decreased excretion.

Metabolic Acidosis

The metabolic functions of the body normally produce about 50–100 mM of acid per day. In acute renal failure, the individual is unable to excrete the H^+ associated with these acids. The buffers of the body fluids can neutralize the H^+ to a certain extent (see Chapter 43); however, when the buffers are used up, the $[H^+]$ of the body fluids increases, and the individual develops metabolic acidosis.

STUDY OUTLINE

TESTS OF RENAL FUNCTION

URINALYSIS

VOLUME Normal is 750–2000 ml; average is 1500 ml.

Oliguria (e.g., chronic renal failure)—< 400 ml/day.

Anuria (e.g., acute renal failure)—< 50 ml/day.

SPECIFIC GRAVITY Assesses concentrating and diluting powers of kidneys.

Concentration test—fluids are withheld for 12–24 hours, maximal specific gravity of 1.026 or more is normal.

Dilution test—one liter of water is drunk in 30 minutes, excretion of urine sample of specific gravity < 1.005 in first hour is normal.

In diabetes mellitus (glucose in urine) or nephrosis (protein in urine), specific gravity is 1.050 or more.

In pyelonephritis (tubules damaged), specific gravity is fixed at 1.010.

MICROSCOPIC EXAMINATION OF SEDIMENT Protein, erythrocytes, leukocytes, renal epithelial cells, or casts indicate and identify disease.

BLOOD ANALYSES

BLOOD UREA NITROGEN (BUN) Accumulation of nitrogenous waste products, mostly urea, indicates renal failure.

SERUM CREATININE Creatinine is produced at a relatively constant rate; increased concentration indicates decreased GFR.

RENAL CLEARANCE TESTS Inulin clearance is most accurate measure of GFR.

Clearance of iodohippurate sodium (Hippuran) or iodopyracet (Diodrast) measures renal plasma flow.

CREATININE CLEARANCE Convenient estimate of GFR, but because of some clearance by tubular secretion, creatinine clearance overestimates GFR in renal disease.

RADIOGRAPHY AND RADIOACTIVE PYELOGRAPHY Radioactive or radiopaque materials provide image of urinary system.

CAUSES OF RENAL DYSFUNCTION

DISTURBANCES OF NONRENAL ORIGIN

CIRCULATORY DISORDERS If renal perfusion is inadequate, GFR decreases, causes oliguria.

In severe circulatory shock, acute renal damage.

HORMONAL IMBALANCE Antidiuretic hormone (ADH)—deficiency causes diabetes insipidus.

Aldosterone—excess causes Na^+ retention, K^+ depletion; deficit causes Na^+ wasting.

Parathormone—deficiency increases plasma phosphate; excess causes loss of phosphate in urine.

DISTURBANCES OF RENAL ORIGIN

Inflammatory and degenerative diseases; entire nephron and function affected.

Disorders of tubular transport mechanisms.

ACUTE RENAL FAILURE Kidney is unable to regulate solute and water balance; onset is abrupt; oliguria or anuria.

Glomerular capillaries are damaged by immune reaction.

Tubular epithelial cells are damaged by ischemia or nephrotoxins.

CHRONIC RENAL FAILURE Gradual, progressive destruction of nephrons.

Immune reaction—chronic glomerulonephritis; glomerular membrane thickens, becomes fibrous; glomeruli eventually are replaced by fibrous tissue.

Infection and inflammation—pyelonephritis; tissue damage in medullary areas decreases ability of kidneys to concentrate urine.

NEPHROTIC SYNDROME Increased permeability of glomerular membrane—plasma proteins are lost in urine (proteinuria).

Loss of oncotic pressure, formation of edema.

SPECIFIC TUBULAR DISORDERS Deficiencies of certain transport mechanisms.

Defective glucose transport—renal glycosuria.

Distal tubules not sensitive to ADH—nephrogenic diabetes insipidus.

Inability to secrete enough H^+—renal tubular acidosis.

Excretion of phosphate in urine—renal hypophosphatemia.

Excretion of amino acids in urine—aminoaciduria.

FUNCTIONAL CHANGES IN RENAL FAILURE

ACUTE RENAL FAILURE Causes oliguria or anuria.

Filtration may be normal but most of filtrate is reabsorbed.

Damaged and sloughed tubular epithelium may occlude tubules.

GFR may be decreased by constricted arterioles.

CHRONIC RENAL FAILURE

FUNCTIONAL ANATOMY Kidneys are small, glomeruli are normal to hypertrophied, total number of tubules is decreased.

Tubules are atrophied, normal, or hypertrophied.

Normal glomeruli may be attached to abnormal tubules, and vice versa.

Compensated by changes of perfusion and transport characteristics.

FUNCTIONAL MASS If fewer than one-third of normal nephrons are functioning, wastes accumulate in body.

ISOSTHENURIA Because of work load, remaining nephrons experience water and osmotic diuresis.

Working at limits, nephrons cannot handle extra water or solute quickly—produce urine isotonic with plasma.

EFFECTS OF RENAL FAILURE ON BODY FLUIDS Depend on dietary intake.

UREMIA Retention of nitrogenous end products, mainly urea.

Urea is not toxic but is evidence of renal failure.

Symptoms are caused by abnormal electrolyte, water, and acid-base balances and by other toxic products of metabolism.

EDEMA Normal intake but decreased output increases body fluid volume, dilutes plasma proteins, allows fluid to accumulate in interstitial space.

Na^+ and water intake must be restricted to match output.

HYPERKALEMIA Depends on intake of K^+, which must be restricted because of cardiotoxic effects.

METABOLIC ACIDOSIS Net products of metabolism are acidic; must be excreted or buffered.

When buffers are exhausted, $[H^+]$ of body fluids increases.

BIBLIOGRAPHY

Batlle, D.C.; Arruda, J.A.L.; and Kurtzman, N.A. 1981. Hyperkalemic distal renal tubular acidosis associated with obstructive uropathy. *N. Engl. J. Med.* 304:373.

Blagg, C.R., and Scribner, B.H. 1980. Long-term dialysis: Current problems and future prospects. *Am. J. Med.* 68:633.

Brenner, B.M.; Hostetter, T.H.; Humes, H.D., et al. 1978. Molecular basis of proteinuria of glomerular origin. *N. Engl. J. Med.* 298:826.

Brenner, B.M., and Stein, J.H. (eds.). 1982. *Nephrotic Syndrome.* New York: Churchill Livingstone.

Conger, J.D., and Schrier, R.W. 1980. Renal hemodynamics in acute renal failure. *Annu. Rev. Physiol.* 42:603.

Chapman, A. (ed.). 1980. *Acute Renal Failure.* New York: Churchill Livingstone.

Fillit, H.M.; Read, S.E.; Sherman, R.L., et al. 1978. Cellular reactivity to altered glomerular basement membrane in glomerulonephritis. *N. Engl. J. Med.* 298:861.

Grantham, J.J. 1976. Fluid secretion in the nephron: Relation to renal failure. *Physiol. Rev.* 56:248.

Harrington, A.R., and Zimmerman, S.W. 1982. *Renal Pathophysiology.* New York: Wiley.

Hayslett, J.P. 1979. Functional adaptation to reduction in renal mass. *Physiol. Rev.* 59:137.

Ibels, L.S.; Alfrey, A.C.; Haut, L., et al. 1978. Preservation of function in experimental renal disease by dietary restriction of phosphate. *N. Engl. J. Med.* 298:122.

Leaf, A., and Cotrans, R.S. 1980. *Renal Pathophysiology* (2nd ed.). New York: Oxford University Press.

Levinsky, R.J.; Malleson, P.N.; Barratt, T.M., et al. 1978. Circulating immune complexes in steroid-responsive nephrotic syndrome. *N. Engl. J. Med.* 298:126.

Maxwell, M.H., and Kleeman, C.R. (eds.). 1979. *Clinical Disorders of Fluid and Electrolyte Metabolism.* New York: McGraw-Hill.

Relman, A.S., and Rennie, D. 1980. Treatment of end-stage renal disease: Free but not equal. *N. Engl. J. Med.* 303:996.

Valtin, H. 1979. *Renal Dysfunction: Mechanisms Involved in Fluid and Solute Imbalance.* Boston: Little, Brown.

Waterfall, W.K. 1980. Dialysis and transplant. *Br. Med. J.* 281:726.

45

Micturition

CHAPTER CONTENTS

FUNCTIONAL ANATOMY

Ureters

The ureters are muscular tubes that convey urine from the kidneys to the urinary bladder. The dilated upper ends form the renal pelves, and the distal ends enter the bladder from the rear (Figure 45-1). The ureters course through the wall of the bladder for some distance before entering the cavity. This arrangement forms a "check valve," which keeps urine from flowing back into the ureters as the bladder fills. The walls of the ureters consist of an outer adventitia, a middle layer of smooth muscle, and an inner mucosa composed of transitional epithelium. Compared to those of other hollow tubes (e.g., the intestine), the muscle layers of the ureters are reversed—the inner layer is arranged longitudinally and the outer layer is circular. During contraction, this arrangement augments the opening of the ureters into the bladder, which facilitates the transfer of urine.

The ureters receive sympathetic, parasympathetic, and sensory nerve fibers, but motor innervation does not appear to be essential for the peristaltic contractions that transport urine. The wall of the renal pelvis contains a pace-

maker, analogous to the pacemaker of the heart, which initiates the peristaltic contractions that travel down the ureter. Increased production of urine dilates the renal pelvis, which initially increases the frequency of the pacemaker. The effect soon wears off, however, and flow is maintained at a higher rate by the increased volume propelled by each contraction.

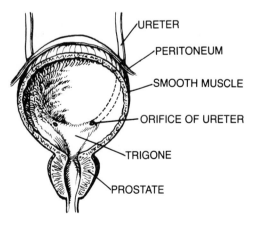

Figure 45-1. The male urinary bladder opened to show the interior.

Bladder

The urinary bladder is a vesicle composed of smooth muscle. It has two principal parts. The base, or *trigone*, is a triangular area that has its upper corners at the entry points of the two ureters and the third corner at the bottom where the urethra exits (Figure 45-1). The *body* of the bladder, which is the main portion, can be distended to store urine; under parasympathetic stimulation (Figure 45-2), contraction of the bladder muscle (the *detrusor muscle*) forces urine through the urethra. Sympathetic innervation of the bladder probably is not important, although some evidence indicates that sympathetic stimulation relaxes the bladder, which enables it to accommodate larger volumes of urine.

Sphincters

Two sphincters prevent involuntary passage of urine from the bladder into the urethra. The *internal urethral sphincter*, which forms a valve at the outlet of the bladder into the urethra (Figure 45-2), is composed of smooth muscle and receives both parasympathetic and sympathetic innervation. Parasympathetic stimulation causes this sphincter to relax during urination. In males, sympathetic stimulation causes the sphincter to contract during orgasm, so that urine is not passed and semen does not enter the bladder. The *external urethral sphincter*, which is formed from skeletal muscle at the point where the urethra pierces the urogenital diaphragm, is controlled voluntarily.

Mucosa

The renal pelves, ureters, and bladder are lined by transitional epithelium. This mucosa is remarkably plastic; it bulges into many folds when the cavities are empty and flattens out as the cavities are distended.

NORMAL MICTURITION

Filling of the Bladder

The bladder is a highly compliant organ that can accommodate about 400 ml of urine with a relatively small increase of pressure. This is because of the structure of the bladder wall and the relationships among intraluminal pressure,

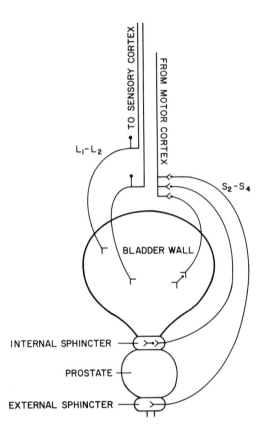

Figure 45-2. Neural control of the bladder (sympathetic fibers have been omitted for the sake of simplicity). Afferent nerves from stretch receptors in the bladder carry impulses to primary parasympathetic motoneurons in the sacral cord and also project to sensory areas of the cerebral cortex. The detrusor muscle of the bladder and the internal urethral sphincter receive parasympathetic innervation; the primary motoneurons are located in the sacral cord and synapse with parasympathetic ganglia in the walls of the tissues that are innervated. The external urethral sphincter receives voluntary innervation via the pudendal nerve.

radius, and wall tension (law of Laplace—see Chapters 1 and 12).

As the bladder fills and its radius increases, the wall tension increases enough to keep the intraluminal pressure fairly constant up to about 300 ml of volume (Figure 45-3). The urge to void, which depends on stimulation of stretch receptors in the wall of the bladder, normally is felt at about 200 ml. When the volume in the bladder approaches about 400 ml, the pressure increases markedly, the wall tension increases rapidly, and the urge to void becomes irresistible.

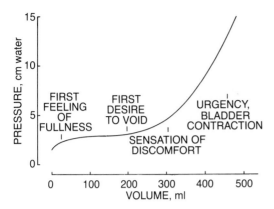

Figure 45-3. Volume-pressure relationship of the bladder. (Redrawn, with permission, from Simeone, F.A., and Lampson, R.S. 1937. A cystometric study of the function of the urinary bladder. *Ann. Surg.* 106:414.)

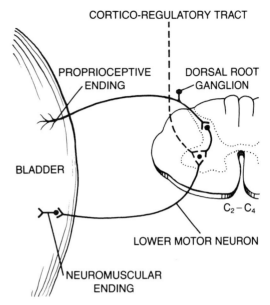

Figure 45-4. The spinal reflex arc related to micturition. (Redrawn, with permission, from Lapides, J. 1976. *Fundamentals of Urology.* Philadelphia: W.B. Saunders Co.)

Emptying of the Bladder

The bladder is emptied by a coordinated activation of parasympathetic nerves, which cause the detrusor muscle to contract and the internal sphincter to relax. The external sphincter is relaxed voluntarily. In infants, the bladder empties uncontrollably because of a reflex centered in the sacral portion of the spinal cord (Figure 45-4). Although the autonomic nervous system is involved, the basic mechanism of this reflex is identical to the stretch reflex in skeletal muscle. Stretch of the bladder wall stimulates proprioceptive endings that send impulses to motoneurons in the sacral cord; these motoneurons, in turn, send back impulses that cause the detrusor muscle to contract and the internal sphincter to relax. The normal system of urinary sphincters does not prevent reflex voiding in the infant but does maintain continence between voidings; thus, the normal infant does not dribble urine continuously.

The child is able to control micturition (becomes "toilet trained") when voluntary control is established over the striated muscle of the external sphincter and the corticoregulatory tract that runs from the cerebral motor cortex to the parasympathetic motor neurons in the sacral cord (Figure 45-5). Through the corticoregulatory tract, the cerebral cortex can augment or inhibit the voiding reflex; thus, the bladder may be emptied at low volumes or kept from emptying at high volumes. In addition, urine flowing along the urethra stimulates a reflex that sustains and augments the primary micturition reflex.

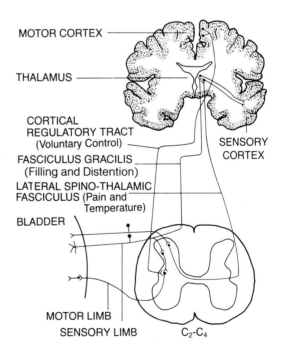

Figure 45-5. The sensory tracts that serve the bladder, and the pathway for high central nervous system control of the spinal reflex related to micturition. (Redrawn, with permission, from Lapides, J. 1976. *Fundamentals of Urology.* Philadelphia: W.B. Saunders Co.)

CLINICAL CORRELATION
45.1   Urinary Retention Associated with Herpes Genitalis

CASE REPORT

The Patient: A 27-year-old woman.

Principal Complaints: Headache and malaise.

History: The patient reported dysuria (painful or burning urination), headache, chills, and fever during the preceding week.

Clinical Examination: Clear, painful vesicles were found on the vulva, and the inguinal lymph nodes were enlarged and tender. The clinical pattern indicated herpes genitalis, which was confirmed by viral culture of material taken from one of the vesicles. Four days later, the patient noticed numbness in the left buttock, inability to feel the passage of feces, and difficulty beginning urination. A neurological examination revealed diminished perception to pinprick in the perineal area and over the right buttock and thigh. The tone of the internal urethral sphincter was low, and cystometric examination disclosed a hypotonic bladder. Lumbar puncture revealed a cell count of 1175 leukocytes/mm^3 in the cerebrospinal fluid (CSF) (normal, 0–5 cells/mm^3, all lympho-

cytes). A differential count showed 15% polymorphonuclear leukocytes (combined neutrophils, eosinophils, and basophils), and 85% monocytes. The total protein content of the CSF was 175 mg/dl (normal, 14–45 mg/dl).

Comment: Infection with herpes simplex virus type II is a venereal disease and the most common cause of genital ulceration. The virus invades the nervous system and can cause dysfunction of the sacral spinal cord (parasympathetic); this dysfunction is characterized by constipation, inability to urinate, and sexual impotency. Pleocytosis (presence of cells in the CSF) also occurs, consistent with the viral infection. The condition is self-limiting and regresses without treatment, but it tends to recur, and there is no cure for it. The urinary retention can be treated by catheterization, by adrenergic α-receptor antagonists, or by cholinergic drugs. This patient did not require such treatment, as her retention was only partial and she regained normal bladder function in four days.

Outcome: The patient recovered without further incident and was dismissed. However, there is no cure, and the disease will recur.

ABNORMAL MICTURITION

Caused by Neurological Damage

GENERAL

Disruption of micturition by neurological injury leads to overfilling and may harm the bladder—excessive distention can damage the detrusor muscle and prevent complete emptying thereafter. Urine left in the bladder tends to become infected, and the renal damage and systemic infections that follow are the leading causes of death in paraplegic patients. Thus, bladder function must be managed carefully in paraplegic patients by catheterization and the use of antibiotics, when needed.

REFLEX BLADDER

Spinal reflexes normally are controlled by higher levels of the central nervous system. For a time after transection of the spinal cord, all reflexes, including the voiding reflex, are suppressed below the area of injury (*spinal shock*). However, because the inhibitory inputs from higher levels of the central nervous system no longer impinge on the parasympathetic motoneurons in the sacral spinal cord, the micturition reflex becomes active after about 2 weeks. The tone of the bladder is increased, the capacity is decreased, and no sensation is felt. The patient tends to void precipitously, and a mass reflex (see Chapter 6), which includes voiding, may be initiated by maneuvers such as stroking the skin of the inner thigh.

ATONIC BLADDER

The atonic, or deafferented, bladder is produced by injury to the afferent nerves that carry proprioceptive (stretch) sensation from the bladder. Trauma rarely causes such a condition, but tabes dorsalis (syphilitic infection of the dorsal nerves and ganglia of the spinal cord) and certain polyneuropathies may do so. Sensation and the desire to void are lost, and, in contrast to the completely denervated or autonomous bladder, the deafferented bladder becomes distended; incontinence occurs when the bladder overfills (*overflow incontinence*).

AUTONOMOUS BLADDER

The autonomous bladder develops when all external nerves to the bladder are destroyed, as in lesions of the conus medullaris or cauda equina. Both voluntary and reflex control of the bladder are lost, and emptying never is complete. In contrast to the deafferented bladder, the autonomous bladder tends not to be distended and may be small and hypertrophied. The high pressure causes urine to dribble, but the bladder can be emptied only by voluntarily increasing intra-abdominal pressure.

Other Dysfunctions

STRESS INCONTINENCE

During childbirth, the urogenital diaphragm sometimes is stretched so severely that the external urethral sphincter is injured. This may cause *stress incontinence,* in which sudden increases of intra-abdominal pressure (e.g., during coughing or sneezing) force small amounts of urine through the malfunctioning sphincter.

BENIGN PROSTATIC HYPERTROPHY

In older men who have benign prostatic hypertrophy, the median lobe of the prostate is enlarged and impinges on the urethra. This causes difficulty in urinating and a predisposition to infection of the urinary tract because of incomplete emptying of the bladder. The most popular treatment for this condition is transurethral resection of the prostate, in which an instrument is passed up the penile urethra to remove a portion of the prostatic tissue that causes the obstruction. Transurethral resection of the prostate disrupts the internal urethral sphincter, but incontinence usually does not develop as long as the external sphincter is intact.

FUNCTIONAL DISORDERS

Incontinence can be caused by functional disorders that prevent adequate control of the micturition reflex by the central nervous system. This condition can occur in senility, in some mentally retarded persons, and in normal adults who have inflamed bladders. In the latter case, such an intense urge to void is felt that it cannot be controlled.

STUDY OUTLINE

FUNCTIONAL ANATOMY

URETERS   Muscular tubes that convey urine from kidneys to urinary bladder.

   Passage through bladder wall forms functional valve.

   Peristaltic waves, originating at pacemaker in renal pelvis, transport urine.

BLADDER   Vesicle composed of smooth muscle.

   Base, or trigone.

   Body is storage portion; contraction of detrusor muscle under parasympathetic control forces urine into urethra.

SPHINCTERS   Internal urethral sphincter forms valve at outlet of bladder; parasympathetic stimulation relaxes it during urination, sympathetic stimulation contracts it during orgasm in males.

   External urethral sphincter, below prostate, consists of skeletal muscle, under voluntary control.

MUCOSA   Transitional epithelium, very plastic.

NORMAL MICTURITION

FILLING OF THE BLADDER   Bladder is highly compliant.

   Filling stimulates stretch receptors, causes urge to void at about 200 ml.

   At about 400 ml, urge to void becomes irresistible.

EMPTYING OF THE BLADDER   Through coordinated action of parasympathetic nerves, detrusor muscle contracts and internal sphincter relaxes; external sphincter relaxes voluntarily.

Bladder emptying is a reflex in infants; stretch receptors in wall of bladder, motoneurons in sacral cord.

Bladder emptying becomes voluntary in a child when control of external sphincter and corticoregulatory tract from motor cortex is attained.

ABNORMAL MICTURITION

CAUSED BY NEUROLOGICAL DAMAGE

GENERAL   Excessive distention damages detrusor muscle, emptying is incomplete.

Retained urine is prone to infections, causes renal damage and systemic infections in paraplegics.

REFLEX BLADDER   After transection of cord.

Initially, all reflexes are suppressed below lesion.

Micturition reflex (spinal) active after about 2 weeks.

ATONIC BLADDER   Injury to afferent nerves, loss of proprioceptive input from bladder.

Desire to void is lost, bladder leaks when overfilled.

AUTONOMOUS BLADDER   All external nerves lost.

Bladder small, hypertrophied, incontinent.

OTHER DYSFUNCTIONS

STRESS INCONTINENCE   External sphincter is injured during childbirth, increases of intra-abdominal pressure force urine through.

BENIGN PROSTATIC HYPERTROPHY Enlarged prostate compresses urethra.

FUNCTIONAL DISORDERS   Loss of control of micturition reflex.

Senility, mental retardation, inflamed bladder.

BIBLIOGRAPHY

Appell, R.A. 1980. Urodynamics I: The functional significance of bladder and urethral innervation. *J. La. State Med. Soc.* 132:22.

Becker, R.F.; Wilson, J.W.; and Gehweiler, J.A. 1971. *The Anatomical Basis of Medical Practice*. Baltimore: Williams & Wilkins.

Boshes, B. 1979. Trauma to the spinal cord. In *Clinical Neurology*. Volume 3. Chapter 35. Edited by A.B. Baker and L.H. Baker. Hagerstown, Maryland: Harper and Row.

Bradley, W.E. 1978. Neural control of urethrovesical function. *Clin. Obstet. Gynecol.* 21:653.

Bradley, W.E., and Scott, F.B. 1978. Physiology of the urinary bladder. In *Campbell's Urology* (4th ed.). Philadelphia: Saunders.

Bradley, W.E. 1980. Cerebro-cortical innervation of the urinary bladder. *Tohoku J. Exp. Med.* 131:7.

Bulmen, D. 1974. *Functional Anatomy of the Urogenital System*. Toronto: Pitman Medical.

Carlsson, C.A. 1978. The supraspinal control of the urinary bladder. *Acta Pharmacol. Toxicol. (Copenh.)* 43:56.

Chusid, J.G. 1979. *Correlative Neuroanatomy and Functional Neurology* (17th ed.). Los Altos, California: Lange.

Kaplan, P.E. 1980. Nervous control of the human urinary bladder. *Electromyogr. Clin. Neurophysiol.* 20:41.

Kiil, F. 1978. Physiology of the renal pelvis and ureter. In *Campbell's Urology* (4th ed.). Philadelphia: Saunders.

Kuru, M. 1965. Nervous control of micturition. *Physiol. Rev.* 45:425.

Lapides, J. 1976. *Fundamentals of Urology*. Philadelphia: Saunders.

Petras, J.M., and Cummings, J.F. 1978. Sympathetic and parasympathetic innervation of the urinary bladder and urethra. *Brain Res.* 153:363.

Simeone, F.A., and Lampson, R.S. 1937. A cystometric study of the function of the urinary bladder. *Ann. Surg.* 106:413.

Snell, R.S. 1973. *Clinical Anatomy for Medical Students*. Boston: Little, Brown.

Sundin, T. 1978. The nervous supply and function of the urinary bladder and urethra. Introduction. *Acta Pharmacol. Toxicol. (Copenh.)* 43:5.

Warwick, R.T. 1979. Observations on the function and dysfunction of the sphincter and detrusor mechanisms. *Urol. Clin. North Am.* 6:13.

PART VIII

GASTROINTESTINAL PHYSIOLOGY

46

The Alimentary Tract

CHAPTER CONTENTS

GENERAL BACKGROUND

Functional Topography

The digestive tract is a muscular tube lined with epithelial cells that secrete and absorb. The secretions break down foodstuffs to molecules small enough to be absorbed by the epithelium of the small intestine. In the stomach and the colon the tube is enlarged, and materials remain in these areas longer. The luminal contents form a noxious environment for the epithelium, and certain highly specialized secretory units, the liver and the pancreas, are separated from the sites of digestion and absorption. This is not a necessity, however, because the mucosa of the stomach and the small intestine are not removed far from the lumen, even though they, too, are highly spe-

cialized. Absorption requires close contact within the contents of the lumen of the small intestine, and sometimes it is a highly regional function. For example, calcium and iron virtually are absorbed only in the duodenum, and cobalamin (vitamin B_{12}) is absorbed only in the terminal ileum.

Bacteria

Bacteria are abundant in the colon, and microorganisms contribute significantly to the function of that organ. However, there are few bacteria in the lumen of the stomach and the small intestine. The regular, intermittent propulsion of debris formed from shed mucosa between meals is believed to be significant in minimizing the growth of bacteria in the small intestine.

GENERAL PRINCIPLES

The relationships among transport, digestion, and absorption can be understood in terms of some general principles that are set forth here.

Processes in the Alimentary Tract

In the alimentary tract, food is broken up, propelled, dispersed, and dissolved in the water of the luminal contents, and then is digested and absorbed selectively into the bloodstream. The term *digestion* implies a breaking up of large molecules into smaller ones by enzymatic action. Although fats, carbohydrates, and proteins are chemically distinct, the processes that are involved in their digestion essentially are similar. All of these substances are hydrolyzed into smaller fragments, which have lower molecular weights and are more soluble in water. A proton is added to one fragment, and a hydroxyl group is added to the other fragment. Because of the different physical and chemical properties of fats, carbohydrates, and proteins, the enzymes that catalyze the hydrolysis also are chemically distinct.

Variation in the Composition of Contents

The contents of the lumen of the alimentary tract vary greatly from time to time and from part to part. This variability in the external environment of the cells of the alimentary tract differs from the constancy of the internal environment, and the contents of the alimentary tract should be thought of as distinct and separate from the body fluids. The contents of the lumen in different parts of the alimentary tract vary because of what is ingested, what is secreted, and what is absorbed. Steep gradients of concentration between parts are maintained by sphincters.

Variation in the Tissue Resistance of the Lining Membrane

The epithelia that line the esophagus, the stomach, and the colon are relatively robust; this is appropriate because the contents of these organs, with which the cells of the organs are in contact, subject the cells to considerable stress. By contrast, the cells that form the membrane of the small intestine are delicate, and the os-

molality in the small intestine is kept within a range of 250–450 mOsm, which is similar to the osmolality of the tissue fluids (about 280 mOsm).

All of the membranes that line the alimentary tract are exposed to chemical and mechanical conditions that tend to damage cells irreparably. In particular, acid in the stomach, enzymes in the small intestine, and bacteria in the colon are unfavorable to the survival of the surface tissues. Therefore, one should not be surprised to discover that all of the cells that line the tract are replaced every 3 or 4 days. This replacement requires a rate of synthesis of proteins and cells that equals the rate of synthesis of cells and hemoglobin in the bone marrow (enough for 50 ml of blood per day).

Separation of the Synthesis of Cells and Enzymes from the Luminal Contents

The synthesis of cells and the protein for enzymes requires organized processes of a kind that can occur only in a stable environment. This stability can be provided, in one instance, because the dividing and synthesizing cells are buried in the mucosa. Thus, the synthesis of the enzymatic protein pepsinogen occurs in cells that are deep within the gastric tubules. On the other hand, the pancreas, which is the main site of the synthesis of digestive enzymes, is separate from the intestinal lumen and connected to it only by a narrow duct.

Residence Times of the Luminal Contents in Various Parts of the Alimentary Tract

The time during which food remains in different parts of the alimentary tract varies greatly; for example, food remains for a very short time in the esophagus and for a very long time in the colon. The residence time varies with the cross-sectional area of the lumen and the function of the muscle (mainly smooth) that propels the contents of the alimentary tract.

Consequences of the Lipid Lining of the Alimentary Tract

SIMPLE DIFFUSION
The entire alimentary tract is lined by cells that are covered by lipid membranes. The contents

of the alimentary tract essentially are aqueous, so that anything absorbed from the alimentary tract must pass from an aqueous phase into a lipid phase. Thus, a substance such as ethanol, which is soluble in both water and lipid, is absorbed rapidly and requires no special mechanisms.

The rate of absorption of a substance into the bloodstream by simple diffusion depends on the solubility of the substance in water and in lipid, the difference between the concentration of the substance in the blood and that in the lumen, and the area of contact between the substance and the surface of the alimentary tract. The area of contact is determined mainly by the structure of the epithelial surface of each part of the alimentary tract. The membrane that lines the esophagus, which does not absorb, is smooth and about 40 cells thick. The ratio of the surface area of the epithelium to the volume of contents is low in the esophagus. By contrast, in the small intestine, which is the main organ of absorption, only a few layers of cells separate the contents of the lumen from the blood in the capillaries, and millions of fingerlike processes, called *villi,* increase the area over which the contents of the lumen make contact with the surface of the intestine. The surface area of the apical region of each cell is increased further by *microvilli*. The area of contact between the luminal contents and the lining of the small intestine is so large that the rate of diffusion of a substance toward the surface of the membrane is the factor that limits the absorption of many solutes.

NONIONIC DIFFUSION

Many drugs are either weak acids or weak bases. In the acid pH of the stomach, a drug that is a weak acid (e.g., aspirin) does not ionize at all. In this state, aspirin is absorbed into the gastric cells and damages the gastric lining. However, if aspirin is taken with enough alkali to raise the intragastric pH to 8, it will be ionized completely. In this state, the drug is not soluble in the lipid membranes of the gastric cells and, hence, does not harm the gastric lining. An understanding of these simple facts about nonionic diffusion is essential for the optimal use of many drugs.

Absorption of Fats

Based on what has been written above, there should be no barrier to the absorption of the triglycerides of food because they are soluble in lipids. However, because fats are insoluble in water, they must be dispersed in the aqueous medium of the intestinal lumen by a complex process before the main products of their digestion, the anions of long-chain fatty acids, will pass through the lipid lining of the intestine into the lymphatic vessels and from there into the bloodstream.

Selective Absorption of Carbohydrates and Proteins

Molecules that essentially are water-soluble, such as carbohydrates and amino acids, ordinarily would not penetrate lipid membranes at all; however, the lipid membrane contains special, selective carriers, probably proteins, that combine with these water-soluble products of digestion, carry them through the membrane, and set them free again in the blood.

ACTIVE TRANSPORT

The selective carrier molecules with which the digestion products of carbohydrates and proteins combine usually are found only in the small intestine, although in some instances the same carriers are found in the renal tubules. The carrier systems, which have an external source of energy and are specific for certain groups of molecules, can move digestion products from an area of low concentration to one of high concentration (active transport). After food is ingested, however, the concentration of material to be absorbed often is higher in the lumen than in the blood that perfuses the intestinal capillaries. Thus, active transport may only increase the rate of absorption of substance-carrier complexes that could proceed passively. Between meals, when the concentration of substances is greater in the blood than in the lumen, the active transport systems serve to prevent the net movement of substances, such as glucose, from the blood to the lumen.

Alimentary Tract as an Organ of Excretion

In addition to absorbing, the alimentary tract also excretes substances. Drugs that are carried in the plasma in lipid-soluble form, bound to albumin, are processed in the liver and conjugated with glucuronate or sulfate to produce water-soluble forms that are excreted into the bile. Because they are water-soluble, these substances are not reabsorbed into the blood after the bile enters the alimentary tract.

Flux of Water

About 3 liters of water enter the alimentary tract each day as food and drink, and another 6 liters of water enter as alimentary secretion. Almost 7 liters of water are absorbed by the small intestine, and almost 2 liters are absorbed by the large intestine, leaving 100–200 ml in the feces. Water moves by osmosis during both secretion and absorption. *Osmosis* is the diffusion of water from an area in which its chemical activity is high to one in which its chemical activity is low. The water is diluted by solute molecules; if the concentration of solute in the lumen of the gut is high, the activity of the water is low, and there is a net flux of water into the lumen. This net flux is composed of two unidirectional fluxes: one flux from the blood into the lumen, which is relatively constant, and one flux from the lumen into the blood, which is reduced by the solute molecules that dilute the water of the lumen. Thus, when the lumen contains solute, the flux out of the lumen is decreased, whereas the flux into the lumen remains unchanged, and water accumulates in it. Thus, movement of water to and from the alimentary tract is determined not only by the amount of water the lumen contains but also by variations in the chemical activity of molecules and ions in the lumen. The movement of water down a hydrostatic pressure gradient, which is called *filtration,* is the reverse of osmosis. Filtration creates osmotic gradients and osmosis dissipates them.

Absorptive Capacity of the Intestine

In 24 hours, the small intestine can absorb at least three or four times the amount of food that normally is eaten. Moreover, the alimentary tract does not control the amount of food that is absorbed; the small intestine absorbs the bulk of the food put into it, regardless of the rate of metabolism of the body. Thus, the amount eaten must be regulated. In a healthy subject, about 95% of the food that is eaten is absorbed; the remainder of the material that enters as food appears in the feces, usually having been changed by the action of the bac-

teria in the colon. In healthy people, this proportion of absorbed to excreted material is relatively constant.

Autonomy of the Alimentary Tract

The alimentary tract is a semiautonomous system of organs that is influenced, but not completely controlled, by the central nervous system. The smooth muscle that propels the contents of the alimentary tract is controlled by a series of nerves that adhere closely to both of its surfaces. This control essentially is local, although events in one part of the gut can influence the rate of propulsion in another part through hormones and other nerves. The secretions of the stomach and the pancreas normally are controlled through the parasympathetic division of the autonomic nervous system, but auxiliary mechanisms allow the pancreas and the stomach to secrete adequately, even after the nerve supply to each organ has been cut. It has proved possible, in the course of treating arterial hypertension in humans, to cut the sympathetic nerves to most of the alimentary tract without causing measurable dysfunction. Similarly, the treatment of duodenal ulcers by cutting the parasympathetic nerves (the vagi) to the abdominal organs also causes no gross dysfunction of the alimentary tract. These statements, however, should not be interpreted to mean that afferent nerves and efferent nerves do not carry impulses and that hormones are not released in normal function. Rather, in the absence of intrinsic impulses or hormones, other elements institute control through extrinsic nerves. Because of the large amount of functional reserve in most alimentary processes, it is difficult to demonstrate minor deficiencies.

Physical Considerations

PRESSURES
The alimentary tract is a hollow tube and, therefore, is subject to the physical constraints of hollow tubes. Material in the alimentary tract is propelled down a gradient of pressure; however, the bores are large and the rates of passage are relatively slow, so that the gradient of pressure often is small and is difficult to measure. Complete closure of the lumen of the intestine every 3 or 4 cm is normal, and the high pressures that may develop in such sequestered

portions of the alimentary canal usually are not related to propulsion.

Pressures in the alimentary tract can be measured by a manometer placed in the tip of a special catheter, which the patient swallows. At the junction of the esophagus and the stomach, which is called the *lower esophageal sphincter,* the luminal pressure normally is higher than it is in the stomach and prevents reflux of the gastric contents into the esophagus. This pressure decreases at the beginning of a swallow. At the same time, the entire esophagus, which is attached to the hyoid bone, moves headward and pulls the stomach over the tip of the catheter, which is fixed in position. Thus, the manometer moves from the esophagus into the gastric cavity, where the pressure is lower. Therefore, it may be difficult to decide whether a decrease of pressure that is recorded by the manometer reflects the relaxation of muscle in one area or the movement of the recording tip into another. This problem is general to the alimentary tract, which is shortened or lengthened according to the state of its longitudinal muscle.

Physiologists are interested in the circumferential tensions in the walls of hollow tubes, either as indicators of the contraction of the smooth muscle or as stimuli to receptors in the walls. According to the law of Laplace (see Chapter 1), the circumferential tension needed to create a given pressure in a tube is proportional to the radius of the tube. Thus, when the radius of a tube is small, the muscle of the wall works at a relative mechanical advantage in generating pressure, and when the radius is large, the muscle works at a relative disadvantage. When the lumen of the esophagus, for example, virtually is closed at the height of the peristaltic wave, and the intraluminal pressure is 100 mm Hg, the circumferential tension in the wall is less than it is when the esophagus is distended fully by a bolus and the intraluminal pressure is 10 mm Hg. Because of the mechanical advantage of the muscle when the lumen of the gut is reduced to a minimum, the high pressures actually are generated after the material has been moved past the tip of the manometer. The radii of different parts of the alimentary tract may change from second to second by as much as a factor of 20. Thus, the pressures that are measured in the alimentary tract are difficult to interpret unless the cross-sectional area of the lumen is measured simultaneously.

The law of Laplace has the same implications for the alimentary system that it has for all systems of hollow muscular tubes: a distended viscus is at a mechanical disadvantage compared to a viscus of smaller bore. Thus, part of the treatment of a small intestine that may be so distended by its contents that it is paralyzed is to pass a nasogastric tube, aspirate the material, and prevent any further distention by swallowed air. Anxiety may cause a person to swallow more air than usual, which by itself may cause abdominal pain.

STUDY OUTLINE

GENERAL BACKGROUND

FUNCTIONAL TOPOGRAPHY   The alimentary tract is a muscular tube that runs from mouth to anus and is lined with various types of epithelia.

Secretions break down food to molecules that can be absorbed.

Contents move slowly in regions where lumen of tube is enlarged.

Secretions are formed by cells in lining of epithelium or by more distant organs (liver and pancreas).

Absorptive functions occur mainly in small intestine, some are highly localized (i.e., iron and calcium in duodenum, vitamin B_{12} in distal ileum).

BACTERIA   Few bacteria in stomach and small intestine; many bacteria in colon.

Forward propulsion and sphincters limit retrograde movement of bacteria.

GENERAL PRINCIPLES

PROCESSES IN THE ALIMENTARY TRACT   Food is broken up, propelled, dispersed, and dissolved in water of luminal contents, digested, and absorbed selectively into bloodstream.

Digestion implies reducing molecular weight of food and making end products soluble in water.

Carbohydrates, fats, and proteins all are broken down by same processes (hydrolysis)—hydroxyl is added to one fragment and a proton is added to other fragment.

Separate enzymes act on three chemically distinct classes of food—lipase on fats, hydrolases on carbohydrates, proteinases on proteins.

VARIATION IN THE COMPOSITION OF CONTENTS   Contents vary from time to time and from part to part.

Variability on luminal side of cells contrasts with constancy on serosal side.

VARIATION IN THE TISSUE RESISTANCE OF THE LINING MEMBRANE   Esophagus, stomach, and colon are lined by different epithelia.

Epithelium of small intestine has delicate, large surface area; osmolality of contents usually is held within range of 250–450 mOsm, as compared to 280 mOsm for tissue fluids.

Cells survive an average of about 4 days.

SEPARATION OF THE SYNTHESIS OF CELLS AND ENZYMES FROM THE LUMINAL CONTENTS   Synthesis occurs in deeper layers of epithelia or in distant organs.

RESIDENCE TIMES OF THE LUMINAL CONTENTS IN VARIOUS PARTS OF THE ALIMENTARY TRACT   Varies widely—seconds in esophagus, days in colon.

Large lumen corresponds to long residence times (e.g., colon).

CONSEQUENCES OF THE LIPID LINING OF THE ALIMENTARY TRACT

SIMPLE DIFFUSION   All cells are covered by lipid membranes; anything entering portal blood from intestine must pass from aqueous phase of luminal contents through lipid layer.

Ethanol, soluble both in water and lipid, is absorbed rapidly by simple diffusion.

Rate of absorption increases with concentration gradient from lumen to blood and with area of contact.

Concentration gradient depends mainly on rate of delivery to intestine; area of contact varies with structure of absorbing membrane (e.g., number of villi).

Millions of fingerlike villi in small intestine and microvilli on each cell increase area of contact; limit to absorption often is set by rate of radial diffusion in contents of lumen.

NONIONIC DIFFUSION   Many drugs are either weak acids or weak bases.

Drugs are absorbed most readily in nonionic state—decreases solubility in water, increases solubility in lipid.

Weak acids are not ionized at low pH—aspirin is absorbed by stomach cells at low pH but not at high pH (> 6); converse applies to absorption of weak bases.

ABSORPTION OF FATS   Insolubility of fats and long-chain fatty acids in water limits rate of diffusion to epithelium.

Complex process disperses products of digestion of fat in luminal contents, aids migration to lipid membrane, where products are absorbed by nonspecific mechanisms.

SELECTIVE ABSORPTION OF CARBOHYDRATES AND PROTEINS   Specific protein carriers in intestinal cell membranes form complexes with water-soluble products—allows passage from lumen to blood through lipid membrane.

ACTIVE TRANSPORT   Selective carriers in small intestine combine with digestion products of proteins and carbohydrates, can move such molecules up a concentration gradient.

Absorption of digestion products usually is down concentration gradient; active transport systems increase rate of absorption, confer selectivity.

ALIMENTARY TRACT AS AN ORGAN OF EXCRETION   Lipid-soluble drugs are carried in plasma, conjugated in liver to water-soluble forms, and excreted in bile into intestine.

Water solubility prevents intestinal absorption because no specific carriers exist for conjugated compounds; drug is excreted in feces.

FLUX OF WATER   Three liters of water as food and drink and 6 liters of water as secretions enter alimentary tract per day; all water except 200 ml in feces is absorbed.

Water moves by osmosis; unabsorbed molecules in lumen dilute water, reducing diffusion from lumen to blood; flux from blood to lumen is unaffected by solutes in lumen, and water accumulates in lumen.

ABSORPTIVE CAPACITY OF THE INTESTINE   Small intestine can absorb about three to four times amount of food that normally enters it; eating is regulated, not absorption.

In healthy individuals, about 95% of ingested food is absorbed; 5% appears in stools, changed by bacteria in colon.

AUTONOMY OF THE ALIMENTARY TRACT   Digestive functions of alimentary system usually are not regulated exclusively by central nervous system, although nerve im-

pulses pass from alimentary tract to medulla and other impulses pass back to alimentary tract.

Control largely is local, although events in one part can influence propulsion in another part through nerves and hormones.

Cutting extrinsic sympathetic nerves to alimentary tract in humans causes no detectable abnormality of digestive function.

Cutting vagus nerves produces some disturbances of alimentary function, but large reserves in alimentary function make relatively minor deficiencies difficult to detect.

PHYSICAL CONSIDERATIONS

PRESSURES Often too small to be measured reliably, cause slow flow along relatively large bore of intestinal tract.

Wall tension needed to generate given pressure is proportional to radius.

With small radius, mechanical advantage; high pressure is generated easily.

With large radius, mechanical disadvantage; alimentary tract may be paralyzed by distention.

BIBLIOGRAPHY

Davenport, H.W. 1977. *Physiology of the Digestive Tract* (4th ed.). Chicago: Year Book.

Davenport, H.W. 1978. *A Digest of Digestion* (2nd ed.). Chicago: Year Book.

Johnson, L.R. (ed.). 1981. *Physiology of the Gastrointestinal Tract.* New York: Raven Press.

McMinn, R.M.H., and Hobdell, M.H. 1974. *Functional Anatomy of the Digestive System.* London: Pitman Medical.

Spiro, H.M. 1983. *Clinical gastroenterology.* New York: MacMillan.

47

Salivation

CHAPTER CONTENTS

FUNCTIONS OF SALIVA

A continuous flow of saliva, which contains water and mucin, is essential for an individual's well-being. Without saliva, speech is impossible, swallowing food is difficult, and growth of bacteria within the oral cavity is excessive. In the acutely ill patient, who may be too weak to take fluids without help, the flow of saliva may be so reduced that serious oral infections develop. The secretion of saliva also can be suppressed by commonly used drugs such as atropine. Understanding the mechanisms involved in control of salivary flow enables one to anticipate and prevent undesirable consequences.

STRUCTURAL FEATURES

Functional Histology

Saliva originates in three pairs of glands: the parotid glands, the submandibular glands, and the sublingual glands. In all three pairs, the fluid part of the secretion is formed by the acinar cells, which also secrete amylase, a starch-splitting enzyme. The fluid formed by the acinar cells drains through intercalated and interlobular ducts into the main duct. The intercalated and interlobular ducts have characteristic structures and modify the secretion as it flows through their lumens (Figure 47-1). Only the submandibular glands and sublingual glands secrete mucus; the parotid saliva is serous, or watery.

Nerve Supply

PARASYMPATHETIC ACTIVITY

Stimulation of the parasympathetic nerves to the salivary glands causes the formation of a large volume of an aqueous secretion; at the same time, the blood vessels of the glands are dilated remarkably. If the parasympathetic nerves to the submaxillary gland are stimulated after the gland has been exposed to atropine, the secretory action of the nerve impulses is blocked completely, which indicates that secretion was mediated by acetylcholine. The vasodilatation persists to some extent. Further studies show that acetylcholine causes the smooth muscles of the arterioles that supply the

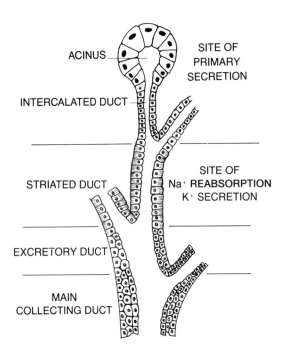

ACINUS

SITE OF PRIMARY SECRETION

INTERCALATED DUCT

STRIATED DUCT

SITE OF Na⁺ REABSORPTION K⁺ SECRETION

SITE OF Na^+ REABSORPTION K^+ SECRETION

EXCRETORY DUCT

MAIN COLLECTING DUCT

Figure 47-1. Characteristic structure of the salivary glands. The primary secretion is formed by the acinar cells. The different histologic appearances of the cells that line the ducts are consistent with their having different functions in modifying the primary secretion. (Redrawn, with permission, from Bell, G., et al. 1976. *Textbook of Physiology and Biochemistry* (9th ed.). Chapter 8. Edinburgh: Churchill Livingstone.)

glands to relax, which increases the blood flow; this action also is abolished by atropine. The residual vasodilatation, which resists the effects of atropine, is caused by *vasoactive intestinal peptide* released from the postganglionic parasympathetic nerves. Atropine does not interfere with the vasodilatation caused by this peptide, which has been shown by immunocytochemical methods to be present in nerve fibers in the salivary glands and in other parts of the gut.

The responses of the salivary gland tissue to cholinergic stimulation include another interesting feature. Usually, the flow of blood through an organ increases in proportion to the use of oxygen by that organ; however, in the salivary glands, the reddening of the venous blood during secretion indicates that the flow of blood is more than the amount that is needed to provide the glandular tissue with oxygen. In 1 minute, the submandibular gland can form a quantity of secretion equal to its own weight; thus, one of the consequences of the increased flow of blood is to provide the water and electrolytes needed to form saliva.

SYMPATHETIC ACTIVITY

Stimulation of the sympathetic nerves that go to the salivary glands causes the release of norepinephrine. The main effect of norepinephrine in this tissue is to reduce the flow of blood and increase slightly the content of amylase in the secretions. When the parasympathetic nerves to the salivary glands are stimulated simultaneously, the output of amylase increases markedly. Although the balance of neural control when salivary secretion is increased physiologically is not known, it seems likely that the additional amylase secreted during the tasting and chewing of food reflects input from both divisions of the autonomic nervous system.

Secretory Mechanisms

Fluid collected by micropuncture techniques close to the acinar cells has concentrations of Na^+, $[Na^+]$, and Cl^-, $[Cl^-]$, close to those of the plasma, but $[HCO_3^-]$, and $[K^+]$ are higher than in the plasma. Thus, Na^+, Cl^-, and much of the water in which they are dissolved are secreted by a filtration process similar to the filtration that occurs in the glomeruli of the kidneys. However, HCO_3^- and K^+ are both filtered and secreted actively by the acinar cells, and further study has shown that K^+ also is secreted in the ducts. The movement of water is secondary to the movement of the solutes. Because of the active transport of HCO_3^- and K^+, the salivary glands can secrete against a head of pressure that is greater than the arterial pressure. The osmotic force exerted by a 1 mM solution of an actively transported substance, which effectively is nonpermeant, corresponds to a pressure of 17 mm Hg. Thus, to exceed a blood pressure of 120 mm Hg, it is necessary to have only a difference of concentration greater than 120/17, or 7 mmole/liter, of actively transported substance.

MODIFICATION OF SECRETION IN DUCTS

The composition of the saliva varies with the rate of secretion; as the rate of secretion increases from the resting state, $[Na^+]$, $[Cl^-]$, and $[HCO_3^-]$ increase and $[K^+]$ decreases and levels off (Figure 47-2). These changes can be ex-

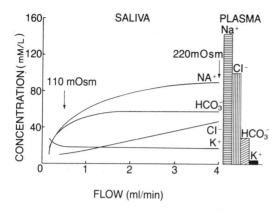

Figure 47-2. Change in the electrolyte composition of human parotid saliva with change in the rate of secretion. A concentration of an ion higher ($[HCO_3^-]$ and $[K^+]$) or lower ($[Na^+]$ and $[Cl^-]$) than that of plasma is taken to indicate active transport. Note that the total concentration of electrolytes is less than that of plasma; thus, the saliva is hypo-osmotic relative to plasma. The increase in the concentration of Na^+ and Cl^- with an increase in the rate of secretion indicates that the ducts absorb Na^+ and Cl^- at a limited rate from a primary secretion that contains a high concentration of Na^+. (Redrawn, with permission, from Thaysen, J.H., Thorn, N.A., and Schwartz, J.L., 1954. *Am. J. Physiol.* 178:155.)

plained by assuming that the composition of the acinar secretion is constant, but that Na^+ and Cl^- are absorbed as the secretion moves slowly through the ducts. As the rate of secretion increases, under the influence of parasympathetic nerves, the fluid passes more rapidly through the ducts, and the opportunity for processing is less. As a result, less Na^+ and Cl^- are reabsorbed per unit volume of secretion, and the $[Na^+]$ approaches that of the primary acinar secretion. Na^+ is believed to be absorbed actively, and Cl^- follows along the electrical gradient that develops. $[K^+]$ decreases because the active secretion of K^+ in the ducts does not match the increased volume that comes from the acini. At high rates of secretion, the $[HCO_3^-]$ of the saliva is twice as great as the $[HCO_3^-]$ of the plasma, although the total concentration of anions and cations still is only two-thirds that of the plasma because of the reabsorption of Na^+ and Cl^- in the ducts. At low rates of secretion, the total concentration of ions is even lower (Figure 47-2).

UTILIZATION OF SALIVARY SECRETION

The HCO_3^- of saliva neutralizes acids that are formed in the mouth from food debris and cause dental caries. Unilateral destruction of the parotid gland by x-radiation in the treatment of tumors often leads to dental caries on the affected side.

The salivary glands are effector organs in reflex arcs; the receptors are in the oral cavity. The afferent nerves from the oral cavity carry impulses that lead to efferent nervous activity and secretion by the glands. Thus, to increase salivary secretion in a clinical situation, the stimulus should be placed in the mouth. The most effective salivary stimuli are chewing (the larger the bolus, the more effective the stimulus) and the flavors of citrus fruits. However, even these stimuli will not be effective in patients who have not drunk enough water or in whom the effective pathway to the salivary glands is blocked by a drug such as atropine. This information should be used to assure the oral well-being of all patients.

STUDY OUTLINE

FUNCTIONS OF SALIVA Essential for speech, swallowing, and hygienic conditions in oral cavity.

Salivary flow is reduced in seriously ill persons who are too weak to drink and is suppressed by commonly used drugs (e.g., atropine).

STRUCTURAL FEATURES

FUNCTIONAL HISTOLOGY Saliva comes from paired glands: parotid, submandibular, and sublingual.

Acinar cells form enzyme and primary fluid component.

Primary secretion flows through ducts that modify its composition.

Submandibular and sublingual secretions are mucous; parotid secretions are serous.

NERVE SUPPLY

PARASYMPATHETIC ACTIVITY Large volume of secretion.

Marked dilation of blood vessels; reddening of venous blood from glands shows that blood flow is greater than is needed to supply oxygen.

Atropine abolishes secretion but not all of vasodilatation, which indicates that secretion, but not all of vasodilatation, is mediated by acetylcholine.

Residual vasodilatation is mediated by vasoactive peptide from peptidergic nerve fibers.

Blood flow supplies water and electrolytes to gland, which can form its own weight of saliva per minute.

SYMPATHETIC ACTIVITY   Decreased flow of blood and slight increase of amylase.

Sympathetic and parasympathetic stimulation simultaneously cause a large increase in the output of amylase.

SECRETORY MECHANISMS Na^+, Cl^-, and water are filtered by acinar cells; HCO_3^- and K^+ are actively secreted.

Water moves from blood to duct by osmosis; active transport of solutes can make duct pressure exceed arterial pressure.

MODIFICATION OF SECRETION IN DUCTS   Primary secretion is high in Na^+, Cl^-, and HCO_3^-; Na^+ and Cl^- are reabsorbed in ducts, K^+ is secreted.

At high rates of secretion, because of less time in ducts, composition is changed less.

UTILIZATION OF SALIVARY SECRETION HCO_3^- protects teeth by neutralizing acids formed in the mouth.

Oral stimulation increases salivary flow.

Secretion requires adequate hydration; secretion is blocked by certain drugs.

BIBLIOGRAPHY

Bell, G.H.; Emslie-Smith, D.; and Paterson, C.R. 1976. Mouth and oesophagus. In *Textbook of Physiology and Biochemistry*. Chapter 8. Edinburgh: Churchill Livingstone.

Bloom, S.R., and Edwards, A.V. 1980. Vasoactive intestinal peptide in relation to atropine resistant vasodilatation in the submaxillary gland of the cat. *J. Physiol.* 300:41.

Cohen, B. 1975. Research in dentistry. *Br. Med. Bull.* 31:99.

Johnson, L.R. (ed.). 1981. *Physiology of the Gastrointestinal Tract*. New York: Raven Press.

Schneyer, L.H.; Young, J.A.; and Schneyer, C.A. 1972. Salivary secretion of electrolytes. *Physiol. Rev.* 52:720.

Sessle, B.J., and Hannam, A.G. 1976. *Mastication and Swallowing*. Toronto: University of Toronto Press.

48

Swallowing

CHAPTER CONTENTS

ANALYSIS OF SWALLOWING

Food is taken in and transferred to the stomach in four stages. Biting, moistening, and preparation for swallowing constitute the first stage. This stage also includes the rejection of ill-tasting food and food that contains sharp or hard particles. The second stage is the transfer of all or part of the contents of the mouth to the superior part of the pharyngeal cavity. The third is the transfer of material into the esophagus, from the superior region of the pharynx through the hypopharynx, while avoiding the ingress of food into the airways. The fourth stage is the transfer of material down the esophagus, from the cricoid sphincter to the cardia, and from there into the stomach.

First Stage

The chewing and preparation of food in the mouth can be started and stopped at will; however, these acts normally are performed reflexly. The muscular action of chewing and the amount of saliva that is formed are determined by the stimulation of receptors in the walls of the buccal cavity or in the bone around the roots of the teeth.

Second Stage

The second stage consists of the sequential elevation of the dorsum of the tongue, which creates an inclined plane that presses against the ventral surface of the hard palate and squeezes the bolus of food rapidly into the pharynx. During this transfer, receptors in the walls of the posterior part of the oral cavity and the pharynx are stimulated. These receptors initiate stages three and four, a series of reflex acts that involve the pharynx and the esophagus. Once begun, the complex sequence of movements of the pharynx and the esophagus cannot be stopped voluntarily.

Third Stage

The third stage is the transfer of material from the pharynx, the region where the pathways for food and air cross, to the esophagus. During the passage of food, the posterior superior exit from the pharynx to the nose and the entrance into the larynx, which form part of the anterior wall of the middle region of the pharynx, both are closed. Muscular contractions decrease the volume of the pharynx from about 40 ml to zero and force food rapidly through the narrow region of the cricoid sphincter.

Fourth Stage

The fourth stage, in which material is transported from the cricoid sphincter through the esophagus to the stomach, has two substages. First, the material is forced into the esophagus. The cervical esophagus is a passive tube into which the pharynx ejects the bolus; if the bolus is large and liquid, the whole length of the esophagus may be filled. In the second substage, the cricoid sphincter closes, and peristaltic muscular contraction occurs. The skeletal muscle of the cervical esophagus contracts first, followed by the smooth muscle of the lower part of the intrathoracic esophagus. Peristalsis is a leisurely process, as a small bolus may require up to 6 seconds to be transported from the region of the cricoid sphincter to the cardia, and the final ejection of the bolus into the stomach may take another 6 seconds. Although the peristaltic waves of the esophagus cannot be inhibited voluntarily, they do stop during repeated swallowing, as material is ejected into the esophagus from the pharynx.

FUNCTIONAL ANATOMY

General

The oral cavity and the pharynx are surrounded by striated muscles controlled through extrinsic nerves. The esophageal muscle is striated in the upper third, smooth in the lower third, and mixed in the middle third. During an ordinary swallow, parasympathetic nerves initiate the peristaltic contractions that move down the esophagus. However, continued peristaltic transport of the contents of the esophagus depends on the organized activity of intrinsic parasympathetic nerve plexuses, which lie between the submucosa and the deep surface of the helical muscles, and between the

layers of muscle. The lumen of the esophagus is lined by squamous epithelium that is 40 cells thick.

Oral Cavity

During the oral stage of swallowing, the mandible is fixed against the maxilla, the lips are sealed, the bolus is moved onto the dorsum of the tongue, and the tongue is elevated sequentially from the front to the back. Although each of the nerves that affect swallowing originates in a different nucleus in the brainstem, during the act of swallowing, each muscle contracts appropriately because the whole process is controlled from a single center in the medulla (Figure 48-1). This center not only controls swallowing, but it also inhibits the respiratory center during the passage of food through the pharynx, which keeps food from being aspirated into the larynx. These multiple actions of the swallowing center, which are directed through somatic and autonomic efferent neurons in several cranial nerves, illustrate some of the properties implied by the term *neural center.*

Pharynx

The pharynx begins at the pillars of the fauces and extends to the cricoid sphincter. The anterior wall of the pharynx consists of the epiglottis and the opening into the larynx; the posterior and lateral walls are formed by the mucous squamous epithelium that covers the three striated constrictor muscles of the pharynx (Figure 48-1).

Esophagus

The esophagus extends from the cricoid sphincter to the lower esophageal sphincter, or cardia. The superior border of the cricoid sphincter is about 17 cm from the incisors, and the region of the lower esophageal sphincter is 40–42 cm from the incisors (Figure 48-2).

LOWER ESOPHAGEAL SPHINCTER

The lower esophageal sphincter is not marked by any thickening of muscle of the esophageal wall, although, to judge from a zone of increased pressure measured with intraluminal catheters, it is a sphincter. The lower esophageal sphincter is mobile and may move in and

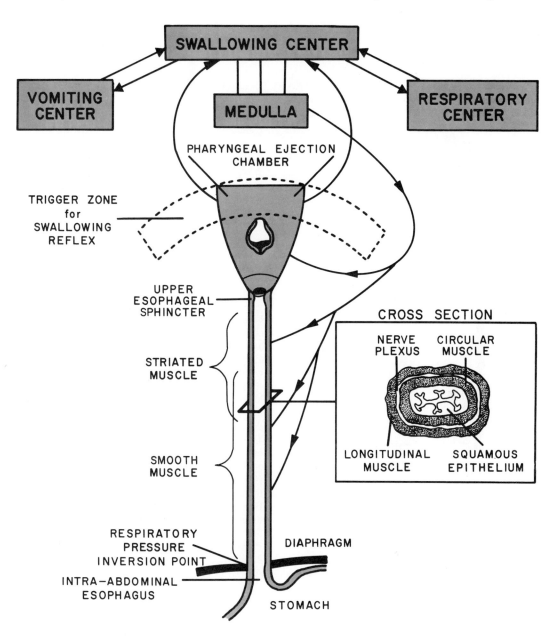

Figure 48.1   The components of the mechanism of swallowing, and the neural control of swallowing.

out of the thoracic cavity during breathing, swallowing, or vomiting.

PRESSURE INVERSION POINT

A functional landmark occurs at the junction of the thoracic cavity and the abdominal cavity (anatomically, this is the location of the diaphragm). When the tip of a manometer is in the intrathoracic esophagus, the pressure falls during inspiration. When the tip is in the intra-abdominal esophagus, the pressure rises during inspiration. Between the two sites is the point of inversion of respiratory pressure (PIP).

EVENTS OF SWALLOWING

Pharynx

During the pharyngeal phase of swallowing, the pressure in the pharynx rises as the pharyngeal muscles contract. Passage of the bolus

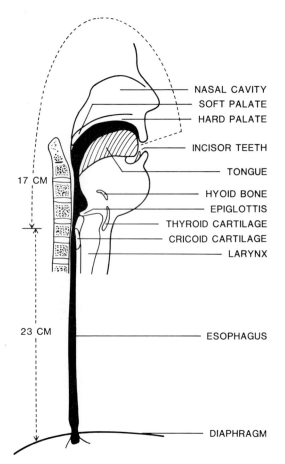

Figure 48-2.   Sagittal section of the pharynx and the esophagus.

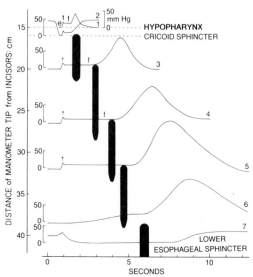

Figure 48-3. Schematic record of pressure changes in the esophageal lumen during the swallowing of a large bolus of radiopaque material (shown in black). The bolus changes in length and width as it moves down the esophagus. The abscissa indicates the time after the bolus is swallowed, and the ordinate gives the site from which the pressure is recorded. Note that the bolus moves down the esophagus ahead of the pressure peak. The **t** wave corresponds to a virtually synchronous increase in pressure all along the esophagus as the cricoid sphincter opens. **f** corresponds to a plateau of pressure as the bolus flows ahead of the wave of pressure. (Redrawn, with permission, from Cohen, B.R., and Wolf, B.S. 1968. Cineradiograph and intraluminal pressure correlations in the pharynx and the esophagus. In *Handbook of Physiology*. Section 6. Alimentary Canal. Chapter 91. Edited by C.F. Code. Washington, D.C.: American Physiological Society.)

from the pharynx back into the mouth is prevented by occlusion of the fauces by the posterior part of the tongue. The nasal passages are sealed by the soft palate. Passage of the bolus from the hypopharynx into the larynx is prevented by the lifting of the larynx forward under the ventral surface of the tongue, by closure of the glottis, and by the down-folding of the epiglottis over the glottis.

The relationship between the pressures recorded in the lumen of the pharyngeal esophagus and the resultant movement of the bolus is shown in Figure 48-3. This figure gives the pressures at several points in the lumen at different distances from the incisors, and sequential frames show the bolus (the black area) as it would be seen during simultaneous radiographic and manometric studies.

Hypopharynx

The first recording in Figure 48-3 refers to the hypopharynx, which is about 15 cm from the

incisors; the tip of the catheter in the second recording is at 16 cm. Note that sudden relaxation of the cricoid sphincter (second recording) precedes the first events in the hypopharynx. The **e** (for elevation wave) on the first recording corresponds to the forward and headward movements of the hyoid bone. This movement breaks the airtight seal of the cricoid sphincter, which normally prevents air from moving in and out of the esophagus during breathing, which now is inhibited. The **t** wave occurs almost synchronously in all of the recordings. The **t** wave is recorded when the tongue drives the oral contents into the pharynx, which is connected through the open cricoid sphincter to a column of air and fluid that runs through the length of the esophagus. The muscles around the superior regions of the pharynx cause the bolus to flow through the hypopharynx (**f** is for flow). During the plateau of pressure (**f** in the second recording), the bolus passes from the pharynx into the esophagus. By the time the pressure in the hypopharynx reaches its peak, the entire bolus is in the cervical esophagus. Catheters in the lumen of a tubular viscus, such as the esophagus, record high pressures only when the lumen is sealed around the catheter tip, which occurs after the contents of the lumen have been driven on.

Cricoid Sphincter

The pressure in the lumen at the cricoid sphincter, 1 cm beyond the hypopharynx, is shown in the second recording; note the contrast with the pressure in the hypopharynx. As breathing is inhibited, the pressure in the lumen falls by about 40 mm Hg to atmospheric pressure (second recording in Figure 48-3). The normal high pressure at the cricoid sphincter is attributed partly to the elasticity of the sphincter and partly to continuous muscular contractions, which are mediated through extrinsic nerves.

Body of the Esophagus

The pressure in the lumen 20 cm from the incisors is shown in recording #3 in Figure 48-3; the **f** plateau is much longer here than it is in the pharyngeal region, although the volume of the bolus that passes is the same. Thus, flow driven by esophageal peristalsis is much slower than that by pharyngeal ejection, although striated muscle provides the motive power for both.

Lower Esophageal Sphincter

In recording #7 in Figure 48-3, the pressure falls initially, which indicates that the lower esophageal sphincter is open during the entire period of swallowing. The events shown in Figure 48-3 occur during a single swallow; if swallowing occurs in rapid sequence, the lower esophageal sphincter remains relaxed throughout the series, and the peristaltic wave sweeps down the esophagus only after the last swallow.

Control of Peristalsis in the Esophagus

Three types of peristalsis in the esophagus have been recognized: primary peristalsis, secondary peristalsis, and neural drive.

PRIMARY PERISTALSIS
When a peristaltic sequence in the esophagus is preceded by a swallow, the events are similar to those shown in Figure 48-3 and are known as *primary peristalsis.*

SECONDARY PERISTALSIS
Secondary peristalsis is initiated by distention of the esophagus in the thorax. In this event, the peristaltic wave begins in the region of the cricoid sphincter, but no pharyngeal swallow precedes it.

NEURAL DRIVE
In primary and secondary peristalsis, impulses carried through the vagus nerve excite each part of the esophagus in turn. Thus, a bolus in the esophagus is not necessary for the propagation of peristalsis. In humans, not every pharyngeal swallowing complex is followed by the complete events of primary peristalsis. Judging from experiments in animals, a bolus increases the frequency of complete peristaltic waves; pharyngeal events and distention of the esophagus combined produce the complete peristaltic complex.

The efferent nerve fibers to the striated muscles of the esophagus and to the nerve plexuses release acetylcholine at nicotinic receptors. The smooth muscle of the body of the esophagus is made to contract by acetylcholine released from postganglionic neurons. This action is weakened by atropine; therefore, the receptors probably are muscarinic. This direct dependence of esophageal smooth muscle on impulses in extrinsic nerves is an unusual feature for smooth muscle in general.

The neural discharge from the swallowing center can be activated at will. Swallowing can be initiated by touching the posterior wall of the pharynx, and the response to this stimulus cannot be inhibited voluntarily. Knowledge of this response is important clinically because this area should not be touched when a mirror is used to examine the posterior aditus of the nose or the larynx.

Actions of Esophageal Sphincters

The action of the cricoid sphincter was discussed previously in this chapter (see the section entitled "Cricoid Sphincter"). When its function is defective, the cricoid sphincter usually fails to relax completely, although the

CLINICAL CORRELATION
48.1   Reflux Esophagitis

CASE REPORT

The Patient: A 57-year-old male.

Principal Complaint: Heartburn.

History: For about five years, the patient had experienced burning discomfort in the substernal area. Initially, the pain occurred only after heavy (fatty) meals or overindulgence in alcohol. For the last three years, he had been troubled every day by symptoms that were more severe after meals, when lying down, or when bending over (for example, to tie his shoelaces). Occasionally, he had a sudden appearance of gastric contents in the mouth, and this was more likely to occur if he reclined after consuming a large meal. He obtained temporary relief by consuming antacid tablets, such as Tums or Rolaids. Similarly, Maalox and other liquid antacids gave relief, although only of the substernal discomfort.

Clinical Examination: All laboratory values were normal. A barium esophagram (x-ray picture taken while barium sulfate—contrast medium—is swallowed) revealed a normal esophagus with a large sliding hiatal hernia (in which the esophago-gastric junction and a portion of the stomach move up into the thorax through the diaphragm (Figure 1).)

Comment: Reflux into the esophagus is a normal event, but when it occurs frequently

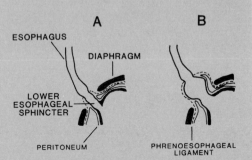

Figure 1.   A. Normal esophagus. **B.** Sliding hernia.

and the esophagus does not drive its contents back into the stomach, retrosternal or epigastric discomfort or pain is experienced. Patients who have reflux usually have low pressure in the lumen at the level of the lower esophageal sphincter (see p. 670) but not to a degree that is diagnostic. Pain of lower esophageal origin is the most common reason for taking antacids bought over the counter.

Outcome: The patient was treated by surgical attachment of the esophago-gastric junction in the abdominal cavity, below the diaphragm. This adjustment stopped the reflux of gastric contents, and he was free of pain. As a preventive measure, he learned to take smaller meals, to avoid fatty foods, and not to eat for 2–3 hours before retiring.

---

individual may not be aware of it. The lower esophageal sphincter, which separates the gastric cavity from the lumen of the esophagus, sometimes fails to relax enough to allow the passage of the bolus. In this instance, swallowed material accumulates in the esophagus until the hydrostatic pressure is great enough to force the sphincter open and allow the material to trickle into the gastric cavity. This condition, called *achalasia of the cardia,* is caused by partial destruction of intrinsic nerves.

The counterpart of the failure of the lower esophageal sphincter to relax is its failure to

contract enough to prevent the reentrance of the gastric contents into the esophagus. Two mechanisms normally prevent this reentrance. The first mechanism is a sphincter, which undoubtedly operates in this region. The term "sphincter" is used here to mean a zone of high intraluminal pressure that exists even when the esophagus is displaced above the diaphragm, out of the abdominal cavity, although no thickening of the circular muscular layer of the esophagus can be shown to account for the high pressure. A zone of high pressure not only exists, but it also is controlled reflexly. This is indicated by the experimental observation that pressure in the sphincter increases when intra-abdominal pressure is increased. In general, it can be said that the mean pressure in the resting sphincter is low in a group of patients who experience reflux from the stomach into the esophagus frequently, but not low enough to permit diagnosis of individual patients. Although hormones can modify the lower esophageal sphincter (e.g., gastrin increases the force of contraction, and cholecystokinin decreases it), they have not been shown to control the lower esophageal sphincter in either health or disease. The second mechanism that keeps the gastric contents within the stomach is the extension of the lower end of the esophagus into the abdomen. When the intra-abdominal pressure is raised, which increases the intraluminal pressure in the stomach, the same external pressure is applied to the part of the esophagus in the abdomen. Thus, the gradient from the stomach into the esophagus does not increase, and the contents remain in the stomach.

STUDY OUTLINE

ANALYSIS OF SWALLOWING

FIRST STAGE   Chewing—reflex action that can be stopped at will.

Oral receptors send afferent impulses to the brainstem; efferent impulses activate glands and muscles in appropriate pattern.

SECOND STAGE   Sequential elevation of dorsum of tongue against hard palate; transfers food to pharyngeal cavity.

Bolus stimulates pharyngeal mucosal receptors, initiates reflex events of stages 3 and 4 of swallowing, cannot be stopped voluntarily.

THIRD STAGE   Pharyngeal cavity is closed, and material is ejected into esophagus by contraction of muscles that surround pharyngeal cavity.

FOURTH STAGE   Esophagus acts as passive tube that receives pharyngeal bolus and develops sequential transporting waves (peristalsis) that last 6–10 seconds.

Peristalsis is inhibited during repeated swallowing.

FUNCTIONAL ANATOMY

GENERAL   Oral cavity and pharynx are surrounded by striated muscle controlled by extrinsic nerves.

Esophagus contains striated muscle in upper third, smooth muscle in lower third, and mixed muscle in middle third.

Impulses in parasympathetic nerves initiate peristaltic contractions by activating nerve plexuses in muscular wall of esophagus.

ORAL CAVITY   During oral stage of swallowing, mandible is fixed against maxilla and lips are sealed.

Bolus is moved to dorsum of tongue, which presses sequentially front to back against hard palate, squeezing food into pharynx.

Entire process is controlled from swallowing center in medulla oblongata.

PHARYNX   Anterior wall consists of epiglottis and opening of larynx.

Posterior and lateral walls are composed of mucous squamous epithelium covering three constrictor muscles of pharynx.

ESOPHAGUS   Extends from cricoid sphincter (about 17 cm from incisors) to lower esophageal sphincter (about 40 cm from incisors).

Lined by robust squamous epithelium; flattened when empty, with folds of redundant epithelium.

LOWER ESOPHAGEAL SPHINCTER   No thickening of muscle layers—sphincter is identified by zone of increased pressure.

Moves longitudinally during swallowing, breathing, or vomiting.

PRESSURE INVERSION POINT   Intrathoracic esophageal pressure decreases during inspiration, intra-abdominal esophageal pressure increases; region of changeover is small—pressure inversion point (PIP).

Useful functional landmark for diaphragm.

EVENTS OF SWALLOWING

PHARYNX   Contraction of muscles increases pressure, ejects bolus into esophagus.

HYPOPHARYNX   First rise of pressure in hypopharynx is caused by backward movement of posterior part of tongue.

Contraction of muscles of pharynx causes contents to flow into esophagus with little increase of pressure, since resistance to flow is slight.

CRICOID SPHINCTER   Pressure falls (by about 40 mm Hg) to atmospheric pressure as breathing is inhibited and swallowing begins.

BODY OF THE ESOPHAGUS   Contents flow past sensor for 2 or 3 seconds without a rise in luminal pressure; bolus migrates ahead of peak intraluminal pressure into region of low resistance.

LOWER   ESOPHAGEAL   SPHINCTER Stays open from beginning of swallowing complex to end—about 8 seconds.

During a series of swallows, sphincter remains relaxed and peristaltic events follow last swallow.

CONTROL OF PERISTALSIS IN THE ESOPHAGUS

PRIMARY PERISTALSIS   Preceded by swallow.

SECONDARY PERISTALSIS   Initiated by distention of esophagus, wave migrates from cricoid sphincter.

NEURAL DRIVE   Vagal nerve impulses to successive parts of esophagus drive peristalsis.

Not every pharyngeal swallowing complex is followed by esophageal peristalsis—presence of bolus increases frequency of peristaltic waves.

Swallowing is activated at will or initiated by touching posterior wall of pharynx.

ACTIONS OF ESOPHAGEAL SPHINCTERS   Defects of cricoid sphincter are uncommon; involve failure to relax completely.

Functional lower esophageal sphincter consists of zone of high pressure (sphincter) and extension of esophagus into abdomen—intra-abdominal pressure seals intra-abdominal part.

Incomplete relaxation of lower esophageal sphincter blocks passage of bolus into stomach (achalasia).

Inadequate contraction of lower esophageal sphincter permits reflux of gastric contents into esophagus (a common problem).

BIBLIOGRAPHY

Code, C.F., and Schlegel, J.F. 1968. Motor action of the esophagus and its sphincters. In *Handbook of Physiology*. Section 6. Alimentary Canal. Chapter 90. Edited by C.F. Code. Washington, D.C.: American Physiological Society.

Cohen, B.R., and Wolf, B.S. 1968. Cineradiographic and intraluminal pressure correlations in the pharynx and the esophagus. In *Handbook of Physiology*. Section 6. Alimentary Canal. Chapter 91. Edited by C.F. Code. Washington, D.C.: American Physiological Society.

Davenport, H.W. 1977. *Physiology of the Digestive Tract* (4th ed.). Chicago: Year Book.

Johnson, L.R. (ed.). 1981. *Physiology of the Gastrointestinal Tract*. New York: Raven Press.

Miller, A.J. 1982. Deglutition. *Physiol. Rev.* 62:129.

The
Stomach

CHAPTER CONTENTS

ACTIONS

The stomach stores food and drink that is taken intermittently and releases them to the duodenum and small intestine at a rate that promotes digestion and absorption. Some digestion occurs in the stomach, and the churning of a meal with the gastric secretions liquifies the food. Despite the considerable benefits of these functions, however, none of them is necessary for life. Only the secretion of intrinsic factor, which takes part in the absorption of cobalamin (vitamin B_{12}), is essential for existence. Provided cobalamin is given by injection, patients can survive after having their stomachs removed.

FUNCTIONAL ANATOMY

The stomach extends from the lower esophageal sphincter to the duodenum; in a healthy person, the stomach will hold about 1.5 liters but can be distended to contain as much as 4 liters. The parts of the stomach that are important physiologically are named in Figure 49-1.

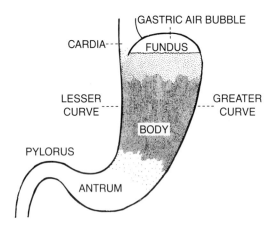

Figure 49-1.   The parts of the stomach, as seen radiologically. The density of stippling indicates the density of acid-secreting (oxyntic) cells.

Blood Supply

The arterial blood supply of the stomach runs along the greater and lesser curvatures. The supply of blood is so ample, relative to the use of oxygen by the stomach, that it is rare for the blockage of an artery to interfere with the function of the secretory cells or the smooth muscle of the gastric wall.

Nerve Supply

The main supply of excitatory (parasympathetic) nerves runs through the vagus trunk, the branches of which pass down the lesser curve of the stomach and give transverse branches to the muscle and the secretory cells. The activity of the sympathetic nerves, which reach the stomach along the blood vessels, inhibit gastric secretion and motility.

Layers of the Gastric Wall

The layers of the wall of the stomach are homologous with the layers of the majority of the gastrointestinal tract. The outer layer is the serosa, which allows the stomach free mobility in the peritoneal cavity, although the esophagus and the duodenum, with which the stomach connects, are fixed. The longitudinal smooth muscle lies beneath the serosa. A plexus (Auerbach's) of nerve cells and fibers lies between the outer layer of longitudinal muscle and the inner layer of spiral muscle. The cells of Auerbach's plexus are connected to the deeper submucosal plexus. The muscularis

mucosae, the contraction of which causes the mucosa to pucker up into folds as the stomach empties, separates the submucosal plexus from the specialized secretory cells. These secretory cells are buried deep in the secretory epithelium; thus, only surface cells that secrete mucus are in contact with the gastric contents, which sometimes are highly acidic. The robust mucosal lining of the gastric lumen is about 0.5 mm thick.

CONTROL OF GASTRIC MOTILITY

The stomach and the duodenum, isolated in a bath of saline solution, are capable of coordinated movements that transfer the gastric contents from the stomach to the duodenum. This activity indicates clearly that the extrinsic efferent fibers in the vagus nerves and sympathetic nerves do not cause the propulsive contractions of the stomach as they do of the esophagus. On the other hand, the nerves of the stomach do adjust the movements, as will be described below.

Electrophysiology

The frequency of the waves of contraction that course over the body of the stomach and the antrum is determined by a spontaneously active electrical pacemaker located in the longitudinal muscle of the greater curvature, at the junction of the fundus and the body of the stomach. The wave of excitation occurs about every 20 seconds and is propagated distally in the longitudinal muscle at a rate of about 0.5 cm/sec. In the gastric antrum, the rate of propagation of the pacemaker potential increases fourfold, with the result that the entire antrum contracts more or less synchronously, as the cardiac ventricle does under the influence of the rapidly propagating Purkinje system (see Chapter 18).

The pacemaker potential determines the maximum frequency of contraction in the stomach, but it does not directly cause the contraction. Records of the electrical and mechanical activity of gastric smooth muscle show that contraction occurs only after an abrupt change of electrical potential (*second potential*) that follows but is distinct from the slowly developing pacemaker potential (Figure 49-2). The second potential, or action potential, which may consist of a single deflection of long

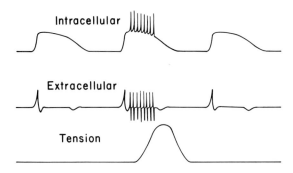

Figure 49-2. Recording of cellular potential (intracellular electrode), surface potential (extracellular electrode), and tension in gastric smooth muscle. The rapid fluctuations are caused by slow depolarization of the cell (upward deflection). The rapid changes in potential (action potentials or "spikes") cause the increase in tension (bottom line) by increasing the concentration of Ca++ inside the smooth muscle cells. (Redrawn, by permission. From *The New England Journal of Medicine* (285:85, 1971.)

duration or a burst of spikes, occurs when the circumferential tension and the concentration of acetylcholine are optimal. The strength of contraction is determined by the magnitude of the second potential, which reflects the amount of Ca++ that enters the gastric muscle cells. Both the pacemaker potentials and the second potentials differ from what is called a "resting potential," although smooth muscle rarely is resting in the sense that it is generating no tension; as a rule, the larger the resting potential, the less the resting tension.

Neural Influences

Nerve impulses carried by fibers of the vagus trunk increase the frequency of contraction of smooth muscle by releasing acetylcholine. The acetylcholine increases the probability that one or more action potentials will follow a pacemaker potential. Norepinephrine, released by sympathetic fibers, hyperpolarizes the cells and decreases the probability that action potentials will follow a pacemaker potential. The nerve fibers terminate at some distance from the muscle fibers and thus create an inhibitory (adrenergic) or excitatory (cholinergic) environment around all of the cells, rather than controlling individual cells. The series of events that relates action potentials and contraction is known as *excitation-contraction coupling*. An increase of [Ca++] inside the cell, caused either by entry of Ca++ through the membrane or by

release of Ca++ from organelles in the cell, is the mediating event.

For several weeks after the parasympathetic (vagal) nerve supply to the stomach has been cut for the treatment of duodenal ulcer, the frequency of the pacemaker potentials and second potentials is decreased, but the electrical activity gradually returns to normal, and the final effect is small after several months have passed.

MECHANICAL FUNCTIONS OF THE STOMACH

Shape of the Stomach

The stomach is shaped like an inverted cone that has its tip bent to the right toward the duodenum (Figure 49-1); this configuration appears to be important to gastric emptying. As the stomach fills, the length of the lesser curve remains constant, but the length of the greater curve increases. During a meal, more food accumulates initially in the fundus and the body of the stomach than in the antrum; thus, the circumferences of the fundus and the body increase more than that of the antrum. In accordance with the law of Laplace (circumferential tension is proportional to pressure × radius) (see Chapter 1), more tension develops in the walls of a compliant tube as the radius of the tube increases. Hence, even though the intraluminal pressure may increase only slightly as the stomach fills, the circumferential tension that balances distention increases more, especially in the distended proximal part.

Relation of Contraction to Distention

As the stomach fills, excitation of the gastric muscle in the proximal part, which has the greatest circumference, is inhibited by the high tension in the gastric wall. As a result, although the site of the pacemaker does not change, peristaltic waves develop farther toward the gastric antrum, where the circumference is smaller. Thus, the shape of the stomach accounts for the origin of the waves of contraction in midbody immediately after a small meal, more distally after a very large meal, and more proximally again as the stomach empties. The antral origin of peristaltic waves in a full stomach leaves the contents of the proximal portion undisturbed. Thus, after a very large meal, acidic gastric secretion does not stop the digestion of starch by salivary amylase for an hour or more.

Receptive Relaxation

After a bolus is swallowed, intragastric pressure decreases before the bolus has passed through the lower esophageal sphincter (*receptive relaxation*). This is a reflex response mediated by fibers in the vagus nerves. After the branches of the vagus nerves to the stomach have been cut for the treatment of duodenal ulcer, greater pressure is required to distend the fundus of the stomach. This reduction of effective gastric capacity is one of the causes of the rapid initial rate of gastric emptying seen in some patients who have undergone vagotomy, if they take liquid meals of more than 300 ml.

Gastric Mixing and Emptying

The contractions of the stomach not only empty the stomach but also mix and liquify the contents. The liquification of food in the stomach hastens the availability of materials that are bound tightly to food and yet are absorbed more effectively in the duodenum than in the jejunum. Iron, calcium, and folic acid are the materials likely to be affected. After several years, some patients who have had operations on the stomach that increase the rate of gastric emptying may develop weak bones from a lack of calcium and anemia from a lack of iron.

The antrum acts as a dynamic filter that usually permits only liquids and very small particles (those less than 1 or 2 mm in cross-section) to pass through the pylorus during the digestive period. Any large, indigestible pieces, such as fruit stones, are cleared from the stomach by the vigorous periodic contractions that travel slowly from the stomach to the terminal ileum during fasting (fasting myoelectric complex; see the section entitled "Myoelectric Complex During Fasting" in Chapter 52).

The antrum has a maximum volume of about 30 ml and can empty almost completely. There are two exits from the antrum: forward into the duodenum through the pylorus and backward into the stomach through the advancing ring of peristalsis. Normally, each stroke of the antral pump squirts about 3 ml or less of material into the duodenum, and the remaining 27 ml or more of material is ejected vigorously back into the stomach. This is an effective way to break up the solids in the gastric contents. Neural input through the vagal trunks can augment gastric emptying by increasing the force of the antral pump, but variation in the resistance to filling of the duodenum is the most important factor that controls gastric emptying (see the section on regulation of gastric emptying that follows).

EFFECT OF VAGOTOMY

Sectioning the branches of the vagus nerves to the stomach, in the treatment of duodenal ulcer, decreases the frequency and force of contraction of the antrum. After several months, however, the antrum again grinds and liquifies solid material effectively. Receptive relaxation of the fundus during a meal, which normally is mediated through the vagus nerves (see the previous section on receptive relaxation), does not occur; as a consequence, fluid is forced into the antrum and the initial emptying is hastened.

REGULATION OF GASTRIC EMPTYING

The stomach and duodenum together can be thought of as a metering pump that is restrained to function at less than full capacity when ejecting pulses of food into the duodenum. Most of the regulation of gastric emptying depends on varying the resistance to filling of the duodenum, which is affected by the composition of the contents of the duodenum. To assess the power of gastric emptying, subjects are given test meals of standard volume, usually 750 ml, and the rate of emptying is measured by the amount of the solution that can be recovered from the stomach through a gastric tube at 10-minute intervals. The stomach usually delivers isotonic saline solution to the duodenum at a rate of 50–100 ml/min, whereas food usually leaves the stomach at a rate of only 3–10 ml/min. The rate of transfer of food from the stomach to the duodenum is slower because the products of digestion stimulate duodenal receptors that increase the resistance of the duodenum to filling and, to a smaller extent, reduce the vigor of the antral pump. The volume of the stomach also affects the rate of emptying, but the significance of the effect depends on the consistency of the contents. The more liquid the contents of the stomach, the more the rate of emptying increases with volume. Solid food leaves only slightly faster when the volume is doubled but the composition is not changed.

Response of Duodenal Receptors to Foodstuffs

Gastric emptying is slowed through duodenal receptors stimulated by the osmotic activity of the digestion products of food.

CARBOHYDRATE AND PROTEIN

Polysaccharides initially are broken down in the stomach by salivary amylase and in the duodenum by pancreatic amylase; polysaccharides are digested to monosaccharides at the surface of the intestinal mucosa. The digestion of protein by gastric pepsin and pancreatic enzymes is somewhat similar, although the product is a mixture of amino acids and short peptides. The osmotic effect of this mixture stimulates receptors located in the walls of the duodenum. Because the receptors are sensitive to osmolarity, all soluble molecules are equally active in slowing gastric emptying. The final result of this process is that 1 g of dietary carbohydrate, either in the form of starch or sugar, and 1 g of digestible protein, such as casein, stimulate the receptors equally because their intermediate products of digestion have equal osmotic effects. Because 1 g of either of these two foodstuffs contains the same amount of energy available for metabolism, the receptors are stimulated equally by solutions that contain equal numbers of calories (Figure 49-3).

TRIGLYCERIDES

The products of digestion of most fats are monoglycerides and the anions of fatty acids. The latter products affect certain duodenal re-

ceptors directly. The combined slowing of gastric emptying by the receptors that respond to the osmotic activity of the digestion products and the receptors that respond to the anions of fatty acids is proportional to the energy of the food. Although no receptor responds directly to the energy of food, the stomach is regulated to deliver about 200 kcal/hr to the duodenum.

EFFECT OF ACID ON GASTRIC EMPTYING

When a meal of ordinary food is taken, the volume of the gastric contents does not change during the first 60 minutes (Figure 49-4A). This constant volume does not mean that the begin-

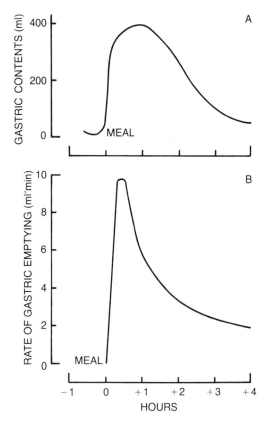

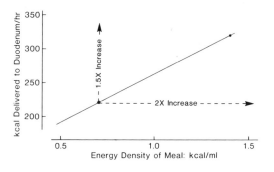

Figure 49-3. The relation between the concentration of energy in a meal and the amount of energy delivered to the duodenum in the first 60 minutes after taking the meal. Note that doubling the energy density of the meal, from 0.7 to 1.4 kcal/ml, increases the energy delivered from 210 to 320 kcal in 60 minutes.

Figure 49-4. The volume of the gastric contents, that is, food mixed with gastric secretions, and the simultaneous rate of transfer of the contents from the stomach to the duodenum. Note that the rate of gastric secretion approximately matches the rate of gastric emptying for the first hour, during which time the volume of the gastric contents changes very little. (Redrawn, with permission, from Malagelada, J.R., et al. 1976. Measurement of gastric functions during digestion of ordinary solid meals in man. *Gastroenterol.* 70:203. © 1976. The Williams & Wilkins Co., Baltimore.)

ning of gastric emptying is delayed for an hour. In fact, the rate of gastric emptying reaches a maximum shortly after the meal is taken (Figure 49-4B); however, the stomach secretes at about the same rate that it empties during the first hour. One might think that the dilution of the food by gastric secretions would interfere with the regulation of the transfer of food to the duodenum. However, the acid that is secreted replaces the food as a stimulus to the duodenal receptors and thus contributes to the control of gastric emptying.

GASTRIC SECRETION

The epithelium of the stomach in humans secretes spontaneously and continuously at a rate of about 0.3–0.6 ml/min (basal secretion). After a meal, the rate may rise to 10 ml/min, and the concentration of acid, which is about 40 mEq/liter of basal secretion, may increase to more than 100 mEq/liter. Healthy people secrete widely differing amounts of acid because they each have different numbers of acid-secreting (oxyntic) cells (Figure 49-5). It has been proposed that the acid of the stomach sterilizes the food, and when food is unhygienic, individuals who secrete little or no stomach acid have a higher risk of bacterial infection than people who secrete stomach acid vigorously. The importance of this hypothesis is uncertain, however, because as much as 20% of a meal may empty into the duodenum before it is acidified or digested.

Structure of Gastric Mucosa

SECRETORY CELLS

The inner surface of the stomach, which comes into contact with the food that is eaten, is composed of cells that secrete mucus continuously and which are shed and replaced at the rate of about 500,000/min. The life span of such a cell, from mitosis to shedding, is 2–4 days. Although the contents of the stomach are particularly noxious, such a high rate of turnover of surface epithelial cells is typical of the lining membrane of the entire alimentary tract. The cells that secrete acid (oxyntic cells) or pepsinogen (chief cells) are arranged as tubules buried in the epithelium at right angles to the surface of the mucosa (Figure 49-6). The inner layer of each tubule is formed by the chief cells, and the acid from the oxyntic cells drains into the tubules between the chief cells. Several

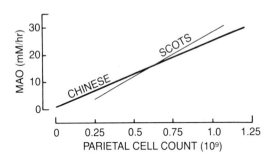

Figure 49-5. Relation between the number of parietal (acid-secreting) cells that were removed during surgery on patients with peptic ulcer and the decrease in maximal acid output (MAO) from the stomach (preoperative output compared with postoperative output). (Redrawn, with permission, from Card, W.I., and Marks, I.N. 1960. The relationship between the acid output of the stomach following "maximal" histamine stimulation and the parietal cell mass. *Clin. Sci.* 19:147, and Cheny, F.C.Y., et al. 1977. Maximum acid output to graded doses of pentagastrin and its relation to parietal cell mass in Chinese patients with duodenal ulcer. *Gut* 18:829.)

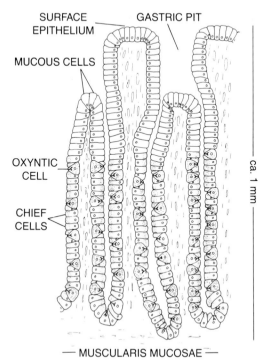

Figure 49-6. Cross-section through a portion of the gastric mucosa showing the arrangement of gastric pits and secretory cells.

tubules join together to form a gastric pit, which drains into the gastric lumen.

GASTRIN—THE GASTRIC SECRETORY HORMONE

Gastrin is a polypeptide that exists in at least four forms: G_{14}, G_{17}, G_{34} (Figure 49-7), and $G_{(unknown)}$; the suffixes indicate the number of amino acids in the respective molecules. The stimulant (agonist) part of the molecule consists of the last four amino acids, which are common to all forms of gastrin. The larger part of the molecule determines the potency of the smaller part. The specificity of the molecule also is determined by the larger part since the last five amino acids also occur in cholecystokinin, which stimulates the gallbladder to contract and the pancreas to secrete enzymes, but is only a weak agonist of the oxyntic cells. Under some circumstances, a high concentration of cholecystokinin inhibits gastric secretion by competing with gastrin, the more potent stimulator, for the excitatory sites on the oxyntic cells.

G_{17} causes about six times the effect that G_{34} causes when the concentration of each in the plasma is the same. When equal molar quantities of G_{17} and G_{34} are injected as an intravenous bolus, however, the two species are about equally effective. This paradox can be explained by the finding that G_{34}, which is the weaker stimulus, has a half-life in the plasma about six times the half-life of G_{17}. Thus, in the gastrin released when a meal is taken (half of which is G_{34} and half of which is G_{17}), each form has about an equal effect on the oxyntic cells.

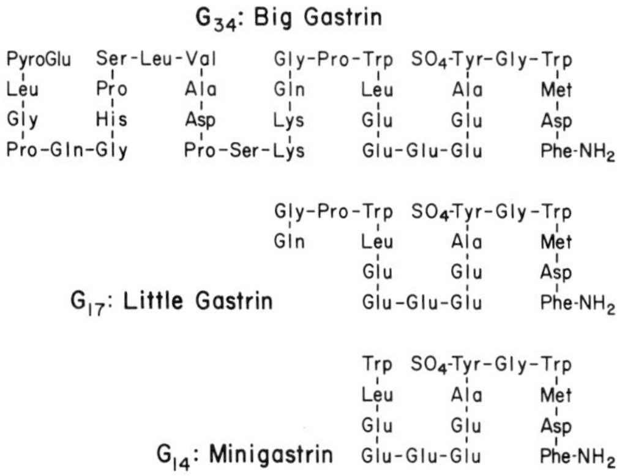

G_{34}: Big Gastrin

PyroGlu	Ser-Leu-Val		Gly-Pro-Trp	SO₄-Tyr-Gly-Trp	
Leu	Pro	Ala	Gln	Leu	Ala	Met
Gly	His	Asp	Lys	Glu	Glu	Asp
Pro-Gln-Gly		Pro-Ser-Lys		Glu-Glu-Glu	Phe-NH₂

	Gly-Pro-Trp	SO₄-Tyr-Gly-Trp	
	Gln	Leu	Ala	Met
		Glu	Glu	Asp
G_{17}: Little Gastrin		Glu-Glu-Glu	Phe-NH₂

	Trp	SO₄-Tyr-Gly-Trp	
	Leu	Ala	Met
	Glu	Glu	Asp
G_{14}: Minigastrin	Glu-Glu-Glu	Phe-NH₂

Figure 49-7. The amino acid sequences of big gastrin (G_{34}), little gastrin (G_{17}), and minigastrin (G_{14}).

ANTRAL MUCOSA

The antrum contains no oxyntic cells and only a few chief cells; however, the antral mucosa has many cells that secrete gastrin, and other cells that secrete a form of mucus that especially adheres to the surface. The antral mucosa is not confined to the antrum proper; usually, a tonguelike area also extends up into the mucosa of the body of the stomach along the lesser curvature. This arrangement is of clinical interest because most gastric ulcers occur at the junction of the acid-secreting mucosa and the antral mucosa.

MUCUS

The mucus of the alimentary tract acts as a lubricant. Mucus is more than 99% water and is not an absolute barrier to diffusion, either in the stomach or in the intestine; this fact is confirmed by the absorption of alcohol or aspirin from the gastric lumen and the whole range of food materials from the intestine. However, the layer of mucus (200–600 μm thick) does reduce the mixing of the luminal contents by intestinal movements, and accounts partly for the "unstirred layer" at the surface of the mucosa, which is believed to limit the rate of intestinal absorption in some circumstances. The final movement of the contents to the luminal face of the absorbing cells is by diffusion.

Secretion of Hydrochloric Acid (HCl)

The H^+ of gastric secretion (H^+Cl^-) is obtained from water, leaving OH^- in the oxyntic cell (Figure 49-8). CO_2 enters the cell and is hydrated to form H_2CO_3; this reaction is catalyzed by carbonic anhydrase. H_2CO_3 dissociates into H^+ and HCO_3^-. The H^+ reacts with the OH^- group left by the formation of gastric H^+, forming water, and the HCO_3^- diffuses into the plasma in exchange for Cl^-. Thus, the blood that leaves a rapidly secreting gastric mucosa contains less CO_2 and more HCO_3^- than the rest of the venous blood. The H^+ secreted into the stomach is delivered to the duodenum, where it is neutralized by HCO_3^- obtained from the plasma by the pancreas (see Figure 50-5).

The millionfold concentration gradient of H^+ between the lumen of the stomach, 4×10^{-2} M (pH 1.4), and the blood, 4×10^{-8} M (pH 7.4), indicates that H^+ is transported actively.

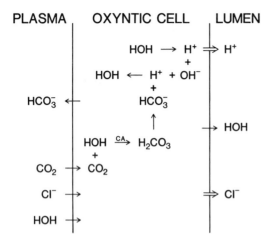

PLASMA | OXYNTIC CELL | LUMEN

$$HOH \rightarrow H^+ \Rightarrow H^+$$
$$+$$
$$HOH \leftarrow H^+ + OH^-$$
$$+$$
$$HCO_3^- \leftarrow HCO_3^-$$
$$\uparrow$$
$$\rightarrow HOH$$
$$HOH \xrightarrow{CA} H_2CO_3$$
$$+$$
$$CO_2 \rightarrow CO_2$$
$$Cl^- \rightarrow \Rightarrow Cl^-$$
$$HOH \rightarrow$$

Figure 49-8. The major processes in the secretion of gastric acid. Single arrows across the cell boundary indicate passive movement, and double arrows indicate active transport (CA = carbonic anhydrase). Because of the movement of water along osmotic gradients, the secretion is approximately isosmotic with the plasma.

Nevertheless, the mucosal surface of the stomach is electrically negative to the blood, despite the transport of H^+ into the lumen. This electronegativity of the luminal face of the mucosa is explained by active transport of Cl^- into the gastric lumen.

CHANGES IN OXYNTIC CELLS DURING SECRETION
The cytoplasm of the oxyntic cell is connected to the gastric tubule by an intracellular canaliculus lined by a secretory membrane; H^+ is released at the surface of microvilli on the membrane. Within minutes of the stimulation of the oxyntic cell, the density of the internal microvilli increases; hence, the area of contact with the canaliculus is greatly enlarged at the time that the rate of secretion of acid is maximal. The microvilli are reabsorbed into the membrane when the period of secretion is over.

EXCITATION OF OXYNTIC CELLS BY HISTAMINE
The rate of output of acid normally is controlled by variation in the concentrations of acetylcholine and gastrin, to which the oxyntic cells are exposed; however, the gastric mucosa also contains relatively high concentrations of

histamine, which stimulates gastric secretion. Although physiological variation in the concentration of histamine in the plasma does not regulate gastric secretion, blocking the action of histamine with an antagonist specific for H_2 receptors does reduce the response of the oxyntic cell to all other stimuli. Currently, this result is taken to mean that the oxyntic cell contains three receptor sites that potentiate each other: one for acetylcholine, one for gastrin, and one for histamine. Thus, the rate of secretion of acid when all three receptors are stimulated is greater than the sum of the rates of secretion when each is stimulated separately. Histamine excites the cells by increasing the concentration of cyclic adenosine monophosphate (AMP); the means by which the other stimuli work are not known.

Pepsinogen-Secreting Cells
The pepsins are gastric proteolytic enzymes that function optimally in the pH range of 1.2–3.5. Pepsins are formed and stored in the gastric mucosa as pepsinogens, which are activated in the gastric lumen, first by acid and then by pepsin, by the removal of a peptide fragment. Pepsins cleave the central regions of proteins (acting preferentially on peptide bonds that involve tyrosine and phenylalanine), yielding short peptides and small amounts of amino acids. Group I pepsinogens are formed by the chief cells, which are associated with the oxyntic cells in the mucosa of the body of the stomach (see Figure 49-6). Group II pepsinogens are formed in the mucosa of the body and also in the mucosa of the antrum, which has no acid-secreting cells. The ratio of chief cells to oxyntic cells is about the same in different individuals. The ratio of the secretion of pepsinogen to the secretion of acid also is constant for a particular type of stimulus, although it is different for different stimuli. Thus, if the stimulus is taken into account, the output of acid, which is convenient to measure, may be used as an index of the output of pepsin.

Pepsinogens also are found in the plasma and filtered into the urine. Group I pepsinogens are the major group in both the mucosa and the plasma. The distinction between the two groups of pepsinogens has no known implications for digestion, but a high concentration of Group I pepsinogens in the plasma is believed to be a genetic marker for one kind of duodenal ulcer, in which the predisposing

CLINICAL CORRELATION
49.1   Peptic Ulcer

CASE REPORT

Patient: A 24-year-old female.

Principal Complaint: Pain in the upper abdomen; relieved by food and antacids.

History: The patient had experienced the same kind of pain, but less severe, since she was 10 years old. She had no pain from age 12, when the menses began, to age 18, but it returned when she was engaged to be married, and again a year after she was married, when her husband went to work in Libya. The pain ceased 3 months after she became pregnant, but returned a week after delivery of her infant, and at the time of admission, was severe. She was breastfeeding her infant. The pain was decreased considerably by antacids that she took 1 hour and 3 hours after meals.

Clinical Examination: Gastroscopy (direct vision through a fiber optic device) revealed a small ulcer in the mucosa of the first part of the duodenum.

Comment: Duodenal ulcer in children is uncommon but not rare. The incidence is the same in both sexes before puberty, but is lower in females after puberty. The symptoms of duodenal ulcer almost always disappear during pregnancy, but they usually return, especially if the woman breastfeeds her infant. Gastric secretion decreases during pregnancy and increases markedly during lactation. The precise hormonal mechanisms are not known. Anxiety can increase the rate of secretion of acid by the stomach and aggravate the ulcer. This patient's symptoms were related to situations that caused her anxiety, which increased the secretion of acid and pepsin, aggravated the ulcer, and caused her pain.

Outcome: With the passage of time, the patient has matured psychologically, her personal life has stabilized, and she now has only trivial pain. It is common for patients who have duodenal ulcer to recover without having definitive treatment. In drug trials, 50% of the cases of ulcer heal in about 8 weeks, even if the patient takes placebo tablets (which have no pharmacological effect).

cause is an abnormally large mass of oxyntic cells and peptic cells in the gastric mucosa.

The secretion of pepsinogen is controlled through the vagus nerves, which form the efferent arm of a local reflex. This reflex is initiated by the action of acid on the gastric mucosa and by the hormone secretin, which is released by the action of acid on the duodenal mucosa. When the ratio of pepsin to acid in a test of gastric secretion is high, it is likely that the main drive to both groups of cells has come through the vagus. If the ratio of pepsin to acid is low, although the secretion of acid is vigorous, it is likely that the effect is mediated mainly by gastrin, which specifically stimulates the oxyntic cells. For example, a patient who has a tumor that secretes gastrin continuously (a gastrinoma) may have a pepsin-to-acid ratio only one-tenth that of a healthy person.

Hyperplasia and Hypoplasia of Gastric Mucosa

The replacement of oxyntic cells and chief cells is under hormonal control. After the anterior lobe of the pituitary is removed experimentally (in the rat), the mucosa becomes thinner, as it does during starvation or during intravenous feeding. The decrease in the numbers of acid-secreting cells and pepsin-secreting cells during intravenous feeding can be prevented by adding a small amount of gastrin to the intravenous infusate. Chronic administration of gastrin elongates the gastric tubules by increasing the number of cells in the mucosa (*hyperplasia*). Distention of the antrum, which increases the rate of release of gastrin, also causes hyperplasia of the oxyntic mucosa.

Although the number of oxyntic cells remains constant under ordinary conditions, this amount can change, and this property is a factor in the genesis of some forms of duodenal ulcer. The hypersecretion of HCl by one genetically determined group of patients who have duodenal ulcers is explained mostly on the basis of an abnormally large number of oxyntic cells. During the ordinary stresses of life, the rate of secretion of gastric acid in response to meals may vary by severalfold at different times. Although it has not been established that these variations are caused by changes in the number of oxyntic cells, it is likely that they are.

BACK-DIFFUSION OF ACID FROM GASTRIC LUMEN TO BLOOD
The healthy gastric mucosa, or gastric mucosal barrier, allows a remarkably small diffusion of acid from the gastric lumen to the blood. The rate of secretion of H^+ may be as much as 20 mEq/hr, and the gradient may be a millionfold (pH range of 1.4–7.4); however, no more than about 2 mEq of H^+ diffuses back from the gastric lumen to the blood. In patients who have gastritis, however, or whose gastric mucosa has been exposed to alcohol or to aspirin in acid solution, the back-diffusion of H^+, mainly in exchange for Na^+ diffusing from the blood to lumen, may increase tenfold. When tested, such an individual appears to have a very low rate of secretion of H^+, although the output of Cl^- is high. When acid is instilled into the stomach of such a patient, only a relatively small proportion of the acid can be recovered because the damaged mucosa permits the H^+ to leak back into the blood.

EFFECTS OF GASTRIC ANACIDITY
Patients who have Addisonian anemia have few or no oxyntic cells and secrete no acid in response to food. These individuals usually do not secrete pepsinogen either, and even if they did, the enzyme would not be effective because it must be activated by acid (see the section entitled "Pepsinogen-Secreting Cells" in this chapter). Although these patients do not digest protein in the stomach, they do not suffer from any special form of malnutrition, apart from a failure to absorb cobalamin. In view of the importance usually attached to the action of acid in liberating secretin, which stimulates the pancreas, the good health of patients who have Addisonian anemia is unexpected. The concentration of gastrin is high in the plasma of such patients; presumably, gastrin is released from the antrum in excess because of the absence of inhibition of release by acid (see the section entitled "Gastric Phase" in this chapter).

Phases of Gastric Secretion
Extensive experiments in animals indicate that gastric secretion occurs in three phases. Although these phases cannot be separated distinctly, they do provide a convenient framework for analysis.

CEPHALIC PHASE
In the cephalic phase of gastric secretory control, sensory perception provides the stimulus. The sight and smell of food or the sounds of food being prepared cause nerve impulses to pass from the cerebral cortex to the medulla, and from there through the vagus nerves to the stomach. Acetylcholine released from vagal nerve endings in the vicinity of the mucosal cells causes the secretion of acid and pepsinogen.

GASTRIC PHASE
Distention of the stomach after food is eaten and the presence of specific amino acids in the food cause the secretion of acid and pepsin. This effect is mediated through the vagus nerves acting either directly on oxyntic cells, chief cells, and mucous cells or through local (cholinergic) nerve nets and by the hormone gastrin. Acid in the antrum inhibits the release of gastrin, and in the absence of acid, the secretion of gastrin increases. Thus, gastric acidity is regulated in part by a negative-feedback mechanism.

INTESTINAL PHASE
The digestion products of protein that enter the small intestine cause gastric secretion. The mediator is hormonal, but it has not been identified specifically. Carbohydrates in the duodenum and fats in the jejunum inhibit gastric secretion. The net effect of food in the ileum is to inhibit the main gastric secretory response to food during the first hour after eating.

VOMITING

Vomiting, or emesis, is mediated through the activity of reflex arcs that activate the appropriate somatic and visceral muscles, although the visceral component is not essential. Indeed, in animal experiments, the stomach has been replaced by an inert bag, and vomiting still occurs. Vomiting involves contraction of the skeletal muscle of the abdomen and thorax in such a way as to create a gradient of pressure from the abdominal cavity to the thoracic cavity. At the same time, constriction of the lower esophageal sphincter and the intra-abdominal segment of the esophagus is abolished by shortening of the longitudinal muscle of the esophagus, which creates a funnellike opening between the stomach and the esophagus that exits through the mouth.

Before vomiting, an individual often has a pale face, feels nauseous, and salivates. Radiological observation of the stomach during nausea shows that peristalsis ceases and the greater curvature elongates. Before emesis begins, the duodenal contents are pushed into the stomach; the antral region contracts, and its contents are forced into the fundus. The combined, stereotyped components of the somatic and visceral organs are coordinated by a center in the medulla oblongata. Central nervous system receptors that initiate vomiting are located either in the vestibular apparatus, which is affected in vomiting caused by seasickness, or in the chemoreceptor zone of the area postrema, which responds to such specific stimuli as apomorphine or digitalis. Electrical stimulation of these medullary regions, separate from the chemoreceptor zone, causes a complete vomiting response, including closure of the glottis and inhibition of breathing.

The receptors of the alimentary tract that most commonly elicit vomiting are located in the back of the throat and in the mucosa of the duodenum and the stomach; simple distention of the stomach or the intestine elicits vomiting, and nausea and vomiting can be caused by any acute pathological process in the abdomen.

STUDY OUTLINE

ACTIONS   Stomach stores food and drink, controls release of ingested material to duodenum for digestion and absorption.

Churning with gastric secretions liquifies meal, and some digestion occurs.

Promotion of cobalamin (B_{12}) absorption is only function essential for life; patients can survive without stomach.

FUNCTIONAL ANATOMY   Stomach extends from lower esophageal sphincter to duodenum; holds 1.5 liters but can be distended to hold as much as 4 liters.

Parts include fundus, body, antrum, and lesser and greater curvatures.

BLOOD SUPPLY   Ample relative to O_2 use; arteries run along lesser and greater curvatures.

NERVE SUPPLY   Excitatory (parasympathetic) fibers run in vagal trunks, on lesser curvature; transverse branches go to fundus—secretory cell area of body—and to gastric antrum.

Sympathetic fibers travel with blood vessels, inhibit gastric secretion and motility.

LAYERS OF THE GASTRIC WALL   Serosa, longitudinal smooth muscle, Auerbach's plexus, spiral muscle, submucosal plexus, muscularis mucosae, and secretory cells (acid, pepsin, mucus, and intrinsic factor).

CONTROL OF GASTRIC MOTILITY   Stomach empties contents peristaltically into duodenum; extrinsic nerves adjust frequency and force of movements but do not cause movement.

ELECTROPHYSIOLOGY   The spontaneous pacemaker in longitudinal smooth muscle of greater curvature at junction of fundus and body; sets frequency of peristaltic waves at 3/min; wave is propagated at rate of 0.5 cm/sec.

Faster propagation in antrum causes synchronous contraction.

Pacemaker potential sets maximal rate; contraction follows variable second potential, occurs when local concentration of acetylcholine and tension in circumferential smooth muscle are optimal.

Resting tension of smooth muscle is related inversely to resting cellular potential.

NEURAL INFLUENCES   Acetylcholine released by vagal nerve fibers increases probability that pacemaker potential will cause contraction.

Norepinephrine hyperpolarizes membrane, decreases probability of contraction.

Effects on contraction are mediated through intracellular $[Ca^{++}]$.

Frequency of pacemaker potentials and action potentials is reduced after vagotomy; effect lasts only few weeks, however.

MECHANICAL FUNCTIONS OF THE STOMACH

SHAPE OF THE STOMACH   Inverted cone with tip bent to right toward duodenum.

Only slight increase of internal pressure increases circumference of cone, which increases wall tension.

RELATION OF CONTRACTION TO DISTENTION   As stomach fills, pacemaker site does not change, but region of circumferential tension optimal for excitation-contraction coupling moves toward antrum; contractions begin at distal edge of food mass.

As stomach empties, contractions begin farther toward fundus.

RECEPTIVE RELAXATION   Intragastric pressure falls immediately after bolus is swallowed; abolished by cutting vagus nerves.

GASTRIC MIXING AND EMPTYING   Mixing and liquefying hasten availability of materials that are bound to food but absorbed best in duodenum.

Antrum acts as dynamic filter; only particles less than 1–2 mm in diameter pass into duodenum in quantity during digestive period.

Maximal volume of antrum is about 30 ml; antrum is able to contract virtually to zero; 3 ml or less enter duodenum, remainder is squirted vigorously back into the body of the stomach.

Vagal activity increases force of antral pump, augments emptying.

Limit on outflow is set mainly by duodenal resistance to filling.

EFFECT OF VAGOTOMY   Frequency and force of antral contraction are decreased, but gradually return to normal.

Emptying of liquids is more rapid—absence of receptive relaxation of body of stomach.

REGULATION OF GASTRIC EMPTYING

Stomach and duodenum form metering pump that usually is restrained to work at less than maximal capacity.

Digestion products of foods stimulate duodenal receptors; mainly increase duodenal resistance to filling; to lesser extent, reduce antral vigor.

Volume and consistency of gastric contents also affect gastric emptying.

RESPONSE OF DUODENAL RECEPTORS TO FOODSTUFFS

CARBOHYDRATE AND PROTEIN   Receptors respond to osmotic effects of digestion products; gastric emptying is slowed.

Equal weights of carbohydrate and protein yield equal amounts of energy; receptors respond to osmotic effects linked indirectly to calories.

TRIGLYCERIDES   Anions of fatty acids stimulate duodenal receptors by binding Ca^{++} from the epithelium; gastric emptying is slowed.

Nine grams of carbohydrate (36 kcal) slows gastric emptying to same extent as 4 g of triglycerides (36 kcal).

Stomach delivers about 200 kcal/hr to duodenum.

EFFECT OF ACID ON GASTRIC EMPTYING   Slows gastric emptying by stimulating duodenal receptors.

GASTRIC SECRETION   Basal secretion (unstimulated) is about 0.3–0.6 ml/min.

After eating, gastric secretion may be 10 ml/min.

Different people have different numbers of oxyntic cells and secrete different amounts of acid in response to standard stimulus.

STRUCTURE OF GASTRIC MUCOSA

SECRETORY CELLS   Surface of stomach is lined by cells that secrete mucus continuously.

Typically, surface cells of alimentary mucosa last 2–4 days; 500,000/min are shed and replaced.

Cells that secrete acid (oxyntic cells) and cells that secrete pepsinogen (chief cells) line tubules of gastric pits that drain into gastric lumen.

GASTRIN—THE GASTRIC SECRETORY HORMONE   Polypeptide; at least four forms: G_{14}, G_{17}, G_{34}, and $G_{(unknown)}$.

Stimulant (agonist) part of molecules is same four amino acids; large part of molecule determines potency and specificity.

Although last five amino acids are common to gastrin and cholecystokinin, cholecystokinin has little effect on gastric secretion.

Gastrin released during meal is half G_{17} and half G_{34}.

ANTRAL MUCOSA   Has mucus, gastrin, and pepsinogen-secreting cells; no oxyntic cells.

MUCUS   Serves as lubricant, forms "unstirred layer" 200–600 μm thick—anything that is absorbed must pass through it.

SECRETION OF HYDROCHLORIC ACID
(HCl) H^+ comes from water (H^+ OH^-); OH^- is neutralized by H^+ produced by hy-

dration of CO_2 to H_2CO_3 and dissociation to $H^+ HCO_3^-$.

Millionfold gradient for $[H^+]$ indicates active transport.

Inward transport of Cl^- makes gastric lumen electronegative to blood.

CHANGES IN OXYNTIC CELLS DURING SECRETION Area of secretory membrane in canaliculus of oxyntic cell is increased by microvilli as process of secretion begins.

After period of secretion, cell microvilli are reabsorbed.

Microvilli are believed to be the site of release of H^+.

EXCITATION OF OXYNTIC CELLS BY HISTAMINE Rate of secretion of oxyntic cells is not related to plasma concentration of histamine, yet histamine H_2 receptor antagonist decreases response to gastrin and acetylcholine.

May mean three receptors on oxyntic cells: one for acetylcholine, one for gastrin, and one for histamine; effect of all three is greater than sum of each alone.

PEPSINOGEN-SECRETING CELLS Gastric proteolytic enzymes with optimum pH range of 1.2–3.5.

Group I pepsinogens are formed by chief cells of body of stomach; associated with oxyntic cells.

High plasma concentration of Group I pepsinogens is an indicator of one form of duodenal ulcer.

Group II pepsinogens are formed by chief cells of antrum and body.

Ratio of secretion of pepsinogen to secretion of acid varies with stimulus but is constant among subjects for each kind of stimulus.

Vagal stimulation yields more pepsin than acid; gastrin yields more acid than pepsin.

HYPERPLASIA AND HYPOPLASIA OF GASTRIC MUCOSA Synthesis of oxyntic cells and chief cells is under hormonal control.

Chronic exposure to gastrin increases number of oxyntic cells and elongates gastric tubules—hyperplasia.

BACK-DIFFUSION OF ACID FROM GASTRIC LUMEN TO BLOOD Gradient for diffusion of acid from gastric lumen (pH 1.4) to blood (pH 7.4) is one millionfold.

In healthy persons, less than 10% of H^+ secreted diffuses back to blood.

Gastric mucosa damaged by aspirin or alcohol permits much greater back-diffusion.

EFFECTS OF GASTRIC ANACIDITY Caused by absence of oxyntic cells.

No acid or pepsin is secreted in response to food.

Stimulus to release of secretin (acid) is missing. Only ill effects are those related to the failure to absorb cobalamin.

Concentration of gastrin in plasma is high because of lack of acid to inhibit release of gastrin in antrum.

PHASES OF GASTRIC SECRETION Three phases, based on animal experiments.

CEPHALIC PHASE Acid is released in response to sensation of food; mediated through vagus nerves.

GASTRIC PHASE Distention of stomach and actions of amino acids; mediated neurally and hormonally.

Acid in antrum—negative-feedback control of release of gastrin.

INTESTINAL PHASE Digestion products of protein in duodenum increase gastric secretion.

Digestion products of carbohydrates in duodenum, fats in jejunum, and of all food in ileum inhibit gastric secretion.

VOMITING Reflex action involving both somatic and visceral muscles; coordinated centrally.

Shortening of thoracic esophagus opens intra-abdominal segment, allows increased abdominal pressure to force gastric contents into esophagus.

Central nervous system receptors are located in vestibular apparatus (activated in seasickness), and chemoreceptor zone of area postrema (stimulated by cardiac glycosides, apomorphine).

Alimentary receptors are in duodenum and stomach.

Pathological processes in abdominal cavity also evoke emesis.

BIBLIOGRAPHY

Burn-Murdoch, R.A.; Fisher, M.A.; and Hunt, J.N. 1978. The slowing of gastric emptying by proteins in test meals. *J. Physiol.* 274:477.

Card, W.I., and Marks, I.N. 1960. The relationship between the acid output of the stomach following "maximal" histamine stimulation and the parietal cell mass. *Clin. Sci.* 19:147.

Cheng, F.C.Y.; Lam, S.K.; and Ong, G.B. 1977. Maximum acid output to graded doses of pentagastrin and its relation to parietal cell mass in Chinese patients with duodenal ulcer. *Gut* 18:827.

Christensen, J. (ed.). 1980. *Gastrointestinal Motility.* New York: Raven Press.

Code, C.F., and Carlson, J.D. 1968. Motor activity of the stomach. In *Handbook of Physiology.* Section 6. Alimentary Canal. Chapter 93. Edited by C.F. Code. Washington, D.C.: The American Physiological Society.

Davenport, H.W. 1977. *Physiology of the Digestive Tract.* (4th ed.). Chicago: Year Book.

Duthie, H.L. (ed.). 1978. *Gastrointestinal Motility in Health and Disease.* Baltimore: University Park Press.

Edwards, D.A.W., and Rowlands, E.N. 1968. Physiology of the gastroduodenal junction. In *Handbook of Physiology.* Section 6. Alimentary Canal. Chapter 97. Edited by C.F. Code. Washington, D.C.: The American Physiological Society.

Elstein, M., and Parke, D.V. (eds.). 1977. *Mucus in Health and Disease.* New York: Plenum Press.

Forte, J.G.; Machen, T.E.; and Öbrink, K.J. 1980. Mechanisms of gastric H^+ and Cl^- transport. *Annu. Rev. Physiol.* 42:111.

Hunt, J.N. 1950. An interpretation of the histamine test of gastric secretion. *Gastroenterol.* 16:231.

Hunt, J.N. 1951. The secretory pattern of the stomach of man. *J. Physiol.* 113:169.

Hunt, J.N. 1959. Gastric emptying and secretion in man. *Physiol. Rev.* 39:491.

Hunt, J.N. 1983. Does calcium mediate slowing of gastric emptying by fat in humans? *Am. J. Physiol.* 244:689.

Hunt, J.N. 1983. Mechanisms and disorders of gastric emptying. *Ann. Rev. Med.* 34:219.

Hunt, J.N., and Wan, B. 1968. Electrolytes of mammalian gastric juice. In *Handbook of Physiology.* Section 6. Alimentary Canal. Chapter 44. Edited by C.F. Code. Washington, D.C.: American Physiological Society.

Hunt, J.N., and Knox, M.T. 1968. Regulation of gastric emptying. In *Handbook of Physiology.* Section 6. Alimentary Canal. Chapter 94. Edited by C.F. Code. Washington, D.C.: American Physiological Society.

Hunt, J.N., and Stubbs, D.F. 1975. The volume and energy content of meals as determinants of gastric emptying. *J. Physiol.* 245:209.

Johnson, L.R. (ed.). 1981. *Physiology of the Gastrointestinal Tract.* New York: Raven Press.

Kelly, K.E., and Code, C.F. 1977. Duodenal gastric reflux by electrical pacing of the canine duodenal pacesetter potential. *Gastroenterol.* 72:429.

Lagerlof, H.O.; Johansson, C.; and Ekelund, K. 1976. Human gastric and intestinal response to meals studied by a multiple indicator dilution method. *Mount Sinai J. Med.* 46:1.

Malagelada, J.R.; Longstreth, G.F.; Summerskill, W.H.J., et al. 1976. Measurement of gastric functions during digestion of ordinary solid meals in man. *Gastroenterol.* 76:71.

Moore, J.G., and Motoki, D. 1978. Gastric secretory and humoral responses to anticipated feeding in five men. *Gastroenterol.* 76:71.

Rotter, J.I.; Sones, J.Q.; Samloff, I., et al. 1979. Duodenal ulcer disease associated with elevated serum pepsinogen I: An inherited autosomal dominant disorder. *N. Engl. J. Med.* 300:63.

Samloff, I.M.; Secrist, D.M.; and Passaro, E. 1976. Serum group I pepsinogen levels and their relation to gastric acid secretion in patients with and without recurrent ulcer. *Gastroenterol.* 70:309.

Soll, A.H., and Walsh, J.H. 1979. Regulation of gastric acid secretion. *Annu. Rev. Physiol.* 41:35.

Walsh, J.H., and Grossman, M.I. 1975. Gastrin. *N. Engl. J. Med.* 292:1324 and 1377 (two parts).

Wormsley, K.G. 1974. The pathophysiology of duodenal ulceration. *Gut* 15:59.

50

The Exocrine Pancreas

CHAPTER CONTENTS

FUNCTIONS

The pancreas is the main source of the enzymes that act in the lumen of the duodenum, the jejunum, and, to a lesser extent, the ileum. These enzymes are amylases (which digest starches), trypsin, chymotrypsin, and carboxypeptidase (which digest proteins), and lipase (the only intestinal enzyme that hydrolyzes triglycerides). In humans, the synthesis of pancreatic enzymes amounts to about 10 g of protein per day. The pancreas of the rat, which contains only about 0.2 g of protein in its tissues, synthesizes about 0.4 g of enzymatic protein in 24 hours. This high rate of production of protein has made the pancreas one of the tissues of choice for studying the details of protein synthesis.

The pancreas also secretes HCO_3^-, which neutralizes the acidic gastric contents that pass into the duodenum. This secretion brings the pH of the duodenum to between 6 and 7, a level at which the digestive enzymes function most effectively. Besides tissues that perform purely digestive (exocrine) functions, the pancreas has islands (of Langerhans) that secrete the hormones insulin and glucagon, which decrease and increase the concentration of glucose in the plasma (endocrine functions), respectively (see Chapter 61).

EMBRYOLOGY

The pancreas is formed by the combination of groups of cells from the entoderm and cells that migrate from the neural crest. Cells from the entoderm secrete HCO_3^- and digestive enzymes, and cells that migrate from the neural crest secrete insulin and glucagon. Insulin and glucagon are polypeptides, as are all of the hormones of the digestive tract. The location of the cells that secrete insulin and glucagon, gathered together as islets deep inside the pancreas, differs from the location of the majority of the cells that release alimentary hormones, which is in epithelium that lines the gut. However, tumors that secrete alimentary hormones sometimes are found far from their usual site in the mucosa.

The concept of an *alimentary hormone* is less clear that it was once; for example, gastrin is secreted into the blood by the antral epithelium of the stomach and is carried in the general circulation. Because of its molecular size, gastrin cannot pass the blood-brain barrier (see Chapter 16). Nevertheless, gastrin is found in the brain; presumably, it is formed there and acts locally. Thus, a more appropriate general term for alimentary hormone might be *polypeptide transmitter*.

FUNCTIONAL ANATOMY

Blood Supply

The pancreas, its head embraced by the duodenum, is applied closely to the posterior wall of the abdominal cavity. The pancreatic body and tail extend away to the left, anterior to the left kidney, as far as the spleen. The blood supply comes from the superior mesenteric artery and the splenic arteries. The pancreatic veins enter the portal vein; thus, all pancreatic hormones inevitably pass through the sinuses of the liver. The concentrations of insulin and glucagon in the interstitial fluid of the liver must be several times higher than those in the extracellular fluid in general, because of degradation in the liver and the kidneys and dilution in the general circulation.

Nerve Supply

Some preganglionic fibers of the vagus nerves enter the pancreatic tissue. The postsynaptic vagal fibers reach the islets, the acinar cells, and the cells of the pancreatic ducts. Impulses that pass through these parasympathetic efferent nerves cause the secretion of enzymes and bicarbonate into the alimentary tract and the release of insulin and glucagon into the blood. The neural transmitter is acetylcholine, and the receptors are muscarinic. Stimulation of the sympathetic fibers to the pancreas causes vasoconstriction.

Secretory Elements

The acinar cells of the pancreas produce the enzymes that digest carbohydrate and fat and the precursors of the enzymes that digest protein. The cells can be stained to show the granules that occupy much of the cytoplasm. After stimulation of the pancreas through the fibers in the vagus trunk, or after hormonal stimulation by cholecystokinin, enzymes are secreted and the acinar cells are depleted of granules (Figure 50-1). The ions of the pancreatic secretion—HCO_3^-, Cl^-, Na^+, and K^+—are secreted by the centroacinar cells and the cells that line the ducts (Figure 50-2).

SYNTHESIS AND RELEASE OF ENZYMES

General Features

The characteristic features of cells that synthesize protein have been identified by studying pancreatic tissue in vitro. The sites at which amino acids are incorporated into enzymes after injection of tracer amounts of radioactive amino acids can be marked by painting the tissue with a radiosensitive emulsion of a silver salt. The grains of silver that form in the proximity of the radioactive amino acids are iden-

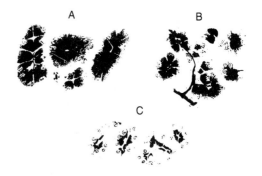

Figure 50-1. Depletion of the acinar cells of the pancreas by hormonal and neural stimulation. **A.** Control cells taken from a fasted, anesthetized dog. **B.** One hour after HCl was instilled into the duodenum. The concentration of granules is decreased somewhat, possibly by the action of cholecystokinin released by the acid. **C.** After stimulation of the vagus nerve. The concentration of granules is decreased markedly.

tified and compared with the structures in the pancreatic tissue that are seen by microscopy. The precursors of the enzymes are formed on the rough endoplasmic reticulum (Figure 50-3) (see Chapter 2). After being transported to the cisternae, these proteins move to the Golgi apparatus, where they are covered by a phospholipid membrane that is similar to the membrane at the surface of the cell. Under the stimulus of acetylcholine or the secretory hormone cholecystokinin, the surface of the package of enzymes fuses with the cell wall, and the enzymes are released into the acini. This process is known as *emiocytosis*. The fusion of the package and the cell wall is mediated by an increase in the concentration of Ca^{++} in the cytoplasm. A similar mechanism also mediates the release of neurotransmitters and many hormones.

Pancreatic Amylase

Pancreatic secretion contains an amylase that splits the 1–4 bonds of unbranched starch to maltose (two glucose molecules) or maltotriose (three glucose molecules) (see Figure 53-1). The sites of branching of the molecule of polysaccharides, the 1–6 bonds, are not affected by pancreatic amylase; hence, the end products of the digestion of branched starch, which are dextrins, are larger than the products of unbranched starch. Salivary amylase also acts in the stomach, but most digestion of starch depends on pancreatic amylase.

Amylase is found in low concentration in the plasma, but most of it is similar to the amylase found in the salivary glands. When the pancreatic tissue is damaged, its amylase is released into the plasma, and the total concentration of amylase in the plasma rises. Pancreatic amylase is filtered by the renal glomeruli, and part of the amylase that is filtered appears in the urine. Because the pancreas is placed deep within the abdomen and has a large reserve of function, mild pancreatic disease often is difficult to diagnose. Thus, an indirect clue to disease, such as a change in the concentration of amylase in the plasma or urine, sometimes is useful diagnostically.

Pancreatic Proteases

The secretion of the pancreas also contains the main intestinal proteolytic enzymes, trypsin, chymotrypsin, and carboxypeptidase. Trypsin and chymotrypsin split specific peptide bonds

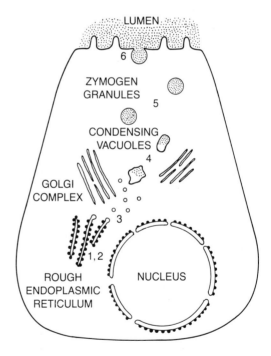

Figure 50-3. Six stages in the synthesis and secretion of pancreatic enzymes. **1.** Synthesized on rough endoplasmic reticulum. **2.** Transported to cisternal space. **3.** Transported to Golgi complex. **4.** Condensed into granules. **5.** Stored as zymogen granules. **6.** Discharged from apical region of cell (exocytosis). (Redrawn, with permission, from Scheele, G.A. 1980. Biosynthesis, segregation, and secretion of exportable proteins by the exocrine pancreas. *Am. J. Physiol.* 238:G470.)

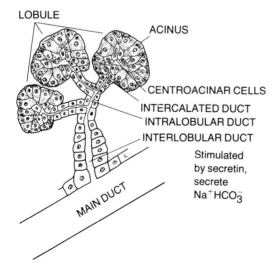

Figure 50-2. The pancreatic secretory elements.

in the middle regions of proteins or polypeptide molecules, and carboxypeptidase acts at the ends of the molecules. These enzymes are held in the granules of the acinar cells in the inactive forms of trypsinogen, chymotrypsinogen, and procarboxypeptidase, respectively. Trypsinogen is activated in the lumen of the duodenum by enterokinase, a proteolytic enzyme formed by the epithelial cells. After it is activated, trypsin activates trypsinogen, chymotrypsinogen, and procarboxypeptidase. Pancreatic cells contain a trypsin inhibitor that normally protects the pancreas from active trypsin. If this protection fails, a sterile pancreatitis (inflammation) ensues.

Pancreatic Lipase

The main pancreatic enzyme that acts on lipids is a triglyceride esterase, lipase, which splits off the long-chain fatty acids from the glycerol molecule at the 1 and 3 positions, leaving a monoglyceride with the fatty acid in the 2 position. This monoglyceride, which is soluble in water, is not split further before it is absorbed. Lipase acts at the oil-water interface in the presence of bile and a co-lipase. The accumulation of lipase at the oil-water interface overcomes the problem of making a water-soluble enzyme react with triglycerides, which virtually are insoluble in water. In patients who have acute pancreatitis, the lipase may react with the triglycerides of the pancreatic tissue to form anions of fatty acids. These anions form insoluble calcium salts. The deposits of calcium that form, which may be seen during radiographic examination, indicate previous inflammation of the pancreas. The pancreas also secretes phospholipases, which hydrolize esters such as cholesterol and lecithin.

FAILURE OF PANCREATIC FUNCTION

By the time pancreatic disease interferes with absorption by the intestine, pancreatic secretion probably is reduced to 10%–20% of its normal value. The sign detected most readily is inadequate absorption of fat, which is indicated by an increased amount of fat in the feces (steatorrhea—more than 6 g/day of fat in a patient who has been taking 100 g of fat per day). No doubt, protein and carbohydrate also are absorbed incompletely, but the bacteria of the colon destroy these molecules, and only the lipids can be detected in the feces. The most

common cause of the deficiency of pancreatic enzymes is fibrocystic disease in children, which is one of the most frequently occurring of the inherited diseases.

Oral Supplements of Pancreatic Enzymes

Pancreatic enzymes, obtained from swine, can be given by mouth, along with food, to counteract deficiencies of pancreatic secretion. Pancreatic enzymes, like all enzymes, are proteins; in the acidic environment of the gastric lumen they are digested by pepsin. However, this digestion can be prevented by using antacids to decrease the acidity of the gastric contents. The least expensive antacid used clinically is calcium carbonate, but it is not suitable for use with pancreatic enzymes. Ca^{++} forms insoluble salts with the fatty acids released by the lipolysis of the triglycerides; thus, fat still is not absorbed, and the effect of the treatment with enzymes is nullified. The antacid of choice is aluminum hydroxide; large amounts are necessary, however, and this antacid may have undesirable side-effects.

Life is possible after complete removal of the pancreas in humans, provided that insulin is given by injection, and pancreatic enzymes, protected as described above, are given by mouth.

SECRETION OF ELECTROLYTES AND WATER

The pancreas secretes HCO_3^-, which helps to neutralize the acidic material delivered to the duodenum from the stomach. The rate of secretion of HCO_3^- by the pancreas does not match the rate of secretion of H^+ by the stomach; however, HCO_3^- also is secreted by Brunner's glands, and H^+ is either exchanged for Na^+ or absorbed by the mucosa of the duodenum. H_2CO_3, formed by the reaction of H^+ with HCO_3^-, exists in equilibrium with CO_2, which accounts for the high partial pressure of CO_2 (P_{CO_2}) in the contents of the duodenal lumen (as much as 600 mm Hg, as compared to 40 mm Hg in venous blood).

Variation of Composition with Rate of Secretion

The way the composition of pancreatic juice changes with the rate of secretion is shown in Figure 50-4. The primary secretion of the cen-

CLINICAL CORRELATION
50.1 Malabsorption

CASE REPORT

The Patient: A 12-year-old boy.

Principal Complaint: Failure to grow.

History: The patient had an older brother, who had died at age 3 of "pneumonia," but 3 other siblings are alive and well. He had suffered from "asthma" since approximately 6 or 7 years of age, and had had two episodes of pneumonia over the past three years. Between these episodes, he had had an increase in cough and production of purulent sputum (which contains pus). He grew normally until the age of 7 or 8 years, but at the time of admission was in a lower percentile for height and weight. His parents had considered him a sickly child, and he had not been able to maintain a normal play schedule with his friends, particularly in the summer. He had a large appetite with no particular food intolerance. He described his bowel habits as normal; however, his feces were large in mass, light colored, poorly formed, somewhat foul smelling, and floated in water.

Clinical Examination: Laboratory examination of the feces revealed a content of fat that comprised about 30% of the amount ingested (normal, less than 6%). Examination of his serum revealed a lowered protein concentration and a prolonged prothrombin time. All of these findings are consistent with cystic fibrosis.

Comment: Cystic fibrosis is an inherited disease in which the central problem is the secretion of unduly viscous mucus. Infection of the air passages (pneumonia) occurs because the cilia do not adequately clear the mucus toward the trachea. Other obstructed or partly obstructed tubes (for example, ureter, eustachian tubes) usually grow excess bacteria. The sweat contains high concentrations of Na^+ and Cl^-; hence, in hot weather salt depletion is a problem. This patient had failed to grow normally because of the decreased absorption of food, although that problem was partly offset by his large appetite. The large amount of feces signifies malabsorption, and the foul smell is caused by bacterial degradation of unabsorbed carbohydrates. The fatty acids in the stool stimulate the colon to secrete, which makes the feces moist and poorly formed. The low concentration of serum protein is a sign of severe undernutrition, specifically of failure to absorb adequate protein. The prolonged prothrombin time is caused by deficient absorption of vitamin K; prothrombin is formed in the liver by a process for which vitamin K is essential. The inadequate absorption is related to blockage of the pancreatic ducts by the viscid mucus and replacement of the pancreatic acini by fibrous tissue. The digestive enzymes, amylase (which digests carbohydrate), lipase (which digests fat), and the proteinases, are not secreted. Thus, digestion of all three major classes of foodstuff is incomplete, and these nutritive materials are excreted in the feces.

Outcome: The patient was given pancreatic enzymes by mouth, protected by antacids, and he began to grow. However, because of the effect of the viscous mucus on pulmonary function, he is unlikely to survive beyond his midtwenties.

---

troacinar cells is believed to be a solution of Na^+, K^+, Cl^-, and HCO_3^- in the same concentrations found in the plasma. The cells of the intercalated, intralobular, and extralobular ducts, stimulated by secretin, increase the $[HCO_3^-]$ to the high levels seen in the pancreatic juice. Cl^- is returned to the plasma in exchange for the HCO_3^- secreted. By giving pure secretin (the hormone that stimulates the secretion of electrolytes by the pancreas), rates of up to 15 ml/min can be obtained. As the rate of secretion rises from 0.5 ml/min to 3 ml/min, the $[HCO_3^-]$ increases from about 10 mEq/liter to 120 mEq/liter. Although the rate of forma-

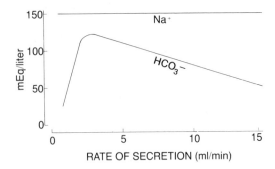

Figure 50-4. Concentration of Na^+ and HCO_3^- in pancreatic secretion formed at different rates. The concentration of HCO_3^- decreases at high rates because the volume of pancreatic juice continues to increase, but the rate of secretion of HCO_3^- reaches a maximum and remains constant (based on the data of Lagerlof, 1942; Wormsley, 1968; and Denyer and Cotton, 1979).

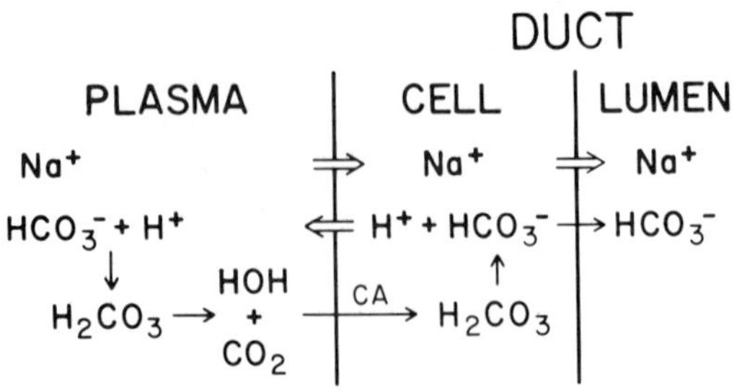

Figure 50-5. Mechanism of formation of HCO_3^- in cells of the pancreatic ducts. The double arrows indicate active transport; CA means carbonic anhydrase. The H^+ secreted actively into the plasma reacts with HCO_3^- to form H_2CO_3, which then breaks down to HOH and CO_2. Na^+ is transported actively into the duct, and HCO_3^- follows the electrical gradient.

tion of fluid continues to increase, the rate of secretion of HCO_3^- does not increase. The output of HCO_3^- reaches a maximum of about 0.7 mEq/min when the rate of flow is 6 ml/min, and remains more or less constant thereafter. Thus, at high levels of stimulation, the $[HCO_3^-]$ in the ducts is decreased by dilution in the primary secretion.

The mechanism of the formation of HCO_3^- in the ducts of the pancreatic cells is illustrated in Figure 50-5. Na^+ is transported from the plasma into the ductal cell in exchange for H^+. The H^+ that is entering the plasma reacts with HCO_3^- to form H_2CO_3, which is in equilibrium with CO_2. Thus, Pco_2 is high in the capillaries of the pancreas and $[HCO_3^-]$ is low. CO_2 diffuses rapidly into the ductal cell because of its high solubility in the lipid membrane. In the cell, under the influence of carbonic anhydrase, CO_2 is hydrated rapidly to H_2CO_3, which dissociates to H^+ and HCO_3^-. Completing the cycle, H^+ is transported back into the plasma, and HCO_3^- follows Na^+ into the lumen of the duct. When pancreatic tissue is bathed in vitro by solutions that contain anions other than HCO_3^- (e.g., acetate), the foreign anions are concentrated in the pancreatic secretion in the same way that HCO_3^- would be. This is taken to indicate that in physiological function, the cation Na^+ is transported actively into the duct and the anion HCO_3^- follows passively. Since water moves easily through all of the membranes that are involved, the secretion is isotonic with the plasma.

CONTROL OF PANCREATIC SECRETION

Discovery of Secretin

Until 1902, the secretion of the pancreas was thought to be controlled entirely through the autonomic nerves. It was determined experimentally that teasing a dog with food made the dog's stomach secrete H^+ and the pancreas secrete HCO_3^-. Both responses were abolished by cutting the vagus nerves. However, H^+ instilled into the duodenum caused the pancreas to secrete HCO_3^-, and the action was not abolished by cutting the vagus nerves. The results were attributed to a local neural reflex initiated at receptors in the duodenal mucosa.

In 1902, Bayliss and Starling infused H^+Cl^- into denervated loops of the jejunum in the dog and noted the output of an alkaline secretion from the pancreas within 2 minutes. These investigators concluded that if this response were not caused by nerves, it might be mediated by some substance that was released from jejunal mucosa and was circulating in the bloodstream. Bayliss and Starling found that the intravenous infusion of an acid extract of jejunal mucosa, but not of other tissues, produced an effect like that caused by acid in the duodenum or the jejunum. They named the class of substances that produce this type of response *hormones* (from the Greek *hormaein*—arouse to activity), and they called this first member of the class *secretin*.

```
His      Glu-Leu-Ser      Leu-Gln-Arg
 |         |    |           |    |
Ser      Ser  Arg         Arg  Leu
 |         |    |           |    |
Asp      Thr  Leu         Ala  Leu      Val
 |         |    |           |    |        |
Gly-Thr-Phe   Arg-Asp-Ser     Gln-Gly-Leu
```

Figure 50-6. Amino acid sequence of secretin.

Alimentary Hormones

Knowledge of alimentary hormones did not develop rapidly until methods of chemical purification by chromatography and methods of synthesizing polypeptides were developed. Chemically pure hormones made possible radioimmunoassay (see Chapter 58), which is more sensitive and convenient than bioassays on denervated organs or isolated tissues (the previous method of study).

Three main alimentary hormones are recognized, and about 15 other "candidate hormones" are known as chemical entities but have not been assigned definite places in the control of function. The hormones accepted currently are gastrin, secretin, and cholecystokinin (once known as pancreozymin for reasons that are given in the section on cholecystokinin later in this chapter).

PROPERTIES OF ALIMENTARY HORMONES

For a substance to be accepted as an alimentary hormone, the changes of concentration of the substance in the plasma after food has been eaten, for example, must be sufficient to cause the changes in activity of the target organ that occur. Because the responsiveness of an organ can be altered by nerves and other hormones, convincing evidence of true hormonal control is difficult to obtain. Alimentary hormones usually are estimated by radioimmunoassay; however, some polypeptide hormones are known to exist in several molecular forms, as gastrin does, for example (see the section on gastrin in Chapter 49). Until an assay that is specific for each form of hormone is available, uncertainty as to whether the hormones produce the effects that may be attributed to them will continue. In the normal control of alimentary function, nerves and hormones may act simultaneously; therefore, it may not be possible to identify completely the part that each plays.

At one time, physiologists thought that each alimentary hormone had a single action (e.g., that secretin stimulated the output of HCO_3^- by the pancreas and did nothing else). If a tissue extract had more than one action, it was supposed that it contained more than one hormone. However, it is clear now that a single polypeptide can act on several organs and probably does so under ordinary circumstances.

HORMONES AND CYCLIC NUCLEOTIDES

The secretion of electrolytes and protein in response to acetylcholine, secretin, and cholecystokinin, all acting at the cell surface, is mediated by the production of cyclic nucleotides from either adenosine triphosphate (ATP) or guanosine triphosphate. This step is common to the excitation of many secretory processes. Cyclic nucleotides stimulate the pancreas directly in vivo. The action of cyclic nucleotides is potentiated by caffeine or theophylline, which inhibit phosphodiesterase, an enzyme that normally destroys cyclic nucleotides.

Actions of Alimentary Hormones

SECRETIN

Secretin increases the output of HCO_3^- by the pancreas and the liver and potentiates the effect of cholecystokinin to increase the output of enzymes by the pancreas. Secretin increases the output of pepsin by the gastric epithelium and antagonizes the effect of gastrin to cause hyperplasia of the oxyntic cells of the gastric mucosa. About half of the 27 amino acids that make up secretin (Figure 50-6) are the same as the amino acids in the corresponding region of the structure of glucagon, a hormone that increases the output of glucose from the liver into the blood (see Figure 55-3). Acid in the lumen of the duodenum is the most effective stimulus to the release of secretin.

CHOLECYSTOKININ

Cholecystokinin has two main actions: it causes the gallbladder to empty and the pancreas to secrete digestive enzymes. The hormonal control of the contraction of the gallbladder was discovered first, and a hormone that controlled the secretion of pancreatic enzymes (pancreozymin) was found about 10 years later. The methods of preparation of the two hormones were similar, both hormones always were found together, and their activities increased in parallel during purification. Ultimately, it was demonstrated convincingly that both properties resided in one hormone, which now is called cholecystokinin (gallbladder mover), or CCK. However, stimulation of the efferent fibers of the vagus nerves also causes the gallbladder to empty. The gallbladder is innervated by the vagus nerves, and after these efferent fibers are cut, as they are in some operations for duodenal ulcer, the likelihood that stones will develop in the gallbladder increases. If the formation of these stones can be related to defective emptying of the gallbladder, it would seem that normal emptying is not achieved by the action of cholecystokinin alone.

Cholecystokinin and secretin acting synergistically are thought to account for most of the secretion of enzymes by the pancreas in response to food, but a neural mechanism also contributes to the secretion of pancreatic enzymes.

The five amino acids at the C (for carboxyl) end of cholecystokinin (Figure 50-7) are the same as the five amino acids at the C end of gastrin (see Figure 49-7); therefore, the specificity of the action of cholecystokinin on the gallbladder and the pancreas must depend on the remaining 28 amino acids in the molecule. The specificity is relative rather than absolute because gastrin injected into the circulation stimulates the pancreas to secrete enzymes; however, it is not known whether this effect occurs physiologically. Cholecystokinin is released by the digestion products of triglycerides (anions of long-chain fatty acids), proteins (peptides and amino acids), and acid in the lumen of the duodenum.

Control of Pancreatic Secretion

The factors that stimulate pancreatic secretion in humans in response to food are difficult to analyze; thus, to some extent, results obtained in the dog have been applied to humans.

CEPHALIC PHASE
When the stimulus to digestive secretion is received by the eyes, ears, or receptors in the tongue or buccal mucosa, the response of the end-organ is called the *cephalic phase*. To measure the cephalic response of the pancreas, the acid that is secreted by the stomach must be aspirated, so that it cannot pass into the duodenum and cause the release of secretin. After this is done, and appetizing food is chewed but not swallowed, the output of HCO_3^- and enzymes still increases fivefold after a latency of 2–4 minutes. This response is mediated through the vagus nerves.

GASTRIC PHASE
In the dog, distention of the gastric antrum causes the release of gastrin, which may be sufficient to increase the output of enzymes by the pancreas. In addition, some evidence indicates that gastric distention causes neural mediation of this phase of pancreatic secretion.

INTESTINAL PHASE
Secretin and cholecystokinin, which are released from the epithelium of the duodenum and the jejunum, act synergistically with impulses through the vagus nerves to mediate the intestinal phase of pancreatic secretion. Activity in a direct intestinal-pancreatic neural reflex arc increases the rate of secretion of enzymes by the pancreas in response to anions of long-chain fatty acids produced during the digestion of fats.

Acid in the duodenal contents causes the release of secretin, and the concentration of secretin in the plasma is related to the output of acid under resting conditions. Thus, preventing the entrance of acid into the duodenum pre-

Tyr	Pro-Ser-Gly	Leu-Gln-Ser	Ser-Asp-Arg	Phe-NH$_2$
Ile	Ala	Asn	Leu	Ile	Asp	Asp
Gln	Lys	Val	Lys	Asp	Arg	Tyr-SO$_4$	Met
Gln-Ala-Arg	Ser-Met-Ile	Pro-Ser-His	Met-Gly-Trp

Figure 50-7.   Amino acid sequence of cholecystokinin.

vents the release of secretin, which is a significant part of the stimulus to pancreatic secretion after food has been taken.

With improved methods, it is possible to measure the secretin in 1 ml of plasma. This led to the discovery that the release of secretin is pulsatile, as intermittent entry of gastric effluent acidifies the duodenum. A pulse of secretin that lasts 3 minutes, for example, appears to cause pancreatic secretion that lasts 10 minutes. Thus, estimating the mean concentration of secretin in plasma may not reveal an earlier peak of secretin concentration to which the pancreas still is responding. This concept of pulsatile release has yet to be explored for other alimentary polypeptide transmitters. Other hormones (e.g., growth hormone, ACTH, and testosterone) already are known to be released in pulses, but the implications of this are not known.

With the development of a highly sensitive method for estimating pancreatic amylase, it is possible now to measure the latency of the pancreatic response to the intraduodenal instillation of sodium oleate (Figure 50-8), which causes the release of cholecystokinin. Cholecystokinin is a mediator for the release of enzymes by the pancreas; however, it cannot be the mediator involved in the enzyme response to an intraduodenal injection of sodium oleate. The latency of secretion when CCK is injected into the portal vein is 37 seconds, whereas the latency when oleate is instilled into the lumen of the duodenum is only 25 seconds. Other evidence also indicates that oleate elicits a neural response: after vagotomy or the admin-

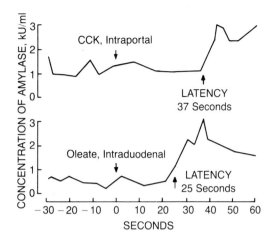

Figure 50-8. Latency of amylase response to intraduodenal instillation of 1 mM of sodium oleate or intraportal injection of 0.66 U/kg of cholecystokinin (CCK). The latency after infusion of oleate into the duodenum was 25 seconds; the latency after injection of CCK into the portal vein was 37 seconds. Physiologically, intraduodenal oleate releases CCK, which causes the pancreas to secrete amylase. However, because oleate acted sooner than CCK, CCK could not have mediated the secretion of amylase in response to oleate in this experiment. The effect was mediated through a neural reflex pathway. (Redrawn, with permission, from Singer, M.V., et al. 1980. *Am. J. Physiol.* 238:G-23.)

istration of atropine, the latency of the response to sodium oleate is increased, but the latency of the response to CCK is not increased.

STUDY OUTLINE

FUNCTIONS   Main source of digestive enzymes in humans.

Secretes HCO_3^-.

Secretes insulin and glucagon.

EMBRYOLOGY   Acinar cells and duct cells migrate from entoderm; secrete enzymes and HCO_3^-.

Cells that form insulin and glucagon migrate from neural crest as do all cells that secrete alimentary hormones.

Most alimentary hormones are secreted by specialized cells in intestinal mucosa; cells that secrete insulin and glucagon are grouped as islets (Langerhans') in the pancreas.

Some alimentary hormones are known to exist in the brain or peripheral nerves; the term *polypeptide transmitter* may be more appropriate than *hormone*.

FUNCTIONAL ANATOMY

BLOOD SUPPLY   Head embraced by duodenum, tail extends to left, reaches spleen.

Blood supply from superior mesenteric artery.

Venous outflow enters portal vein; insulin and glucagon pass through liver before entering general circulation.

NERVE SUPPLY Postganglionic fibers of vagus nerves (parasympathetic) release acetylcholine at acinar cells, duct cells, and islet cells, and cause secretion of HCO_3^-, enzymes, insulin, and glucagon.

Sympathetic nerves mediate vasoconstriction.

SECRETORY ELEMENTS Secretory granules in acinar cells contain amylolytic and lipolytic enzymes and precursors of proteolytic enzymes.

SYNTHESIS AND RELEASE OF ENZYMES

GENERAL FEATURES Precursors of enzymes on rough endoplasmic reticulum; each enzyme is a separate protein.

Enzymes are covered by a phospholipid membrane in the Golgi apparatus.

Stimulated by cholecystokinin or acetylcholine, phospholipid membrane fuses with cell wall; enzymes are extruded into acinus.

Final process is mediated by increased $[Ca^{++}]$ in cytoplasm.

PANCREATIC AMYLASE Splits 1-4 bonds of straight-chain polysaccharides but not 1-6 bonds of branched chains.

Amylase in plasma is mainly from salivary glands; damage to pancreas increases concentration of pancreatic enzyme in plasma and urine.

Increased concentrations of plasma amylase and urinary amylase provide index of pancreatic disease.

PANCREATIC PROTEASES Trypsin, chymotrypsin, and carboxypeptidase are main enzymes that digest protein.

Precursors are secreted (trypsinogen, chymotrypsinogen, procarboxypeptidase); trypsinogen is activated by enterokinase from duodenal epithelium; trypsin then activates precursors.

PANCREATIC LIPASE Main pancreatic enzyme that acts on lipids; acts at lipid-water interface of emulsified fat in presence of bile and co-lipase.

Removes two long-chain fatty acids from each molecule.

Remaining monoglyceride is water-soluble and can be absorbed.

Lipase may be activated in inflamed pancreatic tissue; anions formed from tissue triglycerides are precipitated as radiopaque calcium salts in pancreas.

Phospholipases also are secreted.

FAILURE OF PANCREATIC FUNCTION

Failure to digest and absorb triglycerides (e.g., steatorrhea) is most common sign (more than 6 g/day of fat in feces from 100 g/day of fat in diet).

Fibrocystic disease in children is most common cause.

ORAL SUPPLEMENTS OF PANCREATIC ENZYMES Porcine enzymes are given by mouth with food and antacids.

Patient can survive without pancreas if given insulin by injection and protected enzymes by mouth.

SECRETION OF ELECTROLYTES AND WATER HCO_3^- secreted by pancreas helps to neutralize acid secreted by stomach; HCO_3^- also is secreted by Brunner's glands.

Reaction of HCO_3^- in duodenum with H^+ from stomach causes high partial pressure of CO_2 (Pco_2) in duodenal lumen.

VARIATION OF COMPOSITION WITH RATE OF SECRETION $[Na^+]$, $[K^+]$, $[Cl^-]$, and $[HCO_3^-]$ of primary secretion, from centroacinar cells, are like those of plasma; extra HCO_3^- is added by cells of ducts.

As rate of secretion increases, stimulated by secretin, $[HCO_3^-]$ in pancreatic juice reaches maximum and then decreases as volume continues to increase but the rate of secretion of HCO_3^- does not increase; $[Cl^-]$ increases as $[HCO_3^-]$ decreases.

H^+ is transported from cell to plasma in exchange for Na^+; H^+ reacts with HCO_3^- to form H_2CO_3, which breaks down to HOH and CO_2; CO_2 diffuses into cell and is hydrated to H_2CO_3; H_2CO_3 dissociates to H^+ and HCO_3^-; H^+ is transported back to plasma; HCO_3^- follows Na^+ transported into lumen of duct.

CONTROL OF PANCREATIC SECRETION

DISCOVERY OF SECRETIN Before 1902, secretion of pancreas was thought to be controlled entirely by autonomic nerves.

Acid in jejunum caused pancreatic secretion even after vagus nerves were cut; assumed to involve local neural reflex arc.

Acid found to cause pancreatic secretion after denervation of jejunal loop.

Acid extract of jejunal mucosa injected intravenously caused secretion within 2 minutes; assumed existence of blood-borne factor (hormone) from the jejunum, which was named *secretin*.

ALIMENTARY HORMONES Knowledge depends on radioimmunoassay, purification by chromatography, and synthesis of polypeptides.

Gastrin, secretin, and cholecystokinin currently are accepted as hormones.

PROPERTIES OF ALIMENTARY HORMONES To be accepted as hormone, change of concentration must be enough to cause observed changes of organ function.

Nerves and other hormones may change responsiveness of organ; conclusive evidence that proposed hormone normally controls organ is hard to obtain.

Single polypeptide hormone can act on several organs.

HORMONES AND CYCLIC NUCLEOTIDES Effects of acetylcholine, secretin, and cholecystokinin on secretion of HCO_3^- and protein are mediated by production of guanosine or adenosine cyclic nucleotides.

Effects of cyclic nucleotides are potentiated by caffeine—inhibits phosphodiesterases that break down cyclic nucleotides.

ACTIONS OF ALIMENTARY HORMONES

SECRETIN Increases output of HCO_3^- by pancreas and liver.

Potentiates effect of cholecystokinin to increase output of enzymes from pancreas.

Acid in duodenum is most effective stimulus for release.

CHOLECYSTOKININ Causes pancreas to secrete digestive enzymes—potentiated by secretin.

With parasympathetic nerve activity, causes gallbladder to empty.

Released by H^+ and digestion products of triglycerides and proteins in duodenum.

Related structurally to gastrin, but has considerable specificity of action.

CONTROL OF PANCREATIC SECRETION Studied mostly in dogs, and results are applied to humans.

CEPHALIC PHASE Sensory stimuli cause large increase of pancreatic secretion; mediated through vagus nerves.

GASTRIC PHASE In dogs, distention of antrum releases *gastrin,* which may be sufficient to stimulate enzyme output by pancreas.

Some evidence of neural mediation of pancreatic response to distention of stomach.

INTESTINAL PHASE Mediated by secretin, cholecystokinin, and parasympathetic nerves.

Receptors in small intestine are stimulated by anions of long-chain fatty acids, also cause pancreatic secretion via neural pathways.

Radioimmunoassay studies show that acidification of duodenum causes pulsatile release of secretin; each pulse causes prolonged secretion by pancreas.

BIBLIOGRAPHY

Bloom, S.R., and Polak, J.M. (eds.). 1981. *Gut Hormones.* Edinburgh: Churchill Livingstone.

Denyer, M.E., and Cotton, P.B. 1979. Pure pancreatic juice: Studies in normal subjects and patients with pancreatitis. *Gut* 20:89.

Glass, G.B.J. 1980. *Gastrointestinal Hormones.* New York: Raven Press.

Howat, H.T., and Sarles, H. 1979. *The Exocrine Pancreas.* Philadelphia: Saunders.

Johnson, L.R. (ed.). 1981. *Physiology of the Gastrointes-* functions. *Annu. Rev. Physiol.* 39:135.

Johnson, L.R. (ed.). 1981. *Physiology of the Gastrointestinal Tract.* New York: Raven Press.

Lagerlof, H.O. 1942. Pancreatic function studied by means of secretin. *Acta Med. Skand.* (Suppl. CXXVIII).

Palade, G.E. 1975. Intracellular aspects of the process of protein synthesis. *Science* 189:347.

Schaffalitzky de Muckadell, O.B., and Fahrenkrug, J. 1978. Secretion pattern of secretin in man: Regulation by gastric acid. *Gut* 19:812.

Scheele, G.A. 1980. Biosynthesis, segregation, and secretion of exportable proteins by the exocrine pancreas. *Am. J. Physiol.* 238:467.

Schulz, I., and Stolze, H.H. 1980. The exocrine pancreas: The role of secretagogues, cyclic nulceotides, and calcium in enzyme secretion. *Annu. Rev. Physiol.* 42:127.

Solomon, T.E., and Grossman, M.I. 1979. Effect of atropine and vagotomy on response of transplanted pancreas. *Am. J. Physiol.* 236:E186.

Swanson, H.C., and Solomon, A.K. 1975. Micropuncture analysis of the cellular mechanism of electrolyte secretion by the in vitro rabbit pancreas. *J. Gen. Physiol.* 65:22.

Wormsley, K.G. 1968. Response to secretin in man. *Gastroenterol.* 54:197.

Wormsley, K.G., and Goldbert, D.M. 1972. The interrelationships of the pancreatic enzymes. *Gut* 13:398.

51

The Liver and
the Gallbladder

CHAPTER CONTENTS

STRUCTURAL FEATURES

The liver can be regarded as a three-dimensional, slowly moving lake of blood in which sheets of liver cells, or hepatocytes, float (Figure 51-1). The hepatocytes are the secretory and metabolic cells of the liver. The venous outflow from the abdominal organs, with the exception of the gonads, the kidneys, the adrenal glands, and the rectum, enters the hepatic lake through the portal vein. Thus, all food and drugs that are absorbed from the alimentary tract pass through the liver before they are distributed in the systemic circulation, and all of the alimentary hormones pass through the liver before they reach their target organs. Drugs absorbed from rectal suppositories enter the general circulation without passing through the liver. This route of entry is important when the liver inactivates the drug.

Between the contiguous surfaces of the hepatocytes lie the canaliculi, which carry the bile, secreted continuously by the liver, toward the hepatic bile ducts. Small bile ducts, branches of the portal vein, and branches of the hepatic artery are distributed through the liver lobules, forming the *portal triads*. On the surfaces of the sheets of hepatocytes are many Kupffer cells, which are part of the reticuloendothelial system. These cells project into the hepatic sinusoids and function as phagocytes.

Blood Supply

The blood that flows from the abdominal organs in the portal vein is partly deoxygenated; in the liver capillaries, this blood mixes with the fully oxygenated blood of the hepatic artery. Blood drains from the liver into the inferior vena cava through the hepatic veins.

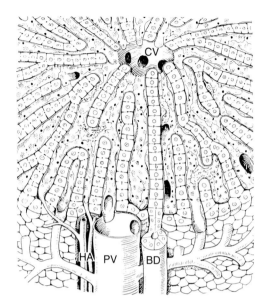

Figure 51-1. The three-dimensional structure of the hepatic lobule. This sketch was taken from a scanning-electron micrograph. CV is the central vein; HA is the branch of the hepatic artery; PV is the branch of the portal vein; and BD is the bile duct. (Modified, with permission, from Muto, M. 1975. A scanning electron microscopic study on endothelial cells and Kupffer cells in rat liver sinusoids. *Arch. Histol. Jap.* 37:369.)

The total flow of blood through the liver is about one-fourth of the cardiac output at rest, and the oxygen consumption of the liver is about one-fifth of the oxygen consumption of the whole body at rest. The uptake of this relatively large amount of oxygen by an organ that weighs only about 1.5 kg indicates a high rate of metabolism. The pressure in the portal vein is about 12 mm Hg, and the pressure in the hepatic vein is about 6 mm Hg. This small gradient of pressure, 6 mm Hg, provides a blood flow of about 1.5 liter/min; thus, the hepatic sinusoids offer very little resistance to flow (see Chapter 12). However, the velocity of flow is low; an average red blood cell takes at least 10 seconds to pass through the liver.

Lymph Flow

The hepatic lymph, which flows at a rate of about 1 liter/day, contains about 50 g of protein. The plasma proteins, which are produced in the liver (5–10 g/day), enter the bloodstream in the hepatic lymph. Consistent with the formation and extrusion of plasma proteins, the

walls of the sinusoids of the liver are relatively permeable. Thus, when the pressure in the hepatic vein is high, as it is in patients who have right-ventricular cardiac failure, for example (see Chapter 22), the rate of filtration increases, fluid collects in the interstitial space, and the liver becomes enlarged and tender. If fluid exudes from the liver and collects in the peritoneal cavity, the condition is called *ascites*.

FUNCTIONS OF THE LIVER

Breakdown and Synthesis

When protein in excess of the needs of the body is consumed, the liver catabolizes the excess amino acids. Some of these amino acids are used for energy, some are used in the production of other amino acids (transamination), and some provide carbon skeletons for the synthesis of glucose, hormones, and other special compounds. The liver stores amino acids and synthesizes a variety of proteins that serve physiological functions, including transport proteins, albumin, and globulins (except γ-globulin). The protein components of the coagulation system are produced mainly in the liver. These elements include fibrinogen (the principal structural element of the blood clot), the enzymes that participate in the clotting process, and fibrinolysin (the enzyme system that removes blood clots). The synthesis of these coagulation factors, in particular that of prothrombin, depends on the absorption of the fat-soluble material phylloquinone, or vitamin K, in the intestine. Absorption of fat-soluble materials involves the action of the bile salts, which also are synthesized in the liver. Cholesterol, the precursor of the bile salts and steroid hormones, is made in the liver and, to a lesser extent, in the intestinal mucosa.

Detoxification

The liver excretes many drugs and other chemicals that are not filtered by the kidneys, predominantly because they are not soluble in water and are carried in the plasma bound to protein. These compounds are made water-soluble in the liver by the microsomal P 450 system. For example, bilirubin is conjugated with glucuronate, and benzoate derivatives are conjugated with glycine. Liver enzymes oxidize, reduce, hydrolyze, or demethylate many drugs and chemicals before conjugating them with the polar (water-soluble) groups.

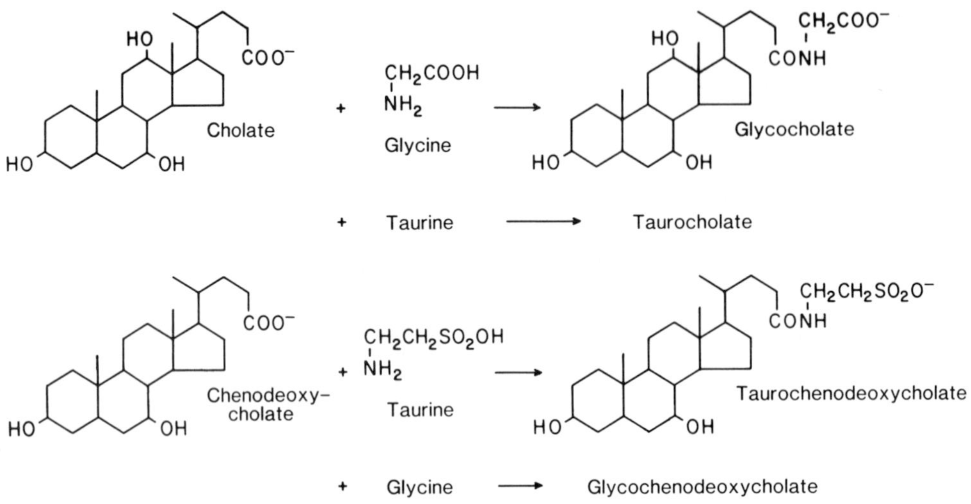

Figure 51-2. The conjugation of the primary bile salts with glycine and taurine.

Storage

Since everything that is absorbed from the alimentary tract must pass through the hepatic portal system, the liver is in a position to act as a storage organ. The most labile material stored in the liver is glycogen. The maximum quantity of glycogen stored is about 100 g, which enables the liver to provide enough glucose to last a person for approximately 8 hours. By contrast, the stores of the fat-soluble vitamins A, D, and E, and the metals iron and copper, would last for months, and the store of cobalamin (vitamin B_{12}) would last for about 3 years. The hepatic store of vitamin K in adults, however, is sufficient for only about 1 month. This is a matter of concern for patients who require surgery but who also have liver disease that interferes with the absorption of fat and, therefore, fat-soluble vitamins. Newborn infants routinely are given supplements of vitamin K because they are born with low stores of that material, and human milk contains amounts of vitamin K that barely are adequate.

Formation of Bile

BILE SALTS

There are two classes of bile salts: the primary salts, which are synthesized in the liver from cholesterol, and the secondary salts, which have been transformed from primary salts by anaerobic bacteria in the colon and, to a much smaller extent, in the jejunum and the ileum. All bile salts contain a sterol nucleus. In humans, the two primary bile salts are cholate, which has three OH (hydroxyl) groups, and chenodeoxycholate, which has two OH groups (Figure 51-2). The OH groups increase the solubility of the hydrophilic portion of the molecule in water. Anaerobic microorganisms in the colon dehydroxylate cholate to form deoxycholate, and dehydroxylate chenodeoxycholate to form lithocholate. Both of these secondary salts are less soluble in water than their corresponding primary forms.

All of the bile salts are detergents; hence, they lower the surface tension of water. This is essential to the formation of *micelles*, particles that consist of bile salts and lipids, which greatly facilitate the digestion and absorption of fat (see the section entitled "Micellar Phase" in Chapter 53).

Besides synthesizing primary bile salts, the liver also conjugates these primary salts with either glycine or taurine. About twice as much glycine conjugate as taurine conjugate is formed because more glycine is available. Conjugation of the bile salts causes them to ionize more completely. As a consequence, the conjugated salts form micelles more readily. In addition, the conjugated salts are absorbed less rapidly from the intestine by nonionic diffusion; this helps to maintain their concentration in the jejunum and ileum until almost all of the dietary lipids have been absorbed.

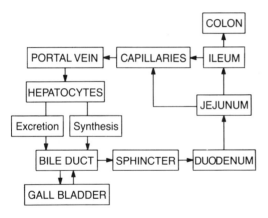

Figure 51-3. The enterohepatic circulation.

BILE-SALT–DEPENDENT SECRETION

One component of bile consists of the bile salts, most of which have been recirculated, although some are newly synthesized. The bile salts are secreted into the bile canaliculi between the hepatocytes. The rate at which bile salts are secreted depends largely on the rate at which they are absorbed in the ileum and returned to the liver in the portal venous blood as part of the enterohepatic circulation (Figure 51-3). The hepatocytes take up the bile salts as the portal blood passes through the liver and secrete them actively into the canaliculi.

The bile salts form micelles in the canaliculi with cholesterol and phosphatidyl choline (lecithin), which also are secreted. The lipid-soluble (steroid) portion of the bile salt associates with the lipid materials, and the polar portion (OH groups and amino acid moiety) associates with the water of the bile. In addition, the greater the ratio of lecithin to cholesterol, the greater the solubility of cholesterol in the bile. This has important consequences because gallstones may begin with the precipitation of cholesterol in the gallbladder, where bile is concentrated ten- to twentyfold between meals.

The bile-salt–dependent flow of bile can be assessed by measuring the concentration of a water-soluble marker such as mannitol, which enters bile only through the canaliculi. The concentration of mannitol in the bile-salt–dependent bile is the same as the concentration of mannitol in the plasma. The bile ducts are impermeable to mannitol; thus, the amount of mannitol that enters the bile from canaliculi during a given time divided by the concentration of mannitol in the plasma during the same time gives the volume of the bile-salt–dependent flow, just as inulin indicates the rate of glomerular filtration (see Chapter 37).

This fraction of the bile also contains bilirubin, the green pigment that is formed from the breakdown products of hemoglobin. As it is secreted, bilirubin is orange-red, which accounts for its name; however, it is oxidized in the intestine, becomes green, and later turns brown. The brown hue gives feces its color. In a patient who has liver disease or in whom the bile duct is obstructed, bilirubin accumulates in the serum. The yellowish hue given to the skin and conjunctiva by excess amounts of this compound is called *jaundice*.

BILE-SALT–INDEPENDENT SECRETION

The other component of bile flow depends on the secretion of Na^+, Cl^-, HCO_3^-, and K^+ by the bile ducts and is controlled partly by the hormones cholecystokinin and secretin. During fasting, after the bile salts have been reabsorbed from the ileum, resecreted, and collected in the gallbladder, only the bile-salt–independent secretion continues.

WATER

The secretion of water in the bile depends on the osmotic effects of the solutes that are secreted; thus, the bile always is isosmotic with plasma. The osmotically active particles are provided by both sources of bile: the bile salts and the Na^+ that are secreted in the canaliculi and the Na^+, HCO_3^-, K^+, and Cl^- that are secreted in the bile ducts. The water that is entrained varies with the amount of bile salts secreted and accounts for about one-half of the total daily output (about 1 liter) of bile.

GALLBLADDER

When food enters the duodenum from the stomach, bile flows directly from the liver through the common hepatic duct, past the entrance of the cystic duct, and through the sphincter of Oddi into the duodenum. During the transition between digestion and fasting, the sphincter of Oddi contracts, less bile enters the duodenum, and more bile passes through the cystic duct into the gallbladder. Water is absorbed in the gallbladder, and the bile is concentrated as much as twentyfold.

Concentration of Bile

The gallbladder has been studied extensively in attempts to understand how water is absorbed, with the expectation that the same principles, appropriately qualified, will apply in other tissues. Briefly, Na^+, Cl^-, and water enter the mucosal cell passively from the lumen, and Na^+ is transported actively into the annular space that surrounds the lateral surfaces of each cell. Water follows the osmotic gradient produced by the movement of Na^+, and Cl^- follows the electrical gradient. The lateral intercellular spaces enlarge while water is being absorbed, which would be expected from the mechanism that has been proposed. The basement membrane is highly permeable, and a slight hydrostatic pressure gradient causes the water, Na^+, and Cl^- to enter the interstitial space, where they are absorbed by the bloodstream. The water is transported passively, and, indeed, *no system that transports water by acting directly on the water molecule is known.*

In spite of the high concentration of bile salts in the gallbladder, the osmotic pressure of the bile in the gallbladder remains the same as the osmotic pressure of the liver bile and the plasma. As water is absorbed, the micelles in the bile aggregate until each one consists of 10–30 anions of bile salt; electrical neutrality is maintained by the positive charges on the predominant cation, Na^+. Each micelle is equivalent to only one osmotically active particle; yet each micelle neutralizes electrically about 20 Na^+. Thus, the total osmotic activity is equivalent to only 21 particles instead of the 40 particles that existed initially. In addition, some Na^+ are sequestered inside the micelles, in association with the anionic bile acids, and have no osmotic effect. This arrangement explains how the concentration of Na^+ in the bile can be much higher than the concentration of Na^+ in the plasma without increasing the osmolarity of the bile above the osmolarity of the plasma.

Reservoir Function

The gallbladder is a component of the system that allows humans to digest and absorb fats by the use of a bile-salt pool of only 3–4 g that is secreted and reabsorbed 4–10 times in 24 hours. The gallbladder will hold about 50 ml of bile, which may have been concentrated from 500 ml of bile as it issued from the liver. Since the gallbladder can concentrate bile salts to 120 mM/liter and the amount of the bile-salt pool is 6 mM/liter, the entire pool *could* be accommodated in the 50 ml-content of the gallbladder between meals. This does not seem to occur, however, because the intestine contains some bile salts even during fasting.

Emptying

When food is taken, the gallbladder begins to discharge its contents slowly into the duodenum. This early contraction of the gallbladder is controlled neurally through efferent cholinergic fibers of the vagus trunk. Cholecystokinin (CCK) also causes the gallbladder to contract. CCK is released from the mucosa of the duodenum and the jejunum mainly in response to the digestion products of fat. The gallbladder delivers its content of bile slowly, mixing it with the bile that flows from the liver. The stomach begins to empty even while the meal is being taken, and the bile salts that enter the duodenum can travel down the lumen of the intestine, be reabsorbed, and be secreted by the liver again within 1 hour.

ENTEROHEPATIC CIRCULATION OF BILE SALTS

The bile salts are a major component of the digestion and absorption of lipids. Bile salts are secreted into the duodenum, where they form micelles that disperse the lipids of the meal in the contents of the duodenum. At the brush-border surface of the small intestine, the fats are absorbed (see the section entitled "Absorption of Fat by Enterocytes" in Chapter 53) and the micelles disintegrate. The bile salts remain in the lumen, are absorbed separately, and are used again (Figure 51-3).

The liver removes most (95%) of the bile salts from the plasma that is presented to it in portal blood. Thus, bile salts are found mostly either in the lumen of the intestine during digestion (Figure 51-4A) or in the gallbladder during the nighttime fast (Figure 51-4B).

Reabsorption

Bile salts are absorbed to some extent by diffusion in the jejunum and the ileum but are absorbed mostly by active transport in the area of ileum near the ileocecal valve. During each circulation of the pool of bile salts, about

CLINICAL CORRELATION

51.1   Gallstones

CASE REPORT

The Patient: A 53-year-old woman.

Chief Complaints: Abdominal pain, nausea, and vomiting.

History: The patient was admitted to the emergency room complaining of recurring severe pain in the right upper quadrant of the abdomen, associated with nausea and vomiting. She had experienced three previous episodes of similar discomfort, but had not sought medical attention. Her history provided no medically significant information except that she was of Southwestern American Indian ancestry, and her mother and three of her sisters had undergone cholecystectomy for symptomatic biliary colic.

Clinical Examination: Further examination revealed a slightly obese woman in moderate distress. Her oral temperature was 37.8 C, her arterial pulse rate was 90/min (normal, 60–100/min), and her respiration rate was 16/min (normal, 13–17/min). Pertinent physical findings were limited to the abdomen, which was tender in the right upper quadrant. The bowel sounds were normal, and neither the liver nor the spleen was palpable (felt by pressing with the fingertips). Laboratory studies revealed a hematocrit of 41% (normal, 37%–48%), white blood-cell count of 11,300 cells/mm^3 (normal, 4,300–10,800 cells/mm^3),

with high concentrations of newly formed polymorphonuclear cells. The results of the urinalysis and the levels of serum electrolytes were normal. The serum bilirubin was 1.8 mg/dl (normal, 0.3–1.0 mg/dl), and the alkaline phosphatase was 127 U/liter (normal, 13–39 U/liter). X-ray films of the abdomen revealed multiple, small calcified densities in the area of the right upper quadrant, which suggests calcified gallstones.

Comment: The location of the pain focuses attention on the gallbladder. The abnormally high serum bilirubin and alkaline phosphatase are consistent with obstruction of the outflow of bile from the liver, and the appearance of small stones in the x-ray film makes it likely that a stone is obstructing the main duct. The increased temperature, high white cell count, and high concentration of newly formed white cells indicate infection proximal to the obstruction. The occurrence of gallstones is endemic among American Indians; thus, her condition is consistent with her ancestry. In the United States and other Western countries, the formation of gallstones in the gallbladder is related to the production of bile supersaturated with cholesterol but deficient in bile acids.

Outcome: The patient was treated by cholecystectomy (surgical removal of the gallbladder) and had no further episodes of gallstones.

98% of the amount that enters the intestine is reabsorbed. Nevertheless, because the entire pool circulates twice during each meal, even this effective rate of reabsorption allows an average loss in the feces of about 0.5 g of bile salts per day. The amount that is lost is matched by synthesis of new bile salts in the liver. The concentration of bile salts in the systemic plasma, which reflects incomplete clearance of portal-venous blood by the liver, is highest about 2 hours after a meal and reaches a peak that is about 10 times the level in a fasting subject. Under these conditions, the rate

of secretion is maximal, and the concentration in the duodenal lumen remains above the minimal level of 1 or 2 mmol/liter that is needed for effective formation of micelles. If the rate of loss in the feces is increased to 0.7 g/day, the pool of bile salts decreases to less than the usual 4 g, but fat still is absorbed adequately because the critical concentration for the formation of micelles is reached through an increased rate of turnover of the bile-salt pool. When the rate of loss exceeds about 0.7 g/day, because of failure of active reabsorption in the terminal ileum or because some drug that binds the bile salts is

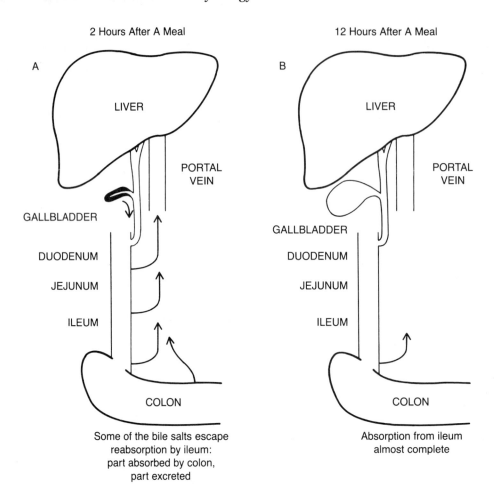

Figure 51-4. The enterohepatic circulation of bile salts after a meal (**A**), and during the nighttime fast (**B**). **A.** Two hours after a meal, the gallbladder is practically empty, so that the entire pool of bile salts is in the intestine and the blood circulation. The liver is secreting rapidly because the rate of return of bile salts from the intestine is high. During each circulation, about 2% of the bile-salt pool escapes reabsorption in the ileum and enters the colon; about half (1% of the total pool) is absorbed and returned to the liver, and about half is lost by excretion. Since the entire pool is secreted and reabsorbed several times a day, about 10% of it is lost and must be replaced by synthesis each day. **B.** Twelve hours after the last meal, at least half of the bile salts are stored in the gallbladder. The rate of secretion by the liver is low because the concentration of bile salts in the portal vein is low. Under these conditions, the mechanism of synthesis of bile salts is released from inhibition by negative feedback, and the rate of synthesis is high.

taken (e.g., cholestyramine), the decrease in the size of the bile-salt pool is not offset adequately by the increased rate of turnover. If the pool of bile salts decreases to about 2 g, the intraluminal concentration is inadequate to form micelles, and steatorrhea (or fat in the feces) is apparent. When an excessive amount of fat (> 6 g/day) that is not absorbed in the small intestine enters the colon as fatty acids (steatorrhea), it may cause diarrhea. The fatty acids are hydroxylated by bacteria, forming compounds similar to the active constituent of castor oil. In addition, the fatty acids form insoluble salts of calcium and magnesium, which may cause a long-term negative balance of Ca^{++} and Mg^{++}.

CLINICAL TEST OF ABSORPTION

One cause of steatorrhea is the deconjugation of bile salts in the small intestine by anaerobic bacteria from the colon. Normally, these microorganisms are found in the small intestine only in low numbers. When this cause of steatorrhea is suspected, the patient can be given a dose of glycocholate that has ^{14}C in the glycine moiety. If the small intestine contains deconjugating bacteria, the glycine is split from the conjugated bile salt, absorbed, and metabolized quickly to CO_2, which comes out in the breath in less than 4 hours. In a healthy individual, such deconjugation occurs only in the colon, so that radioactivity does not appear in the breath until after more than 4 hours.

STUDY OUTLINE

STRUCTURAL FEATURES The liver consists of sheets of hepatocytes bathed on both sides by slowly moving blood.

All materials absorbed by the alimentary tract pass through the liver.

Canaliculi carry bile toward hepatic bile ducts.

Reticuloendothelial cells form part of the body defense system.

BLOOD SUPPLY Liver receives oxygenated blood from hepatic artery and partly deoxygenated blood from portal vein.

About one-fourth of the cardiac output and about one-fifth of the total oxygen consumed in body.

Small gradient of pressure, low vascular resistance.

LYMPH FLOW About 1 liter/day, contains about 50 g of protein, of which about 10 g are plasma proteins synthesized in liver.

Liver sinusoids are relatively permeable, permit passage of plasma proteins; increased venous pressure increases filtration, causes tender liver and collection of fluid in abdominal cavity (ascites).

FUNCTIONS OF THE LIVER

BREAKDOWN AND SYNTHESIS Catabolizes excess amino acids—used for energy and synthesis.

Stores amino acids and synthesizes enzymes, transport proteins, albumin, globulin, and components of the blood coagulation system.

Synthesizes bile salts and cholesterol.

DETOXIFICATION Lipid-soluble materials made soluble by conjugation with polar groups and excreted in bile.

STORAGE Glycogen, vitamins, iron, and copper.

FORMATION OF BILE

BILE SALTS Primary bile salts—synthesized in liver from cholesterol: cholate and chenodeoxycholate.

Secondary bile salts—transformed from primary bile salts by anaerobic bacteria in colon: deoxycholate and lithocholate.

Conjugated in liver with glycine or taurine—increases degree of ionization; form micelles more readily.

Act as detergents to aid absorption of lipids.

BILE-SALT–DEPENDENT SECRETION Consists of newly synthesized salts and salts absorbed and recirculated (mainly the latter).

Cholesterol and lecithin also are secreted; made soluble by forming micelles with bile salts.

Gallstones form when cholesterol precipitates from solution.

Volume is measured by dilution of mannitol, excreted through same pathway.

Route of excretion of bilirubin, breakdown product of hemoglobin.

BILE-SALT–INDEPENDENT SECRETION Depends on secretion of Na^+ by bile ducts; partly controlled by cholecystokinin and secretin.

WATER Secreted down osmotic gradient caused by bile salts, Na^+, HCO_3^-, and Cl^-.

GALLBLADDER Bile secreted continuously, about 1 liter/day, stored in gallbladder between meals; volume is decreased by absorption of water.

CONCENTRATION OF BILE Na^+ is absorbed actively, water and Cl^- follow passively.

Concentrated ten- to twentyfold by reabsorption of water; remains isotonic with plasma—number of particles is decreased by formation of micelles.

RESERVOIR FUNCTION Most of bile-salt pool (3–4 g) could be stored in concentrated bile of gallbladder; turns over 4–10 times in 24 hours.

EMPTYING Occurs in response to food; controlled neurally through vagus nerves and hormonally by cholecystokinin.

ENTEROHEPATIC CIRCULATION OF BILE SALTS Bile salts are sequestered from portal venous blood by liver, are secreted into duodenum in bile, promote the absorption of lipids, are released and absorbed separately, and are returned to portal venous blood.

REABSORPTION   Mostly active transport in ileum near ileocecal junction; some reabsorption by diffusion in jejunum and ileum.

Rapid rate of turnover; some bile salts are lost, replaced by synthesis in liver.

If bile-salt pool is too small, some fat is not absorbed, appears in feces—steatorrhea.

Fatty acids in colon are hydroxylated to compounds that cause diarrhea; also combine with and deplete Ca^{++} and Mg^{++}.

CLINICAL TEST OF ABSORPTION   Deconjugation of glycocholate by bacteria in small intestine is abnormal—revealed by use of ^{14}C glycocholate; $^{14}CO_2$ appears in breath prematurely.

BIBLIOGRAPHY

Brunner, H.; Northfield, T.C.; Hofmann, A.F., et al. 1974. Gastric emptying and secretion of bile acids, cholesterol, and pancreatic enzymes during digestion: Duodenal perfusion studies in healthy subjects. *Mayo Clin. Proc.* 49:851.

Forker, E.L. 1977. Mechanisms of hepatic bile formation. *Annu. Rev. Physiol.* 39:323.

Johnson, L.R. (ed.). 1981. *Physiology of the Gastrointestinal Tract.* New York: Raven Press.

Lautt, W.W. (ed.). 1981. *Hepatic Circulation in Health and Disease.* New York: Raven Press.

Malagelada, J.-R.; Di Magno, E.P.; Summerskill, W.H.K., et al. 1976. Regulation of pancreatic and gallbladder functions by intraluminal fatty acids and bile acids in man. *J. Clin. Invest.* 58:493.

Motta, P.; Muto, M.; and Tryita, T. 1978. *The Liver. An atlas of Scanning Microscopy.* Tokyo: Igaku-Shoin.

Richardson, P.D.I., and Withrington, P.G. 1982. Physiological regulation of the hepatic circulation. *Annu. Rev. Physiol.* 44:57.

Salen, G., and Shefer, S. 1983. Bile acid synthesis. *Annu. Rev. Physiol.* 45:679.

Schalm, S.W.; LaRusso, N.F.; Hofmann, A.F., et al. 1978. Diurnal serum levels of primary conjugated bile acids. *Gut* 19:1006.

Sherlock, S. 1979. Progress report: Hepatic reactions to drugs. *Gut* 20:634.

Sherrick, E.H., and Sherrick, J.C. 1969. *Morphology of the Liver.* New York: Academic Press.

Spellman, S.J.; Shaffer, E.A.; and Rosenthall, L. 1979. Gallbladder emptying in response to cholecystokinin: A cholescintigraphic study. *Gastroenterol.* 77:115.

52

The
Small Intestine

GENERAL BACKGROUND

The primary functions of the small intestine are digestion and absorption, and these functions occur mostly in the duodenum and the jejunum. In addition, the small intestine influences the rate of gastric emptying by providing a varying resistance to gastric propulsion and by a form of feedback in response to the products that reach the duodenum. Thus, the rate of transfer of material to the intestine determines the rate at which foodstuffs are absorbed and subsequently stored in the tissues.

STRUCTURAL FEATURES

Intestinal Wall

The arrangement of the outer layers of the small intestine conforms to the layering that is common to most of the alimentary tract. The entire small intestinal tube, except the duodenum, is covered completely by serosa, except where the reflection of the two layers of mesenteric peritoneum allow the nerves, blood vessels, and lymphatic vessels to reach the external longitudinal coat of muscle. Normally,

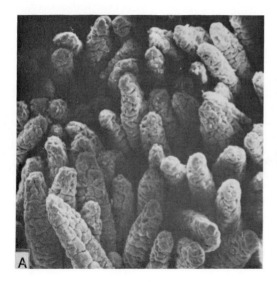 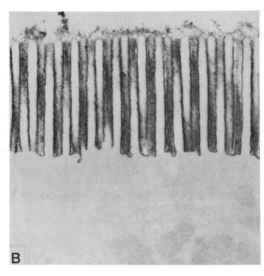

Figure 52-1. Structure of villi. **A.** Three-dimensional view of the villi of the jejunum as seen by scanning electron microscopy. The hexagonal boundaries between enterocytes on the surface of the villi can be seen. Each villus is about 1 mm tall. **B.** Two-dimensional view of the microvilli (brush border) of an enterocyte. The microvilli are about 1 μm tall. Each enterocyte holds about 1000 microvilli. (Reproduced, with permission, from Creamer, B. (ed.). 1974. *The Small Intestine.* London: William Heinemann Medical Books.)

the small intestine is highly mobile in the peritoneal cavity, although this freedom of movement may be limited by adhesions at sites where inflammation has occurred, especially if surgery has been performed. Moving from the outside in, the coats are as follows: longitudinal smooth muscle, Auerbach's plexus (myenteric plexus of nerve cells and fibers), circular (strictly, helical) smooth muscle, the submucosal (Meissner's) plexus, the muscularis mucosae, and the absorbing and secreting elements, the enterocytes, which are interspersed with mucous-secreting cells. The mucosa is formed into permanent circular folds up to 1 cm high, which are more prominent in the duodenum and jejunum than in the ileum. In addition, ever-changing folds, which are invisible from the outside, are caused by the muscularis mucosae without involving the longitudinal or helical muscle. The mucosa has the appearance of fine velvet because it is covered by tightly packed intestinal villi, which are only 1–2 mm high when fully extended (Figure 52-1).

Villi

The structure of each villus is well defined and has functional implications (Figure 52-2). The fingerlike process has a blind central lymphatic vessel that drains into the lymphatic plexus of the submucosa. The arteriole and the vein, neither of which has a muscular coat, run parallel to and close to the lymphatic vessel. The arteriole does not branch, but at the tip of the villus, the arteriole gives off a generous network of capillaries that underlies the absorbing enterocytes. A strand of smooth muscle runs with the vessels and is presumed to be the cause of the rhythmic shortening and lengthening of the villi that can be seen in the living tissue under a dissecting microscope. The villi are covered with enterocytes, which are differentiated from the cells of the three crypts that surround the base of each villus. The enterocytes migrate up the villus in 1 or 2 days, maturing as they go, so that by the time they reach the midregion of the villus, they have developed hydrolyzing enzymes and the carrier systems that absorb sugars, amino acids, Na^+, and so forth. The general arrangement of the villus is shown in Figure 52-2.

COUNTERCURRENT FUNCTION IN INTESTINAL VILLUS

One of the aims of biological science is to condense facts into principles that account for similar function in different tissues. The formation of urine more concentrated than plasma now is explained in terms of the countercurrent arrangement of the nephron and its collecting

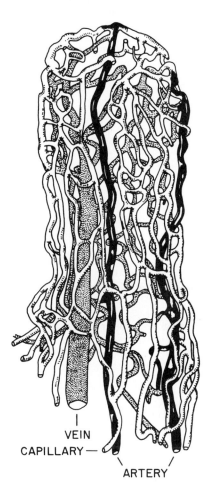

VEIN

CAPILLARY—

ARTERY

Figure 52-2. Blood vessels of an intestinal villus. Note the proximity and parallel course of the artery and vein. The capillaries that connect the artery to the vein immediately underlie the sheath of absorbing enterocytes. (Redrawn, with permission, from Spanner, R. 1932. Neue Befunde uber die Blutwege der Darmwand und ihre funktionelle Bedeutung. *Morph. Jahrbuch* 69:394.)

duct as it dips into the hypertonic region of the papilla of the kidney (see Chapter 41). A corresponding arrangement may account for the ability of the small intestine to absorb water from intestinal contents that are hyperosmolal relative to the plasma. The system appears to work as follows: Na^+ is absorbed by the enterocytes and diffuses into the capillary blood, which flows into the central vein of the villus. The vein is in contact with the central arteriole. As Na^+ is absorbed, the $[Na^+]$ of the vein exceeds the $[Na^+]$ of the arteriole, and Na^+ diffuses from the vein into the arteriole. The arterial blood enters the capillary, and the process is repeated. Several repetitions of this

process would produce the high $[Na^+]$ that is characteristic of the tip of the villus, which may be as much as twice the $[Na^+]$ of the plasma that enters the base of the villus (Figure 52-3). The freezing-point depression of the tissue at the tip of the villus corresponds to an osmotic activity of about 700 mOsm/liter, which provides a gradient for the diffusion of water from lumen to villus and hence to the blood. The countercurrent arrangement also has other implications; for example, when the rate of blood flow through the villus is decreased by local vasoconstriction or by a decrease of central arterial pressure after a large loss of blood, oxygen in the arterial blood diffuses directly into the venous blood, and the tip of the villus is deprived of oxygen. In experimental animals, long-term hypotension causes necrosis of the tips of the intestinal villi.

Enterocytes

The absorbing cell of the small intestine lives for only 2–4 days and is in its functional prime for only 1 day. The surface of the cell is covered by an ordered array of about 1000 microvilli, which is characteristic of secretory and absorptive cells (see Figure 52-1). However, unlike the microvilli of oxyntic cells, which appear only during secretion (see the section entitled "Changes in Oxyntic Cells During Secretion" in Chapter 49), the microvilli of enterocytes are permanent structures. Each microvillus is about 1 or 2 μm long. The surface of the tightly packed microvilli is covered with a material known formally as the *glycocalyx* and informally as the "fuzzy coat," which is believed to contain negative charges that are significant in the process of absorption (see the section entitled "Absorption of Anions" later in this chapter). Only the enterocytes of the luminal part of the villus have been shown to absorb materials and to contain the enzymes that are involved in the hydrolysis of disaccharides and oligopeptides.

INTESTINAL CONTRACTIONS

Propulsion

The contractions of the musculature of the small intestine mix the luminal contents with the secretions of the liver and pancreas and change the area of contact between the contents and the epithelium. The contractions of

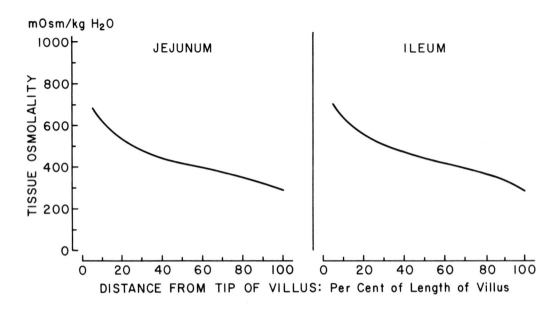

mOsm/kg H₂O

Figure 52-3. Osmolality of the fluid in the interstitial space of a villus that is absorbing Na⁺ and glucose. The osmolality at the tip of the villus is more than twice the osmolality of the plasma. (Reprinted, by permission of the publisher, from "Evidence for the existence of a countercurrent exchanger in the small intestine in man," by D.-A. Hallbäck, et al. *Gastroenterol.* 74:683. Copyright 1978 by the American Gastroenterological Association.)

the intestine determine the rate of onward movement of the luminal contents, which also affects the magnitude of the area of contact. When the intestine is loaded after a meal, the contents usually move backward and forward in the lumen a few centimeters at a time, although the final result is slow progression toward the ileocecal valve. Usually, the small intestine has been cleared of a meal, either by absorption or forward propulsion, by the time the next meal is taken.

Segmentation

Peristaltic transport, as seen in the esophagus, is uncommon in the small intestine, although it may occur when the duodenum fills rapidly. The most typical movement produces segmentation of the contents. Regions of circular muscle 1 or 2 cm wide contract slowly, occlude the lumen, and drive the luminal contents forward or backward. This type of contraction also offers resistance to the transfer of material from other regions. A series of local pacemakers functions in the intestine, and the mean frequency of each pacemaker is less the farther it is away from the pylorus. In the jejunum, the frequency is about 12 contractions/min, while in the ileum the frequency is about 9 contrac-

tions/min. The decreasing frequency of the contractions may explain the forward movement of the intestinal contents. The frequency of the segmenting activity increases after food has been eaten, and the rate of transport is decreased under these conditions. This increased frequency of segmenting activity is not seen when the small intestine is denervated extrinsically; presumably, it is caused by the stimulation of gastric receptors or duodenal receptors.

Pendular Movement

Segmenting movement is the most important method of forward motion of the intestinal contents, but pendular movements also occur. The luminal contents, when made radiopaque over a region of 10–20 cm, can be seen to move in mass either headward or tailward for a short distance. Pendular movements of contents are formed by synchronized contraction of a region 10–20 cm long.

Myoelectric Complex During Fasting

In fasting individuals, a wave of electrical and mechanical activity moves slowly (in about 100 minutes) from the stomach to the ileocecal

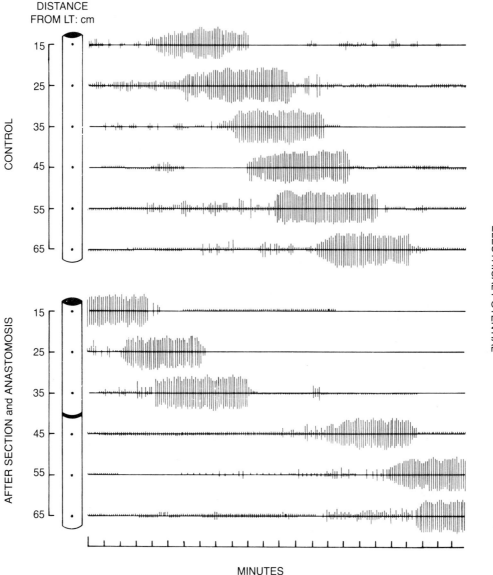

Figure 52-4. Record of electrical activity (corresponding to mechanical activity) of small intestine in a fasting dog (LT is the ligament of Treitz). The ordinate shows the position of the electrodes that were sewn into the intestinal wall. The excitatory front advanced 50 cm in 10 minutes. In the bottom part of the figure, simple transection and resuturing of the gut delayed the onward movement of the complex. This indicates that the mechanical activity depends on excitation moving along the gut rather than being imposed by impulses from extrinsic nerves.

valve. The process is repeated every 100 minutes until food is eaten again (Figure 52-4). The electrical activity is believed to be initiated at the lower esophageal sphincter by a hormone called *motilin,* which is released periodically from the duodenum. The cause of the periodic output of motilin is not known. The *myoelectric* *complex* is called the "intestinal housekeeper" because it sweeps mucosal debris and a population of bacteria from the lumen of the small intestine into the colon. The term "myoelectric complex" reflects its discovery as an electrical phenomenon. All movements of the intestine are preceded and caused by electrical events.

Control of Intestinal Movements

PACEMAKERS

The control systems of the smooth muscle of the different parts of the alimentary tract have similar characteristics. Pacemakers are involved everywhere, except in the esophagus and the anal canal, and electrical and mechanical activities are linked (see Figure 49-2). The pacemaker potentials, which are generated and migrate aborally in the longitudinal muscle, spread directly to the circular muscle. In response to the small pacemaking potential, the circular muscle generates a large action potential that causes contraction of both longitudinal and circular muscle in a limited region. The probability that a pacemaker potential will be followed by a series of spike potentials in the small muscle cells, and, hence, by a contraction, can be increased experimentally by increasing the concentration of acetylcholine and decreased by increasing the concentration of norepinephrine. The spikes and the contractions that follow are caused by sudden changes in the permeability of the cell membranes to Na^+ and Ca^{++}.

EFFECTS OF EXTRINSIC NERVES ON SMALL INTESTINE

Sensory Input

At one time, extensive denervation, including denervation of the abdominal viscera, was performed for the treatment of arterial hypertension. No noticeable effect on gastrointestinal digestive function occurred, but the patients no longer felt the pain that ordinarily is caused by distention of the abdominal viscus. Therefore, it appears that some or all of the afferent fibers from the abdominal organs travel with the efferent fibers of the sympathetic system.

Reflex Control

Section of the vagus nerves in the treatment of patients who have duodenal ulcer causes no dysfunction of the intestine, apart from a slight increase in the frequency of defecation. Although 90% of the 30,000 fibers in the vagus trunk are afferent, sectioning them causes no defect in sensation. This finding is consistent with the notion that the function of the afferent fibers in the vagus trunk is the reflex control of the viscera. The sensation of hunger may be an exception.

Ganglion Blockade

In marked contrast to the lack of effect surgical denervation has on the alimentary tract, inhibition of ganglionic transmission in the gut by drugs stops gut movements; such a condition is known clinically as *ileus*. Awareness of this action is important to the clinician because surgical exploration for treatment of ileus is inappropriate if the condition is caused by a drug. Disturbances of electrolyte balance also can cause ileus.

ABSORPTION

General Characteristics

The multiple foldings and villi of the intestinal epithelium produce an area of potential contact with the luminal contents that is even larger than the area of contact of the pulmonary capillaries with the alveolar air. Under ordinary circumstances, about 80% of the foodstuffs are absorbed in the 100 cm of the alimentary tract immediately distal to the pylorus; however, most materials can be absorbed from all regions of the jejunum and ileum. Some substances are absorbed selectively in specific areas; for example, vitamin B_{12} and bile salts are absorbed actively in the terminal ileum, and the absorption of iron and calcium virtually is limited to the duodenum.

Carrier Systems

Products of digestion that are soluble in water but not in lipid (e.g., glucose, fructose, amino acids, and oligopeptides) do not permeate the cell membrane in their native states. These materials combine with specific carrier systems, which are presumed to be proteins, that extend through the lipid membrane of the enterocyte. By these means, water-soluble compounds can pass from the intestinal lumen through the enterocytes to the extracellular space of the intestine. The carrier systems of the intestine are specific, and different classes of digestion products do not compete with each other for transport. Moreover, many water-soluble substances, such as sulfate and mannitol, are not absorbed because they have no specific transport system.

CLINICAL CORRELATION
52.1   Short-Bowel Syndrome

CASE REPORT

The Patient: A 17-year-old-male.

Principal Complaints: Severe abdominal pain and repeated vomiting.

Clinical Examination: The patient was admitted to the hospital in August 1962, 4 hours after falling from his bicycle. Eight hours later, laparotomy was performed, and the abdominal cavity was seen to be full of black bowel that emitted a musty odor. The dead small intestine was removed; the 30.5 cm length of jejunum that remained was connected to the ileocecal valve, which was intact. The patient passed watery feces for the next 2 weeks and lost 4 kg of body weight. He absorbed no vitamin B_{12}, since he had no terminal ileum (where B_{12} is absorbed specifically), and was given the vitamin by injection.

The patient was discharged after 4 weeks, having regained 2 kg of the body weight he had lost. He passed feces each day. It usually weighed about 1.5 kg, was foul smelling because of bacterial breakdown of unabsorbed protein, and floated in water because of gas formed by bacteria acting on unabsorbed carbohydrates. He developed a large appetite,

and 3 months after discharge, was at his preoperative weight. He had a slight abdominal distention, despite the operative removal of 2.5 kg of dead intestine. The abdominal volume was attributed to his colon distended with feces. His chief problem was decreased absorption of fat because of the loss of absorptive surface; however, the percentage of fat absorbed increased from 10% in 1962 to 60% in 1978. Mucosal hyperplasia is postulated to account for this, but it was not demonstrated. During the first year after surgery, he occasionally developed hypocalcemic tetany. Anions of fatty acids formed by the digestion of fat in the small intestine bind calcium, but normally the calcium is released again when the fat is absorbed. In this patient's case, however, much of the calcium was excreted in the feces along with the unabsorbed fat. His absorption of calcium improved considerably when the content of fat in his diet was decreased, and his plasma $[Ca^{++}]$ returned to normal.

Outcome: The patient has continued to do well. As evidence of his good physical condition, 3 years after his operation, he won his college's 4-mile cross-country race. He is now pursuing a successful career as a parish minister and is the father of two children.

WATER SOLUBILITY

It is not sufficient that a substance be soluble in lipid or have a carrier system that allows it to pass through lipid for it to be absorbed; the substance also must be soluble in water to some extent. Without solubility in water, the substance will not diffuse in the aqueous luminal contents, and it will not obtain an adequate area of contact with the lipid membranes of the cells. Thus, the digestion of insoluble starch to soluble glucose and the breakdown of triglycerides to water-dispersible anions of fatty acids are essential steps in absorption.

Relation of Solutes to Movement of Water

OSMOSIS

The absorption of water from the intestine is secondary to the absorption of solutes, essentially foods, Na^+, and anions. However, if the contents of the lumen are hyperosmolal to the extracellular fluid, additional water enters the alimentary tract. In the stomach, dilution of the hyperosmotic contents depends on the gastric secretions and not on the movement of water from the plasma because the mucosal surface of the stomach is relatively impermeable to water. Thus, the main dilution of food occurs in the duodenum, where the mucosa is permeable to water and where pancreatic secretion is added. Other factors also affect the movement of water. Not only does hyperosmolal food material from the stomach enter the duodenum, but starch is broken down rapidly to maltose, and protein is broken down to oligopeptides; thus, the osmolality of the luminal contents initially increases further. The rate at which water may accumulate in the lumen is moderated, however, because the hyperosmolal solution slows the rate at which material is delivered from the stomach. At the same time, the products of intestinal digestion are absorbed rapidly. Within 5 minutes after starch or protein is taken by mouth, the concentrations of glucose and amino acids in the plasma increase.

NONABSORBABLE SOLUTES

Solutes that are not absorbed from the intestine cause water to accumulate in the lumen. An example of a nonpermeant solute is sodium sulfate. $SO_4^=$, a large heavily hydrated ion, is not absorbed, and it prevents the absorption of Na^+. Another example of clinical importance is lactose, which must be split into glucose and galactose to be absorbed. Patients who lack the enzyme *lactase* cannot absorb lactose. Nonabsorbable solutes cause water to accumulate in the lumen of the intestine by decreasing the chemical activity of water in the lumen, thereby decreasing the flux of water from the lumen to the plasma. According to the same principle, when a solute is absorbed, water also is absorbed because the chemical activity of water is increased in the alimentary tract and decreased in the tissue.

Absorption of Sodium and Water by Small Intestine

MAGNITUDE OF SODIUM AND WATER FLUX

The significance of the fluxes of Na^+ and water into and out of the intestinal lumen is apparent if the amounts and volumes that enter and leave the intestine are viewed in the context of the total volume of extracellular water, which is about 12 liters. The concentration of Na^+ ($[Na^+]$) in the body water is 140 mEq/liter;

thus, the total amount of Na^+ in the extracellular water is 1700 mEq. The fluids secreted into the alimentary tract in 1 day consist of 1 liter of saliva, 1.5 liters of gastric secretion, 1 liter of pancreatic secretion, 0.5 liter of bile, and 3 liters of intestinal influx (see the section entitled "Osmosis" earlier in this chapter) for a total of 7 liters. If the average $[Na^+]$ in the secretions is 110 mEq/liter, 770 mEq, or about 45% of the Na^+ in the extracellular space, is involved. Because the volume of the extracellular space, which includes the plasma, is determined primarily by the amount of Na^+ it contains, the return to the extracellular space of the Na^+ that enters the lumen of the alimentary tract is essential to circulatory function. Despite these large entries of Na^+ into the alimentary tract—in 24 hours, about 800 mEq of Na^+ enters in secretions and about 100 mEq of Na^+ enters from the diet—less than 5 mEq of Na^+ are lost in the feces each day. Although Na^+ is secreted and absorbed mainly in the small intestine, avid reabsorption of Na^+ by the colon reduces the loss in the feces to this low level (see Figure 54-1).

A total volume of food and drink of about 3 liters, which contains 100 mEq of Na^+, is consumed in one day. These 3 liters are mixed with 7 liters of secretion that contain 800 mEq of Na^+; however, the colon receives only 2 liters of fluid that contain 271 mEq of Na^+ (see Figure 54-1). By subtraction, the small intestine must have absorbed 629 mEq of Na^+ (900 mEq − 271 mEq) and 8 liters of water. These figures represent only the net fluxes; that is, the differences between the two-way fluxes, which probably are 10 times larger than the net fluxes. These figures emphasize the significance of the quantities of water and Na^+ that can be lost by vomiting or diarrhea. Although the water lost through these routes can be replaced by drinking, the loss of Na^+ can lead to decreased extracellular volume if it is not corrected.

LATERAL INTERCELLULAR SPACE

Because the absorption of water follows the absorption of solute, the chemical activity of water must be less at some site on the serosal side of the mucosa than on the luminal side. In addition, to maintain the diffusion of water, this gradient of activity must be maintained. Figure 52-5 shows some of the features of this

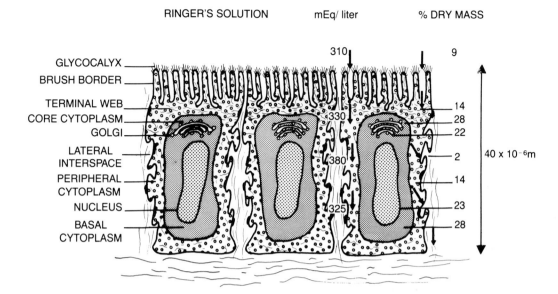

RINGER'S SOLUTION   mEq/ liter   % DRY MASS

GLYCOCALYX

BRUSH BORDER

TERMINAL WEB

CORE CYTOPLASM

GOLGI

LATERAL
INTERSPACE

PERIPHERAL
CYTOPLASM

NUCLEUS

BASAL
CYTOPLASM

Figure 52-5. Diagram of three cells on the surface of a villus from a rabbit ileum. Each cell is about 40 μm long, and the microvilli on the luminal surface are 1 μm long. The values to the right side of the figure indicate the distribution of solids in the cells. The heavy arrows in the cytosol indicate a possible preferred pathway for the passage of water in a region where the concentration of solid matter is low. The numbers in the lateral intercellular space indicate the concentrations of solutes in mEq/liter. The region of maximal concentration of solute (380 mEq/liter) is in the middle part of the lateral intercellular space. Water flows by osmosis from the lumen into the lateral intercellular space; this creates a hydrostatic pressure that causes water to flow farther into the submucosa and hence to the blood in the capillaries (not shown). Thickened regions of the walls of the lateral intercellular spaces represent Na^+ transport ATPase. The results were obtained by electron probe x-ray microanalysis. (Gupta, B.L., and Hall, T.A. Quantitative electron probe x-ray microanalysis of electrolyte elements within epithelial tissue compartments. Reprinted from *Federation Proceedings* 38:144, 1979.)

mechanism, which is thought to be common to the intestine, the gallbladder, and the kidneys.

According to the proposed mechanism, Na^+ is transported actively out of that part of the cytosol where the concentration of solute dry mass in the analysis is low. This is immediately adjacent to the transport ATPase, which is localized in the convoluted walls of the lateral intercellular spaces. This region provides a large area for the rapid diffusion of Na^+ and water from the luminal surface of the cell to the transport sites. When the absorption of water is minimal, the walls of neighboring enterocytes are in contact; as absorption increases, the spaces appear and become wider. As yet, no structural study has indicated where the osmotic gradients that are set up by the transport of glucose might act, but it is possible that these osmotic gradients also involve the lateral in-

tercellular space. The mechanism discussed here presumably is augmented in the intestine by the countercurrent system (see the section on countercurrent function earlier in this chapter), which also depends on the transport of Na^+ by the ATPase in the lateral walls of the enterocytes.

CO-TRANSPORT OF
SODIUM AND GLUCOSE
The absorption of Na^+ is associated with the absorption of glucose or amino acids by a process called *co-transport*. The [Na^+] of the mucosal cell is kept low by a system of active transport that extrudes Na^+ and an anion into the lateral intercellular spaces (Figure 52-5). Glucose is transported from the lumen by combination with a carrier that also combines with Na^+; the complex moves down the con-

centration gradient of Na^+ into the cytosol and can carry glucose up a concentration gradient.

ENTRAINMENT OF SODIUM IN WATER ABSORBED WITH SUGARS

Fructose, unlike glucose and galactose, is not co-transported with Na^+. Nevertheless, absorption of fructose and Na^+ is associated; in humans, the rate of absorption of Na^+ with fructose is about three-fourths of the rate of absorption of Na^+ with glucose. It is postulated that the Na^+ absorbed with fructose is entrained with the water that moves down the osmotic gradient produced by the absorption of fructose. If this is true, Na^+ should be entrained at the same rate by the water absorbed with glucose. This leaves only about one-fourth of the Na^+ that is absorbed to be transported by the carrier along with glucose.

Absorption Related to Hydrolase Activity

Either lactose or maltose given into the intestine is absorbed more rapidly than the same amount of sugar given into the intestine as its constituent monosaccharides, galactose and glucose. This is consistent with the fact that monosaccharides formed from disaccharides hydrolyzed by the enzymes of the brush border mostly do not diffuse back into the luminal space. Thus, it is assumed that the hydrolyzing enzymes and the carrier molecules are located very close to each other in the brush border. Hence, the monosaccharides produced adjacent to the carrier molecules are transported more effectively than the monosaccharides that enter in solution and are distributed throughout the lumen.

Absorption of Anions

For the most part, anions are thought to follow the electrical potential set up by the transport of Na^+. However, as in the kidneys and stomach, Cl^- also is transported actively in the alimentary tract. In the jejunum, and even more in the ileum, HCO_3^- is secreted into the lumen in exchange for Cl^-.

ILEUM

Of the total of up to 10 liters of food, drink, and secretion that enter the alimentary tract in 24 hours, only 2 liters reach the cecum. This is explained by the absorption of almost all of the foodstuffs and 80% of the electrolytes in the small intestine. The ileal mucosa behaves as though it had smaller pores than the jejunal mucosa; thus, the fluxes of ions in the ileum are less. The $[HCO_3^-]$ in the lumen of the ileum is higher than that in the jejunum because of the active secretion of HCO_3^- into the ileum in exchange for Cl^-. The maximum concentration gradient against which the jejunum can absorb Cl^- is 13 mEq/liter, whereas the ileum can create a gradient of 130 mEq/liter. This difference reflects the relative leakiness of the epithelium of each region.

Absorption of Cations

Knowledge of the conditions at the surface of the microvilli is important in understanding why some drugs are absorbed at different rates. The glycocalyx (Figure 52-5) behaves as though it has an excess of negative charges at its surface. These negative sites attract mobile cations, including H^+, so that the $[H^+]$ increases at the interface between the luminal contents and the surface of the intestine. The $[H^+]$ determines the extent to which drugs that are weak acids or weak bases are dissociated. The negative charges facilitate the absorption of drugs that form cations and retard the absorption of drugs that form anions.

INTESTINAL SECRETION

Experiments with isolated pouches of stomach indicate that the normal intestine secretes only in response to direct contact with food in the lumen, if it secretes at all. The enzymes sucrase, maltase, and lactase, which are found in intestinal secretions, normally act while they are fixed to the microvillous (brush) border of the enterocytes; the enzymes that are found in the intestinal secretion come from desquamated cells. However, when the human duodenum is perfused with a nutrient solution and the jejunum is perfused with an electrolyte solution, a net secretion of about (1 ml/min)/30 cm of jejunum can be obtained. Figure 52-6 shows the experimental arrangement in diagrammatic form and the results that were obtained. Although the secretion is approximately isosmotic with plasma, physiologists still do not know whether the secretion is formed by en-

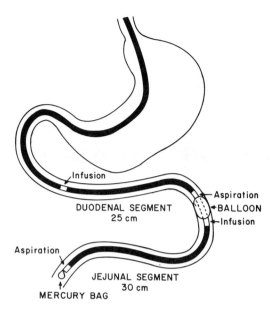

Figure 52-6. Increased secretion of Na^+ and water from 30 cm of human jejunum during 30 minutes while the duodenum was perfused with a nutrient solution. The amount of water was 33 ml and the amount of Na^+ was 5.6 mEq; the $[Na^+]$ was 170 mEq/liter. Note that the $[Na^+]$ is approximately isosmotic with plasma, as predicted by theory.

terocytes that absorb simultaneously or the immature enterocytes in the crypts provide it. These are not idle questions because they are essential to the understanding of diarrhea, a disorder that kills tens of millions of children each year.

Cholera

Cholera is a diarrheal disease that occurs in countries where drinking water may be contaminated by feces or urine. Diarrhea is caused by an exotoxin produced by a microorganism, *vibrio cholerae*. The toxin acts on the enterocytes and causes a profuse diarrhea that drains water and Na^+ from the extracellular space. As a result, the plasma volume decreases, the cardiac output decreases, and the patient dies because the brain is perfused inadequately. If the patient survives the diarrhea, health is restored. *Vibrio cholerae* does not invade the body proper, as the microorganism that causes typhoid fever does.

Although the cholera stool contains no protein, its $[HCO_3^-]$ is higher than that of plasma; hence, the cholera stool is not a filtrate. The

cholera toxin binds to the epithelial cells of the intestine and activates the enzyme adenylate cyclase, which, in turn, causes the intestinal cells to secrete a solution of electrolytes faster than it can be reabsorbed. Despite this deluge of secretions—up to 17 liters/day—the normal absorptive processes continue to function. Since glucose and Na^+ are absorbed together, either by the same carrier molecule or by the entrainment of water and Na^+ in solution, cholera patients usually can maintain a balance of water and Na^+ adequate for survival if they are given a solution of glucose and water by mouth. In fact, the functions of digestion and absorption are affected so little by cholera that rice water (starch water), which is more readily available, can be given instead of glucose. The implication of this treatment is that pancreatic enzymes and intestinal maltase, which are bound to the brush border, continue to function effectively. The current treatment of cholera constitutes a significant advance in coping with a disease that previously was treated by administering intravenous fluids that are not easily obtained in the primitive countries where cholera usually occurs. This treatment also can be applied to some other forms of infective diarrhea. The current treatment is based on knowledge that has been obtained from experiments using pieces of isolated, everted gut in flasks, although it has taken many years of careful clinical studies to learn how to apply that knowledge.

Diarrhea

In the final analysis, one common mechanism may explain the various forms of diarrhea that are seen clinically—an increase in the volume of fluid in the lumen. Water is retained in the lumen rather than being absorbed either because Na^+ is excreted in excess (secretory diarrhea) or because some solute taken by mouth is not absorbed (osmotic diarrhea). The diarrhea that occurs in patients who cannot digest lactose is an example of osmotic diarrhea. In principle, the two forms of diarrhea can be distinguished by measuring the $[Na^+]$ of the fecal water; a $[Na^+]$ of more than 150 mEq/liter indicates a secretory diarrhea because extracellular fluid is being secreted. The fecal water also is isosmotic with plasma in osmotic diarrhea, but the $[Na^+]$ is lower because the main solute is either a sugar or a salt that was taken by the patient; for example, magnesium sulfate ($MgSO_4$).

STUDY OUTLINE

GENERAL BACKGROUND Main functions of small intestine are digestion and absorption; however, by regulation of gastric emptying, small intestine also determines rate of absorption of foodstuffs.

STRUCTURAL FEATURES

INTESTINAL WALL   Conforms to features common to most of alimentary tract.

Serosal covering gives mobility in abdominal cavity.

Epithelium has permanent folds caused by muscularis mucosae; covered by intestinal villi 1 mm high.

VILLI   Fingerlike process with own artery, vein, and lymphatic vessel.

Covered by absorbing cells (enterocytes) that migrate up villus from crypts at base in 2 days.

Only peripheral half of cells on villus are mature, contain digestive enzymes and carrier systems.

COUNTERCURRENT FUNCTION IN INTESTINAL VILLUS   Because of accumulation of Na^+, osmotic pressure at tip of villus is twice the osmotic pressure of plasma; partly responsible for absorption of water.

At low rate of flow, arterial blood at base of villus loses oxygen to venous blood by diffusion—deprives tip of villus of oxygen.

ENTEROCYTES   Absorbing cells of small intestine.

Live only 3–4 days and in functional prime for only 1 day.

Surface is covered with about 1000 microvilli (glycocalyx) 1 μm long.

Enterocytes near tip of villus contain enzymes that are involved in hydrolysis of disaccharides and oligopeptides.

INTESTINAL CONTRACTIONS

PROPULSION   Contractions mix contents with secretions, change area of contact with epithelium, and cause slow onward movement.

Absorption and transport clear intestine of contents by time next meal is taken.

SEGMENTATION   Contraction of 2 cm wide region of circular muscle drives food forward and backward.

Lower frequency in jejunum than in ileum may cause forward transport.

PENDULAR   MOVEMENT   Caused by contraction in 10–20 cm length of intestine.

MYOELECTRIC   COMPLEX   DURING FASTING   Wave of electrical and mechanical activity passes from lower esophageal sphincter to ileocecal valve in approximately 100 minutes.

Wave sweeps contents of intestine before it; is repeated about every 100 minutes until food is taken again.

CONTROL OF INTESTINAL MOVEMENTS

PACEMAKERS   Pacemakers in different areas originate potentials that sweep over smooth muscle at about 5 cm/sec.

Basal electrical rhythm determines when action potentials may occur.

Probability of action potential and contraction following pacemaker is increased by acetylcholine and decreased by norepinephrine.

EFFECTS OF EXTRINSIC NERVES ON SMALL INTESTINE

SENSORY INPUT   Denervation abolishes sensation but has trivial effects on intestinal function.

REFLEX CONTROL   Carried mainly via vagus nerves.

GANGLION BLOCKADE   Ganglion-blocking drugs cause intestinal paralysis; occasionally seen clinically.

ABSORPTION

GENERAL CHARACTERISTICS   Multiple foldings provide large area of contact with luminal contents.

Most materials are absorbed in all regions of jejunum and ileum, except iron and calcium in duodenum and Vitamin B_{12} and bile salts in distal ileum.

CARRIER SYSTEMS   Allow water-soluble digestion products to traverse lipid membranes of enterocytes; specific for each product.

WATER SOLUBILITY   Essential for diffusion in lumen to epithelial surface.

RELATION OF SOLUTES TO MOVEMENT OF WATER

OSMOSIS   In alimentary tract, water moves down osmotic gradients produced by movement of solutes.

Increased osmolality of contents in duodenum causes initial influx of water.

Effect is moderated by slowing of gastric emptying and rapid absorption of products of digestion.

NONABSORBABLE SOLUTES Prevent absorption of water and cause osmotic purge.

ABSORPTION OF SODIUM AND WATER BY SMALL INTESTINE

MAGNITUDE OF SODIUM AND WATER FLUX In 24 hours, about 40% of Na^+ of extracellular fluid enters lumen of alimentary tract in secretions; less than 1% is lost in feces.

Reabsorption of Na^+ by small intestine and colon is essential for maintaining plasma volume.

LATERAL INTERCELLULAR SPACE Active transport of Na^+ into lateral intercellular space sets up diffusion gradient for water from lumen to space.

Hydrostatic pressure in space causes water to flow further into submucosa and eventually into capillaries.

CO-TRANSPORT OF SODIUM AND GLUCOSE Na^+ moves down gradient from lumen to cytosol, is co-transported with glucose and amino acids.

Uphill transport of glucose depends on downhill movement of Na^+.

ENTRAINMENT OF SODIUM IN WATER ABSORBED WITH SUGARS Absorption of glucose and fructose carries water and Na^+ that is dissolved in it.

ABSORPTION RELATED TO HYDROLASE ACTIVITY
Sugars produced from hydrolysis of disaccharides are absorbed more rapidly than corresponding solutions of monosaccharides—indicates hydrolyzing enzymes on brush border are located close to transport mechanism.

ABSORPTION OF ANIONS
Cl^- is transported actively from lumen; HCO_3^- in plasma is exchanged for Cl^-.

ILEUM Has smaller pores than jejunum and, therefore, smaller fluxes of ions.

HCO_3^- is secreted actively into lumen, Cl^- is absorbed actively.

ABSORPTION OF CATIONS
Facilitated by negative charge at mucosal surface.

INTESTINAL SECRETION Small intestine secretes only in response to direct contact with food, if at all.

Enzymes act when fixed to brush border; small quantities in lumen result from desquamated cells of villi.

CHOLERA
Severe diarrhea caused by toxin produced by microorganisms in lumen (*vibrio cholerae*).

Toxin causes intestinal secretion that exceeds reabsorptive capacity.

Concentration of HCO_3^- in cholera stool is greater than that in plasma; indicates cholera stool is formed by secretion rather than filtration.

Digestive and absorptive mechanisms in patient who has cholera are not abnormal.

Giving saline solution and glucose causes sufficient absorption of salt and water to maintain circulating plasma volume.

DIARRHEA
Result of increased volume of fluid in small intestine and large intestine.

Increased volume may be caused by ingestion of nonabsorbed solute (e.g., $MgSO_4$) or by excessive secretion of normally absorbed solute (e.g., Na^+).

BIBLIOGRAPHY

Bueno, L.; Pradduade, F.; and Ruckebusch, Y. 1979. Propagation of electrical spiking activity along the small intestine: Intrinsic versus extrinsic neural influences. *J. Physiol.* 292:15.

Connor, J.A.; Kreulen, D.; Prosser, C.L., et al. 1977. Interaction between longitudinal and circular muscle in intestine of cat. *J. Physiol.* 273:665.

Creamer, B. 1974. *The Small Intestine.* London: Heinemann.

Csaky, T.Z. 1974. *Intestinal Absorption and Malabsorption.* New York: Raven Press.

Duthie, H.L. (ed.). 1977. *Gastrointestinal Motility in Health and Disease.* Baltimore: University Park Press.

Gupta, B.L., and Hall, T.Z. 1979. Quantitative electron probe x-ray microanalysis of electrolyte elements within epithelial tissue compartments. *Fed. Proc.* 38:144.

Hallbäck, D.-A.; Hultén, L.; Jodal, M., et al. 1978. Evidence for the existence of a countercurrent exchanger in the small intestine in man. *Gastroenterol.* 74:683.

Hendrix, T.R., and Paulk, H.T. 1977. Intestinal secretion. In *Gastrointestinal Physiology II.* Volume 12. Edited by R.K. Crane. Baltimore: University Park Press.

Loehry, C.A., and Creamer, B. 1969. Three-dimensional structure of the human small intestinal mucosa in health and disease. *Gut* 10:6.

Lundgren, O. 1974. Progress report: The circulation of the small bowel mucosa. *Gut* 15:1005.

McColl, I., and Sladen, G.E. 1975. *Intestinal Absorption in Man.* New York: Academic Press.

Moog, F. 1981. The lining of the small intestine. *Sci. Am.* 245(5):154.

Smyth, D.H. 1969. The economy of the columnar epithelial cell. *Gut* 10:2.

Tomasini, J.T., and Dobbins, W.T. 1970. Intestinal and mucosal morphology during water and electrolyte absorption. *Am. J. Dig. Dis.* 15:226.

Wood, J.D. 1981. Intrinsic neural control of intestinal motility. *Annu. Rev. Physiol.* 43:33.

Wright, J.P.; Barbezat, G.O.; and Clain, J.E. 1979. Jejunal secretion in response to a duodenal mixed-nutrient perfusion. *Gastroenterol.* 76:94.

53

Digestion and Absorption

CHAPTER CONTENTS

DIGESTION AND ABSORPTION OF CARBOHYDRATES

The term *digestion* signifies the splitting of large molecules into smaller ones that usually are more soluble in water.

Dietary Carbohydrates

More than half of the carbohydrate in the diet is starch; the remainder consists of sucrose and a small quantity of lactose, which is the carbohydrate in milk. Starch consists of chains of glucose molecules; the majority of starch is *amylopectin,* which has branched chains (1–4 and 1–6 links), and the rest is *amylose,* which has straight chains (1–4 links) (Figure 53-1). Different enzymes break the 1–4 links and the 1–6 links. Cellulose, another carbohydrate that occurs in food, is digested in humans to a small extent by the bacteria of the colon, yielding short-chain fatty acids but contributing little energy. The majority of carbohydrate is eaten as polysaccharides, digested, and absorbed as glucose. Disaccharides—sucrose and lactose— also are digested and absorbed in the form of monosaccharides. All carbohydrate from dietary sources enters the portal blood as glucose, fructose, or galactose.

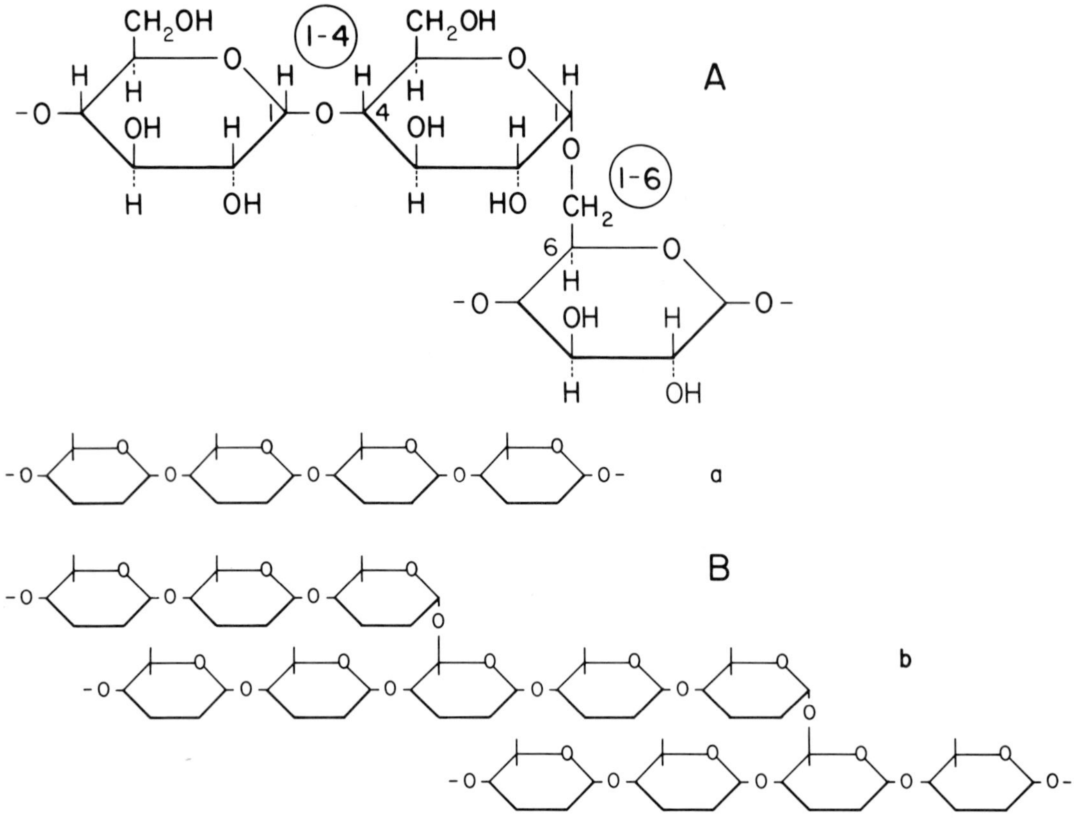

Figure 53-1. Structures of starch. **A.** Details of 1–4 and 1–6 linkages. **B** (a). Straight chain (1–4 linkage only) is characteristic of amylose. (b). Branched chain (1–4 and 1–6 linkages) is characteristic of amylopectin.

Osmotic Implications of Carbohydrates in the Diet

The mucosa of the small intestine has a large surface area, about 250 m², and is highly permeable to water, especially in the jejunum. Thus, any osmotic gradient into the lumen of the intestine increases the volume of water in the lumen and dilutes the contents of the lumen. Excess volume may cause diarrhea; however, certain factors tend to decrease the rate at which fluid accumulates in the duodenum and the jejunum after meals:

1. The hyperosmolality of the duodenal contents decreases the rate at which the gastric contents enter the duodenum (see the section entitled "Response of Duodenal Receptors to Foodstuffs" in Chapter 49).
2. The disaccharides are broken down to monosaccharides while in contact with the enzymes *maltase, sucrase,* and *lactase,* which are bound to the microvilli of the enterocytes. The monosaccharides then are absorbed directly, and only a minor fraction of them diffuses back into the lumen.
3. Carbohydrates are absorbed rapidly after they are delivered from the stomach; the concentration of glucose in the plasma begins to rise less than 5 minutes after a meal has been taken.

After some forms of gastric surgery, gastric emptying can be unusually rapid (see the section entitled "Receptive Relaxation" in Chapter 49). In this circumstance, the fluid that moves into the intestine to dilute the meal decreases the plasma volume and may affect the circulation temporarily. The rapid absorption of carbohydrate also may cause a fall in the plasma $[K^+]$ and temporary muscular weakness because glucose and K^+ are taken into tissues together. These symptoms are part of the "dumping" syndrome.

Digestion of Starch in the Stomach

Because the optimal pH for salivary amylase is 6.5, conditions in the stomach, where strong acid is secreted, appear to be unfavorable for the digestion of starch. However, when the meal is solid, acid penetrates the food mass in the stomach slowly, and up to half of the starch that remains in the stomach 60 minutes after a meal is taken is digested to dextrins. Although salivary amylase does perform a digestive function, some individuals do not produce this enzyme; however, they suffer no deleterious consequences.

Digestion of Starch in the Small Intestine

Table 53-1 lists the enzymes that digest the main carbohydrates of the diet, the end products of the breakdown process, and the sites of action. The disaccharidases listed in this table, which once were thought to be secreted by the intestine ("succus entericus"), now are known to be formed by the mature enterocytes and to remain attached to the microvillous border. These enzymes produce monosaccharides from disaccharides—two molecules of glucose from maltose, one molecule each of glucose and galactose from lactose, and one molecule each of glucose and fructose from sucrose. The enzyme that is involved in the last reaction (sucrase) always is associated with isomaltase, the en-

zyme that splits the 1-6 bonds of branched-chain starch, and both activities may reside in the same protein.

LACTASE DEFICIENCY

A significant proportion of adults, especially Orientals and blacks, either have no lactase or have a smaller concentration of lactase than is normal. If such individuals take a large amount of lactose, say 50 g, they suffer from intestinal gas and may have diarrhea. Even smaller amounts of lactose in foods may cause discomfort in these people. Because lactose is not absorbed, the sugar acts osmotically as a purge and provides a substrate for the colonic bacteria, which make gas.

Intestinal Absorption of Monosaccharides

DIFFUSION

Substances may diffuse through the lipid membranes of the enterocytes; however, monosaccharides are too insoluble in lipids for absorption in this way to be significant. Alternatively, particles can diffuse through pores in cell membranes or through the junctions between cells. However, the molecules of monosaccharides, especially when hydrated, are too large to be absorbed through these routes. This conclusion is supported by the finding that children who are born without the special pathway for the absorption of glucose and galactose (an

TABLE 53-1
The enzymes that digest carbohydrates

Enzyme	Substrate	End product	Site of action
Salivary amylase	Starch (amylopectin) α 1–4 linkages	Maltose; oligosaccharides	Mouth; stomach
Pancreatic amylase	Starch (amylopectin) α 1–4 linkages	Maltose; maltotriose; oligosaccharides	Lumen of small intestine
Maltase	Maltose	Glucose	Microvillous membranes of enterocytes on the luminal half of the intestinal villi in jejunum and ileum
Lactase	Lactose	Galactose; glucose	
Sucrase	Sucrose	Fructose; glucose	
Isomaltase	Oligosaccharides of glucose α 1–6 linkages	Glucose	

inherited defect) do not absorb measurable amounts of glucose and do not survive unless they are given fructose, for which there is a separate, passive carrier system.

FACILITATED DIFFUSION

The rate of absorption of fructose increases with concentration up to a maximum, despite the size of the fructose molecule (which is the same as that of the glucose molecule) and its insolubility in lipid. When absorption is passive, the rate of movement increases linearly with the concentration gradient, and there should be no maximum. The uptake of fructose is considerably faster than that of mannose, which is a hexose of similar molecular weight, and is not affected by glucose or galactose. The latter finding indicates that fructose is not entrained in the water that is absorbed with the other sugars, nor does fructose share a carrier with the other sugars. However, under experimental conditions, in which both glucose and galactose can be shown to be transported against a chemical gradient, active transport of fructose has not been demonstrated. Thus, the evidence suggests that fructose is absorbed by *facilitated diffusion*. In this process, a substance combines with a carrier that allows it to traverse a lipid membrane, but energy is not used in this form of transport.

ACTIVE TRANSPORT

Although glucose and galactose are absorbed actively, they usually are not transported against a concentration gradient because the concentrations of sugars in the lumen of the gut and in the interstitial fluid of the intestine are about the same after meals. However, active transport ensures that carbohydrates are absorbed quickly and almost completely. Since increasing the concentration of glucose decreases the rate at which galactose is transported and vice versa, the two hexoses appear to share the same carrier molecule. Any carbohydrate that escapes absorption is degraded to organic acids, CO_2, H_2, and methane (CH_4) by bacteria in the gut. In infants who have diarrhea, glucose may escape absorption and be found in the feces. Although adults have ample reserves of alimentary function, infants do not.

Co-transport of Glucose and Sodium

In vitro experiments have shown that the gradient of [Na^+] between the outside and the in-side of the cell provides the energy for the transport of glucose (see the section entitled "Co-transport of Sodium and Glucose" in Chapter 52). Glucose and Na^+ are believed to share a common carrier, and the rate of uptake of Na^+ from the intestinal lumen is increased by glucose. There appears also to be another form of transport of glucose that does not involve Na^+, but it has not been characterized.

DIGESTION AND ABSORPTION OF PROTEIN

Sources of Protein

Proteins are an essential part of the diet. If the diet contains plenty of carbohydrate and some fat, the minimum requirement of protein for humans is about 30 g/day (see Chapter 69). In wealthy countries, a person may take as much as 100 g/day of protein, mainly from meat and dairy products. In undeveloped nations, much of the protein that is eaten comes from grain, which is not digested so readily and may contain barely adequate proportions of the essential amino acids (see Chapter 69).

Proteolysis

Proteins are split by a cascade of enzymes (proteases), which act in solution in the lumen of the stomach, in solution in the lumen of the small intestine, and fixed in the brush border of the small intestine. Some of the proteases act in the middle regions of the protein molecules, and other proteases act at the terminal peptide bond. The final intraluminal products are small peptides and amino acids.

GASTRIC PROTEOLYSIS

The gastric proteases (pepsins) (see the section on pepsinogen-secreting cells in Chapter 49) are a group of enzymes that act at pH values of less than 3.5. The pH at which the maximal rate of digestion occurs varies from one enzyme to the next, but pH 2 is a characteristic value. Thus, pepsins act only in the acid content of the stomach and are inactivated in the alkaline environment of the small intestine. Pepsins are secreted in the form of inactive precursors that are activated by acid. Although pepsins do perform a digestive function, only about 10% of the protein in the gastric contents normally is digested in 2 hours. The remainder of the protein is digested in the small intestine by enzymes from the pancreas.

INTESTINAL PROTEOLYSIS

Pancreatic secretions contain two kinds of proteolytic enzymes (see the section entitled "Pancreatic Proteases" in Chapter 50): endopeptidases, which act in the central region of the protein molecule, and carboxypeptidases, which split off amino acids from the C (carboxyl) terminal end of the protein (Figure 53-2). Each enzyme has a preferred site of action; for example, trypsin (an endopeptidase) acts at bonds that contain lysine or arginine. Pancreatic peptidases do not act on peptides that contain fewer than six amino acids (oligopeptides); these peptides are hydrolyzed by enzymes (peptidases) that are fixed in the microvillous border of the enterocytes and are an important part of protein digestion. The main digestion and absorption of protein occurs in the duodenum and jejunum, and a small amount occurs in the ileum.

Absorption

CARRIER SYSTEMS

The enterocytes have transport systems that are selective for two groups of amino acids, and another transport system that is selective for dipeptides and tripeptides. However, the final product that enters the portal blood consists almost entirely of amino acids.

AMINO ACIDS

The carrier systems that selectively transport amino acids from the intestine into the cytosol of the enterocytes react with both L (levorotatory) and D (dextrorotatory) isomers of amino acids, but have greater affinity for the L-amino acid isomer. The higher forms of life use only the L-amino acid isomers. High concentrations of the D-amino acids inhibit the active transport of the L-amino acids when the concentrations of the L-amino acids are low. Amino acids are co-transported with Na^+ in the same way that

TABLE 53-2

Specificities of amino acid transport systems

	Class	Examples
Group I	Neutral amino acids	Glycine; citrulline; leucine; phenylalanine; threonine; and tryptophan
Group II	Basic amino acids	Lysine; arginine; and cystine
Group III	Imino acids	Proline and hydroxyproline

glucose and galactose are; however, the transport of glucose does not interfere with the transport of amino acids.

The chemical specificities of the two carrier systems for amino acids are listed in Table 53-2. This delineation is based on the inhibition of the transport of one amino acid by another. When two amino acids are transported actively but the presence of one does not reduce the rate of transport of the other, the two amino acids are presumed to react with different carrier systems. This classification seems reasonable because the substances in each group have chemical similarities; group I substances are neutral amino acids, and group II substances are basic. The relative rates of absorption of 18 amino acids in humans are shown in Figure 53-3.

DIPEPTIDES AND TRIPEPTIDES

During the study of the absorption of amino acids from the intestine, investigators discovered that the dipeptide glycylleucine was absorbed more rapidly than the amino acid glycine (Figure 53-4). This result was unexpected because physiologists believed that proteins

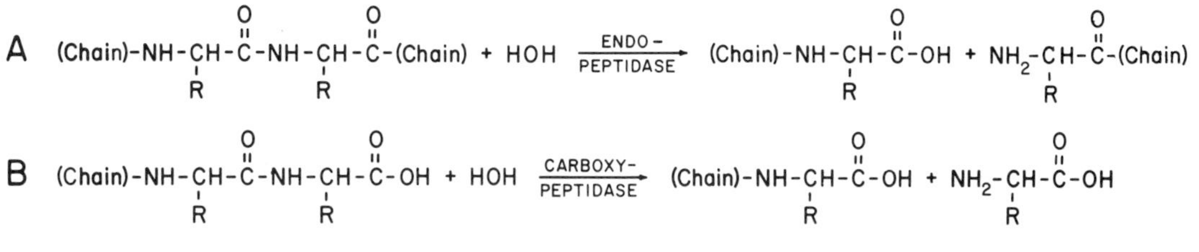

Figure 53-2. Distinction between endopeptidase activity, which breaks the polypeptide chain in the central regions, and carboxypeptidase, which splits off single amino acids.

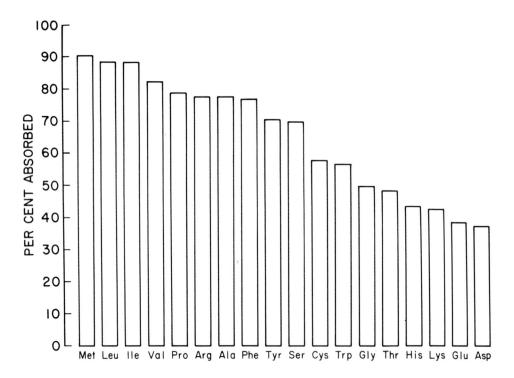

Figure 53-3. Relative rates of absorption of 18 amino acids from a solution that contains 8 mM of each acid. Several factors contribute to the differences: (1) amino acids that have longer side chains are absorbed more rapidly, (2) either positive charge (lysine) or negative charge (aspartic acid) on the side chain decreases the rate of absorption, and (3) amino acids transported more rapidly inhibit the absorption of amino acids transported less rapidly.

were absorbed only after being digested completely to amino acids. It is apparent now that as much as half of the dietary protein may be absorbed as oligopeptides and hydrolyzed in the cytosol of the enterocytes before entering the portal blood. Neonates can absorb protein antibodies intact, and adults can absorb some proteins intact, such as those that cause allergic responses to certain foods (but only in nanogram amounts).

DIGESTION AND ABSORPTION OF FAT

In principle, the absorption of fat from the intestine should be simple because dietary fats

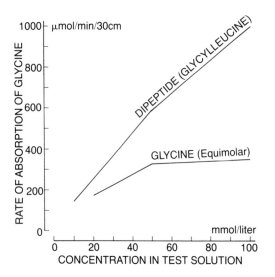

Figure 53-4. Rates of absorption of glycine in the dipeptide glycylleucine, and in a mixture of glycine and leucine as amino acids. Each solution contained the same concentration of glycine. Note the more rapid absorption of the dipeptide and the saturation of the transport system for glycine at a concentration of 50 mmol/liter. (Redrawn, with permission, from Adibi, S.A. 1971. Intestinal transport of dipeptides in man: Relative importance of hydrolysis and intact absorption. *J. Clin. Invest.* 50:2266.)

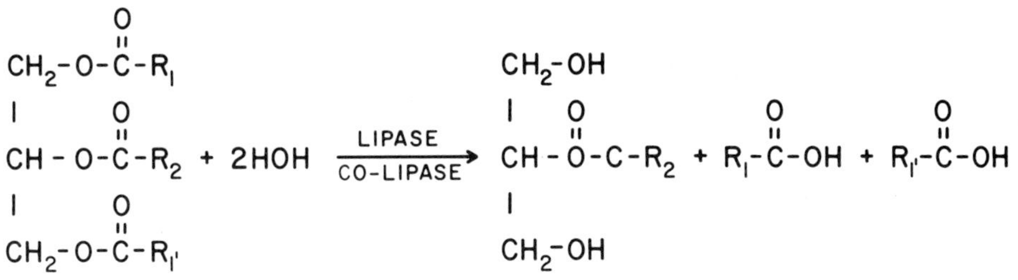

$$CH_2-O-\overset{\overset{\displaystyle O}{\|}}{C}-R_I$$
$$CH-O-\overset{\overset{\displaystyle O}{\|}}{C}-R_2 + 2HOH \xrightarrow[\text{CO-LIPASE}]{\text{LIPASE}} CH-O-\overset{\overset{\displaystyle O}{\|}}{C}-R_2 + R_I-\overset{\overset{\displaystyle O}{\|}}{C}-OH + R_{I'}-\overset{\overset{\displaystyle O}{\|}}{C}-OH$$
$$CH_2-O-\overset{\overset{\displaystyle O}{\|}}{C}-R_{I'}$$

with right products:

$$CH_2-OH$$
$$CH_2-OH$$

Figure 53-5. Hydrolysis of a triglyceride to a monoglyceride and two fatty acids.

are soluble in the lipid surfaces of the cells that line the intestine. In practice, the difficulty to be overcome is the insolubility of fat in the aqueous contents of the intestine, which would prevent the attainment of an adequate rate of diffusion to the intestinal villi.

The most common sign of intestinal malabsorption is steatorrhea, which is defined clinically as more than 6 g of fat/day in the feces. Because the fat-soluble vitamins and triglycerides use the same pathways, malabsorption of fat may cause deficiencies of vitamins A, D, E, and K. Most syndromes of vitamin deficiency cannot be detected for several months; however, deficiency of vitamin K, which decreases the rate of clotting of blood, becomes evident in only a few weeks.

Digestion of Fat in the Stomach

The stomach plays a part in the digestion and absorption of fat, as lipids are partly emulsified with water-soluble proteins and peptides in the gastric antrum. It is now recognized that the digestion of triglycerides in the stomach by pharyngeal lipase releases significant amounts of fatty acids, especially those that have chains of short and medium length.

Digestion of Fat in the Duodenum

PANCREATIC LIPASE
The splitting of fat by lipase and the formation of micelles with bile salts both contribute to the digestion of triglycerides. The triglycerides and the fatty acids formed from them virtually are insoluble in the aqueous contents of the lumen. Lipase, a protein that is soluble in water, acts only at the interface between the triglycerides and the aqueous phase. Thus, emulsification is essential to increase the surface area on which

the lipase can act. The hydrolysis of triglycerides by the combination of lipase and co-lipase removes anions of fatty acids from the 1 and 1' positions of glycerol and leaves a monoglyceride that has a fatty acid at the 2 position (Figure 53-5).

FATTY-ACID SATURATION AND CHAIN LENGTH
Fats that are liquid at body temperature are cleaved more rapidly by lipase. In general, the longer the chain of the constituent fatty acids and the smaller the number of double bonds, the higher the melting point of the fat and the less easily the fat is digested. Thus, tristearin, which has three saturated 18-carbon acids, is digested and absorbed incompletely. The composition of a triglyceride is determined partly by the temperature at which it is formed. For example, in the same animal, the fatty-acid chains of intra-abdominal fat, which exists in a relatively warm area, are longer and more saturated than those of the fat at the periphery of a limb, which is cooler. Consistent with the low temperatures of most bodies of water, fish oils contain a high proportion of unsaturated fatty acids.

MICELLAR PHASE
In the chemical reaction by which triglycerides are broken down, equilibrium is reached when the molar concentrations of triglycerides, monoglycerides, and fatty acids are about the same. For the rapid digestion of fat to continue, the end products (monoglycerides and anions of fatty acids) must be removed to prevent the attainment of equilibrium. Given the usual degree of emulsification and normal concentrations of pancreatic enzymes, the rate of hydrolysis of fat exceeds the rate of absorption. The micelles, each of which contains 20–40 molecules of lipid, provide a sink for the di-

gestion products of fat, thereby promoting the continued digestion of fat. Micelles are formed only if the concentration of bile salts exceeds a critical concentration (1–2 mmol/liter). Bile salts are essential for the production of micelles and are the elements that most commonly are missing when micelles do not form (see the section entitled "Formation of Bile" in Chapter 51). The core of the micellar particle is formed from monoglycerides, fatty acids, cholesterol, phospholipids, fat-soluble vitamins, and the lipid-soluble side of the bile salts. The functional consequences of the formation of micelles are the rapid hydrolysis of triglycerides and the transport of the fatty acids and monoglycerides from the lumen of the intestine to the surface of the enterocyte, where they are absorbed.

The rate-limiting step in the absorption of triglycerides is the passage of the products of fatty acids through the last millimeter of the water phase on the surface of the intestinal mucosa, which is known as the *unstirred layer*. The transport of high concentrations of fatty acids in micelles increases the rate of movement through the unstirred layer by a factor of about 100, as compared with simple diffusion of very low concentrations of fatty acids in an aqueous solution. The micelles transport fat somewhat as hemoglobin transports oxygen. Because of its large size, the micellar particle diffuses only one-seventh as fast as its constituent fatty acids diffuse when they are free in solution. However, the low rate of diffusion of the micelle is more than offset by the amount of fat the micelle transports at one time. The rate of exchange of fatty acids between the micelles and the aqueous environment is high because the average residence time in the micelles is only 10 milliseconds.

Absorption of Fat by Enterocytes

ESTERIFICATION

The fatty acids and monoglycerides in the micelles are believed to pass through the luminal face of the enterocytes by simple diffusion. The gradient for diffusion is maintained by esterification of the monoglyceride in the enterocytes with fatty acids that have been absorbed. Studies with isotopes show that fatty acids in the 1 and 1' positions of ingested triglycerides are randomly allotted to the triglycerides that are synthesized in the enterocytes, but the fatty acid in the 2 position in the ingested fat has a high probability of remaining with the same glycerol molecule and in the same position. Presumably, the monoglyceride is absorbed intact. The reformed triglyceride can be seen collecting in the enterocytes. The majority of the ingested lipid that contains long-chain fatty acids is mixed with phospholipids and is partly enrobed in lipoprotein. The particles that are formed enter the central lymphatic vessel of the villus and eventually pass through the thoracic duct and into the circulation via the lymph. The particles, known as chylomicrons, are large enough (up to 1 μm) to give the intestinal lymph, and even the circulating plasma, a milky appearance after a meal that contains fat. The chylomicrons eventually find their way into the fat depots. Triglycerides that contain chains of less than 10 carbons, and a small amount of triglycerides that contain long-chain acids, are absorbed directly into the portal blood without re-esterification. Short-chain fatty acids are found only in low amounts even in the richest source, which is dairy products. However, triglycerides that contain short-chain fatty acids are available commercially and can be given as food supplements to people who have defective digestion and absorption of lipids that contain long-chain fatty acids.

Steatorrhea

RESERVE FUNCTION

The term *steatorrhea* is used to indicate that a patient has excess fat in the stool (more than 6 g/day), although this amount is only 6%–12% of the fat that usually is taken in the diet per day. The digestive system has a large reserve of function; the rate of secretion of pancreatic enzyme must be reduced by about 90% before steatorrhea becomes apparent. Even then, only about half of the fat in the feces comes from the food; the other half comes from epithelial cells shed by the intestinal mucosa. The general principle of large reserves of function in the alimentary tract does not apply to the bile salts, where a small increase in the amount lost in the feces may reduce the pool of bile salts to a level at which not enough micelles are formed. Figure 53-6 shows that even if the entire biliary output and all of the secretions of the pancreas were diverted from the intestine, 50% of the fat in the diet still would be absorbed. The way in which fat is absorbed under these conditions is not known, but lingual lipase is presumed to be involved.

CLINICAL CORRELATION
53.1 Kidney Stones Occurring After Jejunal Bypass

CASE REPORT

The Patient: A 37-year-old man.

Principal Complaint: Acute abdominal pain radiating into the testicles.

History: The patient reported that the pain had begun abruptly, about 3 hours before he was seen. The pain was severe, with episodic increases, and the patient could not find a position in which he was comfortable. He had suffered 3 other episodes of abdominal discomfort during the preceding 8 years; each of these had lasted 6–10 hours and resolved spontaneously. The patient appeared well but in moderate distress. His oral temperature was 36.7 C, the pulse rate was 85/min (normal, 60–100/min), and the blood pressure was 130/80 mm Hg (normal, 90–140/60–90 mm Hg). Since the onset of the pain, the patient had urinated once and noted that the urine was "cola"-colored. Perusal of the patient's medical record revealed that he had undergone a jejunal bypass because of marked obesity, 5 years before admission. The patient had weighed 350 pounds at that time, and he weighed 186 pounds at the current admission. He had done well after the operation, except for a change in his bowel habits. Ever since the surgery, he had passed watery feces 6–10 times daily.

Clinical Examination: The hematocrit was 44% (normal, 45%–54%); the leukocyte count was 8000 cells/mm³ (normal, 4300–10,800 cells/mm³); the serum electrolytes and the general biochemical profile were normal. The urine contained red blood cells, white blood cells, and hyaline cast (coagulated protein).

An x-ray film of the abdomen revealed multiple calcifications in the area of the right kidney, and an intravenous pyelogram (x-ray film taken of contrast material) provided evidence of a filling defect in the ureter consistent with nephrolithiasis (kidney stones).

Comment: This patient did not absorb all of the fat he ate, because the jejunal bypass had decreased his absorptive surface. Although the decreased absorption of calories had helped him to lose weight, the unabsorbed fatty acids irritated the colon, causing it to secrete sodium and water. This irritation and the subsequent secretions caused the frequent, watery feces. (Because of untoward side effects such as these, this operation no longer is performed.) The same fatty acids combine with the calcium in the intestine (about 1 g/day ingested). Normally, a portion of the calcium combines with oxalate that is ingested and precipitates it as insoluble calcium oxalate, which is excreted in the feces. In this patient, however, very little calcium was left to combine with oxalate; thus, more oxalate was absorbed and subsequently excreted in the urine, where it combined with calcium to form insoluble "stones." These particles blocked the ureter, eroded the renal tissue, and caused bleeding. The reason for their occurrence in only one kidney in this patient is not known.

Treatment: The stones in the ureter were removed surgically. Sometimes stones also are found in the bladder, although none was found in this patient. The patient was instructed to take supplements of calcium salts to trap the oxalate in his gut.

PRECIPITATION OF CALCIUM SALTS

The loss of energy in the feces because of steatorrhea is trivial; the clinical interest in steatorrhea stems from the secondary effects. When the absorption of fat is defective, the feces contain fatty acids that form insoluble salts of Ca⁺⁺ and Mg⁺⁺ and, in the long term, may cause serious deficiencies of these ions. Calcium may be taken from the bones, which causes osteomalacia. Some green vegetables that are part of a typical diet contain oxalate, which usually is not well absorbed because it forms an insoluble salt with Ca^{++}. However,

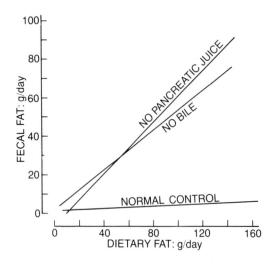

when the Ca^{++} of the colonic contents is complexed with fatty acids, a portion of the oxalate remains soluble, is absorbed, and eventually must be excreted in the urine. The end result is the formation of urinary stones that contain calcium oxalate, and this condition is a hazard for patients who have steatorrhea.

Figure 53-6.   Absorption of fat in a human without bile entering the lumen and without pancreatic lipase. Since these experiments were performed, the effects of lingual lipase in digesting fat in the stomach have been appreciated. (Redrawn, with permission, from Annegers, J.H. 1949. Fecal excretion of nutrients in impaired absorption: Analysis of available quantitative data. *Quart. Bull. Northwest. Univ. Med. School* 23:198.)

STUDY OUTLINE

DIGESTION AND ABSORPTION OF CAR- BOHYDRATES   Digestion decreases molecular weight and usually increases solubility in water.

DIETARY CARBOHYDRATES   Starch— about 25% amylose (straight chains with 1–4 links) and 75% amylopectin (branched chains with 1–4 and 1–6 links).

Disaccharides—sucrose and lactose.

Majority of carbohydrates are eaten as polysaccharides and digested to glucose (monosaccharide) before absorption.

Disaccharides are digested to monosaccharides before absorption.

OSMOTIC IMPLICATIONS OF CARBO- HYDRATES IN THE DIET   Mucosa of small intestine is highly permeable to water, which moves readily down osmotic gradient between plasma and lumen.

Large fluxes of water and Na^+ are minimized by reduced rate of gastric emptying when contents of duodenum are hyperosmolar, tight coupling of hydrolyzing mechanism for disaccharides, and rapid absorption of monosaccharides.

DIGESTION OF STARCH IN THE STOM- ACH   Some polysaccharide may be digested in stomach by salivary amylase before contents become too acidic.

DIGESTION OF STARCH IN THE SMALL INTESTINE   Pancreatic amylase in lumen of small intestine breaks 1–4 links of amylose.

Digestion of oligosaccharides of glucose by isomaltase on brush border breaks 1–6 links.

Digestion of sucrose by sucrase on brush border produces fructose and glucose; digestion of lactose by lactase produces galactose and glucose; digestion of maltose by maltase produces glucose.

Isomaltase and sucrase may be same enzyme.

LACTASE DEFICIENCY   Relatively common among blacks and Orientals; unabsorbed lactose causes intestinal gas and diarrhea.

INTESTINAL ABSORPTION OF MONO- SACCHARIDES

DIFFUSION   Monosaccharides are too insoluble in lipids to pass through cell membranes and too large to pass through pores or between cells.

FACILITATED DIFFUSION   Method of absorption of fructose.

Rate of absorption increases with concentration up to maximum; faster than rate of absorption of mannose, which is sugar of same molecular weight.

Process is specific for fructose.

Active transport of fructose has not been demonstrated.

ACTIVE TRANSPORT   Glucose and galactose are absorbed actively, but usually not against concentration gradient; apparently same carrier molecule for both.

CO-TRANSPORT OF GLUCOSE AND SO- DIUM   Concentration gradient of Na^+ is used to transport glucose on shared carrier.

DIGESTION AND ABSORPTION OF PROTEIN

SOURCES OF PROTEIN   In wealthy countries, protein mostly from meat and dairy products.

In undeveloped countries, protein mostly from grain.

PROTEOLYSIS   Proteins are split by enzymes; final intraluminal products are small peptides and amino acids.

GASTRIC PROTEOLYSIS   Only about 10% in 2 hours.

Characteristic optimum pH is about 2 for gastric proteolysis by pepsins.

INTESTINAL PROTEOLYSIS   Endopeptidases act in central region of molecules, carboxypeptidases are split off amino acids from C (carboxyl) terminal end.

Oligopeptides are hydrolyzed by enzymes fixed on microvillous (brush) border.

ABSORPTION

CARRIER SYSTEMS   Selectively transport amino acids, dipeptides, and tripeptides into enterocytes; only amino acids enter portal blood.

AMINO ACIDS   Higher forms of life use L-amino acids, for which carrier systems have high affinity.

Transported with Na^+, as glucose is, but no interaction between carriage of glucose and carriage of neutral amino acids.

Separate carrier for neutral and basic amino acids.

DIPEPTIDES AND TRIPEPTIDES   Up to half of protein intake may be absorbed into enterocytes as dipeptides and tripeptides; hydrolyzed in cytosol and enter portal blood as amino acids.

DIGESTION AND ABSORPTION OF FAT

Main difficulty is insolubility of digestion products in aqueous contents of intestinal lumen.

Malabsorption of fat is likely to be accompanied by deficiencies of fat-soluble vitamins.

DIGESTION OF FAT IN THE STOMACH

Lipids are emulsified with protein and peptides in gastric antrum.

Pharyngeal lipase releases fatty acids from short- and medium-chain triglycerides.

DIGESTION OF FAT IN THE DUODENUM

PANCREATIC LIPASE   Lipase is soluble in water, acts only at fat-water interface; emulsification increases surface area of interface and increases rate of hydrolysis.

Lipase and co-lipase are split off fatty acids from 1 and 1′ position, leaving monoglyceride with fatty acid in 2 position.

FATTY-ACID SATURATION AND CHAIN LENGTH   Liquidity of fats increases with unsaturation and with decrease in chain length of constituent fatty acids.

Liquidity and low melting point are significant in determining structural roles of fats and in increasing digestibility.

MICELLAR PHASE   Rate of hydrolysis of fat exceeds rate of absorption; removal of fatty acids and monoglycerides depends on removal of digestion products by micelles.

Bile salts are essential to formation of micelles.

Micelles transport fatty materials through aqueous luminal phase; diffuse slowly, but carry large amount of fat to mucosal absorbing surface.

ABSORPTION OF FAT BY ENTEROCYTES

ESTERIFICATION   Diffusion gradient for fatty acids from cytosol of enterocyte is maintained by esterification of fatty acids in cytosol.

Majority of monoglycerides are absorbed into enterocytes and used in resynthesis of triglycerides—fatty acid in the 2 position is not hydrolyzed.

Triglycerides are mixed with cholesterol, enrobed in protein, and exported in lymph as chylomicrons.

Lymph is absorbed into circulation through thoracic duct.

Triglycerides that have fatty acids of fewer than 10 carbons are absorbed directly into portal blood.

STEATORRHEA

RESERVE FUNCTION   Excess fat in feces, more than 6 g/day—about half of excess comes from epithelium shed by mucosa.

Intestine has large functional reserve—secretion of pancreatic lipase must be reduced by 90% to cause steatorrhea.

Small increased loss of bile salts causes steatorrhea because of limited synthetic capacity of liver.

PRECIPITATION OF CALCIUM SALTS   Loss of energy in stools through steatorrhea is trivial; secondary effects are clinically significant.

Deficiencies of Mg^{++} and Ca^{++} caused by precipitation as insoluble salts of fatty acids; prevents complexing and precipitation of oxalates from food with calcium; absorption of oxalate and excretion in urine causes oxalate-containing urinary stones.

BIBLIOGRAPHY

Adibi, S.A. 1978. Intestinal absorption of amino acids and peptides. *Viewpoints in Digestive Diseases.* Volume 10 (4). Thorofare, New Jersey: American Gastroenterological Association.

Annegers, J.H. 1949. Fecal excretion of nutrients in impaired absorption: Analysis of available quantitative data. *Quart. Bull. Northwestern Univ. Med. School* 23:198.

Barrowman, J.A. 1978. *Physiology of the Gastric Intestinal Lymphatic System.* Cambridge, England: Cambridge University Press.

Beazell, J.M. 1941. Re-examination of the role of the stomach in the digestion of carbohydrate and protein. *Am. J. Physiol.* 132:42.

Beck, I.T. 1973. The role of pancreatic enzymes in digestion. *Am. J. Clin. Nutr.* 23:311.

Bisgaier, C., and Glickman, R.M. 1983. Intestinal synthesis, secretion, and transport of lipoprotein. *Annu. Rev. Physiol.* 45:625.

Borgström, B. 1980. Importance of phospholipids, pancreatic phospholipase A_2, and fatty acids for the digestion of dietary fat. In vitro experiments with the porcine enzymes. *Gastroenterol.* 78:954.

Carey, M.C.; Small, D.M.; and Bliss, C.M. 1983. Lipid digestion and absorption. *Annu. Rev. Physiol.* 45:651.

Creamer, B. 1974. *The Small Intestine.* London: Heinemann.

Csaky, T.Z. 1974. *Intestinal Absorption and Malabsorption.* New York: Raven Press.

Desmulle, P. 1968. Pancreatic lipase. In *Handbook of Physiology.* Section 6. Alimentary Canal. Chapter 123. Edited by C.F. Code. Washington, D.C.: American Physiological Society.

Gray, G.M., and Cooper, H.L. 1972. Protein digestion and absorption. *Gastroenterol.* 61:535.

Hamosh, M.; Klaeverman, H.L.; Wolf, R.O., et al. 1975. Pharyngeal lipase and digestion of dietary triglycerides in man. *J. Clin. Invest.* 55:908.

Johnson, L.R. (ed.). 1981. *Physiology of the Gastrointestinal Tract.* New York: Raven Press.

Johnston, J.M. 1968. Mechanism of fat absorption. In *Handbook of Physiology.* Section 6. Alimentary Canal. Chapter 70. Edited by C.F. Code. Washington, D.C.: American Physiological Society.

Lasser, R.B.; Levitt, M.D.; and Bond, J.H. 1976. Studies of intestinal gas after ingestion of a standard meal. *Gastroenterol.* 70:906.

Matthews, D.M. 1977. Protein absorption then and now. *Gastroenterol.* 73:1267.

Semenza, G. 1968. Intestinal oligosaccharides and disaccharides. In *Handbook of Physiology.* Section 6. Alimentary Canal. Edited by C.F. Code. Washington, D.C.: American Physiological Society.

Semenza, G. 1968. Pancreatic amylase. In *Handbook of Physiology.* Section 6. Alimentary Canal. Edited by C.F. Code. Washington, D.C.: American Physiological Society.

54

The Colon

CHAPTER CONTENTS

FUNCTIONS

Absorption

The colon is a drying organ—two liters of ileal contents flow into the cecum and colon and are reduced to less than 200 g of feces every 24 hours. Thus, the colon transports along its lumen material that changes from a liquid to a pasty solid. The colon is essential for comfort and convenience but not for existence. If, for the treatment of disease, the terminal ileum is brought out through the abdominal wall (an ileostomy) and the colon is removed, a normal life span still can be expected. The colon does not absorb food materials to a significant extent; thus, "nutritive enemas" do not nourish. On the other hand, the colon plays a significant part in absorbing Na^+ and water (Figures 54-1 and 54-2).

Propulsion

TYPES OF MOVEMENT

Three types of propulsive movements are recognized, as follows:

1. Haustral shuttling of contents back and forth (Figure 54-3), which mixes the contents and aids the absorption of water (by generating a

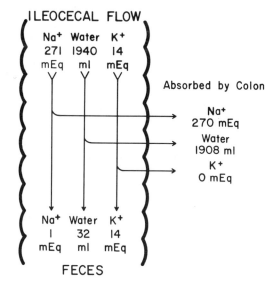

Figure 54-1. The mean volume of water and the content of Na^+ and K^+ in the ileocecal flow of humans. The cations (271 mEq) plus unmeasured anions (271 mEq) in 1908 ml of water absorbed equals 284 mOsm/liter, which is isosmotic with plasma. (Reprinted, by permission of the publisher from "Capacity of the human colon to absorb fluid," by J.C. Debongnie and S.F. Phillips. *Gastroenterol.* 74:698. Copyright 1978 by Elsevier North-Holland, Inc.)

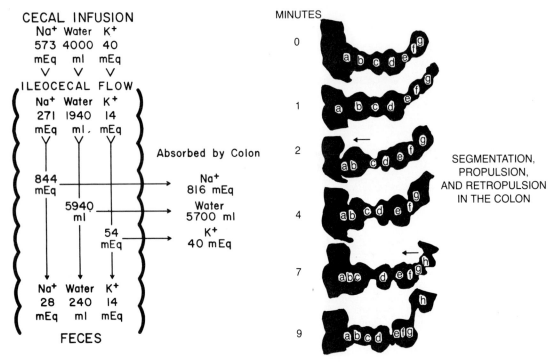

Figure 54-2. The increase of fecal water, Na^+, and K^+ after infusion of 4000 ml of a solution of electrolytes into the cecum during a 24-hour period. Note that fecal water and electrolytes increased slightly (see Figure 54-1). The normal input from the ileum to the cecum plus the infusate was absorbed almost entirely. Note that the colon does not facultatively excrete or fail to absorb Na^+, even when a gross excess of Na^+ is given. The kidney is the only organ that excretes Na^+ and water facultatively. (Reprinted, by permission of the publisher, from "Capacity of the human colon to absorb fluid," by J.C. Debongnie and S.F. Phillips. *Gastroenterol.* 74:698. Copyright 1978 by Elsevier North-Holland, Inc.)

Figure 54-3. Haustral activity, defined as segmentation that does not move colonic contents farther than to neighboring haustra (recesses). This figure is based on tracings from radiographs of contents of a human transverse colon. Barium outlines in the colon developed 12–24 hours after the barium was taken by mouth. The numbers at left are minutes between x-ray frames. Note the slowness of colonic movements. In the frame at 2 minutes, masses *a* and *b* move in the retrograde direction. Between the 4-minute frame and the 9 minutes frame, *a*, *b*, and *c* move forward and *e, f,* and *g* move backward (arrows). The number of haustra is not constant. To create such a lively scene, carbachol (cholinergic) was injected. Normally, the activity would be much less.

pressure gradient). Material is moved forward mainly because of the entrance of ileal effluent proximally and the elimination of feces distally.

2. Contraction of a group of haustra together. This propels liquids and semisolids, but the mechanical effectiveness decreases as the viscosity of the contents increases. Solid contents, especially in the form of discrete masses of feces, are merely compressed and solidified by this form of contraction. Hard feces probably stimulate an increased secretion of mucus, and the feces are thus softened and lubricated.

3. Mass peristalsis, a stripping wave of muscular contraction that advances down a length of bowel at about 30 cm/min, is preceded by a wave of relaxation along its course. About half of the population experience one or occasionally more of these movements in the distal colon each day, usually after breakfast. The rest of the population can achieve this movement by taking a peristaltic stimulant, that is, a laxative that sensitizes the submucosa so that it responds to stretch by a propulsive rather than a localized contraction. "Constipated" people seem never to experience a spontaneous mass peristalsis unless they take supplements of a bulk-producing agent, such as bran, which keeps the mass of bowel contents both soft and continuous (i.e., not broken up into discrete solid masses by haustral contraction).

A

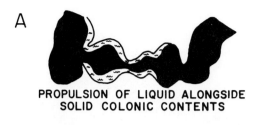

**PROPULSION OF LIQUID ALONGSIDE
SOLID COLONIC CONTENTS**

B

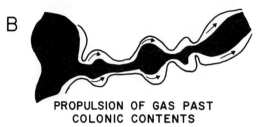

**PROPULSION OF GAS PAST
COLONIC CONTENTS**

Figure 54-4. Propulsion of liquid and gaseous contents. **A.** A few seconds after liquid cecal contents pass slowly into the transverse colon around the fecal masses already present, reflex contraction distally prevents direct passage of the liquid into the rectum. **B.** Because of its lower viscosity, gas passing distally from the proximal colon moves rapidly beyond the region of reflex contraction; then, it can pass through the gut and be voided as flatus. Swallowed air or gas produced in the colon and trapped in either the small intestine or the large intestine is a hazard in intestinal paralysis (ileus) or obstruction. (Redrawn, with permission, from Ritchie, J.A., et al. 1962. Motor activity of the sigmoid colon of humans. *Gastroenterol.* 43:642. © 1962. The Williams & Wilkins Co., Baltimore.)

LIQUID AND GASEOUS CONTENTS

After meals, the liquid contents of the ileum are forced into the colon, where they may distend a number of consecutive haustra and induce a secondary contraction of the distal circumferential smooth muscle. The liquid continues to move forward as long as the primary contraction that propels it lasts longer than the 4-second latency of the secondary contraction. In this way, ileal effluent may be transported over and around masses of more solid consistency, as far as the transverse colon or even farther (Figure 54-4A). Thus, the principle of "last in, last out" does not apply to the contents of the colon.

Gas infused into the duodenum appears at the anus within 30 minutes, which indicates that gases and liquids are transported through the colon separately. In principle, the transport of gas in the colon is similar to the transport of

liquid, but the gas moves forward much more rapidly than the liquid. This occurs because the gas passes around the solid matter, as the liquid does; however, because of its low viscosity, the gas moves as much as 40 cm before each of the successively distended distal segments contracts. These contractions squeeze the tail of the column of gas and drive it onward; thus, the secondary contraction that opposes the advance of liquid aids the advance of gas. This mechanism is illustrated in Figure 54-4B.

SOLID CONTENTS

The colon is about 150 cm long, and the mean rate of transport is such that solid contents are moved the entire length of the colon in about 24 hours. Propulsive movements are intermittent, averaging about one every 2 hours during fasting and about one per hour after a meal. Most movements of the colon are slow (Figure 54-3) and scarcely perceptible without time-lapse cinematography. This contrasts sharply with the peristaltic transport of feces that occurs spontaneously in some people and after laxatives are taken in other people, in which the contents of the descending colon and the distal half of the transverse colon are moved at an average rate of 25 cm/min, usually as a prelude to defecation.

Pressures in the Lumen

EFFECT OF BULK

Many modern, refined foods contain little fiber, so that civilization and small stools are related. In civilized humans, small pouches of mucosa (diverticula) often herniate through the colonic muscle. If these diverticula become inflamed, a condition called *diverticulitis,* they cause pain and may endanger life. It is reasonable to suppose that these diverticula are caused by increased pressure in the colon, although some diverticula may reflect a weakness in the wall of the colon. When the fecal volume is small, as it is when the fiber content of the diet is low, the bowel becomes narrow. The circular muscle of the colon thus is at a mechanical advantage in developing pressure because of the relationship expressed by the law of Laplace (a given tension in circular muscle generates more pressure as the radius decreases). The high intraluminal pressure that develops may cause the diverticula that are formed. Increasing the fiber content of the diet by adding wheat bran, for example, decreases

CLINICAL CORRELATION
54.1   Fecal Incontinence

CASE REPORT

The Patient: A 19-year-old male.

Principal Complaint: Uncontrolled defecation after injury of the spinal cord.

History: After a college fraternity party, the patient dove into the shallow end of a swimming pool and struck his head on the bottom. He was paralyzed immediately.

Clinical Course: In the emergency room, the patient was found to have a high-cervical fracture and quadriplegia (paralysis of all four limbs). He was transferred subsequently to a spinal-care unit, where he slowly regained some function in the upper extremities. His rehabilitative program was complicated by uncontrolled passage of feces; this occurred several times a day and led to the development of an ulcerated area on the skin of his buttocks.

The neurological examination was consistent with a sensorimotor neural defect below C-4. The rectal sphincter had no noticeable tone, and the rectal vault was filled with soft feces. A 5×8 cm area of eroded, ulcerated skin was found on his left buttock.

Comment: Control of defecation in patients who have lesions of the spinal cord depends on reflex activity of the part of the spinal cord isolated from the brain. The system is effective only when the rectum is evacuated periodically. A full rectum is difficult to control even when the puborectal muscle and the external sphincter, which maintain fecal continence, function normally. Both of these muscles depend on somatic nerves for their contraction. Because the section of the spinal cord was so high, this patient was completely unaware of the fullness of his bowel (or bladder). Patients whose spinal cords are damaged at the thoracic level may have vague awareness, probably mediated through visceral afferent nerves.

Outcome: After much effort to deal with his incontinence, the patient elected to have a low-left-sided colostomy and subsequently evacuated once a day. This made possible much better personal hygiene, and he was in much better spirits thereafter.

---

the intraluminal pressure in the sigmoid colon by increasing the volume of and softening the feces.

ANORECTAL FUNCTION

Defecation

NEURAL CONTROL
Defecation is a spinal reflex action that is partly under higher central nervous system control. In cases of accidental complete section of the thoracic spinal cord in humans, reflex actions below the section are suppressed almost completely. Feces are retained and must be removed mechanically (e.g., by means of enemas). After only a few weeks, however, the spinal reflexes resume, and defecation occurs automatically, without control. Patients in this condition are not aware of the need to defecate, nor are they aware that the event has occurred, except indirectly. However, digital stimulation of the anal sphincter enables the patient to initiate defecation reflexly at a convenient time.

ANATOMICAL BASIS
The arrangement and innervation of the structures of the rectum and the anal canal are shown in Figure 54-5. The anal sphincter has an inner sheath of smooth muscle, which is a continuation of the circular muscle layer of the rectum, and an outer sheath of skeletal muscle. The smooth muscle is supplied by extrinsic parasympathetic and sympathetic nerves that extend into the plexus in the wall of the rectum. The skeletal muscle is controlled through a somatic nerve, the pudendal nerve. The lower

CLINICAL CORRELATION
54.2   Spastic Colon

CASE REPORT

Patient: A 43-year-old woman.

Principal Complaint: Abnormal bowel movements.

History: The patient related that her feces had been hard and pencil-thin, and that she had experienced some crampy discomfort in the left upper quadrant of the abdomen. These conditions were not clearly related to meals and were partially relieved by bowel movements. The patient also expressed fear that she had cancer of the colon. She remembered nothing abnormal about her bowel movements before high school, at which time she had begun to notice occasional constipation, and her mother shared laxative with her. When the patient had gone to college, she had begun having episodes of explosive diarrhea with bowel movements 3 or 4 times a day, but not severe enough at night to disturb her sleep. She had been married shortly after she graduated from college and again developed constipation, with the passage of feces in small, rock-hard segments. After the birth of her second child, the patient had begun to experience aching in the lower abdomen, and had had a hysterectomy at age 28. Her diarrhea and constipation had continued to alternate with cycles of a few weeks to a few months. She had developed dyspeptic symptoms in the right upper quadrant, particularly

after fatty meals. Subsequently, she had had a cholecystectomy (gallbladder removal), at age 34.

Clinical Examination: The patient appeared healthy, mildly obese, and slightly anxious. The results of the examination, which included proctoscopy (inspection of the anal canal and rectum) and barium enema (in which barium sulfate is introduced into the colon as a contrast medium for x-ray pictures), were normal. A diagnosis of irritable bowel syndrome, or "spastic colon," aggravated by psychological stress, was reached.

Comment: Spastic colon is an intermittent condition that may occur even in psychologically healthy persons at time of stress, such as examinations, marriage, divorce, or bereavement, but the precise mechanisms are not known. This patient had an abnormally close relationship between her emotions and the secretory and motor functions of her colon. Long-continued, excessive activity of the colonic muscle usually retards the passage of the contents, causing them to be excessively dry and hard. In diarrhea the colon secretes more and contracts less; hence, the contents move faster.

Outcome: The patient was instructed to take a diet high in bran and other fiber, and her condition improved markedly. Unfortunately, not all patients who suffer from "spastic colon" are relieved by this diet.

part of the epithelial lining of the anal canal is supplied by somatic afferent fibers.

ANAL SENSATION

Sensations that enable one to determine the nature of the rectal contents are vital for accepted social behavior; however, the rectal mucosa can be cut, pinched, or burned without any sensation being felt. On the other hand, the lining of the anal canal is sensitive to mechanical and thermal stimulation. When pressure in the colon is measured by the use of a catheter, a zone of high pressure, which is the functional

sign of the presence of the anal sphincter, extends for about 5 cm from the anal verge (Figure 54-5). By inserting a speculum and testing sensation with a stiff hair, it was found that the level of sensation extends only 3 cm from the anal verge. Thus, the normal closure of the anal sphincter prevents the rectal contents from reaching the sensitive region of the anal canal. When the rectum is distended abruptly, the anal sphincter relaxes and allows the sensitive region of the anal canal to give a sensory discharge that signals the nature of the contents, either solid, liquid, or gaseous.

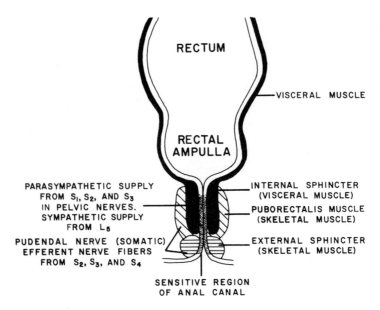

Figure 54-5. Anatomical features of the rectum and anal region. The rectal plexus of nerves and cell bodies that control the internal sphincter and the levator ani are not shown.

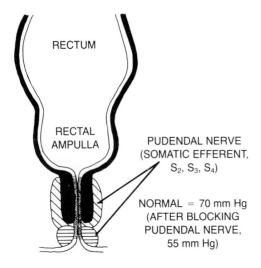

Figure 54-6. Decrease of pressure in the anal canal caused by block of somatic nerves. Major part of resting pressure is maintained by the internal sphincter. The external sphincter and the puborectal muscle have constant tone as a result of nerve impulses in the somatic pudendal nerve.

ANORECTAL REFLEX ACTIONS

When the rectum is empty, as it usually is, the pressure in the anal canal is held at about 28 mm Hg, while the pressure in the rectal ampulla is much less. If the rectum is not emptied by defecation, it tends to empty back into the descending colon. The high pressure in the anal canal mainly is the result of the continued contraction of the smooth muscle of the internal sphincter, which is partly under the influence of the sympathetic nervous system (Figure 54-5). However, the pressure that is generated by the internal sphincter depends mainly on the local nerve plexus. Therefore, this pressure persists after complete extrinsic denervation (Figure 54-6). Normally, when the rectal ampulla is distended slightly, the striated external sphincter and puborectal muscles contract immediately, and the pressure within the anal canal increases. This contraction is followed by inhibition of the internal sphincter for about 8 seconds, after which the internal sphincter resumes its normal resting tone in spite of the continued distention (Figure 54-7). Distention by a volume of less than 50 ml usually causes no sensation, but a volume of 100 ml or more elicits the feeling of a need to defecate.

When the volume that distends the rectal ampulla is greater than 150 ml, the internal sphincter remains inhibited in spite of the persistent distention. The individual now has an urgent desire to defecate, but usually can maintain continence by voluntary contraction of the external sphincter and puborectal muscles. The puborectal muscle pulls the superior part of the anal canal forward toward the pubis and maintains an angulation between the anal canal, which runs upward and toward the pubis, and the rectum, which runs upward

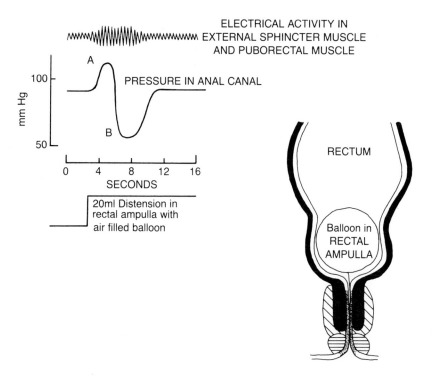

ELECTRICAL ACTIVITY IN
EXTERNAL SPHINCTER MUSCLE
AND PUBORECTAL MUSCLE

Figure 54-7. Pressure and electrical activity in muscle caused by inflation of a balloon in the rectum. Reflex contraction of external sphincter (A) is mediated by impulses through the pudendal nerve. Note the fall in pressure in the anal canal (B) caused by relaxation of the internal sphincter muscle, which contracts again in spite of continued distention. This fall and subsequent rise is seen in patients in whom the somatic pudendal, sympathetic, and parasympathetic nerves are blocked. Thus, changes are caused by local nerve afferent fibers and efferent fibers in the rectal wall. When the rectum is inflated by a volume of 20 ml, contraction of the striated muscle of the external sphincter and the puborectal muscle is mediated through the somatic pudendal nerve. This is a spinal reflex that occurs after spinal transection. Relaxation of the internal sphincter is mediated independent of extrinsic innervation. After about 8 seconds, the internal sphincter regains its previous tone. No sensation is aroused. When the rectum is inflated by 100 ml of air, the same reflex responses occur, but, in addition, a desire to defecate is felt, and the internal sphincter does not increase its tension while the rectum remains inflated. As the rectum is distended further, the desire to defecate increases. The distending balloon may be extruded uncontrollably as contractions of the rectum increase and contractions of the external sphincter decrease.

and toward the sacrum. This angle provides a mechanical device that opposes the entrance of material into the anal canal.

INVOLUNTARY DEFECATION

To initiate defecation requires distention of the rectum, which may be accomplished by a mass movement of the contents of the pelvic colon. Because a mass movement seldom occurs more than once a day, the volume of the colonic contents is enough to inhibit the internal sphincter. When defecation is set in motion or no longer can be prevented, the contractions of the external sphincter and the levator ani muscle usually are reduced. The striated muscle of the external sphincter also is subject to reflex control from the spinal cord through the pudendal nerve. After spinal section in humans, distention of the rectum sets off defecation automatically. The success of the event stems from complete relaxation of the striated muscle. The degree of relaxation of the internal sphincter, which is dominated by local reflexes, is the same as in normal people.

VOLUNTARY DEFECATION

To initiate defecation voluntarily, a sustained contraction of the loaded rectum is needed to drive the rectal contents through the relaxed levator ani muscle and down to the external sphincter. Voluntarily increased intra-abdominal pressure does not augment the expulsive effort until the head of the mass has passed through the muscle wall of the pelvic floor.

Passage of Gas

Studies indicate that when the intra-abdominal pressure is increased to expel gas, voluntary contraction of the puborectal muscle and the external sphincter prevents the entry of solid material into the anal canal. Use of this mechanism leads to occasional mishaps when the rectal contents are liquid.

STUDY OUTLINE

FUNCTIONS

ABSORPTION   Na$^+$ and water are absorbed in the colon, but food materials are not absorbed.

Colon dries ileal contents to feces, greatly reducing volume.

Colon is convenient but not essential to life.

PROPULSION

TYPES OF MOVEMENT Shuttling of contents back and forth, with gradual forward movement.

Contraction of several haustra simultaneously—propels only low-viscosity material.

Mass peristalsis; rapid and complete.

Adequate intake of bulk and water aid movement.

LIQUID AND GASEOUS CONTENTS After meals, liquid ileal contents are forced into colon, pass around pasty material already there.

Distention causes contraction of haustra, but several haustra must be filled before progress of liquid is checked.

Because of lower viscosity, gases run ahead of contracting region—driven by it, not retarded.

Gases can pass from duodenum to anus in 30 minutes; occasionally move 10 cm/sec.

SOLID CONTENTS Travel length of colon in about 24 hours.

Propulsion intermittent—once every 2 hours during fasting, once each hour after meals.

Net movement is slow under fasting conditions, peristaltic transport of feces before defecation is fast—about 25 cm/min.

PRESSURES IN THE LUMEN

EFFECT OF BULK Bulk is reduced in modern diets (less fiber); reduces mass and water content of feces.

Reduced volume, hence radius, of colon gives circular muscle mechanical advantage in generating intraluminal pressure; related to frequent occurrence of colonic diverticuli.

ANORECTAL FUNCTION

DEFECATION

NEURAL CONTROL Spinal reflex action normally is under voluntary control; defecation occurs in few weeks after accidental spinal section in humans, without direct awareness of need.

ANATOMICAL BASIS Smooth muscle of anal sphincter is supplied by autonomic nerves.

Outer sheath of striated muscle is controlled by somatic motor nerves, sensitive mucosal lining of lower anal canal is supplied by somatic sensory nerves.

ANAL SENSATION Rectal mucosa is insensitive to cutting, pinching, or burning.

Distal 3 cm of anal canal is sensitive to tactile stimulation; proximal closure protects this region from stimulation.

Distention of rectum causes relaxation of upper smooth muscle of anal sphincter, sensitive region is stimulated by rectal contents.

ANORECTAL REFLEX ACTIONS When rectum is empty, pressure is less in lumen than in anal sphincter.

Pressure mainly is result of smooth muscle contraction, controlled by autonomic nerves of local plexus.

Slight distention of rectum causes contraction of striated muscle of external sphincter and relaxation of smooth muscle of internal sphincter.

Experimental distention with 100 ml of air causes sensation of need to defecate.

Continence is maintained by voluntary contraction of puborectal muscle and external striated muscle sphincter, even when distention of rectum causes relaxation of internal sphincter and urgent desire to defecate.

INVOLUNTARY DEFECATION Defecation is initiated by distention of rectum; inhibits contraction of sphincters reflexly.

Occurs automatically after spinal section in humans.

VOLUNTARY DEFECATION Sustained contraction of distended rectum augmented by increased intra-abdominal pressure drives rectal contents through reflexly relaxed internal sphincter while external sphincter is not voluntarily contracted.

PASSAGE OF GAS   Deliberate increase of intra-abdominal pressure and voluntary contraction of puborectal muscle and external sphincter are used to empty rectum of gas; hazardous when rectum unexpectedly contains liquid.

BIBLIOGRAPHY

Brodribb, A.J.M.; Condon, R.E.; Cowles, V., et al. 1979. Effect of dietary fiber on intraluminal pressure and myoelectrical activity of left colon in monkeys. *Gastroenterol.* 77:70.

Daniel, E.E.; Bennett, A.; Misiewicz, J.J., et al. 1975. Symposium on colonic function. *Gut* 16:298.

Degongnie, J.C., and Phillips, S.F. 1978. Capacity of the human colon to absorb fluid. *Gastroenterol.* 74:698.

Duthie, H.L., and Bennett, R.C. 1963. The relation of sensation in the anal canal to the functional anal sphincter: A possible factor in anal continence. *Gut* 4:179.

Frenckner, B. 1975. Function of the anal sphincters in spinal man. *Gut:* 16:638.

Frenckner, B., and Euler, C.V. 1975. Influence of pudendal block on the function of the anal sphincters. *Gut* 16:482.

Frenckner, B., and Ihre, T. 1976. Influence of autonomic nerves on the internal anal sphincter in man. *Gut* 17:306.

Hardcastle, J.D., and Mann, C.V. 1968. Study of large bowel peristalsis. *Gut* 9:512.

Johnson, L.R. (ed.). 1981. *Physiology of the Gastrointestinal Tract.* New York: Raven Press.

Lasser, R.B.; Bond, J.H.; and Levitt, M.D. 1975. The role of intestinal gas in functional abdominal pain. *N. Engl. J. Med.* 293:524.

Mendeloff, A.I. (ed.). 1968. Defecation. In *Handbook of Physiology.* Section 6. Alimentary Canal. Chapter 103, part V. Edited by C.F. Code. Washington, D.C.: American Physiological Society.

Phillips, S.F., and Edwards, D.A.W. 1965. Some aspects of anal continence and defecation. *Gut* 6:396.

Ritchie, J.A. 1968. Colonic motor activity and bowel function. *Gut* 9:442.

Ritchie, J.A. 1970. Transport of colonic contents in the irritable colon syndrome. *Gut* 11:668.

Ritchie, J.A.; Ardran, G.M.; and Truelove, S.C. 1962. Motor activity of the sigmoid colon of humans. *Gastroenterol.* 43:642.

Roth, H.P., and Mehlman, M.A. 1978. Symposium on role of dietary fiber in health. *Am. J. Clin. Nutr.* 31 (Suppl.).

PART

IX

ENDOCRINOLOGY AND REPRODUCTION

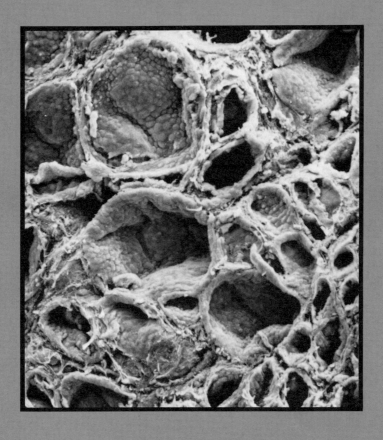

55

General Principles of Endocrine Physiology

CHAPTER CONTENTS

GENERAL BACKGROUND

Two regulatory systems transmit messages and correlate function in the body. One is the central nervous system, which makes direct anatomical connections and releases transmitters in a highly localized fashion; hence, it acts quickly. The other is the endocrine system, which produces its effects through chemical substances released into the blood. These chemicals must reach their target organs through the circulation; hence, the endocrine system acts more slowly but also has a more prolonged effect. These two systems are linked in function and development. The central nervous system, acting through the hypothalamus, strongly influences the endocrine system. In turn, certain hormones act on the central nervous system; in the fetus, these hormones affect the organization of the central nervous system, and in the adult, they affect the activation of the central nervous system.

HORMONES

Hormones are substances that are secreted by endocrine glands, portions of the brain, the gastrointestinal tract, certain tumors, and, possibly, from other cells and tissue. The word *hormone* comes from a Greek word that means *to urge on* (i.e., *to excite*). However, hormones can both stimulate and inhibit. The first substance designated as a hormone was *secretin*, which is released in the gastrointestinal tract and acts on the pancreas. The term *secretin* was coined by two English physiologists, Bayliss and Starling, in 1905. Traditionally, a hormone is defined as being a discrete chemical substance that is produced by an organ or tissue, is discharged into the bloodstream in minute concentrations, and influences markedly the functions of other organs or body systems. This definition may have to be altered, however, because certain hormones, particularly those in the gastrointestinal tract, appear to be released locally by cytoplasmic processes that terminate on other cells.

Steroids

The steroids are derivatives of cyclopentanoperhydrophenanthrene (Figure 55-1); the basic precursor for this structure in the body is cholesterol. The hormones that make up the steroid group are the estrogens, the androgens, progesterone, and the hormones of the adrenal cortex.

Derivatives of Amino Acids

The catecholamines—epinephrine, norepinephrine (Figure 55-2), and dopamine—and the thyroid hormones are derived from single amino acids. Other hormones consist of chains of amino acids, which form polypeptides (Figure 55-3) or proteins. These include the releasing hormones of the hypothalamus, the hormones of the pituitary gland, the pancreatic hormones, and the parathyroid hormone.

Traditional Criteria for the Endocrine Gland

Each endocrine gland is essential for the normal function of some other organ or body system. This can be demonstrated by removing or destroying one of the endocrine glands; the state of impaired function is designated by adding the prefix *hypo* to the name of the gland that is deficient (e.g., *hypothyroid*). The inadequate function that is believed to be caused by the destruction or removal of a particular endocrine gland must be corrected by administering extracts of that gland. If too much of the extract is supplied and the organ or body system becomes overactive, or if an intact gland is overactive, the condition is designated by adding the prefix *hyper* to the name of the gland that is implicated. Finally, the hormone that produced the effect attributed to a gland must be identified in the venous blood coming from that gland.

Newer Concepts of Endocrine Function

A variety of experimental evidence suggests that endocrine functions are not limited to glands and specialized tissues. It has been proposed that hormones initially provided means of intercellular communication in simpler forms of life, and specialized glands developed after organisms had become highly differentiated and complex. Very sensitive methods of radioimmunoassay and receptor identification

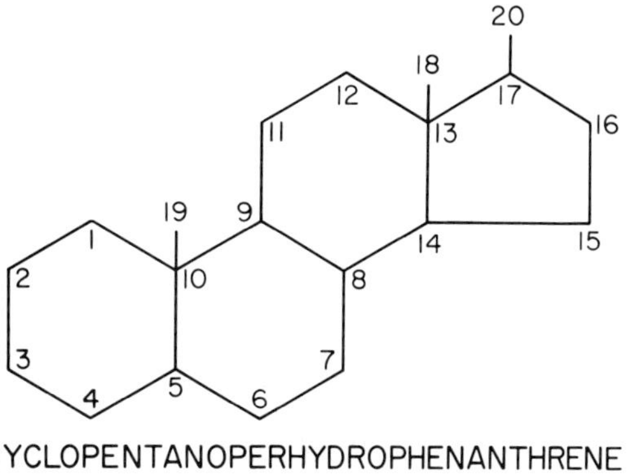

CYCLOPENTANOPERHYDROPHENANTHRENE

Figure 55-1. The chemical structure (and its numbering system) to which all of the steroid hormones are related.

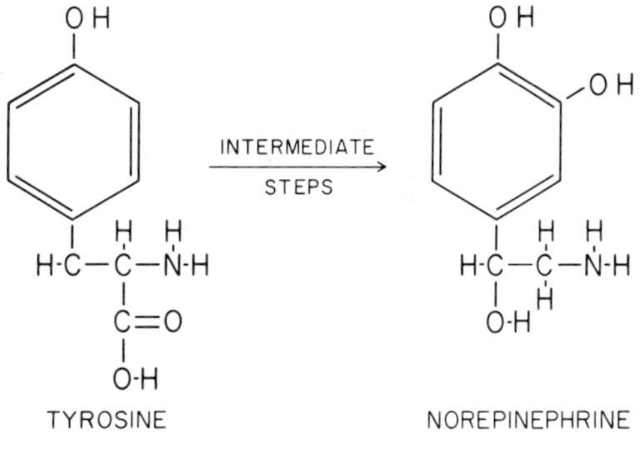

TYROSINE   NOREPINEPHRINE

Figure 55-2. Example of a hormone (norepinephrine) derived from a single amino acid (tyrosine).

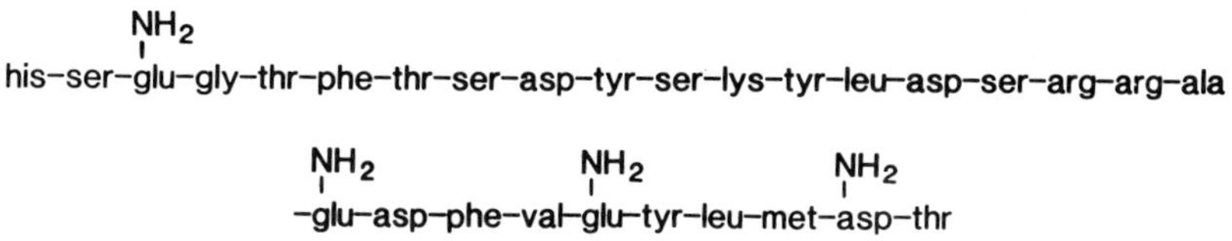

Figure 55-3. The structure of glucagon, a peptide hormone.

suggest that hormones are produced and distributed more widely in the human body than previously was supposed. Hence, some of the simpler systems still may operate, as yet incompletely characterized. Eventually, a broader concept of endocrine function may be demonstrated.

General Characteristics of Hormones

Most hormones are released into the bloodstream and carried throughout the body by the circulating blood; they regulate the processes of the body, such as the synthesis and the degradation of chemicals and the utilization of energy. Other hormones appear to be released locally. Hormones are chemically specific; for example, the removal of an amino group or the hydrogenation of a double bond may decrease considerably or abolish entirely the activity of a particular hormone. The rate of secretion of a particular hormone may vary under different circumstances. In some cases, the resting rate is modified by specific stimuli; for example, the rate of secretion of insulin is increased when the level of glucose in the blood increases, and the rate of release of aldosterone is increased by angiotensin II. In other cases, secretion waxes and wanes cyclically (e.g., the releasing hormones of the hypothalamus and the hormones of the anterior pituitary gland). Quantities of hormones are lost continuously because the compounds are metabolized or excreted; hence, each endocrine organ must produce hormones continuously to maintain the appropriate levels in the circulation. Many hormones do not circulate in the bloodstream in their free forms. Some hormones, which are not soluble in water, are carried in the plasma bound to specific carrier proteins (e.g., thyroid hormone and the steroid hormones). In these cases, the bound hormone is inactive and only the free form produces the characteristic effect.

FEEDBACK

Certain hormones are controlled by negative feedback; that is, an increased concentration in the bloodstream of the substance that is being secreted inhibits the stimulus to secrete, and a decreased concentration increases the stimulus to secrete. This type of regulation tends to maintain a constant level of the hormone. Positive feedback, in which the stimulus to produce increases as the concentration increases or decreases as the concentration decreases, causes extreme instability and is useful only in

special circumstances, such as the burst of gonadotropin that brings about ovulation (see the section entitled "Control Systems" in Chapter 1).

HOMEOSTASIS

Hormones are involved intimately in the maintenance of *homeostasis*, which is the constancy of the internal environment in which most of the cells of the body live (see the section entitled "The Internal Environment: Homeostasis" in Chapter 1).

Mechanisms of Action of Hormones

RECEPTORS

All organs are exposed to hormones, but only certain organs respond to hormones. This happens because hormones interact with active patches or molecules on the surface of the target cells, which are called *receptors* (see the section entitled "Surface Receptors" in Chapter 2). The appropriate hormones bind to the receptors and collect in target organs. The receptors are highly specific for certain molecular configurations, and only slight changes of structure of the hormone decrease its activity markedly, or, if the altered structure binds to the receptor, it may reduce or prevent the hormonal effect by preventing interaction of the true hormone with the receptor. The number of receptors in an organ or tissue is not fixed or constant. Many cells seem to react to persistently high levels of certain hormones by decreasing the number of active receptors. In addition, a particular hormone also may affect the receptors for other hormones. These changes seem likely to represent control mechanisms that currently are not understood.

PERMEABILITY OF MEMBRANES

Certain hormones affect the rate at which specific substances enter the cell. Insulin, for example, increases the rate of movement of glucose into the cell by affecting a specific transport system. Other hormones that affect the permeability of certain specific membranes include antidiuretic hormone (ADH), the estrogens, testosterone, glucagon, the glucocorticoids, and growth hormone.

CYCLIC AMP AND THE SECOND MESSENGER

Every cell that is affected by a particular hormone has receptors on its outer surface for that hormone, and different effector cells have different receptors, depending on the part of the endocrine system to which they react. In many cells, the interaction of the hormone, or *first messenger*, with the receptor stimulates the action of the enzyme adenylate cyclase (formerly adenyl cyclase), which catalyzes the production of cyclic-3′,5′-AMP (*cyclic AMP, or cAMP*) from ATP within the cell. Cyclic AMP then alters the function of the cell by changing the level of activity of some other enzyme, by altering specifically the permeability of the cell, or by affecting some other process that is characteristic of the cell (Figure 55-4). Thus, cyclic AMP acts as a *second messenger*, through which the endocrine organ modulates the physiological actions of the cell. Because different cells contain different enzymes and have different specific structures, such as secretory apparatuses or contractile elements, the effects of the change in the level of cyclic AMP differs from one type of cell to another. Cyclic AMP is inactivated in the cell by phosphodiesterase, which converts cyclic AMP to 5′-AMP; some hormones may act by inhibiting phosphodiesterase, thereby increasing the concentration of cyclic AMP in the cell. Methyl xanthine compounds such as theophylline, which inhibit phosphodiesterase, enhance the effects of hormones that act by stimulating adenylate cyclase. Cyclic guanidine monophosphate (cyclic GMP), prostaglandins, or Ca^{++} also may be second messengers in certain tissues.

CALCIUM

The binding of some hormones to their receptors causes the entry of Ca^{++} into the cell, and, in addition, cyclic AMP causes the release of Ca^{++} from the mitochondria. Thus, as a result of the action of the hormone, the level of Ca^{++} in the cell is increased. In some tissues, the influx and release of Ca^{++} are important parts of the effect of the hormone. For example, the influx of Ca^{++} caused by epinephrine increases the rate of onset and the magnitude of the action potential in the atrionodal junction of the heart and thereby increases the velocity of propagation of excitation and the margin of safety for continued propagation (see Chapter 18).

In general, the hormones that are derivatives of amino acids exert at least a portion of their effects through the cyclic AMP mechanism.

SYNTHESIS OF PROTEIN

One of the basic actions of the steroid hormones is to promote the synthesis of protein (Figure 55-5). To initiate the process, the steroid hormone enters the target cell and binds to a receptor (which is a protein) in the cytoplasm. The hormone-receptor complex then enters the nucleus and binds to DNA. This association causes the transcription of mRNA and leads to the synthesis of protein at an increased rate. In addition, some protein hormones (e.g., insulin, growth hormone, and prolactin) also may affect the synthesis of protein.

OTHER ACTIONS

In addition to the two major mechanisms that have been described here (cyclic AMP and protein synthesis), some hormones act by altering the activities of cellular enzymes, and other hormones induce cellular differentiation.

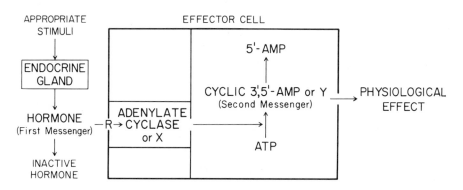

Figure 55-4.   Concept of the second messenger in the effect of an endocrine organ. (Redrawn, with permission, from Sutherland, E.W. 1972. Studies on the mechanisms of hormone action. *Science* 177:401. © The Nobel Foundation 1972.)

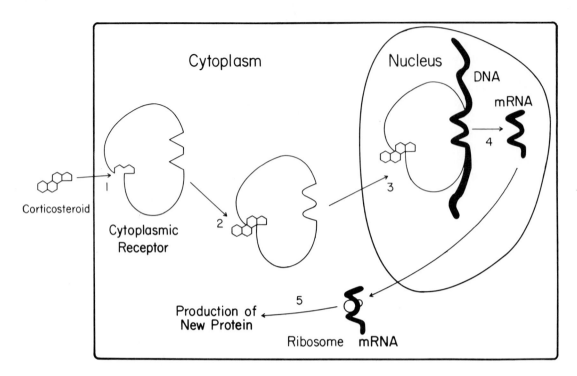

Figure 55-5.   Model of a steroid hormone in the synthesis of a specific protein. **1.** The hormone enters the cell. **2.** It binds to a soluble receptor-protein and induces a slight change in the shape of the protein molecule. **3.** The hormone-receptor complex enters the nucleus and fits to an appropriate segment of DNA. **4.** Messenger RNA (mRNA) is transcribed. **5.** A new protein is produced on the ribosomes in the cytoplasm. (Redrawn, with permission, from Labhart, A. 1974. *Clinical Endocrinology, Theory and Practice.* New York: Springer-Verlag, p. 15.)

STUDY OUTLINE

GENERAL BACKGROUND Two regulatory systems—central nervous system and endocrine system. The two are linked in function and development.

HORMONES   Substances secreted by endocrine glands and certain other tissues.

Word from Greek—"to urge on"; hence, to excite.

Discrete chemical substance produced by organ or tissue and discharged locally or into bloodstream in minute concentrations; influences function of other organs or body systems.

STEROIDS Derivatives of cyclopentanoperhydrophenanthrene—estrogens, androgens, progesterone, and hormones of adrenal cortex.

DERIVATIVES OF AMINO ACIDS Derived from single amino acids—catecholamines and thyroid hormones.

Polypeptides or proteins—releasing hormones of hypothalamus and hormones of pituitary gland, pancreas, and parathyroid glands.

TRADITIONAL CRITERIA FOR THE ENDOCRINE GLAND Essential for normal function of some other organ or gland; demonstrated by destruction or removal.

Inadequate function is corrected by administration of extract of (endocrine) gland.

Hormone is identified in venous blood coming from (endocrine) gland.

NEWER CONCEPTS OF ENDOCRINE FUNCTION Hormones also may be produced by tissues other than those previously known.

GENERAL CHARACTERISTICS OF HORMONES Released into bloodstream and carried throughout body.

Regulate processes of body.

Chemically specific.

Rate of secretion varies.

Produced continuously; metabolized or excreted.

Some are bound to specific carrier proteins in plasma; only free form is active.

FEEDBACK   Concentration in bloodstream affects rate of secretion.

Negative—tends to maintain constant level.

Positive—causes bursts of secretion; unstable levels.

HOMEOSTASIS   Hormones involved in maintenance of constancy of internal environment.

MECHANISMS OF ACTION OF HORMONES

RECEPTORS   Highly specific patches or molecules on surface of target cells with which hormones combine.

Number of receptors is decreased by high levels of certain hormones.

PERMEABILITY OF MEMBRANES   Certain hormones determine rate at which specific substances enter cells.

CYCLIC AMP AND THE SECOND MESSENGER   Hormone (first messenger) reacts with receptor; stimulates enzyme adenylate cyclase and production of cyclic AMP (cAMP)

from ATP within cell.

Cyclic AMP (second messenger) alters function of cell—enzyme activity, membrane permeability, or other function, depending on particular cell.

Cyclic AMP is inactivated by phosphodiesterase; some hormones may increase cyclic AMP by inhibiting phosphodiesterase.

CALCIUM   Hormone action increases $[Ca^{++}]$ inside cell; basis of some actions.

SYNTHESIS OF PROTEIN   One basic action of steroid hormones.

Steroid hormone enters cell, forms hormone-receptor complex that enters nucleus and binds to DNA.

mRNA is transcribed and protein is synthesized.

Protein hormones (e.g., insulin, growth hormone, prolactin) also affect synthesis of protein.

OTHER ACTIONS   Alter activities of cellular enzymes.

Induce cell differentiation.

BIBLIOGRAPHY

Aurbach, H.D. 1982. Polypeptide and amine hormone regulation of adenylate cyclase. *Annu. Rev. Physiol.* 44:653.

Baxter, J.D., and Funder, J.W. 1979. Hormone receptors. *N. Engl. J. Med.* 301:1149.

Baxter, J.D., and MacLeod, K.M. 1980. Molecular basis for hormone action. In *Metabolic Control and Disease* (8th ed.). Edited by P.K. Bondy and L.E. Rosenberg. Philadelphia: Saunders.

Beers, R.F., and Bassett, E.G. 1980. *Polypeptide Hormones.* New York: Raven Press.

Catt, K.J., and Dufan, M.L. 1977. Peptide hormone receptors. *Annu. Rev. Physiol.* 39:529.

Chan, L., and O'Malley, B.W. 1976. Mechanism of action of the sex steroid hormones. *N. Engl. J. Med.* 294:1322, 1372, 1430 (3 parts).

Gorski, J., and Gannon, F. 1976. Current models of steroid hormone action: A critique. *Annu. Rev. Physiol.* 38:425.

Katzenellenbogen, B.S. 1980. Dynamics of steroid hormone receptor action. *Annu. Rev. Physiol.* 42:17.

King, A.C., and Cuatrecasas, P. 1981. Peptide hormone-induced receptor mobility, aggregation, and internalization. *N. Engl. J. Med.* 305:77.

Krieger, D.T., and Liotta, A.S. 1979. Pituitary hormones in brain: Where, how, and why? *Science* 205:366.

Larsson, L.-I.; Goltermann, N.; de Magistris, L., et al. 1979. Somatostatin cell processes as pathways for paracrine secretion. *Science* 205:1393.

Litwack, G. (ed.). 1980. *Biochemical Actions of Hormones.* New York: Academic Press.

Niall, H.D. 1982. The evolution of peptide hormones. *Annu. Rev. Physiol.* 44:615.

Roth, J.; LeRoith, D.; Shiloach, J., et al. 1982. The evolutionary origin of hormones, neurotransmitters, and other extracellular chemical messengers: Implications for mammalian biology. *N. Engl. J. Med.* 306:523.

Starling, E.H. 1905. On the chemical correlation of the functions of the body. *Lancet* 2:339.

Sutherland, E.W. 1972. Studies on the mechanisms of hormone action. *Science* 177:401.

Sutherland, E.W., and Robison, G.A. 1966. The role of cyclic-3′, 5′-AMP in response to catecholamines and other hormones. *Pharmacol. Rev.* 18:145.

Williams, R.H. (ed.). 1981. *Textbook of Endocrinology* (6th ed.). Philadelphia: Saunders.

56

The Neurohypophysis

CHAPTER CONTENTS

FUNCTIONAL ANATOMY

The *neurohypophysis* develops from the floor of the third ventricle of the brain; it is a derivative of the hypothalamus and consists of three parts: the *median eminence*, the *infundibular stem*, and the *infundibular process* (Figure 56-1). The nerves that supply the neurohypophysis, which are unmyelinated, originate in the hypothalamus and pass through the supraopticohypophysial tract into the neural lobe. The neurohypophysial hormones are produced in the neurons of the hypothalamus and are stored in the neural lobe.

HISTORY

Actions of Extracts

The first evidence of physiological effects that might be associated with the neurohypophysis was obtained experimentally by injecting ex-

tracts of this gland into animals. Four effects were established, without concern for the amount of the extract required to produce them. These were: (1) a pressor action, as the arterial blood pressure was increased, (2) an antidiuretic action that delayed the urinary excretion of water and caused the urine to be more concentrated, (3) an oxytocic (which means "rapid birth") action related to enhanced contraction of the uterine muscle, and (4) a galactagogue action that increased the rate at which a lactating female secreted milk.

DIABETES INSIPIDUS

Diabetes insipidus is characterized by excessive production of urine (polyuria) sustained by excessive drinking of water (polydipsia). Diabetes insipidus is distinctly different from *diabetes mellitus*, which is a metabolic disease characterized by the excretion of glucose in the urine. Extracts of the posterior pituitary gland,

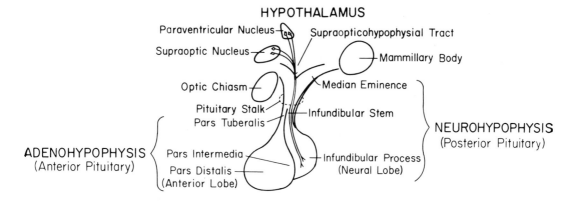

Figure 56-1.   The pituitary gland and its relationship to the structures of the hypothalamus.

which produce antidiuresis in normal individuals, also correct diabetes insipidus; therefore, it appears that a hormone of the posterior pituitary gland normally plays an important role in the water balance of the body. Diabetes insipidus now is thought to be due to a deficiency of the secretion of the posterior lobe caused by damage to the pituitary gland, the hypothalamus, or the nerve tracts that connect the hypothalamus to the pituitary gland. A condition that resembles diabetes insipidus can be produced by compulsive overconsumption of water. In addition, a familial condition exists in which the renal tubule does not respond to antidiuretic hormone (*nephrogenic diabetes insipidus*).

Relation to the Central Nervous System

Using a stereotaxic instrument, which permits relatively accurate placement of probes within the brain, physiologists were able to make discrete lesions in the brain. When the supraopticohypothalamic (SOH) tract was interrupted on both sides of the hypothalamus in laboratory animals, diabetes insipidus developed. This finding was very important because it established that the SOH tract is a link between the hypothalamus and the posterior pituitary gland. Subsequently, it was discovered that the activity of the neurohypophysis depends completely on the innervation of the gland. Electrical stimulation of the SOH tract in the hypothalamus, the median eminence, the infundibular stem, or the neural lobe produces antidiuresis, which is known now to be caused by antidiuretic hormone (ADH, or vasopressin), and contraction of the uterine muscle, which is known now to be caused by oxytocin.

Relatively large doses of ADH cause the pressor effect, which has led to the use of the term *vasopressin* for that hormone.

VASOPRESSIN AND OXYTOCIN

All of the effects of extracts of the mammalian neurohypophysis can be accounted for by two compounds, vasopressin and oxytocin, which have been isolated and purified; the structures of these two substances have been determined, and they have been synthesized.

Vasopressin and oxytocin are nonapeptides, each of which consists of a six-membered disulfide ring and a side chain of three amino acids (Figure 56-2). Vasopressin and oxytocin are related closely in structure; they differ only in the amino acids at positions 3 and 8.

All mammalian species secrete oxytocin, and all mammals secrete a vasopressin that has arginine in position 8 (Figure 56-2) except the pig family, which secretes a vasopressin that has lysine in position 8. There is no species-specificity, however, because either of the versions of vasopressin is effective in all mammals when it is administered as a drug.

Arginine Vasotocin

Arginine vasotocin, which has the ring structure of oxytocin and the side chain of vasopressin (Figure 56-2), was synthesized before it was discovered in animals. It is the natural neurohypophysial hormone of all nonmammalian vertebrates (fish, amphibians, reptiles, and birds), and it is believed to be the stem molecule from which vasopressin and oxytocin have evolved. Arginine vasotocin has been extracted from human pineal glands, and it can

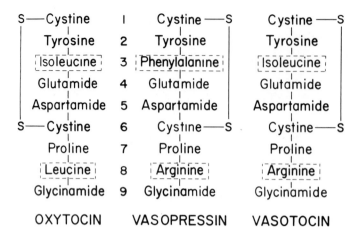

S—Cystine	1	Cystine—S	Cystine—S
Tyrosine	2	Tyrosine	Tyrosine
Isoleucine	3	Phenylalanine	Isoleucine
Glutamide	4	Glutamide	Glutamide
Aspartamide	5	Aspartamide	Aspartamide
S—Cystine	6	Cystine—S	Cystine—S
Proline	7	Proline	Proline
Leucine	8	Arginine	Arginine
Glycinamide	9	Glycinamide	Glycinamide
OXYTOCIN		**VASOPRESSIN**	**VASOTOCIN**

Figure 56-2.   Structure of the nonapeptides oxytocin, vasopressin, and vasotocin. Note that oxytocin and vasopressin differ only in positions 3 and 8. Vasotocin is similar to oxytocin in position 3 and similar to vasopressin in position 8.

be synthesized and secreted in vitro by isolated ependymal secretory cells that have been taken from the pineal glands of human fetuses.

Measurement

Vasopressin and oxytocin in the plasma cannot be measured chemically because the quantities are too small. Two types of assay are used. The older method is a bioassay, in which the effect of the hormone on a target organ is measured, and the activity of the hormone is expressed in units that have been defined. The newer method is radioimmunoassay, in which the hormone is isolated by reaction with an antibody and quantified by measuring the amount of radioactivity (see Chapter 58). Comparison with a prepared standard permits the quantity to be expressed in actual concentration (weight per unit of volume) (Table 56-1).

TABLE 56-1
Plasma level, plasma half-life, and sites of metabolism of vasopressin and oxytocin

	Vasopressin	Oxytocin
Plasma level	< 3µU/ml* (30 pg/ml)	Not detectable in nongravid females 50 µU/ml* during pregnancy 150 µU/ml during labor
Plasma half-life	18 min	2.7 min (in pregnant women)
Sites of metabolism	Kidney and liver	Kidney, liver, and lactating mammary gland

*Determined by bioassay.

Terminology

The terms *vasopressin* and *antidiuretic hormone* are synonymous. The abbreviation *ADH* often is used, and some trade names are well known. Pitressin is a partially purified commercial preparation obtained from the neurohypophysis of cattle and swine; hence, it is a mixture of arginine and lysine vasopressin. Pitressin has predominantly the action of ADH, but it also has a pressor action when given in large doses. Pitressin is the preparation that is used clinically to obtain the action of ADH (see the following section). Pitocin is a partially purified commercial preparation also obtained from the neurohypophysis of cattle and swine. Pitocin has mainly oxytocic activity and is used clinically to achieve the effects of oxytocin (see the section entitled "Actions of Oxytocin" later in this chapter). The synthetic hormone also is available, but it is much more expensive.

Actions of Vasopressin

ANTIDIURETIC EFFECT
The primary effect of vasopressin is *antidiuresis*, or the retention of water in the body. Vasopressin increases the permeability of the distal

CLINICAL CORRELATION
56.1   Inappropriate Secretion of ADH

CASE REPORT

The Patient: A 27-year-old man.

Reason for Admission: Excessive drinking of water.

History: The patient had a history of chronic schizophrenia.* He was admitted to the hospital because he had become psychotic and was drinking more than 10 liters of water/day "to purify himself." Water toxicity developed. He was comatose at the time of admission and underwent several grand mal** seizures after admission. The osmolality of the serum was 231 mOsm/kg water (normal, 285–295 mOsm/kg water), the osmolality of the urine was 232 mOsm/kg water (normal, 500–800 mOsm/kg water), serum [Na$^+$] was 103 mEq/l (normal, 135–145 mEq/liter), serum [Cl$^-$] was 82 mEq/liter (normal, 100–106 mEq/liter), serum [K$^+$] was 3.2 mEq/liter (normal, 3.5–5 mEq/liter), and urinary [Na$^+$] was 109 mEq/liter (normal, 50–130 mEq/liter). Results of the neurological examination were normal, and the EEG showed no abnormality.

Clinical Course: His intake of water was restricted and he was given an infusion of hypertonic NaCl solution; the hyponatremia was corrected and the symptoms of cerebral edema (convulsions) disappeared. However, the psychotic behavior continued. A few days after admission, the patient drank a large quantity of water from a shower bath, and water toxicity developed again. Despite hypo-osmolality of the serum (210 mOsm/kg water), the concentration of urine (275 mOsm/kg water) remained greater than that of the serum. The patient's access to water was restricted more carefully, and the serum concentration and electrolyte content adjusted again. The patient was given psychotherapy and a phenothiazine compound (antipsychotic medication), and his acute psychosis abated. At this time, his serum electrolyte concentration was normal, the osmolality of his serum was 288 mOsm/kg water, and the osmolality of his urine was 595 mOsm/kg water. After he was given a water load (2 liters), the osmolality of his blood did not change, but the osmolality of his urine decreased within an hour to 85 mOsm/kg and remained in that low range for more than 4 hours. The next day, his serum and urinary values were normal again.

Comment: Apparently, during the acute psychosis, the patient had secreted ADH inappropriately (that is, ADH secretion did not decrease when the serum was diluted by the excessive intake of water). The osmolality of the serum had been decreased, and, because of dilution, the concentration of the serum electrolytes had been decreased. Persistence of the inappropriate secretion of ADH with persistence of the psychosis was demonstrated inadvertently when the patient consumed a large amount of water on one occasion. After the psychosis was resolved, he was able to excrete a water load; this indicates normal function of the ADH system (that is, decreased release of ADH when excess water is taken). The release of ADH is known to be increased by pain, emotional stimuli, exercise, and other stimuli (see "Other Stimuli" in this chapter). The results with this patient indicate that acute psychosis has the same effect. Presumably, all of these effects are mediated through tracts from other parts of the brain to the hypothalamic areas that control the release of ADH stored in the neurohypophysis.

Outcome: The patient remained well and was discharged 6 weeks after admission. He has not had another psychotic episode for several months.

---

*A severe mental disorder characterized by unrealistic behavior dominated by private fantasy.

**Generalized convulsions; that is, contortions of the body caused by violent, involuntary contractions of the muscles of the limbs, trunk, neck, and head.

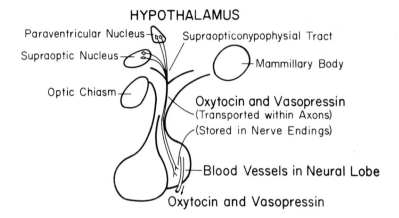

HYPOTHALAMUS

Paraventricular Nucleus

Supraopticonypophysial Tract

Supraoptic Nucleus

Mammillary Body

Optic Chiasm

Oxytocin and Vasopressin
(Transported within Axons)
(Stored in Nerve Endings)

Blood Vessels in Neural Lobe

Oxytocin and Vasopressin

Figure 56-3. Structures associated with the production, transport, storage, and release of oxytocin and vasopressin. See the text for discussion.

tubules and the collecting ducts of the kidneys to water. The result is increased reabsorption of water from the tubular fluid and increased concentration of the urine (see Chapter 41). Water is not transported actively; the movement of water depends on the establishment and maintenance of hyperosmolarity in the interstitial fluid of the medulla of the kidney. Thus, when the permeability of the wall of the collecting duct to water increases, water moves down the osmotic gradient back into the extracellular fluid of the kidney. Subsequently, it enters the renal capillaries and is returned to the general fluid pool of the body. The concentration of cyclic AMP in the cells of the collecting duct is increased by ADH, and it is assumed that cyclic AMP increases the permeability of the cellular membrane to water.

In the absence of ADH, a person may excrete as much as 18 liters of hypotonic urine (50–200 mOsm/liter) per day. Despite the abnormal function in its absence, ADH is not essential to life because a person can compensate for the loss of water in the urine by drinking more water. The compensation is not perfect, however; the homeostasis of water in the body is not as effective, and the plasma usually is slightly hyperosmolar. In addition, to drink and excrete as much as 4–5 gallons of water per day is extremely inconvenient. Although ADH influences the concentration of the urine greatly, its effect is entirely on the absorption of water, and it has no direct effect on electrolyte metabolism in the body. Vasopressin is used clinically to correct for intrinsic deficits of ADH.

PRESSOR EFFECT

The dose of vasopressin that increases the arterial blood pressure significantly is about 100 times the dose that causes antidiuresis. Thus, vasopressin probably is not utilized physiologically to regulate the blood pressure; however, it may be used clinically as a vasoconstrictor (e.g., to control bleeding in a condition such as ruptured esophageal varices).

OTHER PHARMACOLOGICAL EFFECTS

Vasopressin, when given in doses to produce plasma levels that never would be reached physiologically, causes several other effects that cannot be explained easily. These effects include glycogenolysis in the liver, the release of adrenocorticotropic hormone (ACTH) from the pituitary gland (which influences the production of the adrenal steroids), and stimulation of the thyroid gland in some species.

ANTIDIURETIC HORMONE EXCESS (INAPPROPRIATE ADH)

Some patients have tumors that secrete substances resembling ADH (e.g., oat-cell carcinoma of the lung). The symptoms of this condition are retention of water, increased body weight, dilution of body fluids, and relative hyponatremia, although sodium still is excreted in the urine. The treatment for this condition is to restrict the intake of fluids and to remove the tumor.

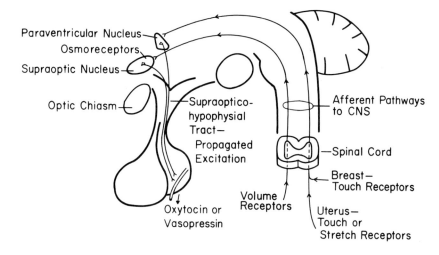

Figure 56-4. The neuroendocrine reflexes involved in the secretion of oxytocin and vasopressin.

Control of the Secretion of Vasopressin

OSMOLARITY OF THE PLASMA

The tonicity of the plasma is sensed by osmoreceptors in the anterior hypothalamus around the supraoptic nucleus, and the input of neurons from that portion of the hypothalamus determines the release of ADH, which is stored in the neurohypophysis (Figure 56-3). The supraoptic neurons themselves may be the osmoreceptors. Increase of the osmotic activity of the plasma causes the osmoreceptors to shrink, which increases the rate of secretion of ADH, and decrease of the osmotic activity of the plasma causes the osmoreceptors to swell, which decreases the rate of secretion of ADH. Thus, a system of negative feedback operates to control the osmolarity of the plasma. A change of osmotic activity of about 1% is sufficient to alter measurably the rate of secretion of ADH. However, one should bear in mind that ADH affects only the rate of excretion of water from the body. If the plasma becomes hypertonic, for example, and more ADH is secreted, the osmolarity of the plasma cannot be restored unless more water is ingested. Normally, the sensation of thirst is elicited, and the person who is affected seeks to drink water; however, if water to drink is not available, as the case might be in a desert or on the ocean, the adjustment of the tonicity of the body fluids will be incomplete.

To evaluate the release of ADH, the individual is required to drink excess water, so that the rate of production of urine is increased; a hypertonic solution of NaCl subsequently is infused into a systemic vein. The volume and the concentration of the urine are measured for a specified period, and the results are compared with normal standards that have been established (Hickey-Hare test). Restriction of the intake of water may be used as a simpler test. In a normal person, the rate of formation of urine decreases and the osmolarity of the urine increases.

VOLUME OF EXTRACELLULAR FLUID

If the volume of the extracellular fluid decreases, the rate of secretion of ADH increases, and if the volume of the extracellular fluid increases, the rate of secretion of ADH decreases. Thus, the release of ADH is modified, so that water is retained or excreted to restore a normal fluid volume. Increased volume of the blood is sensed mainly by stretch receptors in the left atrium, which initiate a neuroendocrine reflex to decrease the secretion of ADH (Figure 56-4). The baroreceptors of the aortic arch and the carotid sinuses sense decreased blood volume and initiate a reflex that increases the secretion of ADH. The stretch of the baroreceptors also is reduced when the arterial blood pressure decreases; hence, ADH also is released in response to hypotension.

OTHER STIMULI

The rate of release of ADH is increased by stress, exercise, pain, trauma, and some emotions. Certain drugs (e.g., morphine, ether, barbiturates, nicotine, and epinephrine) also increase the secretion of ADH. Alcohol decreases the rate of release of ADH.

Actions of Oxytocin

EJECTION OF MILK

The principal physiological effect of oxytocin in mammals is the ejection of milk. Oxytocin causes contraction of the myoepithelial cells of the mammary glands, which surround the alveoli and the ducts; the pressure is increased and the milk is ejected. This effect is necessary for normal lactation in most species; however, some women who have diabetes insipidus, which may indicate damage to the neurohypophysis, still can nurse their babies. Clinically, oxytocin can be used to initiate lactation.

CONTRACTION OF THE UTERUS—PARTURITION

During pregnancy, the actions of oxytocin on the uterus are inhibited by progesterone; however, the sensitivity of the uterus to oxytocin increases during the last 48 hours before the delivery of the fetus, and large quantities of oxytocin are released during parturition. Oxytocin causes contractions of the fundus of the uterus and relaxation of the cervix. In most animal species, destruction of the neurohypophysial system causes *dystocia* (difficult labor). Normal parturition is a complex process, however, and the stimulation of uterine contractions by oxytocin is only one of the factors involved. Some women who have diabetes insipidus have experienced normal labor, and it is probable that, although oxytocin normally augments and helps to maintain labor and delivery, it is not absolutely essential. Oxytocin is used clinically to induce labor and in the immediate postpartum period to increase uterine tone and control hemorrhage.

TRANSPORT OF SPERM

During copulation, oxytocin increases uterine motility and aids the transport of sperm up the female reproductive tract. This is a supporting action, however, rather than an essential one because conception is not impaired in animals whose neurohypophyses have been destroyed.

No function of oxytocin in females of non-mammalian species or in males of any species is known.

Control of the Release of Oxytocin

Oxytocin is released during suckling, during parturition, and during coitus; in each circumstance, a neuroendocrine reflex is involved. Touch receptors in the mammary organs and in the genitalia send stimuli via neural pathways to the paraventricular nucleus; efferent fibers to the neural lobe cause the release of oxytocin stored in that gland (Figure 56-4). There also is a strong psychological component (e.g., the cry of a baby can cause the release of oxytocin and the ejection of milk in a woman who is lactating). The release of oxytocin is inhibited by alcohol.

NEUROSECRETION

The neurohypophysis is a storage organ only—it depends on the hypothalamus and the hypothalamo-hypophysial nerve tract for the synthesis and release of hormones. Vasopressin and oxytocin are synthesized in neurons that originate from cell bodies in the supraoptic and paraventricular nuclei. These neurosecretory cells also synthesize a protein called *neurophysin*, to which the peptide hormones are bound. Neurophysin has a molecular weight of 10,000–14,000 daltons and can be identified by special stains. Most of the synthesis probably occurs in the nerve cell body, and the hormones are transported down the axon and stored in the neural lobe. These axons, which do not synapse, end in relation to blood vessels that are permeable to the hormones. Appropriate stimuli cause nerve impulses, which are necessary for the release of vasopressin and oxytocin into the circulation.

STUDY OUTLINE

FUNCTIONAL ANATOMY

Neurohypophysis—derivative of hypothalamus, develops from floor of third ventricle of brain.

Consists of median eminence, infundibular stem, and infundibular process.

Myelinated nerves from hypothalamus pass through supraopticohypophysial tract into neural lobe.

Hormones are produced in neurons of hypothalamus and are stored in neural lobe.

HISTORY

ACTIONS OF EXTRACTS Injected into experimental animals.

Increased arterial pressure.

Delayed renal excretion of water.

Enhanced contraction of uterine muscle.

Increased rate of secretion of milk.

DIABETES INSIPIDUS Excessive production of urine, drinking of water.

Corrected by administering extracts of posterior pituitary gland.

Caused by deficiency of posterior lobe secretion.

RELATION TO THE CENTRAL NERVOUS SYSTEM Bilateral lesion of supraopticohypophysial (SOH) tract results in diabetes insipidus.

Activity of neurohypophysis depends on innervation.

Electrical stimulation of SOH tract causes antidiuresis (release of antidiuretic hormone, ADH).

VASOPRESSIN AND OXYTOCIN Structures have been determined and compounds have been synthesized: closely related nonapeptides.

ARGININE VASOTOCIN Ring structure of oxytocin, side chain of vasopressin.

Believed to be evolutionary precursor of oxytocin and vasopressin.

Synthesized and stored in human pineal gland.

MEASUREMENT Bioassay (old method) and radioimmunoassay (new method).

TERMINOLOGY *Vasopressin* is synonymous with *antidiuretic hormone* (abbreviated as *ADH*).

Pitressin—commercial preparation; from neurohypophyses of cattle and swine; partially purified; mostly has action of ADH; used clinically.

Pitocin—commercial preparation; from neurohypophyses of cattle and swine; partially purified; mostly has action of oxytocin; used clinically.

ACTIONS OF VASOPRESSIN Primarily retention of water in body.

ANTIDIURETIC EFFECT Increases permeability of distal renal tubules and collecting ducts to water.

Action is assumed to be mediated through cyclic AMP.

Water moves osmotically into hypertonic medulla, is returned to blood in vasa recta.

In absence of ADH, 4–5 gallons of water are excreted per day; no direct effect on electrolytes.

PRESSOR EFFECT About 100 times the antidiuretic dose.

Used clinically as vasoconstrictor.

OTHER PHARMACOLOGICAL EFFECTS Not explained easily; glycogenolysis in liver, release of adrenocorticotropic hormone (ACTH) from pituitary, and stimulation of thyroid in some species.

ANTIDIURETIC HORMONE EXCESS (INAPPROPRIATE ADH) Secreted from certain tumors.

CONTROL OF THE SECRETION OF VASOPRESSIN

OSMOLARITY OF THE PLASMA Sensed by osmoreceptors in hypothalamus; neural activity determines release of ADH stored in neurohypophysis.

Negative-feedback system.

Effects of infusing hypertonic NaCl solution on volume and concentration of urine are used to assess release of ADH.

VOLUME OF EXTRACELLULAR FLUID Negative-feedback system involving ADH.

Increased blood volume is sensed by stretch receptors in left atrium; neuroendocrine reflex decreases secretion of ADH.

Decreased blood volume is sensed by aortic arch and carotid sinus baroreceptors; neuroendocrine reflex increases secretion of ADH.

Arterial hypotension of any cause decreases stretch of baroreceptors, causes release of ADH.

OTHER STIMULI Affect release of ADH.

Increased by stress, exercise, pain, trauma, certain emotions, and certain drugs.

Decreased by alcohol.

ACTIONS OF OXYTOCIN

EJECTION OF MILK   Principal physiological effect in mammals.

Causes contraction of myoepithelial cells of mammary glands.

Can be used to initiate lactation.

CONTRACTION OF THE UTERUS—PARTURITION   Large quantities of oxytocin are released during parturition; sensitivity of uterus is increased.

Aids delivery, but is not essential.

Used clinically to induce labor and control postpartum hemorrhage.

TRANSPORT OF SPERM   Aids transport during copulation, but is not essential.

CONTROL OF THE RELEASE OF OXYTOCIN   During suckling, parturition, coitus; neuroendocrine reflexes.

Touch receptors in mammary organs, genitalia; afferent nerve fibers to hypothalamus; efferent nerve fibers to neural lobe; release of stored hormone.

Strong psychological component.

Inhibited by alcohol.

NEUROSECRETION   Neurohypophysis is a storage organ only.

Vasopressin and oxytocin are synthesized in neuron cell bodies in hypothalamus and transported down axons to neural lobe bound to *neurophysin* (protein).

Stimuli cause nerve impulses, release hormones into adjacent blood vessels for circulation.

BIBLIOGRAPHY

Beardwell, C., and Robertson, G.L. 1981. *The Pituitary*. Boston: Butterworths.

Berson, S.A., and Yalow, R.S. 1967. Radioimmunoassay of peptide hormones in plasma. *N. Engl. J. Med.* 277:640.

Brownstein, M.J. 1983. Biosynthesis of vasopressin and oxytocin. *Annu. Rev. Physiol.* 45:129.

Brownstein, M.J.; Russell, J.T.; and Gainer, H. 1980. Synthesis, transport, and release of posterior pituitary hormones. *Science* 207:373.

Decaux, G.; Waterlot, Y.; Genette, F., et al. 1981. Treatment of the syndrome of inappropriate secretion of antidiuretic hormone with furosemide. *N. Engl. J. Med.* 304:329.

Forsling, M.L. 1979. Antidiuretic hormone. St. Albans, Vermont: Eden Medical Research.

Fuchs, A.-R.; Fuchs, F.; Husslein, P., et al. 1982. Oxytocin receptors and human parturition: A dual role for oxytocin in the initiation of labor. *Science* 215:1396.

Hays, R.M. 1976. Antidiuretic hormone. *N. Engl. J. Med.* 295:659.

Heller, H. 1966. The hormone content of the vertebrate hypothalamo-neurohypophysial system. *Br. Med. Bull.* 22:227.

Knobil, E., and Sawyer, W.H. (eds.). 1974. The pituitary gland and its neuroendocrine control. In *Handbook of Physiology*. Section 7. Endocrinology. Volume IV. Washington, D.C.: American Physiological Society.

Pederson, C.A.; Ascher, J.A.; Monroe, Y.L., et al. 1982. Oxytocin induces maternal behavior in virgin female rats. *Science* 216:648.

Williams, R.H. (ed.). 1981. *Textbook of Endocrinology* (6th ed.). Philadelphia: Saunders.

57

The Adenohypophysis and Neuroendocrinology

CHAPTER CONTENTS

FUNCTIONAL ANATOMY

The *adenohypophysis* arises as an evagination of epithelial tissue from the roof of the mouth. It is classified into three parts (see Figure 56-1): (1) the *pars tuberalis*, which is a strip of tissue that surrounds the median eminence and the upper part of the neural stalk, (2) the *pars intermedia*, which is rudimentary in humans, and (3) the *pars distalis*, or anterior lobe, which is the major secretory portion of the gland. The adenohypophysis is composed of highly vascular tissue that has blood sinuses running between cords of cells.

HORMONES OF THE ADENOHYPOPHYSIS: MAJOR ACTIONS

Gonadotropins

The target organs of the gonadotropins are the testicles in the male and the ovaries in the female.

Follicle-Stimulating Hormone (FSH)

FSH is responsible for spermatogenesis in the male and oogenesis in the female.

Luteinizing Hormone (LH)

In the male, LH stimulates the Leydig cells to secrete testosterone. In the female, LH causes the secretion of estrogens by the ovary, the rupture of the ripe follicle in the ovary and the release of the ovum, the formation of the corpus luteum from the follicular remains, and the secretion of progesterone by the corpus luteum.

Both FSH and LH are secreted by basophilic cells of the adenohypophysis. If these gonadotropins are deficient, the gonads and the accessory glands atrophy, and the individual is sterile.

Prolactin

Prolactin is secreted by acidophilic cells of the adenohypophysis. Prolactin stimulates the mammary glands to produce milk and is responsible for maternal behavior in the female. If prolactin is deficient, no milk is produced and the mammary glands involute.

Adrenocorticotropic Hormone (ACTH, or Corticotropin)

ACTH is secreted by the basophilic cells; it maintains the structure, growth, and secretory activity of the adrenal gland. If ACTH is deficient, the adrenal cortex atrophies and insufficient glucocorticoid hormones are produced. The individual who has this condition is very sensitive to stress (e.g., disease, starvation, exposure, or extremes of temperature).

Thyroid-Stimulating Hormone (TSH, or Thyrotropin)

TSH maintains the structure, growth, and secretory activity of the thyroid gland. TSH is secreted by basophilic cells; if it is deficient, the thyroid gland atrophies and insufficient thyroid hormone is produced.

Growth Hormone (GH), or Somatotropin (SH)

GH, which is secreted by acidophilic cells, is necessary for normal growth and development.

Melanocyte-Stimulating Hormone (MSH, Melanotropin, or Intermedin)

MSH is present in mammalian pituitary glands, but no physiological role for it is known. In fish, amphibians, and reptiles, MSH causes darkening of the skin. A rudiment of this effect may persist in humans, in whom a deficiency of MSH causes pallor. MSH is secreted by basophilic cells.

CONTROL OF THE ADENOHYPOPHYSIS: HISTORICAL AND EXPERIMENTAL

Feedback

At one time, physiologists thought that the secretion of ACTH, TSH, and the gonadotropins by the pituitary gland was controlled by feedback of the hormones of the target organs—the adrenal glands, the thyroid gland, and the gonads, respectively. Feedback does operate as a control; however, it is known now that control exerted through the central nervous system also is very important.

Central Nervous System

External factors influence the endocrine system through the actions of the central nervous system on the adenohypophysis. For example, some animals require genital stimulation to induce ovulation. Although ovulation depends on the release of LH, it does not occur if the neural pathways from the genitals are cut. In the human female, who ovulates spontaneously, anxiety can cause irregularity of the menstrual cycle, or even amenorrhea. This was seen in wartime among women who were in concentration camps or who were in cities that were being bombed. Fear of pregnancy also can affect the menstrual cycle. Stress is known to be an important stimulus for endocrine change; for example, medical students at the time of examinations secrete excess ACTH, which stimulates adrenal secretion. Psychological stress is the most effective stimulus for the release of ACTH in humans. The environment also is a factor because thyroid function is stimulated by low temperatures. These examples of neuroendocrine reflexes demonstrate a true functional relationship by which the external or the internal environment, via the central nervous system, can influence the secretion of ACTH, TSH, and the gonadotropins.

Transplantation of the Pituitary Gland

Most endocrine glands can be transplanted and still maintain normal function. One may infer from this observation that the gland exerts its control via the circulation and that no significant neural interaction occurs. If the pituitary gland is transplanted, however, it does not continue to function normally. The anterior pituitary has no significant nerve supply except for autonomic innervation, and even that is not necessary for pituitary activity.

Pituitary Portal Vessels

A small branch of the internal carotid artery enters the pituitary between the pars tuberalis and the median eminence (Figure 57-1). Further branches of this vessel enter the median eminence and form a series of sinusoidal loops, called the *primary plexus,* which comes into direct contact with neural tissue. The primary plexus drains by portal trunks down the pituitary stalk into the sinusoids of the pars distalis; this is the principal blood supply of the adenohypophysis. It is a true portal system, in which one capillary bed drains into another through an intermediary vein. This system explains how neural control is exerted, even though the gland has no direct nerve supply. Humoral substances are transmitted from the median eminence through the pituitary portal vessels to the pars distalis.

Hypothalamic Influences

Stimulation of certain areas of the hypothalamus increases the activity of one or more of the tropic hormones. If lesions are made in the same areas, the activities of the tropic hormones decrease to less than normal. These experiments confirm that the hypothalamus is involved in the control of the pituitary gland; however, no specific nuclei are implicated.

The central nervous system exerts control over the adenohypophysis through neurohumors rather than by direct neural connections. These neurohumors are secreted by the hypothalamic neurons that end in the median eminence. The neurohumors reach the adenohypophysis by way of the portal vessels and control the secretion of the adenohypophysial hormones.

RELEASING FACTORS

The hypothalamic neurohumors are called releasing factors (RF) or releasing hormones (RH). The term *RH* is used more widely now because the chemical structures of some of these substances are known. The first letter of the name of the pituitary hormone precedes RF or RH (e.g., thyrotropin-releasing hormone is TRH). Some of the hypothalamic neurohumors inhibit the secretion of hormones by the adenohypophysis; such neurohumors are called *inhibitory factors* (IF) or *inhibitory hormones* (IH). The first direct evidence for the existence of the releasing hormones came from experiments in which extracts of the hypothalamus caused the release of pituitary hor-

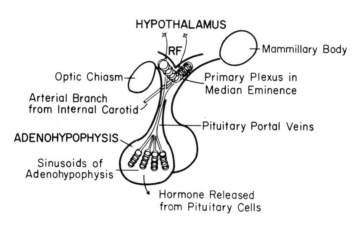

Figure 57-1.   The pituitary portal system.

mones. Chemical purification of the hypothalamic extracts then permitted the chemical structures of several releasing hormones to be determined; all of the releasing hormones that have been characterized in this way are small peptides.

Corticotropin-Releasing Hormone (CRH)

CRH, which causes the release of ACTH, was the first releasing factor to be studied. Its chemical structure has been determined recently; it is a small peptide that contains 41 amino acids.

Thyrotropin-Releasing Hormone (TRH)

Although TRH was one of the later releasing factors to be investigated, it was the first one to be identified chemically and the first one to be synthesized. TRH is a tripeptide that consists of the sequence glutamic acid-histidine-proline (Figure 57-2). Synthetic TRH causes the release of TSH in humans, and it also causes the release of prolactin in humans and in some (but not all) other species.

Luteinizing Hormone-Releasing Hormone (LRH)

LRH causes the release of both LH and FSH in animals and humans (both female and male) and in both adults and prepubertal sub-

jects. The structure of LRH is known—it is a decapeptide (Figure 57-3)—and it has been synthesized.

Follicle-Stimulating Hormone-Releasing Factor (FRF)

FRF is thought to be a small peptide that has a molecular weight of 1200–1400 daltons; however, it is not certain whether FRF really is a separate hormone. It may be that LRH, which acts on both LH and FSH, is the only releasing hormone involved, and that the release of LH and FSH also is influenced by the concentration of estrogens in the plasma (negative feedback).

Growth Hormone-Releasing Hormone (GRH)

GRH is a small peptide that contains 44 amino acids.

Somatostatin, or Growth Hormone-Inhibiting Hormone (GIH)

The chemical structure of GIH is known and the compound has been synthesized. GIH consists of a sequence of 14 amino acids that also contains a disulfide bridge (Figure 57-4). Somatostatin also has been isolated from

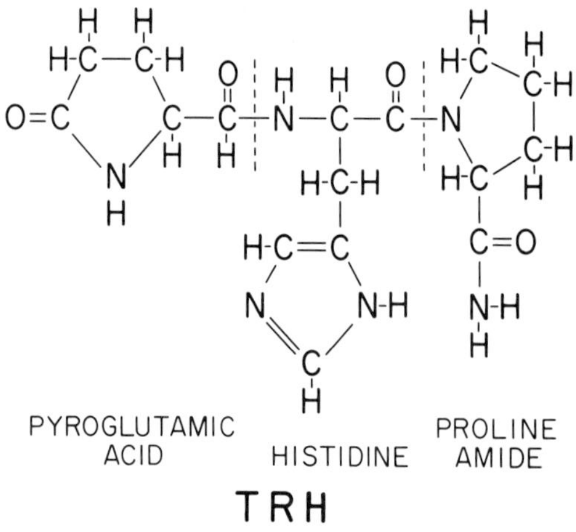

Figure 57-2.   The chemical structure of thyrotropin-releasing hormone (TRH).

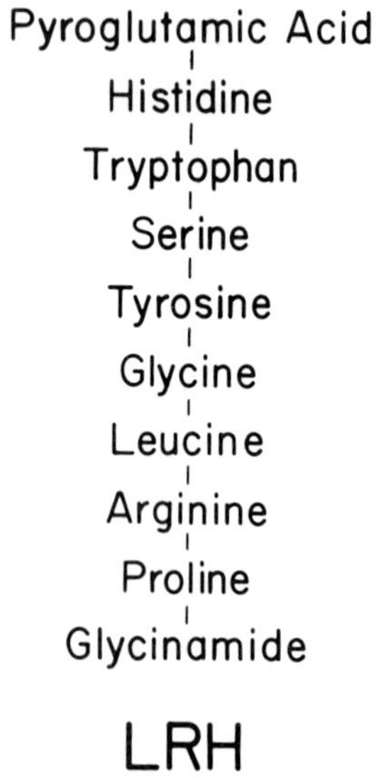

Figure 57-3.   The amino acid sequence of luteinizing hormone-releasing hormone (LRH).

tissues of the small intestine and the pancreas, where it inhibits the secretion of glucagon and insulin (see Chapter 61).

Prolactin-Inhibiting Factor (PIF)

Apparently, PIF is secreted continuously and, hence, inhibits the release of prolactin continuously. This type of action is unique. Experimental procedures that isolate pituitary influences from hypothalamic influences (e.g., lesions in the hypothalamus, section of the pituitary stalk, or transplantation of the pituitary gland) decrease the secretion of all of the other pituitary hormones; however, these procedures *increase* the rate of synthesis and secretion of prolactin. Physiologically, prolactin is secreted when the rate of secretion of PIF decreases. The chemical structure of PIF is not known, but some evidence indicates that dopamine may be PIF.

Prolactin-Releasing Factor (PRF)

PRF is less important than PIF in the control of the secretion of prolactin. The chemical struc-

ture of this factor is not known; in some species, TRH may act as PRF.

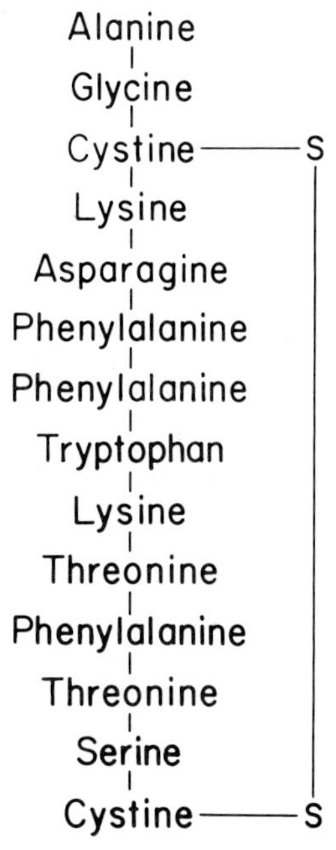

Melanocyte-Stimulating Hormone-Inhibiting Factor (MIF) and Melanocyte-Stimulating Hormone-Releasing Factor (MRF)

MIF and MRF are included only for the sake of completeness; no physiological role for these factors in mammals is known.

General Characteristics of Releasing Factors

Up to the present time, 10 hypothalamic releasing or inhibiting factors have been identified, and three of them have been characterized and synthesized. The releasing factors are secreted by neurons that originate in the hypothalamus and terminate in the median eminence of the pituitary. Because these neurons release peptides at their endings, they may be called *peptidergic* neurons.

The releasing factors reach the adenohypophysis via the pituitary portal vessels. Once there, they act rapidly; for example, TRH increases the concentration of TSH in the plasma in one circulation time, and after 3 minutes, the plasma TSH has increased tenfold. Very small amounts of the releasing factors are secreted, and some of them are inactivated rapidly in the blood. When their rates of secretion are normal, none of them reaches the pituitary via the general circulation, and pituitary glands that are transplanted to other parts of the circulation do not function normally. Thus, the pituitary portal system functions as a special circulation by which hormones are transported only to the anterior pituitary.

The mechanisms by which the releasing factors work are not known. There is some evidence that they increase the permeability of the anterior pituitary cells to Ca^{++}, which depolarizes the cells, and that some of them activate adenylate cyclase. Most of the releasing factors are highly specific; a particular one acts only on certain pituitary cells and causes the release of a particular pituitary hormone. The exceptions to this generalization are LRH, which releases both LH and FSH, and TRH, which releases both TSH and prolactin in some species. Finally, the releasing factors are not species-specific because a given factor from one species produces the same effect in other species.

Alanine
|
Glycine
|
Cystine————S
|
Lysine
|
Asparagine
|
Phenylalanine
|
Phenylalanine
|
Tryptophan
|
Lysine
|
Threonine
|
Phenylalanine
|
Threonine
|
Serine
|
Cystine————S

SOMATOSTATIN

Figure 57-4.   The amino acid sequence of somatostatin (GIH).

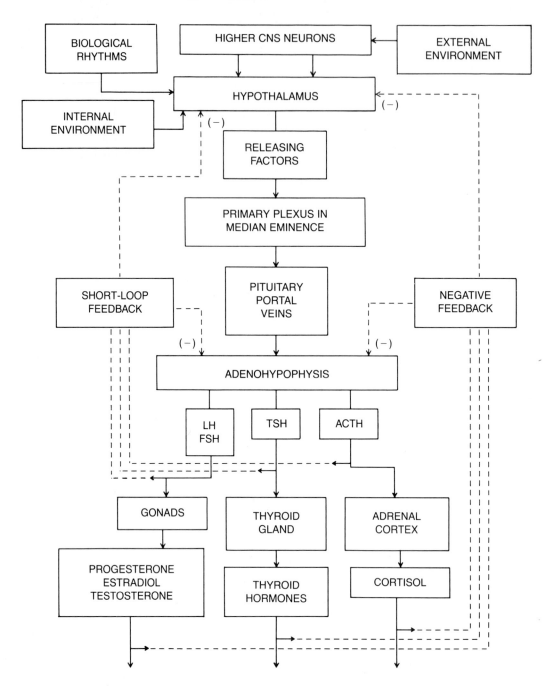

Figure 57-5.   Control of the anterior pituitary by the hypothalamus and the influences that act on the hypothalamus, which include negative feedback from the pituitary hormones and the hormones of the target glands.

ADENOHYPOPHYSIAL CONTROL

Feedback

The tropic hormones released from the pituitary gland cause the target organs to secrete hormones, and the hormones from the target organs "feed back" to regulate the secretion of the pituitary hormones (Figure 57-5). Only the free hormone is active in the feedback process, which may occur at the pituitary, at the hypothalamus, or at both sites. Because this is negative feedback, it tends to maintain endo-

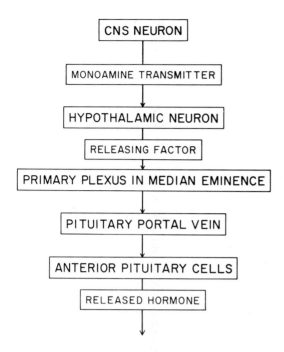

Figure 57-6. The mechanisms by which the central nervous system influences the anterior pituitary gland.

crine activity at a constant level under the conditions of a constant environment. The pituitary hormones themselves exert negative feedback on both the pituitary and the hypo-thalamus; however, negative feedback is less important in the control of the pituitary hormones than feedback from the target organs is.

Control by the Central Nervous System

The neuroendocrine reflex is important to increase or decrease the rate of secretion of the pituitary hormones in response to changing environmental or physiological conditions (Figure 57-6). Neurons from other areas of the central nervous system enter the hypothalamus and secrete various *monoamines* (such as dopamine, norepinephrine, and serotonin), which transmit information to the hypothalamic neurons. The hypothalamic neurons, in turn, secrete the releasing factors in the median eminence. The releasing factors are carried by the portal vessels to the adenohypophysis, where they control the release of specific pituitary hormones. Thus, input from the central nervous system can alter the constancy that negative feedback produces. In this way, the "biological rhythms," which probably are generated in the central nervous system, are superimposed on the resting rates of secretion of the pituitary hormones. One example of this type of rhythm is the circadian (daily) rhythm in the ACTH-adrenal cortex system.

STUDY OUTLINE

FUNCTIONAL ANATOMY Adenohypophysis arises from epithelial tissues of roof of mouth.

Three parts: (1) pars tuberalis, which surrounds median eminence and upper part of neural stalk, (2) pars intermedia, which is rudimentary in humans, and (3) pars distalis, the major secretory portion.

HORMONES OF THE ADENOHYPOPHYSIS: MAJOR ACTIONS

GONADOTROPINS Target organs—ovaries in females; testicles in males.

FOLLICLE-STIMULATING HORMONE (FSH) Spermatogenesis in males; oogenesis in females.

LUTEINIZING HORMONE (LH) Stimulates Leydig cells to secrete testosterone in males.

In females, LH causes (1) secretion of estrogens by ovary, (2) rupture of ripe follicle in ovary and release of ovum, (3) formation of corpus luteum from follicular remains, and (4) secretion of progesterone by corpus luteum.

PROLACTIN Stimulates mammary glands to produce milk; is responsible for maternal behavior in females.

ADRENOCORTICOTROPIC HORMONE (ACTH, OR CORTICOTROPIN) Maintains structure, growth, and secretory activity of adrenal cortex.

THYROID-STIMULATING HORMONE (TSH, OR THYROTROPIN) Maintains structure, growth, and secretory activity of thyroid gland.

GROWTH HORMONE (GH), OR SOMA-TOTROPIN (SH)   Necessary for normal growth and development in general.

MELANOCYTE-STIMULATING HORMONE (MSH, MELANOTROPIN, OR INTERMEDIN)   Rudimentary in humans.

CONTROL OF THE ADENOHYPOPHYSIS: HISTORICAL AND EXPERIMENTAL

FEEDBACK   Important, but is not the only factor.

CENTRAL NERVOUS SYSTEM   Influence of external factors on adenohypophysis.

TRANSPLANTATION OF THE PITUITARY GLAND   Pituitary does not function normally when transplanted, yet does not depend on nerves.

PITUITARY PORTAL VESSELS   Transmit influence of hypothalamus on adenohypophysis.

Arterial branch forms sinusoidal loops in median eminence; receives input from neural tissue.

Portal veins drain down pituitary stalk to pars distalis; form principal blood supply.

Transmit humoral substances and provide neural control in absence of nerve supply to gland.

HYPOTHALAMIC INFLUENCES   Increased by stimulation, decreased by lesions.

Central nervous system controls adenohypophysis through neurohumors (*releasing factors*) that reach gland through portal vessels.

RELEASING FACTORS   Extracts of hypothalamus cause release of pituitary hormones: releasing factors, or releasing hormones; all known ones are small peptides.

CORTICOTROPIN-RELEASING HORMONE (CRH)   Causes release of ACTH; thought to be small peptide.

THYROTROPIN-RELEASING HORMONE (TRH)   First identified chemically and synthesized; also causes release of prolactin in humans.

LUTEINIZING HORMONE-RELEASING HORMONE (LRH)   Causes release of LH and FSH.

FOLLICLE-STIMULATING HORMONE-RELEASING FACTOR (FRF)   May not be separate hormone; LRH may do both; LH and FSH also are influenced by negative feedback from estrogen in plasma.

GROWTH HORMONE-RELEASING HORMONE (GRH)   Probably small peptide.

SOMATOSTATIN, OR GROWTH HORMONE-INHIBITING HORMONE (GIH)   Structure known; has been synthesized.

Also found in small intestine and pancreas; inhibits secretion of glucagon and insulin.

PROLACTIN-INHIBITING FACTOR (PIF)   Secreted continuously; inhibits release of prolactin.

PROLACTIN-RELEASING FACTOR (PRF)   Less important than PIF in control of prolactin.

MELANOCYTE-STIMULATING HORMONE-INHIBITING FACTOR (MIF) AND MELANOCYTE-STIMULATING HORMONE-RELEASING FACTOR (MRF)   No physiological role in mammals is known.

GENERAL CHARACTERISTICS OF RELEASING FACTORS   Ten releasing factors are known; three have been synthesized.

Peptides are released by hypothalamic neurons; reach adenohypophysis through pituitary portal vessels.

Act quickly, of short duration, do not reach general circulation.

Some releasing factors increase permeability of pituitary cells to Ca^{++}; some activate adenylate cyclase.

Most releasing factors cause release of particular hormones.

Not species-specific.

ADENOHYPOPHYSIAL CONTROL

FEEDBACK   Negative—maintains constant level.

Pituitary hormones cause target organs to secrete hormones that feed back to regulate pituitary secretion.

Only free (unbound) hormones are active.

Pituitary hormones feed back on both pituitary and hypothalamus; less important than target-organ feedback.

CONTROL BY THE CENTRAL NERVOUS SYSTEM   Alters constancy of negative feedback.

Neuroendocrine reflex alters pituitary secretion in response to environmental or physiological conditions.

Other central nervous system neurons transmit information to hypothalamus through monoamines.

Hypothalamic neurons secrete releasing hormones; travel to pituitary through portal system, release specific pituitary hormones.

Biological rhythms, generated by central nervous system, are superimposed on resting rates of pituitary secretion.

BIBLIOGRAPHY

Beardwell, C., and Robertson, G.L. 1981. *The Pituitary.* Boston: Butterworths.

Beling, C.G., and Wentz, A.C. 1980. *The LH-Releasing Hormone.* New York: Masson Publishing Co.

Blackwell, R.E., and Guillemin, R. 1973. Hypothalamic control of adenohypophysial secretion. *Annu. Rev. Physiol.* 35:357.

DeGroot, L.J.; Cahill, G.F., Jr.; Odell, W.D., et al. (eds.). 1979. *Endocrinology.* Volume I. New York: Grune & Stratton.

Givens, J.R.; Kitabchi, A.E.; and Robertson, J.T. (eds.). 1982. Hormone-secreting pituitary tumors. Chicago: Yearbook.

Guillemin, R. 1978. Peptides in the brain: The new endocrinology of the neuron. *Science* 202:390.

Harris, G.W. 1948. Electrical stimulation of the hypothalamus and the mechanisms of neural control of the adenohypophysis. *J. Physiol.* (London) 107:418.

Harris, G.W. 1955. The function of the pituitary stalk. *Bull. Johns Hopkins Hosp.* 97:358.

Knobil, E., and Sawyer, W.H. (eds.). 1974. The pituitary gland and its neuroendocrine control. In *Handbook of Physiology.* Section 7. Endocrinology. Volume IV. Washington, D.C.: American Physiological Society.

Krieger, D.T., and Martin, J.B. 1981. Brain peptides. *N. Engl. J. Med.* 304:876, 944 (2 parts).

Leong, L.; Framley, S.; and Neil, J.D. 1983. Neuroendocrine control of prolactin secretion. *Annu. Rev. Physiol.* 45:109.

Lumpkin, M.D.; Negro-Vilar, A.; and McCann, S.M. 1981. Paradoxical elevation of growth hormone by intraventricular somatostatin: Possible ultrashort-loop feedback. *Science* 211:1072.

McCann, S.M. 1982. Physiology and pharmacology of LHRH and somatostatin. *Annu. Rev. Physiol.* 22:491.

McQuillan, M.T. 1980. *Somatostatin.* St. Albans, Vermont: Eden Medical Research.

Meites, J., and Sonntag, W.E. 1981. Hypothalamic hypophysiotropic hormones and neurotransmitter regulation: Current views. *Annu. Rev. Pharmacol. Toxicol.* 21:295.

Morgane, P.J., and Panksepp, J. (eds.). 1980. *Physiology of the Hypothalamus.* New York: Marcel Dekker.

Motta, M. (ed.). 1980. *The Endocrine Functions of the Brain.* New York: Raven Press.

Reichlin, S.; Saperstein, I.; Jackson, M.D., et al. 1976. Hypothalamic hormones. *Annu. Rev. Physiol.* 38:389.

Samson, W.K., and Kozlowski, G.P. 1981. Nerve cells that double as endocrine cells. *Bioscience* 31:445.

Schally, A.V. 1978. Aspects of hypothalamic regulation of the pituitary gland. *Science* 202:18.

Tixier-Vidal, A., and Gourdji, D. 1981. Mechanism of action of synthetic hypothalamic peptides on anterior pituitary cells. *Physiol. Rev.* 61:974.

Vale, W.; Rivier, C.; and Brown, M. 1977. Regulatory peptides of the hypothalamus. *Annu. Rev. Physiol.* 39:473.

Williams, R.H. (ed.). 1981. *Textbook of Endocrinology* (6th ed.). Philadelphia: Saunders.

58

Growth Hormone, or Somatotropin

CHAPTER CONTENTS

HISTORY

Acromegaly

The relationship between the pituitary gland and the growth of the body was indicated first by tumors found in the pituitary glands of patients who had *acromegaly*. This condition is known now to be caused by excessive secretion of growth hormone (GH) in adults, after the growth areas of the bones (*epiphyses*) have closed. Acromegaly is characterized by progressive enlargement of the ends of the long bones and the growth of certain soft tissues. The bones cannot increase in length, but they do increase in width. The hands and the feet enlarge, the skull and the jaw lengthen, and the viscera enlarge.

Gigantism

Gigantism is a relatively rare condition of extreme growth that was found to be a juvenile form of the same disease that causes acromeg-

aly in adults. The excessive secretion of GH occurs before the growth areas of the bones have closed; hence, the person grows to be very large, and the body proportions are approximately normal. Gigantism can be produced experimentally by the injection of GH into animals.

Pituitary Dwarfism

Pituitary dwarfism was produced experimentally in puppies that failed to grow and develop after their hypophyses were removed. These results were interpreted correctly to indicate that the pituitary gland is the source of a hormone that is necessary for normal growth. The clinical counterpart is the human who retains infantile stature and features because of a deficiency of GH in childhood. Dwarfs of this type can be made to grow and mature by injection of GH. Dwarfism also is caused by other conditions, however, which the injection of GH does not correct.

CLINICAL CORRELATION
58.1   Pituitary Gigantism

CASE REPORT

The Patient: A 19-year-old male.

Principal Complaint: Extreme growth (gigantism).

History: The patient has normal parents and siblings; he was normal himself until 10 years of age, when he began to experience abnormally rapid growth. The rate of growth continued at the 99th percentile for 2 years, and then remained between the 50th and 75th percentiles for 2 more years. At age 14 years, the concentration of growth hormone (GH) in the plasma was 113 ng/ml (normal, 10–20 ng/ml) and could not be increased by injection of insulin or decreased by injection of glucose. The fasting blood glucose level was 110 mg/dl (normal, 70–110 mg/dl); the glucose tolerance test (oral) suggested borderline diabetes (see Chapter 61, "Glucose Tolerance Test"), but no glucose was found in the urine. The serum inorganic phosphorous was 8 mg/dl (normal, 3–4.5 mg/dl). In the initial period of rapid growth, the patient was strong and vigorous, but during the last 2 years, he developed muscular weakness and atrophy. Specific weakness developed in his hands, making it difficult for him to hold a pencil and write, or to use table utensils.

Clinical Examination: At admission, all of the limb reflexes were markedly obtunded. Cranial tomograms (sectional radiography) showed no significant abnormality of the sella turcica; no signs of a tumor (such as impaired vision or increased intracranial pressure) were found. Nevertheless, on the basis of the increased plasma levels of GH and its lack of susceptibility to stimulation or suppression, a pituitary tumor (microadenoma) was diagnosed.

Treatment: Surgical hypophysectomy by the trans-sphenoidal approach was performed, and tissue consistent with an acidophilic tumor was removed. Substitution therapy for the pituitary insufficiency was introduced. Although the plasma GH level decreased considerably, it still was slightly greater than normal (20–25 ng/dl); this level suggests that the tumor may not have been removed completely.

Comment: A pituitary tumor that produces one type of hormone often decreases production of the other pituitary hormones by compressing pituitary tissue and destroying cells that produce the other hormones. For example, the muscular weakness and atrophy that pituitary giants subsequently develop reflect adrenal cortical deficiency to some extent. Lack of secretion of pituitary gonadotropin delays puberty, hence the epiphyses do not close, and bone growth continues. Adult women who develop such tumors often have amenorrhea secondary to decreased LH and FSH. Neurological symptoms develop, as abnormal growth of nerves causes compression in the channels through bones and joints. The weakness of the hands in this patient was caused by pressure on the medial nerve in the space formed by the wrist bones and the transverse carpal ligament ("carpal tunnel syndrome").

Outcome: Although substitution therapy with thyroid, adrenal, and growth hormones should bring about normal puberty and its subsequent limitation to linear growth, the continued high levels of GH may produce some degree of *acromegaly*, and further surgery or radiation of the remaining tumor probably will be necessary.

CHEMISTRY

Growth hormone has been characterized and synthesized—it is a protein that contains 191 amino acids, with two disulfide bridges, and has a molecular weight of 21,500 daltons (Figure 58-1). The half-life of GH in the circulation is 20–30 minutes, and the normal concentration in the plasma is about 3 ng/ml.

The first purified extract of GH was obtained from the pituitary glands of cattle. Later, GH was isolated from sheep, whales, rats, monkeys, and humans. Bovine GH is active in rats but not in humans; this discovery was the first evidence of species-specificity of a hormone. GH from monkeys is active in humans, but the only source of human GH is the human pituitary gland. Most of the GH used in the United States is supplied by the National Pituitary Agency of the National Institutes of Health, which collects and processes pituitary glands that have been removed at autopsy. The supply of GH is extremely limited, and it is available only for specific patients approved by the Medical Advisory Committee of the National Pituitary Agency. Some GH also is available commercially for patients who have documented evidence of GH deficiency.

PHYSIOLOGICAL ACTIONS

Effects on Bone

Growth hormone promotes the formation of cartilage and bone; if the epiphyses of the long bones have not closed, GH accelerates the growth of all tissues in normal proportions. After the epiphyses have closed, excess GH causes the growth of bones only at sites where cartilage persists. These places include the mandible, the nasal bones, the bones of the hands and the feet, and the supraorbital ridges. Growth in these areas accounts for the characteristic changes that occur in a person who has acromegaly.

The effects of GH on the growth of the bone may be indirect; GH causes the liver, and perhaps the kidney, to produce *somatomedin*, a peptide that has a molecular weight of about 7000 daltons. Somatomedin stimulates the growth of cartilage and bone. The androgens, which are protein-anabolic hormones, also promote the growth of bone; however, these hormones accelerate the closure of the epiphyses, which stops further growth. This is an important difference between GH and the androgens.

Effects on Soft Tissue

GH increases significantly the mass of skeletal muscle and connective tissue. Excess GH causes enlargement of the heart and general splanchnomegaly, including increase of the size and functional capacity of the kidneys. The central nervous system and its derivatives are not affected. The endocrine glands are not affected directly; however, GH may enhance the effect of a specific tropic hormone to increase the rate of growth of a target organ.

Effects on Metabolism

Consistent with its effects on tissue mass, GH promotes the entry of amino acids into cells and increases the rate of synthesis of protein. This action decreases the concentration of amino acids in the plasma and causes positive nitrogen balance. As the rate of catabolism of protein is decreased, the concentration of urea in the blood (blood urea nitrogen, or BUN) decreases.

GH promotes the mobilization of fats; thus, the concentration of free fatty acids in the plasma increases, and a source of energy is made available. In addition, GH inhibits the synthesis of fat.

GH causes *hyperglycemia*, which is a high concentration of glucose in the blood. This effect is accomplished by increasing the rate of release of glucose from the liver (stimulates phosphatase) and decreasing the uptake of glucose by some cells (inhibits hexokinase), especially muscle and fatty tissues. GH is diabetogenic. In addition to increasing the blood glucose directly, GH antagonizes the action of insulin and promotes other factors that also antagonize insulin. GH alone can produce diabetes in some species, and about 30% of the people who are acromegalic also have diabetes mellitus.

GH causes the retention of potassium and phosphorus by the tissues. The concentration of phosphate in the plasma increases, probably because of increased reabsorption of phosphate by the kidneys. The concentration of calcium in the plasma also increases, although this effect may be caused by an increased rate of absorption of calcium from the gut. GH causes the retention of sodium under certain conditions, but the effect is not as consistent as that on the other minerals.

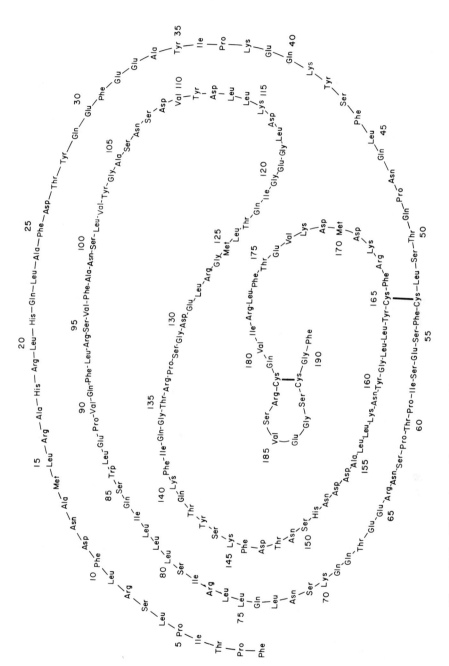

Figure 58-1.   The amino acid sequence of human growth hormone (HGH). Note the two disulfide bridges. (From Li, C.H., et al. 1977. Human somatotropin: Restoration of full biological activity by noncovalent interaction of a natural and synthetic fragment of the hormone. *Proc. Natl. Acad. Sci. U.S.A.* 74:1016.)

ASSAY

Bioassay

For many years, the concentration of GH in a sample was estimated by its action to widen the proximal tibial epiphysial cartilage in young hypophysectomized rats. This test was useful for quantifying GH in extracts of the pituitary gland or for purified preparations of GH, but it was not sensitive enough to measure the concentration of GH in the blood.

Radioimmunoassay (RIA)

The radioimmunoassay procedure was developed by Berson and Yalow, and Yalow shared in the Nobel Prize for this discovery in 1977 (Berson was deceased). The use of RIA to measure the concentrations of hormones in the plasma has increased vastly the knowledge of the physiology of the endocrine system. RIA is a standard procedure now in most clinical laboratories, where it is used to measure pituitary hormones, steroid hormones, and other clinically important substances in the blood.

The principle of RIA is that competition between radioactively labeled hormone and unlabeled hormone determines the amount of each bound to a specific antibody (Figure 58-2). The amount of labeled hormone that is bound can be estimated by measuring the amount of radiation associated with the antibody. A standard curve is prepared by adding known amounts of unlabeled hormone to a solution that contains labeled hormone and the antibody to the hormone. The amount of labeled hormone that is bound decreases as the concentration of unlabeled hormone increases. The unknown sample, which contains unlabeled hormone, then is equilibrated with a solution of the antibody and the labeled hormone, and the concentration of the hormone in the unknown sample can be read from the standard curve.

SECRETION

Although GH produces its most dramatic effects during the phase of growth and development of the body, it is secreted throughout

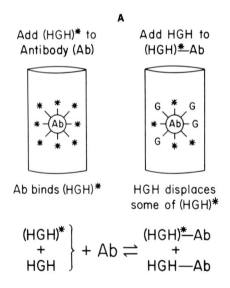

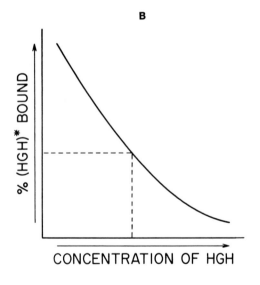

Figure 58-2.   The method of measuring human growth hormone (HGH) by radioimmunoassay. **A.** A specific antibody to HGH is produced by injecting very pure HGH into a laboratory animal. The antibody (Ab) eventually is harvested, and a known amount of it is mixed with HGH that has been labeled with ^{125}I [designated (HGH)*]. The amount of (HGH)* associated with Ab is determined by measuring the amount of radioactivity associated with Ab. Unlabeled HGH then is added, and some of the HGH displaces some of the (HGH)*. The amount of (HGH)* displaced is determined by measuring the radioactivity that remains associated with Ab; the decrease of radioactivity is related to the amount of HGH that is bound, which, in turn, reflects the concentration of HGH in the solution. **B.** A standard curve is constructed by adding graded amounts of HGH. Thus, the concentration of HGH in an unknown sample can be detemined by the amount of radioactivity that remains associated with Ab (dashed lines).

life. The average concentration of GH in the plasma of normal adults is about 3 ng/ml. The concentration is slightly greater in premature infants and in some normal infants; however, it is not significantly greater in normal children than in normal adults.

Under conditions in which the utilization of glucose is decreased or in which danger of such a decrease is imminent, the rate of secretion of GH can increase markedly. These conditions include *hypoglycemia* (low blood sugar), fasting, and the secretion or administration of glucagon. Experimentally, 2-deoxyglucose, which prevents the metabolism of glucose within the cell, also increases the rate of secretion of GH. An increase in the concentration of amino acids in the plasma, which would occur after a meal that contained protein, increases the secretion of GH. The infusion of arginine, an amino acid, is used clinically to test for the capacity to secrete GH. If the concentration of free fatty acids in the plasma decreases, the secretion of GH increases. Stress increases the secretion of GH, even if glucose is infused to produce hyperglycemia (see below). During sleep, the concentration of GH in the plasma increases; it reaches a peak about 70 minutes after the period of sleep begins, and it does so again on several occasions during subsequent deep sleep.

If glucose is injected into a normal person, so that the concentration of glucose in the blood increases, the concentration of GH in the blood decreases. A lack of change of the plasma concentration of GH in response to changes of blood glucose is taken to indicate the hypersecretion of GH; for example, the infusion of glucose into an acromegalic person usually causes no change in the level of GH in the plasma. Cortisol, a glucocorticoid hormone that is secreted by the adrenal cortex and that increases the concentration of free fatty acids in the plasma, decreases the rate of secretion of GH. Finally, a rising level of GH itself, through short-loop feedback (see Figure 57-6), decreases the rate of secretion of GH.

Control of Secretion

Growth hormone, like other pituitary hormones, is controlled by a combination of negative feedback and hypothalamic influence.

NEGATIVE FEEDBACK

The major feedback regulation of GH is the rate of utilization of glucose. This effect probably is monitored by the hypothalamus because patients in whom the pituitary stalk has been sectioned and monkeys in which lesions have been made in the ventromedial nucleus of the hypothalamus do not respond to hypoglycemia with an increased rate of secretion of GH. An additional mechanism is the short-loop feedback of GH on itself at the level of the pituitary gland.

CENTRAL NERVOUS SYSTEM

The rate of secretion of GH is increased by GRF, the hypothalamic releasing factor, and decreased by somatostatin, or growth hormone-inhibiting hormone (GIH), which also comes from the hypothalamus. GIH, administered experimentally, blocks the effect of any stimulus that normally increases the secretion of GH, and GIH decreases the concentration of GH in the plasma of a person who has acromegaly.

STUDY OUTLINE

HISTORY

ACROMEGALY   Caused by excess secretion of GH after growth areas of bones have closed.
  Ends of long bones enlarge.
  Certain soft tissues grow.
  Hands and feet enlarge and skull and jaw lengthen.
  Viscera enlarge.

GIGANTISM   Excess secretion of GH before growth areas of bones close.
  Subject is very large, but body proportions are about normal.

PITUITARY DWARFISM   Caused by deficiency of GH in childhood.
  Subject retains infantile stature and features.

CHEMISTRY   GH has been characterized structurally and synthesized.
  Protein; 191 amino acids; two disulfide bridges.
  Half-life in circulation is 20–30 minutes; normal concentration in plasma is 3 ng/ml.
  Considerable species-specificity; human GH is obtained from human pituitary glands removed at autopsy.

PHYSIOLOGICAL ACTIONS

EFFECTS ON BONE   Promotes formation of cartilage and bone.

If epiphyses are not closed, GH accelerates growth of all tissues in proportion (gigantism).

If epiphyses are closed, GH causes growth only where cartilage persists (acromegaly).

Effects may be indirect, through *somatomedin* (produced by liver and perhaps by kidneys), under influence of GH.

Androgens promote growth of bones, but not after epiphyses close.

EFFECTS ON SOFT TISSUE   Increases the mass of skeletal muscle and connective tissue.

Excess GH causes enlargement of heart and viscera.

EFFECTS ON METABOLISM   Promotes the entry of amino acids into cells, increases rate of synthesis of protein.

Concentrations of amino acids and urea in plasma decrease—causes increased synthesis and decreased breakdown of protein.

Promotes mobilization of fats, inhibits synthesis; free fatty acids in plasma are increased.

Increases release of glucose from liver, decreases uptake by muscle and fatty tissues—leads to increased blood glucose.

Antagonizes action of insulin and promotes diabetes.

Retention of potassium and phosphate by tissues; increased reabsorption of phosphate by kidneys; plasma phosphate increases.

Plasma calcium increases—increased rate of reabsorption from gut.

Retention of sodium under certain conditions.

ASSAY

BIOASSAY   Widening of epiphyseal cartilage in young, hypophysectomized rats; limited sensitivity.

RADIOIMMUNOASSAY (RIA)   Measures concentration of hormone in plasma.

Competition between radioactively labeled hormone and unlabeled hormone, binding by specific antibody; concentration of GH in unknown sample is determined by amount of radioactivity that remains associated with antibody.

SECRETION   Continues throughout life; plasma concentration about same in normal children and normal adults.

Secretion is increased by conditions that decrease utilization of glucose—hypoglycemia, fasting, glucagon, increased plasma amino acids, decreased plasma fatty acids, stress, and sleep.

Decreased by hyperglycemia, cortisol, increased free fatty acid, and increasing plasma GH (negative feedback).

CONTROL OF SECRETION   Combination of negative feedback, hypothalamic influences.

NEGATIVE FEEDBACK   Rate of utilization of glucose (decreased utilization causes increased GH; increased utilization causes decreased GH).

Plasma GH, on pituitary ("short-loop").

CENTRAL NERVOUS SYSTEM   Increased by GRF (releasing factor), decreased by somatostatin.

BIBLIOGRAPHY

Clemmons, D.R.; Van Wyk, J.J.; Ridgway, E.C., et al. 1979. Evaluation of acromegaly by radioimmunoassay of somatomedin-C. *N. Engl. J. Med.* 301:1138.

DeGroot, L.J.; Cahill, G.F., Jr.; Odell, W.D., et al. (eds.). 1979. *Endocrinology.* Volume I. New York: Grune & Stratton.

Guillemin, R.; Brazeau, P.; Böhleh, P.; et al. 1982. Growth hormone-releasing factor from a human pancreatic tumor that caused acromegaly. *Science* 218:585.

Isakson, O.G.P.; Jansson, J.-O.; and Gause, I.A.M. 1982. Growth hormone stimulates longitudinal bone growth directly. *Science* 216:1237.

Knobil, E., and Sawyer, W.H. (eds.). 1974. The pituitary gland and its neuroendocrine control. In *Handbook of Physiology.* Section 7. Endocrinology. Volume IV. Washington, D.C.: American Physiological Society.

Li, C.H.; Bewley, T.A.; Blake, J., et al. 1977. Human somatotropin: Restoration of full biological activity by noncovalent interaction of a natural and synthetic fragment of the hormone. *Proc. Natl. Acad. Sci. U.S.A.* 74:1016.

McCann, S.M. 1982. Physiology and pharmacology of LHRH and somatostatin. *Annu. Rev. Physiol.* 22:491.

Phillips, L.S., and Vassilopoulou, R. 1980. Somatomedins. *N. Engl. J. Med.* 302:371, 438.

Raisz, L.G., and Kream, B.E. 1981. Hormonal control of skeletal growth. *Annu. Rev. Physiol.* 43:225.

Tannenbaum, G.S.; Guyda, H.J.; and Posner, B.I. 1983. Insulin-like growth factors: A role in growth hormone negative feedback and body weight regulation via brain. *Science* 220:77.

Williams, R.J. (ed.). 1981. *Textbook of Endocrinology* (6th ed.). Philadelphia: Saunders.

Yallow, R.S. 1978. Radioimmunoassay: A probe for the fine structure of biological systems. *Science* 200:1236.

59

The
Thyroid Gland

CHAPTER CONTENTS

FUNCTIONAL ANATOMY

The *thyroid gland* is located in the neck, at the level of the fifth to the seventh cervical vertebrae; it develops from the floor of the pharynx. When viewed from the front, the thyroid gland is roughly H-shaped. It is composed of a right lobe and a left lobe, which lie on either side of the trachea and are connected by an isthmus. The gland ultimately is composed of many vesicles, or *follicles*, each of which is lined by a single layer of cuboidal cells. The follicles are filled with *colloid*, a homogeneous material that is the site of storage of the thyroid hormones.

PHYLOGENY

The metabolic need for the thyroid hormone developed first in the higher marine vertebrates, and it was met by the evolution of

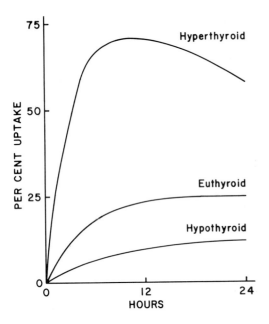

Figure 59-1. Estimation of thyroid activity by measuring the rate of uptake of ^{131}I and the fraction of the total dose that is taken up. The rapid decline of ^{131}I in the hyperactive gland (hyperthyroid) reflects the rapid rate of turnover.

specialized tissue that concentrates iodide and synthesizes the thyroid hormones. When the vertebrates left the oceans, where iodide is a common constituent in the environment, to live on the land, where iodide is a trace element, the mechanisms for concentrating iodide became enhanced. Humans, like all other vertebrates, have discrete, highly developed thyroid glands that store the thyroid hormones; therefore, humans can tolerate periods during which little or no iodide is ingested.

IODINE METABOLISM

The thyroid gland stores iodide to about 25 times the concentration of iodide in the plasma. Because the iodide ion is charged negatively, an electrical gradient develops in addition to the concentration gradient. The mechanism of concentration of iodide is not known, but it is an active process and has been presumed to be related to the hypothetical Na^+-K^+ pump.

Radioactive Iodide

The use of the radioactive isotope ^{131}I has contributed greatly to the understanding of the metabolism of iodide and the biosynthesis, se-

cretion, control, and metabolism of the thyroid hormones. The thyroid gland takes up ^{131}I that is consumed or injected in exactly the same way that it takes up the stable isotope.

CLINICAL USE OF ^{131}I

^{131}I emits both β- and γ-rays. β-rays are charged particles that travel only a few millimeters before they are absorbed, and they damage tissue only in a limited area. γ-rays are emitted from the nucleus and have properties similar to those of x-rays (i.e., they are not charged, travel a considerable distance before being absorbed, cause negligible internal damage, and can be measured externally). The rate and amount of uptake of ^{131}I and, hence, the activity of the thyroid gland can be estimated by external counting after ^{131}I has been administered to a patient (Figure 59-1). Highly localized scanning may be done to locate areas of the gland that take up ^{131}I at an abnormally fast rate (hot nodules) or an abnormally slow rate (cold nodules).

When the uptake of ^{131}I is studied, a very small dose is given (e.g., 100 μCi), so that too few β-rays are emitted to cause harm. A larger dose may be used deliberately (e.g., 5mCi) to destroy a portion of a hyperactive thyroid gland. If too much ^{131}I is given and too much of the gland is destroyed, the patient may become hypothyroid. This is not a serious problem, however, because replacement therapy is easy to maintain.

Children should not be given ^{131}I because of the danger that the radiation will cause thyroid cancer. This admonition is based on the observations that ^{131}I causes cancer of the thyroid in baby rats and that the incidence of cancer of the thyroid was abnormally high in people whose thymus glands were irradiated during childhood. ^{131}I also should not be given to pregnant women or women who are lactating, because it is excreted in the milk, and the nursing infant will be exposed.

Uptake of Iodide

Iodide enters the body chiefly with food and water. It is absorbed quickly from the gastrointestinal tract and transported as inorganic iodide in the circulation. Most of the iodide is removed from the circulation by the thyroid gland, which concentrates it, and the kidneys, which excrete it. After 24 hours, approximately one-third of the iodide that was ingested has been taken up by the thyroid gland, and two-thirds of it has been excreted.

The thyroid gland is not the only tissue or organ that concentrates iodide; the gastric mucosa, the salivary glands, the lactating mammary glands, the skin, the choroid plexus, and the placenta also concentrate iodide. However, the thyroid gland binds I^- and forms organic compounds of iodine. Because these other organs and body systems do not bind the iodide, the concentration of iodide in them decreases rapidly, and most of it is gone after 24 hours.

BIOSYNTHESIS OF THYROID HORMONE

The first step in the biosynthesis of thyroid hormone, and probably the step that limits the rate of synthesis, is the active transport of I^- into the follicular cells of the thyroid gland. I^- is oxidized quickly (by peroxidase) to active $I°$ or to I_2 (Figure 59-2).

Iodine is added to tyrosine, an amino acid, to form *3-monoiodotyrosine* (MIT) and *3,5-diiodotyrosine* (DIT). The iodination probably occurs at the membrane of the follicular cell on the side that borders on the colloid. Once it is bound, the I is considered to be organic iodine. Monoiodotyrosine and diiodotyrosine combine to form *3,5,3'-triiodothyronine* (T_3, or TRIT), and two molecules of diiodotyrosine condense to form *3,5,3',5'-tetraiodothyronine* (*thyroxine*, or T_4) (Figure 59-2).

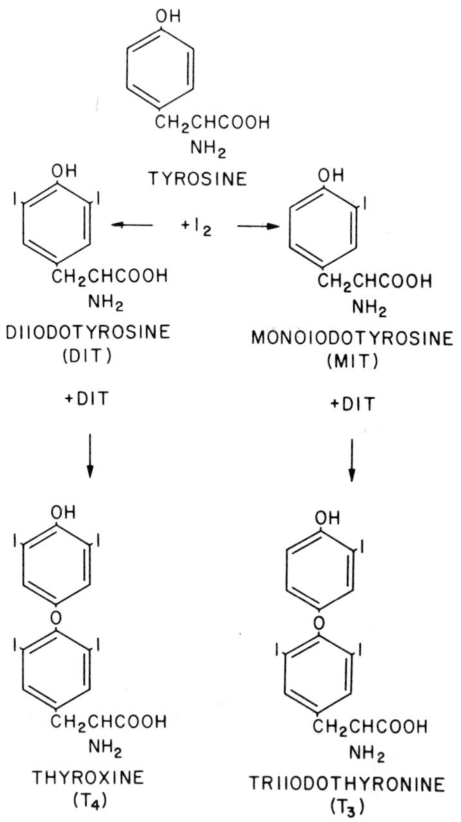

Figure 59-2. Biosynthesis of the thyroid hormones.

THYROGLOBULIN

The follicles of the thyroid gland are filled by an amorphous material (*collagen*) that consists mostly of a large protein (molecular weight is about 650,000 daltons) called *thyroglobulin*. It is synthesized by the cells of the thyroid gland, and the thyroid hormones are synthesized and stored on it. Thyroglobulin is too large to leave the thyroid gland and enter the capillaries at a significant rate; hence, it is not found in the plasma normally, although very small amounts of it may appear in the lymphatic system. In certain pathological conditions, such as thyroiditis or thyroid tumor, or after therapeutic procedures such as radiation or surgery of the thyroid gland, thyroglobulin may be found in the circulation.

The thyroid hormones, triiodothyronine (T_3) and thyroxine (T_4), and their precursors, monoiodotyrosine (MIT) and diiodotyrosine (DIT), are stored in the colloid, bound by pep-

tide linkages to the thyroglobulin. More precursor than hormone is stored, and very little inorganic iodide is free in the gland because most of the iodide that enters the gland is bound. Normally, enough of the thyroid compounds are stored to maintain metabolism for several months, even if none of them is replaced (Figure 59-3).

RELEASE OF THYROID HORMONE (TH)

The release of TH is initiated as colloid droplets are engulfed and hydrolyzed in the cell. Under the influence of thyroid-stimulating hormone, TSH, the thyroid protease cleaves the peptide linkages of the thyroglobulin, and T_3 and T_4 are released into the blood. T_3 and T_4 are the thyroid hormones that are secreted physiologically (Figure 59-4).

The molecules of MIT and DIT that also are released by the proteolysis of thyroglobulin are deiodinated within the thyroid gland. Deficiencies of certain enzymes that are involved in the deiodination or coupling of MIT and DIT (Figures 59-3 and 59-4) permit the appearance of MIT and DIT in the circulation. The individuals in whom this abnormality occurs usually are hypothyroid.

Most of the I^- that is produced by the deiodination of MIT and DIT remains in the thyroid gland and is used again in the biosynthesis of TH. When circulating TH is metabolized, much of the I^- that is freed also is conserved. Thus, the average amount of I^- that must be taken into the diet to maintain a balance, which is about 20 μg/day, is only one-fifth to one-third of the total amount of I^- that is needed for the synthesis of TH.

Abnormal Metabolism of Iodine

At least five forms of congenital goitrous hypothyroidism, which represent specific defects in various stages of the synthesis of TH, have been reported (Figure 59-4). These defects are as follows: (1) defects in the active transport of iodide, (2) inability to bind I° to tyrosine, (3) inability to deiodinate MIT and DIT, (4) lack of coupling enzyme, so that the synthesis of T_3 and T_4 from MIT and DIT fails, and (5) deficiency of thyroid protease, so that abnormal fragments of thyroglobulin are secreted.

CIRCULATING THYROID HORMONE

T_4 in the circulation is bound almost entirely (99.96%) to specific proteins in the plasma. Thyroxine-binding globulin (TBG) binds most of the T_4, and thyroxine-binding prealbumin (TBPA) binds some of it. When T_4 is in excess, it may bind also to serum albumin. The small amount of T_4 that is free in the circulation is in equilibrium with the T_4 that is associated with the thyroxine-binding proteins (TBP):

$$T_4 + TBP \rightleftarrows T_4TBP$$

The physiological significance of the hormone-binding proteins is not understood completely. According to current concepts, only the free T_4 is active, and the bound T_4 is an inactive, circulating store of the hormone. It is assumed that the free T_4 either enters the cell or affects cell membranes to exert the metabolic effects of the thyroid gland, and that the free T_4 also exerts the characteristic effects of negative feedback on the secretion of TSH by the pituitary gland.

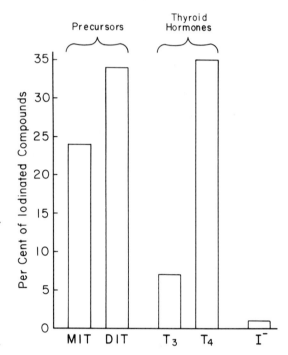

Figure 59-3.   The relative amounts of the thyroid hormones and their precursors that are stored in the thyroid gland.

In clinical laboratories, total T_4 is measured (both free and bound); the direct measurement of free T_4 alone is a research tool. The determination of total T_4 is useful because generally it reflects the amount of free T_4 that is in equilibrium with bound T_4. However, this is true only when the concentration of TGB is normal. Estrogens increase the production of hormone-binding proteins in the liver. Thus, women who are pregnant or who are taking estrogens (birth control pills) to prevent pregnancy have increased concentrations of TBG and plasma T_4 as measured clinically; however, their rates of metabolism are normal and they show no evidence of hyperthyroidism because their plasma concentrations of free T_4 are normal. At the other extreme, patients who are taking androgens, who lack TBG for genetic reasons, or who have abnormally low concentrations of all plasma proteins because of liver or kidney disease have low concentrations of plasma T_4 as measured clinically. Nevertheless, such patients may show no signs of hypothyroidism because their plasma concentrations of free T_4 are normal.

When protein-bound iodine (PBI) is measured, all of the iodine that is combined with

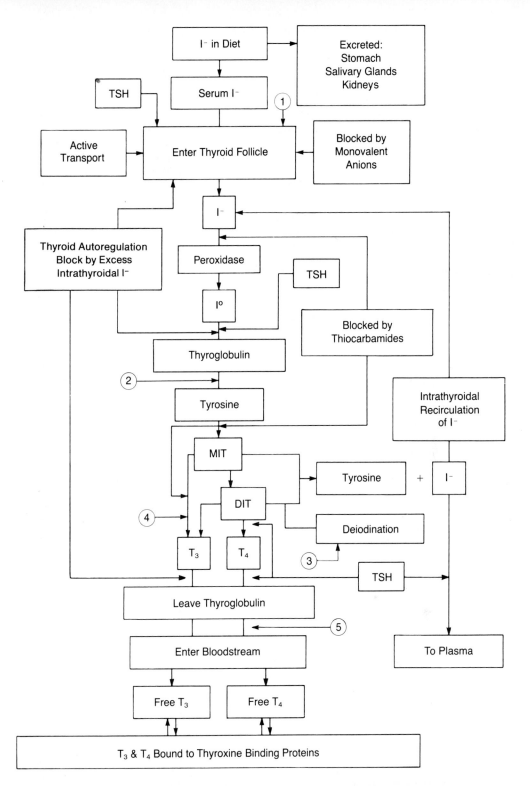

Figure 59-4. The synthesis and binding of TH to thyroglobulin, the hydrolysis of TH from thyroglobulin, and the secretion of TH into the bloodstream. Also shown are the sites at which TSH acts, monovalent anions block, thiocarbamides inhibit, thyroid autoregulation is imposed, and metabolic abnormalities occur. **1.** Defects in the active transport of iodide. **2.** Inability to bind $I°$ to tyrosine. **3.** Inability to deiodinate MIT and DIT. **4.** Lack of coupling enzyme, so that synthesis of T_3 and T_4 from MIT and DIT fails. **5.** Deficiency of thyroid protease, so that abnormal fragments of thyroglobulin are secreted.

organic compounds in the circulation is measured; usually, the organic iodine is contained in T_4. Formerly, this was the most widely used clinical test for thyroid function; however, it has been replaced by the more specific measurement of total plasma T_4.

The control system for the secretion of TSH by the pituitary gland responds to free T_4 and T_3 and acts to maintain a constant level of T_4 and T_3 in the plasma. In pregnant women or in anyone whose levels of estrogen are high, the concentration of TBG is increased. By mass action, the equilibrium between T_4 and TBG is moved to the right (Figure 59-5), more T_4 is bound, and the concentration of free T_4 decreases. Suppression of the production of TSH by negative feedback is relieved; thus, more TSH is released and the thyroid is stimulated to secrete more T_4. At the new equilibrium, T_4 is normal but TBG and bound T_4 are elevated.

Triiodothyronine (T_3) in the Circulation

T_3 binds to specific plasma proteins, but not quite to the extent that T_4 does because T_3 binds to TBG but not to TBPA. T_3 is four to five times as potent as T_4, and the metabolic actions of T_3 begin more promptly and develop more rapidly. T_3 also enters cells more easily. Apparently, the kinetics of T_3 are different because less T_3 is bound. In birds, which lack TBG, T_3 and T_4 are equally potent and the durations of action are the same.

TBG Increases

($\uparrow$TBG)

T_4 + TBG $\rightleftharpoons$ T_4TBG

($T_4\downarrow$)   (T_4TBG$\uparrow$)

More T_4 Secreted

($\uparrow T_4$)

T_4 + TBG $\rightleftharpoons$ T_4TBG

                              (T_4TBG$\uparrow$)

T_4 Returns to Normal

T_4TBG Remains High

Figure 59-5. Increased concentration of thyroid-binding globulin (TBG) increases the concentration of TBG-bound T_4, while the concentration of free T_4 is normal.

T_3, like T_4, is secreted by the thyroid gland; however, about one-third to one-half of the T_3 in the circulation is produced by the conversion of T_4 to T_3 outside the thyroid gland. The normal concentration of T_3 in the plasma is only about one-seventy-fifth that of T_4 (1.2 ng/ml vs. 90 ng/ml); however, the concentrations of free T_3 and T_4 differ by only tenfold (4 pg/ml of T_3 vs. 40 pg/ml of T_4) (Figure 59-6). Despite the fact that the concentration of T_3 is only one-tenth that of T_4, the effect of T_3 is about one-half that of T_4 because T_3 is about five times as potent as T_4. Plasma T_3 is not measured routinely in most clinical laboratories, but it can be determined by radioimmunoassay in some clinical laboratories.

T_3-UPTAKE TEST

T_3-uptake is used clinically as an indicator of the function of the thyroid gland; it is not a measure of plasma T_3, and it should be used in conjunction with the determination of plasma T_4. Radioactive T_3 and charcoal or a resin are added to a sample of the patient's plasma in vitro (Figure 59-7). The test is a measure of the partition of radioactive T_3 between unsaturated TBG in the plasma (TBG that is not bound to T_4) and the charcoal or resin. T_3 binds preferentially to TBG; however, if binding sites on TBG are not available, the T_3 is taken up by the resin. T_3-uptake is an indirect measurement of the saturation of TBG with T_4. Thus, if the TBG is highly saturated because of a high concentration of T_4 in the plasma, only a few binding sites on the TBG are available to T_3, and the uptake of T_3 by the resin is high.

When the level of T_4 and the uptake of T_3 vary in the same direction, the tests indicate the status of the thyroid gland (Figure 59-8). If both values are high, the patient is *hyper*thyroid; if both values are low, the patient is *hypo*thyroid. When the level of T_4 and the uptake of T_3 vary in opposite directions, the binding proteins of the plasma are altered. This combination can occur in pregnancy, when the level of T_4 is high and the uptake of T_3 is low. It can occur also if TBG is deficient; in this event, the level of T_4 is low and the uptake of T_3 is high. In both of these conditions, however, free T_4 is normal and the patient is euthyroid.

The *free T_4 index* is an artificial number obtained by multiplying the total T_4 by the uptake of T_3. The true thyroid status of the patient is determined by the level of free T_4, which is not measured clinically; however, the free T_4 index correlates well with free T_4.

METABOLISM OF THYROID HORMONE

T_4 is secreted at a rate of about 80 µg/day, and its half-life in the plasma is about 7 days. Thus, when thyroxin is given therapeutically, administration once a day is adequate. Some tissues, especially the liver, take up T_4 intracellularly and keep it in a form that is exchangeable with the plasma. The half-life of T_3 in the plasma is about 1.5–3 days.

Deiodination, which occurs in the liver and the kidneys, is the major route of catabolism of T_3 and T_4. Much of the I^- is carried back to the thyroid gland by the circulation; of the I^- that is lost, 85%–90% is excreted in the urine.

Some of the thyroid hormone is conjugated with sulfate or glucuronide, which attaches to the hydroxyl (OH) groups, and then passed via the bile to the gut. Most of the conjugated TH is hydrolyzed back to T_3 and T_4 and reabsorbed from the small intestine. The remaining 10%–15% of the I^- that is lost is excreted via the feces.

CONTROL OF THE THYROID GLAND

Thyrotropin (TSH)

TSH from the pituitary gland influences all aspects of the thyroid gland, including the uptake of I^-, the synthesis and release of TH, and the growth of the gland. The effects of TSH are mediated by the activation of adenylate cyclase in the membrane of the thyroid cell, which increases the concentration of cyclic AMP within the cell. Prolonged stimulation of the thyroid

$$
\begin{array}{cc}
0.04\% & 99.96\% \\
T_4 \;+\; TBP \;\rightleftharpoons\; & T_4\,TBP \\
40 \text{ pg/ml} & 90 \text{ ng/ml}
\end{array}
$$

$$
\begin{array}{cc}
0.3\% & 99.7\% \\
T_3 \;+\; TBP \;\rightleftharpoons\; & T_3\,TBP \\
4 \text{ pg/ml} & 1.2 \text{ ng/ml}
\end{array}
$$

Figure 59-6.   Relative binding of T_4 and T_3 to thyroid-binding protein (TBP). Abbreviations: ng = nanogram (10^{-9}g) and pg = picogram (10^{-12}g).

gland by TSH causes the gland to enlarge; this condition is called *goiter*.

TSH is a glycoprotein secreted by basophilic cells of the pituitary gland. TSH is composed of two subunits, which are designated α and β, and has a molecular weight of about 28,000 daltons. The α-chain is similar to the α-chain of the gonadotropins LH, FSH, and HCG (human chorionic gonadotropin). The β-subunit of each of the glycoprotein hormones is different. Although TSH is immunologically specific, there is no species-specificity with respect to its biological action; for example, TSH from cattle or swine is active in humans. TSH is not used clinically because T_4 is more satisfactory. TSH is used in some tests, however.

NEGATIVE FEEDBACK

The pituitary gland is sensitive to the levels of free T_3 and T_4 in the plasma. If the levels of T_3 and T_4 change in one direction, the rate of secretion of TSH changes in the other direction. Thus, if TH decreases, TSH increases, and the effect is to restore the concentration of TH in the plasma. The increase of TH, in turn, causes the rate of secretion of TSH to decrease again. In primary hypothyroidism, the thyroid gland does not respond to TSH with increased secretion of TH; hence, the plasma levels of TSH remain high. Most of the effect of feedback by TH is manifested in the pituitary gland, by changing the sensitivity of the pituitary to

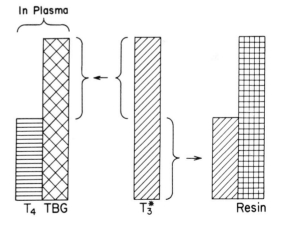

In Plasma

T_4 TBG T_3^* Resin

Figure 59-7. T_3-uptake test. T_3^* is radioactive (^{125}I) T_3. The amount of T_3^* for which there were no binding sites on TBG (thyroid-binding globulin) is bound to the resin. Because the sites not available to T_3 were occupied by T_4, the amount of T_3 bound to the resin indicates the amount of T_4 bound to TBG.

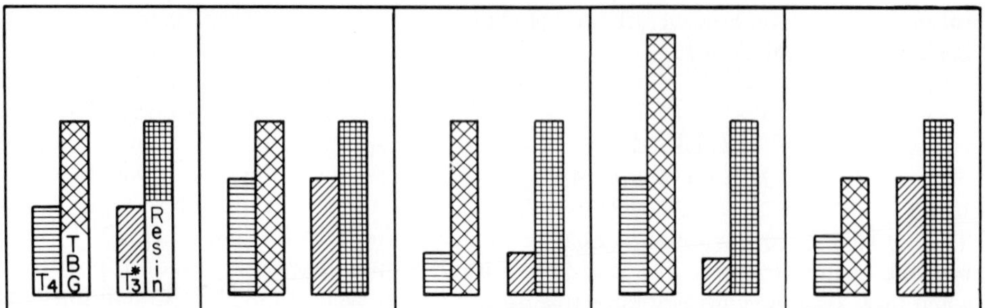

	Euthyroid	Hyperthyroid	Hypothyroid	Pregnancy	TBG Deficiency
Total T$_4$	Normal	High	Low	High	Low
T$_3$ Uptake	Normal	High	Low	Low	High
Free T$_4$	Normal	High	Low	Normal	Normal
Free T$_4$ Index	Normal	High	Low	Normal	Normal

Figure 59-8. Interpretation of T$_4$ level and T$_3$-uptake. TBP is thyroid-binding protein and T$_3$* is radioactive (^{125}I) T$_3$.

thyrotropin-releasing hormone (TRH). Feedback is an important mechanism for maintaining a constant rate of secretion of TH, especially in the absence of environmental changes. Hypothyroid patients are very sensitive to TRH, and a relatively small amount of TRH causes a relatively larger amount of TSH to be released. Hyperthyroid patients are insensitive to TRH. TRH may be used as a diagnostic test, but it is expensive.

CENTRAL NERVOUS SYSTEM EFFECTS

The most important mechanism for regulating the secretion of TSH is mediated through TRH, which is released by hypothalamic neurons and carried to the adenohypophysis through the pituitary portal system. TRH participates in the control of the normal secretion of TSH and, in addition, is responsible for all modifications of the secretion of TSH in response to environmental changes (e.g., increased secretion in response to cold and decreased secretion in response to heat or stress).

Autoregulation of Thyroid Function

Autoregulation of thyroid function is known to depend on intrathyroidal iodine, but the process is not understood well. When iodine is

deficient, the thyroid gland becomes more responsive to TSH. When iodine is in excess, the rate of active transport of iodide and the rate of synthesis and release of TH are decreased (Figure 59-4). This mechanism forms the basis for the administration of iodine to prepare hyperthyroid patients for thyroid surgery. The effect is only temporary.

ANTITHYROID DRUGS

Monovalent Anions

Certain organic anions, such as perchlorate and thiocyanate, inhibit thyroid function; the negative charge and the size of the molecule both are important. The anions block the uptake of I$^-$ at the site of the active transport of I$^-$, mostly by competitive inhibition (Figure 59-4). As a consequence of treatment by monovalent anions, no iodide is taken up by the thyroid for further synthesis of TH; hence, when the stores of TH are gone, the rate of metabolism of the tissues decreases. The lack of negative feedback permits a high rate of secretion of TSH, which stimulates the thyroid gland and eventually causes goiter (enlarged thyroid gland).

Thiocarbamides

Propylthiouracil (PTU) and methimazole, which are thiocarbamide derivatives, are used most commonly to suppress thyroid function. These drugs prevent the formation of TH by blocking the oxidation of I^- to $I°$, by inhibiting the iodination of MIT, and by preventing the coupling of iodothyronines to form T_3 and T_4 (Figure 59-4). The consequences of the use of the thiocarbamides—hypometabolism and enlargement of the thyroid gland—are caused by the lack of TH synthesis. The thiocarbamides are used clinically to control hyperthyroidism. Because they pass through the placental barrier, thiocarbamides can cause hypothyroidism and goiter in the fetus.

Naturally Occurring Goitrogens

Substances found in certain vegetables, such as cabbage, rutabagas, and turnips, inhibit the synthesis of TH. Generally, these foods are not consumed in sufficient quantity to cause goiter; however, "cabbage goiter" sometimes is seen in vegetarians.

EFFECTS OF THYROID HORMONES

Thyroid hormones are not essential for life, but if they are deficient, function is disturbed at various levels, from enzymes to behavior and from organelles to organ systems. No metabolic process or major organ system is spared the effects of an excess or deficit of TH. One of the most fundamental effects is increased consumption of O_2 and production of heat in all tissues except the adult brain, testes, spleen, uterus, and anterior pituitary gland. Many of the effects of the thyroid hormones depend on the quantity of hormone that is secreted—in fact, the effects that have been described usually are those of too much or too little TH—the effects of normal secretion of TH are not known for certain.

Deficiency of TH during the development of the fetus after the twelfth week, when the fetal thyroid gland should begin functioning, causes a condition known as *cretinism*. The development of the skeleton is delayed, and the brain is small and poorly developed. All mammals require TH, in addition to growth hormone (GH), for growth after birth. In hypothyroid children, the growth of bone is slowed and closure of the epiphyses is delayed. In amphibians, metamorphosis requires TH.

Central Nervous System

Impaired formation of the myelin sheath can lead to irreversible brain damage and mental deficiency (cretinism). After the critical period during which TH is essential for normal development of the fetus, replacement therapy cannot restore intellectual function to normal. In humans, this period usually ends in utero or shortly after birth, but it may include the first year of life. After the brain has developed, deficiency of TH causes mental sluggishness and slowing of the tendon reflexes, but these conditions can be reversed by treatment. Excess TH, or hyperthyroidism, causes tremor, hyperactivity, restlessness, and irritability.

Skin

In the hypothyroid patient, mucoproteins are deposited under the skin (*myxedema*), especially in the extremities and the periocular areas of the face. The skin is pale and cool because of cutaneous vasoconstriction, and the patient is sensitive to a cold environment. The hyperthyroid patient is intolerant of heat—the skin is warm and moist because of cutaneous vasodilatation, and the patient sweats excessively.

Cardiovascular System

Deficiency of TH results in decreases of heart rate, blood volume, and arterial pressure. Excess of TH affects all of these variables oppositely; because of the high rate of consumption of O_2 by the myocardium, angina pectoris (pain), cardiac failure, and atrial fibrillation occur frequently. TH increases the sensitivity of the heart and blood vessels to the effects of the catecholamines, which may account for some of the events listed above. Drugs that block adrenergic β-receptors, such as propranolol, may be used to relieve the symptoms of hyperthyroidism that are related to the heart.

Gastrointestinal System

Hypothyroidism may be associated with loss of appetite, decreased intake of food, and occasional constipation. Hyperthyroidism may be associated with increased appetite, increased consumption of food, and more frequent bowel movements. The causes of these changes are not known.

Gonads

Normal gonadal function requires normal thyroid function; hence, deficiency of TH is characterized by retarded development of the gonads. In the female, fertility is decreased and menstruation is irregular; the cycles may be short, and bleeding may occur between periods. TH in excess causes long menstrual cycles and amenorrhea (lack of menstrual bleeding). TH has been used as a drug to increase the production of milk by dairy animals.

Metabolism

Physiological amounts of TH favor the synthesis of protein, which is indicated by positive nitrogen balance. Excess TH causes the catabolism of protein, which results in the wasting of muscle and negative nitrogen balance. The production of phosphocreatine is impaired, which causes myopathy and weakness, especially in the ocular muscles and the myocardium.

TH increases gluconeogenesis and glycolysis, and excess TH may cause hyperglycemia. TH also increases the rate of absorption of glucose from the intestine and, consistent with the overall increased rate of metabolism, enhances the utilization of glucose.

TH increases the turnover of fat by increasing the rates of synthesis, mobilization, and oxidation of fat. Deficiency of TH permits the concentration of cholesterol in the plasma to increase because of decreased rates of metabolism and excretion of cholesterol (in the bile). Excess TH decreases the concentration of cholesterol in the plasma by increasing the rates of consumption and excretion of cholesterol. The d-isomer of T_4 is used therapeutically to decrease cholesterol in the body.

If TH is deficient, the bones do not grow or heal normally because the synthesis of organic matrix is inadequate. Excess TH causes wasting of bone and excretion of Ca^{++}. The renal blood flow and rate of glomerular filtration are increased; hence, the excretion of other electrolytes also may be increased.

TH is necessary for the conversion of carotene to vitamin A in the liver. Excess TH increases the requirements of the body for the vitamin B complex and vitamin C.

MECHANISM OF ACTION OF THYROID HORMONES

The actions of the thyroid hormones involve both of the two major schemes for explaining the actions of hormones: the production of cyclic AMP and stimulation of protein synthesis. Examples of the production of cyclic AMP are the actions in the heart, where TH activates adenylate cyclase, and in adipose tissue, where TH causes the synthesis of adenylate cyclase de novo. The increased rate of metabolism that TH engenders develops slowly and probably depends on the synthesis of certain proteins, particularly in the mitochondria.

GRAVES' DISEASE

Graves' disease has several classic features, not all of which are seen in every case. The principal elements of Graves' disease are: (1) *goiter,* which is an enlarged thyroid gland, (2) *thyrotoxicosis,* which is characterized by the symptoms of excess TH, (3) *exophthalmos,* or protrusion of the eyeballs, which is caused by the accumulation of mucopolysaccharides in the retro-orbital spaces, infiltration of the cells by macrophages, and profound edema, and (4) *nonsuppressibility,* because the administration of TH does not inhibit the uptake of ^{131}I by the thyroid gland.

Long-Acting Thyroid Stimulator (LATS)

LATS is an abnormal factor found in the plasma of most patients who have Graves' disease. LATS is a protein, an immunoactive γ-globulin that probably is an autoantibody directed against some component of the thyroid gland. LATS differs from TSH chemically, although it acts on the thyroid gland in the same way that TSH does. The stimulatory effects of LATS on the thyroid reach a maximum more slowly than those of TSH do, however, and LATS continues to act for a longer time (Figure 59-9). LATS is cleared from the blood much more slowly than TSH is; the half-life of LATS is 1-2 weeks, whereas the half-life of TSH is only 30 minutes.

LATS crosses the placental barrier, while TSH does not. Babies whose mothers have Graves' disease may be born with exophthalmos, goiter, and heart failure; LATS is found in the plasma of most of such infants. The effects on the infants last for 1 or 2 months, after which no LATS can be detected in the plasma.

LATS is produced by lymphocytes in the plasma of patients who have Graves' disease. It is not found in pituitary extracts, and some

CLINICAL CORRELATION
59.1   Primary Hypothyroidism

CASE REPORT

The Patient: A 52-year-old woman.

Principal Complaint: A lump in the neck, determined to be a goiter.

History: Four months before the present admission, a physician had found that the patient's thyroid gland was about three times the normal size and of a hard, rubbery consistency. The concentration of thyroxine (T_4) in the plasma was 3.1 μg/dl (normal, 4–12 μg/dl).

Clinical Examination: A needle-aspiration biopsy of the thyroid gland was taken; microscopic examination revealed markedly atypical epithelial cells associated with chronic inflammation and fibrosis. This pattern is consistent with thyroiditis caused by autoimmune factors. T_4 concentration was 1.6 μg/dl, the free thyroxine index was 0.5 ng/dl (normal, 1–4 ng/dl), the T_3 resin uptake was 25% (normal, 25–35%), and the concentration of TSH in the plasma was 115 U/ml (normal, 0.5–3.5 U/ml). A test for antibodies to colloid was moderately positive. The 24-hour uptake of ^{131}I was 34% of the administered dose, (normal, 5%–30%).

Comment: This combination of findings—a diffusely enlarged, firm thyroid gland; primary hypothyroidism; a positive test for antibodies to colloid antigen; the slightly elevated uptake of ^{131}I; and the atypical cells and fibrosis—is consistent with Hashimoto's thyroiditis (fibrous variant). This condition causes hypothyroidism, but the patient may be well except for the goiter. However, the goiter increases because of a lack of negative-feedback suppression of TSH release, and symptoms of compression of the trachea may appear.

Treatment: A subtotal thyroidectomy was performed, and the diagnosis of thyroiditis was confirmed. Treatment was begun with a low daily dose of L-thyroxine, which was increased every 2 weeks until the proper maintenance dose was reached. At that level of T_4, the TSH is normal, and the patient feels better. Partial thyroidectomy usually is not necessary since treatment with thyroxine often causes the goiter to regress somewhat.

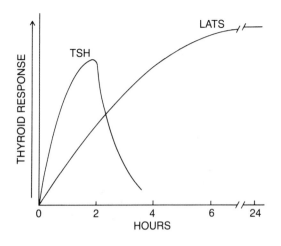

Figure 59-9. Time course of the actions of TSH and LATS on the thyroid gland.

patients still have thyrotoxicosis after their hypophyses have been removed. Graves' disease appears to be an autoimmune disease that involves both humoral and cell-mediated immunity. Human thyroid-stimulator immunoglobulins, or HTSI (a group of three immunoglobulins that include human thyroid stimulator, LATS, and a LATS protector) presently are thought to cause the hyperthyroidism seen in Graves' disease.

Exophthalmos-Producing Substance (EPS)

A substance distinct from LATS is responsible for exophthalmos. Although it probably has a pituitary origin, this substance differs from

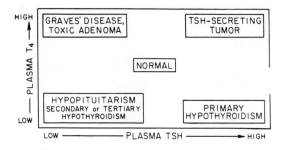

Figure 59-10. The levels of TSH and T$_4$ in various diseases of the thyroid, relative to normal.

TSH because neither excess TSH nor excess TH causes exophthalmos. EPS appears to be a derivative of TSH (perhaps the β-chain and part of the α-chain); the molecular weight of EPS is about 20,000 daltons. The action of EPS also may involve an abnormal γ-globulin other than LATS. The etiology of Graves' disease has not been worked out completely. The evidence suggests that several substances (including HTSI and EPS) are involved.

Most primary thyroid disease is autoimmune because antibodies to thyroid substance or structure are formed. Such antibodies may either stimulate or suppress the thyroid gland or produce effects similar to the effects of the thyroid hormones.

PLASMA LEVELS OF TSH IN VARIOUS THYROID DISEASES

The plasma levels of TSH are elevated in primary thyroid disease, and generally they are normal or low in cases of hyperthyroidism, except in cases of ectopically produced TSH (Figure 59-10).

STUDY OUTLINE

FUNCTIONAL ANATOMY Thyroid gland is located in neck, fifth to seventh cervical vertebrae; develops from floor of pharynx.

Composed of follicles filled with colloid on which thyroid hormone is stored.

PHYLOGENY Specialized tissue that concentrates iodide; evolved from marine vertebrates; on land, concentrating mechanisms were enhanced and storage function developed.

IODINE METABOLISM Thyroid gland concentrates I$^-$, about twenty-fivefold, against electrochemical gradient.

RADIOACTIVE IODIDE ^{131}I, treated same as stable isotope by thyroid gland, provides tracer.

CLINICAL USE OF ^{131}I   Emits both β- and γ-rays.

γ-rays cause negligible damage; can be measured externally.

β-rays cause damage locally, may be used to destroy portion of hyperactive thyroid gland.

^{131}I may cause thyroid cancer in children, should not be used in them.

UPTAKE OF IODIDE Ingested with food and water.

One-third is taken up by thyroid gland and two-thirds is excreted by kidneys.

Taken up temporarily by other glands and tissues but not stored.

BIOSYNTHESIS OF THYROID HORMONE I$^-$ is taken up by thyroid, oxidized to I$^\circ$.

Iodine is added to tyrosine to form 3-monoiodotyrosine (MIT) and 3,5 diiodotyrosine (DIT).

MIT plus DIT forms 3,5,3'-triiodothyronine (T$_3$).

Two DIT form 3,5,3',5'-tetraiodothyronine (thyroxine, or T$_4$).

THYROGLOBULIN Large protein, constitutes most of collagen that fills thyroid.

Synthesized in gland, thyroid hormones are stored on thyroglobulin.

Too large to leave gland normally; may enter circulation in pathological conditions and after radiation and surgery.

Thyroid hormones are bound by peptide linkages to thyroglobulin; normally, several months' supply is stored.

RELEASE OF THYROID HORMONE (TH) Under influence of thyroid-stimulating hormone (TSH).

Thyroid protease splits T$_3$ and T$_4$ from thyroglobulin, released into blood.

MIT and DIT are released, deiodinated in gland, I$^-$ is used again in biosynthesis.

TH is metabolized in circulation, most of I$^-$ is conserved.

ABNORMAL METABOLISM OF IODINE

Defects in active transport of I^-.

Inability to bind $I°$ to tyrosine.

Failure to deiodinate MIT and DIT.

Lack of coupling enzyme: T_3 and T_4 are not synthesized from MIT and DIT.

Deficiency of thyroid protease; abnormal fragments of thyroglobulin are secreted.

CIRCULATING THYROID HORMONE

Most of T_4 in circulation is bound to thyroxine-binding proteins (TBP); excess may bind to serum albumin.

Only free T_4 is active; in equilibrium with bound T_4.

Total T_4 is measured clinically, reflects free T_4 when TBP is normal.

Estrogens (pregnancy, birth control pills) increase TBP and total T_4 but not free T_4; body metabolism is normal.

Androgens, low concentrations of all plasma proteins (genetic conditions or liver or kidney disease) decrease total T_4 but not free T_4; metabolism is normal.

Measurement of protein-bound iodine (PBI) includes all bound iodine; organic iodide usually is T_4.

Secretion of TSH by pituitary is controlled by free T_3 and T_4—negative feedback; keeps T_3 and T_4 levels constant.

Excess TBG (i.e., pregnancy)—more T_4 is bound and free T_4 decreases.

Through negative feedback, TSH increases, T_4 increases; at equilibrium, T_4 is normal, TBG and bound T_4 are increased.

TRIIODOTHYRONINE (T_3) IN THE CIRCULATION

T_3 binds less than T_4, acts quicker, enters cells easier.

One-tenth as much free T_3 as free T_4; T_3 is five times as potent as T_4; half of thyroid activity is from T_3.

T_3-UPTAKE TEST

Used together with measurement of plasma T_4.

Radioactive T_3 and resin are added to sample of plasma.

T_3 binds to TBG not occupied by T_4; rest binds to resin and can be measured.

Indirect measurement of saturation of TBG with T_4.

If T_4 level and T_3-uptake vary in same direction, status of thyroid gland is indicated; if both values are high—hyperthyroid; if both values are low—hypothyroid.

If T_4 level and T_3-uptake vary in opposite directions, plasma proteins are altered.

Pregnancy (TBG increased)—T_4 is high, T_3 uptake is low, thyroid is normal.

T_4 is low, T_3-uptake is high—TBG is deficient and thyroid is normal.

Free T_4 index—multiply total T_4 and T_3-uptake.

Concentration of free T_4 is best indicator; not measured clinically. Free T_4 index correlates.

METABOLISM OF THYROID HORMONE

Rate of T_4 secretion is about 80 μg/day; half-life is about 7 days; T_3 half-life is 1.5–3 days.

Catabolized mainly by deiodination; much of I^- is returned to thyroid, some I^- is excreted in urine.

Some is conjugated with sulfate or glucuronide, enters gut with bile; most is hydrolyzed back to T_3 and T_4 and is reabsorbed; rest is lost in feces.

CONTROL OF THYROID GLAND

THYROTROPIN (TSH)

TSH (pituitary) affects all functions of thyroid gland.

Activation of adenylate cyclase, increased cyclic AMP in cell.

Prolonged stimulation causes goiter (enlarged thyroid gland).

Glycoprotein, α- and β-subunits, molecular weight is about 28,000 daltons.

No species-specificity of function.

NEGATIVE FEEDBACK   TH increases, TSH decreases; TH decreases, TSH increases; maintains constant level of TH.

In primary hyperthyroidism, TH is low and TSH is high.

Feedback mostly TH on pituitary, changes sensitivity to TRH (hypothalamic).

CENTRAL NERVOUS SYSTEM EFFECTS   Through TRH from hypothalamus.

Affected through negative feedback by TH.

Response to change of environment—TRH release is increased by cold, decreased by heat and stress.

AUTOREGULATION OF THYROID FUNCTION

If iodine is deficient, thyroid gland is more responsive to TSH; in iodine excess, synthesis and release of TH is decreased. Mechanism not known; effect is temporary.

ANTITHYROID DRUGS

MONOVALENT ANIONS   Perchlorate, thiocyanate.

Block uptake of I^- by competitive inhibition; thyroid synthesis stops.

Plasma TH decreases, TSH increases (lack of feedback inhibition); gland is stimulated and enlarges (goiter).

THIOCARBAMIDES   Propylthiouracil and methimazole.

Block oxidation of I^- to I°, inhibit iodination of MIT, and prevent coupling of DIT and MIT to form T_3 and T_4.

Used clinically to control hyperthyroidism.

NATURALLY OCCURRING GOITRO-GENS   In cabbage, turnips, and rutabagas.

EFFECTS OF THYROID HORMONES
TH not essential to life but if deficient, function is disturbed; affect all body processes and systems.

Increase consumption of O_2 and production of heat.

If deficient in fetus—small body size, poorly developed brain (cretinism).

Necessary for growth and maturation.

CENTRAL NERVOUS SYSTEM   Deficiency in fetus causes impaired myelination, mental deficiency; irreversible (cretinism).

After brain develops, deficiency causes mental sluggishness, slow reflexes; reversible.

Excess causes muscle tremor, hyperactivity, restlessness, and irritability.

SKIN   Hypothyroid—skin is pale and cool (vasoconstriction); patient is sensitive to cold; mucoproteins are deposited under skin, cause puffy appearance (myxedema).

Hyperthyroid—skin is moist (sweating) and warm (vasodilatation); patient is intolerant of heat.

CARDIOVASCULAR SYSTEM   Deficiency causes decreased heart rate, blood volume, and arterial pressure.

Excess causes increased heart rate and blood pressure, cardiac ischemia (excess consumption of O_2), high-output failure, and dysrhythmia.

Increases sensitivity to catecholamines; adrenergic β-receptor blockers relieve some symptoms of hyperthyroidism.

GASTROINTESTINAL SYSTEM   Hypothyroidism is associated with loss of appetite and constipation.

Hyperthyroidism is associated with increased appetite and more frequent defecation.

GONADS   Necessary for normal development and function.

Hypothyroidism causes decreased fertility and irregular menstruation.

Hyperthyroidism causes long menstrual cycles and lack of menstruation (amenorrhea).

METABOLISM   TH favors protein synthesis; positive nitrogen balance.

Excess TH causes catabolism of protein, muscle wasting, negative nitrogen balance, impaired phosphocreatine production, myopathy, and weakness.

TH increases gluconeogenesis and glycolysis; increases absorption and utilization of glucose.

TH increases rates of synthesis, mobilization, and oxidation of fat.

In hypothyroidism, plasma cholesterol is increased (decreased metabolism and excretion); in hyperthyroidism, plasma cholesterol is decreased (increased metabolism and excretion).

If TH is deficient, growth and healing are slow; inorganic matrix is inadequate.

Excess TH causes bone wasting, excretion of Ca^{++}; renal blood flow and glomerular filtration rate are increased; electrolytes may be lost.

TH is needed to convert carotene to vitamin A in liver.

Excess TH increases requirements of vitamin B complex and vitamin C.

MECHANISM OF ACTION OF THYROID HORMONES   Production of cyclic AMP (e.g., action on heart, adipose tissue).

Synthesis of protein (e.g., in mitochondria).

GRAVES' DISEASE   Enlarged thyroid gland (goiter).

Symptoms of excess TH (thyrotoxicosis).

Protruding eyeballs (exophthalmos).

Not suppressed by administered TH (lack of feedback effect).

LONG-ACTING THYROID STIMULATOR (LATS)   Abnormal factor in plasma of patients who have Graves' disease.

Protein; immunoactive against thyroid.

Different from TSH; stimulates thyroid more slowly, acts longer.

Cleared from blood more slowly than TSH.

Crosses placental barrier; neonate may have symptoms of Graves' disease.

Produced by lymphocytes, not found in pituitary gland.

May include group of 3 immunoglobulins.

EXOPHTHALMOS-PRODUCING SUBSTANCE (EPS)   Substance is distinct from LATS, causes exophthalmos.

PLASMA LEVELS OF TSH IN VARIOUS THYROID DISEASES   Increased in primary hypothyroidism.

Normal or low in hyperthyroidism.

BIBLIOGRAPHY

DeGroot, L.J.; Cahill, G.F., Jr.; Odell, W.D., et al. (eds.). 1979. *Endocrinology*. Volume I. New York: Grune & Stratton.

De Visscher, M. (ed.). 1980. *The Thyroid Gland*. New York: Raven Press.

Emerson, C.H., and Utiger, R.D. 1972. Hyperthyroidism and excessive thyrotropin secretion. *N. Engl. J. Med.* 287:328.

Greer, M.A., and Solomon, D.H. (eds.). 1974. Thyroid. In *Handbook of Physiology*. Section 7. Endocrinology. Volume III. Washington, D.C.: American Physiological Society.

Hershman, J.M. 1974. Clinical application of thyrotropin-releasing hormone. *N. Engl. J. Med.* 290:886.

Holm, L.-E.; Dahlqvist, I.; Israelsson, A., et al. 1980. Malignant thyroid tumor after iodine-131 therapy: A retrospective cohort study. *N. Engl. J. Med.* 303:188.

Jackson, I.M.D. 1982. Thyrotropin-releasing hormone. *N. Engl. J. Med.* 306:145.

Larsen, P.R. 1982. Thyroid-pituitary interaction: Feedback regulation of thyrotropin secretion by thyroid hormones. *N. Engl. J. Med.* 306:145.

Li, C.H. (ed.). 1978. *Thyroid Hormones*. New York: Academic Press.

Oppenheimer, J.H. 1979. Thyroid hormone action at the cellular level. *Science* 203:971.

Stanbury, J.B., and Hetzel, B.S. 1980. *Endemic Goiter and Endemic Cretinism: Iodine Nutrition in Health and Disease*. New York: Wiley.

Sterling, K. 1979. Thyroid hormone action at the cell level. *N. Engl. J. Med.* 300:117 and 173 (two parts).

Sterling, K., and Lazarus, J.H. 1977. The thyroid and its control. *Annu. Rev. Physiol.* 39:349.

Van Herle, A.J.; Vassart, G.; and Dumont, J.E. 1979. Control of thyroglobulin synthesis and secretion. *N. Engl. J. Med.* 301:239.

Williams, R.H. (ed.). 1981 *Textbook of Endocrinology* (6th ed.). Philadelphia: Saunders.

60

Adrenal Cortex and Adrenocorticotropic Hormone (ACTH)

CHAPTER CONTENTS

HISTORY

In 1855, Addison described a fatal disease characterized by anemia, a weak heart, weakness and easy fatigability of the skeletal muscles, anorexia, nausea, vomiting, diarrhea, hypoglycemia, and abnormal pigmentation of the skin. At autopsy, the adrenal glands of patients who had this disease were found to be atrophied. Addison's patients usually had tuberculosis, which certainly contributed to their demise; however, it appeared that the adrenal glands provided some function on which life depended. In 1856, Brown-Séquard adrenalectomized animals and proved that the adrenal glands, indeed, were vital. By the 1920s, physiologists knew that the *adrenal cortex,* but not the adrenal medulla, was essential for life. In the early 1930s, it was learned that the adrenal cortex affected electrolyte and water metabolism, and an addisonian patient, if protected from stress, could remain alive by ingesting extra salt and water.

Also in the early 1930s, the first active extracts of the adrenal cortex were prepared, and crystalline steroids were isolated and identified. In 1937, deoxycorticosterone (DOC), a mineralocorticoid, was synthesized, and in the 1940s, cortisone, a glucocorticoid that soon was available clinically, was synthesized. An amorphous fraction of adrenal extract, which contained most of the vital activity of the extract, remained uncharacterized for another 20 years. Finally, aldosterone, the physiological mineralocorticoid, was crystallized.

STEROID STRUCTURE

More than 46 crystalline steroids have been isolated from the adrenal glands. Most of these steroids are chemical intermediates that occur only within the adrenal cell, and only a few of them are secreted into the bloodstream. All of these steroids have in common the cyclopentanophenanthrene nucleus (see Figure 55-1).

Four main groups of steroids have been isolated (Figure 60-1): (1) *corticosteroids* and (2) *progestins,* which have 21 carbon atoms in the nucleus, including a 2-carbon side chain on C-17, (3) *androgens,* which have 19 carbon atoms in the nucleus, and (4) *estrogens,* in which the nucleus contains 18 carbons and ring A is aromatic. All of the physiologically active adrenal corticoids have in common an α-β unsaturated 3-ketone group and a reducing, α-ketol, side chain.

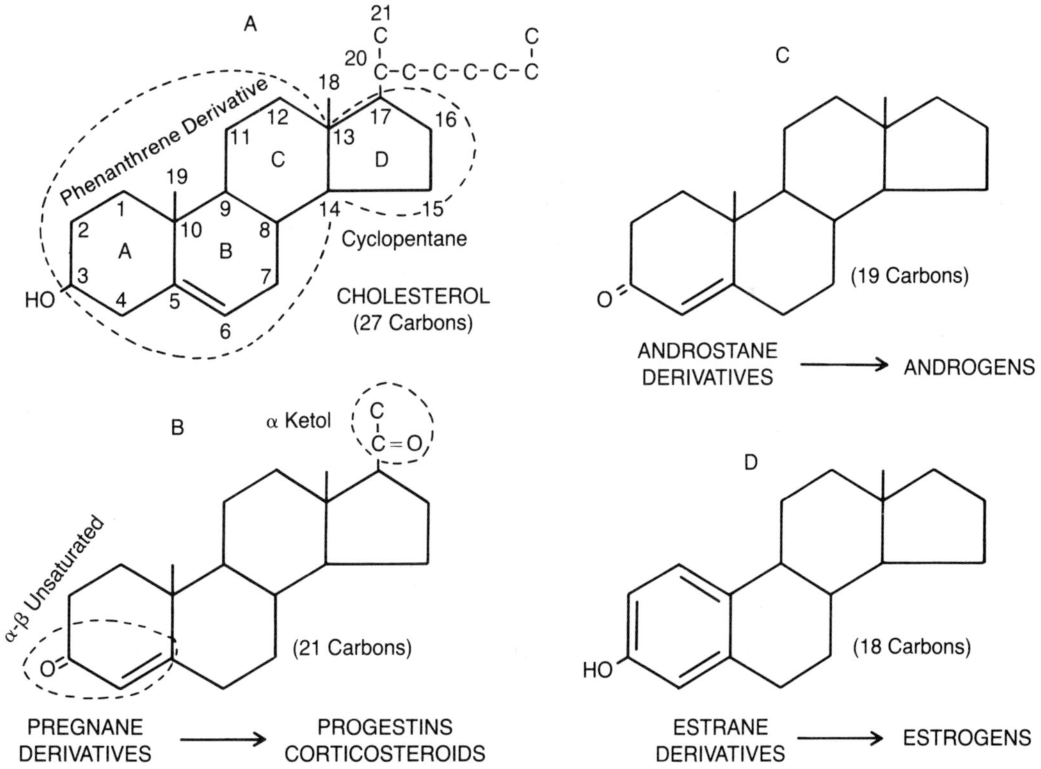

Figure 60-1. Four main groups of steroids. **A.** Chemical structure of cholesterol, which is the precursor of all of the steroid hormones. **B.** Intermediate structure from which the corticoids and the progestins are synthesized. **C.** Basic structure of the androgens. **D.** Basic structure of the estrogens.

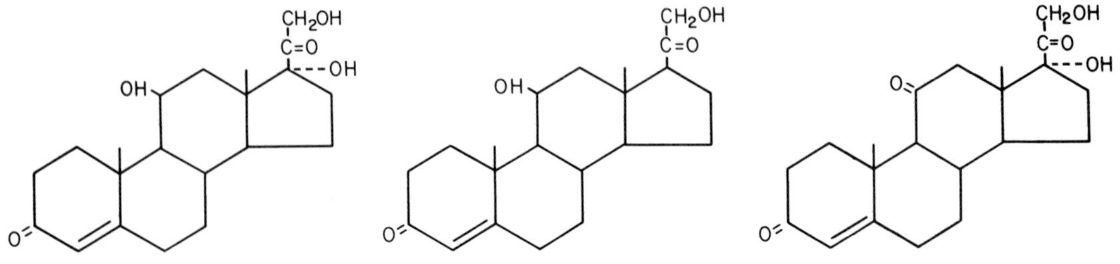

Figure 60-2. Chemical structures of cortisol, corticosterone, and cortisone.

COMPOUNDS SECRETED

Only small quantities of the steroids that have been identified in the adrenal cortex are found in extracts of the glands. Thus, it appears that the hormones are not stored to any great extent; rather, they are synthesized and secreted as they are needed. The natural secretory products of the adrenal glands have been determined by collecting the venous blood that flows from the adrenal cortex.

Glucocorticoids

All of the species that have been studied secrete either *cortisol, corticosterone,* or a mixture of the two; humans secrete mainly cortisol (Figure 60-2). These compounds exert marked effects on intermediary metabolism. The plasma level of cortisol is about 12.5 μg/dl, and the half-life of cortisol in the plasma is 60–90 minutes. Most of the cortisol (96%) is bound to a specific plasma protein, an α-globulin called *cortisol binding globulin,* or *CBG*; only the free hormone (4%) is active. The equilibrium of CBG and the free hormone (C) is as follows:

$$C + CBG \rightleftarrows CCBG$$

CBG, like all hormone-binding proteins, is synthesized in the liver, and its concentration increases during pregnancy or treatment with estrogen. A higher concentration of CBG binds more cortisol; however, after the new equilibrium has been established, the concentration of free cortisol still is the same. The clinical determination of cortisol measures both free cortisol and CBG-bound cortisol. Thus, the total cortisol increases when the CBG increases.

Humans also secrete corticosterone, at an average rate of 2.5–3 mg/day. Corticosterone circulates bound to CBG, and its half-life in the plasma is about 30 minutes. The ratio (concentration of cortisol)/(concentration of corticosterone) is about 7:1. *Cortisone* also is an active glucocorticoid. It was the first glucocorticoid to be synthesized and made available for clinical use; however, it is not secreted by the adrenal cortex normally. A small amount of cortisone is formed from cortisol in the liver.

Mineralocorticoids

The most potent of the mineralocorticoids, which affect electrolyte and water metabolism, is *aldosterone* (Figure 60-3). It is secreted at the rate of 150 μg/day, which is less than one–one-hundredth of the rate at which cortisol is secreted. The average concentration of aldosterone in the plasma is about 7 ng/dl; 50%–60% of aldosterone is bound to plasma albumin, and its half-life is about 20 minutes. *Deoxycorticosterone* (DOC) is secreted in small amounts by the adrenal cortex; however, because DOC is only one-thirtieth as potent as aldosterone, it does not affect the metabolism of salt and water significantly. *Deoxycortisol,* also called *substance S,* has mineralocorticoid action and is about as potent as DOC, but it is not secreted. DOC is used clinically when a mineralocorticoid is needed.

The classification of the adrenal corticoids into glucocorticoids and mineralocorticoids is made on the basis of the most prominent effect; however, most corticoids possess both kinds of activity to some extent. Aldosterone is 500 times as potent as cortisol on water and electrolyte metabolism; it is secreted in such small amounts that it does not affect intermediary metabolism. Although cortisol is much less potent as a mineralocorticoid than aldoster-

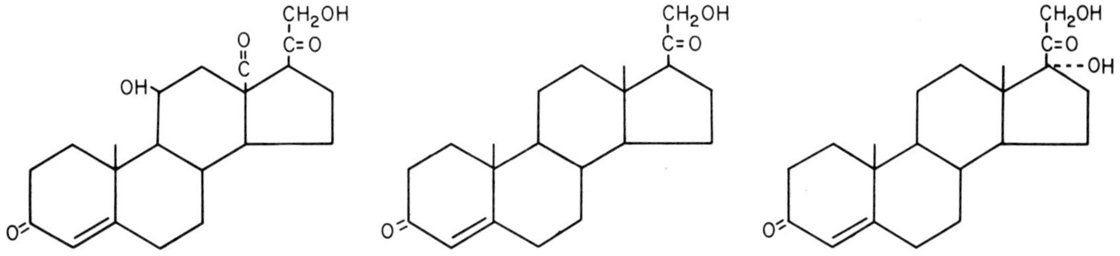

ALDOSTERONE

DEOXYCORTICOSTERONE (DOC)

DEOXYCORTISOL (SUBSTANCE S)

Figure 60-3. Chemical structures of aldosterone, deoxycorticosterone, and deoxycortisol.

one is, enough cortisol is secreted to have some effect on the metabolism of water and electrolytes.

Adrenal Androgens

The androgens can produce masculinizing effects. The principal hormone secreted is *dehydroepiandrosterone* (DHA, DEA, or DHEA) (Figure 60-4), which is secreted at the rate of 15–30 mg/day. Other adrenal androgens, and even testosterone, are secreted in much smaller amounts; however, none of the adrenal androgens is very potent, except testosterone, and no masculinizing effects occur normally. Androgens promote the growth of pubic and axillary hair in women. The secretion of the adrenal androgens is controlled by adrenocorticotropic hormone (ACTH), just as that of the glucocorticoids is; however, the androgens exert no feedback control on the secretion of ACTH. Although the compounds of this group have no sexual function and they do not produce the effects that are most characteristic of the adrenal gland, two-thirds of the 17-ketosteroids (androgens) secreted in the urine come from the adrenal cortex. In addition, minimal amounts of estrogens and progesterone also may be secreted by the adrenals.

EFFECTS OF GLUCOCORTICOIDS

Intermediary Metabolism

The principal metabolic effect of the glucocorticoids is to increase *gluconeogenesis,* which is the formation of glucose from amino acids. In addition, these hormones increase the rate of glycolysis in the liver by stimulating phosphatase activity; glucose-6-phosphatase is broken down to free glucose, which enters the blood. The result of these actions is an increase in the concentration of glucose in the blood, and this effect may be enhanced because the corticoids oppose the entry of glucose into the cells. Thus, these hormones, when secreted in excess, are diabetogenic. Consistent with these observations, 80% of patients who have Cushing's syndrome, which is caused by excessive secretion by the adrenal glands, have abnormal glucose-tolerance curves (see Chapter 61).

Additional effects include increased protein catabolism and the mobilization and redistribution of fat in the body. The typical syndrome of overdosage with cortical hormone is deposition of fat in the face (*moon face*), in the suprascapular region (*buffalo hump*), and on the trunk of the body (*centripetal redistribution*), but not in the extremities. Characteristically, purple striae form over the abdomen because of thinning and stretching of the skin.

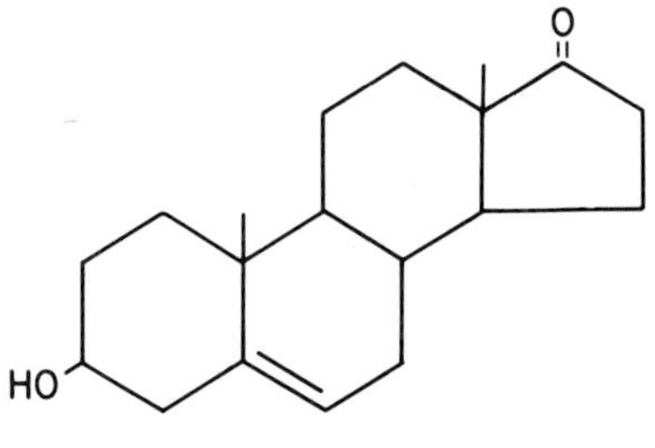

DEHYDROEPIANDROSTERONE (DHA, DEA, DHEA)

Figure 60-4. Chemical structure of dehydroepiandrosterone.

Bone

Excess glucocorticoid opposes the development of cartilage and decreases the rate of formation of new bone, especially the synthesis of the matrix. Excess glucocorticoid decreases the deposition of Ca^{++} and eventually causes the loss of Ca^{++} from bone. *Osteoporosis,* demineralization of the bones, is the most severe factor that limits the long-term therapeutic use of cortisol.

Kidneys

The glucocorticoids increase the glomerular filtration rate and increase the excretion of water in the urine. Because of a slight mineralocorticoid action, these hormones aid the retention of Na^+ directly; however, if the action to increase the rate of formation of urine exceeds the action to retain Na^+, the rate of excretion of Na^{++} also is increased. The rate of excretion of Ca^{++} is increased, and sometimes cortisol is used clinically to decrease the concentration of Ca^{++} in the plasma.

Gastrointestinal Tract

The glucocorticoids increase the rate of secretion of acid and pepsin in the stomach, and this action has been related to the production of peptic ulcers. In an unrelated action the corticoids antagonize the action of vitamin D by decreasing the rate of absorption of Ca^{++} from the gut.

Stress

The glucocorticoids increase the ability of the body to withstand stress by mechanisms that are not known. If the stress is severe, the hormones of the adrenal cortex are necessary for survival. The corticoids help to maintain the plasma volume by preventing the shift of water into the cell. Corticoids also have vascular effects because they oppose inappropriate dilatation and enhance the arteriolar constriction caused by the catecholamines.

Secretion of ACTH

The concentration of cortisol in the plasma is an important factor in the control of the rate of release of ACTH by negative feedback. When the concentration of cortisol in the plasma increases, the rate of secretion of ACTH decreases, and when the concentration of cortisol in the plasma decreases, the rate of secretion of ACTH increases. The effectiveness of any of the cortical hormones in the feedback mechanism is related directly to their potencies as glucocorticoids.

Muscle

Adrenal insufficiency is characterized by extreme weakness and fatigue of the skeletal muscles. Glucocorticoids restore muscle function, but the mechanism of their action is not known.

Nervous System

Either cortical insufficiency or cortical excess may affect a person's mood or adjustment to reality. Patients who have Addison's disease (cortical insufficiency) often are depressed or anxious, and patients who have Cushing's syndrome (excess cortical hormone) often are euphoric or even overtly psychotic. The glucocorticoid hormones lower the threshold for convulsion and may produce seizures in patients who have epilepsy, whereas mineralocorticoids may have the opposite effect. Insufficiency of glucocorticoids causes slowing of the frequency of oscillation in the electroencephalogram (EEG).

Lymphoid Tissue and Elements of Blood

The glucocorticoids decrease the mass of the lymphoid tissue by direct inhibition of mitosis. *Lymphocytopenia* (low concentration of lymphocytes in the circulation) develops because of the destruction of lymphocytes. This effect is sought when the corticoids are used clinically to treat lymphomas and lymphocytic leukemia. Among other effects on the blood cells, the numbers of circulating eosinophils and basophils are decreased, and the numbers of circulating neutrophils, platelets, and red blood cells are increased.

Anti-Inflammatory and Anti-Allergic Effects

The anti-inflammatory and anti-allergic effects of the corticoids are not physiological, because these effects are produced only by amounts of the hormones that never would be secreted naturally. The corticoids stabilize the cellular lysosomes and alter the inflammatory response to tissue injury. Thus, hyperemia and exudation are decreased, and the migration of phagocytic cells and infiltration at the site of the injury is diminished. There are disadvantages, however. The healing of wounds may be impaired because the inflammatory process is a natural defense mechanism of the body. The inhibition of the inflammatory process also largely removes the symptoms of infection; the fever that accompanies inflammation may be prevented by inhibition of the release of pyrogen from granulocytes. Because the inflammatory process is inhibited, the infection is not isolated and contained, and it may spread more readily than it would in the absence of the corticosteroids. Before one undertakes treatment with large doses of glucocorticoids, the infective organism (e.g., in pneumonia or in tuberculosis) should be identified and the appropriate antibiotics should be administered.

The glucocorticoids are useful in treating allergic or hypersensitivity reactions; they probably act by preventing the release of histamine. Glucocorticoids are useful in relieving the symptoms of asthma and hives and in providing symptomatic relief in collagen and autoimmune disease, such as rheumatic arthritis, disseminated lupus erythrematosus, and dermatomyositis.

Permissive Actions

In addition to the actions they exert directly, the steroids also are necessary for certain other hormones to be effective. For example, the mobilization of fat by epinephrine and the response of vascular smooth muscle to all of the catecholamines occur only in the presence of physiological amounts of glucocorticoids.

Adaptation to Environment

The glucocorticoids perform important physiological functions in the adaptation of the organism to changes in its environment. In do-

ing so, the glucocorticoids affect almost every organ system or metabolic function in the body. Because ideal amounts of these hormones produce normal function, the effects identified with the glucocorticoids generally are those associated with their lack (adrenal insufficiency) or oversupply (hyperadrenal states or therapy with large doses of corticoid).

CONTROL OF GLUCOCORTICOIDS

ACTH, or Corticotropin

If the adrenal gland is transplanted in an experimental animal, the adrenal cortex still functions; however, if the animal is hypophysectomized, the adrenal cortex atrophies. Normal function of the cortex depends on the action of ACTH, which also maintains the structure and growth of the adrenal gland. ACTH promotes the synthesis of all of the adrenal steroids, and it also promotes their secretion to some extent, except that of aldosterone. In doing so, ACTH regulates both the basal secretion and any increased secretion that is needed because of environmental change or stress in the organism. In addition, by its support of the adrenal gland, ACTH maintains the responsiveness of the adrenal cortex to its tropic action.

ACTH is a single-chain polypeptide that contains 39 amino acids (molecular weight is 4567 daltons) and is secreted by basophilic cells of the anterior pituitary. The structure of ACTH is known, and the hormone has been synthesized. The first 23 amino acids are the same in all species; this portion may be considered the active core of the ACTH molecule because it is as potent as the full molecule (Figure 60-5). The biological action of ACTH is not species-specific; however, if ACTH from one

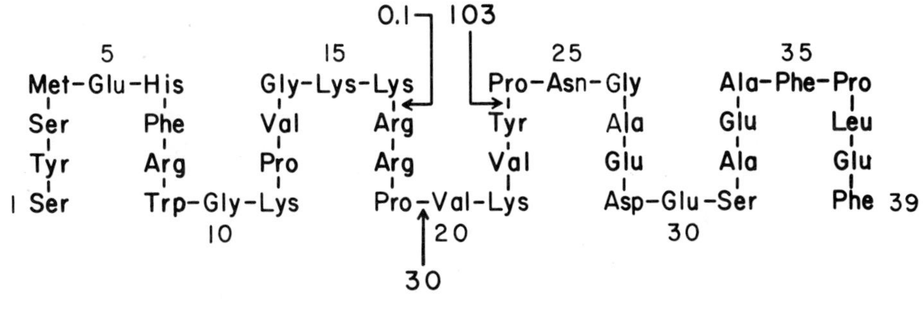

Figure 60-5. Sequence of amino acids in the molecule of ACTH. The numbers at the arrows give the relative biological activity of a peptide that begins at #1 and terminates at the point indicated. Thus, the first 23 amino acids constitute the active portion of the molecule.

species is injected into another species, it may cause a certain number of antibodies to form. ACTH is relatively short-lasting; its half-life in the plasma is only about 10 minutes.

The first 13 amino acids of ACTH are identical to those of α-MSH, and ACTH does have some MSH-like activity (it darkens the skin somewhat). The further biological significance of this common action, if there is any, is not known.

ACTH is derived from a precursor molecule called pro-opiomelanocortin (POMC). The remainder of the POMC molecule consists of an end terminal fragment and a polypeptide called β-lipotropin. Stress or other conditions that cause the secretion of ACTH also cause the release of equimolar quantities of β-lipotropin. The function of β-lipotropin is not clear. β-lipotropin consists of two peptides called γ-lipotropin and β-endorphin. The role of β-endorphin in the pituitary is not known, but in the brain, β-endorphin combines with specific receptors to produce analgesic activity like that of the drug morphine.

CONTROL BY NEGATIVE FEEDBACK

ACTH is controlled significantly through negative feedback by the glucocorticoids (the free hormone) to the pituitary gland and, especially, to the hypothalamus. In the absence of stressful stimuli, this mechanism keeps the concentration of cortisol in the blood relatively constant.

The sensitivity of the adrenal cortex to ACTH seems to require the continuous presence of ACTH. Twenty-four hours after an experimental animal has been hypophysectomized, the response of the adrenal cortex to injected ACTH has decreased. In the human subject, the administration of doses of glucocorticoids large enough to suppress the release of ACTH decreases the response of the adrenal cortex to exogenous ACTH to one-half of normal after only 2 days. For this reason, prolonged treatment of patients by the administration of corticoids must be approached with caution. During the time the release of ACTH is suppressed, the adrenal glands may become unresponsive and even may atrophy. When the treatment is stopped, a considerable delay may ensue before the adrenal glands can function again. In general, the inhibitory potency of the adrenal hormones parallels the glucocorticoid potency. Thus, other steroid hormones that produce some of the same effects as the glucocorticoids, such as aldosterone, deoxycortico-

sterone, and progesterone, also suppress the secretion of ACTH to a slight extent. Steroid hormones that have no glucocorticoid action, such as the adrenal androgens and estrogens, do not inhibit the secretion of ACTH.

ACTH itself may feed back to the pituitary to inhibit its own synthesis and release (short-loop feedback); however, this mechanism is less important than the feedback of the glucocorticoids.

CONTROL BY THE CENTRAL NERVOUS SYSTEM (CNS)

CRF (corticotropin-releasing factor), which is secreted by hypothalamic neurons, reaches the adenohypophysis through the pituitary portal vessels and stimulates the secretion of ACTH. CRF is necessary for the basal secretion of ACTH and, even more important, for the changes of the rate of secretion of ACTH in response to changes of either the external or the internal environment. Nerve impulses from other areas of the CNS feed into the hypothalamus to modify the rate of secretion of CRF. All kinds of "stress," such as cold, heat, pain, emotion, infection, surgery, or trauma, increase the rate of secretion of ACTH and thereby activate the adrenal gland indirectly. Stress is more effective than negative feedback in controlling the secretion of ACTH; for example, experimental surgery increases the rate of secretion of ACTH, even though cortisol is being infused.

CIRCADIAN RHYTHM

The term *circadian rhythm* comes from *circa* (about) and *dian* (day). The biological rhythms probably are generated in the limbic cortex, and their effects are superimposed on the resting rate of secretion of ACTH to produce normal daily variations in the concentration of cortisol in the plasma. The rate of secretion of ACTH is not smooth; irregular "bursts" of ACTH actually occur throughout the day, but the bursts occur most frequently in the early morning. The concentration of cortisol usually increases at the end of the normal period of sleep, but it can be modified greatly, even in humans. It is highest at 6 A.M. to 8 A.M., decreases throughout the day, and reaches a low point between 10 P.M. and midnight (Figure 60-6). This cycle is shifted by 12 hours in nocturnal animals; in rodents, for example, the concentration of cortisol is highest in the evening. The cycle can be altered by changing the periods of light and darkness artificially.

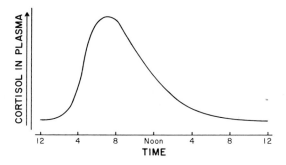

Figure 60-6. Typical daily (circadian) pattern of the concentration of cortisol in the plasma, which reflects the rhythmic secretion of ACTH.

In the course of normal circadian fluctuation, the concentration of cortisol decreases to approximately 50% of the peak by 4 P.M. to 5 P.M. It is abnormal if this fluctuation does not occur; for example, patients who have Cushing's syndrome secrete cortisol at a relatively constant rate. Patients who have hypothalamic disease may lose their circadian rhythm entirely, and the rhythm is altered in patients who have temporal lobe disease.

To summarize, the rate of secretion of ACTH is controlled by a combination of negative feedback, hypothalamic influence, and circadian rhythm.

MECHANISM OF ACTION

ACTH increases the activity of adenylate cyclase and stimulates the synthesis of protein in the cells of the adrenal cortex, probably at the translational level. The net result is to increase steroidogenesis, especially the conversion of cholesterol to pregnenolone. This step is basic to the production of all corticoids and androgens in the adrenal cortex, and all of the corticoids and androgens are affected equally by ACTH or the lack of it.

Increased secretion of the adrenal steroids is secondary to increased synthesis. The response to ACTH is very rapid—an increase of the concentration of corticoids in the plasma can be measured only 2 minutes after the injection of ACTH or the imposition of stress.

ACTIONS OF ALDOSTERONE

The primary effect of aldosterone is to increase the rate of reabsorption of Na^+ by the renal tubules. Aldosterone acts mainly in the distal tubules, but the uptake of Na^+ in the proximal tubules and in the ascending limb of the loop of Henle also may be influenced. In addition, the reabsorption of Na^+ from sweat, saliva, and gastric juice also is increased. Thus, aldosterone decreases the excretion of Na^+ in general.

The retention of Na^+ causes the volume of the extracellular fluid (ECF) to increase because water is retained by osmosis. Aldosterone decreases the rate of reabsorption of K^+. Under its influence, K^+ and H^+ are exchanged for the Na^+ that is reabsorbed in the distal tubules. Thus, more K^+ is excreted in the urine (see Chapter 42).

SECRETION OF ALDOSTERONE

Stimuli

The rate of secretion of aldosterone is increased by a high concentration of K^+ (*hyperkalemia*) or a low concentration Na^+ (*hyponatremia*) in the plasma; however, the most important physiological stimulus for the secretion of aldosterone is a decrease of the volume of the ECF. As would be expected, the secretion of aldosterone is decreased by hypokalemia, hypernatremia, or an increase of the volume of the ECF. The rate of secretion of aldosterone increases when an individual stands up, because the decreased arterial volume in the area of the baroreceptors causes an increase in sympathetic nervous system activity in the kidneys. Thus, the concentration of aldosterone in the plasma normally is higher during the day, when the individual is sitting, standing, or walking most of the time, than at night, when the person is reclining. This is not a true circadian rhythm, however, because the concentration of aldosterone does not change if the individual remains supine. Finally, stress increases the rate of secretion of aldosterone through the secretion of ACTH, which acts on the common biosynthetic pathway.

Control

RENIN-ANGIOTENSIN SYSTEM

The *renin-angiotensin system* is the principal regulator of the secretion of aldosterone (Figure 60-7). Renin is a proteolytic enzyme that is synthesized, stored, and secreted by juxtaglomerular (JG) cells in the kidneys. JG cells are specialized myoepithelial cells located in the media of the afferent arterioles at the entrance to the glomerulus. The distal tubule lies in

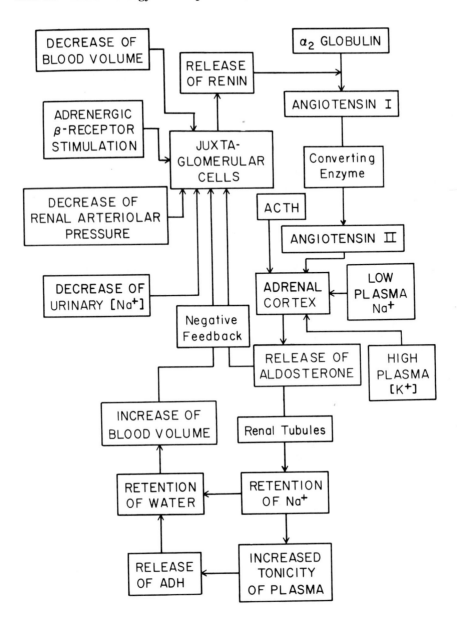

Figure 60-7.   The control and actions of aldosterone.

close approximation to the JG cells; at the site where it touches the afferent arterioles and the glomerulus, it is modified to form the *macula densa.*

Renin is released from the kidneys in response to decreased stretch of the renal arterioles, decreased concentration of Na⁺ in the urine, and sympathetic nervous system activity. The stretch of the renal arterioles may reflect either blood pressure or blood volume; in either case, the JG cells act as stretch receptors.

The concentration of Na⁺ in the urine is sensed by the cells of the macula densa. Sympathetic nervous system activity is mediated through efferent nerves to the JG cells and by circulating catecholamines.

When renin enters the bloodstream, it acts on angiotensinogen, an α_2-globulin that circulates in the plasma, to split off the first 10 amino acids and produce angiotensin I (a decapeptide). A converting enzyme located mostly in the lungs converts angiotensin I to angiotensin

II (an octapeptide). Angiotensin II acts on the glomerulosa cells of the adrenal cortex to cause the release of aldosterone.

PLASMA CONCENTRATION OF SODIUM AND POTASSIUM IONS

Although the electrolytes Na^+ and K^+ affect the cells in the zona glomerulosa of the adrenal cortex directly, as described above, this is not a major mechanism for the regulation of aldosterone.

ACTH

ACTH increases the rate of secretion of aldosterone in response to stress, as described above, and ACTH is necessary for the maximal secretion of aldosterone. ACTH also maintains the morphology of the adrenal gland and the responsiveness of the adrenal gland to stimuli; however, ACTH is not essential for the basal secretion of aldosterone, and animals whose hypophyses have been removed still secrete aldosterone.

BIOSYNTHESIS OF ADRENAL STEROIDS

The adrenal cortex, ovaries, and testes all are derived from the same embryonic tissue. Each of these organs specializes in the production of specific steroid hormones, and the hormones secreted are determined by the enzymes located in the cells that synthesize them.

The pathways of biosynthesis are much the same in all of the cells that produce steroids. Cholesterol is the chief precursor in the biosynthesis of all of the steroid hormones, and progesterone appears to be the key compound, although some physiologists consider pregnenolene to have that distinction (Figure 60-8). The synthesis of the adrenal corticoids proceeds by the successive hydroxylation of progesterone at C-17, C-21, and C-11. The hydroxylation at C-11 occurs only in the adrenal glands.

METABOLISM AND EXCRETION OF ADRENAL STEROIDS

The adrenal steroids are degraded mainly in the liver. The principal metabolites are produced by the reduction of C-3 in ring A (see Figure 60-8) to form an OH group that conjugates with glucuronide or sulfate groups. These conjugates are highly soluble in water and are excreted readily in the urine, although some free cortisol also is excreted in the urine. A small amount of cortisol and all of the adrenal androgens to be excreted are converted to 17-ketosteroids.

DEFECTS IN BIOSYNTHESIS

In some people, the synthesis of cortisol does not proceed correctly. Errors occur because the correct enzyme is deficient or absent or because some other enzyme is too active. Presumably, these defects are transmitted genetically by recessive, autosomal, aberrant genes.

3-β-ol-Dehydrogenase Defect

In the 3-β-ol-dehydrogenase defect, excessive amounts of androgens are produced, and the adrenocortical hormones are deficient because the synthesis of cortisol is blocked early in the process (see Figure 60-8).

21-Hydroxylase Defect

The 21-hydroxylase defect is most common; fortunately, it usually causes only an incomplete block of the synthesis of cortisol. The rate of secretion of cortisol is abnormally low, and, because negative feedback is slight, the rate of secretion of ACTH is abnormally high. Thus, precursors and the end products build up behind the block. Because of the point in the synthetic chain at which the block occurs, excess androgen is produced (Figure 60-8).

The combination of excess ACTH and excess androgen causes a virilizing adrenal hyperplasia. The route to 17-hydroxylation is open, and the production of adrenal androgens and estrogens is stimulated markedly by the increased ACTH (Figure 60-9). This condition is demonstrated by the increased concentration of pregnanetriol in the urine; pregnanetriol is the excretion product of 17-hydroxyprogesterone, which is the precursor immediately prior to the block. The rate of excretion of 17-ketosteroids in the urine also is increased. In some cases, aldosterone still can be produced; however, in the more severe form of the defect, in which the deficiency of the enzyme is greater, not enough aldosterone is produced. Patients who have this condition are called "salt losers," and they show the signs of adrenal insufficiency.

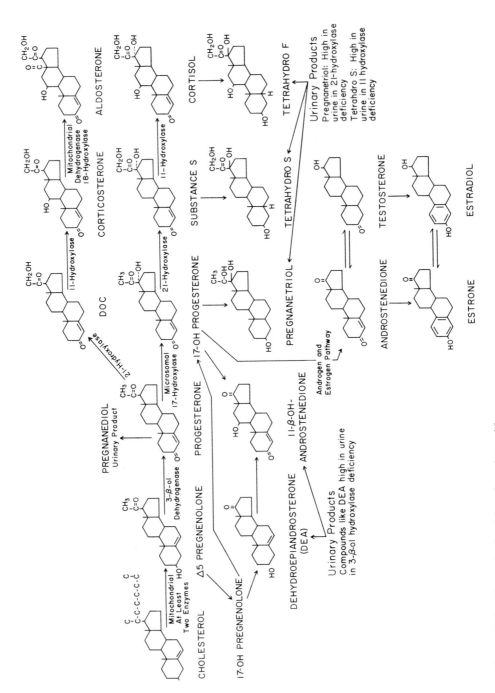

Figure 60-8.   Biosynthesis of the adrenal steroids.

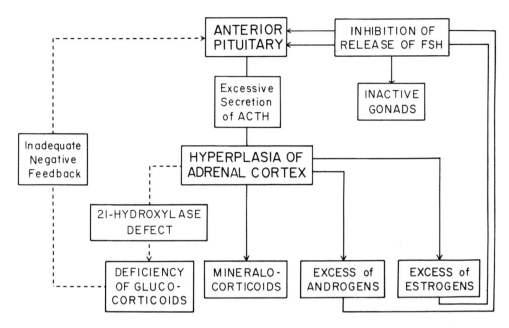

Figure 60-9. The mechanism of adrenal hyperplasia. Deficiency of 21-hydroxylase causes a deficiency of glucocorticoids (see Figure 60-8), and ACTH is produced in excess because of the lack of negative-feedback inhibition by the glucocorticoids. The high concentration of ACTH causes hyperplasia of the adrenal glands and excess production of androgens and estrogens. The androgens promote the male secondary sexual characteristics, but the estrogens have no effect, either on the secondary sexual characteristics or on the sex organs, because they are antagonized by the high concentration of androgens. The high concentration of androgens and estrogens suppresses the secretion of gonadotropins by the pituitary gland, so that the gonads do not develop properly; if the condition is not corrected, it may cause infertility.

Excess adrenal androgens cause virilism. In the presence of excess adrenal androgens, the female fetus in utero develops the external genitalia of the male to varying degrees before the twelfth week of gestation. This condition, combined with internal female genitalia, constitutes *pseudohermaphroditism*. In the adult female, the adrenogenital syndrome consists of a receding hairline or baldness, excess hair on the face and the body, the male pattern of pubic hair, small breasts, an enlarged clitoris, and heavy arms and legs. The male fetus or the prepubertal boy undergoes precocious development of the secondary sex characteristics but does not experience growth of the testes and spermatogenesis. This condition is called *precocious pseudopuberty*. In the adult male, the adrenogenital syndrome merely accentuates the characteristics that exist already.

The 21-hydroxylase defect is treated by the administration of glucocorticoids, which correct the deficiency of cortisol and inhibit the secretion of ACTH by negative feedback. The rate of secretion of adrenal androgens then decreases (Figure 60-10).

11-Hydroxylation Defect

The consequences of the 11-hydroxylation defect are severe because DOC and substance S, both of which have mineralocorticoid activity, are produced in excess; Na^+ and water are retained, and arterial hypertension develops. Thus, patients who have this disease have both virilizing adrenal hyperplasia and hypertension.

PLASMA LEVELS OF CORTISOL AND ACTH IN VARIOUS ADRENAL DISORDERS

The concentrations of cortisol and ACTH in the plasma may be abnormal in several different

CLINICAL CORRELATION
60.1   Cushing's Syndrome

CASE REPORT

The Patient: A 27-year-old woman.

Principal Complaints: Fatigue, muscle weakness, a tendency to bruise easily, and a puffy face.

History: The patient had been well until about 1 year before admission, when she had begun to develop the symptoms given above.

Clinical Examination: The patient was found to have hypertension, swelling of the feet, purple streaks over the buttocks, and some fullness in the supraclavicular areas and over the scapulae. The significant laboratory findings were: 8 A.M. plasma cortisol,* 51 μg/dl (normal, 9–25 μg/dl); fasting 8 A.M. plasma ACTH,* 630 pg/ml (normal, < 150 pg/ml); 24-hour urinary 17-hydroxysteroids, 20 mg (normal, 2–10 mg); 24-hour urinary ketosteroids, 41.7 mg (normal, 3–15 mg); urinary free cortisol, 442 μg (normal, 20–100 μg). Plasma [K$^+$] was 3.1 mEq/liter (normal, 3.5–5 mEq/liter), [Cl$^-$] was 98 mEq/liter (normal, 100–106 mEq/liter), and plasma [HCO$_3^-$] was 33 mEq/liter (normal, 21–28 mEq/liter); these changes of electrolytes are mineralocorticoid effects caused by the high plasma level of cortisol. Selective venograms (close injection of contrast material and observation by x-ray) disclosed that both adrenal glands were moderately enlarged, with no evidence of adrenal tumor. Dexamethasone (a potent synthetic glucocorticoid) was administered at a rate of 2 mg every 6 hours for 48 hours. After this treatment, the 24-hour 17-hydroxysteroid level was not changed significantly (27 mg); this lack of change indicates autonomous secretion of cortisol from an adrenal tumor, secretion of ACTH from a pituitary tumor, or a nonendocrine source of ACTH (lack of feedback suppression by plasma glucocorticoids). X-ray films of the chest revealed a well-defined nodule in the left lower lung-field. A left-sided exploratory thoracotomy was performed. A nodule about 1.7 cm in diameter was found in the left inferior lobe; biopsy showed it to be a carcinoid tumor. Such tumors may produce ACTH or other hormones and are not suppressed by negative feedback. Thus, ACTH levels remain high despite high plasma levels of glucocorticoids.

Outcome: After the nodule was removed, the plasma levels of ACTH and the plasma and urinary levels of cortical steroids decreased to normal. The patient began to lose the features of Cushing's syndrome; the hypertension disappeared, and she did well in all respects.

*The time of taking the samples is standardized because of diurnal variation in secretion of the hormone.

conditions. Using the physiological relationships between the pituitary gland and the adrenal cortex, the physician often can determine which of these conditions exists (Figure 60-11).

Suppression Test

In the suppression test, an effective glucocorticoid, such as dexamethasone (a synthetic compound), is administered to inhibit the secretion of ACTH, and either the concentration of cortisol in the plasma or the concentration of 17-hydroxycorticoids in the urine is measured. If the concentration of target hormone is decreased, the secretion of ACTH has been suppressed, and one can conclude that the corticoids are being controlled by ACTH. If the concentration of corticoids does not decrease, it is not being controlled by negative feedback, and at least three other possibilities must be considered: (1) the adrenal cortex is secreting

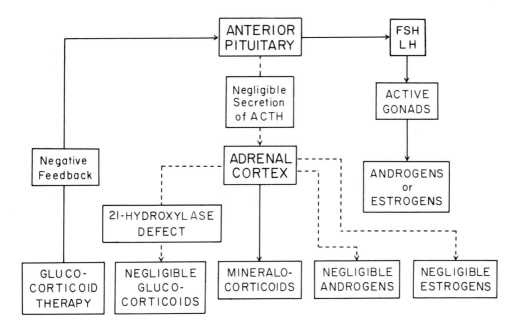

Figure 60-10. The actions of cortisone in the treatment of virilizing adrenal hyperplasia. The cortisone provides a normal concentration of ACTH through negative-feedback inhibition. Thus, androgens and estrogens no longer are produced in excess, so that the pituitary gonadotropins are secreted, and the gonads mature and secrete the normal hormones of the ovary or the testes.

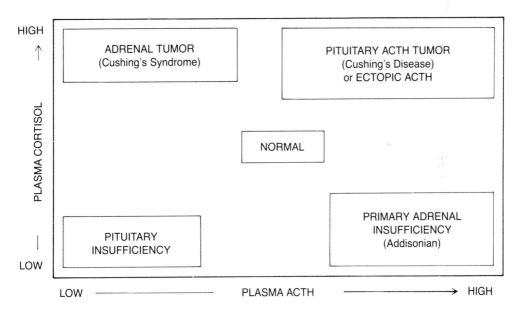

Figure 60-11. Relationship between the concentration of ACTH and the concentration of cortisol in the plasma, relative to the normal state, in various disorders of the adrenal cortex.

autonomously from a tumor (this is part of Cushing's syndrome), (2) a tumor in the pituitary gland is secreting ACTH (Cushing's disease) (in this event, the secretion of ACTH may be suppressed by a large dose of the corticoid), or (3) ACTH is being produced ectopically (ACTH usually comes from a tumor of the lungs).

STUDY OUTLINE

HISTORY   Adrenal cortex was found to be essential to life.

Adrenocortical extracts were prepared, and crystalline steroids were isolated.

Deoxycorticosterone (mineralocorticoid) and cortisone (glucocorticoid) were synthesized.

Aldosterone was isolated from an amorphous fraction of cortical extract.

STEROID STRUCTURE   Has cyclopentanophenanthrene nucleus.

Four main groups have been isolated from adrenal cortex:

Corticosteroids—21-carbon nucleus, C-17 side chain.

Progestins—21-carbon nucleus.

Androgens—19-carbon nucleus.

Estrogens—18-carbon nucleus, ring A is unsaturated.

All physiologically active adrenal corticoids have α-β unsaturated 3-ketone groups, α-ketol side chain.

COMPOUNDS SECRETED   Little storage; compounds are synthesized and secreted as needed.

GLUCOCORTICOIDS   Exert marked effects on intermediary carbohydrate metabolism.

Cortisol is principal hormone in humans.

Plasma level is about 12.5 μg/dl; half-life is 60–90 minutes.

Most are bound to cortisol-binding globulin (CBG); only free hormone is active.

CBG increases during pregnancy or treatment with estrogens; more cortisol is bound and new equilibrium is reached; free cortisol remains the same.

Clinical measurement, total cortisol; increases when CBG increases.

Corticosterone also is secreted by humans; active glucocorticoid. 2.5–3 μg/day; bound to CBG; plasma half-life is about 30 minutes.

Ratio [plasma corticosterone]/[plasma cortisone] is about 7:1.

Cortisone—first glucocorticoid to be synthesized and first used clinically; not secreted by adrenal cortex.

MINERALOCORTICOIDS   Affect electrolyte and water metabolism.

Aldosterone is most potent, approximately 150 μg/day is secreted; plasma half-life is about 20 minutes.

Plasma concentration is about 7 ng/dl; fifty to sixty percent is bound to plasma albumin.

Deoxycorticosterone (DOC) is secreted in small amounts; less potent than aldosterone; not important physiologically but is used clinically.

Deoxycortisol—not secreted; potency is similar to that of DOC.

Most corticoids have both mineralocorticoid and glucocorticoid action; classified by main effect.

ANDRENAL ANDROGENS   Not potent; no masculinizing effects normally.

Principal hormone is dehydroepiandrosterone, 15–30 mg/day; other androgens in smaller amounts.

Secretion is controlled by ACTH, but no feedback.

Promote growth of pubic and axillary hair in women.

Two-thirds of androgens in urine come from adrenal cortex.

EFFECTS OF GLUCOCORTICOIDS

INTERMEDIARY METABOLISM   Principal effect is gluconeogenesis (glucose from amino acids).

Increase liver glycolysis and release free glucose.

Increase blood glucose; effect is enhanced by opposing entry of glucose into cells.

Increase protein catabolism; mobilize and redistribute fat.

Overdose of hormone as drug causes deposition of fat in face, subscapular regions, and trunk, but not in extremities.

BONE   Excess glucocorticoid opposes development of cartilage and formation of bone.

Loss of Ca^{++} from bone; long-term use causes demineralization (osteoporosis).

KIDNEYS   Increase glomerular filtration rate and excretion of water.

Balance between slight mineralocorticoid effect (retention of Na^+) and increased urine volume determines effect on Na^+.

Rate of excretion of Ca^{++} is increased.

GASTROINTESTINAL TRACT   Increase secretion of H^+ and pepsin; may promote peptic ulcer.

Antagonize vitamin D and decrease absorption of Ca^{++} from gut.

STRESS Oppose effects of unknown mechanisms; necessary for survival of severe stress.

Help maintain plasma volume; oppose shift of water to cells.

Enhance vasoconstriction by catecholamines.

SECRETION OF ACTH Controlled by negative feedback.

Plasma concentration of cortisol increases, rate of secretion of ACTH decreases; plasma concentration of cortisol decreases, rate of secretion of ACTH increases.

Effect is related to potency as glucocorticoid.

MUSCLE Weakness occurs in adrenal insufficiency.

NERVOUS SYSTEM Deficit of corticoids may cause depression; excess may produce euphoria or psychosis.

Glucocorticoids lower threshold for convulsions; may cause seizures in epileptics.

Deficit causes decreased frequency of oscillation in electroencephalogram.

LYMPHOID TISSUE AND ELEMENTS OF BLOOD Inhibit mitosis, decrease mass of lymphoid tissue—lymphocytopenia (low concentration of lymphocytes); used to treat lymphomas and lymphocytic leukemia.

Circulating eosinophils and basophils are decreased; neutrophils, platelets, and red cells are increased.

ANTI-INFLAMMATORY AND ANTI-ALLERGIC EFFECTS Hormones are given as drugs; probably prevent release of histamine.

Decrease hyperemia and exudation at site of injury.

Decrease migration and infiltration of phagocytic cells.

Healing may be impaired, infection may spread.

Appropriate antibiotics also should be used.

PERMISSIVE ACTIONS Necessary for other hormones to be effective (e.g., mobilization of fat by epinephrine, vascular effects of all catecholamines).

ADAPTATION TO ENVIRONMENT Almost every organ system or metabolic function is involved.

CONTROL OF GLUCOCORTICOIDS

ACTH, OR CORTICOTROPIN Released from adenohypophysis.

Maintains structure and growth of adrenal cortex.

Promotes synthesis of all adrenal steroids and secretion of all adrenal steroids except aldosterone.

Mediates control from internal (negative feedback) and external (hypothalamic) sources.

Tropic action maintains responsiveness of adrenal cortex.

Single-chain polypeptide; structure is known and has been synthesized.

First 23 amino acids are active part; same in all animal species; not species-specific.

Plasma half-life is about 10 minutes.

Derived from precursor (pro-opiomelanocortin) that also yields β-lipotropin and β-endorphin.

CONTROL BY NEGATIVE FEEDBACK Glucocorticoids on pituitary and hypothalamus.

In absence of stress, maintains cortisol at relatively constant levels.

Administered glucocorticoid suppresses release of ACTH; sensitivity of adrenal cortex to ACTH decreases; adrenal glands may atrophy.

Feedback suppression is related to glucocorticoid potency.

Some feedback suppression by ACTH (short-loop).

CONTROL BY THE CENTRAL NERVOUS SYSTEM (CNS) Through corticotropin-releasing factor (CRF).

Changes in environment ("stress")—input from other areas of CNS modify hypothalamic release of CRF.

CNS influence is dominant over negative feedback.

CIRCADIAN RHYTHM Daily variation is superimposed on resting secretion of ACTH.

Levels of cortisol usually are higher in morning, decrease toward night.

Daily cycle is altered by changing periods of light and dark.

Overall control of ACTH is a combination of negative feedback, hypothalamic influence, and circadian rhythm.

MECHANISM OF ACTION ACTH increases activity of adenylate cyclase; stimulates synthesis of protein in adrenal cortical cells.

Synthesis of steroids is increased; basic step—conversion of cholesterol to pregnenolone; secretion of steroids follows synthesis.

Effect is rapid; plasma corticoids begin to increase within 2 minutes.

ACTIONS OF ALDOSTERONE Primary action—increases reabsorption of Na^+ by renal tubules.

Reabsorption of Na^+ from sweat, saliva,

gastric juice also is increased.

Retention of Na$^+$ causes retention of water and increase of extracellular fluid volume.

Increased excretion of K$^+$ and H$^+$; exchanged for Na$^+$.

SECRETION OF ALDOSTERONE

STIMULI   Decreased extracellular fluid volume is most important; also hyperkalemia and hyponatremia.

Secretion of aldosterone is increased in standing subject—increased sympathetic nervous system activity.

Stress causes increased secretion of ACTH.

CONTROL

RENIN-ANGIOTENSIN SYSTEM   Principal regulator.

Renin—proteolytic enzyme; secreted by juxtaglomerular cells of kidney.

Release of renin is caused by decreased stretch of renal arterioles, decreased [Na$^+$] in urine, and sympathetic nervous system activity.

Action of renin on angiotensinogen in plasma forms angiotensin I.

Converting enzyme, mostly in lungs, converts angiotensin I to angiotensin II.

Angiotensin II causes release of aldosterone.

PLASMA CONCENTRATION OF SODIUM AND POTASSIUM IONS   Not a major mechanism.

ACTH   Increases secretion of aldosterone in response to stress.

Maintains adrenal gland (function and sensitivity).

BIOSYNTHESIS OF ADRENAL STEROIDS   Determined by specific enzymes.

Cholesterol is main precursor.

Successive hydroxylation of C-17, C-21, and C-11.

METABOLISM AND EXCRETION OF ADRENAL STEROIDS   Degraded in liver, conjugated with glucuronide or sulfate; water-soluble, excreted in urine.

Some free cortisol also is excreted in urine.

Some cortisol is converted to 17-ketosteroids.

DEFECTS IN BIOSYNTHESIS   Presumably transmitted by recessive, autosomal, aberrant genes.

3-β-ol-DEHYDROGENASE DEFECT   Excessive amounts of androgens are produced, adrenocortical hormones are deficient because of production block.

21-HYDROXYLASE DEFECT   Usually, incomplete block of cortisol synthesis.

Cortisol is low, feedback is decreased, and ACTH is increased.

Precursors and end products accumulate behind block, include excess androgens.

Excess ACTH and excess androgen cause virilizing hyperplasia.

Synthesis is stimulated by ACTH; route to 17-hydroxylation is open, excess androgens are produced.

If not enough aldosterone is produced, Na$^+$ is lost in urine; signs of adrenal insufficiency.

Androgens cause pseudohermaphroditism in female fetus and masculinization in adult female.

Androgens cause precocious pseudopuberty in male fetus or prepubertal male and accentuation of male characteristics in adult male.

Treat by giving glucocorticoids; ACTH secretion is inhibited by feedback.

11-HYDROXYLATION DEFECT   Deoxycorticosterone and deoxycortisol (mineralocorticoids) are secreted in excess.

Na$^+$ and water are retained—arterial hypertension.

Virilizing hyperplasia.

PLASMA LEVELS OF CORTISOL AND ACTH IN VARIOUS ADRENAL DISORDERS

SUPPRESSION TEST   Synthetic glucocorticoid is administered.

If cortisol is decreased, ACTH has been suppressed by negative feedback.

If cortisol is not decreased, could be adrenocortical tumor (autonomous secretion), pituitary tumor (secreting ACTH), or ACTH produced ectopically (usually from tumor of lungs).

BIBLIOGRAPHY

Baxter, J.D., and Rosseau, C.G. 1979. *Glucocorticoid Hormone Action.* New York: Springer-Verlag.

Blaschko, H.; Sayers, G.; and Smith, A.D. (eds.). 1975. Adrenal gland. In *Handbook of Physiology.* Section 7.

Endocrinology. Volume VI. Washington, D.C.: American Physiological Society.

Byyny, R.L. 1976. Withdrawal from glucocorticoid therapy. *N. Engl. J. Med.* 295:30.

DeGroot, L.J.; Cahill, G.F., Jr.; Odell, W.D., et al. (eds.). 1979. *Endocrinology.* Volume II. New York: Grune & Stratton.

Finkelstein, M., and Shaefer, J.M. 1979. Inborn errors of steroid metabolism. *Physiol. Rev.* 59:353.

Ganong, W.F.; Alpert, L.C.; and Lee, T.C. 1974. ACTH and the regulation of adrenocortical secretion. *N. Engl. J. Med.* 290:1006.

Genazzani, A.R.; Thijssen, J.H.H.; and Siiteri, P.K. (eds.). 1980. *Adrenal Androgens.* New York: Raven Press.

Gorski, J., and Gannon, F. 1976. Current models of steroid hormone action: A critique. *Annu. Rev. Physiol.* 38:425.

Krieger, D.T. (ed.). 1979. *Endocrine Rhythms.* New York: Raven Press.

Krieger, D.T., and Martin, J.B. 1981. Brain peptides. *N. Engl. J. Med.* 304:876 and 944 (two parts).

Leavitt, W.W., and Clark, J.H. (eds.). 1979. *Steroid Hormone Receptor System.* New York: Plenum Press.

Loeb, J.N. 1976. Corticosteroids and growth. *N. Engl. J. Med.* 295:547.

Nelson, D.H. 1980. *The Adrenal Cortex: Physiological Function and Disease.* Philadelphia: Saunders.

Neville, A.M. 1982. *The Human Adrenal Cortex.* New York: Springer-Verlag.

O'Malley, B.W. 1971. Mechanisms of action of steroid hormones. *N. Engl. J. Med.* 284:370.

O'Malley, B.W., and Schrader, W.T. 1976. The receptors of steroid hormones. *Sci. Am.* 234:32.

Parillo, J.E., and Fauci, A.S. 1979. Mechanisms of glucocorticoid action on immune processes. *Annu. Rev. Pharmacol. Toxicol.* 19:179.

Rusak, B., and Zucker, I. 1979. Neural regulation of circadian rhythm. *Physiol. Rev.* 59:449.

Urban, M.D.; Lee, P.A.; and Migeon, C.J. 1978. Adult height and fertility in men with congenital virilizing adrenal hyperplasia. *N. Engl. J. Med.* 299:1392.

Williams, R.H. (ed.). 1981. *Textbook of Endocrinology* (6th ed.). Philadelphia: Saunders.

61

The Endocrine Pancreas

CHAPTER CONTENTS

INSULIN

History

Diabetes is one of the oldest known diseases; it has been a medical problem for more than 3500 years. The name *diabetes,* which was given in 20 A.D., comes from the Greek, *dia,* which means *through,* and *bainen,* which means *go* (i.e., *to go through*). The chief symptoms of diabetes were listed correctly as polyuria, polydipsia, and polyphagia. In 1679, the sweet taste of the urine (*mellitus,* or *sweet*) was used as a diagnostic test to distinguish *diabetes mellitus* from *diabetes insipidus,* and the tasting of the urine became a part of the diagnostic examination. In 1788, diabetes mellitus was associated with pathology of the pancreas, and in 1869, the pancreatic islets were discovered. In 1889, experimental pancreatectomy in a dog produced diabetes mellitus. Although it was known that the pancreas must produce a substance that controls the concentration of glucose in the blood, no one could isolate the substance because the digestive enzymes of the pancreas always destroyed it. In 1921, Banting and Best ligated the pancreatic duct of the dog, and the acinar cells, which produce the enzymes, were destroyed. Only the islet cells remained, and an extract made from them was used to prolong the lives of diabetic dogs. Banting and Macleod received the Nobel Prize for this discovery in 1923. After the extract was purified further, it could be used in clinical trials, and for the first time in history, diabetic patients could be kept alive.

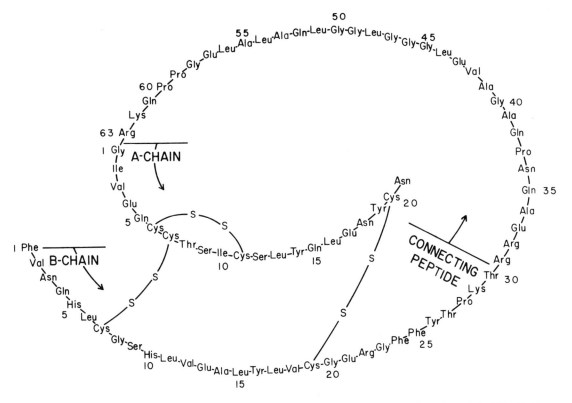

Figure 61-1. Structure of human proinsulin. *New England Journal of Medicine* 283:522, 1970).
(Modified and redrawn, by permission, from the

Chemistry

Insulin is a relatively small protein, which has a molecular weight of 5734 daltons. The structure of insulin was determined in 1955; this was the first time that the structure of a protein was established, and Sanger received the Nobel Prize for this work in 1958. The insulin molecule consists of two dissimilar polypeptide chains (an A-chain that consists of 21 amino acids and a B-chain that consists of 30 amino acids) linked by two disulfide bridges. In addition, the A-chain contains a disulfide ring (Figure 61-1).

Insulin is synthesized in the pancreas as a single, long chain that is called *proinsulin*. A peptide chain that connects the A-chain and the B-chain usually is split off before the insulin is released. Insulins from all species are biologically active in humans; however, there are immunological differences, and some antibodies are formed if insulin from one species is injected into another species. Porcine insulin differs from human insulin only in amino-acid 30 of the B-chain. Human insulin was first synthesized in the laboratory in 1966.

Insulin is synthesized, stored, and secreted by the β-cells of the pancreatic islets. The human pancreas contains about 200 units of insulin, and about 50 units are secreted per day (one unit [U] = 40 μg). Thus, very little insulin is stored, and it must be synthesized at a fairly rapid rate. The concentration of insulin in the plasma averages about 20 μU/ml, and the half-life of insulin in the circulation is 10–25 minutes. Insulin probably is not bound to plasma proteins, but this subject has aroused considerable controversy in the past.

Actions of Insulin on Metabolism

CARBOHYDRATE

Insulin increases the utilization of glucose, facilitating the transport of glucose into the cells, especially those of muscle and fatty tissue. Insulin does not increase the rate of uptake of glucose by the brain (except, perhaps, by the hypothalamus), the renal tubules, the mucosa of the gastrointestinal system, or the red blood cells. Insulin stimulates the transfer of glucose through the cell membrane, but this is not its only effect. Insulin is highly selective in its ac-

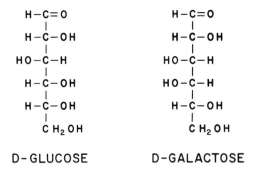

Figure 61-2. Structural formulas of D-glucose and D-galactose. The configuration of each is the same in the first three carbons.

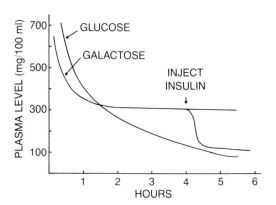

Figure 61-3. The uptake of glucose and galactose in eviscerated-nephrectomized dogs. Each hexose was injected at 0 hours. In the absence of insulin, galactose enters the cells of the liver, kidneys, and intestine, only. The curve for glucose indicates the continuous use (and further uptake) of glucose; the curve for galactose indicates that galactose is not used, its uptake ceases, and its concentration in the blood remains constant. When insulin was injected (arrow), the concentration of galactose decreased and then leveled off again. These experiments show that insulin promotes the uptake of galactose but not the use of it. (Redrawn, with permission, from Levine, R., et al. 1950. Action of insulin on the "permeability" of cells to free hexoses, as studied by its effect on the distribution of galactose. *Am. J. Physiol.* 163: 70.)

tion because only hexoses and pentoses that have the same configuration as D-glucose in the first three carbons are transported (Figures 61-2 and 61-3).

The transport of glucose also can be modified by other factors, including exercise and hypoxia, which increase the rate of entry of glucose into cells, and certain hormones (e.g., growth hormone and cortisol), which decrease the rate of entry of glucose into cells. The entry of glucose is not an all-or-nothing phenomenon. In the absence of insulin, glucose still enters the cell; however, it enters much more slowly, and higher concentrations of glucose in the plasma are required to obtain a reasonable rate of entry (Figure 61-3). Insulin increases the rate of oxidation of glucose in the cell, particularly by the glycolytic pathway, and it increases the synthesis of glycogen, especially in the liver, skeletal muscles, and fatty tissues. Insulin opposes the release of glucose from the liver by inhibiting the intracellular enzyme glucose-6-phosphatase, which dephosphorylates glucose and thereby permits it to enter the bloodstream (Figure 61-4). The net result of all of these effects of insulin is to decrease the concentration of glucose in the blood.

PROTEIN

Insulin increases the rate of transport of amino acids into the cell, increases the rate of synthesis of protein, and decreases gluconeogenesis. Thus, the net result is protein anabolism and decreased concentrations of amino acids in the plasma. Consistent with these effects, insulin is necessary for normal growth and normal repair of damage to the tissues.

FAT

Insulin promotes lipogenesis by activating lipoprotein lipase, and opposes lipolysis by inhibiting hormone-sensitive lipase. The latter is accomplished by decreasing the concentration of cyclic AMP, which is necessary for lipolysis. The net effect is to decrease the concentrations of free fatty acids and triglycerides in the plasma and to store fat.

Effects on Potassium

Insulin increases the rate of uptake of K^+ by the cells and thereby decreases the concentration of K^+ in the plasma. Insulin is used clinically to relieve hyperkalemia temporarily. Because insulin also decreases the concentration of glucose in the plasma, glucose must be administered along with the insulin to prevent hypoglycemia. On the other hand, when insulin is used to treat the uncontrolled diabetic patient, it may cause hypokalemia.

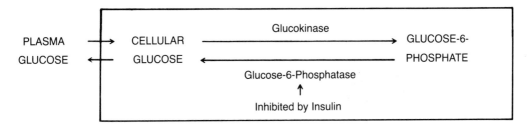

Figure 61-4. The mechanism by which insulin opposes the release of glucose from the liver.

Control of Secretion of Insulin

NEGATIVE FEEDBACK

The concentration of glucose in the blood is the major factor that controls the release of insulin. If the concentration of glucose increases, the rate of secretion of insulin increases, and when the concentration of glucose decreases, the rate of secretion of insulin decreases. This negative-feedback mechanism acts on the pancreas. The effect is rapid; insulin is increased measurably in the plasma only 1 minute after an intravenous injection of glucose.

The mechanism that controls the secretion of insulin also is sensitive to the concentration of amino acids in the plasma, because an increase in the concentration of amino acids increases the concentration of insulin. This effect may be seen after the ingestion of proteins or during the intravenous infusion of amino acids. Increasing the concentration of fatty acids in the plasma also increases the rate of secretion of insulin.

NEURAL CONTROL

Parasympathetic activity, carried in the right vagus nerve, increases the rate of secretion of insulin. Sympathetic nerve activity has a dual effect. Adrenergic α-receptor stimulation inhibits the secretion of insulin, presumably by inhibiting cyclic AMP, and adrenergic β-receptor activity increases the secretion of insulin. However, these effects of the autonomic nervous system are not necessary for the normal control of the secretion of insulin.

INTESTINAL HORMONES

Glucagon, secretin, cholecystokinin, gastrin, and GLI (glucagon-like immunoreactive factor) all stimulate the secretion of insulin. Food in the stomach or in the small intestine causes the release of one or more of these gastrointestinal hormones, which then cause the secretion of insulin. Because of this effect, glucose or amino acids taken orally stimulate the secretion of insulin more effectively than they do when given intravenously. The physiological significance of these effects is not clear.

Glucagon increases the concentration of glucose in the plasma, and this effect also increases the secretion of insulin. The release of insulin by glucagon does not depend on the level of blood glucose, however, because glucagon acts very rapidly and causes the release of insulin before it causes hyperglycemia.

Somatostatin (growth-hormone inhibiting hormone, or GIH) decreases the rate of secretion of insulin. It inhibits both the basal secretion of insulin and the secretion of insulin that is stimulated by the infusion of arginine (an amino acid). The effect of somatostatin appears to be on the pancreas; however, the physiological significance of it is not known. Somatostatin, which is a hormone of the hypothalamus, also is found in the islet cells of the pancreas, in the stomach, and in the duodenum.

DRUGS

Sulfonylurea compounds (tolbutamide and chlorpropamide), which are used orally to lower the blood glucose level, increase the secretion of insulin. Diazoxide, an antihypertensive agent, and the thiazide diuretics decrease the secretion of insulin.

Hormonal Relationships

A number of other hormones increase the concentration of glucose in the blood. Growth hormone (GH) decreases the uptake of glucose in some cells by inhibiting glucokinase, thereby decreasing phosphorylation (Figure 61-5). In

CASE REPORT

The Patient: A 37-year-old woman.

Principal Complaints: Sudden onset of weakness, sweating, anxiety, faintness, and sometimes, unconsciousness, determined to be caused by hypoglycemia.

History: The patient was an insulin-dependent diabetic of 13 years' duration. Her blood glucose was controlled reasonably well most of the time, but she had suffered several attacks of hypoglycemia. The number of attacks had averaged about one/year for several years but were increasing in frequency.

Clinical Examination: There was no evidence of autonomic nervous system neuropathy, and the patient's endocrine evaluation showed normal results, except for the responses of the counter-regulatory hormones epinephrine, glucagon, growth hormone (GH), and cortisol to decreased blood glucose. To test these responses, hypoglycemia was induced by injection of crystalline insulin, venous blood samples were collected, and the concentrations of counter-regulatory hormones were measured. In response to plasma glucose levels as low as 40 mg/dl, the concentrations of glucagon, GH, and cortisol did not increase significantly at any time; the concentration of epinephrine increased slightly but temporarily, and decreased again despite continued hypoglycemia. In additional tests, the concentrations of all of the counter-regulatory hormones increased in response to other stimuli; for example, ACTH increased the plasma concentration of cortisol and growth hormone, infusion of arginine increased the concentration of glucagon, and exercise on a treadmill increased the concentrations of cortisol, epinephrine, and norepinephrine. Thus, the endocrine organs were not defective. Glucagon and epinephrine, the most important counter-regulatory hormones, administered in physiological quantities, stimulated hepatic glucose production and increased the plasma glucose concentration.

Comment: The lesion that caused the patient's lack of counter-regulatory response is not known, but other reports in the literature of insulin-dependent patients who release insufficient glucagon during hypoglycemia indicate that the problem is not rare.

Outcome: No correction was possible for this patient, but careful monitoring of blood glucose levels has decreased the severity of the hypoglycemic attacks.

---

addition, GH increases hepatic gluconeogenesis and stimulates phosphatase, which increases the release of glucose from the liver. Finally, GH promotes factors in the plasma that antagonize the actions of insulin. The hyperglycemia that GH induces stimulates the secretion of insulin, and GH eventually may exhaust the β-cells of the pancreas, causing diabetes.

The glucocorticoids and, indirectly, ACTH, increase the concentration of glucose in the blood by promoting gluconeogenesis, increasing hepatic glucogenesis and the release of glucose from the liver, and antagonizing the actions of insulin.

Epinephrine causes glycogenolysis (the breakdown of glycogen) in liver and muscle and the release of glucose into the blood. Glucagon also causes glycogenolysis (but in the liver only) and promotes gluconeogenesis.

The thyroid hormones and, indirectly, TSH, increase the rate of absorption of glucose from the intestine; hence, they increase further the concentration of glucose in the blood after each meal. In addition, the thyroid hormones favor glycogenolysis (perhaps potentiating the action of epinephrine), augment the secretion of glucocorticoid, and accelerate the degradation of insulin. All of these effects may lead to ex-

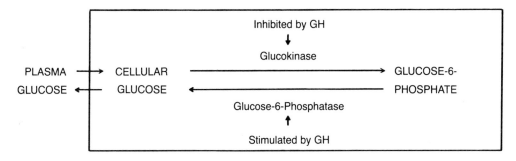

Figure 61-5. The mechanisms by which growth hormone (GH) opposes the uptake and storage of glucose by the liver.

haustion of the pancreas and the development of metathyroid diabetes if the pancreatic reserve is low.

All of these hormones increase the concentration of glucose in the blood and, as a consequence, increase the secretion of insulin, which acts to decrease the concentration of glucose. Therefore, the level of blood glucose reflects the balance of these hormonal influences.

Glucose Tolerance Test

The glucose tolerance test, which is used in the clinical diagnosis of diabetes, measures the ability of the body to handle a load of glucose. In preparation for the test, the amount and type of carbohydrate in the diet are regulated for several days, and the patient fasts overnight before the test is performed. A sample of blood is taken for the measurement of glucose under the condition of fasting, and the patient then drinks a solution that contains 100 g of glucose. Samples of blood and urine are taken for the measurement of glucose, and a curve of concentration versus time is constructed (Figure 61-6). If the patient is normal, the blood level of glucose while fasting is less than 100 mg/dl, and after 2 hours is less than 120 mg/dl. A patient who has diabetes mellitus yields a "diabetic curve," or a "poor glucose tolerance" curve. The level of glucose in the blood during fasting is high (usually more than 120 mg/dl), the peak value is high and is achieved more slowly, and the value still is greater than 120 mg/dl after 2 hours.

The oral glucose tolerance test reflects the rate of absorption of glucose from the intestine, the rate of uptake of glucose by the tissues, and the rate of excretion of glucose in the urine (if the curve is abnormally high). Thus, several factors influence the results of the test, and not all of these factors are related to insulin. In a simple screening test, the level of blood glucose is measured during fasting (fasting blood glucose) and 2 hours after eating a meal.

DIABETES MELLITUS

Etiology

Diabetes mellitus is largely hereditary; probably, it arises from a multifactorial, recessive, genetic defect. Thus, the relatives of known diabetic patients are at higher risk than the average person; however, the occurrence of the disease is not inevitable. In only 60% of the cases in which one member of a set of identical twins has diabetes does the other member also have it, and not all children of two diabetic parents become diabetic.

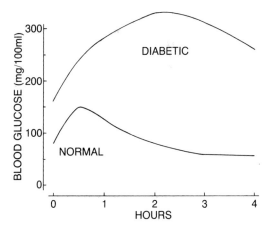

Figure 61-6. Glucose tolerance test. The subject takes glucose by mouth at 0 hours. In the diabetic individual, the concentration of glucose in the blood is higher before the test, increases more after glucose is taken, and returns to the beginning value more slowly.

Diabetes represents either a relative or an absolute lack of insulin. In this condition, the cells do not utilize glucose as they do normally. Diabetes also may reflect a relative or an absolute excess of glucagon, which increases the concentration of glucose in the blood. The concentration of glucagon, which normally is regulated by the concentration of glucose in the blood, may be inappropriate for the degree of hyperglycemia that exists. It is possible that many cases of diabetes are caused by abnormalities of both insulin and glucagon.

Factors That Aggravate Diabetes

ENDOCRINE IMBALANCE

Several hormones affect the level of glucose in the blood and the secretion or the action of insulin (see the previous section on insulin). Thus, an excess of any of these hormones (e.g., growth hormone or the glucocorticoids) makes diabetes more severe.

OBESITY

More than 80% of adults who have diabetes are, or have been, overweight. Many obese persons who do not have the signs and symptoms of diabetes yield abnormal glucose tolerance curves; after these individuals lose weight, their tolerance curves are normal (Figure 61-7). Many obese diabetic patients have abnormally high concentrations of insulin in the plasma,

and obese patients are relatively resistant to the actions of insulin. Studies using radioimmunoassay have shown that cells from obese patients bind less insulin than cells from nonobese patients do. Thus, it has been postulated that in obesity the number of insulin receptors in the tissues decreases, and the tissues become less responsive to insulin.

Juvenile-Onset Diabetes vs. Maturity-Onset Diabetes

Diabetes occurs most often in children or adolescents and in adults who are more than 40 years of age, but the conditions of the disease in these two groups differ in several ways. Diabetes in young people, or *juvenile-onset diabetes,* develops more rapidly and is more severe than diabetes in older people, which is called *maturity-onset diabetes*. Juvenile-onset diabetes is caused by a deficiency of insulin related to pathology of the β-cells of the pancreas. The patient usually is slender and of normal weight. The treatment must include the administration of insulin and is enhanced by a proper diet and regular exercise. Maturity-onset diabetes develops slowly, and most of the patients who have this form of the disease are obese. The β-cells of the pancreas are normal, and normal to excessive amounts of insulin are secreted because of decreased sensitivity to insulin. Thus, drugs that stimulate the β-cells to release more insulin and that tend to increase the number of insulin receptors (*oral hypoglycemic agents;* see Figure 61-8) often provide effective treatment. Diet and weight loss are important, however, because obesity alone causes a de-

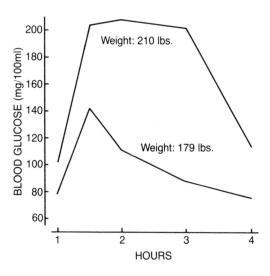

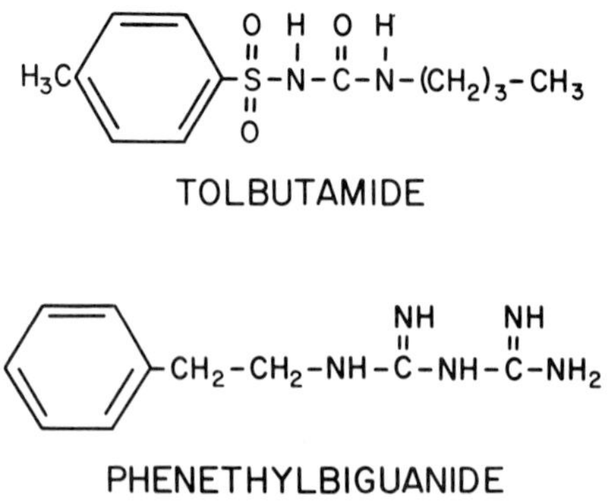

Figure 61-7. Glucose tolerance curves. The upper curve was obtained from an obese subject by conventional techniques (see Figure 61-6). The lower curve was obtained from the same individual after a period of fasting and loss of weight.

Figure 61-8. The structural formulas of the oral hypoglycemic agents tolbutamide (Orinase) and phenethylbiguanide (phenformin, DBI, or Meltrol).

creased sensitivity to insulin (see Figure 61-7). Exercise also is beneficial. Exercise, like insulin, decreases the concentration of glucose in the blood. Exercise promotes the entry of glucose into cells, even in the absence of insulin, and it increases the rate of oxidation of glucose. There is evidence that exercise increases the number of insulin receptors in the tissues. Diabetic individuals can exercise safely and can participate in team sports, but they must be careful to increase their intake of carbohydrates when they increase their physical activity.

Oral Hypoglycemic Agents

The sulfonylurea compounds (Figure 61-8) stimulate the β-cells of the pancreas to secrete insulin. These compounds inhibit the enzyme phosphodiesterase; hence, they increase the concentration of cyclic AMP in the β-cells. With continued use, these compounds increase the number of insulin receptors in the tissues, and some of them also may inhibit the secretion of glucagon. Thus, they increase the effectiveness of pancreata that do not secrete enough insulin, but they are not useful in the treatment of juvenile diabetes, in which insulin is severely deficient. The effects of the sulfonylurea compounds extend over many hours. These compounds include tolbutamide (Orinase), acetohexamide (Dymelor), tolazamide (Tolinase), and chlorpropamide (Diabinese).

The biguanide compounds (Figure 61-8) increase the utilization of glucose by promoting anaerobic glycolysis. These compounds do not stimulate the secretion of insulin; hence, they may be effective in treating juvenile-onset diabetes, in which insulin is severely deficient. An additional effect of the biguanide compounds, which is not beneficial in diabetes, is to decrease the absorption of glucose from the gastrointestinal tract. The only biguanide compound that was approved for use, phenethylbiguanide (phenformin, DBI, or Meltrol), was removed from the market by the Food and Drug Administration (FDA) in July, 1977 (see *Science* 203:1094, 1977).

The use of hypoglycemic agents is very controversial. The report of the University Group Diabetes Program (UGDP) concluded that therapy with tolbutamide is associated with an increased risk of death from cardiovascular disease (see *Diabetes* 19:747, 1970). This report has been criticized by some researchers and defended by others (see *J.A.M.A.*, 1975, 231:583, 624; and 232:806, 825, 853).

Deficiency of Insulin

The events that occur in an untreated diabetic patient involve carbohydrate, fat, protein, electrolyte, and water metabolism. All of these events are initiated by a decrease in the utilization of glucose.

HYPERGLYCEMIA

When the concentration of glucose in the blood increases in a normal person, the liver stops releasing glucose, and the rate of utilization of glucose by peripheral tissues is accelerated. In the diabetic patient, however, these hormone-dependent mechanisms fail, and both failures contribute to *hyperglycemia* (abnormally high concentration of glucose in the blood).

GLUCOSURIA

When the concentration of glucose in the blood is within the normal range, all of the glucose filtered by the kidneys is reabsorbed. When insulin is deficient, the concentration of glucose in the blood is high, the renal threshold (limit of the capacity of the kidneys to reabsorb) for glucose is exceeded, and glucose is excreted in the urine (*glucosuria*) (see Chapter 40).

POLYURIA

Glucose increases the osmolarity of the renal tubular fluid and opposes the reabsorption of water in the collecting ducts. Thus, urine is formed and must be excreted at an abnormally high rate (*polyuria*).

POLYDIPSIA

The loss of water through polyuria provokes thirst and causes the individual to drink more water (*polydipsia*).

POLYPHAGIA

Despite the excess of glucose in the blood, the cells are deficient because glucose does not enter the cells fast enough. Thus, the patient is hungry and consumes more food. The feeling of hunger may arise from a satiety center in the ventromedial nucleus of the hypothalamus (see Chapter 67).

KETOSIS

Because of the abnormal limitation of carbohydrate metabolism, lipids are catabolized more rapidly than normal in the diabetic patient, and the concentrations of triglycerides and free fatty acids in the plasma increase. Metabolic products of the fats include acetoacetic acid, β-hydroxybutyric acid, and acetone, which collectively are called *ketone bodies.* The ketone bodies are a good source of energy, especially in the person who is fasting; however, because of the abnormal carbohydrate metabolism in the diabetic patient, the ketones are produced faster than the tissues can oxidize them, and they accumulate in the plasma. The ketones are acidic, and because of their high concentration in the plasma, they may exhaust the buffering capacity of the body and produce metabolic acidosis (see Chapters 32 and 43). Because of the effect of H^+ on the respiratory center, systemic acidosis causes rapid, deep, breathing (*Kussmaul breathing*), which is one of the diagnostic signs of metabolic acidosis. The state of metabolic acidosis is intensified by the loss of Na^+ and K^+ in the urine in association with keto-acids. Diabetic acidosis is a medical emergency that can lead to hypovolemic shock, coma, and death.

LOSS OF NITROGEN
The catabolism of proteins also is accelerated because of the deficient metabolism of carbohydrates, and the uncompensated diabetic patient is in negative nitrogen balance (see Chapter 69). The result is protein wasting, loss of weight, and low resistance to infection.

Excess Insulin

Too much insulin causes *hypoglycemia,* which is an abnormally low concentration of glucose in the blood. The principal deleterious effects involve the brain, which, except in a person who has adapted through prolonged fasting, depends almost entirely on glucose for its energy. The initial manifestations of hypoglycemia are hunger, nervousness, anxiety, sweating, tachycardia, weakness, tremor, lack of coordination, and slurred speech. As the condition progresses, the individual experiences headaches, visual disturbances, mental confusion, and spasms. In the final stages of hypoglycemia, the patient becomes comatose and has shallow respiration, bradycardia, miosis, loss of the pupillary light reflex, atonia, and hyporeflexia; death is caused by depression of the respiratory center. Coma also can be caused by ketosis. If the physician is not sure whether the comatose patient is hypoglycemic or ketotic, he or she should draw blood for the determination of the glucose concentration and then administer glucose intravenously. If the patient has hypoglycemia, the glucose may be vital. If the patient has ketosis, the glucose will do no harm, and the proper therapy can be given later.

Prediabetic Condition

A person may be disposed to diabetes (*prediabetic*) without giving any obvious indication of it. However, the reserve capacity of the pancreas may be small. The glucose tolerance of such an individual may be normal, but it can be made abnormal by a moderate dose of a glucocorticoid, which increases the body's need for insulin and thereby reveals the limited ability of the pancreas to supply insulin on demand. Prediabetic subjects often experience hypoglycemia several hours after eating because the secretion of insulin continues after the need for it has diminished. This indicates some disorder in fine regulation of the system. Of all diabetic patients who have a family history of diabetes, 25% go through a prediabetic stage, whereas only 3% of diabetic patients who have no family history of the disease go through such a stage.

Prediabetic women who become pregnant have a greater probability of miscarriage, spontaneous abortion, and carrying fetuses who have various congenital lesions than normal women do. Some women become *gestational diabetics,* who have abnormal glucose tolerance curves during pregnancy. The symptoms usually disappear after delivery, but many of these women become diabetics later. The actions of placental lactogen and the destruction of endogenous insulin by the placenta are among the probable causes. The birth of a large baby (4–4.5 kg or more) suggests that the mother is prediabetic. The fetus is fattened by the high concentration of glucose in the mother's blood. The mother's glucose increases the concentration of glucose in the blood of the fetus, which stimulates the secretion of insulin by the fetus (insulin does not cross the placental barrier). The excess secretion of insulin by the fetus may cause hypoglycemia in the neonate.

Some prediabetic individuals have vascular abnormalities, such as thickening of the basement membrane of the capillaries in the pancreas, glomeruli, brain, myocardium, conjunctiva, and retina. The prediabetic condition also can be demonstrated in biopsies taken from the earlobe. The vascular changes may be seen months or years before the effects on glucose metabolism (*chemical diabetes*) are manifest.

Late Complications of Diabetes

Although diabetes appears to be a metabolic disease related primarily to a relative deficiency of insulin, it has serious complications that involve the blood vessels. The vascular effects may be caused by the abnormal metabolism that is characteristic of diabetes, but this conclusion is not certain. Both small vessels and large vessels are affected. Proliferative lesions appear in the small blood vessels, particularly in the glomerular capillaries, where they cause renal insufficiency, and in the retinal vessels, where they impair vision and may cause blindness. Diabetic patients are 17 times as likely to have kidney problems as normal individuals are, and 25 times as likely to become blind. Diabetes mellitus is the third most common cause of blindness.

Atherosclerosis also is a frequent complication of diabetes mellitus. All of the large arteries are involved, and coronary artery disease is the most common cause of mortality among diabetics. Taken together, 78% of the deaths of diabetic patients are related to the cardiovascular system and the kidneys. Neuropathies, which also occur frequently, may be caused by impairment of the circulation to nerve trunks.

If the cardiovascular complications are caused by abnormal metabolism in the diabetic patient, careful maintenance of nearly normal levels of glucose in the blood should prevent or decrease the severity of these cardiovascular complications. Unfortunately, "good" control of glucose levels does not seem to prevent the complications, although there is disagreement about this issue. At present, it is not known whether one basic defect is responsible for both the metabolic disturbances and the vascular lesions or whether they are separate defects that sometimes are inherited together. Recent evidence suggests that excess glucose harms cells directly by attaching to critical cellular proteins. This is an attractive hypothesis that remains to be proved.

GLUCAGON

Glucagon is secreted by the α_2-cells of the pancreatic islets. The structure of glucagon has been determined, and the compound has been synthesized. Glucagon is a polypeptide that has a molecular weight of 3485 daltons and consists of 29 amino acids in one long chain (see Figure 55-3). The mean concentration of glucagon in the plasma is about 0.1 ng/ml, and its plasma half-life is 5–10 minutes. Glucagon is degraded by many tissues, especially the liver and the kidneys. Glucagon is active in all species, but some antibodies are formed if glucagon from one species is injected into another species.

Extrapancreatic Glucagon

Some areas of the stomach and the duodenum secrete a form of glucagon that is identical to pancreatic glucagon; however, the glucagon secreted by the intestine beyond the duodenum is not the same as that secreted by the pancreas. The two different glucagons can be distinguished by the use of specific antibodies, and the nonpancreatic form is called *glucagon-like immunoreactive factor* (GLI), or GI glucagon. GLI is released in response to glucose in the small intestine.

Actions of Glucagon

Glucagon increases the concentration of glucose in the blood by causing glycogenolysis in the liver and by promoting gluconeogenesis. The promotion of gluconeogenesis also decreases the concentration of amino acids in the plasma. Glucagon promotes lipolysis, but it actually decreases the concentration of free fatty acids and triglycerides in the plasma, perhaps by stimulating the uptake and catabolism of fatty acids by other tissues.

Injected glucagon causes the release of various hormones, but it is not known whether the secretion of all of these hormones represents physiological actions. GI glucagon, which is released by glucose in the small intestine, causes the release of insulin. This appears to be a physiological effect that accounts for the release of insulin before the concentration of glucose in the blood increases. In addition, glucagon causes the release of calcitonin and growth hormone. The latter effect is used as a clinical test.

Control of Glucagon

The secretion of glucagon is regulated primarily by the concentration of glucose in the blood, through negative feedback at the level of the pancreas. Glucagon increases when the concentration of glucose decreases; the subsequent inhibition of the secretion of glucagon in response to increasing glucose may require insulin. GI glucagon is secreted in response to glucose in the small intestine.

SUMMARY OF CONTROL OF PANCREATIC HORMONES

Secretion	NUTRIENTS			G.I. HORMONES					SYMPATHETIC NERVOUS SYSTEM
	GLUCOSE	AMINO ACIDS	FREE FATTY ACIDS	CCK*	GASTRIN	SECRETIN	GLUCAGON	SOMATO-STATIN	
INSULIN	↑	↑	↑	↑	↑	↑	↑	↓	↓ α AGENTS
GLUCAGON	↓	↑	↓	↑	↑	↓	—	↓	↑ β AGENTS

*CHOLECYSTOKININ

Figure 61-9. Control of pancreatic hormones. An upwardly directed arrow indicates increased secretion of the hormone (insulin or glucagon), and a downwardly directed arrow indicates decreased secretion of the hormone.

Increased levels of amino acids in the plasma increase the secretion of glucagon. This mechanism may be used to maintain a normal concentration of glucose when insulin is secreted in response to amino acids during a meal that contains more protein than carbohydrate. Decreased levels of free fatty acids in the plasma also increase the rate of secretion of glucagon. Several other hormones influence the rate of secretion of glucagon; cholecystokinin increases it, and secretin and somatostatin decrease it. The stomach and pancreas contain more somatostatin than the hypothalamus does, but the significance of this fact is not known.

The autonomic nervous system also influences the secretion of glucagon. Adrenergic β-receptor stimulation increases it, and α-receptor stimulation decreases it; however, neural control is not necessary for the normal secretion of glucagon.

The control of the pancreatic hormones insulin and glucagon is summarized in Figure 61-9. Because of its actions that oppose the actions of insulin, glucagon has been implicated in the pathogenesis of diabetes mellitus. Because glucagon increases the concentration of glucose in the plasma, it is possible that patients who have hypoglycemia may be deficient in glucagon, but this is not known.

STUDY OUTLINE

INSULIN

HISTORY Diabetes mellitus is associated with excretion of sugar in the urine and with pathology or removal of the pancreas.

Eventually, extract of pancreas that prolonged life of diabetic animal was prepared.

Substance was identified as insulin.

CHEMISTRY Small protein; two peptide chains, one with disulfide ring, connected by two disulfide bridges.

Synthesized as single long chain (proinsulin), connected by peptide chain split off before release.

Insulin from all species is active in humans.

Synthesized, stored, and secreted by β-cells of pancreatic islets.

Synthesized rapidly; little is stored.

About 20 μU/ml in plasma; half-life is 10–25 minutes.

Probably not bound to plasma proteins.

ACTIONS OF INSULIN ON METABOLISM

CARBOHYDRATE Insulin increases utilization of glucose by cells, decreases concentration of glucose in blood.

Enhances transfer of glucose into cells.

Affects only hexoses and pentoses with configuration of glucose in first three carbons.

Does not affect brain, renal tubules, gastrointestinal mucosa, or red blood cells.

Exercise increases rate of entry of glucose into cells; growth hormone and cortisol decrease it.

Without insulin, glucose enters cells slower; higher plasma concentration is required.

Increases cellular oxidation of glucose, increases synthesis of glycogen.

Opposes release of glucose from liver (inhibits glucose-6-phosphatase).

PROTEIN Promotes anabolism, decreases concentration of amino acids in plasma.

Increases transfer of amino acids into cells, increases synthesis of proteins, decreases gluconeogenesis.

Necessary for normal tissue growth and repair.

FAT   Decreases plasma concentrations of free fatty acids and triglycerides; stores fat.

Decreases lipogenesis, opposes lipolysis (decreases cyclic AMP).

EFFECTS ON POTASSIUM   Increases uptake of K^+ by cells, decreases plasma $[K^+]$.

Clinically, relieves hyperkalemia temporarily.

Glucose is administered to prevent hypoglycemia.

May cause hypokalemia in diabetic patient.

CONTROL OF SECRETION OF INSULIN   Major factor is concentration of glucose in blood.

NEGATIVE FEEDBACK   Plasma glucose on pancreas.

Glucose increases, insulin increases; glucose decreases, insulin decreases; tends toward constant plasma glucose level.

Effect is rapid; insulin increases 1 minute after glucose is injected.

Increase of amino acids or fatty acids in plasma increases secretion of insulin.

NEURAL CONTROL   Parasympathetic (vagal) nerve activity increases insulin secretion.

Sympathetic, α-adrenergic receptor stimulation opposes secretion; β-adrenergic receptor stimulation increases secretion.

Neural effects are not necessary for normal control.

INTESTINAL HORMONES   Glucagon, secretin, cholecystokinin, gastrin, and glucagon-like immunoreactive factor (GLI) stimulate secretion of insulin.

Food in stomach or gut causes release of one or more gastrointestinal hormones; causes secretion of insulin.

Glucose or amino acids more effective orally (to increase insulin secretion) than intravenously.

Glucagon increases plasma glucose, hence insulin; also acts directly to increase insulin secretion.

Somatostatin decreases insulin secretion.

DRUGS   Sulfonylurea compounds (oral hypoglycemic agents) increase insulin secretion and increase number of insulin receptors; diazoxide (antihypertensive agent) and thiazide diuretics decrease insulin secretion.

HORMONAL RELATIONSHIPS   Several other hormones increase blood glucose concentration; hyperglycemia increases secretion of insulin.

Growth hormone decreases uptake and utilization of glucose; increases gluconeogenesis and release of glucose from liver; promotes factors that antagonize actions of insulin.

Glucocorticoids promote gluconeogenesis, increase release of glucose from liver, and antagonize actions of insulin.

Epinephrine and glucagon cause liver glycogenolysis; epinephrine causes skeletal muscle glycogenolysis.

Thyroid hormones increase intestinal absorption of glucose, favor glycogenolysis (potentiate epinephrine), increase secretion of glucocorticoids, and accelerate breakdown of insulin; may exhaust pancreas.

GLUCOSE TOLERANCE TEST   Measures ability of body to handle load of glucose.

Normal—fasting glucose $<$ 100 mg/dl of blood; two hours after glucose is given, $<$ 120 mg/dl of blood.

Diabetic curve—fasting glucose $>$ 120 mg/dl of blood; increases after glucose is given; remains $>$ 120 mg/dl of blood after 2 hours.

Several factors are involved, not all are related to insulin.

DIABETES MELLITUS

ETIOLOGY   Largely hereditary.

Absolute or relative lack of insulin; cells do not utilize glucose normally.

Absolute or relative excess of glucagon; blood glucose concentration is increased.

Both factors may be involved.

FACTORS THAT AGGRAVATE DIABETES

ENDOCRINE IMBALANCE   Several hormones affect level of glucose or secretion of insulin (see sections on "Intestinal Hormones" and "Hormonal Relationships").

OBESITY   Majority of adults who have diabetes are or have been overweight.

Many obese people have abnormal glucose tolerance curves.

Obese people are relatively resistant to actions of insulin.

Many obese diabetic patients have high blood levels of insulin.

JUVENILE-ONSET DIABETES VS. MATURITY-ONSET DIABETES   Diabetes is most common in children or adolescents and in adults more than 40 years old.

Juvenile-onset diabetes—severe; develops rapidly; deficiency of insulin (pathology of pancreatic β-cells); patient of normal weight; treat with insulin, diet, and exercise.

Maturity-onset diabetes—develops slowly; patient usually is obese; β-cells are normal; normal to excess insulin is secreted; sensitivity to insulin is decreased; treat with diet, weight loss, exercise, and oral hypoglycemic agents.

Exercise decreases blood glucose; promotes entry of glucose into cells, increases rate of oxidation of glucose.

Diabetics must increase intake of carbohydrate to match physical activity.

ORAL HYPOGLYCEMIC AGENTS   Sulfonylurea derivatives—stimulate β-cells to secrete insulin, increase number of insulin receptors; some compounds may inhibit secretion of glucagon; not useful in treating juvenile-onset diabetes.

Biguanide derivatives—increase use of glucose by promoting anaerobic glycolysis; would aid juvenile diabetic.

No biguanide is approved for use by FDA, alleged to be associated with increased risk of cardiovascular disease; not everyone in field agrees.

DEFICIENCY OF INSULIN   Conditions of untreated diabetic patient are all related to decreased utilization of glucose.

HYPERGLYCEMIA   Normal subject—when plasma glucose increases, more is used by tissues, less is produced by liver; these are effects of insulin.

Diabetic patient—mechanisms are not regulated; both mechanisms contribute to hyperglycemia.

GLUCOSURIA   Plasma glucose exceeds reabsorptive capacity of kidneys; glucose appears in urine.

POLYURIA   Glucose increases osmolarity of urine, more water is retained in tubules; more urine is excreted.

POLYDIPSIA   To replace water lost in urine, patient drinks more.

POLYPHAGIA   May reflect satiety center; failure of glucose to enter cells fast enough; patient is hungry.

KETOSIS   Because less glucose is used, fats are catabolized more rapidly.

Metabolic products are acetoacetic acid, β-hydroxybutyric acid, and acetone; called *ketone bodies;* more are produced than can be used.

Ketones are acidic, exhaust body buffers; cause metabolic acidosis.

Systemic acidosis produces rapid, deep breathing.

Na^+, K^+ are excreted in urine combined with keto-acids: makes acidosis worse.

Result can be hypovolemic shock, coma, and death.

LOSS OF NITROGEN   From catabolism of proteins; causes loss of weight and low resistance to infection.

EXCESS INSULIN   Causes hypoglycemia.

Affects brain, which depends on glucose; symptoms are related to neural effects; coma, respiratory depression, death; alleviated by glucose.

Coma also is caused by ketosis; can be determined by blood glucose level.

PREDIABETIC CONDITION   Glucose tolerance curve is normal, but reserve capacity of pancreas is decreased.

Revealed by glucocorticoids, pregnancy (*gestational diabetic*).

Large baby at birth suggests prediabetic condition.

Vascular abnormalities may precede effects on glucose metabolism.

LATE COMPLICATIONS OF DIABETES   Vascular damage.

Capillaries are damaged, particularly in kidneys and retinas.

Atherosclerosis in large arteries.

Effects may be related to abnormal metabolism or may be separate defect that is inherited along with diabetes.

Excess glucose may harm cells directly by attaching to critical proteins.

GLUCAGON   Secreted by $α_2$-cells of pancreatic islets.

Single-chain polypeptide; active in all species, plasma half-life is 5–10 minutes.

EXTRAPANCREATIC GLUCAGON   Secreted from stomach and duodenum; similar to pancreatic glucagon.

Glucagon secreted from intestine beyond duodenum is different; *glucagon-like immunoreactive factor* (GLI or GI glucagon).

Secreted in response to glucose.

ACTIONS OF GLUCAGON   Increases blood glucose (glycogenolysis and gluconeogenesis).

Promotes lipolysis, uptake, and catabolism of fats.

GI glucagon causes release of insulin.

Causes release of calcitonin and growth hormone.

CONTROL OF GLUCAGON   Negative feedback; glucose on pancreas.

Secretion is increased by increased amino acids and decreased free fatty acids in plasma.

Secretion is increased by cholecystokinin, decreased by secretin and somatostatin.

Secretion is increased by adrenergic β-receptor stimulation, decreased by adrenergic α-receptor stimulation.

Hyperglycemia is a factor in diabetes mellitus; hypoglycemia may be caused by glucagon deficiency.

BIBLIOGRAPHY

Andreani, D.; De Puro, R.; Lauro, R., et al. (eds.). 1981. *Current Views on Insulin Receptors.* New York: Academic Press.

Balodimas, M.D.; Camerini-Davalos, R.A.; and Marble, A. 1966. Nine years' experience with tolbutamide in the treatment of diabetes. *Metabol.* 15:957.

Bennion, L.J., and Grundy, S. 1977. Effects of diabetes mellitus on cholesterol metabolism in man. *N. Engl. J. Med.* 296:1365.

Burrow, G.N.; Hazlett, B.E.; and Phillips, M.J. 1982. A case of diabetes mellitus. *N. Engl. J. Med.* 306:340.

Cahill, G.F., Jr.; Etzwiler, D.D.; and Freinkel, N. 1976. Blood glucose control in diabetes. *Diabetes* 25:237.

Campfield, L.A., and Smith, F.J. 1983. Neural control of insulin secretion: Interaction of norepinephrine and acetylcholine. *Am. J. Physiol.* 244 (Regulatory Integrative Comp. Physiol. 13):R629.

Cooperstein, S.J., and Watkins, D. (eds.). 1981. *The Islets of Langerhans: Biochemistry, Physiology, and Pathology.* New York: Academic Press.

Czech, M.P. (chairman). 1982. Cellular dynamics of insulin action (symposium). *Fed. Proc.* 41:2717.

DeFronzo, R.A., and Lang, R. 1980. Hypophosphatemia and glucose intolerance: Evidence for tissue insensitivity to insulin. *N. Engl. J. Med.* 303:1259.

DeGroot, L.J.; Cahill, G.F., Jr.; Odell, W.D., et al. (eds.). 1979. *Endocrinology.* Volume II. New York: Grune & Stratton.

Fitzgerald, P.J., and Morrison, A.B. (eds.). 1980. *The Pancreas.* Baltimore: Williams and Wilkins.

Flier, J.S.; Kahn, C.R.; and Roth, J. 1979. Receptors, antireceptor antibodies, and mechanisms of insulin resistance. *N. Engl. J. Med.* 300:413.

Gerich, J.E.; Charles, M.A.; and Grodsky, G.M. 1976. Regulation of pancreatic insulin and glucagon. *Annu. Rev. Physiol.* 38:353.

Hedeskov, C.J. 1980. Mechanism of glucose-induced insulin secretion. *Physiol. Rev.* 60:442.

Johnson, I.S. 1983. Human insulin from recombinant DNA technology. *Science* 219:632.

Lang, D.A.; Matthews, D.R.; Peto, J., et al. 1979. Cyclic oscillation of basal plasma glucose and insulin concentrations in human beings. *N. Engl. J. Med.* 301:1023.

Levine, R.; Goldstein, M.; Huddlestun, B., et al. 1950. Action of insulin on the "permeability" of cells to free hexoses, as studied by its effect on the distribution of galactose. *Am. J. Physiol.* 163:70.

Marks, V., and Rose, F.C. 1981. *Hypoglycaemia.* Oxford: Blackwell Scientific.

McMillan, D.E. 1975. Deterioration of the microcirculation in diabetes. *Diabetes* 24:944.

Misbin, R.I.; O'Leary, J.P.; and Pulkkinen, A. 1979. Insulin receptor binding in obesity: A reassessment. *Science* 205:1003.

Paz-Guevara, A.T.; Hsu, T.H.; and White, P. 1975. Juvenile diabetes mellitus after 40 years. *Diabetes* 24:559.

Pederson, O.; Beck-Nielsen, H.; and Heding, L. 1980. Increased insulin receptors after exercise in patients with insulin-dependent diabetes mellitus. *N. Engl. J. Med.* 302:886.

Raskin, P., and Unger, R. 1978. Hyperglucagonemia and its suppression: Importance in the metabolic control of diabetes. *N. Engl. J. Med.* 299:433.

Rizza, R.A.; Gerich, J.E.; Haymond, M.W., et al. 1980. Control of blood sugar in insulin-dependent diabetes: Comparison of an artificial endocrine pancreas, continuous subcutaneous insulin infusion, and intensified conventional insulin therapy. *N. Engl. J. Med.* 303:1313.

Schnatz, J.D. (ed.). 1982. *Diabetes Mellitus.* Menlo Park, California: Addison-Wesley.

Shen, S.W., and Bressler, R. 1977. Clinical pharmacology of oral antidiabetic agents. *N. Engl. J. Med.* 296:493.

Siperstein, M.D.; Foster, D.W.; Knowles, H.C., Jr., et al. 1977. Control of blood glucose and diabetic vascular disease. *N. Engl. J. Med.* 296:1060.

Steiner, D.F., and Freinkel, N. (eds.). 1972. Endocrine pancreas. In *Handbook of Physiology.* Section 7. Endocrinology. Volume I. Washington, D.C.: American Physiological Society.

Tamborlane, W.V.; Sherwin, R.S.; Genel, M., et al. 1979. Administration of insulin to juvenile diabetics via portable pump. *N. Engl. J. Med.* 300:573.

Unger, R.H., and Orci, L. 1981. Glucagon and the A cell: Physiology and pathophysiology. *N. Engl. J. Med.* 304:1518, 1580.

Unger, R.H., and Orci, L. 1981. *Glucagon.* New York: Elsevier.

Unger, R.H.; Dobbs, R.E.; and Orci, L. 1978. Insulin, glucagon, and somatostatin secretion in the regulation of metabolism. *Annu. Rev. Physiol.* 40:307.

Valverde, I.; Vandermeers, A.; Anjaneyulu, et al. 1979. Calmodulin activation of adenylate cyclase in pancreatic islets. *Science* 206:225.

Williams, R.H. (ed.). 1981. *Textbook of Endocrinology* (6th ed.). Philadelphia: Saunders.

Wollheim, C.B., and Sharp, G.W.G. 1981. Regulation of insulin release by calcium. *Physiol. Rev.* 61:914.

Woods, S.C., and Porte, D., Jr. 1974. Neural control of the endocrine pancreas. *Physiol. Rev.* 54:596.

Zonana, J., and Rimoin, D.L. 1976. Inheritance of diabetes mellitus. *N. Engl. J. Med.* 295:603.

62

Parathyroid Glands, Vitamin D, and Calcitonin

CHAPTER CONTENTS

PARATHYROID GLANDS

The parathyroids are the smallest of the endocrine glands, and they are essential for life. Generally, the parathyroid gland has four parts, two of which are embedded in each of the two lobes of the thyroid gland. Care must be taken not to remove the parathyroid glands during surgery of the thyroid, but the parathyroids often are difficult to identify. Shortly after the parathyroid glands were rediscovered, in 1898, surgeons found that if these glands were removed, the patient went into *tetany,* which is hyperexcitability and rapid, spontaneous contraction of skeletal muscle. A few years later, in unrelated work, substances that decrease the concentration of calcium ions, [Ca^{++}], were found to cause tetany. Eventually, physiologists realized that the parathyroid glands were involved with Ca^{++}.

Later, on the basis of changes in the parathyroid glands seen in patients who had certain bone disorders, investigators concluded that the parathyroids were involved with bone. It is known now that the parathyroid glands secrete a hormone, called *parathormone,* that is important in the metabolism of calcium and phosphate and in the physiological remodeling of bone.

Parathormone

Parathormone (PTH) is secreted by the chief cells of the parathyroid glands. Although the first active extracts of the parathyroids were made in 1925, the structure of PTH was not known until 1959. PTH is a polypeptide that is made up of 84 amino acids and has a molecular weight of 9500 daltons (Figure 62-1). It is synthesized and secreted rapidly, and little of it

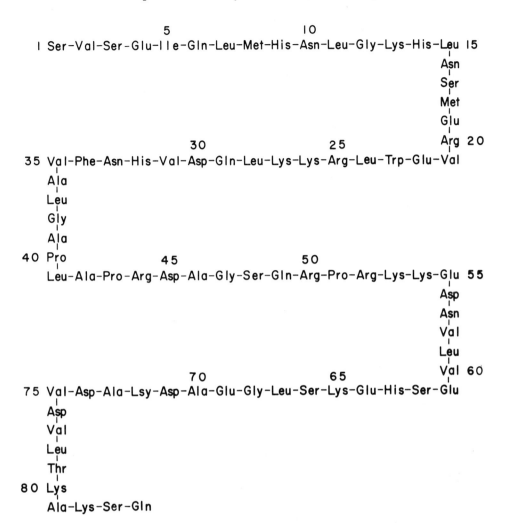

Figure 62-1.   The amino acid sequence of human parathyroid hormone (parathormone, or PTH). (Reprinted, with permission, from Keutmann, H.T., et al. 1978. Complete amino acid sequence of human parathyroid hormone. *Biochem.* 17:5728. Copyright 1978. American Chemical Society.)

is stored in the gland. The rate of turnover of the total content of the glands is 10–15 times per hour. PTH appears not to be bound to protein in the circulation, and its half-life in the plasma is 10–20 minutes.

PTH is not species-specific, but bovine PTH causes the formation of antibodies when injected into humans. PTH is active only when administered parenterally. It is usually not given to treat hypoparathyroid patients, however, because it is expensive, short-lasting, must be injected, and forms antibodies. Ca^{++} and/or vitamin D are used instead. Not much is known about the metabolism of PTH. Probably it is inactivated in the liver and the kidneys; little or none is excreted in the urine.

Calcium

The maintenance of an adequate and constant concentration of ionized calcium, $[Ca^{++}]$, in the extracellular fluid is essential for the normal function of many tissues of the body. Calcium is absorbed from the intestine and enters a pool in the plasma and the extracellular fluid. It circulates in the plasma in three forms; the total concentration is about 10 mg/dl, or 5 mEq/liter. About one-third to one-half of the calcium in the plasma is bound to protein (primarily albumin). About one-sixth is associated in complex with phosphate or bicarbonate, and about half is ionized. Together, the calcium that is complexed and that which is ionized (Ca^{++}) form the "diffusible" calcium, so designated because it can diffuse through capillary walls. Ca^{++} is the fraction of greatest biological interest. It is involved in the various active functions of calcium, and the concentration of ionized calcium, [Ca^{++}], is the variable that is controlled. Clinical determinations measure the total concentration of calcium, and the normal distribution between ionized forms and bound forms is assumed. If the concentration of albumin in the plasma is abnormally low, total calcium may be low, but [Ca^{++}] may be normal.

FUNCTIONS OF CALCIUM

Calcium participates in the formation of bones and teeth; in fact, the skeleton contains 99% of the total calcium in the body. Ca^{++} is important in regulating membrane permeability and in determining the excitability of nerves and muscles. Decrease of [Ca^{++}] increases the excitability of the motor nerves and the end plates of the skeletal muscles by decreasing the threshold of excitation, and if [Ca^{++}] becomes low enough, tetany, or rapid spontaneous muscular contraction, occurs. Ca^{++} is essential for the normal contraction of skeletal muscle (coupling of excitation and contraction) and for the normal contractility and rhythmicity of the heart. Ca^{++} also is necessary for the coagulation of blood because it is involved in the formation of thrombin from prothrombin. Anticoagulant compounds such as citrate, ethylenediaminetetraacetate (EDTA), and versenate prevent clots by forming complexes with Ca^{++}. [Ca^{++}] must be lower to affect clotting than it must be to cause tetany. Finally, appropriate [Ca^{++}] is needed to maintain the normal activity of enzymes.

Bone

Bone consists of about two-thirds mineral and one-third organic material. The mineral predominantly is a complex salt of calcium and phosphate, which is called *hydroxyapatite* and has the following formula:

$$3\ Ca_3\ (PO_4)_2 \cdot Ca\ (OH)_2$$

Bone also contains a small amount of noncrystalline salts. The organic matrix of bone is mostly collagen, about 90%–95% in mature bone, which contains a large amount of hydroxyproline. The ground substance consists mostly of mucopolysaccharides. The live matter of bone consists of cells that elaborate the structural material. Bone is formed by osteoblasts (cells)

that first make osteoid, which is a mixture of ground substance and collagen. The collagen them becomes calcified.

Bone is formed and resorbed continually. Osteocytes probably are responsible for the rapid resorption. Osteoclasts, which are large multinucleated cells, are involved with the active resorption of bone (both mineral and collagen-matrix) that leads to structural remodeling. Remodeling occurs in response to the stress of bearing weight, or gravity. Thus, bone is not static, because turnover—formation and resorption—occurs continually.

Calcium Homeostasis

The product of Ca^{++} and HPO$_4^=$ is a constant: [Ca^{++}] × [HPO$_4^=$] = K; because the salt is partially ionized, this is a dissociation constant. In general, any condition that alters one component will cause an opposite change in the other component; thus, if [Ca^{++}] increases, [HPO$_4^=$] decreases.

Bone is conceived of physiologically as having two compartments. One compartment consists of a stable, or nonexchangeable, fraction that is large and contains about 1100 g of calcium, and the other compartment consists of a labile, or exchangeable, fraction that is small and contains about 4 g of calcium. Ca^{++} and HPO$_4^=$ exchange freely between the extracellular fluid and the labile fraction of bone (Figure 62-2). This exchange function acts as a buffer mechanism that reduces the fluctuation of plasma [Ca^{++}] and helps to keep it more nearly constant. The concentration of Ca^{++} is controlled more rigidly than that of any other ion in the circulation. The daily fluctuation of [Ca^{++}] in humans is less than about 3%, in spite of considerable variation in the rates of intake and excretion of calcium.

Three organ systems participate in the maintenance of calcium homeostasis: the intestines, the bones, and the kidneys. All three of

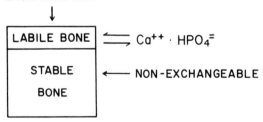

Figure 62-2. Equilibrium between Ca^{++} and HPO$_4^=$ in the extracellular fluid and labile bone.

these systems act to some extent in the absence of PTH; however, PTH affects the rate at which calcium is absorbed by the intestines, transported out of the bone, and reabsorbed by the renal tubules. PTH is not necessary merely to keep [Ca^{++}] constant in the plasma; it is necessary for a constant [Ca^{++}] of normal magnitude. In the absence of PTH, the total concentration of calcium in the plasma is about 7 mg/dl, which is near the level at which tetany occurs. In an animal that has normally functioning parathyroid glands, the total concentration of calcium in the plasma is about 10 mg/dl. The difference between the two concentrations is maintained by PTH.

Actions of Parathormone

The primary function of PTH is to maintain the plasma [Ca^{++}] at a high level and within narrow limits. This is accomplished by the mobilization of calcium to increase the plasma [Ca^{++}] and the excretion of phosphate to decrease the plasma [HPO$_4^=$], which favors the solution of Ca^{++}. PTH also is involved in the remodeling of bone.

BONE

The main action of PTH is to increase the rate of resorption of bone; the overall effect is to transfer Ca^{++} and HPO$_4^=$ from stable bone to the extracellular fluid. The rate of osteolysis in the area around the large osteocytes is increased, although this action is not understood completely. Somehow, PTH makes the calcium soluble and allows it to get from the bone into the circulation, and this event takes place rapidly enough to influence the moment-to-moment plasma [Ca^{++}].

The number of active osteoclasts and the rate of function of the osteoclasts are increased; the osteoclasts actively absorb the fully calcified, stable bone. Thus, calcium and phosphate are removed from a nonexchangeable fraction of bone, made soluble, and returned to the extracellular fluid. This is a slow process, and the effects are not seen for 5 or 6 hours; however, this process of resorption has almost unlimited capacity because of the very large portion of the total calcium and phosphate of the body that is contained in bone. The action is mediated by the stimulation of adenylate cyclase, which increases the concentration of cyclic AMP.

KIDNEY

PTH increases the rate of excretion of HPO$_4^=$ in the urine. It decreases the rate of reabsorption of HPO$_4^=$ in the proximal tubules, and it may increase the rate of secretion of HPO$_4^=$ in the distal tubules; however, there is some controversy about whether the latter action occurs. The net result is *phosphaturia,* or excessive loss of phosphate in the urine, and an associated decrease of plasma [HPO$_4^=$]. This renal effect is appropriate because the resorption of bone under the influence of PTH releases both Ca^{++} and HPO$_4^=$ into the plasma. If HPO$_4^=$ were not excreted, the dissociation constant [Ca^{++}] $\times$ [HPO$_4^=$] = K might be exceeded, and the normal [Ca^{++}] might not be maintained. The kidney responds rapidly to PTH (within less than 1 hour), but its capacity to correct changes of plasma [Ca^{++}] is limited.

The increased rate of reabsorption of Ca^{++} by the renal tubules might be expected to decrease the urinary [Ca^{++}]; however, because of the PTH-induced hypercalcemia, the [Ca^{++}] of the tubular fluid may be increased more than the rate of reabsorption of Ca^{++} is increased, and the urinary [Ca^{++}] may be increased (*hypercalciuria*). The actions of PTH on the kidney are mediated by increased activity of adenylate cyclase and, consequently, increased concentration of cyclic AMP. The effects of PTH on the kidney are summarized in Table 62-1.

TABLE 62-1
Effects of parathormone on the kidney

	Reabsorption	Secretion	Urinary excretion	Serum
Ca^{++}	↑	—	↑ or ↓	↑
HPO$_4^=$	↓	↑(?)	↑↑	↓

↑ = increased

↓ = decreased

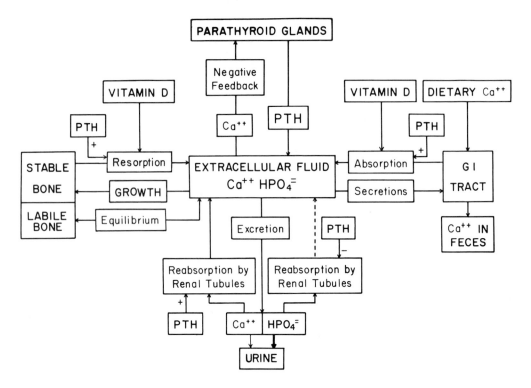

Figure 62-3.   The control of [Ca^{++}] in the extracellular fluid. A (+) at the site of action of PTH indicates that the function is increased; a (−) indicates that the function is decreased.

PTH also may cause the synthesis of 1,25-dihydroxycholecalciferol (active vitamin D) in the kidney; however, this point is controversial.

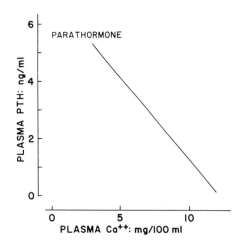

Figure 62-4.   Effect of plasma [Ca^{++}] on plasma PTH. (Redrawn, with permission, from Potts, J.T., Jr., et al. 1968. *Parathyroid Hormone and Thyrocalcitonin (Calcitonin).* New York: Excerpta Medica.)

GASTROINTESTINAL TRACT

PTH increases the rate of absorption of Ca^{++} from the small intestine; however, this effect is apparent only in animals that have adequate vitamin D. In fact, an appropriate concentration of vitamin D appears to be necessary for PTH to exert its effects at all levels—bone, kidney (except the excretion of phosphate), and gastrointestinal tract.

All of the actions of PTH to regulate plasma [Ca^{++}] are summarized in Figure 62-3.

Control of the Secretion of Parathormone

The pituitary does not secrete a tropic hormone for the parathyroid glands, and no neural control is exerted. The principal regulator is a feedback mechanism that involves the plasma [Ca^{++}] (Figure 62-4). Decreased plasma [Ca^{++}] increases the rate of secretion of PTH, and increased plasma [Ca^{++}] decreases the rate of secretion of PTH. This system acts rapidly; the rate of secretion of PTH changes within minutes after a change of plasma [Ca^{++}]. The effect is mainly on the synthesis of PTH, and release

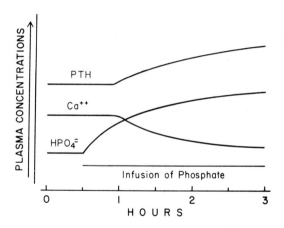

Figure 62-5. Effects of infusion of phosphate on plasma PTH, [HPO$_4^=$], and [Ca^{++}]. Note that PTH did not increase until [Ca^{++}] decreased. If [Ca^{++}] is kept constant, infusion of phosphate does not alter PTH.

follows synthesis because very little PTH is stored in the parathyroid gland. High plasma [HPO$_4^=$] increases the rate of secretion of PTH indirectly, by causing plasma [Ca^{++}] to decrease via the equilibrium expressed by: [Ca^{++}] × [HPO$_4^=$] = K. HPO$_4^=$ does not influence the secretion of PTH directly (Figure 62-5).

Hypoparathyroidism

The most common cause of hypoparathyroidism is damage to or removal of the parathyroid glands, either during thyroid surgery or because of parathyroid adenoma. Idiopathic (spontaneous) hypoparathyroidism is less common; it occurs mostly in children and twice as frequently in females as in males.

HYPOCALCEMIA
Low plasma [Ca^{++}] decreases the threshold for stimulation of nerves. A common symptom of low plasma [Ca^{++}] is numbness and tingling of the extremities, which reflects increased activity of the sensory nerves that mediate light touch. Certain signs are used clinically. These are Chvostek's sign, which is twitching of the facial muscles (especially those of the upper lip) in response to tapping the facial nerve at the angle of the jaw (hyperexcitable facial nerve), and Trousseau's sign, which is flexion of the wrist and thumb and extension of the fingers when the blood supply to the arm is decreased

by the use of a pressure cuff. In the electrocardiogram, the Q-T interval is prolonged and cardiac dysrhythmia may occur. Finally, if the plasma [Ca^{++}] is low enough, tetany occurs as a result of the decreased threshold for excitability of the motor nerves to the skeletal muscles.

Laboratory tests show that in hypoparathyroidism the [Ca^{++}] of the plasma and urine are low, while the plasma [HPO$_4^=$] is high. The treatment of hypoparathyroidism consists of large doses of calcium salts and/or vitamin D.

Hyperparathyroidism

The etiology of hyperparathyroidism often is not known; generally, the condition is caused by an adenoma that is not responsive to negative feedback suppression by [Ca^{++}]. This problem rarely is seen before puberty, and it occurs two to three times more often in females than in males. Laboratory tests show that the plasma [Ca^{++}] is high, the plasma [HPO$_4^=$] is low, and both [Ca^{++}] and [HPO$_4^=$] in the urine are high.

Among the symptoms of hypercalcemia are pain in the back and lower extremities caused by renal problems—kidney stones and deposits of calcium in the renal tubules. In addition, pathological fractures, bone cysts, and generalized decalcification of bone (osteoporosis) occur, and an abnormally short Q-T interval appears in the electrocardiogram. Generally, the only treatment of hyperparathyroidism is surgery to remove the abnormal glandular tissue.

VITAMIN D

The term *vitamin D* denotes a group of biologically active sterols that affect mineral metabolism and are necessary for the actions of PTH. The principal compounds of this group are vitamin D$_3$, or *cholecalciferol*, which is the natural animal vitamin, vitamin D$_2$, or *calciferol* (also called ergocalciferol), and A.T. 10, or *dihydrotachysterol*, which is available commercially as Hytakerol. Calciferol and dihydrotachysterol are derived from ergosterol, which is a steroid of plant origin.

Sunlight or ultraviolet light causes vitamin D to be formed in the skin by the conversion of 7-dehydrocholesterol (provitamin D) to cholecalciferol (Figure 62-6). Vitamin D also is found in oily foods and is absorbed from the gut after it has been changed to another active compound, if bile is present.

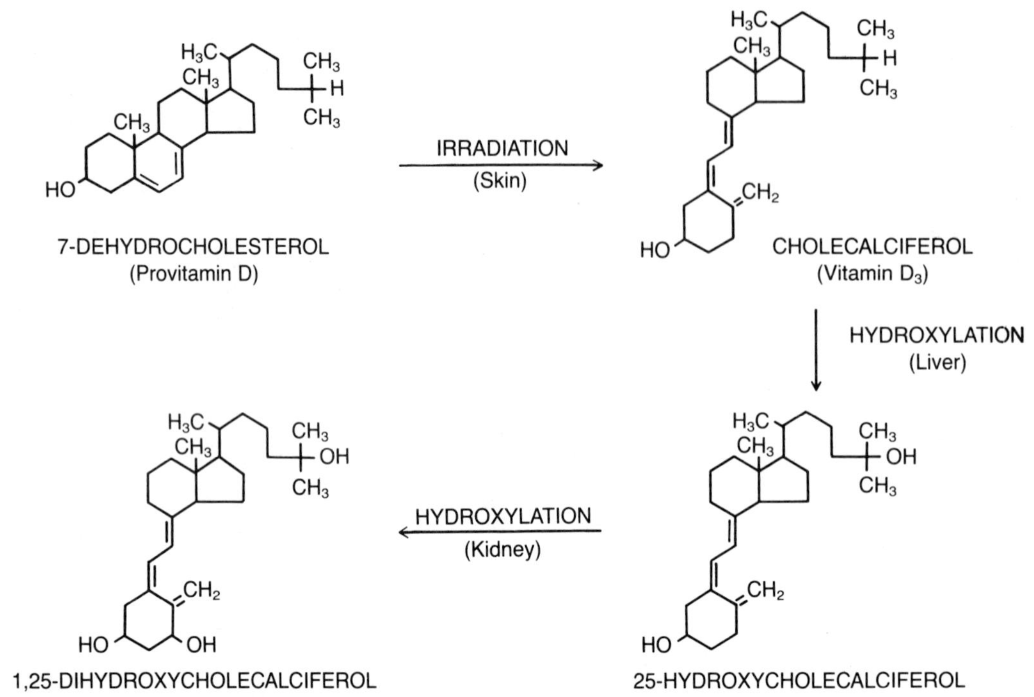

Figure 62-6. The metabolites of vitamin D and their sites of formation.

Although cholecalciferol (vitamin D$_3$) is a natural form of the vitamin, certain of its metabolites are more potent. Cholecalciferol is transformed in the liver to 25-hydroxycholecalciferol (Figure 62-6), which is 1.4 times as potent, and the transformation continues in the kidney to form 1,25-dihydroxycholecalciferol, which is 13 times as potent as cholecalciferol. Because of its higher potency, 1,25-dihydroxycholecalciferol is considered to be the active form of vitamin D. The synthesis of this active form in the kidney is stimulated by hypocalcemia.

Actions

Vitamin D is necessary for the absorption of calcium from the intestine by active transport; it is more important than PTH for this function (see Figure 62-3). In the bone, vitamin D is necessary for the mobilization of Ca^{++} and HPO$_4^{=}$ by PTH. Vitamin D acts with PTH to enhance the resorption of bone, although it does not affect the concentration of cyclic AMP as PTH does. Vitamin D also is very important in the formation and remodeling of bone.

In the kidney, vitamin D is necessary for PTH to increase the reabsorption of calcium by the renal tubules. Vitamin D opposes the action of PTH on HPO$_4^{=}$ by increasing the rate of reabsorption of HPO$_4^{=}$ in the renal tubules.

In general, vitamin D and PTH act synergistically. Small doses of each are ineffective when given alone to parathyroidectomized animals, but when they are given together, vitamin D and PTH bring the plasma [Ca^{++}] back to normal. Very large doses of each can act alone; for example, 50,000–100,000 units of vitamin D may be used successfully to treat a hypoparathyroid patient. However, a patient who has functioning parathyroid glands might need only 400 units of vitamin D for successful results.

Control

There is no evidence that the amount of vitamin D made in the skin or absorbed from the intestine is determined by changes in the metabolism of calcium. However, the rate of biogenesis of 1,25-dihydroxycholecalciferol, which is the most active form of vitamin D, is regulated strongly by the plasma [Ca^{++}]. Decreased plasma [Ca^{++}] stimulates the conversion of 25-hydroxycholecalciferol to 1,25-dihydroxycholecalciferol in the kidney, and increased plasma [Ca^{++}] decreases the rate of this conversion.

CLINICAL CORRELATION
62.1 Abnormal Secretion of Parathormone

CASE REPORT

The Patient: A 34-year-old woman.

Principal Complaints: Persistent fatigue, fever, weight loss, and frequent headaches.

History: The symptoms had begun to develop about 1 year before admission, and the patient had been first seen 1 month before the present admission.

Clinical Examination: Because of the non-specific nature of the symptoms, general laboratory studies were performed. The only significant abnormal findings were the plasma concentrations of calcium, 13.7 mg/dl (normal, 8.5–10.5 mg/dl), phosphorous, 1.2 mg/dl (normal, 3.4–5 mg/dl), and alkaline phosphatase, 95 U/liter (normal, 13–39 U/liter). These values are consistent with hyperparathyroidism. The concentration of parathyroid hormone (PTH) in the plasma, determined by radioimmunoassay, was 301 mU/ml (normal pre-ovulatory level, 5–22 mU/ml). Although PTH increases the rate of absorption of calcium by the renal tubules, the concentration of calcium in the tubular fluid more than offsets the effects of the increased reabsorption, and urinary calcium was increased. The calcium content of the urine during 24 hours was 365 mg (normal, 150 mg, or less). Hypercalcemia can be caused by adrenal insufficiency, possibly due to opposing actions of glucocorticoids and vitamin D on plasma calcium. However, the value of plasma cortisol (morning sample),* 14.6 µg/dl, was normal (range, 5–25 µg/dl) and increased (42.3 µg/dl) after the administration of ACTH.

Treatment: Two weeks after admission, the neck was explored surgically; the four parathyroid glands appeared normal, and biopsy of each revealed no abnormality. Since the evidence suggested a parathyroid adenoma (a benign tumor) in a supernumerary (extra) parathyroid gland, a search for the extra gland was begun. Injection of radiographic contrast material into the left internal mammary artery revealed an area of abnormally high perfusion, which is characteristic of parathyroid adenomas, in the anterior mediastinum. Subsequent surgical exploration of the area disclosed a large parathyroid nodule within the left lobe of the thymus gland.

Outcome: The abnormal tissue was removed, the patient's plasma calcium concentration became normal, and the symptoms of hyperparathyroidism disappeared.

*The time of taking the samples is standardized, because of diurnal variation in secretion of the hormone.

Deficiency of vitamin D causes rickets in children and osteomalacia in adults. In both conditions, the calcification of bone is inadequate, and plasma $[Ca^{++}]$ and $[HPO_4^=]$ are abnormally low.

Vitamin D toxicity is manifested by hypercalcemia and hyperphosphatemia. Vitamin D toxicity can be caused by ingesting too much vitamin D or, occasionally, by an abnormal sensitivity to vitamin D. The treatment of this disorder is prevention; one avoids vitamin D and sunlight.

CALCITONIN

Before 1964, parathormone (PTH), together with vitamin D, was the only hormone that was known to regulate $[Ca^{++}]$ directly. When the plasma $[Ca^{++}]$ was low, PTH would increase it, and when the plasma $[Ca^{++}]$ was high, it inhibited the secretion of PTH; however, no hormone was known to have as its principal action the lowering of plasma $[Ca^{++}]$. One might expect the level of plasma $[Ca^{++}]$ to oscillate more than it does, if it were controlled only by nega-

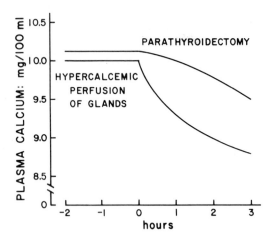

Figure 62-7. Effects on the plasma [Ca^{++}] of dogs caused by parathyroidectomy and by perfusion of the thyroid-parathyroid apparatus with hypercalcemic blood. (From the data of Copp et al., 1961.)

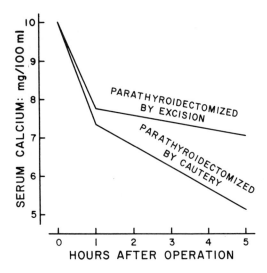

Figure 62-8. Decrease of plasma [Ca^{++}] caused by surgical excision or cautery of the parathyroid glands of young male rats. (Redrawn, with permission, from Hirsch, P.F., et al. 1963. Thyroid hypocalcemic principle and recurrent laryngeal nerve injury as factors affecting the response to parathyroidectomy in rats. *Endocrinol.* 73:249.)

tive feedback on PTH. However, the plasma [Ca^{++}] is remarkably constant.

Investigators observed that isolated perfusion of the thyroid-parathyroid apparatus of the dog with hypercalcemic blood caused the systemic [Ca^{++}] to decrease too rapidly to be explained solely by inhibition of the secretion of PTH. In addition, the effect could not be duplicated by removal of the parathyroid glands (Figure 62-7). When the perfusate was collected and injected into another dog, the plasma [Ca^{++}] of the second dog decreased. Thus, something in the perfusate from the first dog decreased the plasma [Ca^{++}] actively. The substance was assumed to be a previously unknown hormone from the parathyroid glands, and it was named *calcitonin*. This was the first postulate that a hormone lowers plasma [Ca^{++}].

In another series of experiments, the parathyroid glands of rats were removed surgically, and the plasma [Ca^{++}] decreased slowly (Figure 62-8). If the parathyroid glands were removed by cautery, the plasma [Ca^{++}] decreased more rapidly. It was proposed that the cautery had damaged the thyroid glands and some substance that lowered the plasma [Ca^{++}] was released from the thyroid. This proposal was confirmed when a material that decreased the plasma [Ca^{++}] was extracted from the thyroid gland. This new hormone was called *thyrocalcitonin*.

Additional experiments were performed on goats, in which the thyroid and the parathyroid are supplied by different blood vessels (Figure 62-9). When the parathyroid was perfused with hypercalcemic blood, the systemic plasma [Ca^{++}] was not affected. When the thyroid was perfused with hypercalcemic blood, the systemic plasma [Ca^{++}] was decreased; thus, it was concluded that the hormone comes from the thyroid gland.

In a further series of experiments, the thyroid glands of chickens were extracted and no thyrocalcitonin was found. When the ultimobranchial glands were extracted, they were found to be rich in calcitonin. Thus, it was concluded that calcitonin was the only hormone present and that it came from neither the thyroid nor the parathyroid.

The ultimobranchial glands arise from the fifth pharyngeal pouch, whereas the parathyroid glands develop from the third and fourth pharyngeal pouches. The ultimobranchial glands are separate structures in birds, reptiles, amphibians, and fish. In mammals, the ultimobranchial glands are embedded in the thyroid glands but are outside the follicles. Ultimobranchial tissue is composed of *parafollicular cells* ("light cells" or "C cells"), which do not take up iodide and are not influenced by

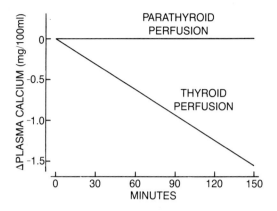

Figure 62-9. Effects on plasma $[Ca^{++}]$ caused by isolated perfusion of the thyroid and parathyroid glands of goats. (Reprinted, by permission, from *Nature.* Vol. 202, p. 1303. Copyright © 1964. Macmillan Journals Ltd.)

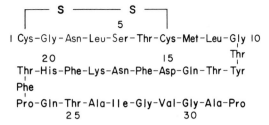

Figure 62-10. The amino acid sequence of human calcitonin.

TSH. In humans, some ultimobranchial tissue that secretes calcitonin may occur in the thymus and perhaps also in the parathyroid glands.

Calcitonin is a peptide that consists of 32 amino acids. The structure is known, and the compound has been synthesized (Figure 62-10). Calcitonin extracted from salmon ultimobranchial glands is 20 times as potent in humans as human calcitonin.

Actions

Calcitonin decreases plasma $[Ca^{++}]$ by inhibiting the resorption of stable bone; this also is the fraction of bone on which PTH acts. Calcitonin is more effective as a hypocalcemic agent in young animals than in adult animals. It may be more important physiologically in regulating the rate of skeletal remodeling, especially in young animals, than it is in maintaining the homeostasis of calcium.

Calcitonin decreases plasma $[HPO_4^=]$. It does not act on the excretion of Ca^{++} by the kidneys or the absorption of Ca^{++} by the intestines, and it does not inhibit the secretion of PTH or inactive PTH. The actions of calcitonin do not require vitamin D.

Control

The principal control of calcitonin is through negative feedback by Ca^{++} at the level of the cells that secrete calcitonin. When the plasma $[Ca^{++}]$ increases, the secretion of calcitonin

increases, and plasma $[Ca^{++}]$ is decreased again. When plasma $[Ca^{++}]$ decreases, the secretion of calcitonin decreases, and plasma $[Ca^{++}]$ is permitted to increase again (Figure 62-11). In addition, the gastrointestinal hormones glucagon, gastrin, and cholecystokinin stimulate the secretion of calcitonin. The physiological role of these gastrointestinal hormones in the control of calcitonin is not known. The principal hormonal influences on calcium are summarized in Table 62-2.

Calcitonin probably has a physiological role in the maintenance of calcium homeostasis and in the remodeling of bone. Calcitonin may be more important in the development of the skeleton than in the stabilization of the plasma $[Ca^{++}]$; however, it complements the action of parathormone (PTH) in the control of $[Ca^{++}]$. A decrease of plasma $[Ca^{++}]$ of about 0.3

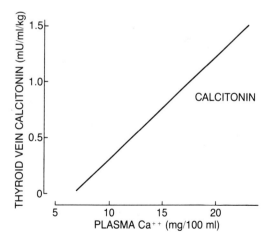

Figure 62-11. Effects of plasma $[Ca^{++}]$ on plasma calcitonin. (Redrawn, with permission, from Care, A.D., et al. 1968. *Parathyroid Hormone and Thyrocalcitonin (Calcitonin).* New York: Excerpta Medica.)

TABLE 62-2
The principal hormonal influences on calcium

	Plasma Ca^{++}	Plasma HPO$_4^=$	Secretion stimulated by
PTH	↑	↓	↓ [Ca^{++}]
Vitamin D	↑	↑	↓ [Ca^{++}] (biogenesis of active D$_3$)
Calcitonin	↓	↓	↑ [Ca^{++}]

↑ = increased

↓ = decreased

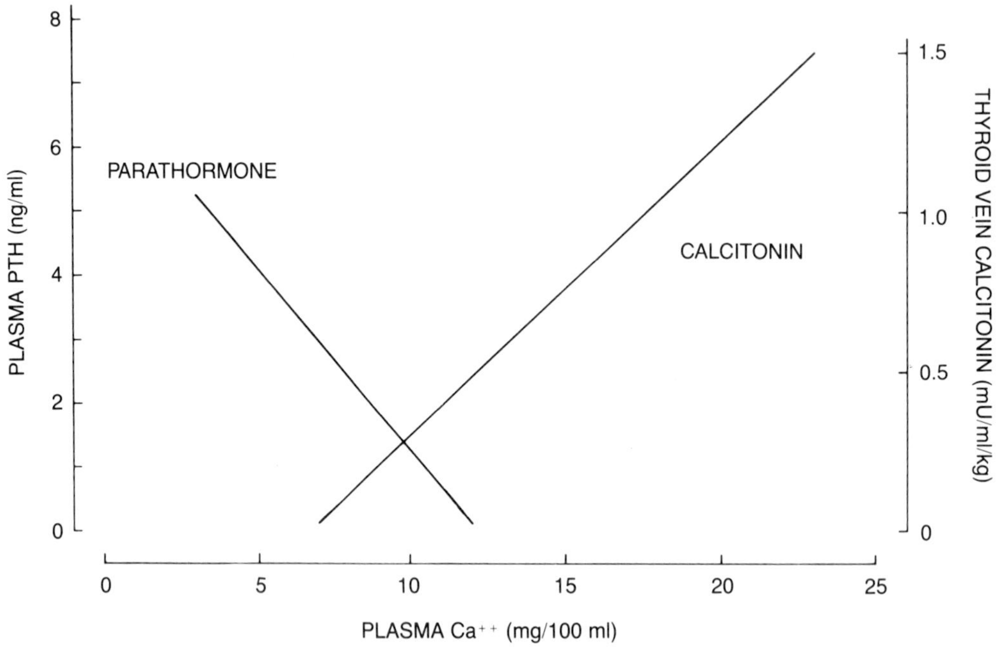

Figure 62-12.   The dual control of plasma [Ca^{++}] by parathormone (PTH) and calcitonin. Any deviation from the normal [Ca^{++}] of 10 mg/dl evokes an increase in the concentration of one of the hormones that oppose the change. (Redrawn, with permission, from Copp, D.H. 1968. *Parathyroid Hormone and Thyrocalcitonin (Calcitonin).* New York: Excerpta Medica.)

mg/dl causes the release of PTH, and an increase of plasma [Ca^{++}] of about 0.5 mg/dl causes the release of calcitonin. PTH and vitamin D increase plasma [Ca^{++}], and calcitonin decreases plasma [Ca^{++}]. Acting together, the two hormones form a dual feedback mechanism that is sensitive and effective (Figure 62-12).

STUDY OUTLINE

PARATHYROID GLANDS   Essential for life.

Four parts; embedded in thyroid gland.
Removal causes low plasma [Ca^{++}] and tetany.

Glands secrete parathormone; affects metabolism of calcium and phosphate.

PARATHORMONE Polypeptide, has 84 amino acids; synthesized and secreted, little is stored.

Plasma half-life is approximately 10–20 minutes; not protein-bound.

Not species-specific.

CALCIUM   Adequate and constant plasma $[Ca^{++}]$ is essential for many normal functions.

Total plasma calcium exists in three forms: protein-bound, complexed with phosphate or bicarbonate, and ionized.

Ca^{++} fraction is controlled; most important.

Total calcium is measured clinically; normal ionization is assumed.

FUNCTIONS OF CALCIUM   Formation of bones and teeth.

Factor in excitability of nerves and muscles.

Necessary for muscle contraction.

Affects rhythm of heart.

Participates in blood coagulation.

Needed for normal activity of enzymes.

BONE   About two-thirds is mineral; one-third is organic material.

Mineral is hydroxyapatite.

Organic matter is collagen, mucopolysaccharides (ground substance), and cells.

Formed and resorbed continually.

Remodeling is related to stress of bearing weight.

CALCIUM HOMEOSTASIS   Reciprocal relationship: $[Ca^{++}] \times [HPO_4^=] = K$.

Two compartments of bone—exchangeable (labile) and nonexchangeable (stable).

Ca^{++} and $HPO_4^=$ exchange between extracellular fluid and labile fraction.

Helps keep plasma $[Ca^{++}]$ constant.

Homeostasis involves intestines (absorption), bone (resorption), and kidneys (excretion of Ca^{++} and $HPO_4^=$); PTH affects all three.

PTH is necessary for adequate level of plasma $[Ca^{++}]$.

ACTIONS OF PARATHORMONE

BONE   Increases rate of resorption of Ca^{++} and $HPO_4^=$ from stable bone.

Rapid action—dissolves calcium around osteocytes.

Slow action—increases activity of osteoclasts; mediated by stimulating adenylate cyclase, increasing cyclic AMP.

KIDNEY   Increases excretion of $HPO_4^=$ by decreasing reabsorption in proximal tubules; may increase secretion in distal tubules.

Decreases plasma $[HPO_4^=]$, permits plasma $[Ca^{++}]$ to increase: $[Ca^{++}] \times [HPO_4^=] = K$.

Increases reabsorption of Ca^{++} in proximal tubules.

Renal effects through adenylate cyclase–cyclic AMP system.

May increase synthesis of vitamin D in kidneys.

GASTROINTESTINAL TRACT   Increases rate of absorption of Ca^{++} in small intestines.

Requires also vitamin D.

CONTROL OF THE SECRETION OF PARATHORMONE   Negative feedback by plasma $[Ca^{++}]$.

HYPOPARATHYROIDISM   Usually caused by damage to or surgical removal of parathyroid glands; idiopathic form is rare.

HYPOCALCEMIA   Decreased threshold for nerve stimulation; moderate—revealed by clinical tests; severe—causes tetany.

Prolonged Q-T interval in electrocardiogram; dysrhythmia may occur.

Treat with calcium salts or vitamin D.

HYPERPARATHYROIDISM   Usually from adenoma.

Kidney stones and calcium deposits in renal tubules.

Decalcification of bones.

Short Q-T interval in electrocardiogram.

Treat by surgical removal of abnormal glandular tissue.

VITAMIN D   Group of sterols that affect mineral metabolism and are necessary for action of PTH.

Principal compounds are D_3 (cholecalciferol—natural animal vitamin), D_2 (calciferol), and A.T. 10 (dihydrotachysterol; commercial preparation is Hytakerol).

Formed in skin in sunlight (ultraviolet light); 7-dehydrocholesterol is converted to cholecalciferol.

Contained in certain oily foods, absorbed from intestines.

Certain metabolites are more potent; 1,25-dihydroxycholecalciferol is considered the active form; synthesis in kidney is stimulated by hypocalcemia.

ACTIONS   Necessary for active transport of calcium during absorption by gut.

Necessary for mobilization of Ca^{++} and $HPO_4^=$ from bone by PTH.

Important in formation and remodeling of bone.

Necessary for reabsorption of Ca^{++} by renal tubules.

Increases reabsorption of $HPO_4^=$ in renal tubules.

Generally, acts synergistically with PTH; small amounts of each are made more effective by the other.

CONTROL   Absorption or synthesis in skin is not controlled.

Biosynthesis of 1,25-dihydroxycholecalciferol, most active form, is regulated by negative feedback of plasma $[Ca^{++}]$.

Deficiency causes rickets in children and osteomalacia in adults; plasma $[Ca^{++}]$ and $[HPO_4^=]$ are abnormally low.

Excess causes hypercalcemia and hyperphosphatemia; corrected by decreasing intake of vitamin D and avoiding sunlight.

CALCITONIN   Before 1964, no hormone was known to lower plasma $[Ca^{++}]$; experiments indicated existence of such a hormone.

Once thought to come from thyroid—called *thyrocalcitonin*.

Eventually found to come from ultimobranchial glands—called *calcitonin*.

Peptide; has 32 amino acids.

ACTIONS   Inhibits resorption of stable bone.

Regulates skeletal remodeling; more important in young animals.

Decreases plasma $[HPO_4^=]$.

CONTROL   Negative feedback by Ca^{++} on secreting cells is most important.

Glucagon, gastrin, and cholecystokinin stimulate secretion.

Calcitonin functions in calcium homeostasis and bone remodeling.

Calcitonin and PTH form sensitive and effective dual feedback mechanism.

BIBLIOGRAPHY

Adams, J.S.; Clemens, T.L.; Parrish, J.A., et al. 1982. Vitamin D synthesis and metabolism after ultraviolet irradiation of normal and vitamin D-deficient subjects. *N. Engl. J. Med.* 306:722.

Aurbach, G.D., and Geiger, S.R. (eds.). 1976. Parathyroid gland. In *Handbook of Physiology*. Section 7. Endocrinology. Volume VII. Washington, D.C.: American Physiological Society.

Aurbach, G.D.; Keutmann, H.T.; Niall, H.D., et al. 1959. Structure, synthesis, and mechanism of action of parathyroid hormone. *Recent Prog. Horm. Res.* 28:353.

Austin, L.A., and Heath, H., III. 1981. Calcitonin: Physiology and pathophysiology. *N. Engl. J. Med.* 304:269.

Care, A.D.; Cooper, C.W.; and Orimo, H. 1968. The direct measurement of thyrocalcitonin secretion rate in vivo. In *Parathyroid Hormone and Thyrocalcitonin (Calcitonin)*. Edited by R.V. Talmage and L.F. Belanger. New York: Excerpta Medica.

Copp, D.H. 1970. Endocrine regulation of calcium metabolism. *Annu. Rev. Physiol.* 32:61.

Copp, D.H.; Davidson, A.G.F.; and Chehey, B.A. 1961. Evidence for a new parathyroid hormone which lowers blood calcium. *Proc. Can. Fed. Biol. Soc.* 4:17.

DeGroot, L.J.; Cahill, G.F., Jr.; Odell, W.D., et al. (eds.). 1979. *Endocrinology*. Volume II. New York: Grune & Stratton.

DeLuca, H.F. 1981. Recent advances in the metabolism of vitamin D. *Annu. Rev. Physiol.* 43:199.

Fraser, D.R. 1980. Regulation of the metabolism of vitamin D. *Physiol. Rev.* 60:551.

Habener, J.F. 1981. Regulation of parathyroid hormone secretion and biosynthesis. *Annu. Rev. Physiol.* 43:211.

Hirsch, P.F., and Munson, P.L. 1969. Thyrocalcitonin. *Physiol. Rev.* 49:548.

Holick, M.F.; Uskokovic, M.; Henley, J.W.; et al. 1980. The photoproduction of 1α, 25-dihydroxyvitamin D_3 in skin. *N. Engl. J. Med.* 303:349.

Keutmann, H.T.; Sauer, M.M.; Hendy, G.M., et al. 1978. Complete amino acid sequence of human parathyroid hormone. *Biochem.* 17:5723.

Martin, K.J.; Hruska, K.A.; Freitag, J.J., et al. 1979. The peripheral metabolism of parathyroid hormone. *N. Engl. J. Med.* 301:1092.

Norman, A.W., and Henry, H. 1974. 1,25-dihydroxycalciferol—a hormonally active form of vitamin D_3. *Recent Prog. Horm. Res.* 30:431.

Omdahl, J.L., and DeLuca, H.F. 1973. Regulation of vitamin D metabolism and function. *Physiol. Rev.* 53:327.

Parfitt, A. 1976. Mechanism of calcium transfer between blood and bone and their cellular basis: Morphological and kinetic approaches to bone turnover. *Metab.* 25:809.

Parsons, J.A. 1982. *Endocrinology of Calcium Metabolism*. New York: Raven Press.

Queen, S.F., and Bell, N.H. 1975. Calcitonin: A general survey. *Metab.* 24:555.

Raisz, L.G., and Kream, B.E. 1981. Hormonal control of skeletal growth. *Annu. Rev. Physiol.* 43:225.

Raisz, L.G., and Kream, B.E. 1983. Regulation of bone formation. *N. Engl. J. Med.* 309:29, 83 (two parts).

Rasmussen, H., and Goodman, D.B.P. 1977. Relationships between calcium and cyclic nucleotide in cell activation. *Physiol. Rev.* 57:421.

Reiss, E., and Canterbury, J.M. 1969. Primary hyperparathyroidism. *N. Engl. J. Med.* 280:1381.

Wasserman, R.H., and Fullmer, C.S. 1983. Calcium transport proteins, calcium absorption, and vitamin D. *Annu. Rev. Physiol.* 45:375.

Williams, R.J. (ed.). 1981. *Textbook of Endocrinology* (6th ed.). Philadelphia: Saunders.

63

The Gonads and the Gonadotropins

CHAPTER CONTENTS

GONADS

The principal function served by the gonads is the continuation of the species by the production of germ cells and hormones. The male gonads are the *testes,* which carry out the de-velopment and maturation of sperm and the synthesis and secretion of testosterone. The female gonads are the *ovaries,* which are responsible for the development and release of ova and the synthesis and secretion of estrogens and progesterone.

GONADOTROPINS

The gonadotropins, which are hormones of the anterior pituitary gland, control the gonads in both the male and the female. The gonadotropins foster the structural and functional growth of the gonads, and under their influence ova develop, spermatozoa are produced, and the hormones of the gonads are synthesized and secreted. Gonadotropins have no direct influence on the accessory sex organs. The pituitary gonadotropins are follicle-stimulating hormone (FSH), luteinizing hormone (LH), and prolactin (see Chapter 57 for additional information about the release of these hormones).

FOLLICLE-STIMULATING HORMONE (FSH)

FSH is secreted by basophilic cells of the anterior pituitary gland. FSH is a glycoprotein that is made up of α- and β-subunits and has a molecular weight of about 30,000 daltons. The α-subunit is similar to the α-subunits of LH, HCG (human chorionic gonadotropin), and TSH (thyroid-stimulating hormone); however, the β-subunit is different in each of the glycoprotein hormones of the pituitary gland. Follicle-stimulating hormones from other species are not active in humans. Pregnant mare's serum (PMS), a commercial preparation, has actions in the human that resemble the actions of FSH.

In the male, FSH stimulates adenylate cyclase in the seminiferous tubules of the testicles, producing cyclic AMP, which induces and maintains spermatogenesis. Cyclic AMP causes the Sertoli cells and androgen-binding protein (ABP) to take up and bind testosterone in high concentration. FSH increases the weight of the testicles but does not induce the secretion of testosterone.

In the female, FSH stimulates the growth of the primary ovarian follicle to form the mature graafian follicle. FSH does not induce steroidogenesis or ovulation, but it does prepare the follicle for the action of LH.

Control

CENTRAL NERVOUS SYSTEM
Luteinizing hormone-releasing hormone (LRH) is synthesized by hypothalamic neurons, released in the median eminence, and carried via the pituitary portal vessels to the anterior pituitary gland, where it causes the release of FSH (Figure 63-1). A follicle hormone-releasing factor (FRF) may be produced, but this factor currently is thought to be identical to LRH. LRH has been synthesized and is available for clinical use in some countries; it is available only for clinical research in the United States.

FEEDBACK IN THE MALE
The most important control of FSH in the male is negative feedback. A glycoprotein called *inhibin*, which is released from the Sertoli cells of the seminiferous tubules, inhibits the secretion of LRH.

Testosterone, when administered in large doses as a drug, can inhibit the secretion of FSH and even has been tried as a male contraceptive; however, in physiological concentration, testosterone does not exert negative feedback. In low doses, testosterone exerts positive feedback. Thus, small amounts of the hormone reinforce further release up to a limit, but this is not considered to be an important mechanism of control.

FEEDBACK IN THE FEMALE
The most important negative feedback in the female is provided by the estrogens released from the mature follicle of the ovary; estradiol is the principal member of this group. The estrogens act on the hypothalamus to inhibit the release of LRH and on the adenohypophysis to inhibit the release of FSH (Figure 63-1). Large concentrations of progesterone, which is released by the corpus luteum (after ovulation), also inhibit the release of FSH. In low concentration, the estrogens may reinforce their own secretion through positive feedback, but this mechanism is relatively unimportant.

LUTEINIZING HORMONE (LH)

LH is secreted by basophilic cells of the anterior pituitary gland. It is a glycoprotein that has a molecular weight of about 28,000 daltons (in the human) and is composed of α- and β-subunits. Luteinizing hormones from other species are not active in humans. Human chorionic gonadotropin (HCG) has actions that are similar to those of LH and is available for clinical use.

LH acts on adenylate cyclase to increase the concentration of cyclic AMP in both sexes. In

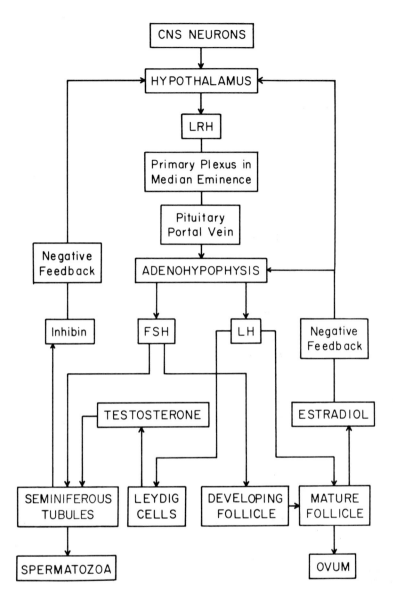

Figure 63-1.   Actions and control of FSH. FSH, released by LRH, acts in both the male and the female, and in both genders some of the effects depend on interplay of FSH with LH. In the male, FSH is responsible for spermatogenesis, but testosterone, which is secreted under the influence of LH, also is necessary. The secretion of FSH in the male is controlled by negative feedback on the hypothalamus through inhibin. In the female, FSH stimulates the maturation of the follicles in preparation for ovulation, under the influence of LH. The secretion of FSH in the female is controlled by negative feedback on the hypothalamus and the adenohypophysis, through estrogen.

the male, LH promotes the synthesis and secretion of testosterone by the Leydig (interstitial) cells of the testes. It acts mainly on the biosynthesis of pregnenolone from cholesterol. In the female, LH is responsible for the final maturation of the ovarian follicle, the synthesis and secretion of estrogen, and ovulation from the mature follicle. Estrogen is produced by the theca interna cells of the follicle; LH acts on the biosynthesis of pregnenolone from cholesterol, just as it does in the production of testosterone in the male.

A large amount of LH—a "burst," or a "surge"—is needed to produce ovulation. The burst of LH appears to be caused by a combination of a neural timing-mechanism and positive feedback by estrogen. The neural mechanism is most striking in species that ovulate reflexly, only after copulation, such as the cat or the rabbit. This mechanism involves afferent pathways from the genitalia to the hypothalamus and is a neuroendocrine reflex in which LH is the efferent link. It can be duplicated by stimulation of the genitalia with a glass rod or by electrical stimulation of certain areas of the brain.

In species that ovulate spontaneously, such as humans and rodents, ovulation occurs cyclically rather than in response to sexual stimulation. In rats, the electrical activity of the brain changes in a specific way several hours before the animal ovulates. Pentobarbital or certain psychopharmacological drugs can prevent this electrical activity and delay ovulation for 24 hours. Certain psychopharmacological agents also can delay ovulation and interfere with the normal menstrual cycle in women.

After ovulation has occurred, LH promotes the formation of the *corpus luteum* from the remains of the follicle. The theca interna cells and the granulosa cells are organized ("luteinized"), and progesterone and estrogen are synthesized and secreted by the luteal cells of the corpus luteum.

Control

CENTRAL NERVOUS SYSTEM

In both male and female humans, a center in the mid to posterior hypothalamus controls the continuous, or baseline, secretion of LH through the LH releasing hormone, LRH (see Chapter 57). This is the only center for the control of LH in the male. In the female, a center in the anterior hypothalamus controls the cyclic production of LH responsible for the "surge" that causes ovulation.

FEEDBACK

In the female, both estrogen and progesterone exert negative feedback on the pituitary gland and the tonic center of the hypothalamus (Figure 63-2). This inhibitory action of estrogen probably is the most important physiological mechanism to decrease the secretion of LH. Progesterone, in large amounts, also can inhibit the cyclic center and thereby block ovulation. Estrogen, in rising levels, exerts positive feedback on the cyclic center of the hypothalamus. This mechanism provides the burst of LH that is needed to cause ovulation. In the male, testosterone exerts negative feedback on the tonic center of the hypothalamus and, probably, the pituitary gland.

The concentrations of the gonadotropins and the gonadal steroids do not remain constant throughout the day. The plasma levels vary randomly, as if these hormones were secreted in small quantities rather than continuously.

PROLACTIN

Prolactin is secreted by acidophilic cells of the anterior pituitary gland. It is a protein, a globulin that has a molecular weight of about 30,000 daltons and consists of about 198 amino acids. Prolactin is related closely in structure to growth hormone (GH) and a placental hormone, human chorionic somatomammotropin (HCS), or human placental lactogen (HPL). Prolactin contains disulfide bridges that are necessary for biological activity (insulin, GH, ADH, and oxytocin also have disulfide bridges).

Prolactin has no well-established actions in the male. In the human female, it causes the production of milk by the mammary gland after estrogen and progesterone have acted on the breast, and it is responsible for maternal behavior.

Control

Prolactin is secreted tonically, and control is introduced through prolactin inhibiting factor (PIF), which is secreted by hypothalamic neurons (Figure 63-3). Stimuli that lead to the secretion of prolactin do so by inhibiting PIF. The prolactin-releasing factor (PRF) of the hypothalamus is of minor physiological importance. Feedback is not an important mechanism in the control of prolactin, although prolactin in high concentrations can stimulate the secretion of PIF and thereby inhibit its own secretion through short-loop feedback.

The secretion of prolactin is facilitated by physiological levels of estrogens indirectly, via inhibition of PIF in the hypothalamus, and directly, by stimulation of the adenohypophysis. Large doses of gonadal steroids (estrogens and testosterone have been used) can be given to prevent the production of milk in a woman who does not wish to nurse her baby. These hormones may act on the breast to prevent the effects of prolactin; however, feedback on the hypothalamus or the pituitary cannot be ruled out completely.

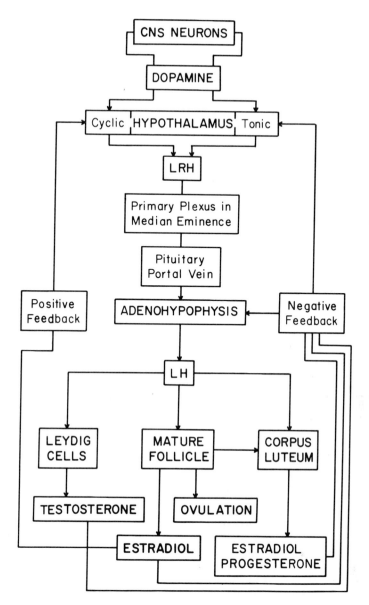

Figure 63-2. Actions and control of LH. In both the male and the female, LH is released by LRH under the influence of a "tonic" center in the hypothalamus. In the male, LH promotes the synthesis and secretion of testosterone by the interstitial cells of Leydig and is controlled by negative feedback of testosterone on the adenohypophysis and the tonic center of the hypothalamus. In the female, LH promotes the final maturation of the follicle, the synthesis and secretion of estrogen, and ovulation from the mature follicle. Continuous, or tonic, secretion of LH, which is responsible for the maturation of the follicle and the maintenance of the corpus luteum, is controlled by negative feedback of estrogen and progesterone on the adenohypophysis and the tonic center of the hypothalamus. Rising levels of estrogen stimulate the production of LH by positive feedback on the cyclic center of the hypothalamus to produce the burst of estrogen that causes ovulation.

STIMULI FOR SECRETION

Stimulation of the nipples by suckling, stimulation of the genitalia, the actions of estrogens, stress, anesthesia, exercise, thyrotropin-releasing hormone (TRH), and drugs such as phenothiazines, reserpine, and methyldopa all increase the rate of secretion of prolactin. The physiological significance of the stimulation by TRH is not known; occasionally, a hypothyroid patient may have high levels of prolactin

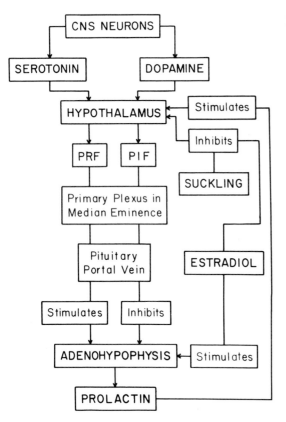

Figure 63-3. Control of prolactin. Prolactin is secreted tonically and controlled primarily by prolactin inhibiting factor (PIF), which is secreted by the hypothalamus and acts on the adenohypophysis. Suckling at the breast is the main stimulus that inhibits PIF and increases the secretion of prolactin and milk. Prolactin is controlled to a minor extent by short-loop feedback on the hypothalamus that increases the release of PIF, by feedback of estrogen on the hypothalamus that inhibits the release of PIF and on the adenohypophysis that stimulates the secretion of prolactin. The hypothalamus also releases prolactin releasing factor (PRF), which is of only minor importance.

---

and experience *galactorrhea* (abnormal production of milk). L-dopa and bromocriptine decrease the rate of secretion of prolactin, and the latter, especially, is used clinically to treat galactorrhea.

MENSTRUAL CYCLE

The reproductive cycle in the female human provides periodically for fertilization and pregnancy. During a period of about 30–40 years, uterine bleeding occurs after intervals of approximately 1 month, due to the interplay among the central nervous system, the anterior pituitary gland, the ovaries, and the response of the endometrium. The menstrual cycle is dated from the first day of bleeding, which is day 1. For convenience, the length of the typical cycle is considered to be 28 days, although the cycles vary among individuals and in the same women at different times. Only primates have such a menstrual cycle.

Proliferative, or Follicular, Phase

The proliferative phase is the beginning of the menstrual cycle (Figure 63-4). The follicle develops under the influence of FSH, and estrogen is secreted under the influence of LH. The endometrium of the uterus thickens, becoming glandular and vascular. The estrogen exerts positive feedback on the secretion of FSH and LH; however, as the level of estrogen increases, it inhibits FSH by negative feedback. The increasing concentration of estrogen, through continued positive feedback on the cyclic center in the hypothalamus, produces the surge of LH that causes ovulation. If the increased level of estrogen is prevented or if the level of estrogen remains high continuously (as it does when birth control pills are given), the burst of LH does not occur and ovulation does not take place.

Secretory, or Luteal, Phase

After ovulation, the corpus luteum is formed from the remains of the follicle, under the control of LH, and begins to secrete estrogen and progesterone (Figure 63-4). As the concentrations of estrogen and progesterone increase, these gonadal hormones begin to inhibit the secretion of LH by negative feedback, and, subsequently, their own rates of secretion decrease. As the levels of estrogen and progesterone diminish, the thick, glandular, and vascular endometrium sloughs and bleeds because of a lack of hormonal support. This is *menstruation*.

Figure 63-4. (Opposite page.) Hormonal influences and the phases of the menstrual cycle. See the text for further discussion. ➤

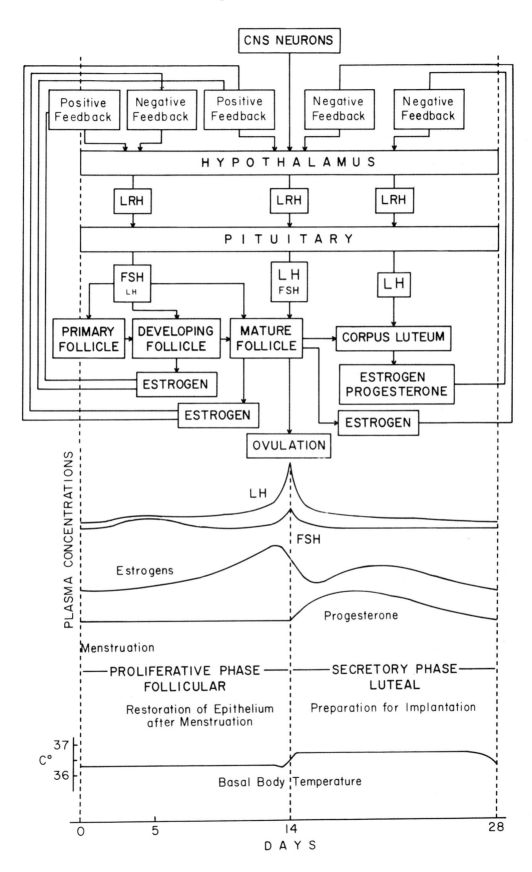

The factors that make this series of events cycle spontaneously are not known. The corpus luteum is fully mature 8 or 9 days after ovulation, and if the ovum is not fertilized and implanted, the corpus luteum begins to regress.

Ovulation is not necessary for menstrual bleeding to occur. Whenever the endometrium is built up, a fall in the level of estrogen or progesterone or both will cause menstruation. The endometrium may be built up by the action of estrogen alone to such an extent that it outgrows its blood supply and menstruation occurs.

Basal Body Temperature (BBT)

After ovulation has occurred, the rectal temperature of the typical woman, taken before rising in the morning, increases from about 36.3 C to about 36.7 C (Figure 63-4). This effect is believed to be caused by a calorigenic action of progesterone. BBT is a good clinical indicator of the occurrence of ovulation and the secretion of progesterone. The BBT remains above 36.7 C if pregnancy occurs and the secretion of progesterone continues.

Although the length of the menstrual cycle varies, the duration of the luteal phase remains fairly constant at about 13–14 days. Thus, ovulation usually occurs 13–14 days before the beginning of menstruation, and most of the variation of the cycle occurs during the follicular phase (between menstruation and ovulation).

Estrous Cycle

The estrous cycle is the reproductive or sexual cycle in animals. It differs from the human cycle because the period of sexual desire is localized to one interval during the cycle, and bleeding occurs at the time of ovulation (e.g., in dogs and horses) rather than between ovulations, as it does in humans.

Rhythm Method of Birth Control

The ovum survives for 1–3 days if it is not fertilized, and the sperm survives for about 2 days; hence, the fertile period begins about 2 days before ovulation and ends 3 days after ovulation. The interval between the twentieth day of one regular cycle and the ninth day of the next cycle is considered to be a "safe period," during which the occurrence of pregnancy is improbable.

Despite the evidence that appears to support it, the rhythm method fails in 25%–30% of the cases. There are several reasons for these failures. The menstrual cycle is variable, and ovulation is not regular; the occurrence of ovulation on any day of the cycle has been documented. The luteal phase of the cycle is fairly regular, however, so that ovulation occurs about 13–14 days before menstruation. Thus, in a regular cycle of 35 days' duration, ovulation will occur on day 21. If this factor is taken into account, the effectiveness of the rhythm method can be improved. The rhythm method can be made most accurate by keeping a chart of BBT and observing when ovulation occurs rather than predicting it.

HUMAN CHORIONIC GONADOTROPIN (HCG)

Fertilization occurs in the fallopian tube, forming the *blastocyst,* which remains free in the tube and uterus for 7 or 8 days after ovulation (until about days 21–23 of the cycle). During this time, the blastocyst is nourished by the secretions of the endometrium. This is the secretory phase of the cycle, and the levels of estrogen and progesterone are high. The correct balance of these hormones is essential to the survival of the fertilized egg. Eventually, the blastocyst implants in the endometrium of the uterus; the placenta is formed and begins to secrete HCG, which maintains the corpus luteum (Figure 63-5).

HCG is a glycoprotein that has a molecular weight of about 46,000 daltons and consists of α- and β-subunits (as LH, FSH, and TSH also do). HCG probably is secreted by syncytial cells of the placenta.

Actions

HCG acts very much as LH does. HCG maintains the corpus luteum throughout most of the first trimester of pregnancy, and it causes the corpus luteum to secrete estrogen and progesterone during this time. HCG can be used clinically in humans when LH is needed.

The detection of HCG in the urine or blood is the basis of most tests for pregnancy. Very sensitive tests can detect HCG only 2 or 3 days after implantation has occurred. The usual clinical tests are less sensitive than this, however, and they do not detect HCG in the urine

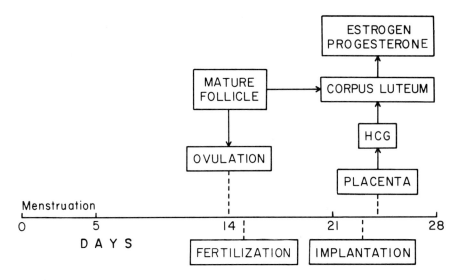

Figure 63-5. Maintenance of the corpus luteum by human chorionic gonadotropin (HCG) from the placenta. In this example, the fertilized ovum was implanted on day 23, and on day 24 the placenta began to secrete HCG.

until about 40 days after the last menstrual period, or about 2 weeks after a period has been missed.

ANDROGENS AND ESTROGENS

The pathways of biosynthesis of androgens and estrogens essentially are the same in the adrenal cortex, the ovary, and the testis (see Figure 60-8). Cholesterol is the chief precursor in all of the pathways. LH is responsible for the synthesis and secretion of androgens and estrogens by the gonads in both sexes. *Testosterone,* the principal androgen, is formed from androstenedione, and the estrogens are formed in subsequent steps (Figure 63-6). *Estradiol* is the most potent estrogen secreted; testosterone is its immediate precursor or it is formed from androstenedione through estrone. Androgens and estrogens are synthesized in both the testes and the ovaries and normally are secreted in both sexes. Thus, there are normal levels of androgens in the plasma of the female and normal levels of estrogens in the plasma of the male.

Chemistry and Secretion of Androgens

Testosterone is the major androgen secreted. It is synthesized and secreted by the Leydig cells (interstitial cells) and is controlled completely by LH. Two-thirds of the testosterone in the circulation is bound to a plasma globulin (testosterone–estrogen-binding globulin, or TEBG), which also binds estradiol. Only free testosterone is biologically active. The normal concentration of testosterone (bound plus free) in the plasma of males is about 0.6 µg/dl, and the normal concentration of testosterone in the plasma of females is about 0.03 µg/dl. Males secrete about 4–9 mg of testosterone per day. Testosterone is metabolized to 17-ketosteroids, mainly in the liver (Figure 63-6); 17-ketosteroids are excreted in the urine. About one-third of the ketosteroids excreted by males come from the testes and about two-thirds come from the adrenal cortex; hence, the concentration of 17-ketosteroids in the urine is not a good indicator of testicular activity.

Actions of Androgens

FEEDBACK
Testosterone exerts negative feedback on LH at the level of the hypothalamus. Testosterone feeds back on FSH only in very high concentration; in physiological concentrations, it does not affect FSH.

ACCESSORY REPRODUCTIVE ORGANS OF THE MALE
Androgens are necessary for the development and maintenance of the ducts associated with the transport of the spermatozoa and the ac-

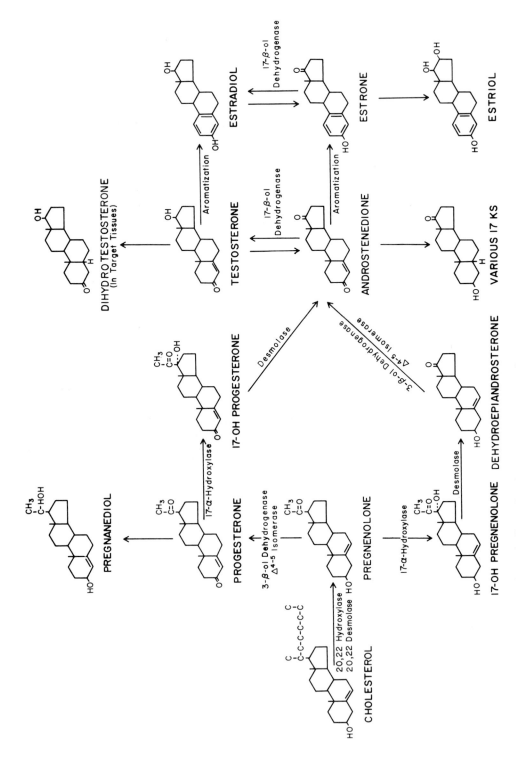

Figure 63-6.   Biosynthesis and metabolism of androgens, estrogens, and progesterone.

cessory glands that secrete the seminal fluid. These ducts and glands are the epididymis, the vas deferens, the bulbourethral glands, the prostate gland, and the seminal vesicles. The secretion of fructose from the seminal vesicles, which is necessary for the nutrition of the spermatozoa that are ejaculated, depends on testosterone. In a male who has been castrated, the prostate gland atrophies because of the lack of testosterone. This is the rationale behind performing castration in an effort to control cancer of the prostate. Estrogen also may be administered because it inhibits the secretion of LH and thereby decreases the rate of secretion of testosterone. The size and width of the penis, the formation of rugae in the scrotum, and the pigmentation of the scrotum all are affected by testosterone. Some of the accessory glands concentrate testosterone and convert it to *dihydrotestosterone* (DHT) (Figure 63-6). In those tissues, DHT is the physiologically active form of testosterone.

SPERMATOGENESIS

The concentration of testosterone in the seminiferous tubules, where spermatogenesis occurs, is 100 times that in the plasma. FSH also is necessary for spermatogenesis. Large doses of testosterone given exogenously inhibit FSH and thereby inhibit spermatogenesis. Thus, testosterone may be used in this way as a contraceptive.

SECONDARY SEXUAL CHARACTERISTICS OF THE MALE

The secondary sexual characteristics distinguish the male from the female of the species. The pubic hair, which is the first to appear, forms a triangular pattern with the apex superior. Under the influence of testosterone, the facial, axillary, and general body hair increase, but the hair of the scalp decreases. The receding hairline is characteristic of males. Baldness is determined genetically, but it does not occur if androgens are lacking. The vocal cords lengthen and thicken to produce a deeper voice. The body build changes; the shoulders broaden, and the mass of the skeletal muscles increases. The sebaceous glands of the skin produce oil (sebum), and acne frequently is a problem after puberty.

GENERAL METABOLIC EFFECTS

Protein anabolism is a major effect of the androgens. The rate of synthesis of protein increases, and the rate of catabolism decreases. The skeletal muscles and the accessory sexual structures are changed the most, but all tissues are affected. Synthetic compounds that have strong anabolic effects but little androgenic action would be important clinically.

The androgens promote the growth of bone, but they also cause the epiphyses to close. At the time of puberty, the rate of secretion of testosterone increases, and the rate of growth increases greatly for 1 or 2 years; thereafter, the epiphyseal plates close and further growth is prevented. By contrast, growth hormone does not close the epiphyses (see Chapter 58). During adolescence, the development of the skeleton and the degree of sexual maturation are correlated closely. Early sexual maturity produces the characteristic spurt of growth, but early closure of the epiphyses; hence, individuals who follow this pattern usually are shorter of stature. Gonadal deficiency, in which the production of androgens is inadequate from childhood (*eunuchoidism*), causes long arms and legs (because the epiphyses remain open longer), narrow shoulders, small muscle-mass, a rounded, feminine body, and small genitalia. The androgens also cause moderate retention of Na^+, Cl^-, K^+, Ca^{++}, and water.

BEHAVIOR

Aggressive, dominant behavior is associated with androgens, especially in animals. The psychosexual pattern of the adult human is more complex because it involves social conditions in addition to hormonal influences. Testosterone increases the libido, but it does not determine the means by which sexual desire is expressed. A minimum level of testosterone is necessary for the maintenance of the libido; however, the level of testosterone and the degree of sexual desire are not correlated directly.

EFFECTS OF INCREASING AGE

The male human does not experience a climacteric; that is, spermatogenesis and the secretion of testosterone do not decline suddenly to negligible levels at a certain age in males (in contrast to the nearly complete failure of ovarian function in females). As the male grows older, spermatogenesis and the secretion of testosterone decrease slightly, and sexual response and performance are slowed; however, as long as the male remains healthy, these functions will continue. The rate of secretion of testosterone can be decreased by pathological conditions; in this event, symptoms comparable to the female climacteric appear. These include hot flashes, irritability, and depression. The libido and sexual ability also would be decreased in the male, which is not necessarily the case in post-menopausal women.

Chemistry and Secretion of Estrogens

The estrogens cause cornification of the vaginal mucosa and other changes in the female genital organs. In animals, estrogens evoke changes of behavior and a state of *estrus* (acceptance of the male, or "heat"). There is no precise counter-part of this phenomenon in the female human.

Three estrogens occur naturally in humans (Figure 63-7): *estrone* (E_1), *estradiol* (E_2), and *estriol* (E_3). These compounds are character-ized by an unsaturated ring A and a phenolic OH group at C-3. 17β-estradiol is the most potent estrogen biologically, and it is the major secretory product.

The estrogens are synthesized and secreted by the ovary (cells of the theca interna), the corpus luteum, the placenta, and in small amounts by the testes and the adrenal cortex. The rates of secretion by the ovary and the corpus luteum are controlled by LH. The bio-synthetic pathway proceeds through the an-drogens (see Figure 63-6); in addition, an-drogens are converted to estrogens in the periphery (away from the source of secretion) to some extent, especially in fat tissue.

The estrogens are secreted throughout the menstrual cycle; two peaks occur—one before ovulation and another during the middle of the luteal phase (see Figure 63-4). Estrogens circu-late bound to a specific plasma globulin, which also binds testosterone (gonadal-steroid-bind-ing globulin [GBG], or testosterone-estrogen-

TABLE 63-1

The rates of secretion and plasma levels of estradiol during the menstrual cycle of adult women

	Secretion rate	Plasma level
Follicular phase	70 µg/day	6–8 ng/dl
Ovulation	600 µg/day	30 ng/dl
Luteal phase	250 µg/day	20 ng/dl
Adult male	—	2 ng/dl

binding globulin [TEBG]). About two-thirds of the estrogens in the circulation are bound. Ta-ble 63-1 gives the rates of secretion and the concentrations of estrogen in the plasma dur-ing the different phases of the menstrual cycle. The liver inactivates the estrogens and conju-gates them for excretion in the urine. After menopause, the secretion of estrogens by the ovaries is negligible.

Actions of Estrogens

FEEDBACK

The estrogens exert negative feedback on the secretion of FSH and on the tonic secretion of LH (see Figure 63-2); both of these actions are important physiologically. In low concentra-tion, the estrogens exert positive feedback on the secretion of FSH and the tonic secretion of LH; neither of these actions is very impor-tant physiologically. When the concentrations of estrogen are increasing, positive feedback helps to produce the surge of LH that causes ovulation (see Figure 63-4); this effect is very important.

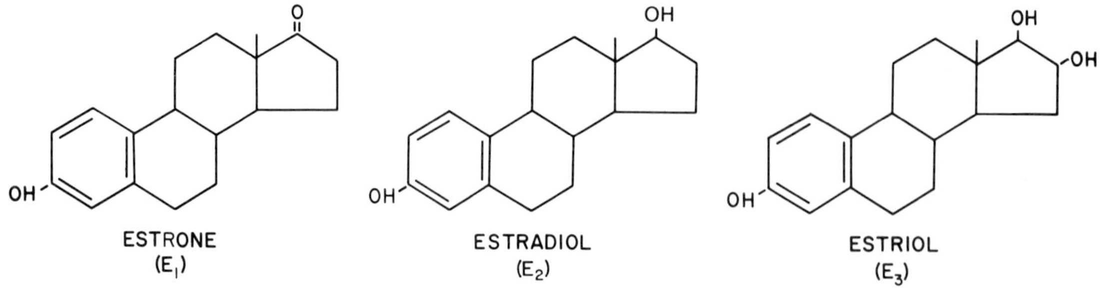

Figure 63-7.   Structural formulas of the estrogens.

ACCESSORY REPRODUCTIVE ORGANS OF THE FEMALE

The estrogens provide for the reproductive processes of ovulation, implantation, pregnancy, parturition, and lactation by stimulating the development and maintaining the structure and function of the accessory organs. The estrogens stimulate the growth of the follicles in the ovary and promote motility in the fallopian tubes. In the uterus, the estrogens are responsible for the changes that occur during the follicular, or proliferative, phase of the menstrual cycle. These changes include the growth of the endometrium, an increased rate of synthesis of proteins, proliferation of the uterine glands, and an increase of the blood supply. The estrogens cause the uterus to enlarge to the adult size; in addition, they increase the motility of the myometrium and the sensitivity of the myometrium to oxytocin. Thus, estrogens stimulate all of the smooth muscle of the genital tract. In the cervix, the estrogens increase the opening of the os (mouth of the uterus) and the quantity of (alkaline) mucus that is secreted; the estrogens decrease the viscosity and the cellularity (leukocytes) of the cervical mucus. All of the changes in the cervix favor the survival and transport of the sperm. The changing qualities of the mucus can be used clinically to determine when a woman is ovulating. This information is important when a patient is being inseminated artificially.

The estrogens cause the vagina to develop and enlarge to the adult size, and they promote cornification, which is thickening of the epithelial mucosa of the vagina. The latter action is so characteristic that it can be used to verify the secretion of estrogen.

The mammary glands enlarge at the time of puberty, and their normal growth requires both estrogen and progesterone. Estrogens stimulate primarily the growth of the mammary ducts. In pharmacological doses, estrogen preparations inhibit the secretion of prolactin and can be used to prevent lactation and to dry up the breasts after birth. For this inhibition to be effective, however, the suckling stimulus must not be applied.

SECONDARY SEXUAL CHARACTERISTICS OF THE FEMALE

The female pelvis is widened to aid in the carriage and delivery of the fetus. This is an important attribute of the human, particularly because of the relatively large head of the human fetus. The female body contours generally are rounded and curved because of the uniform distribution of a layer of adipose tissue subcutaneously. In addition, adipose tissue is concentrated in the breasts, buttocks, hips, and thighs. In contrast to the actions of the androgens, the estrogens promote more hair on the scalp and less hair on the body in general. The pattern of the pubic hair is a triangle with the apex down. The growth of pubic and axillary hair in females at puberty is caused by adrenal androgens and not by estrogens.

GENERAL METABOLIC EFFECTS

The estrogens increase protein anabolism, but not to the extent that the androgens do. The spurt of growth and closure of the epiphyses also occur in females (Figure 63-8); however, there is some controversy about the role of the estrogens in this process. Some physiologists believe that the sudden, rapid growth actually is caused by an increased rate of secretion of adrenal androgens induced by estrogen at the time of puberty.

The estrogens cause moderate retention of Na^+, Cl^-, and water (mineralocorticoidlike activity). Most women retain salt and water and gain weight just before menstruation (this is related to premenstrual tension), when the concentrations of estrogen and progesterone are high. The estrogens also stimulate the

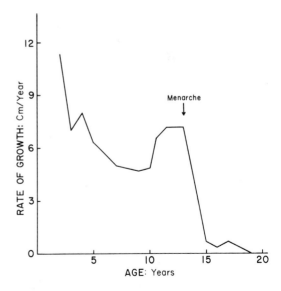

Figure 63-8.   Rate of growth of a typical female human from infancy to adulthood.

synthesis of plasma proteins in the liver. This action is important with respect to proteins that bind hormones in the circulation (see Chapter 59).

BEHAVIOR

In animals, estrogen conditions the receptivity of females and establishes stereotyped patterns of sexual behavior (estrous behavior). Estrogens may affect sexual drive in humans, but they do not determine the means by which it is expressed.

Menopause

The ovaries change with age; they become unresponsive to gonadotropins and do not secrete estrogens. This change occurs mostly between the ages of 45 and 55 years. Because the ovaries do not secrete estrogens, the endometrium does not build up, and menstruation does not occur. Ovulation does not occur. It should be emphasized that this is a failure of the ovaries and not of the pituitary. Because the concentration of estrogens in the plasma is low, the rates of secretion of FSH and LH increase (lack of negative feedback). Human menopausal gonadotropin can be extracted from the urine of postmenopausal women and used clinically for its FSH-LH activity. Human menopausal gonadotropin is one of the "fertility" drugs, which, in combination with human chorionic gonadotropin (HCG), has produced multiple births.

Most of the effects seen after menopause are related to the lack of estrogen. "Hot flashes" are common. These are sensations of heat that move in waves up the chest to the head; they may be caused by the large concentrations of gonadotropins that are circulating. Emotional disturbances such as anxiety, tension, depression, irritability, headaches, insomnia, myalgia, and palpitations also occur. Protein anabolism is decreased, the skin becomes thinner, and the protein matrix of the bone may be decreased to the extent that osteoporosis develops. The genital tissues atrophy slowly; the vaginal epithelium becomes thin, the vulva may itch, and urinary difficulties may appear. Usually, the menopausal woman experiences little or no change of libido.

Some women experience few or none of the reactions listed above, but most women require some degree of medical treatment. Low-level replacement therapy is applied. If the uterus has not been removed, an estrogen preparation is given cyclically, along with progesterone, for a few days every second or third month, so that the endometrium will slough periodically and prevent excessive buildup. If the uterus has been removed, estrogen is given continuously.

PROGESTERONE

The general term *progestin* means a substance that aids in maintaining pregnancy. *Progesterone* is an intermediate compound in the production of all of the steroid hormones in the ovaries, the testes, and the adrenal cortex (see Figures 60-8 and 63-6). Progesterone is secreted in large amounts by the corpus luteum (and by the placenta during pregnancy) and in very small amounts by the adrenal cortex, the testes, and, perhaps, the follicular cells of the ovary. LH alone is responsible for control of the secretion of progesterone by the corpus luteum.

Progesterone circulates bound to a specific plasma globulin. The rate of secretion and the concentration of progesterone in the plasma vary during the menstrual cycle (Table 63-2). Progesterone is metabolized in the liver to *pregnanediol* (Figure 63-9), in which ring A is reduced completely, and conjugated with glucuronide for excretion in the urine.

Actions

FEEDBACK

Progesterone, especially in large amounts, exerts negative feedback to inhibit the rates of secretion of LH and FSH. Progestin in birth control pills acts in this way to prevent ovulation.

TABLE 63-2

The rates of secretion and plasma levels of progesterone during the menstrual cycle of adult women

	Secretion rate	Plasma level
Midfollicular phase	3–6 mg/day	0.9 ng/ml
Midluteal phase	20–40 mg/day	15 ng/ml
Pregnancy	–	140 ng/ml
Adult males	0.75 mg/day	0.3 ng/ml

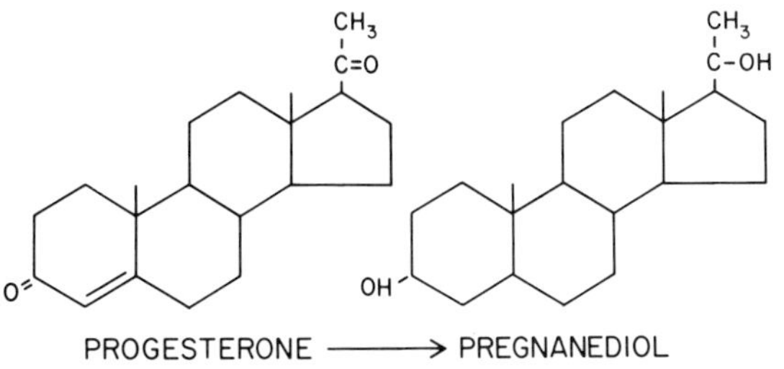

Figure 63-9. Progesterone is metabolized to pregnanediol in the liver.

UTERUS

Progesterone appears after ovulation and induces a secretory type of uterine endometrium. It promotes the secretion of mucus of high glycogen content by the uterine glands and allows for implantation of the fertilized ovum. Progesterone acts on endometrium that has been influenced previously by estrogen. Withdrawal of progesterone usually causes uterine bleeding and desquamation of the secretory endometrium. Progesterone inhibits uterine contraction and, true to its name, maintains gestation.

Progesterone causes the mucus of the cervical glands to be thick, tenacious, and cellular. Thus, it helps to establish conditions unfavorable for the penetration and survival of spermatozoa. This action is consistent with the function of progesterone to support and protect the pregnancy that already has begun. These actions also are desirable in birth control medication.

MAMMARY GLANDS

In the mammary glands, progesterone stimulates the development of lobules and alveoli. Most of the development of the breasts at puberty is under the influence of estrogen, although progesterone secreted during the last half of the menstrual cycle causes some alveolar proliferation and swelling of the breasts. True alveoli do not develop until the first pregnancy, when the concentration of progesterone in the plasma reaches high levels.

CONTROL OF FERTILITY

Oral Birth Control Pills

The term *pill* is used incorrectly in this expression, because technically a pill is medication in the form of a hardened plastic mass, and medication for the control of birth usually is supplied in the form of tablets. The term has become established thoroughly in the popular language, however, and in addition, the true pill no longer is used; therefore, *pill* will be used in this text simply as a nonspecific term for any solid oral medication.

After the completion of successful clinical trials in the late 1950s, birth control pills (BCP) first were sold as contraceptive agents in 1960. At present, more than 20 million women throughout the world, including about 10 million in the United States, use steroids for contraception. When they are used properly, BCP are about 99.9% effective. This rate of effectiveness is greater than the effectiveness of any other method, except abstinence and sterilization.

BCP contain synthetic estrogens and progestins (Figure 63-10); the naturally occurring estrogens and progestins are not effective orally. The combination BCP, which contain both synthetic estrogen and progestin, are taken daily for 3 weeks, then stopped for 7 days, during which time menstruation occurs. Thereafter, the cycle is repeated.

BCP inhibit the secretion of LH and FSH through negative feedback; the estrogen blocks especially FSH and the progestin blocks especially LH. Under these conditions, the ovarian follicles grow very little and do not mature. Thus, no mature follicle is available for ovulation. Measurement of LH in the plasma by radioimmunoassay shows that the surge of LH, which is needed for ovulation, does not occur. In addition, the endometrium is not suitable for implantation, and the cervical mucus is not appropriate for the penetration of sperm.

If the administration of BCP is stopped, menses and ovulation resume normally in most women. After 3 months, the menstrual cycles are normal in 98% of the subjects, and fertility and pregnancy can occur in most women. A small portion of women do not resume normal cycles. The reasons for this are not known; however, patients who have a history of menstrual irregularity experience *postpill amenorrhea* more frequently than other women do.

There is no evidence to suggest that BCP have changed the rate of occurrence of cancer of the breast or genitalia; however, women who have estrogen-sensitive cancer of the breast should not use BCP.

THROMBOEMBOLISM

A statistical association between death from thromboembolism and the use of BCP has been reported; however, this subject is contro-

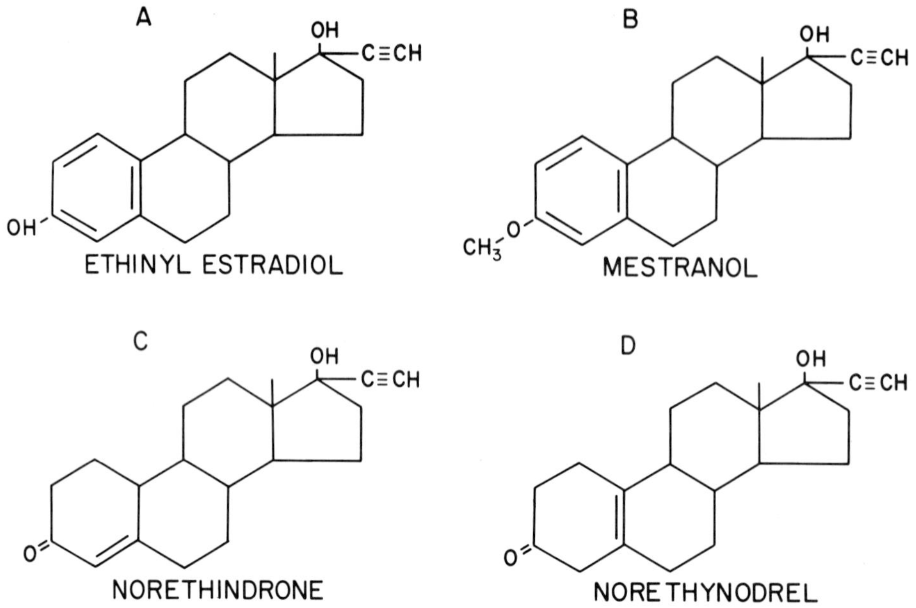

Figure 63-10. Synthetic estrogens and progestins. **A.** and **B.** Representative synthetic estrogens. **C.** and **D.** Representative synthetic progestins. C is contained in the commercial preparations Novum, Norinyl, and Norlutin. D is contained in the commercial preparation Enovid.

versial. The original work has been criticized, and other investigators have not confirmed the original results. There is general agreement, however, that BCP with low-dose estrogens are preferred. In any event, the risk is slight and considerably less than the risk associated with pregnancy.

There is no evidence that BCP prolong the period of reproduction. Because a woman who is taking the pill does not know when menopause begins, usually it is recommended that, for complete protection, she continue to take the pill until she is well past the average age of menopause. Many gynecologists recommend that women stop taking BCP after the age of 40 years, however, because of increased risk of cardiovascular disease, hypertension, and stroke and use other means of contraception.

HORMONE-BINDING PROTEINS

One should keep in mind that, because of the estrogen content, BCP increase the concentration of hormone-binding proteins in the plasma; hence, measurements of total thyroxine (T_4) or cortisol will yield high values (see Chapter 59). Another variation of the use of the gonadal hormones for birth control is the use of synthetic progestin alone. In this method, the pill is taken every day. Its effect is to change the cervical mucus and inhibit the transport of sperm.

POSTCOITAL CONTRACEPTION

Postcoital contraception is more convenient for some women. Prostaglandins, which are luteolytic in animals and can cause abortion in women, show some promise of being effective when used after coitus. Progestins are effective, but it appears that they would have to be given too many times during the menstrual cycle. Estrogens also are effective, and they have been used (e.g., after a woman has been raped). The estrogens alter the secretory endometrium to prevent implantation, and they may increase the rate of transport of the ovum from the tube to the uterus, so that the ovum arrives before the uterus is ready for implantation. If this method is used, the treatment should begin within 48 hours after coitus and last from 4 to 6 days. It is adequate after a single sexual contact, but it involves too many side-effects to be used after several sexual contacts each month.

Intrauterine Device (IUD)

The IUD is a very old method; descriptions of it have been found in writings from ancient Egypt. The IUD was used first in modern times by a German physician in the early 1900s, and devices have been on the market since the early 1960s.

Devices of various shapes are inserted into the uterus. The method is simple, inexpensive, and effective. The IUD is used by about 4 million women in the United States and has failed in only about 1.9% of the cases. Most of the failures have been found subsequently to be related to accidental and undetected expulsion of the device.

The IUD does not prevent ovulation; the woman has regular menstrual cycles, and the burst of LH still precedes ovulation. The mechanism of action is not known completely, but somehow the device prevents implantation of the fertilized ovum. The IUD might interfere with implantation simply by filling space and being in the way, it might distend the uterine cavity and compress the endometrial tissue, or it may act by eliciting an inflammatory response. The latter explanation is accepted most widely. Among the newer IUDs are those made of copper, which is toxic to spermatozoa. Another new IUD releases progesterone locally and thereby prevents the transport of sperm and alters the motility of the fallopian tubes.

OTHER HORMONAL INFLUENCES

Genitalia

INTERNAL GENITALIA

The differentiation of the primitive gonads into testes or ovaries is determined genetically. Internally, the ducts initially are undifferentiated and will become female if they are not influenced by substances from the testes. This occurs in normal females, in males whose testes do not secrete during early fetal development, and in males whose tissues do not respond to the secretions of the testes. The *müllerian duct system* develops into the fallopian tubes, the uterus, and the upper portion of the vagina. The formation of male internal ducts and accessory structures depends on functional testes and their secretions. The testes secrete *müllerian regression factor* (MRF), which sometimes is called *müllerian duct inhibiting substance,* a polypeptide that causes the müllerian system to atrophy. Testosterone, along with MRF, causes the *wolffian duct system* to differentiate into the epididymis, the vas deferens, and the seminal vesicles. This system acts locally; therefore, unilateral development is possible.

EXTERNAL GENITALIA

In the external genitalia, also, female is the basic condition (clitoris, labia minora, labia majora, and the lower portion of the vagina) and is expressed if testicular secretion is absent. If androgen is present (normally, testicular testosterone), the male external genitalia (the penis and the scrotum) develop. This effect is produced by testosterone acting systemically. Gonadotropin from the placenta probably is responsible for this secretion of testosterone, which occurs between the eighth and the thirteenth week of gestation. This series of events provides the explanation for the varying degrees of masculine external genitalia (pseudohermaphroditism) in female infants who have virilizing adrenal hyperplasia.

Central Nervous System

Sexual maturation, or differentiation, of the central nervous system (CNS), probably the hypothalamus, also is influenced by androgens during the development of the fetus. Here, also, the basic condition is female; that is, the hypothalamus has a center for the cyclic secretion of gonadotropin. During a critical period in development, late fetal or early neonatal (depending on the species), androgen changes the hypothalamus into one that provides only tonic control of the secretion of gonadotropin (i.e., a "male" hypothalamus). In the female rat, a single injection of testosterone before 5 days of age abolishes permanently the cyclic release of gonadotropin and the female patterns of mating. If this animal, as an adult, is placed with a responsive female, it displays male sexual behavior, and the administration of estrogen and progesterone do not restore female estrous behavior. Thus, both behavior and the hypothalamic-controlled release of gonadotropin appear to be influenced by the hormonal milieu during fetal life. The hormonal influences on genital and CNS development are summarized in Table 63-3.

PUBERTY

Puberty may be defined in various ways; functionally, it is the age at which reproduction becomes possible. Generally, puberty occurs between 10 and 17 years of age. In the United States, the average age of puberty for girls is 12 years, and the average age of puberty for boys is 14 years. In girls, puberty is marked by the

CLINICAL CORRELATION
63.1   Testicular Feminization

CASE REPORT

The Patient: A 47-year-old woman.

Principal Complaint: A pelvic mass that interfered with bladder function.

History: The patient had been well until about 2 weeks before she was seen, when she had begun to be aware of "fullness" in the pelvis and to have difficulty controlling her bladder.

Clinical Examination: The patient appeared well at examination. Although she had never menstruated and had no axillary or pubic hair, she had moderately large breasts and feminine contours. She was married, but had never been pregnant. She disclosed that she had never had a strong libido. The external genitalia appeared normal, but the vagina was short, and no uterus was found. A firm mass was located in the right side of the pelvis. Laboratory studies revealed normal thyroid function, normal serum electrolytes, luteinizing hormone (LH) 5.9 U/liter (normal, 5–22 U/liter), follicle stimulating hormone (FSH) 1.4 U/liter (normal, 3–16 U/liter), serum testosterone 878 ng/dl (normal, 25–90 ng/dl), 24-hour urinary 17-hydroxysteroids 4.6 mg (normal, 2–10 mg) and 24-hour urinary ketosteroids 13 mg (normal, 3–15 mg). The karyotype (pattern of chromosomes) was 44 + xy, which is characteristic of the genetic male. Pelvic tomograms (sectional x-rays) revealed a mass above the bladder, and an intravenous pyelogram (x-ray films showing the progress of contrast medium through the urinary system) showed the mass to be compressing the bladder.

Treatment: A laparotomy (abdominal incision) was performed and a benign tumor of the right gonad (adenoma of the seminiferous tubules) was removed. No uterus or fallopian tubes were found. The left gonad was removed, and microscopic examination showed it to be a testis.

Comment: Because the growth of axillary and pubic hair is caused by adrenal androgens, the absence of those secondary sexual characteristics in the patient suggests either the failure to produce androgens or the lack of end-organ response to the hormone. The patient's adrenal function is normal and provides adequate androgens. The circulating testosterone is secreted by the testes and is within the normal range for a male. Thus, the patient is a male chromosomally and hormonally but has almost complete lack of tissue response to androgens. Because of this insensitivity, the wolffian ducts were not stimulated to develop into epididymis, vas deferens, and seminal vesicles, and male external genitalia were not formed. The testes secreted müllerian-inhibitory factor *in utero*, which prevented development of the uterus. Estrogens were produced by conversion from androgens, at sufficient levels to allow development of the female breasts at puberty, in the absence of androgen effects. The relative lack of libido and the female psychosocial orientation can be attributed to the lack of androgen sensitivity by the central nervous system. Tumors of the essentially undescended testes are common in cases of testicular feminization.

Outcome: The patient has done well since the surgery. She was told that a large ovarian cyst had been removed. Because her function within the female gender is successful, no useful purpose would have been served by disclosing the abnormal development.

menarche, which is the first menstrual bleeding (Figure 63-8). This may be anovulatory at first (ovulation does not occur), and the bleeding may be caused only by the withdrawal of estrogen. The onset of puberty is less dramatic in males, and it is indicated by the first appearance of mature spermatozoa in the ejaculate. Penile erection is possible shortly after birth, and the capacity for intercourse and orgasm precedes spermatogenesis.

Puberty is initiated by increased output of the pituitary gonadotropins. Relatively little

TABLE 63-3
Summary of hormonal influences on genital and central nervous system development

	Basic condition	If present	Influence	Anatomical expression
Internal structures	Female	Testes—MRF; testosterone	Local ⟶	Male ducts
External genitalia	Female	Testes—testosterone	Systemic ⟶	Male external genitalia
Central nervous system maturation	Female (cyclic)	Testes—testosterone	Systemic ⟶	Male hypothalamus with noncyclic gonadotropin secretion and male behavior

gonadal activity occurs between birth and puberty, and very little gonadal steroid hormone is secreted during childhood. The concentration of gonadotropins increases gradually between the ages of 7 and 10 years and reaches adult levels by about 15 or 16 years of age. The gonads can respond to gonadotropins long before puberty, and the pituitary can release gonadotropins. The pituitary of the immature animal or human secretes LH and FSH in response to injected LRH. The hypothalamus of the immature animal contains LRH and FRF, but apparently these releasing hormones are not secreted. Thus, the degree of maturation is not determined by the gonads or the pituitary, but rather by the CNS, and some neural mechanism is responsible for the onset of puberty.

Theories about the Initiation of Puberty

CESSATION OF INHIBITION BY GONADAL HORMONES
According to one theory, small amounts of hormones secreted by the immature gonads are sufficient to inhibit the output of gonadotropins at the level of the CNS. At puberty, the sensitivity of the CNS changes, the small concentration of gonadal steroids no longer is an effective inhibitor, the gonadotropins are released, and the gonads mature.

CESSATION OF INHIBITION BY THE HYPOTHALAMUS
Another theory holds that the anterior hypothalamus and its specific connections exert tonic inhibitory control over the LRH center. LRH is secreted to stimulate the secretion of gonadotropins only after inhibition by the hypothalamus is relaxed. This theory is supported by the observation that animals and children who have lesions in certain parts of the brain, and especially in the hypothalamus, mature sexually early in life (precocious puberty). No one knows what sets this "biological clock" to change the sensitivity of the hypothalamus or to remove hypothalamic inhibition so that puberty occurs.

STUDY OUTLINE

GONADS Produce germ cells and hormones.
  Testes—male; sperm and testosterone.
  Ovaries—female; ova, estrogens, and progesterone.

GONADOTROPINS Hormones of anterior pituitary: FSH, LH, and prolactin.
  Promote growth and development of go-

nads, production of spermatozoa, and development of ova.
  Synthesis and secretion of hormones.

FOLLICLE-STIMULATING HORMONE (FSH) Glycoprotein; α-, β-subunits; stimulates adenylate cyclase, increases cyclic AMP.

Male—induces and maintains spermatogenesis in seminiferous tubules.

Female—stimulates growth of ovarian follicle and prepares follicle for action of LH.

CONTROL

CENTRAL NERVOUS SYSTEM Through LRH of hypothalamus.

FEEDBACK IN THE MALE *Inhibin,* released by seminiferous tubules, inhibits secretion of LRH.

FEEDBACK IN THE FEMALE Estrogens inhibit release of LRH by the hypothalamus and FSH by the adenohypophysis.

Progesterone (corpus luteum) inhibits release of FSH.

LUTEINIZING HORMONE (LH) Glycoprotein; α-, β-subunits; stimulates adenylate cyclase; increases cyclic AMP.

Male—synthesis and secretion of testosterone.

Female—maturation of ovarian follicle, synthesis and secretion of estrogen, and ovulation from mature follicle.

Burst of LH is needed to cause ovulation; combination of neural timing and positive feedback by estrogen.

Ovulation is cyclic in humans; not initiated by external genital stimulation.

LH promotes formation of corpus luteum from remains of follicle; estrogen and progesterone are secreted.

CONTROL

CENTRAL NERVOUS SYSTEM Hypothalamus controls continuous, or tonic, secretion of LH through release of LRH (in both male and female); cyclic production of LH is controlled by anterior hypothalamus (in females).

FEEDBACK Male, negative—testosterone on tonic center of hypothalamus and on pituitary.

Female, negative—estrogen and progesterone on pituitary and tonic center of hypothalamus; positive—estrogen on cyclic center of hypothalamus.

PROLACTIN Protein (globulin); contains disulfide bridge; similar to GH.

Causes production of milk; maternal behavior.

CONTROL Secreted tonically; controlled through PIF from hypothalamus.

STIMULI FOR SECRETION Primary stimuli are suckling at breast, stimulation of genitalia, actions of estrogens; inhibit release of PIF.

MENSTRUAL CYCLE Reproductive cycle; period of fertility is followed by uterine bleeding at approximately monthly intervals.

PROLIFERATIVE, OR FOLLICULAR, PHASE Beginning of menstrual cycle.

Follicle develops under influence of FSH; estrogen is secreted under influence of LH.

Endometrium thickens; becomes vascular and glandular.

Positive feedback by estrogen produces LH surge; causes ovulation.

SECRETORY, OR LUTEAL, PHASE Corpus luteum is formed from remains of follicle under influence of LH; secretes estrogen and progesterone.

Increasing estrogen and progesterone inhibit LH secretion.

Levels of estrogen and progesterone diminish; endometrium sloughs and bleeds.

Corpus luteum regresses if not fertilized.

Ovulation is not necessary for menstruation; caused by withdrawal of estrogen and progesterone after buildup of endometrium.

BASAL BODY TEMPERATURE (BBT) After ovulation, body temperature increases about 0.5 C; reflects progesterone.

Indicator of ovulation.

Usually 13–14 days before menstruation; most constant part of cycle.

ESTROUS CYCLE Reproductive cycle in animals, except primates.

RHYTHM METHOD OF BIRTH CONTROL Fertile period is from about 2 days before ovulation to 3 days after.

"Safe period" is from about day 20 of one cycle to day 9 of next cycle; fails in 25%–30% of cases.

Menstrual cycle is variable; ovulation is not regular.

Luteal phase is more dependable; ovulation occurs 13–14 days before menstruation; identified by basal body temperature.

HUMAN CHORIONIC GONADOTROPIN (HCG) Glycoprotein; α-, β-subunits.

Ovum is fertilized in fallopian tube, forms blastocyst; is free in fallopian tube and uterus for 7–8 days after ovulation.

Nourished by the endometrium (secretory phase).

Blastocyst implants in endometrium; placenta is formed, secretes HCG.

ACTIONS Similar to actions of LH.

Maintains corpus luteum during first trimester of pregnancy.

Causes corpus luteum to secrete estrogen and progesterone.

Detection in blood is basis of pregnancy test.

ANDROGENS AND ESTROGENS Cholesterol is chief precursor.

Stimulated by LH.

Testosterone (androgen) is immediate precursor of estradiol (estrogen).

Both hormones are synthesized and secreted in both testes and ovaries.

CHEMISTRY AND SECRETION OF ANDROGENS Testosterone is major androgen secreted.

From Leydig cells, controlled by LH.

Two-thirds is bound to globulin in plasma; one-third is free, active.

ACTIONS OF ANDROGENS

FEEDBACK Negative, on LH, at hypothalamus.

ACCESSORY REPRODUCTIVE ORGANS OF THE MALE Ducts and glands—epididymis, vas deferens, bulbourethral and prostate glands, and seminal vesicles.

Developed and maintained by androgens.

Size of penis and rugae and pigmentation of scrotum also are affected.

SPERMATOGENESIS FSH also is necessary.

SECONDARY SEXUAL CHARACTERISTICS OF THE MALE Pubic hair has characteristic male pattern.

Facial and axillary body hair is increased; hair of scalp is decreased, receding hairline is characteristic of males.

Vocal cords lengthen, voice deepens.

Shoulders broaden, skeletal muscle mass increases.

Sebaceous glands produce oil (acne).

GENERAL METABOLIC EFFECTS Protein anabolism; synthesis is increased, catabolism is decreased.

Bone growth; spurt at puberty; terminated by closure of epiphyses.

Moderate retention of ions and water.

BEHAVIOR Favors dominant behavior; necessary for libido.

EFFECTS OF INCREASING AGE Gradual decline in spermatogenesis and testosterone secretion but no menopause; sexual function of male is decreased but continues.

CHEMISTRY AND SECRETION OF ESTROGENS Three compounds are secreted: estrone, estradiol (main estrogen), and estriol.

Synthesized and secreted principally by ovary, corpus luteum, and placenta; some secreted by testes and adrenal cortex.

Ovary and corpus luteum are controlled by LH.

Biosynthetic pathway through androgens.

Secreted continuously, peaks before ovulation and during middle of luteal phase.

Bound in plasma to globulin that also binds testosterone; about two-thirds is bound and one-third is free (active).

Negligible secretion by ovaries after menopause.

ACTIONS OF ESTROGENS

FEEDBACK Negative on FSH and tonic LH; positive on cyclic LH (ovulation).

ACCESSORY REPRODUCTIVE ORGANS OF THE FEMALE Developed and maintained by estrogens.

Growth of ovarian follicles and motility of fallopian tubes.

Growth of uterus to adult size and motility of myometrium.

Uterine changes and proliferative phase.

Changes in cervix to favor survival and transport of sperm.

Growth of vagina to adult size and thickening of mucosa.

Enlarge mammary glands at puberty (requires progesterone also).

SECONDARY SEXUAL CHARACTERISTICS OF THE FEMALE Wide pelvis—accommodate large head of fetus.

Body contours rounded by subcutaneous fat; deposits in breasts, buttocks, hips, and thighs.

Distribution of hair—more on scalp, less on body (pubic and axillary hair of females are caused by androgens).

GENERAL METABOLIC EFFECTS Increase protein anabolism.

Growth spurt and closure of epiphyses at puberty—may be caused by secretion of adrenal androgens induced by estrogens.

Moderate retention of salt and water.

Stimulate synthesis of plasma proteins.

BEHAVIOR Increases libido.

MENOPAUSE Occurs between 45 and 55 years of age.

Ovaries become insensitive to gonadotropins; do not secrete estrogens.

Ovulation and menstruation do not occur.

FSH and LH secretion are increased—lack of feedback inhibition (low estrogen levels).

Effects are related to lack of estrogen—emotional disturbances, decreased protein metabolism, thinning of bones, and slow atrophy of genital tissues; libido usually is not changed.

Estrogen replacement therapy.

PROGESTERONE Intermediate in synthesis of all steroid hormones.

Large amounts are secreted by corpus luteum and placenta; small amounts are secreted by adrenal cortex and testes, and perhaps by ovarian follicles.

Controlled by LH.

Bound to specific plasma globulin; secretion varies during menstrual cycle.

Metabolized in liver and secreted in urine.

ACTIONS

FEEDBACK   Negative on LH and FSH.

UTERUS   Effects are produced when progesterone is secreted after ovulation.

Prepares endometrium for implantation; withdrawal causes sloughing and bleeding.

Inhibits contractions; opposes penetration and survival of spermatozoa.

MAMMARY GLANDS   Stimulates development of lobules and alveoli.

CONTROL OF FERTILITY

ORAL BIRTH CONTROL PILLS   Synthetic estrogens and progestins.

Inhibit LH and FSH through negative feedback.

Follicles do not mature.

No LH "surge"; endometrium is not prepared for implantation.

When pills are stopped, menstruation and ovulation usually resume.

THROMBOEMBOLISM   Statistical association; controversial.

HORMONE-BINDING PROTEINS   An increased binding of thyroxine (T_4) and cortisol.

POSTCOITAL CONTRACEPTION   Prostaglandins—luteolytic in animals; show promise.

Progestins—effective, but must be given too frequently.

Estrogens—alter endometrium to oppose implantation; too many side-effects to be used repeatedly.

INTRAUTERINE DEVICE (IUD)   Various devices are inserted into uterus; effective in practice.

Prevents implantation, means unknown.

Copper—toxic to spermatozoa.

Local release of progesterone prevents transport of sperm.

OTHER HORMONAL INFLUENCES

GENITALIA

INTERNAL GENITALIA   Ducts are undifferentiated; become female if not influenced by substances from testes.

Müllerian regression factor (MRF) is polypeptide secreted by testes; causes müllerian ducts to atrophy.

Testosterone and MRF cause wolffian ducts to form epididymis, vas deferens, and seminal vesicles.

EXTERNAL GENITALIA   Will be female in absence of testicular secretions.

Testosterone causes male genitalia to develop.

Gonadotropin of placenta causes secretion of testosterone.

Masculine external genitalia in female infants who have virilizing adrenal hyperplasia.

CENTRAL NERVOUS SYSTEM   In absence of androgen, hypothalamus has center for cyclic secretion of gonadotropins (female).

At critical time, androgen changes hypothalamus to provide tonic secretion (male).

PUBERTY   Age at which reproduction is possible.

In human female, beginning of menstruation.

In human male, mature spermatozoa are present in ejaculate.

Initiated by increased output of pituitary gonadotropins.

Unknown neural mechanism is responsible.

THEORIES ABOUT THE INITIATION OF PUBERTY

CESSATION OF INHIBITION BY GONADAL HORMONES   Hormones from immature gonads inhibit CNS secretion of gonadotropins; sensitivity of CNS changes, gonadotropins are released, and gonads mature.

CESSATION OF INHIBITION BY THE HYPOTHALAMUS   Anterior hypothalamus inhibits LRH center; inhibition is relaxed for unknown reasons.

BIBLIOGRAPHY

Adler, N.T. 1981. *Neuroendocrinology of Reproduction: Physiology and Behavior.* New York: Plenum Press.

Bardin, C.W., and Catterall, J.F. 1981. Testosterone: A major determinant of extragenital sexual dimorphism. *Science.* 211:1285.

Bremmer, W.J., and deKrester, D.M. 1976. The pros-

pects for new, reversible male contraceptives. *N. Engl. J. Med.* 295:1111.

DeGroot, L.J.; Cahill, G.F., Jr.; Odell, W.D., et al. (eds.). 1979. *Endocrinology.* Volume III. New York: Grune & Stratton.

Ehrhardt, A.A., and Meyer-Bahlburg, H.F.L. 1981.

Effects of prenatal sex hormones on gender-related behavior. *Science* 211:1312.

Fink, G. 1979. Feedback actions of target hormones on hypothalamus and pituitary, with special reference to gonadal steroids. *Annu. Rev. Physiol.* 41:571.

Frantz, A.G. 1978. Prolactin. *N. Engl. J. Med.* 298:201.

Gordon, J.W., and Ruddle, F.H. 1981. Mammalian gonadal determination and gametogenesis. *Science* 211:1265.

Greep, R.O., and Astwood, E.B. (eds.). 1975. Male reproduction. In *Handbook of Physiology*. Section 7. Endocrinology. Volume V. Washington, D.C.: American Physiological Society.

Haseltine, F.P., and Ohno, S. 1981. Mechanisms of gonadal differentiation. *Science* 211:1278.

Heinonen, O.P.; Slone, D.; Monson, R.R., et al. 1977. Cardiovascular birth defects and antenatal exposure to female sex hormones. *N. Engl. J. Med.* 296:67.

Hennekens, C.H.; Evans, D.A.; Castelli, W.P., et al. 1979. Oral contraceptive use and fasting triglyceride, plasma cholesterol, and HDL cholesterol. *Circulation* 60:486.

Knobil, E.; Plant, T.M.; Wildt, L., et al. 1980. Control of the rhesus monkey menstrual cycle: Permissive role of hypothalamic gonadotropin-releasing hormone. *Science* 207:1371.

Kruhlich, L. 1979. Central neurotransmitters and the secretion of prolactin, GH, LH, and TSH. *Annu. Rev. Physiol.* 41:603.

Lipsett, M.B. 1980. Physiology and pathology of the Leydig cell. *N. Engl. J. Med.* 303:682.

MacLusky, N.J., and Naftolin, F. 1981. Sexual differentiation of the central nervous system. *Science* 211:1294.

Mainwaring, W.I.P. 1977. The mechanism of action of androgens. In *Monographs in Endocrinology*. New York: Springer-Verlag.

McCann, S.M. 1977. Luteinizing-hormone-releasing hormone. *N. Engl. J. Med.* 296:797.

McEwen, B.S. 1981. Neural gonadal steroid actions. *Science* 211:1303.

McEwen, B.S., and Parsons, B. 1982. Gonadal steroid action on the brain: Neurochemistry and neuropharmacology. *Annu. Rev. Pharmacol. Toxicol.* 22:55.

Means, A.R.; Dedman, J.R.; Tash, J.S., et al. 1980. Regulation of the testis Sertoli cell by follicle-stimulating hormone. *Annu. Rev. Physiol.* 42:59.

Parkes, D. 1979. Drug therapy. Bromocriptine. *N. Engl. J. Med.* 301:873.

Reiter, E.O., and Grumbach, M.M. 1982. Neuroendocrine control mechanisms and the onset of puberty. *Annu. Rev. Physiol.* 44:595.

Richards, J.S. 1980. Maturation of ovarian follicles: Actions and interactions of pituitary and ovarian hormones on follicular cell differentiation. *Physiol. Rev.* 60:51.

Rosenberg, L.; Armstrong, B.; and Jick, H. 1976. Myocardial infarction and estrogen therapy in postmenopausal women. *N. Engl. J. Med.* 294:1256.

Rubin, R.T.; Reinisch, J.M.; and Haskett, R.F. 1981. Postnatal gonadal steroid effects on human behavior. *Science* 211:1318.

Spaziani, E. 1975. Accessory reproductive organs in mammals: Control of cell and tissue transport by sex hormones. *Pharmacol. Rev.* 27:207.

Troen, P., and Nankin, H. (eds.). 1977. *The Testis in Normal and Infertile Man*. New York: Raven Press.

Weiss, N.S., and Sayvetz, T.A. 1980. Incidence of endometrial cancer in relation to the use of oral contraceptives. *N. Engl. J. Med.* 302:551.

Wildt, L.; Marshall, G.; and Knobil, E. 1980. Experimental induction of puberty in the infantile female rhesus monkey. *Science* 207:1373.

Williams, R.H. (ed.). 1981. *Textbook of Endocrinology* (6th ed.). Philadelphia: Saunders.

Wilson, J.D.; George, F.W.; and Griffin, J.E. 1981. The hormonal control of sexual development. *Science.* 211:1278.

64

Human Sexual Function

CHAPTER CONTENTS

GENERAL BACKGROUND

Besides its importance in reproduction, sex pervades human life in many important ways. Humans are "the sexiest primates"—intercourse occurs more frequently, lasts longer, and is more intense in humans than in other primates. As humans evolved, the existence of strong pair-bonds between the adult male and female aided survival because: (1) early humans were hunters, and stable sexual bonding at home permitted cooperation among males on the hunt, (2) the development of efficient weapons made sexual competition especially dangerous, and (3) the prolonged childhood and adolescence of the human required a stable, long-lasting pair-bond between parents. One of the most effective ways to maintain a strong pair-bond was to share complex, intense, and rewarding sexual activity. The result is a female who, in contrast to other primates, can achieve orgasm and is sexually re-

ceptive virtually at any time, and a male who has a prodigious desire for sex. Behavioral observation indicates that the vast bulk of human sexual activity is concerned with emotional closeness and mutual enjoyment rather than reproduction. Truly, sex is recreational as well as procreational, and the apparent preoccupation of modern society with sex may reflect the unmasking of natural drives rather than the development of decadence.

MALE SEXUAL FUNCTION

Functional Anatomy

The male reproductive system is located partly inside and partly outside the pelvic cavity (Figure 64-1). The external reproductive organs are the scrotum, penis, and testicles, and the internal organs are the ducts and accessory glands.

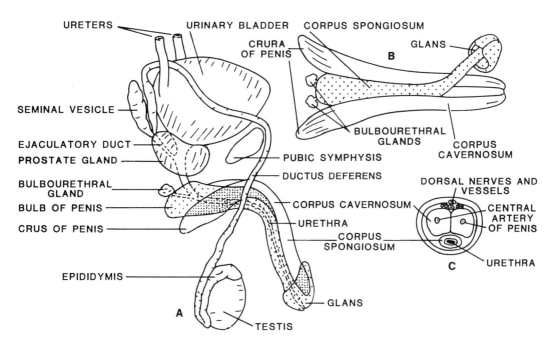

Figure 64-1. A. The male reproductive system. **B.** Inferior view of a dissected penis with the distal portion of the corpus spongiosum displaced to one side. **C.** Cross-section of the penis.

PENIS

The penis, which is the male organ for copulation, consists of three cylinders of erectile tissue. The most ventral (when the glans is pointed superiorly), called the *corpus spongiosum,* has the urethra running through its center (Figure 64-1). The distal end of the corpus spongiosum expands into the *glans penis,* which covers the ends of the corpora cavernosa. The glans penis has special sexual importance because it is highly sensitive to tactile stimulation. The other two erectile cylinders, the *corpora cavernosa,* provide the main structural support for the erect penis. The proximal ends of the cylinders, the *crura,* are attached to the pubic bones.

SCROTUM

The scrotum is a multilayered pouch that consists of two separate compartments, each of which contains a testis* (Figure 64-2). The skin of the scrotum is darker than the skin of the rest of the body and has numerous sweat glands. Directly beneath the scrotal skin is the dartos muscle, which contracts under involuntary (sympathetic) control in response to cold or sexual excitement.

TESTES

The testes, which weigh about 30 g each, produce sperm and androgens. The testes are encased separately in a tough fibrous capsule (*tunica albuginea*), which also forms septa that penetrate and divide the testis into lobes. The lobes are packed with seminiferous tubules, in the walls of which spermatogenesis proceeds (Figure 64-2). After about 74 days, the sperm migrate to the epididymis, where they mature for about 3 weeks and attain motility. The testes also function as endocrine organs—Leydig cells, located in the spaces between the seminiferous tubules, produce testosterone.

EPIDIDYMIS, VAS DEFERENS, AND SEMINAL VESICLES

The seminiferous tubules converge at one pole of the testis and empty into the head of the *epididymis* (Figure 64-2), a tortuous tube that partially wraps around the testis and becomes

---

*Testis is derived from the Latin for *witness.* This stems from an ancient custom of placing one hand over the genitalia when taking an oath; the word *testify* has the same derivation.

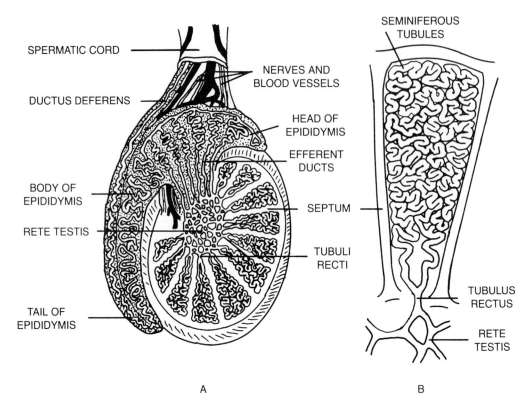

SPERMATIC CORD

DUCTUS DEFERENS

BODY OF
EPIDIDYMIS

RETE TESTIS

TAIL OF
EPIDIDYMIS

NERVES AND
BLOOD VESSELS

HEAD OF
EPIDIDYMIS

EFFERENT
DUCTS

SEPTUM

TUBULI
RECTI

SEMINIFEROUS
TUBULES

TUBULUS
RECTUS

RETE
TESTIS

A

B

Figure 64-2. Ductus deferens, epididymis, and testis. **A.** Sagittal section. **B.** Seminiferous tubule within a single compartment of the testis.

the *ductus deferens* (also called the *vas deferens*). The ductus deferens enters the abdominal cavity through the inguinal canal, runs posteriorly around the bladder (Figure 64-3), widens into an ampulla, in which sperm are stored, and becomes an ejaculatory duct when joined by a duct from one of the bilaterally paired seminal vesicles. The ejaculatory ducts empty into the urethra. The seminal vesicles produce a viscous secretion that contains *activating principle* and contributes to the volume of semen. Until acted on by the activating principle, the sperm largely are immobile, which conserves their energy resources until ejaculation occurs. Seminal fluid also contains a variety of other materials, including fructose, which the sperm utilize for energy, and prostaglandins, which may cause uterine contractions that help to move the sperm toward the fallopian tubes, where fertilization occurs.

URETHRA AND PROSTATE
The urethra serves two functions in the male: to transport sperm and to excrete urine. The ure-

thra begins at the base of the bladder, passes through the prostate (*prostatic urethra*), pierces the urogenital diaphragm (*membranous urethra*), and courses through the corpus spongiosum of the penis as the *cavernous urethra* (also called the *penile urethra*). The urethra receives numerous small ducts from the prostate; during ejaculation, the capsule of the prostate contracts and prostatic fluid is expressed into the urethra to become part of the ejaculate. Prostatic fluid, a milky, alkaline secretion, adds to the volume of ejaculate and neutralizes the acidic environment of the vagina, which otherwise might be spermicidal.

BULBOURETHRAL (COWPER'S) GLANDS
After it leaves the prostate, the urethra enters the fibrous and muscular urogenital diaphragm, in which the *bulbourethral glands* are embedded. During intercourse, these glands are compressed by the contractions of the urogenital diaphragm, which causes them to empty a small amount of alkaline fluid into the

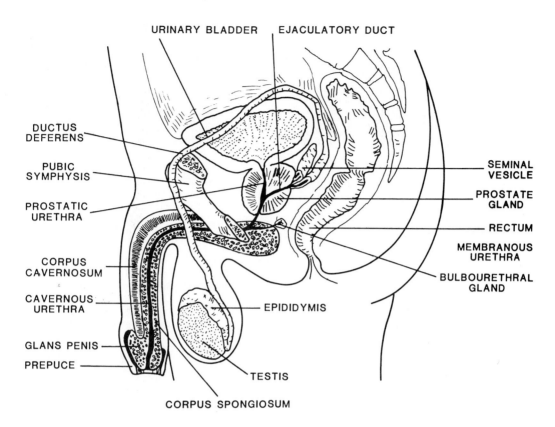

URINARY BLADDER   EJACULATORY DUCT

DUCTUS
DEFERENS

PUBIC
SYMPHYSIS

PROSTATIC
URETHRA

CORPUS
CAVERNOSUM

CAVERNOUS
URETHRA

GLANS PENIS

PREPUCE

SEMINAL
VESICLE

PROSTATE
GLAND

RECTUM

MEMBRANOUS
URETHRA

BULBOURETHRAL
GLAND

EPIDIDYMIS

TESTIS

CORPUS SPONGIOSUM

Figure 64-3.   Median sagittal section of the male pelvis with a portion of the left pubic bone at-tached to illustrate the path of the ductus deferens.

---

urethra. The alkalinity of this fluid helps to protect the sperm from the acidic environment of the urethra, and the presence of a few stray sperm in these secretions may account for occasional pregnancies that follow intercourse in which ejaculation never seems to occur.

SEMEN
Semen is composed of fluids derived from the testis, seminal vesicles, bulbourethral glands, and prostate. Most of the semen (about 60%) comes from the seminal vesicles—this is the last fluid to be ejaculated and serves to wash sperm out of the urethra. About 20% of the ejaculate comes from the prostate, and the remaining 20% comes from the vas deferens and bulbourethral glands. Most of the sperm in the ejaculate come from the vas deferens and ampullae of the vas deferens, where they are stored. The typical volume of ejaculate, 3–4 ml, contains about 100 million sperm per milliliter. A man is considered to be sterile if his sperm count is less than 20 million per milliliter. Sperm can live for several weeks in the male genital tract, but, once ejaculated, they live for only 2 or 3 days in the female genital tract.

Male Sex Act
EXCITEMENT PHASE
Different men become sexually aroused by different things; visual, olfactory, verbal, and tactile cues are especially important. The first response to sexual stimulus is erection of the penis, which is caused by parasympathetic impulses that flow from the sacral portion of the spinal cord through the pelvic nerve. This neural activity causes dilatation of the helicine arteries of the corpora cavernosa and corpus spongiosum. The penis is engorged by excessive inflow of blood and restricted outflow caused by compression of the venules in the corpora. A man cannot will an erection, but by relaxation and erotic concentration, he may maintain an erection for a relatively long time.

PLATEAU PHASE
The plateau phase occurs when the glans penis undergoes a slight additional enlargement and

CLINICAL CORRELATION
64.1   Impotence

CASE REPORT

The Patient: A 37-year-old man.

Principal Complaints: Impotence and loss of sexual interest.

History: The patient came for help at the insistence of his wife. He was embarrassed to be seeking help and had difficulty talking about his problem, which he described in simplistic terms. He contended that he just wasn't interested in sex anymore, and never really had been interested. At other times, he attributed the problem to his wife, whom he described as sexually demanding. He and his wife had not even attempted to have intercourse for 6 months or more, and the last time or two that they had tried, "it just didn't work." He justified himself in vague terms, stating that he worked overtime a great deal and was tired, or that his wife was too aggressive, which he did not like. About a year earlier, he had begun to drink alcohol more, to "relieve his nerves." Inquiry into his background revealed early problems of a sexual nature. When he was 15 years old, he had attempted to participate in a group activity, in which he and several friends were to take turns having intercourse with a willing girl. He said that although he was excited, when his turn came, he couldn't perform. All of them, including the girl, then laughed at him, and he was the subject of ridicule afterward. "Everyone" knew about it, and he was accused of being homosexual. During the subsequent years, he had convinced himself that he was a "latent homosexual." Every time he had attempted to have intercourse, he had remembered the incident at age 15.

Comment: Physical examination, which included a neurological study and examination of the genitals, revealed no pathology. The patient had no history of diabetes, spinal cord injury, or surgery of the pelvis or the neck of the bladder. He did not take antihypertensive medication or other drugs that would affect his libido, and endocrine studies, which included LH, FSH, testosterone, prolactin, T_3 uptake, and T_4, were normal. The blood sugar was normal after overnight fast and 2 hours after a meal. Thus, this was a case of psychological impotence. The problem was the patient's image of himself, beginning with the incident described above, and reinforced by his contemporaries. Each failure to perform sexually had reinforced his fears and assured the continuance of his problem. He had married a domineering woman, who added pressure on him. Sexual activity never was pleasurable to him—it always was associated with anxiety and displeasure.

Outcome: Through psychological counselling, the patient re-examined his experience as a teenager and re-interpreted his role in it. He had to share this experience with his wife; the sharing was painful and embarrassing, but it brought him significant relief. He realized that he was still thinking as an adolescent rather than as an adult. Both he and his wife were involved in the therapy, and both learned to understand his problem and to alter their expectations. Eventually, he was able to approach sex without anxiety and to enjoy the experience. His wife played a major role in the treatment by recognizing how she had worsened the problem by her demands on him. Working together, they developed a healthy and rewarding sexual relationship.

This study is courtesy of David M. McLendon, Ph.D.

---

a small amount of fluid is released from the bulbourethral glands. The testes also are enlarged by vascular congestion and are pressed against the body by contraction of the cremaster muscles and the dartos muscle.

ORGASMIC PHASE

Orgasm is a highly pleasurable, involuntary response to sexual stimulation. In the male, orgasm is mediated by sympathetic nervous impulses that emanate from the lumbar portions of the spinal cord. First, contraction of the musculature of the epididymis, vas deferens, and ampullae forces sperm into the urethra. Next, muscular contraction in the prostate and seminal vesicles forces fluids from these glands, which flushes the sperm down the penile urethra to the outside. During this time, the external urethral sphincter (see Chapter 45, Figure 45-2), located in the pelvic diaphragm, relaxes because the frequency of somatic motor impulses traveling to it over the pudendal nerve decreases. Sympathetic and somatic motor stimulation cause rhythmic contractions of the urethra and perineal musculature, which expel the semen. In addition, sympathetic nerve stimulation causes the internal urethral sphincter (see Chapter 45, Figure 45-2) to contract, which prevents retrograde ejaculation of semen into the bladder. Orgasm is an intense physiological response—this is indicated by striking increases in heart rate, blood pressure, and respiratory rate.

REFRACTORY AND RESOLUTION PHASES

Immediately after orgasm, men find further sexual stimulation physically unpleasant or even painful. This phase, which lasts for a few minutes, is called the refractory phase. It is followed by the resolution phase, during which the man can become ready for more sexual excitement but may go back to the prestimulated stage.

FEMALE SEXUAL FUNCTION

The female reproductive system serves the following functions: (1) production of ova, (2) transport of fertilized ova to the uterus, (3) development of the fertilized ovum from zygote up to the time of birth, and (4) sexual activity. The female reproductive system is located partly inside and partly outside the pelvic cavity (Figures 64-4 and 64-5). The external female genitalia are the mons pubis, labia ma-

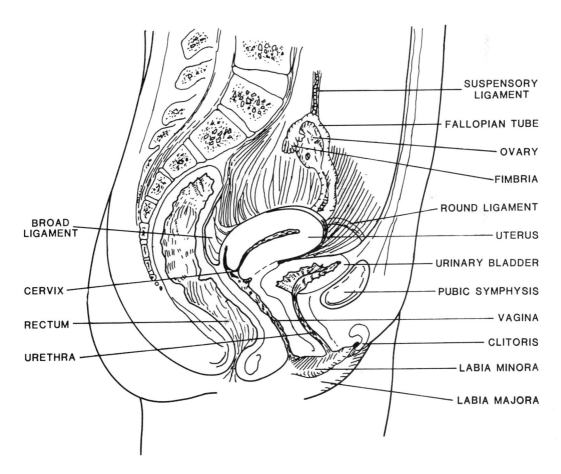

Figure 64-4. Median section of the female pelvis.

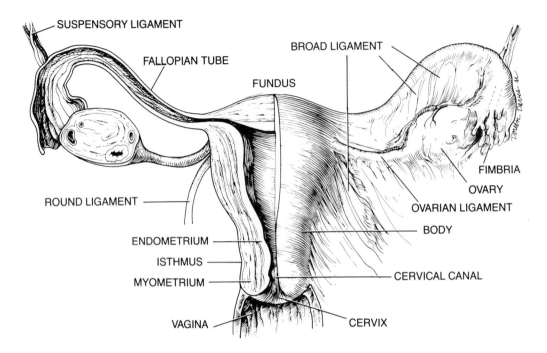

Figure 64-5. Structures of the female reproductive system seen from behind. The posterior walls of the vagina, the left side of the uterus, the left uterine tube, and the entire left broad ligament have been removed.

jora and labia minora, clitoris, and vaginal opening, which collectively are called the vulva. The internal genitalia are the ovaries, fallopian tubes, uterus, and vagina. Despite obvious anatomical differences between female and male sexual anatomy, most parts of the two reproductive systems are functionally and/or developmentally similar.

Functional Anatomy

MONS PUBIS AND LABIA

The *mons pubis* is an elevated layer of fatty tissue that overlies the symphysis pubis. The *labia majora* are two elongated and elevated folds of skin that correspond developmentally to the male scrotum; the mons and outer surface of the labia majora become covered with hair at puberty. The *labia minora,* two folds of skin encompassed by the labia majora, enclose the urethral and vaginal openings and cover the clitoris (prepuce of the clitoris).

CLITORIS

The *clitoris* is analogous developmentally to the male penis, and, because of its copious innervation, the clitoris is a major focus of sexual stimulation. The clitoris contains two cords of erectile tissue (corposa cavernosa, but no corpus spongiosum) that are engorged with blood during sexual excitement.

VAGINA

The *vagina* is a hollow tube that extends from the vaginal vestibule to the cervix. During sexual intercourse, the vagina serves as a receptacle for the penis, and at term, as the birth canal. Because of elastic tissue and redundant folds of mucosa, the vagina is capable of appreciable contraction or expansion during intercourse and birth. During sexual excitement, the vaginal mucosa secretes a fluid that is important for lubrication during coitus. The bilaterally paired *Bartholin's glands* empty into an area just inside the vestibule of the vagina; during sexual excitement, these glands produce a small amount of mucoid secretion that helps to lubricate the vestibule.

OVARIES

The two *ovaries,* the female gonads, 2–3 cm long, are located on either side of the uterus (Figure 64-5). These glands have dual functions—to produce ova and to secrete the female sex hormones estrogen and progesterone (see Chapter 63).

UTERUS

The nongravid *uterus* is a thick, muscular, pear-shaped organ about 8 cm long (Figure 64-5). The uterus receives two fallopian tubes from above and opens into the vagina below. Its layers, from outside to inside, are a fibrous *perimetrium,* a muscular *myometrium,* and a glandular *endometrium.* The muscular myometrium expels the fetus at birth; the glandular endometrium proliferates cyclically (see Chapter 63) in preparation for implantation of a fertilized ovum, and then sloughs during the menses if fertilization does not occur.

FALLOPIAN TUBES

The *fallopian tubes,* about 10 cm long, extend between each ovary and the uterus. The ovarian ends are covered with *fimbria,* which cling to the ovary and catch the released ovum. After capture, the ovum is directed down the tube. If fertilization occurs, it usually does so in the upper part of the fallopian tube. Unlike sperm, ova are not mobile; numerous beating cilia on the inner surface of the fallopian tubes transport the fertilized ovum to the uterus for implantation.

Female Sex Act

EXCITEMENT PHASE

Women are aroused sexually by various things; visual, olfactory, verbal, and tactile cues are especially important. The first response to sexual stimulation is lubrication of the vagina by a transudate from the richly vascular mucosa; lubrication is the functional counterpart of erection in the male and is mediated by parasympathetic nerve stimulation that passes from the sacral cord through the pelvic nerve. Parasympathetic nerve stimulation also causes engorgement of the vagina, the labia minora, the labia majora, and the corpora cavernosa of the clitoris.

PLATEAU PHASE

In the plateau phase, the vascular congestion of vagina, clitoris, and labia continue, the breasts increase in size because of congestion, and Bartholin's glands produce a few drops of mucoid secretion that lubricates the vaginal vestibule. In addition, uterine contractions usually occur during this phase.

ORGASMIC PHASE

In the woman, orgasm is a highly pleasurable, involuntary response to sexual stimulation, mediated by sympathetic neural impulses that emanate from the lumbar portions of the spinal cord. During orgasm, the uterus and the outer third of the vagina contract rhythmically, which may aid the transport of sperm during intercourse, and thereby, increase the probability of fertilization. Copulation in animals causes the posterior pituitary gland to release oxytocin, which increases uterine contraction and, thereby, may enhance the transport of sperm; whether this also occurs in human females is not known. Female orgasm is a very intense experience that causes striking increases in heart rate, blood pressure, and respiratory rate.

RESOLUTION PHASE

Unlike men, women do not reach a refractory phase after orgasm. If stimulation continues, most women can experience successive orgasms. The resolution phase consists of disgorgement of blood from the genitalia and a return to the resting state.

ABNORMALITIES OF SEXUAL FUNCTION

Male

Impotence, or the inability to achieve an erection, usually is caused by psychic factors, but diseases such as diabetes, alcoholism, syphilis, vascular occlusive diseases (e.g., aneurysms or arteriosclerosis), neurological disorders, and some drugs also may cause it. Other disorders, such as premature ejaculation, retarded ejaculation, and sexual anhedonia (lack of pleasure during orgasm) generally are caused by mental disorders.

Female

Female functional disorders include frigidity (inability to experience sexual pleasure), dyspareunia (painful coitus), and vaginismus (spasm of the vagina). Analogous to impotence in males, frigidity usually is caused by psychic factors, but physical diseases such as infections of the reproductive tract, diabetes, neurological disorders, and drugs also may cause it. Dyspareunia may be caused by psychic factors, infections, or anatomical abnormalities of the vagina or introitus. Vaginismus usually is secondary to dyspareunia.

STUDY OUTLINE

GENERAL BACKGROUND Pair-bonding, based on shared sexual activity, is essential to human development and survival.

MALE SEXUAL FUNCTION

FUNCTIONAL ANATOMY

PENIS Organ for copulation, contains urethra and erectile tissue; highly sensitive to tactile stimulation.

SCROTUM Pouch that contains testes.

TESTES Produce sperm and androgens.

EPIDIDYMIS, VAS DEFERENS, AND SEMINAL VESICLES Transport, store, and activate sperm; contribute seminal fluid to semen.

URETHRA AND PROSTATE Urethra transports sperm and excretes urine.

Prostate adds alkaline fluid to ejaculate; neutralizes acidity of vagina.

BULBOURETHRAL (COWPER'S) GLANDS Add alkaline fluid to urethra during intercourse (before ejaculation).

SEMEN Sixty percent from seminal vesicles, 20% from prostate, and 20% from vas deferens and bulbourethral glands.

Contains sperm released from storage in vas deferens—approximately 400 million sperm in approximately 4 ml of semen.

MALE SEX ACT

EXCITEMENT PHASE Erection through parasympathetic neural activity—engorgement because of increased blood flow and partial occlusion of venous drainage.

PLATEAU PHASE Slight additional enlargement of glans penis and release of fluid from bulbourethral glands.

Testes are congested and pulled against body.

ORGASMIC PHASE Highly pleasurable, involuntary response mediated by sympathetic neural activity.

Sperm are forced into urethra from epididymis and vas deferens.

Fluid forced from seminal vesicles and prostate flushes sperm through urethra.

External urethral sphincter relaxes, rhythmic urethral and perineal contractions expel sperm.

Internal urethral sphincter contracts, prevents retrograde movement of semen into bladder.

Increased heart rate, blood pressure, and respiration.

REFRACTORY AND RESOLUTION PHASES Further sexual stimulation undesirable immediately after orgasm—gradual return to normal.

FEMALE SEXUAL FUNCTION Produce ova, transport fertilized ova to uterus, support development of fertilized ovum until birth, and sexual activity.

FUNCTIONAL ANATOMY

MONS PUBIS AND LABIA Mons pubis—layer of fatty tissue that overlies symphysis pubis; covered with hair after puberty.

Labia majora—elevated and elongated folds of skin on either side of vaginal opening; covered with hair after puberty.

Labia minora—two folds of skin encompassed by labia majora; enclose urethral and vaginal openings and cover clitoris.

CLITORIS Major focus of sexual stimulation; contains erectile tissue.

VAGINA Receptacle for penis during sexual intercourse, birth canal during delivery of fetus.

During sexual excitement, mucosa and glands at vaginal vestibule secrete lubricating fluid.

OVARIES Produce ova and secrete estrogen and progesterone.

UTERUS Thick-walled, muscular organ.

Endometrium proliferates and sloughs cyclically.

Supports fetus during development; expels it at birth.

FALLOPIAN TUBES Extend between uterus and ovaries on each side.

Capture released ovum.

Site of fertilization of ovum.

Transport ovum to uterus.

FEMALE SEX ACT

EXCITEMENT PHASE Secretion of lubricant; engorgement of vagina, labia, and clitoris.

PLATEAU PHASE Congestion and lubrication; uterine contractions.

ORGASMIC PHASE Highly pleasurable, involuntary response mediated by sympathetic neural activity.

Uterus and outer vagina contract rhythmically, may aid transport of sperm.

Increased heart rate, blood pressure, and respiration.

RESOLUTION PHASE No refractory phase in females.

Disgorgement of blood from genitalia and return to resting state.

ABNORMALITIES OF SEXUAL FUNCTION

MALE Impotence—lack of erection; usually

caused by psychic factors; also may be caused by organic disease or drugs.

Premature or retarded ejaculation or lack of pleasure during orgasm—usually caused by mental disorders.

FEMALE   Frigidity—lack of sexual pleasure; usually caused by psychic factors; also may be caused by organic disease or drugs.

Dyspareunia—painful coitus; caused by psychic factors, infections, or anatomical abnormalities.

Vaginismus—spasm of the vagina; usually caused by painful coitus.

BIBLIOGRAPHY

Adler, N.T. 1981. *Neuroendocrinology of Reproduction: Physiology and Behavior.* New York: Plenum Press.

Dickinson, R.L. 1949. *Atlas of Human Sex Anatomy* (2nd ed.). Baltimore: Williams and Wilkins.

Hamilton, D., and Naftolin, F. (eds.). 1982. *Reproductive Function in Men.* Cambridge, Massachusetts: MIT Press.

Katchadourian, H.A., and Lunde, D. 1975. *Fundamentals of Human Sexuality* (2nd ed.). New York: Holt, Rinehart, and Winston.

Kinsey, A.C.; Pomeroy, W.B.; and Martin, C.E. 1948. *Sexual Behavior in the Human Male.* Philadelphia: Saunders.

Kinsey, A.C.; Pomeroy, W.B.; Martin, C.E., et al. 1953. *Sexual Behavior in the Human Female.* Philadelphia: Saunders.

Marberger, H. 1974. The mechanisms of ejaculation. In *Basic Life Sciences.* Volume 4B. Physiology and Genetics of Reproduction. Edited by E.M. Countinho and F. Fuchs. New York: Plenum Press.

Masters, W.H., and Johnson, V.E. 1966. *Human Sexual Response.* Boston: Little, Brown and Co.

Masters, W.H., and Johnson, V.E. 1970. *Human Sexual Inadequacy.* Boston, Little, Brown and Co.

Pritchard, J.A., and MacDonald, P.D. 1980. *Williams Obstetrics* (16th ed.). New York: Appleton-Century-Crofts.

Sadock, B.J.; Kaplan, H.I.; and Freedman, A.M. 1976. *The Sexual Experience.* Baltimore: Williams and Wilkins.

Schulz, D.A. 1979. *Human Sexuality.* Englewood Cliffs, New Jersey: Prentice-Hall.

Sherfey, M.J. 1972. *The Nature and Evolution of Female Sexuality.* New York: Random House.

65

Pregnancy and Parturition

CHAPTER CONTENTS

PREGNANCY

Development of Follicles and Ovulation

Beginning during the fetal life of female humans, primary oocytes develop from the germinal epithelium that forms the outer surface of the ovaries. Carrying a coating of epitheloid cells, these *primordial ova* migrate inward from the germinal epithelium and form *primordial follicles* (Figures 65-1 and 65-2). At birth, the ovaries contain nearly 1 million primary oocytes, but most eventually degenerate, and only about 400 or 500 of these oocytes develop into follicles that are expelled during ovulation. The *primary oocyte* contains 46 chromosomes (44 + XX), the same number of chromosomes that somatic cells contain. The first meiotic (reduction) division occurs during maturation of the

follicle, which produces *secondary oocytes* that have 23 chromosomes (22 + X). The secondary oocyte, called an *ovum* after it is expelled from the ovary, is caught by the fimbriated end of one fallopian tube and directed into the tube, where it can be fertilized by sperm. After fertilization, the ovum is called a *zygote*. The zygote implants into the wall of the uterus and develops into an embryo and a placenta.

FOLLICLES

Hormonal regulation of the development of the follicles and ovulation are discussed in Chapter 63. After the last day of the menses, increasing plasma levels of FSH stimulate the theca cells and granulosa cells to proliferate. The granulosa layer covers the ovum. The theca interna cells, immediately outside the gran-

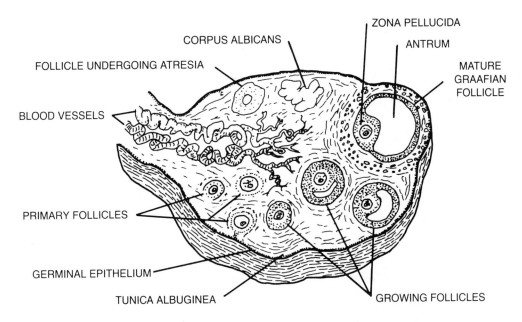

Figure 65-1. Section of an ovary showing follicles in various stages of development.

ulosa layer, secrete follicular fluid and estrogen. The theca externa is a connective tissue sheath around the developing follicle (Figure 65-2). Liquor folliculi accumulate and form the antrum of the follicle as the primary oocyte undergoes the first state of meiosis and develops into a secondary oocyte in a mature graafian follicle (see Figures 65-1 and 65-2). FSH causes the follicle to develop, but LH is necessary for the production of estrogen by theca interna cells.

OVULATION

At the beginning of a menstrual cycle, approximately 10–20 primary follicles begin to mature, but only one eventually is ovulated—the rest degenerate and become atretic follicles. The mechanism by which only a single follicle matures is unknown, but physiologists believe that one follicle grows and matures a little faster than the others and secretes more estrogen into its liquor folliculi. The estrogen has two effects—by local action, it enhances growth of the follicle, and by systemic action, it feeds back on the anterior pituitary and hypothalamus to inhibit the secretion of FSH (see Figure 63-1). Because of the decreased concentration of FSH, all of the follicles degenerate except the largest one, which grows under the influence of the estrogen it produces. As described in Chapter 63, the steadily increasing

concentration of estradiol in the serum causes a sudden burst of LH, and ovulation occurs; subsequently, the corpus luteum is formed from the remnants of the follicle.

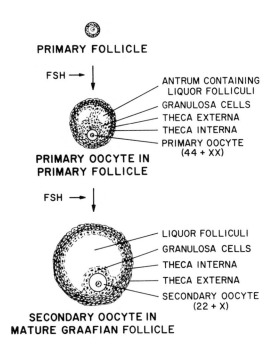

Figure 65-2. Development of mature graafian follicle.

Fertilization

During coitus, about 4 ml of semen, which normally contains about 100 million sperm per milliliter, is ejaculated. After the sperm are deposited in the vagina, they must overcome the obstacle formed by the mucus that fills the cervical canal. The sperm that first make contact with the mucus bore through it with the help of enzymes released from a small cap on their heads, called the *acrosome*. This action clears a path for other sperm. After 1–1.5 hours, the sperm reach the ovum in the ampullae of the oviduct (fallopian tube). This rate of transport is much faster than can be explained by the flagellar action of the sperm and has been attributed to a dual cilliary action by the fallopian tubes. Thus, one set of cilia move ova down the oviduct while another set appears to help move sperm up the oviduct.

Several sperm reach the ovum and penetrate a layer of adherent follicular cells, the *corona radiata* (Figure 65-3). The acrosomal enzymes of several sperm then act on the nearly impervious *zona pellucida* (see Figure 65-2), which was produced earlier by the follic-

ular cells, and one sperm enters the cytoplasm of the ovum. After this entry, the zona pellucida suddenly becomes very impermeable and no more sperm can enter. The ovum undergoes the second meiotic division, and the genomes of sperm and ovum fuse.

The developing placenta produces human chorionic gonadotropin (HCG), a glycoprotein that has a molecular weight of 30,000 daltons; HCG has LH activity and, thereby, maintains the corpus luteum (see Figure 63-5). The corpus luteum is important for the developing embryo because it produces progesterone, which aids the continuation of pregnancy by maintaining a rich secretory endometrium and inhibiting uterine contractions. After a few weeks, however, the corpus luteum no longer is needed because the developing placenta begins to secrete progesterone.

Implantation of the Fertilized Ovum

After fertilization, the ovum becomes a zygote, which undergoes successive mitotic cleavages to form *blastomeres*. Fluid accumulates among

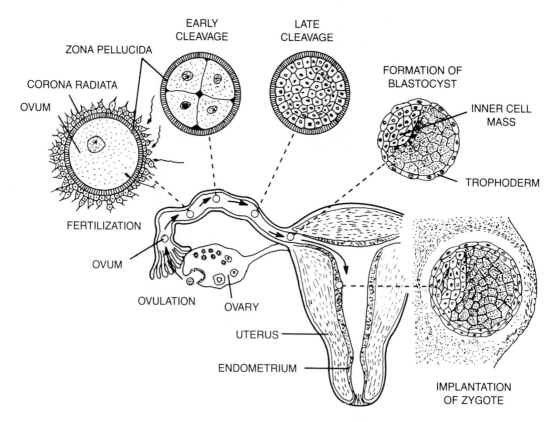

Figure 65-3.   Fertilization of an ovum within the uterine tube—cleavage and implantation of the zygote.

the blastomeres, and the aggregate, called the *blastocyst* (Figure 65-3), implants into the endometrium of the uterus. The fetal membranes and placenta are formed from a portion called the *trophoblast* (or *trophoderm*), and the embryo develops from a portion called the *inner cell mass* (Figure 65-3).

Placenta

The continued secretion of progesterone is important in maintaining a rich secretory endometrium, or *decidua,* which provides nutrients for the developing embryo. The decidua is the sole source of nutrients for the embryo for about the first week and continues to supply some of the nutrients for the developing embryo for about 3 months. The trophoblast invades the endometrium gradually, by sending

in fingers of vascular tissue that become the chorionic villi of the mature placenta (Figure 65-4).

CIRCULATION IN THE MATURE PLACENTA

Branches of the single fetal umbilical vein and the paired umbilical arteries grow into the chorionic villi and form the fetal side of the fetal-maternal circulation. Continued erosion of the endometrium by the chorionic villi forms pools of maternal blood that bathe the villi (Figure 65-4). Thus, deoxygenated blood from the fetal umbilical artery flows into the capillaries of the fetal side of the placenta, is oxygenated, and returns to the fetus through the single umbilical vein. A total surface area of about 10 m^2 is available for the exchange of nutrients and waste products between mother

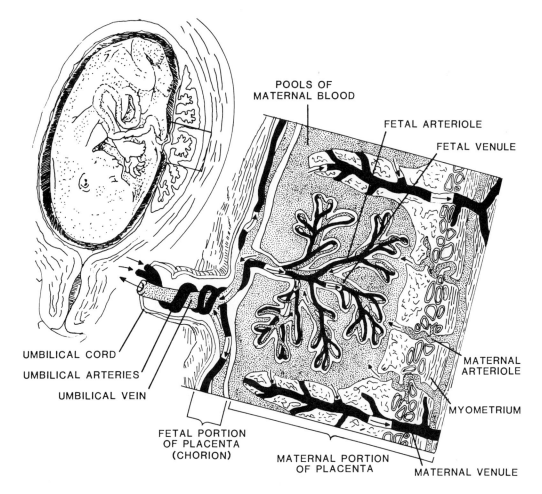

POOLS OF
MATERNAL BLOOD

FETAL ARTERIOLE

FETAL VENULE

UMBILICAL CORD

UMBILICAL ARTERIES

UMBILICAL VEIN

MATERNAL
ARTERIOLE

MYOMETRIUM

FETAL PORTION
OF PLACENTA
(CHORION)

MATERNAL PORTION
OF PLACENTA

MATERNAL VENULE

Figure 65-4.   Vascular arrangement of the placenta. Arrows indicate the direction of blood flow. One chorionic villus is shown enlarged.

and fetus. The "placental barrier" is several cells thick (fetal capillary endothelium covered by cells from the trophoblast) and usually permits little or no mixing of fetal and maternal blood. Generally, substances that have molecular weights of less than 500 daltons can cross the placenta readily.

NUTRITION OF THE FETUS

Ultimately, the diet of the mother is the source of all nutrients for the developing fetus. Triglycerides do not cross the placenta, but glycerol does. Glucose and amino acids cross the placenta readily. Glucose appears to cross by facilitated (carrier-mediated) diffusion and active transport.

Glucose is the major nutrient for the growing fetus, but maternal plasma levels of glucose vary. These fluctuations are modified by *human placental lactogen* (HPL), (also called *human chorionic somatomammotropin*), a protein that has a molecular weight of about 38,000 daltons. Produced in the placenta and found only in the maternal circulation, HPL blocks the use of glucose and favors the use of fatty acids by the mother.

GROWTH OF THE FETUS

Many factors can either retard or accelerate growth of the fetus. In maternal diabetes, because of the high concentration of glucose in the maternal blood, the fetus usually is larger than normal; however, if the diabetes has damaged the mother's vascular system appreciably, the blood vessels of the uterus also may be affected and the fetus may be small. Maternal malnutrition affects the outcome of pregnancy less than might be expected. During the winter of 1944–45, when a famine occurred in an area of the Netherlands, the average daily caloric intake of the population was as low as 450 kcal/day. Surprisingly, the mean birth weight of infants born during this time was only 8 ounces less than normal, and no abnormal intellectual impairment was detected in the children as they grew up. The effects of maternal malnutrition on the offspring appear to be related to the length of gestation and the ratio of fetal weight to maternal weight. Thus, in rats, in which gestation lasts only 21 days and the total fetal weight is 25% of maternal weight, materal malnutrition appears to have more deleterious effects than in the human, in which gestation lasts for approximately 266 days and fetal weight is only 5% of maternal weight.

In general, supplementation of the maternal diet with vitamins and minerals other than iron and folate, which are needed for maternal and fetal production of erythrocytes, has not been proven to be necessary. The increased requirement for vitamins and minerals in pregnant women can be met by any reasonable diet that supplies adequate calories and protein.

MATERNAL TOBACCO SMOKING

The effects on the fetus of tobacco smoking by the mother are clear. Mothers who smoke tobacco have smaller infants and an increased incidence of miscarriage and perinatal deaths. Some studies indicate that children of mothers who smoke have lower I.Q.s than normal. It has been estimated that nearly 5000 fetuses and infants die in the United States each year because their mothers smoke tobacco. These deaths might be caused by increased maternal and fetal levels of carbon monoxide and the vasoconstrictor action of nicotine, combined with reduced maternal appetite and nutrition.

MATERNAL DRUG USE

The effects on the fetus of excessive intake of ethanol by the mother are appreciable. Chronic maternal alcoholism may lead to alcohol withdrawal symptoms in the infant, growth retardation, a variety of birth defects, and a decreased I.Q. Addiction of the mother to narcotics, barbiturates, or amphetamine derivatives causes postpartum drug withdrawal, low birth weight, fetal distress, and a low I.Q. in the infant. The use of any drugs by the mother generally is discouraged because many drugs affect developing fetuses in a variety of ways.

PRODUCTION OF HORMONES BY THE PLACENTA

Human chorionic gonadotropin produced by the placenta maintains the corpus luteum, which, in turn, produces the progesterone that maintains the early pregnancy (Figure 65-5). Later, the placenta produces its own progesterone, and the corpus luteum no longer is needed. Progesterone promotes the development of decidual cells in the endometrium for nourishment of the early embryo, depresses uterine contractility to prevent early expulsion of the fetus, and prepares the breasts for lactation by increasing alveolar growth. Human placental lactogen, which occurs only in maternal plasma (Figure 65-6) and antagonizes

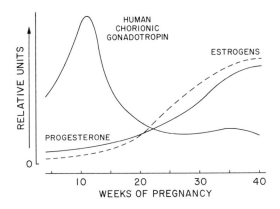

Figure 65-5. Relative concentrations of human chorionic gonadotropin (HCG), estrogen, and progesterone in the maternal blood during pregnancy.

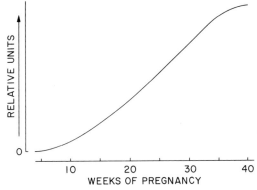

Figure 65-6. Relative concentration of human placental lactogen (HPL) in the maternal blood during pregnancy.

the action of insulin in the mother, spares glucose and amino acids for the fetus. In fact, the functional condition of the placenta is associated with the level of placental lactogen, and decreased levels of HPL in maternal plasma have been associated with syndromes of "placental insufficiency."

ESTROGENS IN PREGNANCY

The production of estrogen each day by a pregnant woman near delivery may exceed the total amount of estrogen produced by the ovaries of a nonpregnant woman in 3 years. This high rate of production of estrogen terminates abruptly at delivery; therefore, it is related to the fetal-placental unit. The predominant estrogen in nongravid women is estradiol; the predominant estrogen in pregnant women is estriol. The placenta does not have the enzymes 17-α-hydroxylase and desmolase (see Figure 63-6), which are necessary for the conversion of progesterone to androstenedione. However, the placenta is a rich source of the enzymes necessary for the conversion of C-19 steroids (dehydroepiandrosterone, androstenedione, and testosterone) to estrogens and the conversion of cholesterol to progesterone (see Figure 63-6). Thus, the placenta can convert cholesterol to progesterone efficiently. Progesterone is shuttled to the maternal and fetal adrenal glands for conversion of dehydroepiandrosterone or androstenedione, which, in turn, are sent back to the placenta for conversion to estrogens (mostly estriol). The large size of the fetal adrenals makes them a rich source of these hormone precursors. The no-

tion of this arrangement is supported by the observation that mothers of anencephalic fetuses (congenitally deformed fetuses that lack cerebral hemispheres), which have no adrenal cortices, have diminished levels of estriol in their blood and urine.

The high concentration of estrogen in pregnant women serves several purposes. Estrogen increases the vascularity of the endometrium, promotes the development of the ductal system of the breasts (in the human, estrogen also causes some lobular growth), and maintains the decidua that is needed for early nutrition of the embryo.

Maternal Adaptations to Pregnancy

Pregnancy lasts for approximately 266 days, and during this time, truly remarkable physiological and anatomical adaptations that accommodate the growing fetus take place in the mother.

REPRODUCTIVE ORGANS

In the nonpregnant woman, the uterus weighs about 70 g, and the volume of the uterine cavity is about 10 ml. At term, the pregnant uterus weighs about 1100 g and contains a volume of about 5 liters. This phenomenal increase in size of the uterus is caused by hypertrophy of the smooth muscle cells, a marked increase in the content of collagen and elastin in the myometrium, and hyperplasia of the endometrium. Early in pregnancy, the uterus increases in size because of the actions of estrogen and progesterone. Later in pregnancy, it increases because of pressure exerted by the growing fetus.

Other reproductive organs also change markedly. In preparation for distention during labor, the vagina and vulva increase in vascularity, secretory activity, and size.

GAIN OF BODY WEIGHT

Perhaps the most notable change during pregnancy is the gain of body weight by the mother, which is 11 kg on the average. Only about 1 kg is gained during the first trimester (3 months), but about 5 kg are gained during each of the last two trimesters. At term, the average fetus weighs 3.5 kg, the placenta weighs 0.7 kg, the amniotic fluid weighs 1 kg, and the uterus weighs 1 kg. Thus, the uterus and its contents account for a little more than half of the weight that is gained. The weight of the breasts increases by about 0.5 kg, and the blood volume increases by 1.5 liters. About 2.7 kg of fat are added, and some fluid is retained, mostly in the tissues below the uterus, in which venous flow is compromised somewhat by the increasing size of the conceptus.

METABOLISM OF NUTRIENTS

The conceptus is rich in protein and accounts for about half of the 1 kg of protein gained during pregnancy; the other 0.5 kg comes from increases in the breasts, plasma proteins, and maternal hemoglobin.

In general, pregnancy is a diabetogenic experience. HPL, estrogen, and progesterone all oppose the effects of insulin on glucose, and an increased glomerular filtration rate (GFR) plus decreased reabsorption may cause glucose to appear in the urine.

Plasma lipids in the mother increase about 40% in later pregnancy, caused in part by increased resistance to the lipid-storing action of insulin. In addition, a "lipostat" in the hypothalamus may be set at a higher level, which allows appetite to be maintained despite increased body stores of fat. This amount of stored fat decreases in later pregnancy because of the increased demands of the conceptus.

CARDIOVASCULAR SYSTEM

The circulation is affected remarkably by pregnancy because 500–1000 ml of blood flows through the placenta each minute. The decrease in peripheral vascular resistance produced by this additional vascular bed causes the cardiac output and the heart rate to in-crease. In later pregnancy, the maternal cardiac output depends strongly on body position. When the mother lies on her side, her resting cardiac output is maximal, but in the supine position, it decreases markedly because the gravid uterus compresses the inferior vena cava. Blood pressure is increased in the veins of the legs, vulva, and hemorrhoidal circulation by the supine position, and varicosities may develop in these areas.

Maternal blood volume increases by about 45%; plasma volume increases more than red cell volume; hence, hematocrit and hemoglobin concentration decrease somewhat. The increased blood volume may reflect, in part, fluid retained because of increased plasma levels of estrogen and aldosterone. Plasma erythropoietin levels also increase, possibly due to an effect of HPL that increases the red cell mass. The extra blood volume fills the additional vascular space created by the pregnancy. At delivery, the mother loses one-half to one-third of this extra blood; thus, it also provides a safety factor against peripartum hemorrhage.

RESPIRATION

The increasing mass of the uterus compromises the downward movement of the diaphragm somewhat, but increased minute ventilation, blood hemoglobin, and cardiac output actually diminish the a-$\bar{\text{v}}$ O_2 difference. Increased minute ventilation is related to progesterone, which increases respiratory effort by a direct effect on the respiratory center in the brain.

GASTROINTESTINAL TRACT

Increased levels of progesterone cause generalized relaxation of smooth muscle, including the smooth muscle of the gastrointestinal tract. The rates of gastric emptying and intestinal transit are diminished, which often contributes to constipation. "Heartburn" caused by gastroesophageal reflux is common. Gastroesophageal reflux appears to be related to the altered position of the stomach, which causes increased intragastric pressure and decreased tone of the lower esophageal sphincter.

Toxemia of Pregnancy (Eclampsia)

Toxemia, a serious syndrome that may occur during the last trimester of pregnancy, is characterized by hypertension, generalized edema, convulsions, and/or coma. When only hypertension and edema occur, the syndrome is called *preeclampsia*. The cause of toxemia is unknown, but it appears to be related to vasospasm and damage to vascular endothelium. Vasospasm causes hypertension by increasing peripheral vascular resistance, and vasospasm plus endothelial damage can occlude arteries that supply the brain, which causes neurological symptoms. The generalized edema reflects decreased plasma oncotic pressure caused by excessive loss of plasma proteins through the glomerular capillaries (which are damaged by deposition of fibrin or immune complexes). Ultimately, eclampsia is related to disordered function of the placenta because, if the damage has not progressed too far, delivery of the placenta promptly reverses the symptoms. The fetus is not involved necessarily, since eclampsia has occurred in the absence of a fetus (in cases of *hydatidiform mole*, a tumor of placental origin).

Nausea and Vomiting

Some degree of nausea and vomiting occurs in about 50% of women during the first trimester of pregnancy and in some cases persists until delivery. Nausea and vomiting are more common in the morning (hence, the term *morning sickness*) and can be initiated by emotional disturbances or the smell of food. Occasionally, the nausea and vomiting are so severe and intractable that therapeutic abortion is necessary. Since this condition is most common during the first trimester, when HCG levels are highest, it may be caused by HCG or some other product released from the invading trophoblast.

PARTURITION

Initiation of Labor

Normally, after about 270 days of growth, the uterus begins to expel the conceptus in the process of labor and delivery. Beginning in the first trimester of pregnancy, the uterus undergoes episodic, slow, irregular contractions called *Braxton-Hicks contractions*. The intensity and frequency of contractions increase in the later months of pregnancy. As labor begins, the contractions change in character by becoming more painful, more frequent, more intense, and of longer duration. After an hour in which contractions have occurred every 5 minutes and lasted for 1 minute each, it is time to go to the hospital.

Several theories are available to explain why the ineffective Braxton-Hicks contractions become effective labor contractions. Each theory involves a positive feedback in which a contraction sets off a train of events that causes a stronger contraction. Thus, the intensity of contraction tends to build.

RELEASE OF OXYTOCIN

Oxytocin often is given to women to initiate labor, and endogenously released oxytocin may be involved in the physiological initiation of labor. According to this theory, impingement of the head of the growing fetus on the cervix activates neural pathways to the neurohypophysis, causing the release of oxytocin, which increases uterine contractions and, hence, further stimulation of the cervix. Despite the attractiveness of this theory, increased plasma levels of oxytocin normally are found only while the fetus is being delivered. Thus, the role of oxytocin may be to facilitate contraction of the uterus after delivery, which compresses endometrial vessels and decreases blood loss.

FETAL CORTISOL

Recent work in animals has indicated that the function of the hypothalamic-pituitary-adrenal axis may be important for the initiation of parturition. In pregnant sheep, adrenalectomy, hypophysectomy, or transection of the hypophysial-portal vessels of the fetus causes prolonged gestation. The counterpart of this circumstance in the human is the anencephalic fetus, in which the brain and adrenal glands fail to develop properly and gestation is markedly prolonged. Although these observations suggest that fetal cortisol has some role in the initiation of parturition, fetuses that have diminished cortisol production because of enzymatic defects do not undergo prolonged gestation, and injection of corticosteroids into the amniotic fluid does not initiate labor.

PROGESTERONE WITHDRAWAL

Progesterone decreases uterine contractility and is used to maintain pregnancy when spontaneous abortion is threatened. By contrast, estrogens increase myometrial contractility and are used to induce abortion. Some investigators have suggested that a decrease in the ratio of progesterone to estrogen may be a factor in the initiation of labor.

PROSTAGLANDINS

Prostaglandins $F_2\alpha$ and E_2 evoke strong myometrial contractions. Glycerophospholipids of the fetal membranes contain arachidonic acid, which serves as a precursor for the synthesis of prostaglandin. Investigators have shown that the amniotic fluid of women in labor contains higher concentrations of arachidonic acid than the amniotic fluid of women not in labor. In addition, lysosomes in the fetal membranes contain the enzyme phospholipase, which cleaves arachidonic acid from the glycerophospholipids. After arachidonic acid is released from the fetal membrane, prostaglandin synthetase, which is present in the fetal membranes and the decidua, generates prostaglandins from arachidonic acid. The prostaglandins then enhance myometrial contractions (Figure 65-7). This theory has many correlates, including the following observations:

1. Amniotomy (rupture of the amnion), infection, or instillation of hypertonic NaCl solutions into the amnion all may initiate labor, possibly by activating the phospholipase and prostaglandin synthetase in the fetal amnion.
2. Progesterone binds avidly to lysosomes in fetal membranes, and this may be the mechanism by which it inhibits myometrial contractility (i.e., by preventing release of phospholipase and subsequent synthesis of prostaglandins).
3. Aspirin and indomethacin, both inhibitors of prostaglandin synthetase, prolong gestation.

Labor and Delivery

The process of labor and delivery usually is divided into three stages. The *first stage* begins when uterine contractions reach sufficient intensity, frequency, and duration to begin to cause dilation and *effacement* (thinning) of the cervix. The first stage ends when the cervix is dilated enough (usually 10 cm) that the fetal head can pass through. This stage may last for 8–24 hours in the first pregnancy, but due to stretching of the maternal tissues, it is much shorter after multiple pregnancies. The *second stage of labor* begins when the cervix is fully dilated and ends when the child is delivered. *The third stage,* delivery of the placenta, usually lasts about 15 minutes.

FIRST STAGE

The pressure of the fetal head causes dilation and effacement of the cervix. When the amnion is ruptured, the amniotic fluid rushes out, and the loss of buoyancy causes the fetal head to exert even more pressure on the cervix. After the head enters the birth canal, pressures on the cranium are so great during uterine contractions that Cushing's reaction (increased arterial pressure—see Chapter 16) is evoked, which increases fetal vagal tone and decreases the fetal heart rate. Other possible causes of fetal bradycardia during contractions, all of which are abnormal, include uteroplacental vascular insufficiency and compression of the umbilical

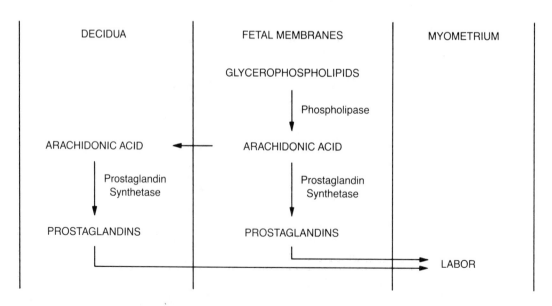

Figure 65-7. Pathways by which prostaglandins may be generated in vivo for the induction of labor.

CLINICAL CORRELATION
65.1   Spinal Anesthesia During Delivery

CASE REPORT

The Patient: A 24-year-old woman, gravida 1 (first pregnancy).

Reason for Admission: Spontaneous labor.

History: The patient had received excellent prenatal care, had gained only 10 kg, and had experienced an uneventful prenatal course.

Clinical Examination: At the time of admission, all physical findings were normal, including arterial pressure of 110/60 mm Hg (normal, 90–140/60–90 mm Hg). Four hours after admission, however, the arterial pressure was 140/105 mm Hg. Six and one-half hours after admission, the uterus was contracting every 3–4 minutes (characteristic of active labor), and the patient was sedated (given sedative medication). Two hours after active labor had begun, the uterine cervix was dilating satisfactorily, and other vital signs were normal, but the arterial pressure had increased to 150/105 mm Hg. Antihypertensive medication was given, and the arterial pressure decreased to 130/90 mm Hg. Four and one-half hours after active labor had begun, the arterial pressure had increased slightly, to 135/95 mm Hg. Her sedative medication was renewed, as labor continued, and 4 hours later she was given another injection of antihypertensive medication. Twelve hours after active labor had begun, the amniotic membrane was ruptured surgically (a painless procedure that eventually enhances labor). The arterial pressure had increased again, to 150/105 mm Hg, and she was given another form of antihypertensive medication, along with renewal of her sedation. Twenty-two hours after active labor had begun, a spinal anesthetic was administered.

The blood pressure was 110/60 mm Hg, the heart rate was 85 beats/min, and the respiratory rate was 23/min (normal, 13–17/min). A midline episiotomy (an incision of the perineum and vaginal mucosa to avoid laceration) was performed, and the baby was delivered successfully. The mother did not fare as well. No heart beat could be felt, and cardiac arrest was presumed. External cardiac massage was begun, and oxygen was administered by endotracheal tube. Intravenous fluid (dextrose in saline) was administered. An electrical shock was applied to the chest wall, after which a pulse was felt. Norepinephrine was added to the intravenous infusion, the blood pressure increased to 140/90 mm Hg, and spontaneous breathing resumed. The patient was kept in intensive care for 24 hours, and she eventually recovered without additional untoward events.

Comment: This patient's first difficulty was the onset of hypertension (pre-eclampsia), which was treated adequately. However, the combination of antihypertensive drugs and spinal anesthesia precipitated a hypotensive crisis. Local anesthetic is injected into the spinal fluid in the lumbar segments of the cord. In this case, however, the anesthetic rose too high in the cord—up to the lower thoracic region—and blocked the outflow of sympathetic nervous system activity that provides arteriolar and venous tone and, hence, helps to maintain the cardiac output and the systemic arterial pressure. The prolonged labor (22 hours) also provided considerable additional stress (labor that lasts more than 18 hours is considered high risk). Nevertheless, the good initial condition of the patient, due to good prenatal care, and the prompt and expert resuscitation provided a happy outcome.

cord. By monitoring the patterns of intrauterine pressure and changes of fetal heart rate, the obstetrician can ascertain the cause of fetal bradycardia during contractions and, if need be, intervene to protect the fetus and the mother.

SECOND STAGE

The second stage may last only a few minutes in women who have borne several children, but usually lasts about 1 hour in women who have had no children. In the later parts of this stage, each uterine contraction causes the head of the fetus to distend the mother's perineum more and more. When birth is imminent, local or regional anesthesia is given to the mother, an episiotomy is performed, and the mother is instructed to augment the force of uterine contractions by taking deep breaths and "bearing down" with the abdominal muscles (Valsalva

maneuver). The obstetrician performs various manipulations to aid delivery and to protect the infant and mother; the infant is expelled, and the umbilical cord is clamped and cut.

THIRD STAGE

Usually about 5 minutes after birth, the placenta is delivered when the chorionic villi tear away from the endometrium. This causes bleeding from the open villous sinuses, but the loss of blood usually is kept to a minimum because the uterus contracts rapidly, which closes the villous sinuses and constricts the uterine arterioles. Endogenous oxytocin, released from the neurohypophysis, acts physiologically to cause contraction of the uterus after delivery of the placenta. In addition, oxytocin usually is given intravenously to the mother after delivery of the placenta to augment uterine contractions further.

STUDY OUTLINE

PREGNANCY

DEVELOPMENT OF FOLLICLES AND OVULATION   Almost 1 million primary egg cells in ovaries of female human at birth; 400–500 eventually are expelled during ovulation.

Primary oocyte—46 chromosomes (44 + XX).

Secondary oocyte—23 chromosomes (22 + X).

Expelled from surface of ovary (ovulation), secondary oocyte enters fallopian tube and can be fertilized there.

Ovum is called zygote after fertilization, implants into wall of uterus, develops into embryo and placenta.

FOLLICLES   FSH stimulates theca and granulosa cells to proliferate.

Theca interna cells secrete follicular fluid and estrogen under influence of LH.

Primary oocyte divides (meiosis), develops into secondary oocyte in mature graafian follicle.

OVULATION   Approximately 10–20 follicles begin to mature during each menstrual cycle, but only one eventually is ovulated.

Estradiol produced by follicle stimulates abrupt release of LH, which causes ovulation.

Corpus luteum is formed from remains of follicle.

FERTILIZATION   Sperm contact ovum in fallopian tube.

Ovum becomes impermeable after one sperm enters; sperm and ovum fuse.

Developing placenta produces human chorionic gonadotropin (HCG), which maintains corpus luteum.

Corpus luteum produces progesterone, supports pregnancy during first trimester.

IMPLANTATION OF THE FERTILIZED OVUM   Successive mitotic divisions produce blastomeres; fluid accumulates among blastomeres; aggregate, called blastocyst, implants into endometrium.

Fetal membranes and placenta develop from trophoblast; embryo develops from inner cell mass.

PLACENTA   Progesterone maintains secretory endometrium (decidua), which nourishes embryo initially.

Vascular tissue invades endometrium to form chorionic villi.

CIRCULATION IN THE MATURE PLACENTA   Deoxygenated fetal blood is in capillaries on fetal side of placental barrier, maternal blood is on other side.

Nutrients and wastes exchange; little or no mixing of blood.

NUTRITION OF THE FETUS Obtained solely from mother.

Glucose and amino acids cross placental barrier, triglycerides do not.

Glucose is major nutrient of fetus; human placental lactogen (HPL) in maternal circulation opposes use of glucose, favors use of fatty acids by mother.

GROWTH OF THE FETUS High concentration of glucose in diabetic mother accelerates growth of fetus.

Fetus is highly resistant to effects of maternal malnutrition.

Normally adequate diet provides for both mother and fetus; iron and folate supplement aids production of erythrocytes.

MATERNAL TOBACCO SMOKING Smaller infants, increased incidence of miscarriage and perinatal deaths, possible mental impairment.

Deaths possibly caused by carbon monoxide levels, vasoconstriction, and inadequate nutrition.

MATERNAL DRUG USE Alcohol, narcotics, barbiturates, and amphetamine derivatives.

Symptoms of withdrawal in infant, retarded growth, fetal distress, birth defects, and mental impairment.

PRODUCTION OF HORMONES BY THE PLACENTA Human chorionic gonadotropin maintains corpus luteum in early pregnancy.

Progesterone promotes development of decidua, depresses uterine contractility, and increases growth of alveoli in breasts.

Later, placenta produces progesterone and estrogen.

Human placental lactogen antagonizes action of insulin in mother, spares glucose and amino acids for fetus.

ESTROGENS IN PREGNANCY High rate of production by placenta, mostly estriol.

Increases vascularity of endometrium, promotes development of ductal system and lobules of breasts, and maintains decidua for early nutrition of fetus.

MATERNAL ADAPTATIONS TO PREGNANCY

REPRODUCTIVE ORGANS Increase in size and weight of uterus.

Increase in vascularity, secretory activity, and size of vagina and vulva.

GAIN OF BODY WEIGHT Average is about 11 kg.

Most is in last two trimesters.

About half of increase is by uterus and contents.

Increased blood volume; fluid is retained and body fat is added.

METABOLISM OF NUTRIENTS Approximately 1 kg of protein is gained; half in conceptus (uterus and contents) and half in breasts, plasma proteins, and maternal blood volume.

Placental hormones oppose effects of insulin; GFR is increased, reabsorption is decreased—glucose may appear in urine.

Fat is stored early, used later to supply conceptus.

CARDIOVASCULAR SYSTEM Cardiac output increases to supply placenta.

In supine maternal position, fetus compresses inferior vena cava; increases venous pressure in legs, vulva, and hemorrhoidal vessels.

Blood volume increases significantly; most of gain is lost during and after delivery.

RESPIRATION Stimulated centrally by progesterone; mass of uterus compromises downward movement of diaphragm.

GASTROINTESTINAL TRACT Progesterone decreases smooth muscle activity, contributes to constipation.

Gastroesophageal reflux ("heartburn") is common—position of stomach is altered, increases intragastric pressure; decreased tone of lower esophageal sphincter.

TOXEMIA OF PREGNANCY (ECLAMPSIA) May occur in last trimester—hypertension, generalized edema, convulsions, and/or coma.

Vasospasm and vascular damage cause hypertension and compromise blood supply to brain.

Renal capillary damage permits loss of plasma proteins; decreased plasma oncotic pressure leads to edema.

Causes unknown, but related to placenta.

NAUSEA AND VOMITING Related to human chorionic gonadotropin or other placental hormone.

PARTURITION

INITIATION OF LABOR Several theories, all involve positive feedback, as intensity of uterine contraction builds.

RELEASE OF OXYTOCIN Oxytocin promotes uterine contraction.

In theory, impingement of head of fetus on cervix causes release of oxytocin through neural reflex.

Plasma concentration of oxytocin normally does not increase until fetus is being delivered—too late to initiate contractions.

Main function of oxytocin may be after delivery, as uterine contraction compresses endometrial blood vessels and decreases blood loss.

FETAL CORTISOL   Experimental evidence suggests role of cortisol in parturition, but administration of cortisol does not initiate labor.

PROGESTERONE WITHDRAWAL   Progesterone decreases uterine contraction—progesterone/estrogen ratio may affect initiation of labor.

PROSTAGLANDINS   Certain prostaglandins evoke uterine contractions.

Fetal membranes contain precursors of prostaglandins and enzymes that act on prostaglandins.

Inhibitors of prostaglandins prolong gestation.

LABOR AND DELIVERY

FIRST STAGE   Dilation and thinning (effacement) of cervix by head of fetus, from force of uterine contraction.

Ends when cervix is dilated enough to pass head of fetus.

Lasts 8–24 hours in first pregnancy, less in successive pregnancies.

SECOND STAGE   Fetus is delivered, cord is tied and cut.

Lasts about 1 hour in first pregnancy and a few minutes in successive pregnancies.

THIRD STAGE   Placenta is expelled.

Endogenous oxytocin causes uterine contraction, decreases bleeding; oxytocin also may be administered.

BIBLIOGRAPHY

Adler, N.T. 1981. *Neuroendocrinology of Reproduction: Physiology and Behavior.* New York: Plenum Press.

Baker, T.G. 1963. Quantitative and cytological study of germ cells in human ovaries. *Proc. Roy. Soc. (Biol.)* 158:417.

Boyd, J.D., and Hamilton, W.J. 1970. *The Human Placenta.* Cambridge, England: Heffner.

Fuchs, F. 1977. *Endocrinology of Pregnancy* (2nd ed.). Hagerstown, Maryland: Harper and Row.

Greep, R.O. 1975. Reproductive physiology. Volume 8. *International Review of Physiology.* Baltimore: University Park Press.

Greep, R.O. 1977. Reproductive physiology II. Volume 3. *International Review of Physiology.* Baltimore: University Park Press.

Greep, R.O. 1980. Reproductive physiology III. Volume 22. *International Review of Physiology.* Baltimore: University Park Press.

Katz, R.; Karliner, J.S.; and Resnik, R. 1978. Effects of natural volume overload state (pregnancy) on left ventricular performance in normal human subjects. *Circulation* 58:434.

MacDonald, D.C.; Porter, J.C.; Schwarz, B.E., et al. 1978. Initiation of parturition in the human female. *Sem. Perinatol.* 2:273.

MacDonald, D.C.; Schultz, F.M.; Dunhoelter, J.H., et al. 1974. Initiation of human parturition. I. Mechanism of action of arachidonic acid. *Obstet. Gynecol.* 44:629.

MacDonald, R.R. (ed.). 1978. *Scientific Basis of Obstetrics and Gynaecology* (2nd ed.). Edinburgh. Churchill Livingstone.

Mistell, D.R., and Davajon, U. 1979. *Reproductive Endocrinology, Infertility and Contraception.* Philadelphia: F.A. Davis.

Nathanielsz, P.W. 1978. Endocrine mechanisms of parturition. *Annu. Rev. Physiol.* 40:411.

Pritchard, J.A., and MacDonald, D.C. (eds.). 1980. *Williams Obstetrics* (16th ed.). New York: Appleton-Century-Crofts.

Ramsey, E.M., and Davis, R.W. 1963. A composite drawing of the placenta to show its structure and circulation. *Anat. Rec.* 145:366.

Shearman, R.P. (ed.). 1979. *Human Reproductive Physiology.* Oxford: Blackwell Scientific.

Siiteri, P.K.; Febres, F.; Clemens, L.E., et al. 1977. Progesterone and maintenance of pregnancy: Is progesterone nature's immunosuppressant? *Ann. N.W. Acad. Sci.* 286:384.

Simpson, E.R., and MacDonald, P.C. 1981. Endocrine physiology of the placenta. *Annu. Rev. Physiol.* 43:163.

Strickland, S., and Beers, W.H. 1979. Studies of the enzymatic basis and hormonal control of ovulation. In *Ovarian Follicular Development.* Edited by A.R. Midgleg and W.P. Sadler. New York: Raven Press.

Tulchinsky, D., and Ryan, K.J. 1980. *Maternal-Fetal Endocrinology.* Philadelphia: Saunders.

PART
X

METABOLISM
AND NUTRITION

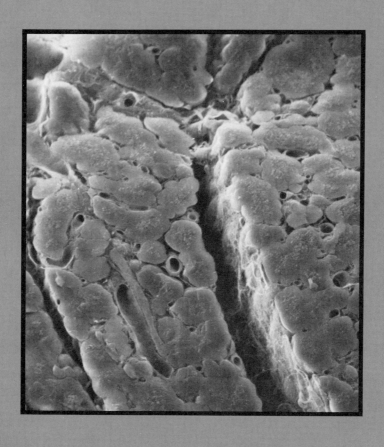

66

Thermoregulation

CHAPTER CONTENTS

GENERAL BACKGROUND

Humans are *homeotherms,* which means that their internal temperatures must be regulated closely. This characteristic is shared by all mammals, whose internal temperatures are maintained between 36 C and 38 C, and birds, whose temperatures are kept at about 40 C. If their bodies are protected, humans can function in ambient temperatures that vary from −50 C to +50 C. Individual cells cannot tolerate such a range of temperature, however; at −1 C, ice crystals begin to form, and at +45 C, protein begins to coagulate, or denature. For short periods only, an internal temperature of about 41 C can be tolerated. Thus, humans live only a few degrees from the point of thermal death, and the evidence suggests that the physiological control mechanisms of humans are organized to protect against overheating. Modern humans probably can protect themselves against overcooling, depending on their behavioral skills and energy supplies.

The body temperature of the mammal, near the maximum that can be tolerated by protein, provides for the maximum rate of chemical reactions, which are catalyzed by enzymes. The viscous fluids—blood, synovial fluids, and so on—flow well at warmer temperatures; in addition, excitation is propagated more rapidly in nerves at warmer temperatures, and muscles contract more rapidly in mammals than in "cold-blooded" animals such as the frog, for example. Thus, the capacity of the body for rapid action and the ability to support the action with rapid metabolism make intense physical activity possible. It follows that the body temperature must be regulated accurately, by balancing the loss of heat with the production of heat. At the practical level, physical exercise, which is widely recognized as necessary for good health, may place considerable stress on the system that regulates the temperature of the body. The flexibility of the homeotherm, which permits a wide range of behaviors, habitats, and travel in a wide variety of geographic, thermal, and environmental conditions, requires a continuous input of energy into the system and complicates the problem of thermal regulation.

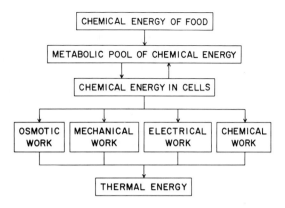

Figure 66-1. Transformation of energy in biological systems.

ENERGY, METABOLISM, AND THERMAL BALANCE

Forms of Energy

Energy may be thought of as the capacity to do work. *Kinetic energy* is the energy of motion, and *potential energy* is the energy stored or bound physically or chemically. Kinetic energy has limited, although important, use in biological systems. The two forms of energy may be exchanged easily; for example, some of the kinetic energy of blood flowing from the heart into the aorta is converted to potential energy during systole, as the walls of the arteries are stretched, and is converted back into kinetic energy during diastole, as the elastic arteries rebound and pressure is used to sustain flow (see Chapter 12).

Potential, or stored, energy is released as *free energy,* which is work, and heat. The production of heat from a source of potential energy represents inefficient use. Typically, biological systems are about 20% efficient; that is, about 20% of the energy liberated does work, and about 80% appears as heat. Chemical energy is the only biological source of energy (Figure 66-1).

ENTROPY

In a classical sense, the amount of energy in an isolated system remains constant, but *entropy* increases; that is, the proportion of energy that is available to do work diminishes. Thus, biological systems function on the pathway from high-grade energy to entropy and exist in a steady state (i.e., not changing with time), rather than in equilibrium (i.e., no free energy).

Thermal Balance

Thermal homeostasis, or the balance between the production of heat and the loss of heat, is essential to the life of a homeothermic animal. To maintain the body temperature within the narrow optimal range, unneeded thermal energy must be removed efficiently.

In the resting person, the production of heat approaches 37–40 kcal/m^2 of body surface per hour, or about 1500–1700 kcal/day. Light work may increase heat production to 2500–3000 kcal/m^2/day, and heavy work may produce 6000 kcal/m^2/day. During short, extreme bouts of exercise, the rate of production of heat may reach 10–16 times the basal level. If no heat were lost by the human body at rest, the temperature of the body would increase at the rate of 1 C/hr, and if the body were doing light work, the temperature would increase at the rate of 2 C/hr.

BODY TEMPERATURE

The temperature of the body can be measured using a thermometer (mercury or alcohol), which utilizes the expansion of a liquid, a thermocouple, which utilizes the flow of current between unlike metals, or by a thermistor, which utilizes the conductivity of an element.

Sites of Measurement

Because the body produces heat within its core and dissipates heat at its surface, the surface is cooler than the core. The vital organs—heart, brain, liver, kidneys, and endocrine organs—lie within the core of the body, and the tempera-

CLINICAL CORRELATION
66.1   Malignant Hyperthermia

CASE REPORT

The Patient: A 63-year-old man.

Reason for Admission: Surgery for benign prostatic hypertrophy.

History: The patient had undergone general anesthesia on three previous occasions, for unrelated illnesses. Agents used previously included thiopental, succinylcholine, and halothane. On the last occasion of general anesthesia, the patient had experienced fasciculations (uncoordinated, isolated, localized muscle twitching) and some rigidity after the succinylcholine was administered, but the procedure had been uneventful otherwise.

Anesthetic Procedure: In preparation for the surgery on the prostate, anesthesia was induced with thiopental and succinylcholine, and no abnormality was observed at that time. Anesthesia was continued with 1% halothane and 50% nitrous oxide. When surgery was begun, it was noted that the venous blood

appeared unusually dark, although the arterial blood was well oxygenated. Forty-five minutes after anesthesia was begun, the body temperature began to increase, the extremities were somewhat rigid, and evidence of premature ventricular contractions was seen on the ECG. The plasma potassium concentration, $[K^+]$, was 6.3 mEq/liter, the pH of the arterial blood was 6.9, the heart rate was 125 beats/min, the arterial oxygen tension (Pa_{O_2}) was 150 mm Hg, and the Pa_{CO_2} was 177 mm Hg.* It was concluded that the patient was in malignant hyperthermia. The surgery was completed as quickly as possible, and emergency treatment was begun.

Emergency Procedures: Anesthesia was terminated, the patient was hyperventilated with 100% oxygen, and intravenous infusion of iced lactated Ringer's solution was begun. The patient was placed on a cooling blanket (through the coils of which ice water was circulated), and ice packs were placed around the neck and the axillae. Sodium bicarbonate,

---

ture of the core is sensed and regulated. The most widely accepted measurement of body temperature is that obtained from the rectum at a depth of 5–8 cm. In the resting person, the rectal temperature is slightly higher than the temperature of the arterial blood, about the same as that of the liver, and slightly lower than that of the brain. The temperature of the brain can be estimated by measuring the temperature of the tympanic membrane, which is close to, but slightly less than, that of the hypothalamus.

The temperature of the esophagus is very close to that of the arterial blood. The temperature in the axilla and the oral temperature, both of which are convenient to obtain, are about the same—approximately 0.65 C less than the rectal temperature. The temperatures measured in the sites that have been listed, although not all the same, bear a fixed relationship to the core temperature and reflect changes in the core temperature.

SKIN TEMPERATURE

Estimations of the temperature of the skin vary widely; skin temperature is different at different sites and under different conditions. The range of temperatures measured at different sites is about 10–12 C. The skin closest to organs that produce heat at a high rate is the warmest. Estimates of the mean temperature of the skin, $\bar{T}_S$, are obtained by weighting measurements from different areas. The weightings are determined empirically. One such equation is as follows:

$$\bar{T}_s = 0.21\, \bar{T}_{face} + 0.17\, \bar{T}_{abdomen} + 0.11\, \bar{T}_{chest} \\ + 0.10\, \bar{T}_{back} + 0.15\, \bar{T}_{thigh} + 0.08\, \bar{T}_{calf} \\ + 0.12\, \bar{T}_{upper\,arm} + 0.06\, \bar{T}_{lower\,arm}$$

$\bar{T}_{skin}$ at an air temperature of 24–25 C is about 33 C. The range is 28.6–34.6 C. The temperature of the skin is lower than that of the core, and the skin is not affected adversely by a con-

---

(CLINICAL CORRELATION continued)

insulin, glucose, and mannitol were administered. Nevertheless, the patient's body temperature continued to increase, reaching 41.3 C, and the systemic acidosis persisted. The plasma [K$^+$] increased to 7.3 mEq/liter. At this time, the patient was placed on partial cardiopulmonary bypass, using a femoral artery and the accompanying vein. The rate of blood flow was 2.5 liters/min. The heat-exchanger was used for cooling, and the temperature of the blood returning to the patient was 34 C. After 20 minutes, the rectal temperature had decreased to 37.5 C, and the bypass was discontinued. The patient recovered without further incident.

Comment: The cause of malignant hyperthermia is not known, but it may involve a defect in uptake of Ca^{++} by the sarcoplasmic reticulum. In this model, the [Ca^{++}] of the sarcoplasm becomes abnormally high, and the skeletal muscles undergo prolonged contracture. The high metabolic rate of the continuously contracting muscle accounts for the high rate of oxygen consumption and production of CO_2 and lactate. The high plasma [K$^+$] also reflects the high level of muscular activity. A susceptibility to the condition is inherited, and the event is produced by anesthetic agents. The probability that the condition will develop increases with successive anesthetic experiences. Control of the body temperature and removal of the anesthetic agents is the preferred treatment. Respiratory support is important to provide for the high consumption of O_2 and production of CO_2. Bicarbonate helps to offset the metabolic acidosis caused by the high rate of production of lactate by glycolysis. Insulin helps to decrease the plasma [K$^+$] and assists in the cellular uptake of glucose. The cold fluids help to remove heat, and together with the mannitol, an osmotic diuretic, support renal function. The tachypnea is related to the high Pa$_{CO_2}$, the tachycardia is caused by the hyperthermia, and the cardiac dysrhythmia is related to the increased plasma [K$^+$]. Once a patient is known to be susceptible to malignant hyperthermia, general anesthesia should be avoided. If surgery is necessary, neuroleptoanalgesia (a state of altered consciousness produced by combinations of tranquilizers and narcotics), which appears to be safe to use, may provide adequate anesthesia.

*These values do not reflect normal conditions and spontaneous respiration. The patient is breathing 49% O_2, he is anesthetized, and the respiration is controlled externally.

---

siderable range of temperatures. However, prolonged periods of temperature as low as 10 C may damage the skin.

Mean Body Temperature

The mean temperature of the body, $\bar{T}_b$, is obtained by weighting the core temperature (rectal measurement) and the mean temperature of the skin:

$$\bar{T}_b = 0.67 \bar{T}_r + 0.33 \bar{T}_s$$

The purpose of this operation is to estimate how much body heat is gained from or lost to the environment and the rate of storage of heat in the skin; this method provides only an approximation.

Variation

The normal body temperature is not a single value but varies among individuals and with the time of day. At any given time, the oral temperatures of a group of healthy people may differ by as much as 1.5 C (Figure 66-2). The body temperature of a given individual who follows a reasonably regular schedule varies cyclically by about 2 C during a 24-hour period. The body temperature is lowest just before the person rises in the morning, increases during the day, and reaches a peak before bedtime. The body temperature decreases steadily during the night, while the individual sleeps (Figure 66-3). In nocturnal creatues, including many humans, this cycle is reversed.

CORE-SHELL CONCEPT

The core-shell concept is a physiological notion about the body. This concept is based largely on the source of heat, the gradient of temperature along which heat is lost from the body, and the principal site of the loss of heat.

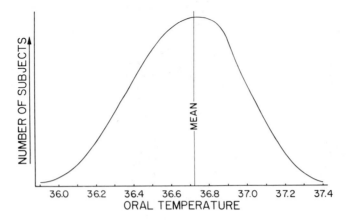

Figure 66-2. Range of oral temperatures measured in a group of healthy, young people at mid-   morning. The mean is 36.72 C.

Heat Production

In the person at rest, heat is produced in the core of the body. The cavities of the cranium, the thorax, the abdomen, and the pelvis are relative "hot spots" (Figure 66-4). This pattern changes dramatically when the person exercises, and the skeletal muscles become major producers of heat.

Heat Loss

The loss of heat is associated with the "shell" of the body, which is close to or in contact with the external environment (Figure 66-5). Bodies covered by clothing, hair, or feathers possess a "microenvironment" around their surfaces. Bodies that are nude and hairless exist essentially in the macroenvironment.

Shell Thickness

The thickness of the shell is a factor in the loss of heat from the body. A layer of fat under the skin contributes significantly to the insulative qualities of the shell. In humans, most of the heat lost from the shell is brought from the core by the circulating blood. Thus, the cardiovascular system is a major factor in the physiological control of heat loss. When warm blood is brought to the surface in the vessels of the skin, the shell effectively is thinner. Thus, the relative sizes of the shell and the core depend on the temperatures of the body and the environment. In a warm environment, the ratio of core to shell increases, and the temperature of the shell increases. In a cold environment, the ratio

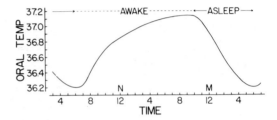

Figure 66-3. Range of oral temperature during 24 hours in a normal, healthy, young man. Although individuals vary, this is a typical pattern.

of the core to the shell decreases, and the temperature of the shell decreases. Among terrestrial species, the pig has a very effective shell. The pig's shell can be as thick as 10 cm, and it cools well, without invoking large alterations of metabolism to correct for losses of heat. Among aquatic species, the Alaskan seal retains heat well, even in water at −2 C. This animal has a subcutaneous layer of fat that constitutes as much as one-third of the radius of the body. Consistent with the insulating qualities of fat, obese humans tolerate cold with less metabolic response than thin ones do.

TRANSFER OF HEAT EXTERNALLY

Mechanisms

Heat is transferred from the shell to the environment by conduction, convection, radiation, and evaporation (Figure 66-6).

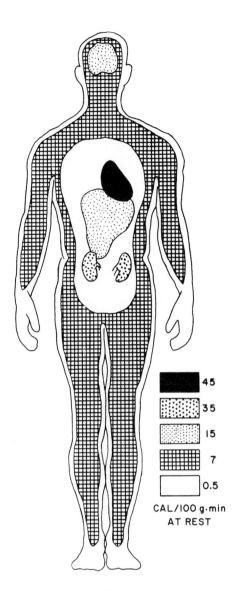

Figure 66-4. Production of heat in the human body at rest. During exercise, the production of heat by the skeletal muscles increases markedly. (Redrawn, with permission, from Aschoff, J., and Wever, R. 1958. *Naturwissenschaften* 45:477.)

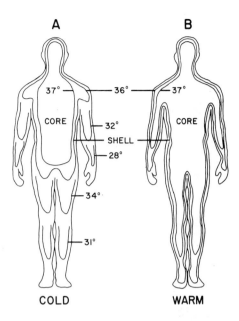

Figure 66-5. Core-shell concept in the human body. The temperature of the core is kept constant over a wide range of ambient temperatures. The temperature of the surface and underlying areas (shell) varies with the ambient temperature. The shell is "thicker" in a cold environment (**A**) and "thinner" in a warm environment (**B**). (Redrawn, with permission, from Aschoff, J., and Wever, R. 1958. *Naturwissenschaften* 45:477.)

Figure 66-6. Exchange of heat by radiation, conduction, convection, and evaporation. The person in this illustration receives heat by radiation from the sun and loses heat by radiation to the environment, loses heat by conduction to the floor, loses heat by convection, as air warmed at the surface of his body expands and rises, displaced by cooler ambient air, and loses heat by both sensible and insensible evaporation.

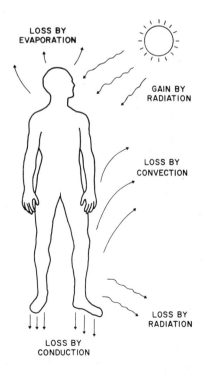

CONDUCTION

Conduction is the transfer of heat by direct contact of a warmer body with a cooler one. Kinetic energy is transferred from one atom or molecule to another atom or molecule. Conduction is not a problem for the person who is protected by clothing in a dry environment, but for bodies in cool water, such as swimmers, it is a problem. The amount of heat transferred depends on the difference of temperature and the area of contact. Heat may be either gained or lost by this mechanism.

CONVECTION

Convection is the transfer of heat by the flow of a fluid that has been warmed or cooled by conduction or radiation. As an example, *natural convection* occurs when fluid that has been warmed, which expands and becomes lighter, is pushed away from a source of heat by colder, heavier fluid. *Forced convection* is caused by a fan or an impellor that moves fluid past a source of heating or cooling. Because of the role of conduction in convection, the transfer of heat by the two mechanisms sometimes is classified together as "convective" transfer.

RADIATION

Radiation is the transfer of heat by infrared waves from one dense object to another dense object, regardless of the distance or the temperature of the environment between the objects. Heat may be either gained or lost by this mechanism. At a room temperature of 20 C, as much as 40%-50% of a person's heat production may be lost by radiation. The position of the body can be a factor. If an individual assumes a position that decreases the area of exposed surface to a minimum—for example, the fetal position—the loss of heat by radiation is decreased. To lose heat, a recumbent position in which the arms and legs are thrust outward from the body is most effective.

EVAPORATION

Evaporation is an important but highly variable mechanism of heat loss. Profuse sweating is the most effective means of losing heat when the rate of production is high. The conversion of 1 g of water from liquid to gas requires 0.58 kcal of heat, the latent heat of vaporization. Evaporation is affected by the *relative humidity*— the amount of water vapor already in the air relative to the amount the air can hold.

Evaporation has a basal component, called *insensible*, which involves the vaporization of water through the skin (*transpiration*), from the respiratory passages, and from the mucosa of the mouth. Approximately 20%-25% of the basal production of heat may be lost by insensible evaporation.

SENSIBLE TRANSFER OF HEAT

The transfer of heat by conduction, convection, or radiation, each of which is a *sensible* means (i.e., the process is *sensed*), can be described by the following equation:

$$C = kS(T_s - T_a)$$

where C is the rate of transfer of heat, T_s is the temperature of the surface, T_a is the ambient (or surrounding) temperature, S is the surface area, and k is a constant that is characteristic of the process. The "constant of cooling," k, sometimes is called *body conductance* because it describes the speed at which heat moves out of the body. This movement occurs in three stages: (1) from the core to the skin (k_t), (2) from the skin, through clothing or fur (k_{cl}), and (3) from the clothing or the fur to the air (k_a). The serial addition of these conductances takes the usual form:

$$\frac{1}{k_{total}} = \frac{1}{k_t} + \frac{1}{k_{cl}} + \frac{1}{k_a}$$

If the reciprocals of conductance (resistance, or insulation) are added,

$$I_{total} = I_t + I_{cl} + I_a$$

Finally, heat balance, in which no heat is stored, is expressed by:

$$M \pm R \pm C \pm K - E = 0$$

where M is the production of heat by metabolism, R is the loss or gain of heat by radiation, C is the loss or gain of heat by convection, K is the loss or gain of heat by conduction, and E is the loss of heat by evaporation.

TRANSFER OF HEAT INTERNALLY

Mechanisms

To keep the core temperature constant, heat that is produced by metabolism must be transferred out of the cells and down a gradient of

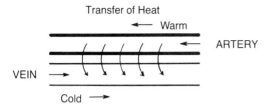

Transfer of Heat

Figure 66-7.   The temperature of arterial blood is approximately equal to the mean temperature of the core of the body. The temperature of venous blood depends on the organ or tissue perfused. Venous blood draining from the skin or from the ears, hands, or feet may be several degrees cooler than arterial blood. If an artery and a vein are contained in the same sheath, as often they are, heat is transferred from the warmer blood of the artery to the cooler blood of the vein. Thus, a certain amount of heat does not reach the periphery. This is one means by which the effective thickness of the shell is varied when the temperature of the environment varies.

temperature to the surface of the shell. This transfer is accomplished by conduction and convection.

CONDUCTION
Within the body, heat is transferred from cell to cell or to adjacent fluids, in both the core and the shell. The rate of transfer within the core by conduction is slow because the gradient is small. In the shell, the rate of transfer is high because the gradient is large. If the body depended on conduction alone for the dissipation of heat, and the difference of temperature between the core and the shell were 4 C, the resting human body would gain 40–70 kcal/hr, and the active human body would gain 175–200 kcal/hr. Thus, conduction alone would not be adequate to maintain a balance between the production of heat and the loss of heat.

CONVECTION
A system of forced convection is used, in which the heart pumps the blood through the circulation. Transfer by this means requires a gradient of temperature between the blood and the tissues. Cooler blood, returning from the periphery, is warmed by the tissues that are metabolizing actively; warmed blood, going to the periphery, is cooled by the tissues of the shell, which are in contact with the external environment. Blood, the carrier of the heat, has

a high heat capacity, which is that of its principal constituent, water. A rapid, well-controlled system is formed.

COUNTERCURRENT EXCHANGE
The close apposition of arteries and veins helps to conserve heat, to a certain extent, in the limbs and the digits. Some heat is transferred from the warmer arterial blood to the cooler venous blood and never reaches the periphery (Figure 66-7).

PHYSIOLOGICAL THERMOREGULATION

Response to Environmental Temperature
Within a certain range of environmental temperatures, the resting body temperature is controlled without altering metabolism (Figure 66-8). In this zone of thermal neutrality, heat is lost by conduction, convection, radiation, and insensible evaporation, and the overall process is influenced by vasomotor control and the choice of clothing. At lower ambient temperatures, the rate of metabolism increases to

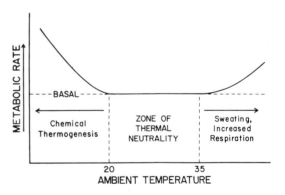

Figure 66-8.   In a range of ambient temperatures between about 20 and 35 C, the core temperature of the resting body is controlled by manipulation of the body shell, and metabolism remains at the basal level. At ambient temperatures below about 20 C, extra heat is produced by shivering and by thyroid action, which increases the rate of metabolism. At ambient temperatures above 35 C, active processes of heat loss are initiated, permitting control of the core temperature but increasing the rate of metabolism and ultimately limiting the tolerable range of ambient temperatures.

produce more heat, and at higher ambient temperatures, metabolism is increased by the active mechanisms of heat loss that are brought into play.

Control System

To keep the body temperature constant despite changing environmental temperatures, a control system is required. The control system in the human body has sensors in the shell and the core, an integrator in the hypothalamus, and an effector system that varies the production and dissipation of heat (see Chapters 5 and 16).

SENSORY RECEPTORS

The most numerous receptors in the skin, which is the principal component of the shell, are the naked nerve endings, which monitor pain caused by large changes of temperature. The end-organs of Ruffini respond specifically to warming, and the end-bulbs of Krause respond specifically to cooling (see Chapter 5). Thermoreceptors also occur in the tongue, the respiratory tract, and the viscera. Thermoreceptors in the hypothalamus are sensitive to changes in the temperature of the core.

INTEGRATION

Apparently, the temperature of the core, rather than the content of heat, is regulated. The hypothalamus is the center of control because it senses the temperature of the arterial blood and has access to the means of altering the production and dissipation of heat (Figures 66-9 to 66-11).

EFFECTOR SYSTEM

In the anterior hypothalamus (preoptic), receptors sensitive to heat initiate sweating and vasodilatation (panting in the dog). In the posterior hypothalamus, receptors sensitive to cold initiate vasoconstriction, shivering, and the release of epinephrine, which causes thermogenesis. Heating also suppresses the responsiveness of the posterior hypothalamus. The release of thyroid hormone is controlled by the hypothalamus through the pituitary gland.

The somatic nervous system controls voluntary adjustments by the person in the environment, such as seeking shelter or exposure, choosing clothing, and assuming the appropriate posture. The somatic nervous system also provides the efferent pathway for the control of shivering, although the initiation and maintenance of shivering is involuntary.

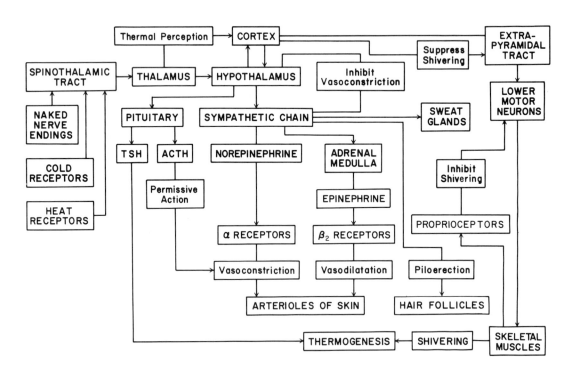

Figure 66-9.   Control of core temperature by control of skin blood flow, shivering, and thyroid activity.

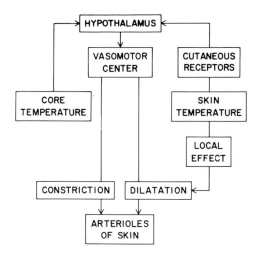

Figure 66-10.   Control of blood flow to the skin in response to core temperature.

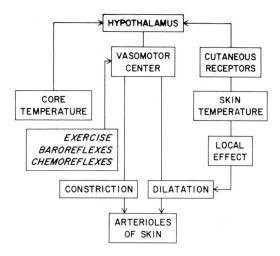

Figure 66-11.   Nonthermoregulatory influences on skin blood flow. Increased metabolism (exercise) increases the core temperature and induces vasodilatation, but vasoconstriction to divert blood to active muscles also is imposed. Baroreceptor and chemoreceptor influences also induce cutaneous vasoconstriction that is related to the maintenance of central arterial pressure.

HYPOTHERMIA

Accidental Hypothermia

If a person is exposed to the cold in an unprotected environment, the rate of loss of heat may exceed the rate of production, and the temperature of the body may decrease. Examples of this include people who have been shipwrecked and are exposed in an open lifeboat or in the water, mountain climbers who are trapped on a ledge, or elderly people who may have inadequate food and fuel. The problem for the elderly is made worse by a naturally declining rate of metabolism and may be compounded by the use of sedatives or tranquilizers, which oppose a vigorous metabolic response to the cold.

The ability of the body to oppose hypothermia is impaired at a core temperature of about 33 C, and it is lost entirely at about 31–29 C. This occurs because of the decreased rate of metabolism of the cells at lower temperatures and because of the loss of consciousness at about 30 C, which depresses the drive of the central nervous system to increase the production of heat by muscular activity. Death may occur when the core temperature decreases to about 25 C, although people have survived after experiencing core temperatures as low as 19 C.

Induced Hypothermia

In some surgical procedures that involve the heart or the brain, the body temperature is decreased deliberately to a range of 25–21 C to decrease the oxygen consumption of tissues that may be perfused only slightly or not at all. In these cases, the period of hypothermia is brief, and both cooling and rewarming are controlled carefully.

Adaptation to Cold

The ability to tolerate a lowered body temperature is poorly developed in humans; however, there are exceptions to this generalization. The Australian aborigines, for example, can endure relatively cold nights with scant shelter and little clothing. Apparently, marked peripheral vasoconstriction permits the temperature of the shell to decrease markedly, but the temperature of the core decreases only slightly.

HYPERTHERMIA

Fever

PYROGENS

Certain substances, which are called *pyrogens*, alter the function of the thermoregulatory center. The production of heat is increased and the loss of heat is curtailed; thus, the temperature of the body increases. The temperature is regulated at the higher level, and the thermoregulatory system acts as if some control

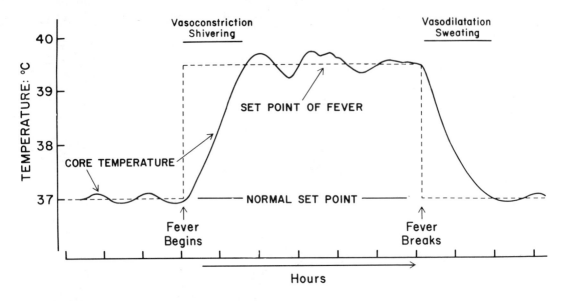

Figure 66-12. The onset and decline of fever. See the text for discussion. (Redrawn, with permission, from Brenglemann, G., and Brown, A.C. 1965. In *Physiology and Biophysics,* 19th ed., eds. T.C. Ruch, and H.D. Patton. Philadelphia: W.B. Saunders Co.)

point has been reset. Fever may be a form of defense for warm-blooded animals, but the mechanism is not clear.

INFECTION

Infectious microorganisms (bacteria or viruses) release pyrogens that cause fever. The onset of fever may be preceded by headache, nausea, fatigue, and muscle pain. The actual increase of body temperature begins with the *chill phase,* in which the body acts as if it were not warm enough (i.e., a sensation of chill is felt). Cutaneous vasoconstriction produces a cool, dry skin, and shivering increases the rate of production of heat. As a result, the core temperature increases. After the fever is established, the skin is warm, and the individual may feel warm (Fig-

ure 66-12). The increased temperature caused by the fever is superimposed on the daily variation, and a mild fever may seem to disappear at times when the body temperature normally decreases and to return when the body temperature normally increases (see Figure 66-3).

RECOVERY

When the cause of the fever is removed, normal thermoregulation resumes because the "set point" of the hypothalamus has been restored. The skin is flushed, and the cardiac output may increase as the excess heat is dissipated. The blood pressure may decrease. When the temperature of the skin reaches 34 C, sweating begins, and the rate of loss of heat exceeds the rate of production (Figure 66-12).

STUDY OUTLINE

GENERAL BACKGROUND Human body temperature is regulated between 36 C and 38 C; with protection, can function in environment with temperatures from −50 C to +50 C.

Body produces excess heat; physiological controls balance heat production with heat loss.

Warm body temperature permits rapid, intense activity.

Continuous input of energy is required to maintain body temperature.

ENERGY, METABOLISM, AND THERMAL BALANCE
FORMS OF ENERGY   Kinetic (motion) and potential (stored).

Two forms are exchanged easily.

Potential energy is converted to work (about 20%) and heat (about 80%)−efficiency is about 20%.

Chemical energy is only biological source.

ENTROPY   Measure of energy not available to do work.

At equilibrium, no free energy.

Biological systems exist in steady state, not equilibrium.

THERMAL BALANCE   Essential for homeothermic animal.

Body produces heat continuously; rate increases with activity.

If heat is not lost, body temperature increases.

BODY TEMPERATURE

SITES OF MEASUREMENT   Body is heated by core, cooled by surface.

Core contains vital organs; temperature of core is sensed and regulated.

Temperature usually measured orally, axially, or rectally.

Temperatures are different at different sites, but relationship to core temperature is fixed.

SKIN TEMPERATURE   Varies; temperature warmest close to organs that produce heat.

Lower than core temperature; not affected adversely by considerable range.

MEAN BODY TEMPERATURE   Obtained by weighting mean temperatures of core and skin.

VARIATION   Normal body temperature is a range, not a single value.

Varies among individuals.

Varies cyclically during 24 hours.

CORE-SHELL CONCEPT

HEAT PRODUCTION   In head and trunk at rest, in skeletal muscles during activity.

HEAT LOSS   At surface of body, in contact with environment.

SHELL THICKNESS   Determines insulative qualities.

Fat contributes significantly.

Control of blood flow to surface controls effective thickness of shell—variable transfer of heat from warm core to cooler shell.

Shell becomes thinner in warm environment and during exertion.

Shell becomes thicker in cold environment and in resting body.

TRANSFER OF HEAT EXTERNALLY

MECHANISMS

CONDUCTION   Transfer of heat by direct contact—heat may be either gained or lost.

CONVECTION   Transfer of heat by flow of fluid that is warmed or cooled by contact.

Natural—fluid moves because of change of density.

Forced—fluid is pumped.

RADIATION   Transfer of heat between bodies by infrared waves.

EVAPORATION   Loss of heat through latent heat of vaporization.

Enhanced by sweating; affected by relative humidity.

Insensible loss by vaporization through skin, from respiratory passages, and from mucosa of mouth.

SENSIBLE TRANSFER OF HEAT   By conduction, convection, or radiation—can be *sensed.*

Body conductance—speed at which heat moves out of body.

TRANSFER OF HEAT INTERNALLY

MECHANISMS   Must have temperature gradient from core to surface of shell.

CONDUCTION   From cell to cell or to adjacent fluids.

Slow in core because gradient is small.

Faster in shell because gradient is large.

Alone, not adequate mechanism.

CONVECTION   Forced circulation of blood.

Warm blood from core is pumped to surface, cools, is pumped back to warm core, and so on.

Effective system; blood has high heat capacity (that of water).

COUNTERCURRENT EXCHANGE   Some heat is transferred from warm blood of artery to cool blood of vein, never reaches periphery.

PHYSIOLOGICAL THERMOREGULATION

RESPONSE TO ENVIRONMENTAL TEMPERATURE   In middle zone, controlled by varying loss of heat without change of production of heat.

At low ambient temperature, heat production is increased (increased metabolic rate).

At high ambient temperature, metabolism is increased by active mechanisms of heat loss.

CONTROL SYSTEM

SENSORY RECEPTORS   Naked nerve endings; sense pain caused by large differences of temperature.

Special end-organs sense warming and cooling.

Thermoreceptors in tongue, respiratory tract, and viscera.

Thermoreceptors in hypothalamus sense changes in core temperature (from blood).

INTEGRATION   In hypothalamus.

EFFECTOR SYSTEM Autonomic nervous system—vasoconstriction/dilatation, sweating, and release of epinephrine.

Thyroid hormone is released.

Involuntary—shivering.

Voluntary adjustment—appropriate clothing, shelter, posture, and activity.

HYPOTHERMIA

ACCIDENTAL HYPOTHERMIA Exposure to cold environment; inadequate shelter or fuel; sedatives or tranquilizers.

Body function is impaired; consciousness is lost at about 30 C core temperature; death occurs at about 25 C.

INDUCED HYPOTHERMIA In surgical procedures, to allow interruption of perfusion; brief and controlled.

ADAPTATION TO COLD Peripheral vasoconstriction—thickens shell, protects core.

HYPERTHERMIA

FEVER Pyrogens alter function of thermoregulatory center.

PYROGENS Increased heat production, decreased loss—chill phase; shivering, sense of being cold.

Control point is reset higher.

Subject may feel warm after fever is established.

INFECTION Bacteria and viruses release pyrogens.

RECOVERY Normal set point is restored.

Vasodilatation and sweating warm skin as heat is dissipated.

BIBLIOGRAPHY

Bennett, A.F., and Ruben, J.A. 1979. Endothermy and activity in vertebrates. *Science* 206:649.

Benziger, T.H. 1969. Heat regulation: Homeostasis of central temperature in man. *Physiol. Rev.* 49:671.

Brengelmann, G.L. 1983. Circulatory adjustments to exercise and heat stress. *Annu. Rev. Physiol.* 45:91.

Clark, G.; Magoun, H.W.; and Ranson, S.W. 1939. Hypothalamic regulation of body temperature. *J. Neurophysiol.* 2:61.

Crawshaw, L.I. 1980. Temperature regulation in vertebrates. *Annu. Rev. Physiol.* 42:473.

Crawshaw, L.I.; Moffitt, B.P.; Lemons, D.E., et al. 1981. The evolutionary development of vertebrate thermoregulation. *Am. Sci.* 69:543.

Dinarello, C.A., and Wolf, S.M. 1978. Pathogenesis of fever in man. *N. Engl. J. Med.* 298:607.

Dubois, E.F. 1948. *Fever and the Regulation of Body Temperature.* Springfield, Illinois: Charles C. Thomas.

Glotzbach, S.F., and Heller, H.C. 1976. Central nervous regulation of body temperature during sleep. *Science* 194:537.

Grav, H.J., and Blix, A.S. 1979. A source of nonshivering thermogenesis in fur-seal skeletal muscle. *Science* 204:87.

Hardy, J.D. 1965. The "set-point" concept in physiological temperature regulation. In *Physiological Controls and Regulations.* Edited by W.S. Yamamoto and J.R. Brobeck. Philadelphia: Saunders.

Hensel, H. 1973. Neural processes in thermoregulation. *Physiol. Rev.* 53:948.

Hensel, H. 1981. *Thermoreception and Temperature Regulation.* New York: Academic Press.

Horowitz, B.A. 1979. Metabolic aspects of thermogenesis: Neuronal and hormonal control (Symposium). *Fed. Proc.* 38:2147.

Kleiber, M. 1975. *The Fire of Life.* Malabar, Florida: Krieger.

Rowell, L.B. 1983. Cardiovascular aspects of human thermoregulation. *Circ. Res.* 52:367.

Satinoff, E. 1978. Neural organization and evolution of thermal regulation in mammals. *Science* 201:16.

67

Hunger
and Thirst

CHAPTER CONTENTS

REGULATION
OF FOOD INTAKE

Working Definitions

HUNGER
Hunger is a complex of sensations evoked by
the depletion of body nutrient stores; in humans, it evokes an awareness of the need to
ingest food. Hunger may be disagreeable, and
it may even be painful ("hunger pangs"). It can
cause aggressive, frantic behavior in the subject
attempting to satisfy it. In lower forms of animal life, hunger is a condition that causes an
organism to ingest food if it is available, and to
search for food if none is nearby.

APPETITE
Appetite is the desire to ingest food. Appetite is
an affective state that is associated with pleasure, does not depend entirely on need, and

may persist after hunger has been appeased.
Thus, appetite may lead to the storage of energy as fat. Psychological conditioning is an
important part of appetite.

SATIETY
Satiety is an affective state that is achieved
when hunger has been satisfied and the desire
to ingest food has been removed.

Constancy of Energy Stores

Physiologists generally believe that animals,
including humans, balance the intake and expenditure of energy so that a relatively constant
amount is retained in the body. Presumably,
hunger indicates that the store of energy is being depleted, and satiety indicates that the restoration of energy is adequate. The observation
that humans and most other animals keep their
body weights and compositions relatively con-

899

stant supports this notion. Some experimental data also substantiate this belief. Most animals that are force-fed above their normal caloric needs will decrease their intake if they are allowed to do so. If their food is diluted by roughage, rats will increase their intake until their caloric needs are met. However, some humans who normally are obese seem to lack signals that tell them when their caloric needs have been satisfied.

History

Clinical observations that brain tumors sometimes were associated with obesity led eventually to the production of obese animals by experimental lesioning of the hypothalamus. Destruction of the ventromedial nuclei (VMN) caused an increased intake of food (Figure 67-1), while stimulation of the same area decreased the intake of food and suppressed food-related behavior. Thus, the concept of a "satiety center" in the VMN emerged. Stimulation of the ventrolateral region of the hypothalamus produced voracious eating, and lesioning of the same area produced an aversion to eating and drinking (Figure 67-1). Thus, the concept of a "feeding center" developed. Apparently, the feeding center is tonically active and must be inhibited by the satiety center.

Satiety Signals

GLUCOSTATIC HYPOTHESIS

Studies using radioactive tracers have shown that the VMN takes up glucose avidly, and the rate of uptake is influenced by insulin. Investigators concluded that receptors (cells) in the VMN, which are sensitive to the concentration of glucose they contain, influence the intake of food. These receptors are not influenced by the concentration of glucose in the blood, which may help to explain the persistent hunger of diabetic individuals. Goldthioglucose, injected in mice, is taken up by the cells of the VMN along with regular glucose, but destroys the glucose-sensitive cells. The animals eat excessively and become obese. Thus, when the receptors of the VMN are inactivated or destroyed, the animal loses the sense of satiety that comes from eating. In addition, electrical activity recorded from the VMN was increased by hyperglycemia. These experiments support the idea of a satiety center. Together, the feeding center and the satiety center might ensure the balance of energy in the body.

LIPOSTATIC HYPOTHESIS

Some evidence suggests that fat or products of the metabolism of fat may affect sensors in the VMN. Animals that have been force-fed by stomach tube until they are grossly obese voluntarily decrease their intake when given food ad libitum, until their weight returns to normal. Conversely, animals that have been starved overeat when given food again, until their body weight and energy stores have been replenished.

THERMOSTATIC HYPOTHESIS

Physiologists have observed that animals increase their intake of food in cold weather and decrease it in hot weather. Heating and cooling of the hypothalamus by implanted probes provide some support for the notion that food intake may be regulated partly by responses to the environmental temperature. The specific dynamic action of food, which is the increase of metabolism related to digestion and absorption (see Chapter 68), has been associated with increased hypothalamic temperature. Thus, the results of the intake of food may modify the drive for further intake. Experimental destruction of the rostral portion of the hypothalamus prevents any effect of changes in the temperature of the blood on food-related behavior. The possible role of this mechanism in the control of food intake has not been fully assessed.

AMINOSTATIC HYPOTHESIS

There is evidence that the level of amino acids in the plasma controls the intake of food to some extent. In addition, a deficiency of one or more of the essential amino acids in experimental animals causes the animals to increase their total intake of food.

Gastrointestinal Tract

Both hunger and satiety may be influenced by input from the alimentary tract. Some form of satiety signal seems to originate in the oropharynx. A small amount of food ingested by a dog in the usual way decreases the amount of a regular meal taken later more than placing the same amount of food directly into the stomach does. Patients who are unable to swallow food and must take their meals through gastric fistulae are more satiated by chewing food first and then placing it into the stomach than by placing the food directly into the stomach. On the other hand, the presence of food in or

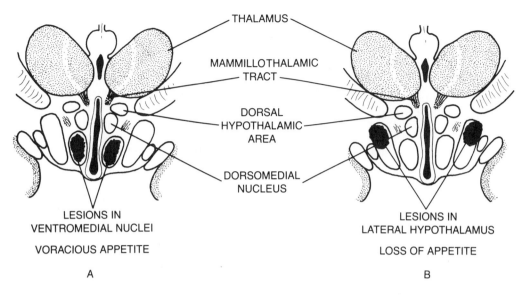

THALAMUS

MAMMILLOTHALAMIC TRACT

DORSAL HYPOTHALAMIC AREA

DORSOMEDIAL NUCLEUS

LESIONS IN VENTROMEDIAL NUCLEI

VORACIOUS APPETITE

A

LESIONS IN LATERAL HYPOTHALAMUS

LOSS OF APPETITE

B

Figure 67-1. Effects of specific lesions in the hypothalamus on appetite in the cat.

passing through the oropharynx does not substitute for actual ingestion of food. Dogs in which esophageal fistulae were produced, so that food was swallowed but did not reach the stomach, "consumed" larger amounts of food than normal. Hunger pangs may be felt in the empty stomach, and a sense of fullness depresses the appetite. Even inert bulk in the stomach satisfies briefly; thus, mechanoreceptors appear to function in satiety. However, only actual assimilation of substrates into the body satisfies the need for food.

REGULATION OF WATER INTAKE

Water

Water is the matrix of life. It is the largest single component of living cells and tissues, and it provides the medium for, or is involved in, all of the chemical reactions that occur in the body. Life began in an aqueous environment, and water provided the milieu for the primitive unicellular organism. When animals left the ocean, they carried the milieu for the cells of the body in their internal environment.

Most tissues that are exposed to the external environment are bathed by an aqueous medium, for example, the alveoli of the lungs, the respiratory and nasal passages, the oropharynx, the gastrointestinal tract, the genitourinary tract, and the corneal surfaces of the eye. Even the skin, which lives partly in the external environment, is only a few cells away from being wet.

INTAKE
The high degree of dependence of life on water requires effective mechanisms for balancing intake and output. The average intake of water is about 2.5 liters/day. Approximately 1.4 liters are taken as beverage, about 0.9 liter is contained in the food that is ingested, and 150–200 ml is obtained by the oxidation of hydrogen (metabolic water).

OUTPUT
Approximately 1 liter of water is excreted in the urine, 0.2 liter accompanies the feces, and 0.3–0.6 liter is lost as insensible evaporation from the skin. Sensible evaporation, or sweating, can vary from virtually nothing to several liters per day. A person who exercises vigorously in a warm, humid environment can deplete his body fluids rapidly. Na^+ and Cl^-, the principal ions of the extracellular fluid, also are lost and must be replaced along with water. About 0.5 liter of water evaporates from the respiratory tract during breathing; this loss varies depending on the water content of the air. It is greater in cold weather, when the air is dry after it has been warmed, and less in warm

weather, when the air usually contains more moisture. The skin is the major barrier against the loss of fluid from the body. When the skin has been burned, the fluid loss rate can be great enough to cause circulatory shock (see Ch. 23).

Thirst

Thirst is a sensation that causes one to seek water; it is analogous to hunger. Humans are known to experience thirst, and we assume that it precedes drinking in other animals.

DRINKING

Animals, including humans, drink in response to a relative lack of water in one or more fluid compartments of the body. This need may be accentuated by circadian rhythm and by activity. In addition, drinking usually accompanies meals and is associated with psychological and social behavior.

DRY MOUTH

Water deprivation eventually produces a dry mouth, which is caused by decreased flow of saliva. A dry mouth produces chronic thirst

and a compelling search for relief. It has been proposed as the basis of thirst. When the mouth is dry, chewing and swallowing food becomes difficult. Some animals (the laboratory rat, for example) may stop eating under this condition.

Thirst is not caused by dry mouth alone. Local wetting of the oropharynx does not relieve the feeling of thirst, although small quantities of very cold water, such as can be obtained by sucking on ice cubes, may provide temporary and partial relief. Even complete local anesthetization of the oropharynx does not obtund thirst. Artificial drying of the mouth, by the use of atropine, for example, which blocks muscarinic receptors and stops the salivary flow, does not produce the true sensation of thirst. The individual feels the need to wet the oropharynx but not to consume large quantities of water.

CELLULAR DEHYDRATION

Cellular dehydration is an important stimulus to drinking. It can be produced by the injection of a hyperosmolal solution of NaCl, which distributes primarily in the extracellular fluid (ECF) and causes water to leave the cells along

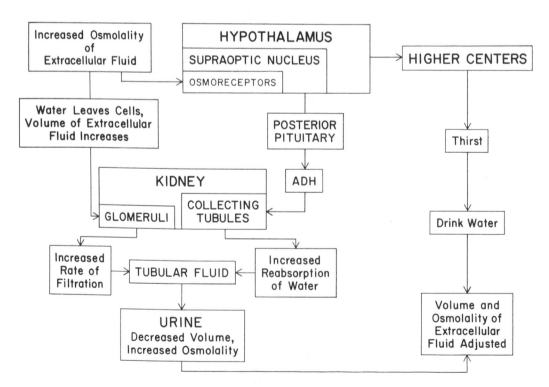

Figure 67-2.   Effects of increased osmolality of extracellular fluid and subsequent cellular dehydration.

an osmotic gradient (see Chapter 42). The effect can be localized by the injection of hypertonic solution into the blood supply of the hypothalamus. Cells of the supraoptic nucleus and the lateral preoptic area act as osmoreceptors and sense changes of cellular hydration. The response of these receptors not only engenders thirst, which increases the voluntary intake of water, but also causes the release of antidiuretic hormone (ADH) by the posterior pituitary, which conserves the water content of the body (see Chapter 42). The scheme for cellular dehydration is given in Figure 67-2. As water leaves the cells along the osmotic gradient, the volume of the ECF increases, and the glomerular filtration rate increases. This tends to increase the volume of the urine; the balance between increased filtration and the action of ADH determine the final volume and concentration of the urine. Increased filtration followed by selective reabsorption of water results in a net excretion of electrolytes and helps to adjust the osmolality of the ECF back toward normal. The feeling of thirst leads to the ingestion of water, which also tends to dilute the ECF. This is a sensitive system in humans since a small (1%–2%) decrease in the volume of the cellular water initiates drinking and the release of ADH.

EXTRACELLULAR DEHYDRATION

Thirst has long been associated with the loss of ECF by hemorrhage, severe vomiting, or diarrhea. Cholera, a former scourge that causes severe extracellular dehydration, produces a "burning thirst" that can be relieved by intravenous fluids. A person who sweats excessively but does not take adequate replacement of fluid and electrolytes will experience extracellular dehydration followed by cellular dehydration. The ECF volume must be maintained within narrow limits because it influences the volume and consistency of the circulating blood. The proper balance of the ECF is attained by appropriate intake, through drinking, and by appropriate excretion, through the kidneys. The ECF volume is sensed by low-pressure stretch receptors in the atria, the great veins, and the pulmonary vessels. The scheme for depletion of both extracellular fluid and intracellular fluid compartments is given in Figure 67-3. Increased osmolality of the ECF evokes the release of ADH and the sensation of thirst, as also is shown in Figure 67-2. The loss of ECF volume decreases the rate of tonic input from the volume receptors, releasing the medullary centers from suppression. As a result, sympathetic nervous system outflow to the kidneys increases the release of renin. Renin

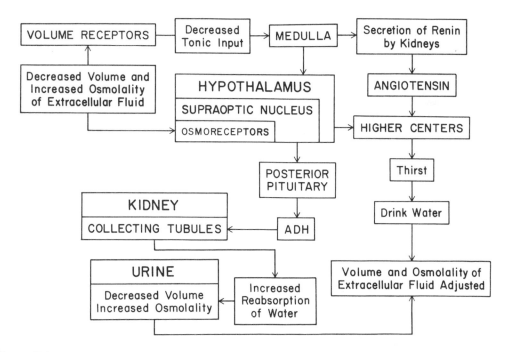

Figure 67-3.   Effects of decreased volume and increased osmolality of extracellular fluid and subsequent cellular dehydration.

catalyzes the formation of angiotensin (angiotensin I, which is converted to angiotensin II), which engenders the sensation of thirst in the forebrain. Increased intake and decreased excretion of water tend to increase the volume and decrease the osmolality of the ECF and to restore the volume of the cellular fluid, which is in equilibrium with the ECF.

Satiety

PERIPHERAL EFFECTS
The voluntary intake of water stops when thirst has been relieved. Experimental evidence indicates that both peripheral and central receptors are involved. Animals that have been dehydrated drink enough to rehydrate themselves, and no excess is ingested. Intake is stopped before the water has been absorbed, which suggests gastric or intestinal receptors. Animals in which esophageal fistulae have been produced, so that the water they swallow does not reach the stomach ("sham drinking"), drink greatly in excess of their normal requirements. Thus, oral or pharyngeal metering is not adequate. Water given intragastrically, or even distention of the stomach with a balloon, decreases sham drinking.

HYPOTHALAMIC CENTERS
Stimulation of the lateral hypothalamus produces thirst and the release of ADH, and lesions in the same area cause a failure to drink. However, no clear-cut satiety center for thirst has been identified.

STUDY OUTLINE

REGULATION OF FOOD INTAKE

WORKING DEFINITIONS
HUNGER   Awareness of need to ingest food.
APPETITE   Desire to ingest food.
SATIETY   Satisfaction of hunger and removal of desire to ingest food.

CONSTANCY OF ENERGY STORES
Normally, intake and expenditure of energy are balanced.
Related to maintenance of constant body weight and composition.
Absence of appropriate signals may lead to obesity.

HISTORY   Concept of "satiety center" in hypothalamus—experimental lesion of ventromedial nuclear (VMN) caused increased intake of food.
Stimulation of VMN decreased food intake—"feeding center."

SATIETY SIGNALS
GLUCOSTATIC HYPOTHESIS   Receptors in VMN take up glucose under influence of insulin; influence intake of food.
Receptors are destroyed by goldthioglucose; animals become obese.
May reflect satiety center.
LIPOSTATIC HYPOTHESIS   Fat or products of metabolism of fat may affect sensors in VMN.
THERMOSTATIC HYPOTHESIS   An increased hypothalamic temperature decreases food intake.
May reflect increased metabolism related to digestion and absorption (specific dynamic action).
AMINOSTATIC HYPOTHESIS   Plasma levels of amino acids may affect food intake.

GASTROINTESTINAL TRACT   Input may affect hunger and satiety.
Satiety signal from oropharynx.
Satiety signal from food in stomach.
Distention of mechanoreceptors may be involved.

REGULATION OF WATER INTAKE

WATER   Largest component of cells and tissues; necessary for life.
INTAKE   As beverage, in food, and from metabolism.
OUTPUT   Must balance input.
Excreted in urine and feces.
Sweating and evaporation from skin and respiratory tract.

THIRST   Sensation of need for water.
DRINKING   Related to need for fluid.
Psychological and social behavior.
DRY MOUTH   Decreased flow of saliva.
Produces thirst, but not only factor involved.
CELLULAR DEHYDRATION   Stimulates drinking.
Sensed by osmoreceptors in hypothalamus.
Causes the release of antidiuretic hormone (ADH)—water is conserved by avid reabsorption in kidneys.

EXTRACELLULAR DEHYDRATION
Causes thirst.
  Hemorrhage, vomiting, diarrhea, and sweating.
  ECF volume is sensed by receptors in atria, great veins, and pulmonary vessels.
  Causes cellular dehydration.
  Release of ADH—retention of water.
  Release of renin, which catalyzes formation of angiotensin—causes thirst, retention of Na^+.

SATIETY
PERIPHERAL EFFECTS   Intake of water is stopped when thirst is relieved.
  Gastric or intestinal factors are involved.
HYPOTHALAMIC CENTERS   Stimulation causes thirst and release of ADH.
  Lesions cause failure to drink.
  No clear-cut satiety center.

BIBLIOGRAPHY

Adolph, E.F. 1982. Termination of drinking: Satiation. *Fed. Proc.* 41:2533.

Andersson, B. 1978. Regulation of water intake. *Physiol. Rev.* 52:468.

Andersson, B.; Leksell, L.G.; and Rundgen, M. 1982. Regulation of water intake. *Annu. Rev. Nutr.* 2:73.

Baile, C.A., and Forbes, J.M. 1974. Control of food intake and regulation of energy balance in ruminants. *Physiol. Rev.* 54:160.

Booth, D.A. (ed.). 1978. *Computable Theory of Feeding Control.* New York: Academic Press.

Bray, G.A., and York, D.A. 1979. Hypothalamic and genetic obesity in experimental animals: An autonomic and endocrine hypothesis. *Physiol. Rev.* 59:719.

Fitzsimons, J.T. 1972. Thirst. *Physiol. Rev.* 52:468.

Fitzsimons, J.T. 1978. Angiotensin, thirst, and sodium appetite: Retrospect and prospect. *Fed. Proc.* 37:2669.

Fitzsimons, J.T. 1979. *The Physiology of Thirst and Sodium Appetite.* New York: Cambridge University Press.

Grossman, S.P.; Dacey, D.; Halaris, A.E., et al. 1978. Aphagia and adipsia after preferential destruction of nerve cell bodies in hypothalamus. *Science* 202:537.

Kissileff, H.R., and Van Italli, T.B. 1982. Physiology of the control of food intake. *Annu. Rev. Nutr.* 2:371.

Le Magnen, J. 1983. Body energy balance and food intake: A neuroendocrine regulatory mechanism. *Physiol, Rev.* 63:314.

Liebowitz, S.F. 1971. Hypothalamic alpha- and beta-adrenergic systems regulate both thirst and hunger in the rat. *Proc. Natl. Acad. Sci.* 68:334.

Morgensen, G.J., and Kucharaczyk, J. 1978. Central neural pathways for angiotensin-induced thirst. *Fed. Proc.* 37:2683.

Penicaud, L., Larue-Achagiotis, C., and LeMagnen, J. 1983. Endocrine basis for weight gain after fasting or UMH lesion in rats. *Am. J. Physiol.* 245:E246.

Phillips, M.I.; Hoffman, W.E.; and Beales, S.L. 1982. Dehydration and fluid balance: Central effects of angiotensin. *Fed. Proc.* 41:2520.

Ramsay, D.J. 1978. Beta-adrenergic thirst and its relation to the renin-angiotensin system. *Fed. Proc.* 37:2689.

Ritter, R.C.; Slusser, P.G.; and Stone, S. 1981. Glucoreceptors controlling feeding and blood glucose: Location in the hindbrain. *Science* 213:451.

Smith, G.P.; Gibbs, J.; and Young, R.C. 1974. Cholecystokinin and intestinal satiety in the rat. *Fed. Proc.* 33:1146.

Stricker, E.M. 1978. Hyperphagia. *N. Engl. J. Med.* 298:1010.

Thompson, C.I. 1979. *Computable Theory of Eating.* New York: Spectrum Publications.

Thompson, C.I. 1980. *Controls of Eating.* New York: SP Medical and Scientific Books.

Wurtman, R.J., and Wurtman, J.J. 1979. *Disorders of Eating.* New York: Raven Press.

Zimmerman, M.B., and Blaine, E.H. 1981. Water intake in hypovolemic sheep: Effects of crushing the left atrial appendage. *Science* 211:489.

68

Energy

CHAPTER CONTENTS

SOURCES

Energy Content

Energy is provided in the diet by carbohydrate, fat, protein, and alcohol. The principal unit of measurement is the *calorie* (cal), which is the amount of heat needed to increase the temperature of 1 g of water from 15 C to 16 C. A larger, more convenient unit frequently is used—the *kilocalorie* (kcal), or *large calorie* (Cal)—which is equal to 1000 calories. Another unit of work, or energy, is the *joule* (j), which is equivalent to 0.24 calories. The *kilojoule* (kj) is equal to 1000 joules.

COMPLETE OXIDATION

The potential caloric contribution of each of the sources of energy in the diet can be determined experimentally by measuring the heat evolved when the particular dietary substance is burned completely to CO_2 and H_2O. The average values obtained are 4.1 kcal/g of carbohydrate, 9.4 kcal/g of fat, 5.6 kcal/g of protein, and 7.0 kcal/g of alcohol. Since the body cannot produce oxides of nitrogen, the energy of the nitrogenous component of protein is not available to the body. Oxidation of nitrogen produces 1.3 kcal of the 5.6 kcal produced when 1 g of protein is burned; therefore, only 4.3 kcal/g of protein potentially are available to the body.

DIGESTIBILITY COEFFICIENTS

The fuel value of the diet is compromised further by the apparent digestibility of various foodstuffs. The digestibility varies significantly among food sources; however, in the typical American diet, *digestibility coefficients* (amount absorbed/amount ingested) for carbohydrate, fat, and protein are 0.98, 0.95, and 0.92, respectively. Alcohol is virtually totally absorbed. These factors yield physiological fuel values of 4 kcal/g (17 kj) for carbohydrate, 9 kcal/g (38 kj) for fat, 4 kcal/g (17 kj) for protein, and 7 kcal/g (30 kg) for alcohol.

ENERGY DENSITY

Specific foodstuffs vary widely in their energy densities (kcal/g). For example, the amounts of different foods required to provide 10% of the daily energy needed by an "average" adult male (2700–3000 kcal) are 14 heads of lettuce, 6 tablespoons of sugar, 3 tablespoons of butter, or 4 large eggs. The amount of energy that each of these foodstuffs represents may not be appreciated. If burned completely, each of the various quantities of food listed above could increase the temperature of 300 liters of water from 15 C to 16 C, or approximately 3 liters of water from 0 C to 100 C.

Energy is stored in the body primarily in fat (Figure 68-1), which is a convenient form because of its high energy density. The amount of energy stored as carbohydrate is small; therefore, unless adequate amounts of energy are taken in, the stores of fat or protein must be used. Because all of the protein of the body serves a purpose, either structural or functional, the body is compromised to some extent whenever protein stores are used as fuel. Excess protein in the diet (i.e., the quantity consumed above that needed for maintenance of structure or function) is converted to carbohydrate (gluconeogenesis) and/or fat. If adequate calories are provided in the diet, the stores of carbohydrate and fat can supply the energy needed between meals.

Efficiency

The body transforms about 20% of food energy into mechanical, osmotic, chemical, and electrical energy, and about 80% of food energy is converted to heat. Most of the energy is transformed through adenosine triphosphate (ATP), using the terminal phosphate bond. In the production of free energy from glucose, 38 mol of ATP is produced from 1 mol of glucose and 6 mol of O_2. Thus, the ratio of phosphate produced to oxygen consumed ($P:O_2$) is 6.33. If palmitic acid is used as an example, the $P:O_2$ for fat is 5.61. Thus, fat is only 89% as efficient as glucose when the utilization of O_2 is the basis for comparison. The higher $P:O_2$ for glucose is caused largely by the production of ATP in the anaerobic phase of glucose metabolism and the greater role of FADH (flavin-adenine-dinucleotide-H^+) in fat metabolism. FADH and NADH (nicotinamide-adenine-dinucleotide-H^+) are important carriers of chemical energy. They are used in the transfer of energy from foodstuffs to triphosphate energy carriers such

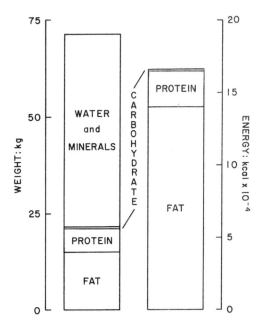

Figure 68-1. Relative proportions of mass and energy in the body. (Redrawn, with permission, from "How Metabolism Affects Clinical Problems," by G.F. Cahill, Jr., and T.A. Aoki in *Medical Times* [Vol. 98, No. 10.])

CLINICAL CORRELATION
68.1   Deficient Use of Energy
Because of Cystic Fibrosis

CASE REPORT

The Patient: A 1-month-old male.

Principal Complaint: Failure to grow and gain weight.

History: The gestation of this infant had been complicated by his mother's use of diphenyl-hydantoin (an anti-epileptic medication) during the first two months of the pregnancy and by the infant's premature birth at 34 weeks. The birthweight, 2.5 kg, was appropriate for the infant's gestational age. The postnatal course was complicated by jaundice* (plasma bilirubin, direct, 12.9 mg/dl [normal, 0.4 mg/dl], and indirect, 2.6 mg/dl [normal, 0.6 mg/dl]), which was treated successfully with phototherapy** for four days. It was noted during a routine clinical examination that the infant, at one month of age, was not growing normally (length 47.5 cm, weight 2.70 kg, head circumference 33.2 cm) despite an ap-

petite described as voracious. The child tolerated his diet (artificial formula) well. No other signs or symptoms of illness were noted in the history.

Clinical Examination: The infant was thin, wasted, and irritable. No signs of acute or chronic infection were noted, and the lungs and heart were normal. The abdomen was mildly distended and the liver was enlarged (determined by palpation). The neurological examination revealed no abnormality. The hematocrit was 25% (normal, 45%–52%), the hemoglobin was 8.6 mg/dl (normal, 13–18 mg/dl), mean corpuscular hemoglobin was 33.5 pg (normal, 27–32 pg), mean corpuscular volume was 97.5 μm^3 (normal, 80–94 μm^3), the total leukocyte count was 13,200/mm^3 (normal, 4300–10,800 mm^3), with a normal differential (distribution of cell types). The amount of liver transaminases was increased slightly, the plasma bilirubin was normal, and the amount of alkaline phosphatase was increased slight-

as ATP. Only 2 mol of ATP is produced for each mol of FADH oxidized, while 3 mol of ATP is produced for each mol of NADH oxidized. This difference is important when O_2 transport becomes a limiting factor.

The energy released from a unit of substrate also is of interest when substrate efficiency is considered. Glucose provides 2.11 kcal/g (in the form of ATP), while palmitic acid yields 5.05 kcal/g. Therefore, palmitic acid is 2.5 times as efficient as glucose on the basis of weight.

The overall efficiency with which work is done is the product of the efficiency of storing energy in phosphate bonds and the efficiency of transforming the energy of phosphate bonds into work. The efficiency of phosphorylation from both glucose and palmitic acid is 55%, if one assumes an average of 10 kcal/mol for the terminal phosphate bond of ATP. This efficiency factor is calculated by comparing the energy content of the terminal phosphate

bonds produced in the enzymatically controlled oxidation of glucose (380 kcal/mol of glucose) with the total amount of heat released when glucose is burned completely to CO_2 and H_2O (690 kcal/mol of glucose). However, the efficiency of transforming bond energy into work in the body is difficult to measure because efficiency is affected by such factors as physical training and the type of work done.

USE OF ENERGY

The use, or expenditure, of energy is divided into three principal categories: (1) energy required to maintain the basal metabolism, (2) energy used for "specific dynamic action," and (3) energy used for activity, or the performance of work.

Under specific physiological conditions, the use of energy may be partitioned further to include the cost of growth and/or the production of milk. The energy required for growth of

ly. Serum concentrations of calcium and phosphorus were normal, total plasma protein was 5.6 g/dl (normal, 6.0–8.4 g/dl), and the plasma albumin was 3.1 g/dl (normal, 3.5–5.0 g/dl). A 72-hour stool collection, obtained to evaluate fat absorption, showed that the child was losing 8.7 g of fat/day (normal, <5 g/day) in the feces. Radiological examination revealed no abnormality of the skeletal system. The NaCl concentration of the sweat was high. A diagnosis of cystic fibrosis was made, with malabsorption and anemia secondary to the primary disease.

Comment: The nutritional effects of cystic fibrosis are mediated through the exocrine pancreas, in which the acini are replaced by fibrous and fatty tissue. Digestion and absorption are deficient because of the lack of pancreatic enzymes (proteases, amylase, and lipase; see Chapter 50). All glands are affected, and a common feature is the production of abnormally viscous mucus, which blocks small, tubular structures. The sweat glands also are involved, however, and they secrete no mucus. The concentrations of sodium and chloride in the perspiration are abnormally high, and this finding is diagnostic of cystic fibrosis. In this patient, the high content of fat in the feces (steatorrhea), because of the

deficiency of pancreatic lipase, confirmed the diagnosis.

Treatment: The patient was given supplemental pancreatic enzymes by mouth, accompanied by antacid compounds to protect against digestion by gastric protease (see Chapter 49). He was also placed on a diet that contained a large proportion of triglycerides composed of fatty acids of middle length, which are absorbed without being broken down and re-esterified (see Chapter 53, "Absorption of Fat by Enterocytes"); thus, lipase is not needed for their absorption. Fat-soluble vitamins and iron also were supplemented.

Outcome: The patient's nutritional state was improved markedly by the special diet, and he began to grow and gain weight. However, his long-term prognosis is not favorable because of the debilitating pulmonary changes that will occur, leading to chronic bronchitis, emphysema, and occasional bronchopneumonia (see Chapter 35).

*Yellow pigmentation of the skin caused by bilirubin.
**Strong white or blue light causes the oxidation of bilirubin to water-soluble derivatives that are excreted readily.

the body or synthesis of milk is accounted for by the cost of the metabolic transformations of foodstuffs to tissues and specific milk components such as lactose, stereospecific triglycerides, and a variety of specialized proteins.

Basal Metabolism

Basal metabolism is the metabolism needed to sustain the minimal normal activity of all cells of the body under normal conditions. It is expressed as the basal metabolic rate, or BMR. The conditions under which the BMR is measured must be specified. Usually, the expenditure of energy must be measured in the morning, when the individual is at rest (neither losing heat to nor gaining heat from the environment) and at least 12–15 hours after the last meal. The basal metabolic rate is assumed to be proportional to the area of the body surface. Thus, the BMR usually is expressed as kcal/m^2.

Because the area of body surface is difficult to measure, formulas have been developed to relate the BMR to body weight. In a wide range of animal species of various sizes, the relationship

$$BMR = 70 \text{ kcal/kg}^{0.75}/\text{day}$$

seems to hold. (Body weight raised to the 0.75 power is referred to as the *metabolic body size*.) However, a number of other factors also must be taken into account when the energy needs of individuals are estimated.

GENDER

Differences between the two genders are seen after about 2 years of age; the BMR of females typically is about 5%–10% less than that of males of the same size and age. The largest difference (18%–27%) occurs during adolescence and in young adults. This difference has been attributed to different body composition;

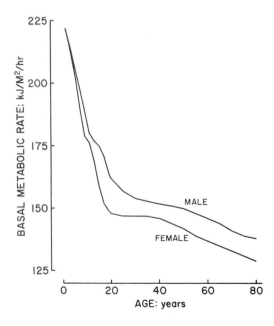

Figure 68-2. Basal metabolic rate for humans from 1 to 80 years of age.

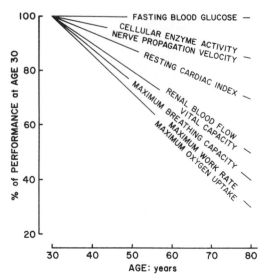

Figure 68-3. Performance levels of specific organs, systems, and tissues relative to values at age 30. (Redrawn, with permission, from Carlson, L.A. (ed.). 1972. *Nutrition in Old Age.* Uppsala, Sweden: The Swedish Nutrition Foundation.)

however, this factor does not account entirely for the dissimilarity.

AGE

The changes of metabolic rate with age (Figure 68-2) reflect changes in metabolism due to growth, alterations in body composition, and alterations caused by senescence. The decline of the BMR with age is paralleled by a decrease of lean body mass. To a considerable extent, the decline of the BMR (per unit of body weight) may reflect mass of different composition (more fat) added to or replacing lean body mass. However, a number of physiological characteristics change with age (Figure 68-3), and these changes also may contribute to the decline in the BMR.

RACE AND/OR NATIONALITY

A number of studies have indicated differences in the BMR among various racial and national groups. Differences in diet, exercise, and body composition have been offered as explanations for the differences in the BMR.

TEMPERATURE OF THE ENVIRONMENT

The environmental temperature at which the heat produced by basal metabolism is adequate

to maintain the normal body temperature is called the *critical temperature* (Figure 68-4). Above this temperature, excess heat is dissipated by the evaporation of water; below this temperature, more heat must be produced to keep the body warm (see Chapter 66).

DISEASE

The energy needs of the body may vary markedly in different disease states; energy needs are increased most in patients who are undergoing extensive healing and replacement of tissues. In burn patients, the rate of metabolism may be three to four times normal, and similar increases have been reported for patients who have malaria. In patients who have fever, the rate of metabolism increases about 13% with each centigrade degree of body temperature above normal. The metabolic rate is approximately unchanged in patients who undergo elective surgery, although in cases of major surgery it may double. After multiple bone fractures, increases in metabolic rate of 10%–25%, sustained for as long as 1 month, have been reported. Increased metabolic rates have been reported in cancer patients, but the increases depend on the age of the patient, the stage of disease, the type of cancer, and the mode of therapy.

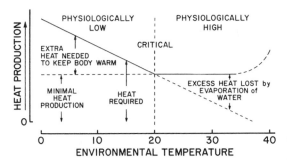

Figure 68-4. Heat production required to maintain body core temperature. At a critical temperature of the environment, minimal heat produced by the basal functions maintains the body core temperature. Below the critical temperature, more heat must be produced, and above the critical temperature, heat must be dissipated. (Redrawn, with permission, from Kleiber, M. 1975. *The Fire of Life: An Introduction to Animal Energetics.* p. 167 (Fig. 9.8). Robert E. Krieger Publishing Co., Inc., Malabar, Florida.)

SLEEP
The BMR is measured while the individual is awake. Measurements in sleeping subjects show that the metabolic rate is about 7% less than that obtained when the person is awake.

DIURNAL RHYTHM
Daily and seasonal variations in BMR of about 15% have been reported. Most of the studies have been done in small animals; few data on humans are available.

NUTRITIONAL STATE
Inadequate nutrition decreases the BMR substantially; however, decreased lean body mass cannot account for all of the decreased use of energy. In carefully controlled studies of partial starvation, 65% of the decrease in BMR could be attributed to decreased lean body mass, and the remaining 35% simply reflected decreased metabolic activity. The nature and cost of this adjustment are not understood completely.

The BMR is influenced markedly by recovery from malnutrition, particularly in children, who may gain weight at rates up to 20 times normal. During the period of rapid growth, the BMR is increased correspondingly. The energy costs of protein synthesis are be-lieved to account for a significant proportion of the basal metabolic expenditure. The rate of synthesis of protein in severely malnourished children before refeeding is low; after 8 days of refeeding, protein synthesis and the BMR both are increased significantly.

HORMONAL FACTORS
The production of hormones at different rates also contributes to the differences of metabolic rate among individuals. These variations may be caused by genetic, environmental, nutritional, pathological, and/or physiological conditions. The predominant role of thyroid hormones in the regulation of energy is well known. In addition, insulin, glucagon, glucocorticoids, growth hormone, prolactin, and melanocyte-stimulating hormone (MSH) are thermogenic to some extent. All of these hormones, except prolactin and MSH, act only in concert with the permissive action of the thyroid hormones. This relationship is not clear; however, the necessity of accompanying thyroid action suggests some factor in common. Adenylate cyclase, acting on the mitochondria to uncouple synthesis along the chain of electron transport or simply helping to increase the number of mitochondria, is the most likely common factor.

The thyroid hormones potentiate the calorigenic action of the catecholamines, norepinephrine and epinephrine, which also are important in maintaining the body temperature during adaptation to cold (see Chapter 66). Increased heat production during exposure to cold and after the administration of catecholamines at normal temperature is blocked by adrenergic β-receptor antagonists. Evidence obtained recently suggests that lean subjects produce more heat after the administration of catecholamines than obese subjects do. This response reflects more efficient use of energy in obese individuals, which may account in part for their excess storage of energy in adipose tissue. The mechanisms by which the catecholamines act may include increased oxidation of brown fat, increased glycolysis, and increased turnover of triglycerides.

Thermogenesis
Specific dynamic action (SDA) is a term applied to the increased production of heat after the ingestion of food. In the past, SDA has been

related to energy used in the digestion and metabolism of protein and, more specifically, to the production of urea. However, more recent studies have revealed little correlation between the magnitude of the SDA and the amount of urea that is produced. Furthermore, postprandial heat production is more complex than originally was thought.

Because of the nonspecific characteristics of SDA, the more general term *thermogenesis* often is used to designate the production of heat not associated with basal metabolic needs, work, growth, or the synthesis of milk. The variability of the thermogenic component of energy metabolism may account for many of the discrepancies observed between food intake and body weight. Many studies have shown that lean subjects maintain stable weight despite a wide range of energy intakes, and other studies have indicated that subjects of normal weight who are made obese experimentally by forced overeating require more energy to maintain the increased weight than spontaneously obese individuals do. These studies support the existence of a physiological mechanism that regulates the use of energy. The thermogenic component may be modulated by the efficiency with which energy is produced from substrates; thus, individuals who are "predisposed" to obesity may use energy more efficiently than those who are "predisposed" to leanness. The thermogenic component may be modulated through the recycling of glucose-6-phosphate, fructose, 1,6-diphosphate, and Cori cycle intermediates, through the fluxes of fatty acids between liver and adipose tissue, through the efficiency of active transport processes, and through the efficiency of ATP coupling in the mitochondria. Thermogenesis has been divided into five subgroups: (1) dietary-induced, (2) produced by isometric contraction of muscle, (3) cold-induced, (4) drug-induced, and (5) psychological.

DIETARY-INDUCED THERMOGENESIS

Dietary-induced thermogenesis is potentiated by exercise, frequent eating, and large meals. The mechanism of this increase of heat production is not understood. Possible explanations include increased rate of synthesis of protein and increased activity of high-energy-using metabolic cycles. Dietary-induced thermogenesis explains why some subjects need

more energy than others do to maintain weight gained by experimental overeating (see the previous section on thermogenesis).

MUSCLE TENSION

Muscle tension accounts for increased production of heat when muscles contract but no work is done. One example of this is supporting a load without moving; energy is expended but no work is performed.

COLD-INDUCED THERMOGENESIS

Cold-induced thermogenesis is a mechanism for maintaining body temperature. Cold-induced heat production usually is divided into shivering thermogenesis (muscular) and non-shivering thermogenesis (see Chapter 66). In adults, heat is produced mainly by contraction of muscles and in infants, by metabolism of brown fat. Recent studies indicate that adult humans also maintain significant amounts of brown fat, which may be important in the regulation of energy use. This regulation may be accomplished by cycles that produce heat but do not change the net amounts of substrates involved ("futile cycles"), that is, increased turnover of triglycerides in brown fat with no change in net synthesis or breakdown. People who have abnormally small amounts of brown fat or whose brown fat is unresponsive may be predisposed to obesity.

DRUG-INDUCED THERMOGENESIS

Drug-induced thermogenesis is common in modern society. Caffeine, alcohol, and nicotine all are calorigenic, but the mechanisms are not fully known. Ephedrine also is calorigenic, and obese animals treated with ephedrine lose body fat without decreasing their intake of food and without necessarily experiencing negative nitrogen balance (see Chapter 69). The effects of ephedrine and other drugs like it are more pronounced in obese subjects than in lean ones; nevertheless, drug treatment for obesity seldom is acceptable because of possible adverse side-effects. Positive energy balance (i.e., gain of weight) occurs only when intake exceeds use. Decreased intake and increased activity are the only physiological approaches to losing weight. Identifying the causes of inappropriate levels of energy intake or energy use should suggest the best approach to the treatment of obesity.

PSYCHOLOGICAL THERMOGENESIS

Psychological thermogenesis occurs in stressful situations and during emotional turmoil; increased sympathetic nervous system activity is one factor, but all of the mechanisms are not known.

Activity

Basal metabolism accounts for approximately 60% of the energy needs of the average adult and SDA accounts for about 5%; a person has little control over either of these factors. Activity, which accounts for the remaining 35% in the sedentary person, varies widely. People who have very active occupations (e.g., stevedores and construction workers) may require as much as 5000 kcal/day. In these individuals, activity may account for 60% of the net use of energy. For most people, various forms of intense athletic activity require the greatest amount of energy. To compare sources of energy intake and means of use, a person could, by activity alone, for example, expend the amount of energy provided by an "average" banana split (about 800 kcal) by sawing wood or rowing a boat for about 100 minutes. Exercise and controlled dietary intake are the only means known to maintain energy balance, although dietary-induced thermogenesis is a modifying factor.

MEASUREMENT OF ENERGY USE

Calculation

The use of energy can be measured directly by measuring the production of heat, although it usually is measured indirectly by calculating the consumption of O_2 and the production of CO_2. To use the latter method, one must know the number of calories produced per mole of CO_2 produced or O_2 consumed. Data for making these calculations are obtained most accurately under fasting conditions, in which catabolic processes predominate. When only glucose is oxidized, 5.1 kcal are produced per

mole of O_2 consumed, and when only fat is oxidized, 4.5 kcal are produced per mole of O_2 consumed. In practice, the rate of production of energy per mole of O_2 consumed varies between 4.5 and 5.1, depending on the proportions of fat and glucose metabolized. These proportions are determined from the respiratory quotient (RQ), which is the ratio of CO_2 produced to O_2 consumed. For glucose, the RQ is 1, and for fat it is 0.7. The relative contributions of energy from glucose and fat are calculated from measurements of RQ on the basis of stoichiometric relationships in the chemical equations that describe the oxidation of glucose and fat. Experimental methods that eliminate the effects of the oxidation of protein and minimize the errors introduced by anabolic processes have been developed.

Measurement in the Field

The use of energy is measured under field conditions by continuous monitoring of O_2 consumption or heart rate or by methods that document time spent in specific activities. The measurement of O_2 consumption requires cumbersome equipment that interferes with the performance of work and decreases efficiency. The second method requires the calibration of individual heart rates in terms of O_2 consumption. The effects on heart rate of posture and other factors not related to work limit the accuracy of this method. The third method is the least precise of all because it relies on tables of average values for energy required to perform specific activities and requires that the subject keep a diary of the time spent in performing those activities in the field.

Measurement in the Laboratory

The production of heat can be measured directly in the laboratory, using two principal types of calorimeters. The *heat-sink calorimeter* measures the loss of heat by the body into the ventilatory system of an insulated chamber. The *gradient-layer calorimeter* measures the production of heat by evaluating the temperature gradient across a well-described surface. Both methods are accurate, but the gradient-layer calorimeter has a much shorter response time.

ENERGY COST OF DEPOSITION OF FAT AND PROTEIN

Age and Rate of Growth

After infancy, under most conditions, the chemical composition of the fat-free portion of the body can be altered very little by nutritional means, except for the mineralization of bone. Chronic and severe undernutrition produces some change in this compartment, since stores of glycogen are small, the distribution of water between extracellular space and intracellular space is abnormal, intracellular concentrations of K^+ are decreased, and intracellular concentrations of Na^+ are increased. However, major changes in body composition involve the content of fat. In addition, the lipid and the lipid-free compartments do not grow synchronously—the lipid-free compartment reaches maximum size and levels off before the lipid compartment does. Therefore, the composition of weight gained depends on an individual's age, rate of growth, and, in selected circumstances, nutritional status.

Dietary Factors

Dietary factors influence the amount of fat deposited, and the net effect of diet is modulated by the maturity of the subject. The interrelationships between diet and maturity have been summarized as follows:

1. In growing animals, a decrease in the amount of an adequate diet slows the rate of deposition of fat more than it slows the rates of deposition of protein and minerals. Thus, at a given age, animals given less food contain less fat than animals given more food. At the end of the total growth period, the animals that are fed less food still contain less fat, even though they weigh the same as the animals who were fed more.
2. If the amount or quality of protein in the diet is decreased until the deposition of protein is impaired, the body accumulates fat. Animals fed diets low in protein are fatter than those given normal diets; this is true for animals that are both the same age and the same body weight.
3. The fat content of the body increases markedly as mature weight is approached. Even in adult animals, the deposition of fat is associated with the simultaneous deposition of protein. Approximately 10 mg of N (which is a measure of the deposition of protein) are deposited with each gram of fat. More substantial gains in lean body mass are possible only with the stimulation that accompanies physical activity.

Synthesis of Fat from Glucose

Theoretical calculations indicate that 0.43 kcal is lost from each gram of glucose converted to fatty acid. This is 10% of the heat available from the complete oxidation of glucose. Glucose is converted to glycogen at a cost of only 5% of the energy it contained initially. However, each gram of fat contains nine times as many calories as each gram of glycogen does, mainly because of the greater energy density of fat, but also because the water stored with glycogen decreases the energy density of the carbohydrate. By comparison, 0.28 kcal is lost from each gram of triglyceride that is hydrolyzed and re-esterified. This amount equals approximately 3% of the heat available from the complete oxidation of fat.

Synthesis of Proteins from Amino Acids

The estimation of the cost of protein synthesis is based on the assumption that each peptide bond requires four molecules of ATP. On this basis, one can calculate that 0.85 kcal is required to synthesize 1 g of protein. In growing animals, it is estimated that 1.37 g of protein must be synthesized for each gram of protein actually laid down. The complete oxidation of protein yields 5.4 kcal/g; therefore, the efficiency of net protein synthesis is

$$\frac{5.4 \text{ kcal/g}}{(0.85 \times 1.37) \text{ kcal/g} + 5.4 \text{ kcal/g}} = 0.82$$

These estimates of efficiency are higher than experimental values, but the reasons for the discrepancies are not well understood. The thermogenic components of energy use may be involved, and the rate of turnover of protein may have been underestimated.

ENERGY REQUIREMENTS

Energy requirements usually are calculated by summing the factors involved. In adults, energy use is grouped into three principal components: basal metabolism, activity, and thermogenesis. In children, growth also is considered.

Adults

The average energy requirement for moderately active men is 46 kcal/kg, and the average requirement for moderately active women is 42 kcal/kg. These amounts are based on measurements of the dietary intakes of moderately active adults 20–39 years of age. The range of energy intake in this group is wide—the best estimates are that 95% of the intakes are within ±30% of the mean. Recommended intakes of energy are set at the mean of the population to avoid recommending overconsumption of calories. In contrast, the recommended intakes of other nutrients are set high enough to cover the needs of 98% of the population for which they are intended.

As discussed earlier, age also affects energy need (see the sections entitled "Age" and "Age and Rate of Growth" earlier in this chapter). The rate of use of energy remains stable between 20 and 39 years of age but decreases by 5% during each decade between 40 and 59 and declines by 10% during each subsequent decade.

Pregnancy and Lactation

During pregnancy, additional energy is needed for the growth of the fetus, accumulation of various maternal tissues, and movement of the heavier mother. Increases in requirements of energy vary throughout pregnancy because the rates of accumulation of fetal and maternal tissues change. Currently, an additional 300 kcal/day is recommended during the first trimester, and an extra 350 kcal/day is recommended during the second and third trimesters. The difference between the estimate for the first trimester and the estimates for the second and third trimesters reflects the increased rate of deposition of fat in maternal tissues during the second trimester and in fetal tissues during the third trimester. Maternal fat stored during this period is mobilized during lactation. The consequences of inadequate deposition of fat by either the mother or the fetus are not well understood. The mother may not provide enough milk for the infant, and the infant may not adapt well to extrauterine conditions.

Lactation also requires additional energy. The average lactating woman produces about 850 ml of milk, which has an average energy content of 0.7 kcal/ml, or 600 kcal, per day. Experiments with animals suggest that the conversion of food energy to milk is 80% efficient. Therefore, about 750 kcal/day are needed. Part of this increased need is met by energy stored during pregnancy, which amounts to about 36,000 kcal. If the woman lactates for 6 months, an additional 100,000 kcal, or about 550 kcal/day, must be obtained from the diet.

Infants and Children

Infants and children need additional energy for growth; during the first 4 months of life, 20%–30% of the caloric intake is used for that purpose. Between 4 months and 1 year, 5% is needed, between 1 and 2 years of age, about 2% is needed, and between 2 and 3 years, less than 1% is needed. If one assumes that normal tissue added during growth contains 10% fat, 18% protein, and 70% water, an energy cost of 4–5 kcal/g of tissue is obtained. This value reflects about 15 kcal/g of protein and 13 kcal/g of fat deposited. These estimates include the energy used for synthesis and the energy content of the protein and fat synthesized.

After periods of infection or inadequate diet, the rate of growth is accelerated. Rates up to 20 times normal have been reported, but rates about five times normal are more common. This factor should be taken into account when determining the energy needs of children under these conditions.

Hospitalized Patients

Most hospitalized patients are significantly less active than healthy people. If the hospitalized patients are severely restricted, their energy requirements may be only about 5%–10% more than basal metabolic needs. Most ambulatory patients require about 20% more than basal needs, but these values do not include increased needs due to fever, repair of tissues, neoplasms, neurological disorders, malabsorption, or other causes.

ENERGY CONSUMPTION OF VARIOUS TISSUES

Energy Stores

Energy stores are regulated through the control of intake, activity, and the efficiency of use. At all ages, the major store of energy is fat. Although the means of regulating the adipose compartment are unclear, they probably exist. The lean body mass decreases slightly during adult life, but it is fairly well stabilized after infancy and is used as a source of energy only during periods of prolonged fasting (see Chapter 69).

Substrate Use by Different Tissues

Tissues may be classified according to the energy substrate used. Tissues that obtain most of their energy from the oxidation of free fatty acids are cardiac muscle, liver, renal cortex, and, except in severe exercise, skeletal muscle. Cardiac muscle, renal cortex, skeletal muscle, and brain can obtain energy from the oxidation of ketone bodies. Many tissues depend on glucose as a major source of energy; these are brain, leukocytes, lymphocytes, mammalian erythrocytes, renal medulla, retina, some fetal tissues, some malignant tumors, and skeletal muscle during severe exercise.

ENERGY USE DURING STARVATION

Studies of starving animals reveal that the effects on organ systems vary among different species. The liver, small intestine, heart, and pancreas are among the organs most affected by starvation. No comparable data for humans are available; however, clinical observations of cases of partial starvation suggest that fat stores are diminished and lean body mass is lost in humans approximately as they are in lower animals.

Partial Starvation

The effects of partial starvation depend on the degree of starvation (extent and duration of deprivation) and the energy substrate provided. Partial starvation in human subjects—1579 kcal/day derived from 54.5 g of protein, 27.1 g of fat, and normal amounts of vitamins and minerals, except for riboflavin and vitamin A—causes loss of active tissue equivalent to about 28 g/day during the first 12 weeks and 10 g/day during the second 12 weeks. In these subjects, fat was lost at the rate of 56 g/day during the first 12 weeks and 26 g/day during the second 12 weeks. These changes indicate that the energy deficit decreases as starvation continues; the reasons are decreased BMR and

decreased spontaneous activity (Figure 68-5). The reduction of BMR is disproportionately greater than the loss of actively metabolizing tissue, which indicates a decreased rate of metabolism in the surviving tissue. Severely malnourished individuals in undeveloped countries, who have chronically low intakes of protein and calories, also have lower BMRs than the loss of actively metabolizing tissues alone would cause.

Fasting

Studies of fuel used during fasting show that 17% of the calories come from protein during the early phase. The human subject cannot tolerate loss of protein beyond one-third to one-half of the lean body mass, and would die in 25–46 days if the use of protein continued at the same rate. In total and partial starvation, adaptive mechanisms permit significant sparing of lean body mass by increasing the oxidation of free fatty acids (Figure 68-6) in response to the decreased concentration of insulin in the blood or the decreased ratio of insulin to glucagon. This makes more free fatty acids available for oxidation and the production of ketones. The success of this adaptation is due principally to increased use of ketones by the central nervous system. The rate of use of protein in gluconeogenesis decreases as the production and use of ketones increase.

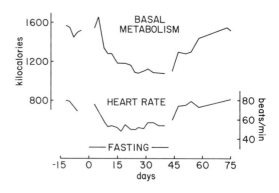

Figure 68-5. Decrease of basal metabolic rate (BMR) during 42 days of starvation in humans. The decreased heart rate reflects the decreased rate of work by various organ systems, which is partially responsible for the decreased BMR. (Redrawn, with permission, from Kleitman, N. 1926. Basal metabolism in prolonged fasting in man. *Am. J. Physiol.* 77:236.)

INFANTS

The normal fasting infant switches from dietary carbohydrate to endogenous fat as the major source of energy much faster than the adult does. However, infants experience relatively less ketosis. In a series of studies, malnourished infants were subjected to periods of fasting before and after they were placed on an adequate diet. After 21 hours of fasting, the malnourished infants obtained 94% of their energy from fat, and after 27 hours of fasting, previously malnourished infants who had been repleted with a normal diet obtained 92% of their energy from fat. During fasting, protein provided 4% of the energy needed by the malnourished infants and 7% of that needed by the repleted infants. By contrast, well-nourished adults who fasted for comparable periods obtained about 13% of their energy from protein. Despite their quicker adaptation, the overall rate of catabolism in infants still is 40% greater than that of adults. Plasma concentrations of glycerol, free fatty acids, β-hydroxybutyrate, and acetoacetate increased in the infants during fasting, both before and after repletion.

However, free fatty acids, β-hydroxybutyrate, and acetoacetate increased less in the infants studied before repletion.

Amino Acids

The adaptation to fasting also is reflected in the plasma concentrations of amino acids. Three compounds particularly are affected (Figure 68-7): (1) the concentration of valine first increases and then decreases, (2) the concentration of alanine decreases, and (3) the concentration of glycine increases. The temporary increase of valine represents an increased breakdown of muscle, and the early decrease of alanine reflects increased use of that compound for gluconeogenesis early in starvation. The delayed increase of glycine has not been explained adequately.

Ketoacids

The production and use of ketoacids increase early in starvation. The increased production of ketones is made possible by increased lipolysis, and the increased use of ketones apparently depends on their increased availability. Thus, increased production increases use until a steady state is reached.

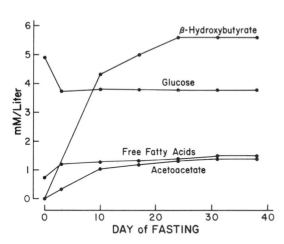

Figure 68-6. The concentrations of free fatty acids and ketones in the blood during fasting. The increased contribution of free fatty acids to net energy use depends on increased hydrolysis of triglycerides, subsequent release of fatty acids from fat depots, and increased production of ketone bodies. Increased oxidation of fat spares body proteins and decreases the concentration of glucose in the blood. (Redrawn, with permission, from "How Metabolism Affects Clinical Problems" by G.F. Cahill, Jr., and T.A. Aoki in *Medical Times* [Vol. 98, No. 10.])

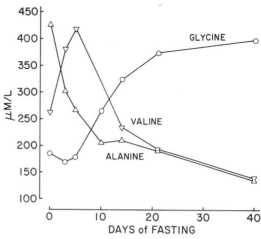

Figure 68-7. Changes in serum amino acid levels during prolonged fasting. (Redrawn, with permission, from "How Metabolism Affects Clinical Problems" by G.F. Cahill, Jr., and T.A. Aoki in *Medical Times* [Vol. 98, No. 10.])

Insulin and Glucagon

The changes in the plasma concentrations of hormones during prolonged fasting are illustrated in Figure 68-8. Insulin appears to be the most important hormone in the adaptation to starvation; the other hormones fulfill secondary but supportive functions. The interactions of insulin and glucagon are shown schematically in Figure 68-9. According to this scheme, a decrease of insulin allows increased lipolysis. The increased glucagon:insulin ratio apparently causes increased conversion of fatty acids to ketone through an undefined mechanism.

NORMAL SUBSTRATE USE

In a person at rest after a meal, mainly glucose is oxidized if the diet is balanced in carbohydrate, fat, and protein. Protein not used in normal maintenance is catabolized to urea, glucose, and/or fat. Excess carbohydrate is stored as glycogen and/or fat, depending on glycogen stores and total caloric intake. Excess fat is stored in adipose tissue; no fat is converted to glucose.

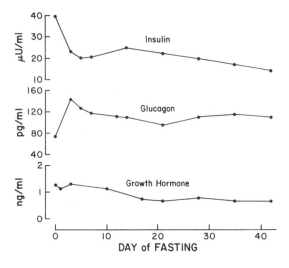

Figure 68-8. Changes in hormone levels as fasting continues. The decreased concentration of insulin is essential to the increased hydrolysis of triglycerides. Increased glucagon promotes the use of fatty acids and may help to direct the oxidation of those compounds toward the production of ketones. The changes in growth hormone are consistent with catabolism and the altered use of substrates. (Redrawn, with permission, from "How Metabolism Affects Clinical Problems" by G.F. Cahill, Jr., and T.A. Aoki in *Medical Times* [Vol. 98, No. 10.])

ENERGY USE DURING EXERCISE

Substrates

During light and moderate work, carbohydrate and fat each provide about half of the energy used; protein provides little energy. The relative contributions of fat and carbohydrate to energy usage depend on the type and duration of work performed, the diet, the state of physi-

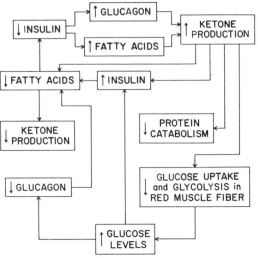

Figure 68-9. Homeostatic control of substrate use during fasting.

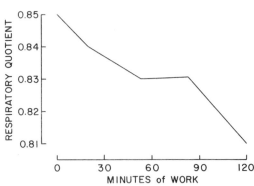

Figure 68-10. Increased use of fat, indicated by decrease of the respiratory quotient (RQ) as work proceeds. The use of substrates depends on the duration and intensity of the work and the physical condition and diet of the subject. (From *Textbook of Work Physiology: Physiological Bases of Exercise* by P.O. Aastrand and K. Rodahl (2nd ed.). Copyright © 1977. Used with the permission of McGraw-Hill Book Company.)

cal training, and the health of the subject. As work continues, an increasing proportion of fat is used (Figure 68-10); however, the more intense the work, the greater the use of carbohydrate. The dependence on glucose during exercise is significant. In people who are fasting, the concentration of glucose in the blood may decrease enough to cause adverse symptoms. Glycogen stores in muscle are exhausted after about 90 minutes of exercise at 77% of maximum aerobic power (Figure 68-11). Although the liver provides some glucose for the muscles, about 60% of liver glycogen is allocated to the central nervous system.

Hormonal Effects

The decrease of plasma insulin that accompanies the decrease of plasma glucose, and the decrease of hexokinase activity that occurs when the products of glycogen breakdown accumulate in muscle serve to decrease the uptake of glucose by muscle, which permits more glucose to be used by the brain. The hormonal modulation of energy use during work is summarized in Figure 68-12.

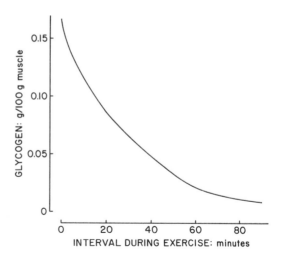

Figure 68-11. Depletion of muscle glycogen with increasing duration of exercise. (From *Textbook of Work Physiology: Physiological Bases of Exercise* by P.O. Aastrand and K. Rodahl (2nd ed.). Copyright © 1977. Used with permission of McGraw-Hill Book Company.)

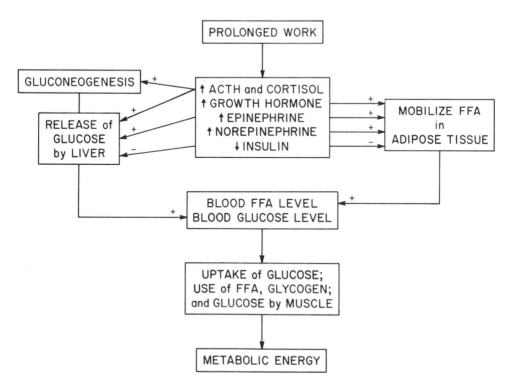

Figure 68-12. Secretion of hormones and use of substrates during exercise. The changes are similar to the changes that occur during fasting. (Redrawn, with permission, from Pruett, E.D.R. *Fat and Carbohydrate Metabolism in Exercise and Recovery and Its Dependence on Work Load Severity.* Universitetsforlagets Trykkningssentral, Oslo, Norway, p. 20, 1971.)

STUDY OUTLINE

SOURCES   Carbohydrate, fat, protein, and alcohol; energy is measured in calories (cal), kilocalories (kcal), and kilojoules (kj).

ENERGY CONTENT
COMPLETE OXIDATION   Carbohydrate—4.1 kcal/g; fat—9.4 kcal/g; protein—5.6 kcal/g.
Oxidation of nitrogen produces 1.3 kcal/g of protein not available to body; net is 4.3 kcal/g of protein.
DIGESTIBILITY COEFFICIENTS   Decrease energy used physiologically.
Carbohydrate and protein—4 kcal/g; fat—9 kcal/g; alcohol—7 kcal/g.
ENERGY DENSITY   Fat is greatest; principal energy store.
All protein stores are structural or functional.
Excess protein in diet is converted to carbohydrate or fat.

EFFICIENCY   About 20% of food energy is used for work; 80% goes to heat.
Transformed through phosphate bonds of ATP.
Carbohydrate is most efficient per O_2 used.
Fat is most efficient per weight.

USE OF ENERGY   Basal metabolism, thermogenesis, and work; under special conditions, also for growth and production of milk.

BASAL METABOLISM   Need for minimal normal maintenance.
BMR is measured at rest, postabsorptive; related to kcal/m² or body weight raised to 0.75 power.
GENDER   BMR of adult males is approximately 5%–10% more than females'; caused partly by different body composition.
AGE   BMR decreases with age, parallels decrease of lean body mass.
RACE AND/OR NATIONALITY   Differences of BMR are caused by diet, exercise, and body composition.
TEMPERATURE OF THE ENVIRONMENT   Below critical temperature, BMR increases to keep body warm; above critical temperature, excess heat is dissipated.
DISEASE   BMR is normal or increased.
SLEEP   BMR decreases slightly.
DIURNAL RHYTHM   BMR varies approximately 15% during day.
NUTRITIONAL STATE   BMR decreases in starvation; increases with repletion and growth.
HORMONAL FACTORS   Several hormones are thermogenic, but require permissive action of thyroid hormones.

Thyroid hormones potentiate actions of catecholamines.
Effect of cold is largely through catecholamines.
Catecholamines increase glycolysis, turnover of triglycerides, and heat produced by brown fat; effects are greater in lean subjects than in obese subjects.

THERMOGENESIS   Production of heat not associated with basal metabolism, activity, growth, or synthesis of milk.
Difference may determine predisposition to leanness or obesity.
DIETARY-INDUCED THERMOGENESIS   Increased production of heat after ingestion of food; potentiated by exercise, frequent eating, and large meals.
Important factor in efficiency of using energy.
MUSCLE TENSION   When no work is done, produces only heat.
COLD-INDUCED THERMOGENESIS   Mechanism for maintaining body temperature.
Shivering—involuntary contraction of muscle.
Nonshivering—metabolism of brown fat.
DRUG-INDUCED THERMOGENESIS   Caffeine, nicotine, and alcohol.
Drug treatment of obesity usually is not acceptable because of possible adverse side-effects; diet and exercise are preferable.
PSYCHOLOGICAL THERMOGENESIS   Caused by emotional stress.

ACTIVITY   About 35% of average energy use in sedentary person, but under voluntary control.
Sixty percent or more of energy use in very active people.

MEASUREMENT OF ENERGY USE

CALCULATION   Estimate production of heat associated with consumption of O_2 and production of CO_2.
RQ (respiratory quotient)—ratio of CO_2 produced to O_2 consumed in fasting state.
Varies with proportions of carbohydrates and fat in diet.

MEASUREMENT IN THE FIELD   Crude at best.
Measure O_2 consumption.
Measure heart rate.
Use standard rates for specific activities.

MEASUREMENT IN THE LABORATORY   Use calorimeters.

ENERGY COST OF DEPOSITION OF FAT AND PROTEIN

AGE AND RATE OF GROWTH   Help determine composition.

DIETARY FACTORS   In growing animals, decreased amount of adequate diet decreases fat stores more than lean mass.

If calories are adequate but protein intake is inadequate, body accumulates fat.

Fat content increases with maturity.

SYNTHESIS OF FAT FROM GLUCOSE   Glucose to fat uses 10% of energy of glucose.

Glucose to glycogen uses 5% of energy of glucose.

Fatty acid to triglyceride uses 3% of energy of fat.

SYNTHESIS OF PROTEINS FROM AMINO ACIDS   Uses 18% of energy.

ENERGY REQUIREMENTS   Sum of basal metabolism, thermogenesis, and activity; in children, also growth.

ADULTS   Stable during ages 20–40, decreases 5% per decade from ages 40–60, decreases 10% per decade thereafter.

PREGNANCY AND LACTATION   Additional energy is needed for growth of fetus, accumulation of maternal tissues, and to move heavier mother; extra 300 kcal/day is recommended during first trimester, 350 kcal/day during second and third trimesters.

Lactation requires about 750 kcal/day extra.

INFANTS AND CHILDREN   Extra energy is needed for growth—4–5 kcal/g of tissue deposited.

More energy is needed after periods of infection or inadequate diet.

HOSPITALIZED PATIENTS   Less active—energy needs are decreased, depending on fever, wound healing, and other factors.

ENERGY CONSUMPTION OF VARIOUS TISSUES

ENERGY STORES   Mainly fat.

Regulated through intake, activity, and efficiency of use.

SUBSTRATE USE BY DIFFERENT TISSUES   Cardiac muscle, liver, renal cortex, and skeletal muscle (except in severe exercise) use mostly free fatty acids.

Cardiac muscle, renal cortex, skeletal muscle, and brain can oxidize ketone bodies.

Many other tissues depend mostly on glucose.

ENERGY USE DURING STARVATION   Fat stores and lean body mass are lost.

PARTIAL STARVATION   Effects depend on extent and duration of deprivation.

Caloric deficit decreases as BMR and activity decrease.

FASTING   At first, protein is lost rapidly.

Increased oxidation of free fatty acids spares lean body mass.

Central nervous system uses ketones more.

INFANTS   Switch to endogenous fat faster than adults do.

AMINO ACIDS   Plasma levels reflect metabolic changes.

KETOACIDS   Production and use increase early in starvation.

INSULIN AND GLUCAGON   Decreased insulin allows lipolysis.

Increased glucagon:insulin ratio increases conversion of fatty acids to ketone.

NORMAL SUBSTRATE USE   Mainly glucose oxidized if diet is balanced.

Excess protein is catabolized.

Excess carbohydrate is stored as glycogen or fat.

Excess fat is stored in adipose tissue.

ENERGY USE DURING EXERCISE

SUBSTRATES   Carbohydrate and fat are used but little protein.

As rate of work increases, proportion of fat used increases.

HORMONAL EFFECTS   Adrenocorticotropic hormone (ACTH), growth hormone, and catecholamines increase; insulin decreases.

Effects combine to increase gluconeogenesis in liver, mobilize fat from adipose tissue.

BIBLIOGRAPHY

Åstrand, P., and Rodahl, K. 1977. *Textbook of Work Physiology: Physiological Bases of Exercise* (2nd ed.). New York: McGraw-Hill.

Atkinson, R.L., Jr., and Bray, G.A. 1978. Energy balance in obesity and its relationship to diabetes mellitus. *Diabetes, Obesity, and Vascular Disease: Metabolic and Molecular Interrelationships.* Edited by H.M. Katzen and R.J. Mahler. New York: Wiley.

Bell, G.H.; Emslie-Smith, D.; and Paterson, C.R. 1976. *Textbook of Physiology and Biochemistry* (9th ed.). Edinburgh: Churchill Livingstone.

Blaxter, K.L. 1973. Energy utilization and obesity in domesticated animals. In *Obesity in Perspective.* Volume 2. Part 2. Edited by G.A. Bray. Bethesda, Maryland: Government Printing Office (DHEW Publication No. [NIH] 75–708).

Fomon, S.J. 1974. *Infant Nutrition* (2nd ed.). Philadelphia: Saunders.

Grande, F., and Keys, A. 1980. Body weight, body composition, and calorie status. In *Modern Nutrition in Health and Disease* (6th ed.). Chapter 1. Edited by R.S. Goodhart and M.E. Shils. Philadelphia: Lea & Febiger.

Himms-Hagen, J. 1976. Cellular thermogenesis. *Ann. Rev. Physiol.* 38:315.

Joint FAO/WHO Ad Hoc Expert Committee. 1973. Energy and protein requirements. *World Health Organization Technical Reports Series*, No. 522. Geneva, Switzerland: World Health Organization.

Keys, A.; Brozek, J.; Henschel, A., et al. 1950. *The Biology of Human Starvation.* Volume 1. Minneapolis: The University of Minnesota Press.

Kleiber, M. 1975. *The Fire of Life: An Introduction to Animal Energetics.* Malabar, Florida: Krieger.

Kleitman, N. 1926. Basal metabolism in prolonged fasting in man. *Am. J. Physiol.* 77:233.

Krebs, H.A.; Williamson, D.H.; Bates, M.W., et al. 1970. The role of ketone bodies in caloric homeostasis. *Adv. Enzyme Regul.* 9:387.

Lehninger, A.L. 1975. *Principles of Biochemistry.* New York: Worth Publishers.

Miller, D.S. 1973. Overfeeding in man. *Obesity in Perspective.* Volume 2. Part 2. Edited by G.A. Bray. Bethesda, Maryland: Government Printing Office (DHEW Publication Co. [NIH] 75–708).

Munro, H.N. 1964. General aspects of the regulation of protein metabolism by diet and by hormones. In *Mammalian Protein Metabolism.* Volume I. New York: Academic Press.

Symposia of the Swedish Nutrition Foundation. 1972. *Nutrition in Old Age.* Uppsala, Sweden: Almqvist & Wiksell.

Van Itallie, T.B.; Gale, S.K.; and Kissileff, H.R. 1978. Control of food intake in the regulation of depot fat: An overview. *Diabetes, Obesity, and Vascular Disease: Metabolic and Molecular Interrelationships.* Edited by H.M. Katzen and R.J. Mahler. New York: Wiley.

Wannemacher, R.W., Jr.; Pace, J.G.; Beall, F.A., et al. 1979. Role of the liver in regulation of ketone body production during sepsis. *J. Clin. Invest.* 64:1565.

Williamson, D.H., and Hems, R. 1970. Metabolism and function of ketone bodies. In *Essays in Cell Metabolism.* Edited by W. Bartley, H.L. Kornberg, and J.R. Quayle. New York: Wiley.

Wimpfheimer, C.; Saville, E.; Voirol, M.J., et al. 1979. Starvation-induced decreased sensitivity of resting metabolic rate to triiodothyronine. *Science* 205:1272.

69

Protein

CHAPTER CONTENTS

GENERAL BACKGROUND

The body requires protein in the diet, and certain amino acids in particular. The body needs protein because it cannot synthesize specific amino acids de novo or reuse hydrolyzed endogenous protein with 100% efficiency. Certain amino acids can be synthesized from others, but eight or nine of the 20 amino acids that make up most proteins must be included in the diet because the body cannot synthesize the appropriate carbon skeletons. These amino acids are classified as *essential,* or *indispensable.* In two of these compounds, threonine and lysine, the system cannot attach amino groups to the appropriate carbon skeletons. The 11 remaining amino acids are called *nonessential,* or *dispensable*—the latter term is gaining popularity. However, the body probably could not synthesize enough of all 11 nonessential amino acids to maintain normal turnover of protein if those compounds were eliminated from the diet completely for a long time.

The amount of protein assimilated depends on the food ingested and the hormonal balance and individual variation of the subject. In addition, it also depends on age, gender, race (possibly), body composition, nutritional factors, presence of diseases, extent of physical activity, what drugs have been taken, and whether the subject is pregnant or lactating.

The terms *protein* and *nitrogen* often are used interchangeably in discussions of protein metabolism. This is done because protein can be identified most easily by the nitrogen it contains. Nonprotein compounds of nitrogen also occur in the diet and the body, but they are only a small part of the total. Because the average protein is 16% nitrogen, the amount of nitrogen in a sample multiplied by 6.25 gives the amount of protein represented in the sample.

923

REQUIREMENTS

Estimation

The amount of protein required usually is estimated by adding the obligatory losses in the urine, feces, and skin, and, when appropriate, the needs for growth and/or lactation. However, no protein is used with 100% efficiency, and the greater the amount of protein in the diet, the less efficiently the protein is used. Egg albumin, for example, is used with only about 70% efficiency when enough is consumed to satisfy the minimum requirement for protein. Dietary intakes of protein less than the minimum requirement are used more efficiently but do not satisfy the needs of the body. Intakes above the minimum requirement are used with progressively less efficiency. Because protein is not stored, in the sense that carbohydrates and lipids are deposited for later use, excess protein in the diet is catabolized in the liver and the kidneys. The carbon skeletons are used immediately for energy or are stored as glycogen or fat, and the nitrogen is excreted as urea and ammonia. Requirements of protein at various ages are summarized in Table 69-1 as milligrams of nitrogen per kilogram of body weight (100 mg of nitrogen is equivalent to 625 mg of protein). Requirements related to body weight decrease with age.

Caloric Intake and Protein Use

The relationship between total calories consumed and efficiency of using protein in normal adults is illustrated in Figures 69-1 and

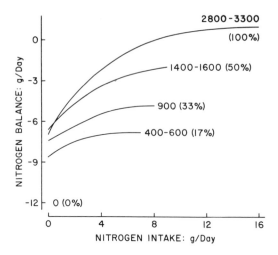

Figure 69-1.   Nitrogen balance at various levels of intake of nitrogen (protein) and energy. The numbers above or to the right of each curve give the energy ingested per day, in kilocalories, and the numbers in parentheses give the percentage of the total energy use provided by the diet. At any level of ingestion of protein, increasing the intake of energy improves the nitrogen balance, and at any level of ingestion of energy, increasing the intake of protein improves the nitrogen balance. (From Greene, H.L., Holiday, M.A., Monroe, H.N. (eds.). *Clinical Nutrition Update: Amino Acids.* Chicago: American Medical Association, 1977.)

69-2. If the intake of protein is not severely restricted, increasing the number of calories consumed improves the balance between uptake and excretion of nitrogen, and if the intake of energy is not severely restricted, increasing the content of protein improves the balance. However, when energy is severely limited, the

TABLE 69-1
Protein requirements of humans
(milligrams of nitrogen per kilogram of body weight per day)

Age	Maintenance	Growth	Efficiency (%)	Total requirement
6–8 mo	112	42	77	200
9–11 mo	110	26	77	177
1 yr	104	16	77	156
3 yr	96	10	77	138
5 yr	86	10	77	126
7 yr	73	8	77	114
9 yr	73	7	77	104
Adult	54	0	77	70

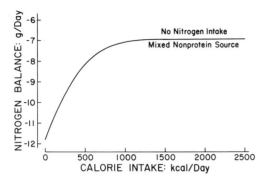

Figure 69-2. Nitrogen balance at various levels of ingestion of energy when no protein is taken. Endogenous nitrogen made available by normal protein turnover is used more efficiently as energy intake is increased from 0 to 750 kcal/day. Further increase does not increase the efficiency of use. This observation is significant clinically when a patient may be provided with only protein-free energy sources. (Redrawn, with permission, from Greene, H.L., Holiday, M.A., and Monroe, H.N. (eds.). *Clinical Nutrition Update: Amino Acids.* Chicago: American Medical Association, 1977.)

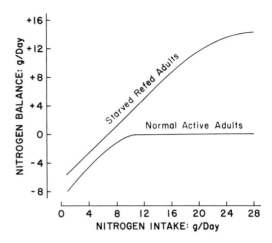

Figure 69-3. Nitrogen retention in normal adults, refed after a period of starvation, and in normally fed adults. Depleted subjects can use protein more efficiently than normally nourished subjects can. (Redrawn, with permission, from Greene, H.L., Holiday, M.A., and Monroe, H.N. (eds.). *Clinical Nutrition Update: Amino Acids.* Chicago: American Medical Association, 1977.)

addition of protein has little effect on the nitrogen balance (Figure 69-1), and when protein is severely limited, additional calories have little effect on the use of protein (Figure 69-2). When protein and calories both are ingested in either adequate or slightly subadequate amounts, the addition of calories improves the use of protein by 2–4 mg of nitrogen per kilocalorie of nonprotein energy. Adding protein to the diet under the same conditions causes the retention of about four times as much nitrogen per kilocalorie of protein added. Individuals recovering from severe protein deficiencies use the protein in the diet much more efficiently (Figure 69-3), provided they are under no other significant stress, such as infection or trauma.

USE OF PROTEIN

Overview

The daily turnover of protein is illustrated in Figure 69-4. The turnover of protein decreases significantly with age (Table 69-2), which probably accounts for the different requirements of children and adults for essential amino acids and protein. Since the amount of protein consumed affects the efficiency of protein use, the daily turnover and rate of oxidation of protein should vary with the intake. In animal experiments, rates of oxidation and turnover increase as much as 10%–20% above control several hours after a meal. In contrast, under the usual dietary conditions, the net rate of synthesis of protein (total synthesis minus breakdown) in normal children and adults does not depend immediately on the amount of protein in the diet. However, in obese adults on very low-energy diets, the intake of protein does influence the rate of synthesis. Subjects on low-energy diets that contain protein synthesize protein at higher rates than do subjects on low-energy diets that do not contain protein. These data suggest that when neither energy

TABLE 69-2
Turnover of body protein and rate of synthesis of total body protein in humans at various ages

Age group	Nitrogen flux (mg/kg/hr)	Total body protein synthesis (g/kg/day)
Newborn (premature)	124	17
Infant (10–20 mo)	65	7
Young adult	26	3
Elderly	19	2

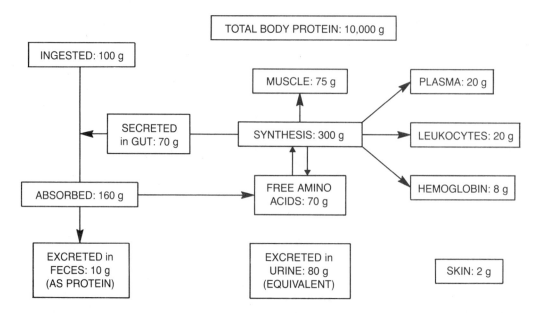

Figure 69-4.   Turnover of body protein in a 70-kg person. Under steady-state conditions, about 300 g of protein is synthesized and broken down each day. The protein requirement is only about 60 g/day because of the reuse of the products of endogenous protein hydrolysis. (Redrawn, with permission, from Greene, H.L., Holiday, M.A., and Monroe, H.N. (eds.). *Clinical Nutrition Update: Amino Acids.* Chicago: American Medical Association, 1977.)

nor protein is a limiting factor, the net rate of synthesis is determined by the body mass or the capacity for growth, but when energy is a limiting factor, protein synthesis is affected.

A subject's nutritional status also influences the rate of synthesis of protein. The rate is much lower in malnourished children than in rapidly growing and repleted infants (Figure 69-5). When the intakes of both calories and protein are increased, the rates of synthesis and breakdown of protein are increased (Figure 69-6). These data, like those given above, suggest that when energy is limited, the system may adapt by changing the rates of breakdown and synthesis of protein.

Studies of the synthesis of protein in the whole body have been difficult to conduct and interpret because at least five variables must be controlled: age, nutritional state, the level of dietary energy, the level of dietary protein, and levels of stress. Metabolic stress, caused by infection or trauma, is particularly important because it decreases the efficiency of use of protein. No clear evidence indicates whether the loss of nitrogen under stress is caused by increased breakdown or decreased synthesis. In one condition, diabetes mellitus, the rate of synthesis of protein is low in the absence of

treatment with insulin but increases one and one-half to twofold after treatment. However, this example may not be representative because of the direct role insulin plays in the synthesis of protein.

Role of the Gastrointestinal Tract

The gastrointestinal tract affects protein metabolism significantly through the secretion of protein (enzymes), the frequent replacement of cells (see Chapter 46), digestion-absorption, and the transamination of amino acids, especially glutamic acid and aspartic acid. The effect of bypassing the gut (total parenteral nutrition) on the utilization of amino acids has not been completely evaluated. The rapid turnover of gastrointestinal tissue makes this system particularly sensitive to deficiencies of protein and energy.

Liver

CATABOLISM

In the absorptive phase, the liver is an important factor in the catabolism of excess amino acids. It can degrade as much as half of the

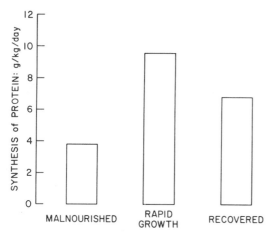

Figure 69-5. Protein synthesis in malnourished, convalescing (rapid growth), and repleted children. The rate of synthesis of protein depends on the state of nutrition. (Redrawn, with permission, from Waterlow, J.C., et al. 1978. *Protein Turnover in Mammalian Tissues and in the Whole Body.* New York: Elsevier North-Holland.)

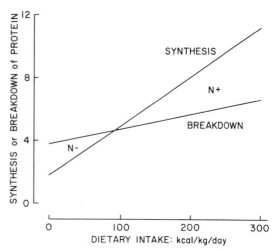

Figure 69-6. General relationship between the energy content of the diet and the rates of synthesis and breakdown of protein. N$^+$ is positive nitrogen balance, and N$^-$ is negative nitrogen balance. The rates are affected by the amount of protein consumed, the amount of energy consumed, the nutritional state of the subject, any stress the subject experiences, and the age or physiological state of the subject. If none of the other factors is abnormal, the rates of synthesis and breakdown of protein increase with increasing ingestion of energy. (Redrawn, with permission, from Waterlow, J.C., et al. 1978. *Protein Turnover in Mammalian Tissues and in the Whole Body.* New York: Elsevier North-Holland.)

amino acids that come to it in the portal vein. The liver is the major, perhaps exlusive, site for the degradation of most essential amino acids, although branched-chain amino acids are degraded in muscle and the kidneys. Nonessential amino acids are degraded by most tissues. The catabolism of amino acids in the liver is limited by the capacities of the appropriate enzymes.

CONTENT

The protein content of the liver, unlike that of most organs, may change continuously. In animals trained to eat only once a day, liver protein reaches a maximum about 12 hours after the meal and then decreases, reaching a minimum 24 hours after the meal. The activities of specific enzymes also change. This modulation of total protein content is caused primarily by changes in the rate of breakdown. Feeding malnourished animals increases the protein content of the liver markedly, because the rate of synthesis increases, and the rate of breakdown decreases.

SYNTHESIS AND RELEASE

Proteins that serve various physiological functions are synthesized and released by the liver (see Chapter 51). These compounds are important clinically because they indicate the

protein status of the body. The liver also is important in the interconversion of amino acids through transamination and deamination reactions. A decrease in the supply of amino acids to the liver decreases the synthesis of such proteins as retinol-binding protein and prealbumin. In very severe cases of protein deficiency, the synthesis of albumin also decreases. Although the rates of synthesis of these proteins are known to decrease, any changes in the rates of breakdown are not clear. The effects of a protein-free diet on protein balance in the liver are shown in Figure 69-7.

When the intake of energy is restricted chronically, without changing the proportions of carbohydrate, fat, and protein, the synthesis and release of proteins from the liver are maintained. However, if the total intake of energy is increased to normal, but the protein content is not normal, the synthesis and release of proteins decrease, the concentration of plasma proteins decreases, and generalized edema, fatty liver, and marked skin changes develop.

CLINICAL CORRELATION
69.1   Neonatal Jaundice

CASE REPORT

The Patient: A 2-month-old male.

Principal Complaint: Prolonged neonatal jaundice.

History: The child's gestation and early neonatal course had been uncomplicated. His birthweight (3.0 kg) and length (43 cm) were appropriate for his gestational age of 40 wk. The infant had breastfed exclusively the first month, after which he was given artificial formula. At two months of age, he had not gained weight and was jaundiced (yellow pigmentation of the skin caused by bilirubin), although he had no other signs or symptoms of illness. There was no history of infection, allergies, or drug ingestion, and there was no family history of hepatic or other gastrointestinal illnesses. An older sibling was healthy.

Clinical Examination: The infant was small, irritable, and mildly jaundiced. Weight and length were below the 3rd percentile. Examination of the head, eyes, ears, nose, and throat revealed no abnormality except for marked dolichocephaly (the head is much longer than it is broad). The chest was clear on auscultation, and no cardiac murmurs were noted. The abdomen was soft, and the span of the liver was 3 cm, with the edge 1 cm below the right costal margin; this span is normal. No splenomegaly or other abdominal masses were noted, and all extremities were normal. Results of the neurological examination were appropriate for the age of the child.

All hematological indices were normal, and the urinalysis was normal. The liver function studies were abnormal, however. Serum transaminases were high: serum glu-

tamic oxalacetic transaminase (SGOT) was 205 IU/liter (normal, 6–18 IU/liter), and serum glutamic pyruvic transaminase (SGPT) was 332 IU/liter (normal, 3–26 IU/liter). Serum alkaline phosphatase was 332 IU/liter (normal, 21–91 IU/liter), serum bilirubin, direct, was 2.0 mg/dl (normal, 0.4 mg/dl), and indirect was 3.7 mg/dl (normal, 0.6 mg/dl). Concentrations of total protein, albumin, and immunoglobulin were normal. Blood clotting studies, serum T4 and amino acids, and sweat tests for cystic fibrosis* all were normal. Significant antibody titers to toxoplasmosis, rubella, cytomegalovirus, and herpes were not noted, and the infant was HBs negative (no surface antigen for hepatitis B was found). A liver-spleen scan and ultrasound studies of the abdomen revealed no abnormality. These studies ruled out diagnoses of tyrosinemia, galactosemia, hypothyroidism, neonatal hepatitis, and biliary atresia (failure of the bile ducts to develop). α_1-antitrypsin activity was found to be very low, and liver biopsy revealed anatomical changes consistent with that deficiency. α_1-antitrypsin, which inhibits several proteolytic enzymes, is the major α_1-globulin in the plasma. The biopsy also demonstrated liver cell necrosis, increase of connective tissue, and inflammation of the portal tract system (the hepatic portal vein and its tributaries).

Comment: Studies of the patient's mother and father revealed that both were carriers of the trait responsible for the patient's autosomal inherited metabolic disorder. This inherited disorder accounts for cholestatic jaundice in a significant number of infants. The term is

*The concentrations of sodium and chloride are abnormally high in the sweat of a subject who has cystic fibrosis.

No current hypothesis explains the apparent protective effect of a balanced, even though inadequate, intake of energy.

Despite the fact that the proteins of the liver are regulated mainly through their rates of

breakdown, rather than through synthesis, few data are available to explain how this is done. The best evidence suggests that it is accomplished by the modulation of lysosomal proteases.

(CLINICAL CORRELATION continued)

used to describe jaundice caused by either mechanical obstruction or a functional disorder that results in failure to produce bile.

Treatment: The child was given a fat-soluble vitamin, phenobarbital, and a formula high in middle-chain triglycerides (MCT). Fat-soluble vitamins must be taken because they, along with other lipid-soluble materials, are absorbed poorly in this condition. Phenobarbital increases the conjugation of bile salts in the liver by inducing the synthesis of conjugating enzymes. Because conjugated bile salts are more water-soluble, they form micelles more readily (see Chapter 51, "Formation of Bile"). Conjugated bile salts also are absorbed less rapidly in the duodenum and the jejunum (non-ionic diffusion); hence, they remain in the small intestine longer and aid the absorption of fat. Conjugated bile salts are absorbed

more rapidly in the ileum (active transport); hence, the flow of bile-salt-dependent bile is increased. This increased flow in turn increases the excretion of serum bilirubin in the feces, which decreases the symptoms of hyperbilirubinemia. MCT in the diet increase the absorption of fat, because MCT are taken up by mucosal cells without undergoing lipolysis. Thus, their absorption does not depend on the formation of micelles, which require bile salts.

Outcome: At one year of age, the patient is doing well. His future still is uncertain, however, because more than 60% of patients who have liver disease during the neonatal period eventually develop cirrhosis. In addition, the risk of hepatic carcinoma is increased in these patients.

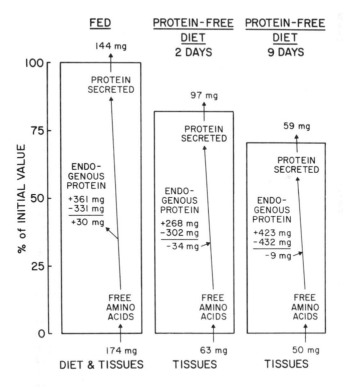

Figure 69-7. Protein synthesis in the liver, and protein content, as percent of initial value, when the diet contains no protein. Under "endogenous protein," a (+) value means synthesis, and a (−) value means breakdown. Although the secretion, or "export," of protein decreases steadily, the synthesis of endogenous liver protein decreases only during the initial period of protein-free intake (2 days). If this condition is prolonged (9 days), both synthesis and breakdown increase. (Redrawn, with permission, from Waterlow, J.C., et al. 1978. *Protein Turnover in Mammalian Tissues and in the Whole Body.* New York: Elsevier North-Holland.)

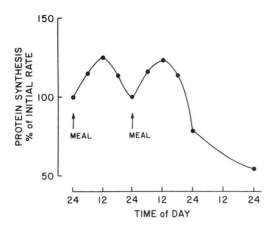

Figure 69-8. Increased synthesis of protein in muscle after meals. This appears to be one important component of the homeostatic mechanism that regulates the use of dietary protein. (Redrawn, with permission, from Waterlow, J.C., et al. 1978. *Protein Turnover in Mammalian Tissues and in the Whole Body.* New York: Elsevier North-Holland.)

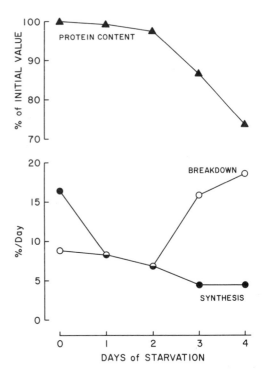

Figure 69-9. Rates of synthesis and breakdown of protein in muscle during starvation. The marked increase of breakdown as starvation continues helps to provide essential amino acids to the liver for the synthesis of plasma proteins. (Redrawn, with permission, from Greene, H.L., Holiday, M.A., and Monroe, H.N. (eds.). *Clinical Nutrition Update: Amino Acids.* Chicago: American Medical Association, 1977.)

Muscle

Muscle accounts for 32% of the total protein stores of an adult human; therefore, muscle should be expected to play an important role in protein homeostasis. After a meal, arteriovenous differences of plasma amino acid concentrations indicate uptake, which is consistent with the synthesis of muscle protein (Figure 69-8). This anabolic effect also helps to stabilize the concentration of amino acids in the plasma. During starvation, the protein content of muscle decreases because of decreased synthesis and increased breakdown of protein (Figure 69-9). The decrease in the rate of synthesis decreases the basal use of energy. In experimental animals given a protein-free diet, the protein content of muscle decreases; both synthesis and breakdown decrease, but synthesis decreases more (Figure 69-10). The decreased turnover helps to conserve essential amino acids but also decreases their availability to the liver and other organs.

In the fasting state, muscle provides much of the substrate for gluconeogenesis needed by tissues that depend on glucose (e.g., the brain). Breakdown exceeds synthesis, and amino acids not released intact into the circulation are transformed to alanine and glutamine, which subsequently provide the carbon skeletons for gluconeogenesis.

The amino acids made available by increased breakdown of muscle proteins during fasting permit the synthesis of essential proteins in the viscera to continue. This fortunate condition does not occur in all forms of dietary restriction. When energy is provided, but protein is not provided, synthesis and breakdown of protein in muscle both decrease. Protein-free diets, regardless of whether they contain adequate energy, cause marked abnormalities in visceral function. These facts help to explain the preservation of visceral protein when diets balanced in protein and calories are taken, even though the amounts of both protein and calories are inadequate. By contrast, synthesis and breakdown of protein in the liver both *increase* when a protein-free diet is taken (see Figure 69-7).

Experimentally Induced Nutritional Stress

Two patterns of breakdown of protein are seen in normal subjects. In one pattern, a deficiency of protein and energy may decrease both

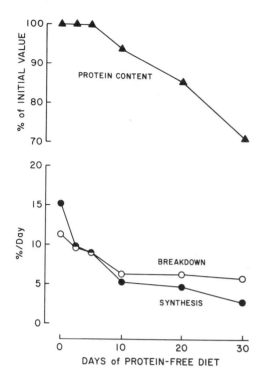

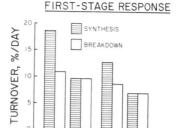

FIRST-STAGE RESPONSE

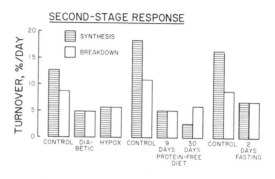

SECOND-STAGE RESPONSE

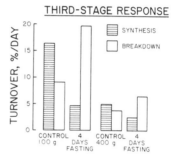

THIRD-STAGE RESPONSE

Figure 69-10.   Rates of synthesis and breakdown of protein in muscle of rats that were subjected to a protein-free diet. The decrease of both rates decreases the supply of essential amino acids to the liver and may account for the decreased production of plasma proteins by the liver. (Redrawn, with permission, from Waterlow, J.C., et al. 1978. *Protein Turnover in Mammalian Tissues and in the Whole Body.* New York: Elsevier North-Holland.)

synthesis and breakdown. In the other pattern, the rate of breakdown increases, while the rate of synthesis decreases. The second pattern is seen in prolonged starvation and, possibly, in severe trauma or infection. Both patterns are seen in the three-stage response to experimentally induced nutritional stress (Figure 69-11). In the first stage, early in protein deprivation or later in a restricted diet, the rate of synthesis decreases and the rates of synthesis and breakdown become nearly the same. In the second stage, both synthesis and breakdown decrease, and in the third stage, synthesis decreases, but breakdown increases. The third stage is the hypercatabolic state usually seen under conditions of severe stress.

QUALITY OF PROTEIN

The foods that provide protein vary in their ability to meet the requirements of the body for protein. The quality of a protein food depends

Figure 69-11.   Protein turnover in muscle of rats during starvation, protein-free diet, and hormone deficiencies. (Redrawn, with permission, from Waterlow, J.C., et al. 1978. *Protein Turnover in Mammalian Tissues and in the Whole Body.* New York: Elsevier North-Holland.)

on its digestibility, its total content of amino acids, the amino acids that comprise it, and the ratio of protein calories to total calories.

Digestibility

NORMAL DIGESTION

Absorption depends on the hydrolysis of protein to a mixture of small peptides and amino acids on the brush border of the intestine (see Chapter 53). Peptides are the principal end products of protein digestion; dipeptides and tripeptides are absorbed into the enterocytes, where they are hydrolyzed into amino acids (see Chapter 53). At least three systems transport the various amino acids into the enterocytes, and another system transports the small peptides. Although these systems have in common certain structural requirements for greatest efficiency, small peptides and free amino acids are absorbed independently. The ability of the gut to absorb small peptides partially offsets the effects of competition among the amino acids for the three transport systems and thereby increases the efficiency of absorption.

APPARENT DIGESTIBILITY

The digestibility of protein is expressed by the ratio of protein apparently absorbed to protein consumed. This ratio is called the *apparent digestibility* (expressed as a percentage). The apparent digestibility of mixed proteins in the typical American diet is about 92%, although this number varies from about 74% for vegetable protein to 97% for the protein of eggs and meat. The digestibility of protein in fruits is about 85%, in most cereals, about 75%–80%, and in legumes, about 78%. Apparent digestibility is decreased by pathological processes that interfere with the production of digestive enzymes or significantly impair absorption. These conditions can be treated with exogenous enzymes or by taking an elemental or partially hydrolyzed diet. In severe cases, total parenteral nutrition must be provided.

TRUE DIGESTIBILITY

True digestibility is determined by correcting for endogenous nitrogen in the feces. Significant amounts of endogenous protein appear in the gut, and not all of this protein is digested and absorbed. The quantity of endogenous protein released from tissues is uncertain, but a reasonable estimate is 150 g/day, of which 85 g comes from desquamation of mucosal cells. The total amount of endogenous protein is approximately two times the usual intake of protein by an adult human. Apparently, proteins that are difficult to digest cause the release of even more endogenous protein.

Endogenous protein is digested more slowly than exogenous protein. Most exogenous protein is absorbed in the upper small intestine, but endogenous protein is digested and absorbed along the entire length of the intestine. Endogenous protein is released and digested intermittently, depending on the frequency of meals. The difference of digestibility between endogenous protein and exogenous protein may decrease the variability in the amount of amino acids absorbed at any given time and

improve the quality of exogenous protein that is absorbed. Because of this circumstance, dietary proteins may be utilized more effectively.

Amino Acid Composition

ESSENTIAL AMINO ACIDS

The requirements for essential amino acids and the recommended ratios of essential amino acids to total amino acids in the diet are summarized in Table 69-3. Histidine is not included as an essential amino acid for adults. Although some evidence indicates that an adult human needs histidine in the diet to sustain normal nitrogen metabolism, this has not been confirmed.

The amount of essential amino acids needed relative to body weight and the ratio of essential amino acids to total amino acids both decline with increasing age. Thus, infants and children need protein of higher quality than adults do. Although adults may be able to compensate at times for proteins of lower quality by consuming greater amounts of protein food, children often are unable to do so. The requirements of infants and adults for particular essential amino acids also differ. This is important when the ability to sustain growth is used as a criterion to estimate the quality of protein (see the section entitled "Protein Efficiency Ratio" in this chapter) because the rate of growth may be the factor most responsible for the differences. The values in Table 69-3 represent needs under normal conditions; stress may alter these needs substantially.

Methods of Estimating Protein Quality

Although other methods for estimating the quality of a protein are available, the ones used most routinely are biological value (BV), net protein utilization (NPU), protein efficiency ratio (PER), and chemical score.

BIOLOGICAL VALUE

The *biological value* (BV) gives the fraction of absorbed protein that is retained in the body:

$$BV = \frac{\text{Nitrogen retained} + \text{obligatory loss of nitrogen}}{\text{Nitrogen absorbed}}$$

This method removes the factor of digestibility from consideration. Thus, the BV expresses how well the protein that is absorbed is used.

TABLE 69-3
Estimated requirements of essential amino acids

Amino acid	Infants (mg/kg)	Children (mg/kg)	Adults (mg/kg)
Histidine	34	0	0
Isoleucine	119	30	10
Leucine	229	45	14
Lysine	103	60	12
Methionine + cystine	45 + cys	27	13
Phenylalanine + tyrosine	90 × tyr	27	14
Threonine	87	35	7
Tryptophan	22	4	3.5
Valine	105	33	10
Total essential (E)	834	261	84
Total protein needs (T)	2000	820	570
E/T	0.42	0.32	0.15

(*Nitrogen absorbed* is defined as nitrogen intake minus nitrogen loss in the feces. *Nitrogen retained* is defined as nitrogen intake minus the sum of nitrogen in the urine, the feces, and other miscellaneous routes of loss.)

NET PROTEIN UTILIZATION
Net protein utilization (NPU) estimates the fraction of ingested protein that is used:

$$NPU = \frac{Nitrogen\ retained + obligatory\ loss\ of\ nitrogen}{Nitrogen\ intake}$$

Digestibility is a factor in this method. Thus, a protein that is digested poorly has a lower NPU value. Since both BV and NPU measure the protein retained in the body, the two methods rank proteins in the same order; however, because of the effect of digestibility, the numerical value of NPU is less than that of BV.

PROTEIN EFFICIENCY RATIO
The *protein efficiency ratio* (PER) is the simplest and most widely used method. It is the ratio of net weight gained to amount of protein consumed:

$$PER = \frac{Growth\ (g)}{Protein\ intake\ (g)}$$

Obviously, this method can be used only in growing animals. It is used often to evaluate synthetic foods proposed to replace natural foods (e.g., meat substitutes made from soybeans).

CHEMICAL SCORE
The *chemical score,* or *amino acid score,* is based on the amino acid composition of the protein:

$$Chemical\ score = \frac{mg\ of\ amino\ acid/g\ of\ test\ protein}{mg\ of\ amino\ acid/g\ of\ reference\ protein}$$

The amino acid that has the lowest test score is the "limiting" amino acid; that is, if one amino acid is not available, no more protein can be synthesized. Thus, the lowest score is used to express the quality of the dietary protein.

LIMITATIONS OF THE METHODS
The results of the BV and NPU tests can be influenced by the use of endogenous protein. Even though a protein that contains none of a certain essential amino acid were fed, it would receive a value higher than zero because at least some of the missing amino acid would be supplied from endogenous sources such as muscle. Thus, the new protein would be synthesized at the expense of a protein already in existence, and the dietary protein would receive a higher rating than it deserved. The PER penalizes proteins that may be adequate for maintenance but not for growth. The chemical score is a nonbiological assessment that requires chemical analysis not readily available to most laboratories. In addition, the chemical score does not take into account any differences of bioavailability among different proteins.

USES OF MEASUREMENTS OF PROTEIN QUALITY
The measurements of protein quality are used to determine how much of a specific protein is required to supply the protein a subject needs. The formula used is as follows:

Intake of test protein

= Requirement for standard protein

$$\times \frac{Quality\ of\ standard\ protein}{Quality\ of\ test\ protein}$$

TABLE 69-4
Biological value (BV) of representative proteins

Food	Biological value
Egg	100
Milk	93
Rice	86
Fish	75
Beef	75
Casein	75
Corn	72
Cottonseed flour	60
Peanut flour	56
Wheat gluten	44

TABLE 69-5
Chemical score and net protein utilization (NPU) values of common foods

Protein	Chemical score	Net protein utilization*
Whole egg	100	—
Human milk	100	95
Cow's milk	95	81
Soybean milk	74	75
Sesame	50	54
Ground peanut	65	57
Cottonseed	81	41
Maize	49	36‡
Rice	67	63‡
Whole wheat	53	49‡

The ratio obtained is larger than 1, and the amount of the test protein taken is adjusted proportionately.

*Based on values for children 3–7 years old receiving 6.7% of energy from protein.

‡Based on values for children 8–12 years old.

QUALITY OF VARIOUS PROTEINS

Estimates of the quality of various protein foods are given in Tables 69-4 and 69-5. Note that the quality of some inexpensive sources of protein, for example, rice and corn, compares well with some more prestigious and expensive sources (e.g., beef). Although the numerical values vary among the different methods of evaluation, the order of most of the foods is the same.

STUDY OUTLINE

GENERAL BACKGROUND   Protein is needed in the diet because the body cannot synthesize protein from other substrates.

Certain amino acids can be synthesized from others—*nonessential* amino acids.

Certain amino acids cannot be synthesized from others—*essential* amino acids.

The term "nitrogen" is used to mean protein because protein is identified through nitrogen.

Average protein is 16% nitrogen; amount of protein = 6.25 × amount of nitrogen measured.

REQUIREMENTS

ESTIMATION   Protein is needed for replacement and for growth.

Use is not 100% efficient; intake must exceed amount needed for replacement and growth.

The more protein consumed, the less efficiently it is used.

Protein is not stored except in structures of tissues—excess in diet is catabolized for energy or converted to glucose and/or fat, which are stored.

CALORIC INTAKE AND PROTEIN USE Increasing either caloric or protein intake improves nitrogen balance, but effect is small or absent if either intake is severely limited.

Subjects recovering from severe protein deficiency use dietary protein more efficiently.

USE OF PROTEIN

OVERVIEW   Turnover of protein decreases with age.

Rates of turnover and oxidation of protein are influenced by intake.

When neither energy nor protein is a limiting factor, rate of synthesis is limited by capacity for synthesis.

When energy intake is limiting factor, system adapts by changing rates of breakdown and synthesis of protein.

Synthesis of protein is affected by age, nutritional status, energy in diet, protein in diet, and stress.

ROLE OF THE GASTROINTESTINAL TRACT Secretion of protein (enzymes); frequent replacement of cells.

Digestion-absorption.

Transamination of amino acids.

Rapid turnover—sensitive to protein deficiency.

LIVER

CATABOLISM Liver degrades excess amino acids.

CONTENT Varies with intake; modulated through rate of breakdown.

SYNTHESIS AND RELEASE Synthesizes specific proteins for physiological functions.

Synthesis depends on supply of amino acids.

Synthesis and release are maintained if all components of diet are decreased proportionately.

Synthesis and release are decreased if energy intake is normal but protein intake is not normal.

MUSCLE One-third of protein stores of adult body.

Protein content decreases during starvation—synthesis decreases and breakdown increases; provides amino acids for essential visceral proteins and for gluconeogenesis, which supplies tissues that need glucose (e.g., brain).

On protein-free diet, both synthesis and breakdown decrease—decreases energy usage; preserves essential amino acids, but decreases their availability to other organs.

EXPERIMENTALLY INDUCED NUTRITIONAL STRESS First stage—early in protein deprivation or later in restricted diet—rate of synthesis of protein decreases until rates of synthesis and breakdown are about the same.

Second stage—both synthesis and breakdown decrease.

Third stage—severe stress—synthesis decreases and breakdown increases.

QUALITY OF PROTEIN

DIGESTIBILITY

NORMAL DIGESTION Protein is hydrolyzed to amino acids and small peptides on brush border of intestine.

Small peptides are absorbed into enterocytes; digestion to amino acids is completed.

One transport system for peptides, and three transport systems for amino acids.

APPARENT DIGESTIBILITY Ratio of *protein apparently absorbed* to *protein intake.*

Varies with foods; average is about 92%.

TRUE DIGESTIBILITY Corrected for endogenous nitrogen in feces.

About twice as much endogenous protein as exogenous protein—secretion of enzymes and shedding of mucosal cells.

AMINO ACID COMPOSITION

ESSENTIAL AMINO ACIDS Need declines with age.

Because of growth and higher rates of turnover of protein, specific needs of children are more urgent than those of adults.

METHODS OF ESTIMATING PROTEIN QUALITY

BIOLOGICAL VALUE Fraction of *absorbed* protein retained in body.

NET PROTEIN UTILIZATION Fraction of *ingested* protein used.

Poorly digested protein has lower NPU value.

PROTEIN EFFICIENCY RATIO Ratio of net weight gained to amount of protein consumed.

Useful only in growing animals.

CHEMICAL SCORE Based on amino acid composition.

Ratio of amino acid in test protein to same amino acid in reference protein.

Amino acid with lowest ratio limits protein synthesis; determines score of entire protein.

LIMITATIONS OF THE METHODS BV and NPU are influenced by use of endogenous protein.

PER is applicable only to growth.

Chemical score does not take bioavailability into account.

USES OF MEASUREMENTS OF PROTEIN QUALITY Determine how much of specific protein is required to meet needs of subject.

QUALITY OF VARIOUS PROTEINS Not always related to price.

Numerical values vary, but order is about the same in all methods.

BIBLIOGRAPHY

Allison, J.B. 1964. The nutritive value of dietary proteins. In *Mammalian Protein Metabolism*. Volume II. Edited by H.N. Munro and J.B. Allison. New York: Academic Press.

Baracos, V., Rodemann, P., Dinarello, C.A., et al. 1983. Stimulation of muscle protein degradation and prostaglandin E_2 release by leukocytic pyrogen (interleukin-1): A mechanism for the increased degradation of muscle proteins during fever. *N. Engl. J. Med.* 308:553.

Clowes, G.H.A., Jr., George, B.C., Villee, C.A., Jr., et al. 1983. Muscle proteolysis induced by a circulating peptide in patients with sepsis or trauma. *N. Engl. J. Med.* 308:545.

Elwyn, D.H. 1970. The role of the liver in regulation of amino acid and protein metabolism. In *Mammalian Protein Metabolism*. Volume IV. Edited by H.N. Munro and J.B Allison. New York: Academic Press.

Goodhart, R.S., and Shils, M.E. (eds.). 1980. *Modern Nutrition in Health and Disease* (6th ed.). Philadelphia: Lea & Febiger.

Joint FAO/WHO Ad Hoc Expert Committee. 1973. Energy and protein requirements. In *World Health Organization Technical Reports Series,* No. 522. Geneva, Switzerland: World Health Organization.

Gunthrie, H.A. 1975. *Introductory Nutrition* (3rd ed.). St. Louis: Mosby.

Munro, H.N. 1974. Protein hydrolysates and amino acids. In *Total Parenteral Nutrition*. Edited by P.L. White and M.E. Nagy. Acton, Massachusetts: Publishing Sciences Group.

Munro, H.N. 1977. Parenteral nutrition: Metabolic consequences of bypassing the gut and liver. In *Clinical Nutrition Update: Amino Acids*. Edited by H.L. Greene, M.A. Halliday, and H.N. Munro. Chicago: American Medical Association.

Waterlow, J.C.; Garlick, P.J.; and Millward, D.J. 1977. Amino acid supply and protein turnover. In *Clinical Nutrition Update: Amino Acids*. Edited by H.L. Greene, M.A. Halliday, and H.N. Munro. Chicago: American Medical Association.

Waterlow, J.C.; Garlick, P.J.; and Millward, D.J. 1978. *Protein Turnover in Mammalian Tissues and in the Whole Body.* New York: Elsevier North-Holland.

Willmore, D.W. 1977. Energy requirements for maximum nitrogen retention. In *Clinical Nutrition Update: Amino Acids.* Edited by H.L. Greene, M.A. Halliday, and H.N. Munro. Chicago: American Medical Association.

Young, V.W.; Perera, W.D.; Winterer, J.C., et al. 1976. Protein and amino acid requirements of the elderly. In *Nutrition and Aging.* Edited by M. Winick. New York: Wiley.

70

Micronutrients

CHAPTER CONTENTS

DEFINITIONS

Although *essential micronutrients* have not been defined inclusively, the term is applied to substances that occur naturally in foods and are needed in small quantities to sustain health. Most organic essential micronutrients are called *vitamins*. However, recent information indicates that this classification is more significant historically than metabolically. The fat-soluble and water-soluble substances that have been recognized as vitamins are listed in Tables 70-1 and 70-2. The absence of the essential fatty acids is noteworthy—although the

TABLE 70-1
Description of fat-soluble vitamins

Vitamin	Major body functions	Deficiency	Excess
Vitamin A (retinol)	Constituent of rhodopsin (visual pigment). Maintenance of epithelial tissues. Role in mucopolysaccharide synthesis	Xerophthalmia (keratinization of ocular tissue), night blindness, permanent blindness	Headache, vomiting, peeling of skin, anorexia, swelling of long bones
Vitamin D	Promotes growth and mineralization of bones. Increases absorption of calcium	Rickets (bone deformities) in children. Osteomalacia in adults	Vomiting, diarrhea, loss of weight, kidney damage
Vitamin E (tocopherol)	Functions as an antitoxicant to prevent damage of cell membranes	Possibly anemia	Relatively nontoxic
Vitamin K (phylloquinone)	Important in blood clotting (involved in formation of active prothrombin)	Conditioned deficiencies associated with severe bleeding, internal hemorrhages	Relatively nontoxic. Synthetic forms at high doses may cause jaundice

From "The requirements of human nutrition" by N.S. Scrimshaw and V.R. Young. *Sci. Am.* 235(3):63–64. Copyright © 1976 by Scientific American, Inc. All rights reserved.

TABLE 70-2
Description of water-soluble vitamins

Vitamin	Major body functions	Deficiency	Excess
Vitamin B₁ (thiamine)	Coenzyme in reactions that involve the removal of CO_2	Beriberi (peripheral nerve changes, edema, heart failure)	None reported
Vitamin B₂ (riboflavin)	Constituent of two flavin nucleotide coenzymes involved in energy metabolism (FAD and FMN)	Reddened lips, cracks at corners of mouth (cheilosis), lesions of the eye	None reported
Niacin	Constituent of two coenzymes involved in oxidation-reduction reactions (NAD and NADP)	Pellagra (skin and gastrointestinal lesions, nervousness, mental disorders)	Flushing, burning, and tingling around neck, face, and hands
Vitamin B₆ (pyridoxine)	Coenzyme (pyridoxal phosphate) involved in amino acid metabolism	Irritability, convulsions, muscular twitching, dermatitis near eyes, kidney stones	Sensory neuropathy
Pantothenic acid	Constituent of coenzyme A, which plays a central role in energy metabolism	Fatigue, sleep disturbances, impaired coordination, nausea (rare in humans)	None reported
Folacin (folic acid)	Constituent involved in transfer of single-carbon units in nucleic acid amino acid metabolism	Anemia, gastrointestinal disturbances, diarrhea, red tongue	None reported
Vitamin B₁₂ (cyanocobalamin)	Coenzyme involved in transfer of single-carbon units in nucleic acid metabolism	Pernicious anemia, neurological disorders	None reported
Biotin	Coenzyme required for fat synthesis, amino acid metabolism, and glycogen formation	Fatigue, depression, nausea, dermatitis, muscular pains	None reported
Choline	Constituent of phospholipids. Precursor of acetylcholine	None reported in humans	None reported
Vitamin C (ascorbic acid)	Maintains intercellular matrix of cartilage, bone, and dentine. Important in collagen synthesis	Scurvy (degeneration of skin, teeth, blood vessels; epithelial hemorrhages)	Relatively nontoxic. Possibility of kidney stones

From "The requirements of human nutrition" by N.S. Scrimshaw and V.R. Young. *Sci. Am.* 235(3):63. Copyright © 1976 by Scientific American, Inc. All rights reserved.

constituents of this group fulfill the criteria for vitamins given above, they have not been classified as vitamins. Inorganic micronutrients classified as *essential trace elements* are listed in Table 70-3. To be recognized as essential, a trace element must meet the following criteria:

1. It is present in all healthy tissues of all living things.
2. Its concentration in animals is nearly constant.
3. When it is missing, the same structural and physiological abnormalities occur in all animal species, and when it is present, these abnormalities are prevented or reversed.

TABLE 70-3
Description of the essential trace elements

Mineral	Amount in adult body (g)	Major body functions	Deficiency	Excess
Iron	4.5	Constituent of hemoglobin and enzymes involved in energy metabolism	Iron-deficiency anemia (weakness, decreased resistance to infection)	Siderosis, cirrhosis of liver
Zinc	2.0	Constituent of enzymes involved in digestion	Failure to grow; small sex glands	Fever, nausea, vomiting, diarrhea
Copper	0.1	Constituent of enzymes associated with iron metabolism	Anemia, bone changes (rare in humans)	Rare metabolic condition (Wilson's disease)
Silicon	0.024	Function unknown (essential for animals)	Not reported in humans	Industrial exposures: silicon—silicosis; vanadium—lung irritation; tin—vomiting; nickel—acute pneumonitis
Vanadium	0.018			
Tin	0.017			
Nickel	0.010			
Selenium	0.013	Functions in close association with vitamin E	Anemia (rare)	Gastrointestinal disorders, lung irritation
Manganese	0.012	Constituent of enzymes involved in fat synthesis	In animals, poor growth, disturbances of nervous system, reproductive abnormalities	Poisoning in manganese mines: generalized disease of nervous system
Iodine	0.011	Constituent of thyroid hormones	Goiter (enlarged thyroid)	Very high intakes depress thyroid activity
Molybdenum	0.009	Constituent of some enzymes	Not reported in humans	Inhibition of enzymes
Chromium	0.006	Involved in glucose and energy metabolism	Impaired ability to metabolize glucose	Occupational exposures: skin and kidney damage
Cobalt	0.0015	Constituent of vitamin B_{12}	Not reported in humans	Industrial exposure: dermatitis and diseases of red blood cells

From "The requirements of human nutrition" by N.S. Scrimshaw and V.R. Young. *Sci. Am.* 235(3):64. Copyright © 1976 by Scientific American, Inc. All rights reserved.

PHYSIOLOGICAL FUNCTIONS

Vitamins

The physiological functions of the vitamins are given in Tables 70-1 and 70-2. The functions of the B-complex, niacin, folacin, and pantothenic acid have been defined better than those of any other vitamins except vitamin D. The actions of most other vitamins are poorly understood. For example, although ascorbic acid participates in various hydroxylation reactions, it can be replaced by other reducing agents.

CLINICAL CORRELATION
70.1   Vitamin B_{12} Deficiency on a Vegan Diet

CASE REPORT

The Patient: A 46-year-old woman.

Principal Complaints: Loss of appetite, weakness, and sore tongue.

History: The patient had been well until about six months before admission, when she had begun to experience the symptoms that brought her to admission. She had experienced a psychological change five years earlier and become a "vegan" (one who eats no food of animal origin).

Clinical Examination: The patient was pale, with a moderate yellowish tinge to the skin, but did not appear acutely ill. The tongue was red and smooth, with a glazed appearance. The heart rate was 82 beats/min (normal, 60–100 beats/min), the respiratory rate was 16/min (normal, 13–17 min), and the arterial pressure was 125/75 mm Hg (normal, 90–140/60–90 mm Hg). The chest was clear, no masses were felt in the abdomen, and renal function was normal. The hematocrit was 34% (normal, 37%–48%), the hemoglobin content was 11 g/dl (normal, 12–16 g/dl), the mean corpuscular volume* was 101 fl† (nor-

*The mean volume of a red cell, determined by hematocrit/red cell count.
†Femtoliter, 1 μm³

mal, 83–97 fl), the leukocyte count was 4,500 cells/mm³ (normal, 4300–10,800 cells /mm³) with a normal differential (distribution of cell types). The blood smear revealed macrocytosis (abnormally large erythroctyes) and hypersegmented neutrophils. Since these findings suggested pernicious anemia, levels of vitamin B_{12} and folate were measured. Folate levels were normal: serum folate was 8.9 ng/ml (normal, 6–15 ng/ml), and erythrocyte folate was 281 ng/ml (normal, 160–640 ng/ml). Serum vitamin B_{12} was 48 pg/ml (normal, 200–600 pg/ml). Examination of the bone marrow revealed large, immature red cells (megaloblasts), large leukocytes with bizarrely shaped nuclei, and decreased stores of iron. The concentration of iron in the serum was 89 μg/dl (normal, 50–150 μg/dl), and the total iron-binding capacity** was 302 μg/dl (normal, 250–410 μg/dl). Because the principal cause of pernicious anemia is failure to absorb vitamin B_{12} associated with lack of gastric acidity, gastric secretory function was

**Iron is transported in the plasma bound to *transferrin* (see Chapter 24), a β-globulin. Normally, only about 25% of the binding sites on transferrin are occupied by iron, and the remainder represent the latent iron-binding capacity of the plasma. If iron is deficient, less transferrin is occupied, and the iron-binding capacity is increased.

However, none of the substitutes has antiscorbutic activity.

New information indicates that the fat-soluble vitamins may function as hormones; vitamin D is a good example. Recent work has demonstrated that a metabolite of vitamin D, 1,25-dihydroxycholecalciferol, enhances the absorption of calcium (see Chapter 62). The mechanism of action of this metabolite is similar to that of other recognized steroid hormones. Recent evidence suggests that vitamin A also acts in a regulatory capacity consistent

with that of a hormone. However, one fat-soluble vitamin has been identified as a cofactor—vitamin K appears to act as a cofactor in the carboxylation of a precursor of prothrombin.

Essential Trace Elements

The major functions of the trace elements in the body are given in Table 70-3. Trace elements operate primarily as catalysts in enzyme

(CLINICAL CORRELATION continued)

tested. Stimulation of the gastric parietal cells by pentagastrin (see Chapter 49) revealed normal gastric secretion, and no antibodies to parietal cells or intrinsic factor†† were found.*** The absorption of vitamin B_{12} was measured by the Schilling test††† and found to be normal.

Comment: The normal gastric secretory function and uptake of B_{12} indicated that the low concentration of vitamin B_{12} in this patient's plasma, which indicates inadequate stores of vitamin B_{12} in the body, were related to her diet. The body normally stores about 5000 μg of vitamin B_{12}, mostly in the liver, and several years may be required for its depletion, even when no B_{12} is absorbed. The patient had been on her exclusively vegetable (vegan) diet for about 5 years. The best sources of vitamin B_{12} in the diet are fresh meat and dairy products; vegetable tissues contain no vitamin B_{12}.

Deficiency of vitamin B_{12} alters DNA synthesis in many tissues of the body, but its effects are especially evident in the hematopoietic (blood-forming) system. Impaired synthesis of DNA retards mitosis (cell division), and this retardation causes the production of large blood cells, both erythrocytes and leukocytes. Mitosis of epithelial cells also is affected, which probably accounts for the abnormalities of the mouth and the gastrointestinal system.

The patient's diet probably also accounts for the mild deficiency of iron that was observed, because iron from vegetable sources is not absorbed well.

Treatment: The patient was given vitamin B_{12} supplement, 5 μg/day, and her condition improved dramatically.

Outcome: Six weeks after the beginning of therapy, all of the symptoms relating to deficiency of vitamin B_{12} were gone and the patient's hematologic profile was normal. Since she is committed to her vegan diet, she will have to continue to take supplementary vitamin B_{12}.

††Intrinsic factor is a glycoprotein, released by the parietal cells of the gastric mucosa, that combines with vitamin B_{12} and facilitates its absorption by specific receptors in the wall of the distal ileum. Patients who lack gastric secretory function do not absorb enough vitamin B_{12}.

***The majority of cases of pernicious anemia are associated with autoantibodies directed against the gastric mucosa, and many cases may be related to antibodies directed against intrinsic factor. The production of the antibodies may be determined genetically or by injury to the gastric mucosa by a virus.

†††2 μg of radioactive vitamin B_{12} (^{60}Co) are administered by mouth, and a large amount (1000 μg) of nonradioactive vitamin B_{12} is injected intramuscularly. Normal subjects excrete 5% to 40% of the radioactivity in the urine in 48 hours (indicating absorption), whereas subjects who do not absorb B_{12} well excrete less than 5%.

systems. Their association with these systems may vary from loose to highly specific. Very specific complexes of enzymes and trace elements are known as *metalloenzymes*. The principal actions of trace elements in enzyme systems are to induce or maintain active conformations, to act as bridges in the formation of complexes, or to alter the electronic configuration of a substrate. These actions permit the trace elements to take part in basic physiological functions in two ways: (1) to act in catalytic centers of enzymes, and (2) to act as components of vitamins or as hormone activators.

Unlike most other water-soluble nutrients, which may be consumed safely in relatively large amounts, all of the essential trace elements produce toxic effects when taken in excess. Despite this, they are widely available commercially in nutritional supplements.

Among all of the recognized trace elements, deficiencies of iron, iodine, copper, and zinc are the most important clinically.

STUDY OUTLINE

DEFINITIONS   Essential micronutrients—substances that occur naturally in foods and are needed in small quantities to sustain health.

Most organic essential micronutrients are called *vitamins*.

Essential inorganic micronutrients are called *essential trace elements* (see text for criteria).

PHYSIOLOGICAL FUNCTIONS

VITAMINS   See Tables 70-1 and 70-2 for descriptions.

B-complex vitamins—cofactors in energy and amino acid metabolism.

Most fat-soluble vitamins function more nearly as hormones.

ESSENTIAL TRACE ELEMENTS   See Table 70-3 for descriptions.

Operate primarily as catalysts in enzyme systems.

Narrow safe range of levels of intake.

Deficiencies of iron, iodine, copper, and zinc are most important clinically.

BIBLIOGRAPHY

Bieri, J.G.; Corash, L.; and Hubbard, V.S. 1983. Medical uses of vitamin E. *N. Engl. J. Med.* 308:1063.

DeLuca, H.F. 1978. The fat-soluble vitamins. In *Handbook of Lipid Research.* Volume 2, Chapter 2. Edited by D. DeLuca. New York: Plenum Press.

Evans, G.W. 1976. Zinc absorption and transport. In *Trace Elements in Human Health and Disease.* Volume 1, Chapter 12. Edited by S.A. Prasad. New York: Academic Press.

Hathcock, J.N. (ed.). 1982. *Nutritional Toxicology.* New York: Academic Press.

Hoffbrand, A.V. 1974. Synthesis and breakdown of natural folates (folate polyglutamates). *Prog. Hematol.* 9:85.

Karcioğlu, Z.A., and Sarper, R.M. (eds.). 1980. *Zinc and Copper in Medicine.* Springfield, Illinois: Charles C. Thomas.

Krumdieck, C.L. 1976. Folic acid. In *Present Knowledge in Nutrition* (4th ed.). Chapter 18. Edited by D.M. Hegsted, et al. Washington, D.C.: The Nutrition Foundation, Inc.

Marks, J. 1975. *A Guide to the Vitamins: Their Role in Health and Disease.* Baltimore: University Park Press.

Mertz, W. 1981. The essential trace elements. *Science* 213:1332.

Owen, C.A., Jr. 1982. Biological aspects of copper: Occurrence, assay, and interrelationships. Park Ridge, New Jersey: Noyes.

Schaumburg, H., Kaplan, J., Windebank, A. et al. 1983. Sensory neuropathy from pyridoxine abuse: A new megavitamin syndrome. *N. Engl. J. Med.* 309:445.

Scrimshaw, N.S., and Young, V.R. 1976. The requirements of human nutrition. *Sci. Am.* 235(3):50.

Sebrell, W.H., Jr. (Chairman). 1981. Conquest of pellagra (Symposium). *Fed. Proc.* 40:1519.

Young, V.R. 1981. Selenium: A case for its essentiality in man. *N. Engl. J. Med.* 304:1228.

71

Physiology of
Human Lactation

CHAPTER CONTENTS

FUNCTIONAL ANATOMY

Basic Anatomy

Human mammary glands consist of 15–20 *lobes*, each composed of numerous *lobules*. Each lobule contains many *acini*, or *alveoli*, which are the secretory units. Each alveolus consists of secretory cells surrounded by contractile myoepithelial cells. The secretory cells empty into small ducts that channel milk from the alveoli to a *lactiferous sinus*, or *ampulla*, beneath the nipple. From the ampullae, 10–15 ducts extend to openings in the surface of the nipple. The glandular and ductal tissues are supported by connective tissue.

After Puberty

At puberty, the epithelial duct system develops, but the most obvious change in the mammary gland is in the proliferation of the surrounding fatty tissue. True alveoli do not develop until after the first pregnancy. The mammary gland changes at puberty in response to hormones from the anterior pituitary and, later, in response to hormones from the ovaries (see

Chapter 63). Other hormones, from the pancreas (insulin) and the thyroid gland, also are essential for normal development of the breast. Estrogen is especially important in the maturation of the ductal system, in the transient increases of vascularity of the gland, and in the proliferation of supporting connective and fatty tissues during each menstrual cycle. The anatomy of the breast changes cyclically, as the levels of estrogen rise and fall. During the first part of the cycle, when the level of estrogen is increasing, some ductal and glandular proliferation occurs in women who have been pregnant. During the second part, the progestational phase, epithelial activity increases and may be accompanied by vascular engorgement and edema of the supporting stroma.

During Pregnancy

During pregnancy, the blood vessels of the breast are dilated and engorged, the intralobular connective tissue is edematous, and the acini and ducts dilate, under the influence of estrogen, progesterone, placental lactogen, and chorionic gonadotropin. The secretory units are formed in response to these hormones; however, milk is not secreted until after the infant is born, when expulsion of the placenta markedly decreases the levels of estrogen and progesterone, and prolactin is secreted. Prolactin is the main stimulus to lactation (see Chapter 63); the alveoli synthesize and secrete colostrum and, later, milk.

LACTATION

Initiation

The initiation and endocrine control of lactation have been studied in cultured tissues, by the administration of hormones to animals, and by measurement of the concentrations of lactogenic hormones in animals and women.

IN VITRO EXPERIMENTS

Studies in tissue culture suggest that hyperplasia of the alveolar cells depends on insulin and adrenocortical steroids. Prolactin or other hormones that have properties similar to those of prolactin (e.g., growth hormone and placental lactogen) are necessary for lactogenesis under these conditions. Lactogenesis is indicated by de novo synthesis of lactose, various fatty acids, and casein (Figure 71-1). Experiments with animals have confirmed the contributions of endogenous insulin, adrenocorticoids, and prolactin that these in vitro experiments indicated.

IN VIVO EXPERIMENTS

Measurements during pregnancy, parturition, and lactation show that lactation is initiated by two distinct components—the onset of stimulation by prolactin and the cessation of inhibition by progesterone. At parturition, the release of prolactin increases greatly, and with expulsion of the placenta, progesterone in the body decreases. After several months of lactation, the concentration of prolactin is much less but still measurable. These observations suggest that larger amounts of prolactin are needed to initiate lactation than to maintain it.

The role of prolactin also has been demonstrated by the administration of either prolactin or a drug (bromocriptine) that inhibits prolactin. Animals given prolactin under appropriate conditions undergo biochemical and morphological changes that result in the secretion of milk. Bromocriptine given to an animal after parturition prevents the secretion of milk.

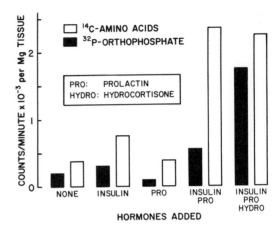

Figure 71-1.   The additive effects of hormones on the synthesis of casein, as indicated by measurement of ^{14}C-amino acids or ^{32}P-orthophosphate. (Redrawn, with permission, from Yokoyama, A., et al. (eds.). 1978. *Physiology of Mammary Glands.* Tokyo: Japan Scientific Societies Press.)

Experiments with animals also have confirmed the inhibitory effect of progesterone. Removal of the ovaries or the corpus luteum from pregnant animals, which removes the source of progesterone, can initiate lactation. Adding progesterone again blocks this response.

POSSIBLE MECHANISMS

The mechanisms by which prolactin and the supporting hormones induce the secretion of milk are not known. Prolactin receptors have been identified in alveolar tissue and observed to increase at parturition. This effect seems to be essential to the subsequent production of milk. Apparently, prolactin induces the proliferation of its own receptors by both increasing the number of alveolar cells and increasing the number of receptors in each cell (Figure 71-2). Estrogen also increases the number of prolactin receptors, and progesterone suppresses that effect.

The mechanisms that follow the interaction of prolactin with its receptor are not known. Two theories have been proposed: the second messenger mechanism (see Chapter 55) and the introduction of some prolactin fragment into the cell. The first theory is more widely accepted at present.

Control of Prolactin Secretion

The secretion of prolactin appears to be controlled by several mechanisms that operate independently via the hypothalamus. Prolactin

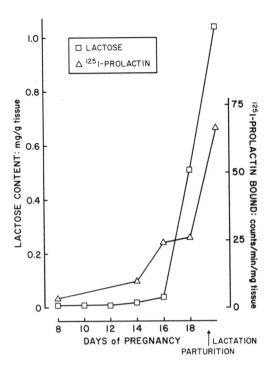

Figure 71-2. Increased binding of ^{125}I-prolactin and increased lactose content in mammary glands of mice during pregnancy and lactation. These data are interpreted to indicate an increased number of receptors for prolactin. (Redrawn, with permission, from Yokoyama, A., et al. (eds.). 1978. *Physiology of Mammary Glands.* Tokyo: Japan Scientific Societies Press.)

is secreted in bursts in response to suckling. Afferent fibers from the nipple and areola transmit through the spinothalamic tract signals that ultimately reach the pituitary by way of the hypothalamus. The secretion of prolactin appears to be inhibited tonically by dopamine (prolactin inhibiting factor, or PIF; see Chapter 57) and activated by serotonin. Thyrotropin-releasing factor (TRF) directly causes the secretion of prolactin, and the possible existence of a specific prolactin-releasing factor has not been ruled out.

QUALITY OF SECRETION

As lactation begins, the breast secretes colostrum, which contains more protein and less fat and carbohydrate than mature milk does. Colostrum also is particularly rich in immunoglobulins, mainly secretory IgA and a variety of immunologically functional mononuclear cells. Colostrum is produced for about 3 days, "transitional milk" is secreted for 5–10 days, and after 2 weeks, mature milk is made.

The nutritional and immunological components of human milk are unique to the human species. As human lactation is studied more, the functions of its components become more clear; however, at present, truly synthetic human milk cannot be produced.

Release of Milk

The *let-down reflex,* or *milk-flow reflex,* is stimulated by suckling, but it also can be induced by auditory, visual, or olfactory stimuli related to nursing. The let-down reflex is mediated primarily by oxytocin (see Chapter 56), which is released by signals carried through the spinothalamic tracts to the hypothalamus and from there to the posterior pituitary. Oxytocin is directly responsible for the contraction of myoepithelial cells, which transfers fat and other components of milk from the secretory cells into the acini and moves milk stored in the distal alveoli into the larger ducts and lactiferous sinuses. This reflex occurs repeatedly during a feeding; it seems to be necessary to increase the amount of fat in the milk and to bring milk from the distal ducts in which it is stored between feedings. Sympathetic nervous system activity opposes the let-down reflex by causing vasoconstriction, which decreases the amount of oxytocin that reaches the breast, and by inhibiting contraction of the myoepithelial cells directly.

Maintenance of Lactation

Normal production of milk depends on adequate intake and storage of nutrients by the mother and appropriate hormonal stimulation. Release of enough prolactin and oxytocin is particularly important. Milk is produced on demand; thus, unless suckling occurs, the production of milk diminishes quickly. The more the baby suckles, the more milk is produced, and the converse also is true. The supply of milk is increased if both breasts are offered at each feeding, and if the feedings are frequent. This prevents milk stasis, which significantly inhibits the production of milk. Frequent nursing increases blood flow to the breasts (Figure 71-3), which enhances the delivery of nutrients and hormones to the cells. Frequent removal of milk also promotes the rate of proliferation and activity of secretory cells, possibly because of increased blood flow and greater exposure to hormones.

CLINICAL CORRELATION
71.1   Malnutrition

CASE REPORT

The Patient: A 2½-year-old male.

Principal Complaints: Chronic diarrhea and failure to thrive.

History: The patient's gestation had been uncomplicated, and his immediate postnatal course had been uneventful. The birthweight, 3.0 kg, and length at birth, 48.5 cm, were appropriate for the gestational age of 38 weeks. He had been breast-fed exclusively for the first three months and given artificial formula after that. At four months of age, he had de-

veloped frequent, intermittent diarrhea. The mother recalls that he had produced about four stools/day; she described these as non-bloody, but foul-smelling, greenish in color, and rather liquid in consistency, with large amounts of mucus. Before this, the child's feces had been soft, yellow in color, and not particularly foul-smelling. The casein-based formula had been changed to a soy milk. This had not been tolerated, however, and the episodes of diarrhea had persisted. A sucrose-casein hydrolyzed formula had been begun, but this trial also had failed. Goat's milk had been tried, but the pattern of diarrhea had

Use of Nutrients

Mature human milk is about 7% carbohydrate, 3.5%–4% fat, and 0.8% protein.

CARBOHYDRATE
The carbohydrate of milk is lactose, which is derived from plasma glucose under the in-

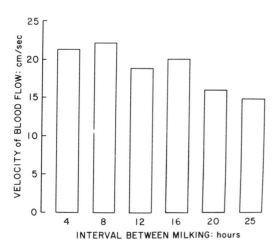

Figure 71-3. Effect of interval between milking on velocity of blood flow in mammary vessels of cows. (Redrawn, with permission, from Yokoyama, A., et al. (eds.). 1978. *Physiology of Mammary Glands.* Tokyo: Japan Scientific Societies Press.)

fluence of lactose synthetase. One of the components of this enzyme, α-lactalbumin, is not synthesized until after parturition. Therefore, the presence of α-lactalbumin and lactose in breast secretions indicates that lactation is beginning.

FAT
Milk fat is synthesized from glucose, free fatty acids of the blood, and triglycerides obtained from low-density lipoproteins and chylomicrons. Fatty acids of triglycerides are made available by the action of lipoprotein lipase, an enzyme present in breast tissue and activated by prolactin.

PROTEIN
The precursors for the proteins of mature milk come from the amino acids of the blood. Animal studies indicate that an excess of amino acids is taken up by the mammary tissue for the synthesis of milk proteins. Plasma proteins provide the bulk of the immunoglobulins contained in colostrum early in lactation.

ENERGY
Indirect studies of the energy required for the production of milk suggest an overall efficiency of about 80%.

recurred. Cereals and solids had been begun at five months of age, but these foods did not diminish the frequency of diarrhea. At that time, the episodes were complicated further by fever and vomiting that would last for about one day, after which the feces would improve temporarily. The child finally had been weaned from goat's milk at 18 months of age and maintained on whole pasteurized (cow's) milk and a limited variety of infant foods. At 24 months of age, the child's significant failure of growth was noted. The child's weight and length were below the third percentile. At that time, his diet consisted of whole cow's milk, applesauce, carrots, spinach, and crackers. The total intake of energy, as deduced from the mother's account, was approximately 450 kcal/day. All solid foods were strained, and milk was given in a bottle to coax a greater intake. The pattern of intermittent diarrhea remained unchanged. The child's developmental milestones were appropriate for his age, there was no history of recurrent infections or allergies, and the family had no history of gastrointestinal disease.

Clinical Examination: The child appeared alert and active. Although he was small, he was proportionate for his size. His height was 83 cm, he weighed 9.8 kg, his head circumference was 48 cm, and the ratio of his mid-arm circumference to fronto-occipital circumference was 0.3; this ratio supports the clinical impression of proportional stunting. Examination of his head, eyes, ears, nose, and throat revealed no abnormalities. His heart and lungs also were normal. No evidence of rickets (frontal bossing,* rachitic rosary,** or widened wrists) was noted. The abdomen was mildly protuberant, and the lower edge of the liver was palpable 1 cm below the costal margin, with a span of 4 cm; these findings are normal. No splenomegaly or abnormal masses were palpable in the abdomen. The rectal examination was normal, and the quaiac test (for blood in the feces) was negative. The skin was carotenemic (yellowish, due to ingestion of large amounts of carotene-containing foods).

Laboratory Data: All laboratory values—hematocrit and hemoglobin, serum iron, total iron-binding capacity, leukocyte count and differential (distribution of cell types), liver function studies, and serum immunoglobulin—were within normal limits. The possible abnormalities were serum albumin and total concentration of protein, which were in the lower limits of the normal range. The feces were negative for pathogenic bacteria and for ova and parasites. Xylose absorption and the 72-hr fecal-fat content were normal, and the sweat-test for cystic fibrosis† was negative. The gastrointestinal and skeletal systems were normal by radiological examination.

Hospital Course: No diarrhea or fever was observed during two weeks of hospitalization. The child gained weight and his borderline laboratory indices improved during a regimen that included nasogastric feeding. During this time, interactions between the mother and the child were noted to be abnormal, and the failure to thrive was ascribed to inadequate intake of food secondary to inadequate parent-child interaction. The mother demonstrated two extreme forms of behavior toward the infant: she was either unconcerned or overly solicitous. Minimal time was devoted to stimulation and arousal of the child in play situations, and his care could be described as almost "scientific" in its rigor, and cold in its delivery. Neither the child nor the mother demonstrated the expected degree of mutual dependence for emotional security. The family was referred for counseling.

Outcome: The mother revealed during counseling that she felt inadequate in caring for the child. When he had been ill, she had seen full-time, trained specialists attend to him, and she felt that she never could duplicate that care. Gradually, she came to realize that the child no longer needed such special treatment and that she could provide for him adequately. As she gained confidence, she treated the child with greater warmth, and he responded with an improved appetite and improved tolerance for a variety of foods. Six months after his dismissal from the hospital, his rate of growth had increased, and, although he still was small for his age, he was progressing towards normal size.

*Protuberance of the forehead.

**Prominence of the costochondral junction to form a series of knobs or "beads," fancied to resemble the rosary used by some Roman Catholics.

†The concentration of sodium and chloride are abnormally high in the sweat of a subject who has cystic fibrosis.

STUDY OUTLINE

FUNCTIONAL ANATOMY

BASIC ANATOMY Mammary glands consist of lobes, lobules, alveoli, and secretory cells.

Myoepithelial (contractile) cells surround secretory cells.

Secretory cells empty into ducts and then into ampullae (sinuses) beneath the nipple.

AFTER PUBERTY Epithelial duct system develops and fatty tissue proliferates; no alveoli.

Influenced by anterior pituitary hormones; later, also influenced by ovarian hormones.

Insulin and thyroid hormones also are essential.

Estrogen promotes mature ductal system and cyclical changes during first part of menstrual cycle.

Progesterone stimulates epithelial activity, and often vascular engorgement and edema of supporting stroma, during second part of cycle.

DURING PREGNANCY Effects of estrogen, progesterone, placental lactogen, and chorionic gonadotropin.

Secretory units (alveoli) form.

Blood vessels dilate and fill; connective tissue becomes edematous; acini and ducts dilate.

No milk is secreted until after infant is born.

LACTATION

INITIATION

IN VITRO EXPERIMENTS Hyperplasia of alveolar cells depends on insulin and adrenocortical steroids.

Prolactin causes lactogenesis.

IN VIVO EXPERIMENTS Stimulation by prolactin at parturition.

Removal of inhibition by progesterone when placenta is expelled.

With appropriate conditions, prolactin causes secretion of milk; blocked by bromocriptine.

Removal of ovaries or corpus luteum of pregnant animal removes source of progesterone and thereby initiates lactation.

POSSIBLE MECHANISMS Prolactin increases number of alveolar cells and prolactin receptors in cells.

Estrogen increases and progesterone decreases number of prolactin receptors in cells.

Prolactin-receptor combination may cause release of second messenger or entrance of prolactin fragment into cell.

CONTROL OF PROLACTIN SECRETION

Stimulated reflexly by suckling.

Inhibited tonically by dopamine (or PIF); activated by serotonin, thyrotropin-releasing factor (TRF), and possible specific prolactin-releasing factor.

QUALITY OF SECRETION First 3 days, colostrum—more protein, less carbohydrate and fat; rich in immunoglobulins.

"Transitional milk" for 5–10 days.

Mature milk after about 2 weeks.

RELEASE OF MILK Stimulated by suckling or other stimuli associated with nursing.

Oxytocin is released, which causes contraction of myoepithelial cells; milk is moved into larger ducts and sinuses.

MAINTENANCE OF LACTATION Adequate nutrition.

Adequate release of prolactin and oxytocin.

Continued suckling and removal of milk.

USE OF NUTRIENTS

CARBOHYDRATE Lactose that is derived from plasma glucose; enzyme is lactase synthetase.

FAT Synthesized from glucose, free fatty acids, and triglycerides.

PROTEIN From amino acids of blood.

Plasma proteins provide immunoglobulins.

ENERGY Production of milk is about 80% efficient.

BIBLIOGRAPHY

Cowie, A.T.; Forsyth, I.A.; and Hart, I.C. 1980. *Hormonal Control of Lactation.* New York: Springer-Verlag.

Goldfarb, J., and Tibbetts, E. 1980. *Breastfeeding Handbook.* Hillside, New Jersey: Enslow Publishers.

Green, T.H., Jr. 1971. *Gynecology: Essentials of Clinical Practice* (2nd ed.). Boston: Little, Brown.

Patton, S., and Jensen, R.G. 1976. *Biomedical Aspects of Lactation.* New York: Pergamon Press.

Peaker, M. (ed.). 1977. *Comparative Aspects of Lactation.* New York: Academic Press.

Shiu, R.P.C., and Friesen, H.G. 1980. Mechanism of action of prolactin in the control of mammary gland function. *Annu. Rev. Physiol.* 42:83.

Townsend, C.M. 1980. Breast lumps. *Clin. Symp.* 32(2):3

Yokoyama, A.; Mizuno, H.; and Nagasawa, H. (eds.). 1978. *Physiology of Mammary Glands.* Baltimore: University Park Press.

72

The Physiology of Work

CHAPTER CONTENTS

FOREWORD

From a physiological standpoint, physical work and exercise are synonymous, even though in our culture, quite different meanings usually are implied by the two terms. In this chapter, both work and exercise will be used to refer to movements of the body that require expenditure of energy above that used at rest. The following section will stress the immediate or acute physiological consequences of work— how the body acts to maintain its homeostatic balance during exercise and how it supports the activity metabolically.

RESPONSES TO ACUTE PHYSICAL ACTIVITY

Cardiovascular Responses

HEART RATE
The most easily measured physiological change that occurs during acute exercise is an increase in heart rate, which may begin before the exercise begins, as a neurohormonal anticipatory response (see Chapter 15). The heart rate increases rapidly at the beginning of a strenuous bout of work and then may rise less rapidly or level off, depending on the work load. In gen-

CLINICAL CORRELATION

72.1 Cardiovascular Responses to Stress of Acute Exercise

CASE REPORT

The Patient: A 32-year-old male.

Reason for Testing: To determine the maximal exercise tolerance as a basis for recommending a program of exercise training, and to screen for latent coronary heart disease.

History: The patient has a family history of heart disease; his father has had angina pectoris for several years, and his mother has congestive heart failure.

Clinical Examination: The patient's physical examination was normal, except for a small pulmonic flow murmur. The resting heart rate was 75 beats/min (normal, 60–100 beats/min), the arterial pressure was 114/68 mm Hg (normal, 90–140/60–90 mm Hg), and the ECG was normal.

Testing Procedure: A progressive, graded treadmill-exercise test was used to determine exercise capacity. The ECG, heart rate, and blood pressure were recorded at the end of each 3-minute stage. To determine the maximal uptake of O_2, expired air was collected during the last minute of the test and analyzed for oxygen and carbon dioxide content. The test was terminated at the end of 12 minutes (4.2 mph, 16% grade) because of leg fatigue. The maximal heart rate was 190 beats/min, arterial pressure was 182/70 mm Hg, and oxygen uptake was calculated to be 2.48 liter/min, or 42.5 ml/kg body weight/min. The heart rate, arterial pressure, and ECG were normal for the intensity of exercise, and the rate of uptake of oxygen indicated a good level of physiological fitness. Measurements during recovery were normal except for the occurrence of occasional premature atrial contractions during the second and third minutes. No indications that physical activity should be limited were noted during or after the test.

eral, during moderate, graded exercise, the heart rate increases linearly with the work load, or the rate of expenditure of energy (Figure 72-1). The heart rate may increase to approximately three times the resting value during maximal work in young, healthy individuals. It usually declines rapidly after the exercise, but the rate of decline depends somewhat on the state of physical training of the person.

ARTERIAL BLOOD PRESSURE

The changes of arterial pressure that occur during exercise are relatively easy to detect and are important consequences of physical activity. Systolic and mean arterial pressures normally increase with the exercise work load. Diastolic pressure normally does not increase with increased work loads and even may decrease slightly. The increase of arterial pressure in response to static, or *isometric*, muscle contractions and to arm work is much greater than

that in response to dynamic, or *isotonic*, contractions and to leg work. These differences are caused by the restriction of blood flow during static muscle contraction and the smaller amount of muscle mass used in arm work. The systolic blood pressure may increase to more than 200 mm Hg during strenuous exercise in normal individuals. It usually returns rapidly to normal after exercise and, because of dilation of the arterioles in the working muscles and decreased resistance to blood flow to the skin, may fall below the resting level.

OTHER EFFECTS

Other cardiovascular parameters that change during exercise, but which are not so evident, are the cardiac output and the rate of uptake, or consumption, of O_2, which increase in proportion to the work load. The cardiac output, as was discussed in Chapter 15, is the product of heart rate and stroke volume. Stroke volume

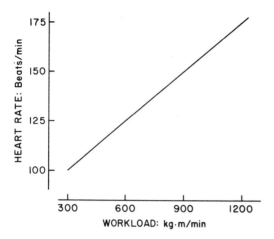

Figure 72-1. Estimation of physical work capacity (PWC) from submaximal heart rates at known work loads (line is constructed from measured responses to 600 and 900 kg-m/min work load). For an estimated maximum heart rate of 175 beats/min, the PWC is 1200 kg-m/min.

normally increases early in work and then rises only slightly with further increase of work intensity. An increase of one and one-half times in stroke volume and a threefold increase in heart rate during maximal exercise produce a maximum cardiac output almost five times the resting value.

EXTRACTION OF OXYGEN FROM BLOOD

More O_2 is extracted from arterial blood by the working muscles, and the arteriovenous O_2 difference increases as the work load increases. Since the total uptake of O_2 by the body is the product of the cardiac output (blood delivered)

and the arteriovenous O_2 difference (O_2 extracted), the uptake of O_2 may increase when either factor increases. Since the arteriovenous O_2 difference may increase as much as five times from rest to maximal exercise, the maximal uptake of oxygen ($\dot{V}O_{2max}$) may increase to as much as 25 times the resting value (0.2 liter/min–5.0 liter/min) in well-trained young men.

DISTRIBUTION OF BLOOD FLOW

The distribution of blood flow to various tissues and organs of the body is changed in such a way that the working skeletal muscles, heart, and brain receive adequate supplies at the expense of visceral organs and nonactive muscles (Table 72-1). The skeletal muscles, which comprise 40%–50% of the body weight, require only a small part of the total blood flow at rest, but they may need as much as 75%–80% of the blood flow during heavy work. This diversion of blood is accomplished by a marked dilation of the arterioles of the working muscles and an increase in the number of open capillary beds, while the arterioles of the inactive muscles and certain other tissues are constricted.

Respiratory Responses

DEPTH AND RATE OF BREATHING

The depth of breathing (*tidal volume*) increases during mild work, and the rate of respiration increases as the work load increases. During heavy work, these two changes cause a large increase in the minute ventilation ($\dot{V}E$), which generally is proportional to the work load until the anaerobic threshold is reached. An increase

TABLE 72-1
Blood flow to different tissues and organs at rest and during heavy exercise

	Rest		Exercise	
	Percent	Flow (ml/min)	Percent	Flow (ml/min)
Heart	4	200	4	1000
Brain	14	700	3	700
Kidneys	22	1100	1	250
Liver	27	1350	1	300
Muscle	15	750	80	20,000
Bone	5	250	1	250
Skin (cool weather)	6	300	6	1500
Other tissues	7	350	4	1000
Total	100	5000	100	25,000

in tidal volume is a more efficient way to increase the rate of exchange of gas because of the anatomical dead space (see Chapter 27, Table 27–1). Alveolar ventilation is greater when a large tidal volume is combined with a moderate rate of respiration than it is when a small tidal volume is combined with a high rate of respiration. The rate of respiration may increase from a resting value of 10–20 breaths/min to more than 40 breaths/min in adults exercising maximally. The tidal volume may increase from an average of 0.5 liter at rest to 4.0 liters during a peak bout of work in an adult male. $\dot{V}E$ varies from approximately 5 liters/min at rest to more than 200 liters/min in large males during maximal exercise. Lung diffusion capacity increases by 25%–50% or more during maximal exercise in healthy persons.

USE OF OXYGEN BY
MUSCLES OF RESPIRATION

The muscles of respiration, which must overcome the elasticity of the lungs and the resistance to airflow, consume more O_2 as the volume of ventilation increases. At rest, the work of breathing requires 0.5–1.0 ml of O_2 per liter of ventilation (0.25%–0.5% of $\dot{V}O_2$), while during heavy work, it may require as much as 10% of the total $\dot{V}O_2$. Ventilation probably does not limit the capacity to take up O_2; this is known because ventilation may be increased either voluntarily or by increasing the work load after $\dot{V}O_{2max}$ has been reached.

BLOOD GASES

During moderate work, the partial pressure of O_2 (Pao_2) and CO_2 ($Paco_2$) and the concentration of H^+, $[H^+]$, of the arterial blood are about the same as they are at rest. During heavy exercise, the $[H^+]$ increases as lactic acid accumulates, and the Pao_2 decreases slightly in spite of an increased alveolar O_2 tension (Pao_2). Thus, chemical changes in the arterial blood fail to explain fully the large increase in ventilation that occurs during heavy exercise. The $Paco_2$ also decreases during heavy exercise, but the $Pvco_2$ (venous) tends to increase.

Muscular Responses

FATIGUE

The physiology of muscular contraction has been discussed in detail in Chapters 9 and 15, and only a few very specific exercise-related phenomena will be considered here. Fatigue of skeletal muscle often is associated with heavy physical activity, but the exact cause of fatigue is unclear. Although some research indicates that the site of muscular fatigue is local, other studies conclude that some component of fatigue may be located in the central nervous system or at the neuromuscular junction.

Fatigue develops rapidly during heavy isometric (static) contraction, and, since the blood flow to the muscle is interrupted, lactic acid or H^+ produced during anaerobic metabolism may accumulate and contribute to fatigue by local mechanisms. Apparently, the ability to maintain static contractions depends on the flow of blood to "wash out" the products of metabolism.

During a period of several hours, rhythmic muscular contractions well below the maximum intensity that can be achieved may cause the maximum intensity of exercise to decline only gradually. The rhythmic nature of such contractions allows for adequate flow of blood, and lactic acid does not accumulate in amounts that would limit performance. Some factors that might cause fatigue during prolonged exercise include an alteration of the properties of the muscle-fiber membrane, disturbance of the ATP-ADP mechanism, and depletion of stores of energy substrate such as glycogen.

The loss of intracellular K^+ and gain of intracellular Na^+ also may increase the frequency of afferent nerve impulses from a fatigued muscle, inhibit the motor fibers, and thereby decrease the force of contraction. Other neural changes that have been found might contribute to a sensation of local fatigue, a feeling of pain, and the inability of the muscle to maintain the tension that is intended during rhythmic or static contractions.

ENVIRONMENTAL
CONSIDERATIONS

Heat Balance

TEMPERATURE OF THE BODY

The core, or internal body, temperature (see Chapter 66) must be maintained within narrow limits if the body is to function efficiently. The average core temperature is 37 C (98.6 F), and an increase to 41 C (105.8 F) may be lethal. The core temperature in humans is regulated mainly by dissipating heat, although some animals regulate their core temperatures by varying the rate of production of heat.

PRODUCTION OR GAIN OF HEAT

The human body produces heat through the contraction of muscles and metabolic activity in other tissues. The body also may gain heat from the environment in several ways, including radiation, conduction, and convection, all of which depend on a difference between the temperature of the core and that of the shell, or skin (see Chapter 66). For thermal regulation to be effective, the temperature of the shell must remain at least 2 C below that of the core; otherwise, the skin acts as an insulator and prevents the loss of heat.

LOSS OF HEAT

The body loses heat by several methods: mainly through the skin (by radiation, conduction, convection, and evaporation), but also through the lungs and by the excretion of wastes. Under conditions of intense sweating, heat is lost almost entirely by the evaporation of water from the skin. The rate of sweating is high when the temperature of the air exceeds the temperature of the skin or when high humidity prevents effective evaporation. Sweat must evaporate to produce cooling; if it runs off or is dried away, it does no good, and if clothing prevents evaporation, the effect is lost.

The rate of gain or loss of heat by the body is expressed in the following equation:

$$S = M \pm R \pm C - E$$

where S is storage, M is metabolic heat production, R is radiation, C is convection, and E is evaporative heat loss. The storage of 60 kcal of heat increases the core temperature of a 70-kg person by 1 C.

CIRCULATION

The circulatory system is very important in maintaining thermal balance. Heat is carried by the blood from the deep tissues to the skin, where dilation of peripheral vessels allows an increase in blood flow. In addition, the blood supplies the fluid the sweat glands secrete. The heart rate increases with an increase of temperature, thereby meeting the need to maintain a high cardiac output.

THERMOREGULATORY CENTER

The thermostat, or center of temperature regulation of the body, is located in the hypothalamus and the adjacent preoptic region. The anterior hypothalamus is sensitive to local changes of temperature, and the posterior hypothalamus receives impulses from thermal sensors in the skin. This regulatory center may increase the rate of loss of heat from the body during exercise or exposure to heat by stimulating the sweat glands and by inhibiting vasoconstriction in the skin, which allows dilation and increased blood flow to the periphery.

Exercise in the Heat

LOSS OF FLUID

A person may sweat at a rate of more than 2 liters/hr while doing heavy work in a hot environment. To work efficiently, the individual must be sure to drink enough water. Water is lost primarily from the extracellular fluid (plasma volume), if the person is exposed to heat alone, or mainly from the intracellular fluid, if the individual sweats while exercising vigorously. The ability to do work declines progressively if fluid is lost and not replaced (dehydration). If a quantity of fluid equal to 5% of the body weight is lost, the cardiac stroke volume decreases and the heart rate increases, although the maximal capacity to do work may not be affected until the fluid loss is greater.

The body opposes the loss of fluid by increasing the secretion of antidiuretic hormone (ADH). This reaction is initiated by an increase in the osmotic pressure of the plasma or a decrease in the blood volume. ADH causes the kidneys to decrease the rate of excretion of urine by reabsorbing more water (see Chapter 41).

REPLACEMENT OF FLUID

Thirst alone is not an adequate stimulus for the replacement of fluid, which is necessary during strenuous work. The amount of fluid that has been lost through sweat may be determined by weighing the person, and only then can it be determined whether the intake of fluid has been adequate. When fluid is lost, the osmotic pressure of most body fluids increases; this change is sensed in the hypothalamic area, producing the sensation of thirst.

ELECTROLYTE BALANCE

Normally, the replacement of water lost during sweating is all that is required, if the period of sweating is short and the individual eats a normal diet. In cases of prolonged sweating, however, such as during heavy work in a hot, humid environment or in an extremely hot industrial job, Na^+ and K^+ may be lost more rapidly than they are replaced by the diet.

Na^+ is conserved by increased reabsorption in the kidneys, which is caused by the action of aldosterone, but there is no such mechanism for conserving K^+. Na^+ can be replaced by increasing the amount of table salt in the diet, if that is necessary, but K^+ must be obtained from foods such as bananas, oranges, tomatoes, and other fruits and vegetables.

Acclimatization

HEAT

A person acquires a tolerance for working in the heat by repeated, graded exercise in a hot environment. The process of acclimatization takes place during about 5–12 days of exposure. The changes are as follows:

1. Increased effectiveness of sweating.
2. Beginning to sweat at a lower body temperature.
3. Increase of the volume of the extracellular fluid, and improved transfer of heat to the periphery.
4. Loss of smaller quantities of electrolytes in the sweat.

Exercise training alone produces only a limited ability to withstand work in the heat, and exercise training in the heat is necessary to produce the adaptive changes listed above. Conversely, exposure to heat alone will not cause acclimatization to work in the heat or improve the tolerance for simple exercise. Training in the heat should be gradual; the duration and intensity of exercise and the temperature of the environment initially should be moderate and then increased progressively, if that is possible.

COLD

The adaptation to a cold environment is not as dramatic as the acclimatization to heat. Humans have a limited ability to reduce the loss of heat by constricting cutaneous vessels and to increase the production of heat by shivering. However, these responses are acute, and research has not shown any chronic increase of the metabolic rate caused by exposure to cold. Chronic exposure of the extremities to cold causes periodic increases of local blood flow, causing greater loss of heat, but probably preventing damage to tissue (from frostbite).

PHYSICAL CAPACITY TO DO WORK

Uptake of Oxygen

The recognized physiological standard for the (aerobic) capacity to perform work is the maximal O_2 uptake ($\dot{V}O_{2max}$), which is measured in a laboratory. This test requires an individual to meet increasingly demanding work loads while the $\dot{V}O_2$ is measured periodically until it reaches a maximal value. The uptake of O_2 usually is measured by an open-circuit method, in which room air is inhaled and expired air is collected for determination of volume and analyzed for content of O_2 and CO_2. The rate of uptake, or consumption, of O_2 is calculated by subtracting the volume of O_2 in the expired air from that in the inspired air. The production of CO_2 may be calculated in the same way.

Oxygen uptake is the product obtained by multiplying cardiac output and arteriovenous O_2 difference. In equation form, this can be written as:

$$\dot{V}O_2 = (HR \times SV) \times a\text{-}\bar{v}O_2 \text{ difference}$$

where HR is heart rate and SV is stroke volume. The following equation illustrates the calculation of O_2 uptake in a young subject at rest:

$$\begin{aligned} \dot{V}O_2 &= (60 \text{ beats/min} \times 85 \text{ ml/beat}) \\ &\quad \times 4 \text{ ml } O_2/100 \text{ ml blood} \\ &= 204 \text{ ml } O_2/\text{min} \end{aligned}$$

In the same subject performing moderate work:

$$\begin{aligned} \dot{V}O_2 &= (150 \text{ beats/min} \times 100 \text{ ml/beat}) \\ &\quad \times 13.5 \text{ ml } O_2/100 \text{ ml blood} \\ &= 2025 \text{ ml } O_2/\text{min} \end{aligned}$$

Although the physiological determinants of $\dot{V}O_{2max}$ are cardiac output and arteriovenous O_2 difference, several other factors merit consideration in predicting work capacity. In addition to the cardiorespiratory system, muscular strength and endurance must be adequate for the activity undertaken, and environmental factors, such as altitude and temperature, also must be considered. Since body weight is a factor in the relative $\dot{V}O_2$, the lower the weight, within limits, the greater the aerobic capacity. Absolute rates of uptake of oxygen are expressed in liters per minute, but it is difficult to compare individual values without considering the size of the body. Since the larger the body, the greater the demand for O_2 at the cellular level, the absolute $\dot{V}O_2$ is divided by the body weight, and the result (aerobic capacity) usually is expressed in milliliters of O_2 consumed per kilogram of body weight per minute (ml/kg/min). It is not known whether $\dot{V}O_{2max}$ is limited by the capacity for delivery of O_2 or the ability of the active muscle cells to extract O_2.

Work Load

The work load imposed during the measurement of $\dot{V}O_{2max}$ may consist of stepping up and down on a bench or steps, pedalling a bicycle ergometer, or walking or running on a motor-driven treadmill. All three methods have advantages and disadvantages, but the bicycle ergometer and the treadmill are used more commonly at this time.

INDIRECT MEASUREMENT
The direct relationship between an increase in heart rate and an increase in work load may be used to estimate the physical work capacity (PWC). In this case, the work load required to elicit a specified heart rate is used as a measure of the PWC (Figure 72–1). Another method of estimating PWC uses the relationship between heart rate and $\dot{V}O_2$. In this test, the subject pedals the ergometer at a constant rate until a steady-state heart rate is achieved, and a nomogram is used to estimate the $\dot{V}O_{2max}$. Other tests, which are based on the rate of decrease of the heart rate to normal after standard work loads, also may be used to estimate PWC, but these generally are less reliable and not as valid. Factors such as neuromuscular coordination, agility, and skill should not enter the determination of physical work capacity.

Energy Costs of Various Activities

METABOLIC EQUIVALENTS
The amount of energy required by any particular activity can be determined by measuring the amount of O_2 used during the activity. The relative rate of uptake of O_2 at rest is about the same for all persons (3.5–4.0 ml/kg/min). Therefore, the energy requirement of any activity can be expressed in multiples of the resting $\dot{V}O_2$, which are called *metabolic equivalents* (MET). For example, walking at the rate of 3

mph on level terrain requires an expenditure of energy about three times the resting level, or 3 METs.

KILOCALORIES
The energy cost also may be expressed in kilocalories (kcal), or units of heat. Direct calorimetry seldom is used in practical situations because the equipment is so expensive, but the caloric cost may be estimated by using the rate of uptake of O_2. The caloric equivalent of 1 liter of O_2 is approximately 5 kcal, or, conversely, the value of $\dot{V}O_2$ may be obtained by dividing the caloric value by 5. Since this conversion is related to absolute values of $\dot{V}O_2$ (liters/minute), the caloric expenditure derived also is absolute for a certain body size. Caloric expenditure usually is expressed as that of a standard 70-kg man.

WORK STANDARDS
The physiological stress of work or exercise may be evaluated according to several standards. The easiest variable to measure is the change of heart rate during a given task, which is expressed as a fraction of the maximal rate. A heart rate of 125 beats/min does not represent to a person who has a maximal heart rate of 185 beats/min the same degree of stress that it does for another individual who has a maximal rate of 150 beats/min. Maximal heart rate tends to decline approximately 10 beats per decade; therefore, age must be considered when heart rate is used to indicate the intensity of work.

The rate of doing work may be evaluated as exhausting, very heavy, heavy, moderate, or light, based on the caloric expenditure, the uptake of O_2, the heart rate, the volume of ventilation, the body temperature, and the increased concentration of lactate in the blood (Table 72–2). Only the latter two of these factors may be used accurately, without regard to the maximal work capacity of the individual, and even these two factors may be affected by the individual's state of physical training.

The length of time that a certain level of work can be sustained depends on the maximal work capacity. Forty percent of the $\dot{V}O_{2max}$ is considered to be the greatest work load that a person can sustain for an entire 8-hour day. Some jobs demand a higher rate of use of energy than this but not for such a long period, and the intervals of work must be alternated with intervals of rest.

TABLE 72-2
Work classification by various physiological standards

Work classification	Energy requirement		Heart rate (beats/min)	Lactate accumulation
	$\dot{V}o_2$ (liters/min)	kcal/min		
Exhausting	3.0	15.0	180	6 times normal
Very heavy	2.5	12.5	180	5 times normal
Heavy	2.0	10.0	160	2 times normal
Moderate	1.5	7.5	140	1.5 times normal
Light	1.0	5.0	120	normal
Sedentary	0.5	2.5	72	normal

STUDY OUTLINE

FOREWORD   Work or exercise—movements of body that require use of energy above resting level.

RESPONSES TO ACUTE PHYSICAL ACTIVITY

CARDIOVASCULAR RESPONSES

HEART RATE   Increases linearly with work load; maximal value is three times resting value; decreases quickly after exercise.

ARTERIAL BLOOD PRESSURE   Systolic and mean pressures increase with work load; diastolic pressure may decrease during exercise.

Increases more during static contraction and in arm work than in leg work.

Systolic pressure may increase to 200 mm Hg during maximal exercise.

OTHER EFFECTS   Cardiac output increases. Stroke volume increases early in exercise.

EXTRACTION OF OXYGEN FROM BLOOD   Increased arteriovenous O_2 difference; increased uptake because of increased cardiac output and arteriovenous O_2 difference.

DISTRIBUTION OF BLOOD FLOW   Changes ensure that working muscle and brain get adequate blood supplies; accomplished by arteriolar constriction in nonessential tissues and dilation in active muscles.

RESPIRATORY RESPONSES

DEPTH AND RATE OF BREATHING   Tidal volume increases during mild exercise; rate increases during moderate and heavy work.

Alveolar ventilation is more efficient when large tidal volume and moderate rate are combined.

Minute volume (rate × tidal volume) increases greatly during exercise.

USE OF OXYGEN BY MUSCLES OF RESPIRATION   Increases as intensity of work increases.

BLOOD GASES Po_2, Pco_2, and $[H^+]$ in arterial blood during moderate exercise are same as at rest.

In heavy exercise, Pao_2 decreases and $[H^+]$ increases.

Large increase in ventilation is not explained by chemical changes.

MUSCULAR RESPONSES

FATIGUE   Cause unclear, may be local (muscular) or related to central nervous system.

Develops rapidly during static contractions.

Loss of intracellular K^+ and increase of Na^+ may induce neural changes that cause decreased force of contraction.

ENVIRONMENTAL CONSIDERATIONS

HEAT BALANCE

TEMPERATURE OF THE BODY   Regulated by heat dissipation; core temperature must remain in narrow range for optimum function.

PRODUCTION OR GAIN OF HEAT   Produced by metabolic activity; gained from environment by radiation, conduction, and convection.

LOSS OF HEAT   Lost by radiation, conduction, convection, and evaporation—latter is most important during exercise and high heat conditions.

Gain or loss is expressed by S = M ± R ± C − E (Storage = metabolic production ± radiation ± convection − evaporative loss).

CIRCULATION   Carries heat from core to surface, provides fluids for sweat.

THERMOREGULATORY CENTER   Located in hypothalamus—stimulates sweat glands and inhibits vasoconstriction in skin.

EXERCISE IN THE HEAT

LOSS OF FLUID   Up to 2 liters/hr during heavy work in hot environment; replacement is essential if exercise efficiency is to be maintained.

Counteracted by secretion of antidiuretic hormone—causes renal reabsorption of water.

REPLACEMENT OF FLUID Thirst is not adequate stimulus during high rate of fluid loss.

ELECTROLYTE BALANCE Loss usually is not enough to justify supplementation except in extreme cases over several days.

Na^+ is conserved by renal reabsorption—action of aldosterone.

K^+ is replaced by diet.

ACCLIMATIZATION

HEAT Tolerance to exercise in heat is increased by repeated, increased work during heat exposure—takes 5–12 days.

COLD Humans have limited ability to reduce heat loss or increase heat production at rest—increased local peripheral blood flow may help prevent frostbite.

PHYSICAL CAPACITY TO DO WORK

UPTAKE OF OXYGEN Maximal O_2 uptake is physiological standard for aerobic work capacity.

Measured by analysis of expired O_2 and CO_2.

Determined by product of cardiac output and arteriovenous O_2 difference.

Usually expressed as liters per kilogram of body weight.

WORK LOAD Assessed by step tests, treadmill, bicycle ergometer.

INDIRECT MEASUREMENT Relationship between heart rate and work load is used to estimate physical work capacity (PWC).

Heart rate response to steady work load is used to estimate $\dot{V}o_{2max}$.

Rate of heart rate decline is not as valid or reliable.

ENERGY COSTS OF VARIOUS ACTIVITIES

METABOLIC EQUIVALENTS Resting $\dot{V}o_2$ is same for all persons (3.5–4.0 ml/kg/min).

Energy requirement of any activity is expressed as multiples of resting $\dot{V}o_2$.

KILOCALORIES Units of heat; estimated from $\dot{V}o_2$.

Caloric equivalent of 1 liter of O_2 is about 5 kcal.

WORK STANDARDS Based on heart rate, $\dot{V}o_2$, caloric cost, ventilation volume, body temperature, and accumulation of lactate.

Evaluated as light, moderate, heavy, very heavy, and exhausting; relative to maximal work capacity and state of training.

Maximum—sustained work at 40% of $\dot{V}o_{2max}$ for 8 hours.

BIBLIOGRAPHY

Andersen, K.L. 1968. The cardiovascular system in exercise. In *Exercise Physiology.* Edited by H.E. Falls. New York: Academic Press.

Åstrand, P.O., and Rodahl, K. 1977. *Textbook of Work Physiology* (2nd ed.). New York: McGraw-Hill.

Blomqvist, C.G., and Saltin, B. 1983. Cardiovascular adaptations to physical training. *Annu. Rev. Physiol.* 45:169.

Brengelmann, G.L. 1983. Circulatory adjustments to exercise and heat stress. *Annu. Rev. Physiol.* 45:191.

Christensen, N.J., and Galbo, H. 1983. Sympathetic nervous activity during exercise. *Annu. Rev. Physiol.* 45:139.

Clausen, J.P. 1977. Effect of physical training on cardiovascular adjustments to exercise. *Physiol. Rev.* 57:779.

Eldridge, F.L.; Millhorn, D.E.; and Waldrop, T.G. 1981. Exercise hyperpnea and locomotion: Parallel activation from the hypothalamus. *Science* 211:844.

Holloszy, J.O., and Booth, F.W. 1976. Biochemical adaptations to endurance exercise in muscle. *Annu. Rev. Physiol.* 38:273.

Shephard, R.J. 1982. *Physiology and Biochemistry of Exercise.* New York: Praeger.

73

The Physiological and Metabolic Effects of Exercise Training

CHAPTER CONTENTS

EXERCISE TRAINING AND FUNCTIONAL FITNESS

Effects of Chronic Inactivity

The human body has evolved and adapted to movement in the upright position. Inactivity, whether in the form of prolonged bed rest, immobilization of a limb, or a relatively sedentary existence, decreases the normal capacity of the body to function voluntarily.

DEMINERALIZATION OF BONE

Prolonged bed rest causes increased excretion of calcium in the urine, which indicates a loss of calcium from the bones. Studies have shown that the stress of gravity on the long bones in the upright position is necessary to maintain the normal mineral composition of the bones. Exercise in the supine position or sitting quietly does not reduce the excretion of calcium caused by bed rest, but standing quietly for 3 hours each day does decrease the excretion of calcium.

DECREASED MUSCLE POWER

Bed rest or the immobilization of a limb also may cause atrophy of muscle; strength and muscular endurance are lost, and the size of the muscle decreases. Loss of muscle strength may not occur as rapidly as some other effects of chronic inactivity do, but it can be substantial during periods of complete immobilization. The loss of muscle strength may be kept small by brief intervals of isometric (static) contraction to less than 50% of maximal strength several times per day.

ORTHOSTATIC HYPOTENSION

Bed rest also decreases the sensitivity of the baroreceptor reflexes in response to upward tilting of the head. *Orthostatic hypotension*, or fainting, in this situation seems to be related to the absence of normal gravitational stress because exercise in the supine position does not improve the condition.

DECREASED CARDIOVASCULAR FUNCTION

Cardiovascular responses to chronic inactivity include decreased heart volume, plasma volume, red blood cell volume, maximal stroke volume, maximal cardiac output, and maximal oxygen uptake ($\dot{V}o_{2max}$). During submaximal exercise after a period of bed rest, stroke volume and cardiac output may decline, and heart rate and arteriovenous O_2 difference may increase. The decline in $\dot{V}o_{2max}$ has been found to range from 17% to 31%. Thus, prolonged bed rest causes significant impairment of the cardiovascular adjustment to exercise and in exercise-related adaptations to physical training.

In summary, the major effects of chronic inactivity or bed rest are bone demineralization, orthostatic intolerance, and decreased maximal aerobic capacity. Although different physiological processes are responsible for each of these conditions, physical activity in the upright position will prevent or alleviate each of them. Obviously, prolonged bed rest is not the best type of rest and even is harmful to the functional health of the individual.

PRINCIPLES OF EXERCISE TRAINING

Physical training, exercise training, or conditioning, as it sometimes is called, may be considered a paradox. The more work the human body does, within certain limits, the easier the work becomes and the more the body becomes capable of doing. This ability to adapt may be clarified by several principles that are related to physical training.

Overload

For adaptive changes to occur, physical stress greater than that of the normal level of activity must be imposed. Thus, to improve cardiorespiratory endurance, one must engage in movements that require large muscle masses to contract repeatedly for a relatively long time. The activity must cause the heart rate to increase to about 70%–80% of maximal, and it must tax the entire system that transports O_2.

Adaptability

When an increased work load is imposed on the body, functional and structural changes occur that enable the body to adjust to the extra work. For example, the muscles may hypertrophy as a result of a chronic work load and, after training, produce less lactate while accomplishing the same task. However, after the body has adapted to a specific work load, no further changes occur unless the load is changed.

Specificity

Each adaptation in structure or function that occurs during physical training is caused by a certain stimulus, and the ability to perform specific tasks is increased. The specificity of training is peculiar not only to the muscle groups or physiological systems that are stressed, but also to the manner in which they are exercised. For example, muscles subjected to heavy loads for short periods develop strength, while muscles exercised lightly for long periods develop endurance.

Reversibility

Adaptations that occur during exercise training are not permanent, and to maintain the benefits that are derived, the training must be continued. All functional and structural changes are reversible in time, and after a person becomes inactive, little, if any, of the benefits derived from a previously active style of life persist.

EFFECTS OF EXERCISE TRAINING

Muscular Effects

Chronic exercise training increases the number of myofibrils (or contractile elements) in each skeletal muscle fiber, the thickness of the connective tissue between and around the muscle fibers, and the content of phosphocreatine and glycogen stored in the muscle. Training does not increase the number of fibers in a muscle, but the larger muscle mass is caused by enlargement of the individual fibers.

The number of capillaries also increases, so that the supply of O_2 and nutrient materials to the muscle and the removal of the products of metabolism are improved. All of these factors contribute to increased muscular endurance. The transmission of nerve impulses to the muscle fibers is improved, resulting in an increase in the number of fibers that can be used in a task for contraction. Training also increases the strength of muscular contraction by bringing into play motor units that are not recruited by the unconditioned person.

Cardiovascular Effects

ADAPTIVE CHANGES FOUND AT REST

1. *Heart rate*—the heart rate is decreased. The ultimate cause of this change is not known; however, the effect is mediated through a greater inhibitory tone (frequency of impulses) applied through the vagus nerve at the sinoatrial node, which is the normal pacemaker of the heart.
2. *Stroke volume*—since the cardiac output is the same and the heart rate is less, the stroke volume is greater.
3. *Cardiac volume*—the volume of the heart at the end of diastole is greater than normal. Increased end-diastolic volume is related to increased stroke volume and may reflect increased ventricular compliance (see Chapter 15).
4. *Heart weight*—the mass of the heart increases because of both increased thickness of the ventricular walls (*cardiac hypertrophy*) and increased length of the muscle fiber (*cardiac dilatation*).
5. *Density of myocardial capillaries*—most investigators agree that new capillaries form in the heart, although there is controversy as to whether collateral vessels that interconnect small arteries develop as a result of training.

6. *Density of skeletal muscle capillaries*—the increased number of capillaries in skeletal muscle may be stimulated by the lowering of O_2 tension in working muscle. This structural change allows a greater rate of blood flow to the muscle fibers.
7. *Arterial blood pressure*—the resting arterial pressure usually is not altered by endurance training if it is normal at the beginning.
8. *Blood volume*—increased blood volume is a distinct advantage in endurance exercise because it allows for effective dissipation of heat while maintaining an adequate flow of blood to the muscles.
9. *Total hemoglobin*—a larger amount of hemoglobin facilitates the transport of O_2 to the muscles and CO_2 from the muscles during work. The increased hemoglobin parallels the increased blood volume, so that both fluid volume and the total number of red blood cells are increased.

ADAPTIVE CHANGES DURING SUBMAXIMAL WORK AT FIXED INTENSITY

The following is a list of the cardiovascular changes that occur during submaximal work at fixed intensity (Figure 73-1):

1. *Smaller increase of heart rate*—at a given work load, the amount the heart rate increases becomes less as training proceeds (Figure 73-2), because the stroke volume at the beginning of the task is greater, and the cardiac output is about the same.
2. *Greater ventricular stroke volume*—increased stroke volume during exercise is related to the increased stroke volume at rest and is consistent with the slower heart rate.
3. *Oxygen uptake unchanged or decreased*—the O_2 required by the body at a given work load could decrease with training because of increased mechanical efficiency. (Mechanical efficiency = work done ÷ energy expended × 100.)
4. *Increase of cardiac output unchanged or decreased slightly*—the cardiac output may increase slightly less in the trained subject than in the untrained subject during submaximal work. This condition would be consistent with a decreased uptake of O_2 caused by increased mechanical efficiency. However, studies report no effect of training on cardiac output during a fixed work load.
5. *Arteriovenous oxygen difference*—an increased arteriovenous O_2 difference would indicate increased extraction of O_2 by the tissues, but this change has not been documented in all studies.

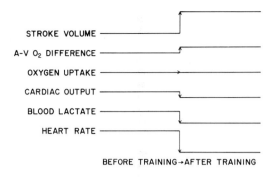

Figure 73-1. Training responses to submaximal work.

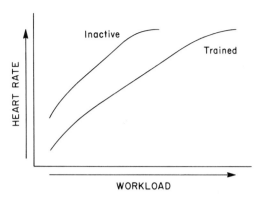

Figure 73-2. Heart rate response to increased work load in inactive and trained subjects.

6. *Decreased plasma lactate*—a decrease of lactic acid probably reflects both a decreased rate of production of lactate, because of a greater utilization of aerobic energy sources, and an increased rate of removal of lactate by the body.

7. *Decreased lung ventilation per liter of oxygen consumed*—decreased need for ventilation may be related to the decreased accumulation of lactate in the blood as training proceeds and a subsequent reduction of the respiratory drive.

RESPONSES TO TRAINING DURING MAXIMAL WORK

The following is a list of the cardiovascular responses to training during maximal work:

1. *Greater maximal cardiac output*—a larger maximal cardiac output is necessary to meet the increased requirements of the muscles for O_2. Since training increases the circulating blood volume and the ability to provide a larger cardiac output, the rate of blood flow during exercise usually is sufficient to provide for the demands of the various tissues and organs during sustained exercise in the trained individual.

2. *Increased arteriovenous oxygen difference*—the arteriovenous O_2 difference increases because of the increased concentration of red blood cells, which increases the O_2 content and the Po_2 in the capillaries. Another factor may be a shift of the O_2 dissociation curve to the right during exercise, because of increased temperature, production of CO_2, and accumulation of lactate.

3. *Increased maximal uptake of oxygen*—the increased maximal uptake of O_2 by the cells is a result of changes in the mitochondria that increase the cellular oxidative capacity and use.

The responses achieved during cardiorespiratory conditioning will not be the same for all persons because many factors determine the results of a training program. These factors include the genetic endowment of body structure and function, the initial level of fitness, the age of a person, any previous training, and the level of motivation.

Respiratory Effects

No definite changes in external respiratory (breathing) factors can be identified as a result of exercise training. The depth of breathing may increase slightly, but the respiratory rate declines, so that the volume of air moved per minute does not change. Maximal lung volumes do not increase with training in normal adults. However, the diffusion capacity of the lungs during maximal exercise may be improved by training.

FITNESS FOR EVERYDAY LIFE

The human body is made for movement; if the body is not allowed to be active, it loses its ability to do so. An individual's physical fitness is related directly to the activity experienced on a regular basis. Generally, individuals are less active today than their ancestors were because the occupations of modern people demand less physically, and modern people depend on the automobile and labor-saving devices rather than on their muscles. The tasks of daily living frequently do not provide enough vigorous exercise to develop and maintain good muscle tone or cardiovascular and respiratory fitness. The degree of inactivity and poor personal health practices have resulted in a massive physical fitness problem.

Physical Fitness

Physical fitness is difficult to define precisely. It involves the relationship between the task to be performed and the ability to perform it. Fitness for a specific task depends on the suitability of the body structure and the effectiveness with which the organs and body systems support the effort required. Maintenance of a reserve capacity to engage in physical activity greater than that required on the job or in normal daily routines is essential to effective functioning in emergency situations.

For most adults, physical fitness involves the ability to perform daily activities without undue fatigue and strain, to participate in leisure-time activities, and to have a reserve of energy in case of emergency. Physical fitness is that part of total fitness that indicates the capacity of the body to do work. It is composed of many elements, the most important of which are (1) freedom from disease, (2) cardiorespiratory or general endurance, (3) flexibility, (4) muscular strength, and (5) muscular endurance. Additional elements have been mentioned by other investigators, but these other elements are related more to preparing an individual to compete in sports and are not included here. The elements discussed in this chapter are related closely to the health and vigor of the individual and are those most susceptible to change due to activity or the lack of it.

FREEDOM FROM DISEASE

Freedom from disease is included because a dysfunctioning organ, invading viruses or bacteria, or other similar disorders can diminish greatly an individual's capacity to function, regardless of how well the person rates with respect to the other four elements.

CARDIORESPIRATORY ENDURANCE

Cardiorespiratory endurance is the ability to perform well on tasks that require work by the large muscles of the body for relatively long periods. Running, swimming, rowing, and bicycling are examples of such tasks. This type of work is characterized by heavy breathing, a high heart rate, and, often, sweating. These exercises are called "aerobic exercises," and the ability to participate in them is called "aerobic capacity." Cardiorespiratory endurance requires efficient working of the heart, lungs, blood vessels, and muscles. Cardiorespiratory endurance may be the most important of all of the elements of fitness because failure of the cardiorespiratory organs will cause death or significant loss of function. An individual who scores high on this fitness element is less likely to have a heart attack, a stroke, high blood pressure, or a respiratory ailment. Furthermore, the ability to recover from these disorders is improved.

FLEXIBILITY

Flexibility refers to the range of movement around the various joints of the body. Flexibility does not depend on the other elements of fitness; thus, whether a person scores high or low on tests of strength or endurance has no relationship to his or her flexibility. Flexibility is specific to the joint. An individual may have a great deal of flexibility around one joint and relatively little around another. Flexibility is a factor in physical fitness only when the range of movement is insufficient to allow a person to assume correct alignment of all body parts or to allow correct movement of all body parts in whatever tasks the individual participates. Sometimes, excessive flexibility will cause a joint to become unstable and may predispose an individual to injury.

MUSCULAR STRENGTH

Muscular strength is the ability of the muscles to exert force. Strength is an important fitness element for people of all ages and both sexes because of its close relationship to endurance. The stronger a person is, the more endurance he or she has. Also, the stronger a person is, the smaller is the fraction of maximum strength required to perform work tasks and to participate in various forms of physical activity. Very few tasks could not be done more efficiently if the performer were stronger.

MUSCULAR ENDURANCE

Muscular endurance is the ability to continue less than maximum muscular contractions. Endurance of postural muscles is required to maintain the body correctly in an erect position. Endurance of extensor muscles of the legs is required in all locomotive movements and in most daily activities.

Cardiovascular Disease and Exercise

ATHEROSCLEROSIS

Cardiovascular diseases take several forms, but the most common condition, and the one that is most serious and perplexing, is *atherosclerosis*, which affects the arteries, including those of the coronary system. Atherosclerosis is a complex process that involves the mechanism of the body for handling certain fats and fatlike substances such as cholesterol. These substances collect beneath the linings of the walls of the arteries and eventually narrow the channel through which blood flows. Atherosclerosis in the coronary arteries causes a gradual decrease in the blood flow to the heart muscle. Atherosclerosis may begin to develop at an early age; however, the person usually is middle-aged or older before symptoms appear.

Coronary Heart Disease

A *heart attack* usually refers to the sudden blockage of a coronary artery. The vessel may be blocked by a temporary spasm or by a clot in a narrowed area; hence, no symptoms of coronary heart disease may have been detected. Chest pains (*angina pectoris*), shortness of breath, and other symptoms of *coronary heart disease* (CHD) may develop in some individuals; these symptoms indicate that the heart muscle is not getting enough O_2 and that a heart attack may occur. Not all of the causative factors in coronary heart disease are known, but risk factors such as smoking, high levels of fat and cholesterol in the blood, high arterial pressure, heredity, obesity, and physical inactivity have been identified tentatively.

Individuals who have a high level of cardiorespiratory fitness are less likely to have coronary heart disease. The influence of exercise training and various types of physical activity on the incidence of CHD has been studied by epidemiological methods. Most research has supported the conclusion that chronic exercise training decreases the incidence or risk of CHD. These studies, however, have been criticized on the grounds that many were retrospective and that both the diagnosis of CHD and the exact quantification of physical activity may not have been accurate.

RISK FACTORS

Exercise training has a positive influence on most of the risk factors for CHD. The beneficial effects of chronic activity on body fat, elevated blood pressure, plasma triglycerides, psychological stress, and tension have been documented. The lowering of total plasma cholesterol by exercise training is somewhat controversial, but the ability of exercise to change the cholesterol-carrying lipoprotein combinations has been demonstrated. Specifically, the cholesterol carried by low-density lipoprotein (LDL) is decreased, and the cholesterol associated with high-density lipoprotein (HDL) is increased. Increased levels of HDL cholesterol are associated with a decreased incidence of CHD.

Exercise Program for Prevention and Rehabilitation

Programs of exercise therapy are used commonly in the process of rehabilitation following heart attacks, and beneficial effects have been claimed for such programs. However, research has not proved that some of the beneficial effects claimed, such as increased collateral circulation in the coronary bed and regression of atherosclerotic plaques, really do occur. It has been established that selected patients, whose remaining myocardium is functioning normally for the most part, can increase their work capacity, efficiency of myocardial contraction, ventricular stroke volume, and psychological state by exercise training. While physical training cannot with certainty be shown to increase the life expectancy of patients who have had heart attacks or to reduce the chance of a recurrent attack, the patient can lead a life of normal activity rather than that of a "cardiac cripple" for his or her remaining years.

PHYSICAL EVALUATION PROGRAM

Before an exercise program is developed for an inactive patient, a complete medical evaluation, which includes physical examination, 12-lead electrocardiogram taken at rest, history, and a maximal or near-maximal multistage graded exercise test with electrocardiographic monitoring, should be performed. For the patient who has coronary artery disease, the initial purpose of the exercise test is to deter-

CLINICAL CORRELATION
73.1   Exercise Training in Coronary Artery Disease

CASE REPORT

The Patient: A 47-year-old male.

Reason for Training: Coronary artery disease: post-coronary-bypass-graft surgery.

History: The patient had been discovered to have electrocardiographic abnormalities during an examination related to gallbladder problems. An exercise stress test provoked cardiac ischemia, and selective coronary angiography subsequently showed 100% occlusion of the right coronary artery with severe lesions of the left coronary artery. Triple coronary-bypass-graft surgery was performed without complications, and the patient was advised to enroll in a comprehensive program of risk-factor modification and exercise.

Treatment: The initial exercise prescription involved walking at a speed of 3.6 mph at a 2.5% incline on a treadmill, or cycling on an ergometer at a work load of 450 kg-m/min at 50 rpm three times/week. The exercise was performed at the rehabilitation center while the ECG was monitored. The patient soon

was advised to exercise additionally at home by walking at a speed of 4 mph for 30 minutes at least two times/week. After 3 months in the program, he had lost 10 lb, his resting arterial pressure had decreased from 155/105 to 145/98 mm Hg (normal, 90–140/60–90 mm Hg), and he had stopped smoking. His fasting plasma cholesterol had decreased from 235 to 196 mg/dl (normal, 120–220 mg/dl), and his plasma triglycerides had decreased from 200 to 105 mg/dl (normal, 40–150 mg/dl). His exercise tolerance had improved from 6 minutes to 9 minutes on a standard treadmill test, with an oxygen uptake of 34.4 ml/kg of body weight/min compared to the initial rate of 22.9 ml/kg of body weight/min. Persistent findings included a high resting heart rate (98 beats/min), (normal, 60–100 beats/min), and nonspecific T wave changes on the ECG at rest. The ECG taken during exercise did not show ischemic changes, so the patient was advised to increase his level of exercise to include intermittent slow jogging at 5.0 mph interspersed with periods of walking, for 40–50 minutes, four or five times/week.

---

mine the functional capacity and maximal heart rate. Other factors to be considered when preparing an exercise program include the patient's age, sex, and orthopedic or neurological limitations, any major risks of CHD (such as obesity, hypertension, diabetes, and tobacco smoking), and environmental conditions such as temperature, humidity, terrain, and levels of air pollution in the location where the patient will exercise. Later, a follow-up test can be used to revise the program, to evaluate the effects of the exercise, and to serve as motivation for further participation in such a program.

MAXIMAL AEROBIC CAPACITY
The patient's maximal aerobic capacity should be measured during the graded exercise test or estimated from the results of the test. If the test

is terminated for clinical reasons (such as angina or ST depression) before the maximal work capacity is reached, the point of termination is considered to be the patient's maximal functional capacity and is used as the basis for the exercise program. The heart rate at the maximum level of work attained during the test also is used to determine the regimen of exercise training.

INTENSITY
The intensity of exercise should be a fraction of the maximal aerobic capacity ($\dot{V}_{O_{2max}}$) or the maximal heart rate. Usually, 60% of the $\dot{V}_{O_{2max}}$, initially, or 70%–75% of the maximal heart rate is prescribed for the unfit individual. The heart rate prescription will remain the same until another graded exercise test is performed;

however, periodic increases in the work load will be necessary to maintain the training heart rate at the prescribed level.

FREQUENCY

Cardiorespiratory endurance may be improved by training sessions that vary in frequency from twice weekly to several times daily. A frequency of three or four exercise sessions per week seems to be optimal for the improvement achieved and the time required. For best results, the sessions should be spaced throughout the week after equal intervals of no more than 2 days.

DURATION

The duration of each exercise session depends in part on the intensity and frequency of training, the functional capacity of the patient, and any symptoms of illness the patient has. Roughly 10% of the total daily energy expenditure may be used to estimate the necessary duration. This translates into 20 minutes or less for sedentary persons or cardiac patients and 40–50 minutes for more active people.

TYPE OF ACTIVITY

The activity prescribed for cardiac patients and sedentary middle-aged and older persons should improve cardiorespiratory endurance (aerobic fitness). Dynamic exercises that provide low resistance to movement of the large muscle groups should be prescribed. Such activities as brisk walking, jogging, bicycling, swimming, certain games, sports, dances, and calisthenic exercises generally provide the desired level of intensity.

WARM-UP AND COOL-DOWN

Any type of exercise should be preceded by a period of gradually increased activity, or warm-up. Warm-up permits gradual accommodation of the cardiovascular system to increased exercise stress and slow stretching of muscles, tendons, and ligaments before more vigorous activity. After endurance exercise, a tapering-off, or cool-down, period of reduced activity should be required. The warm-up period should last 10–15 minutes and include brisk walking or slow jogging and calisthenic exercises of various types. The cool-down should last for 10 minutes, or until the heart rate and blood pressure return to near resting levels.

STUDY OUTLINE

EXERCISE TRAINING AND FUNCTIONAL FITNESS

EFFECTS OF CHRONIC INACTIVITY
Decreases normal functional capacity.
DEMINERALIZATION OF BONE   Increased calcium excretion.
  Stress on long bones in upright position prevents calcium loss.
  Supine exercise or sitting does not overcome demineralization; standing does.
DECREASED MUSCLE POWER   Muscles atrophy with disuse.
  Substantial loss during complete immobilization.
  Loss of strength is minimized by repeated, brief, isometric contractions.
ORTHOSTATIC HYPOTENSION   Decreased sensitivity of baroreceptor reflexes to upward tilting of body.
DECREASED CARDIOVASCULAR FUNCTION   Decreased resting heart volume, plasma volume, red blood cell volume, ventricular stroke volume, cardiac output, and $\dot{V}_{O_{2max}}$; increased heart rate and arteriovenous O_2 difference.

PRINCIPLES OF EXERCISE TRAINING
The more work the body does, the more work it can do.

OVERLOAD   Physical activity greater than normal level must be imposed.

ADAPTABILITY   Functional and structural changes occur with time as result of overload.

SPECIFICITY   Effect of training is specific to particular muscle group or physiological system involved.

REVERSIBILITY   Training adaptations are not permanent; benefits are lost when training ceases.

EFFECTS OF EXERCISE TRAINING

MUSCULAR EFFECTS   Number of myofibrils, thickness of muscle fibers, and thickness of connective tissue increase.
  Increased storage of nutrients and energy substrates.
  Increased number of capillaries.
  More efficient transmission of neuromuscular impulses.

CARDIOVASCULAR EFFECTS Significant adaptation of entire O_2 transport and utilization system.

ADAPTIVE CHANGES FOUND AT REST Heart rate—decreased; increased vagal tone.

Stroke volume—increased; more complete emptying.

Cardiac volume—increased end-diastolic volume; reflects increased ventricular compliance.

Heart weight—increased mass; mainly hypertrophy of ventricular walls.

Density of myocardial capillaries—increased, but collateral vessels connecting arterioles are not found in humans.

Density of capillaries in skeletal muscle—increased; stimulated by decreased O_2 tension; allows increased blood flow to working muscle.

Arterial blood pressure—usually not changed unless high initially.

Blood volume—increased; allows for adequate flow during exercise, especially in hot environment.

Total hemoglobin—increased; facilitates transport of O_2 and CO_2.

ADAPTIVE CHANGES DURING SUBMAXIMAL WORK AT FIXED INTENSITY Smaller increase of heart rate.

Greater ventricular stroke volume—consistent with slower rate.

O_2 uptake is unchanged or decreased—decreased if work efficiency is improved.

Cardiac output is unchanged or decreased slightly—most studies show no effect at a fixed work load.

Arteriovenous O_2 difference—generally no change during submaximal work.

Decreased plasma lactate—decreased rate of production and increased rate of removal.

Decreased lung ventilation per liter of O_2 consumed—decreased respiratory drive caused by decreased lactate production.

RESPONSES TO TRAINING DURING MAXIMAL WORK Greater maximal cardiac output—necessary to meet demands for increased O_2 delivery; made possible by increased resting stroke volume.

Increased arteriovenous O_2 difference—increased hemoconcentration, increased O_2 content, and a shift of O_2 dissociation curve to the right.

Increased maximal uptake of O_2—delivery is increased by increased cardiac output and arteriovenous O_2 difference; mitochondrial changes effect greater utilization.

RESPIRATORY EFFECTS No definite changes in external respiration; maximal capacities and volumes normally are not increased.

FITNESS FOR EVERYDAY LIFE Most jobs and daily tasks do not provide enough exercise to maintain optimal fitness.

PHYSICAL FITNESS Relationship of task to be performed and ability of body to perform it.

Reserve of energy.

Perform daily tasks without fatigue.

Energy for leisure activities.

FREEDOM FROM DISEASE Disease or physical disorder can decrease capacity to function optimally.

CARDIORESPIRATORY ENDURANCE Efficient operation of heart, lungs, blood vessels, and muscles; improved by prolonged aerobic exercises of large muscle groups.

FLEXIBILITY Specific to joint involved in movement.

MUSCULAR STRENGTH Ability to exert force; related to endurance and efficiency of performing work.

MUSCULAR ENDURANCE Ability to continue submaximal contractions; important in postural muscles and muscles of locomotion.

CARDIOVASCULAR DISEASE AND EXERCISE

ATHEROSCLEROSIS Involves mechanism for handling fats and cholesterol in blood.

Cholesterol is deposited in arterial walls; gradual narrowing of artery; begins at early age, but symptoms appear later.

CORONARY HEART DISEASE Blockage of coronary artery; "heart attack."

Caused by atherosclerosis, clot, or spasm of artery; symptoms may include chest pain and shortness of breath.

Physical activity may decrease incidence or risk.

RISK FACTORS Exercise training may improve many risk factors.

Arterial hypertension may be reduced.

Excess body weight is reduced, plasma triglycerides are lowered.

Stress and tension are reduced.

Beneficial changes in lipoprotein cholesterol patterns.

EXERCISE PROGRAM FOR PREVENTION AND REHABILITATION Exercise therapy commonly is used for cardiac patients to improve functional capacity; may not increase life expectancy, but helps patient to lead a more active life.

PHYSICAL EVALUATION PROGRAM
Complete physical examination, history, electrocardiogram, and maximal exercise test are necessary to determine advisability of exercise for sedentary person or cardiac patient.

MAXIMAL AEROBIC CAPACITY Determined at maximal heart rate—used as basis for exercise prescription.

INTENSITY Percentage of maximal heart rate (70%–75%) or aerobic capacity (60%).

FREQUENCY Optimal, 3–4 days/week at regular intervals.

DURATION Each session should last 20–50 minutes or more; depends on intensity, frequency, and patient's functional capacity.

TYPE OF ACTIVITY Dynamic aerobic exercise to improve cardiorespiratory function—walk, jog, bicycle, swim, dance, and so forth.

WARM-UP AND COOL-DOWN Precede all exercise with warm-up; gradual increase of activity accommodates cardiorespiratory and musculoskeletal systems to activity.

Cool-down—period of reduced exercise allows gradual return to resting levels.

BIBLIOGRAPHY

Blocker, W.P., Jr., and Cardus, D., eds. 1983. *Rehabilitation in Ischemic Heart Disease.* New York: Spectrum.

Blomqvist, C.G., and Saltin, B. Cardiovascular adaptations to physical training. *Annu. Rev. Physiol.* 45:169.

Brengelmann, G.L. 1983. Circulatory adjustments to exercise and heat stress. *Annu. Rev. Physiol.* 45:191.

Clausen, J.P. 1977. Effect of physical training on cardiovascular adjustments to exercise. *Physiol. Rev.* 57:779.

Froelicher, V.F., Jr. 1973. The hemodynamic effects of physical conditioning in healthy young and middle-aged individuals and in coronary heart disease patients. In *Exercise Testing and Exercise Training in Coronary Heart Disease.* Edited by J.P. Naughton and H.K. Hellerstein. New York: Academic Press.

Froelicher, V.F. 1983. *Exercise Testing and Training.* New York: LeJacq.

Hartung, G.H.; Foreyt, J.P.; Mitchell, R.E., et al. 1980. Relation of diet to high-density lipoprotein cholesterol in middle-aged marathon runners, joggers, and inactive men. *N. Engl. J. Med.* 302:357.

Holloszy, J.O., and Booth, F.W. 1976. Biochemical adaptations to endurance exercise in muscle. *Annu. Rev. Physiol.* 38:273.

Saltin, B.; Blomqvist, G.; Mitchell, J.H., et al. 1968. Response to exercise after bed rest and after training: A longitudinal study of adaptive changes in oxygen transport and body composition. *Circulation* 38(7): VII-1.

Shephard, R.J. 1982. *Physiology and Biochemistry of Exercise.* New York: Praeger.

Appendix 1:
Units and
Their Abbreviations

LENGTH

m   = meter
cm = centimeter, 10^{-2} m
mm = millimeter, 10^{-3} m
μm = micrometer, 10^{-6} m
nm = nanometer, 10^{-9} m
pm = picometer, 10^{-12} m

MASS

kg = kilogram, 10^3 g
g   = gram
mg = milligram, 10^{-3} g
μg = microgram, 10^{-6} g
ng = nanogram, 10^{-9} g
pg = picogram, 10^{-12} g

TIME

hr   = hour
min = minute
sec = second
msec = millisecond, 10^{-3} sec
μsec = microsecond, 10^{-6} sec

ENERGY

cal   = calorie
Cal   = Calorie, 10^3 cal
kcal = kilocalorie, 10^3 cal

VOLUME

l   = liter
dl = deciliter, 10^{-2} l
ml = milliliter, 10^{-3} l
μl = microliter, 10^{-6} l

CONCENTRATION AND CHEMICAL ACTIVITY

Osm   = osmole, osmolar
mOsm = milliosmole, milliosmolar, 10^{-3} Osm
M   = mole, molar
mM   = millimole, millimolar, 10^{-3} M
Eq   = equivalent
mEq = milliequivalent, 10^{-3} Eq

ELECTRICAL

v   = volt
mv = millivolt, 10^{-3} v
μv = microvolt, 10^{-6} v
f   = farad

FREQUENCY

Hz = Hertz (cycles per second)

Appendix 2: Symbols and Abbreviations Used in Respiratory Physiology*

PRIMARY SYMBOLS

For gases and blood (large capital letters)

F = fractional concentration of dry gas
P = pressure, partial pressure, or tension
V = volume of gas
Q = volume of blood
$\dot{V}$ = volume of gas per unit time, that is, rate of ventilation
$\dot{Q}$ = volume of blood per unit time, that is, rate of blood flow
C = content of gas in blood (ml/100 ml)
S = saturation of hemoglobin with O_2 (%)
R = respiratory exchange ratio

SECONDARY SYMBOLS

For gases (small capital letters)

I = inspired gas
E = expired gas
T = tidal air
A = alveolar air
D = dead space air
B = barometric
STPD = 0 C, 760 mm Hg, dry
ATPS = ambient temperature and pressure, saturated with water vapor
BPTS = body temperature and pressure, saturated with water vapor

For blood (small letters)

a = arterial blood
v = venous blood
$\bar{v}$ = mixed venous blood
c = capillary blood

EXAMPLES

$F_{I_{O_2}}$ = fractional concentration of oxygen in inspired air
$\dot{V}_{CO_2}$ = volume of CO_2 produced/min
$\dot{V}_{O_2}$ = oxygen uptake/min
R = $\dot{V}_{CO_2}/\dot{V}_{O_2}$
$C_{\bar{v}_{O_2}}$ = oxygen content of mixed venous blood (ml of O_2/100 ml blood)
V_E = volume of expired air; that is, V_T or tidal volume
$P_{a_{CO_2}}$ = partial pressure of CO_2 in arterial blood
$P_{\bar{v}_{O_2}}$ = partial pressure of O_2 in mixed venous blood
$\dot{Q}_c$ = capillary blood flow/min
$\dot{V}_A$ = alveolar ventilation/min
V_D = volume of dead space air
P_B = barometric pressure
$P_{A_{O_2}}$ = partial pressure of O_2 in alveolar air
$\dot{V}_A/\dot{Q}_c$ = ventilation-perfusion ratio

*Recommended by the Committee for Standardization of Definitions and Symbols in Respiratory Physiology. Pappenheimer, J.R., Comroe, J.H., Cournand, A., et al. 1950. Standardization of definitions and symbols in respiratory physiology. *Fed. Proc.* 9:602–605.

Index